Introduction to
THEORETICAL ORGANIC CHEMISTRY

Introduction to

THEORETICAL ORGANIC CHEMISTRY

Arno Liberles
Fairleigh Dickinson University

The Macmillan Company, New York
Collier-Macmillan Limited, London

THE MACMILLAN COMPANY
866 THIRD AVENUE, NEW YORK, NEW YORK 10022
COLLIER-MACMILLAN CANADA, LTD., TORONTO, ONTARIO

Printed in the United States of America

To My Parents, Who Have Done So Much for Me

Preface

The emphasis in organic chemistry is continuously shifting from an experimental to a more theoretical approach. The knowledge of a number of name reactions is no longer sufficient, and concepts previously left to the physicist are today taught to and used by organic chemists. This trend, which seems certain to continue, makes the writing of a text extremely difficult. Today the subject encompasses a far wider area than at any previous time, and there is little agreement concerning which topics a text ought to cover. The major problem is not one of finding enough material but rather determining what to include.

This book covers both principles and applications. Courses for which the book is intended are often called physical organic chemistry or theoretical organic chemistry. It is designed for a second course in organic chemistry and contains material generally not included in an introductory course, as well as treating in greater detail subject matter already familiar to the reader. The first ten chapters are more concerned with principles, the last ten with applications. The core of the material stems from my notes on a course in theoretical organic chemistry given on separate occasions to undergraduates and to first-year graduate students. The original notes were supplemented and expanded into the present text.

I have included a chapter on chemical spectroscopy; this emphasizes principles rather than applications, for an understanding of principles is basic to this tool. A number of books emphasizing applications have already appeared. A chapter on the valence-bond method and resonance theory is included, although the molecular orbital approach is currently more popular. It is not certain what the future will bring, the pendulum may swing back, and the valence-bond technique or something akin to it may someday be in vogue again.

I naturally want to mention the assistance of my wife. I should like to thank Mrs. Leonard Parnes, who typed the entire manuscript, as well as two former graduate school classmates, Dr. R. W. Murray and Dr. G. B. Borowitz, who read sections of it. I should also like to thank Dr. I. J. Borowitz. I am very much indebted to Dr. J. E. Leffler, who read the manuscript prior to its publication and who offered many helpful and stimulating suggestions.

A. L.

Contents

Chapter 1

Chemical Reaction and Energy Change

1.1 Introduction

A study of organic chemistry is more than a study of certain isolated reactions and simply knowing which products are formed in any chemical process is not enough. In order to understand a reaction properly we must know how fast it proceeds and upon which factors this rate depends. We must know the factors that govern the equilibrium and how these differ from those influencing the rate. Finally, we must know why the reaction proceeds, which structural changes we are effecting, and why they occur. Theories have been developed that allow us to understand, at least to some extent, why chemical reactions occur, and we discuss some of the underlying principles in a general way in this chapter.

A hydrogen molecule is composed of two nuclei and two electrons, and we begin our discussion by considering a hydrogen molecule whose nuclei are separated by the equilibrium distance 0.74 Å. At this point the coulombic energy of the molecule is at a minimum. Decreasing the internuclear distance raises this energy for repulsion between the positively charged nuclei increases, and this is the dominating factor at short distances. Increasing the internuclear distance also raises the energy. This operation initiates bond breakage into hydrogen atoms. Thus, the coulombic energy of hydrogen molecules is a minimum when the internuclear distance is 0.74 Å, increases sharply as the distance is decreased, and also increases when the distance is increased. If we plot the coulombic energy of the molecule as a function of the distance between the nuclei, we obtain the curve shown in Figure 1–1.

We have assumed in this curve that the molecule is neither vibrating nor rotating. We must now add the vibrational and rotational energy levels of the molecule. The hydrogen molecule has zero-point energy (6.3 kcal/mole) and can exist in vibrationally and rotationally excited states. These are shown in Figure 1–2.

The curve presented here is for the electronic ground state of hydrogen; we can draw similar curves not only for the ground state but for the excited states

1

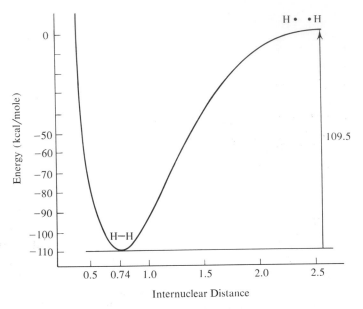

Figure 1–1

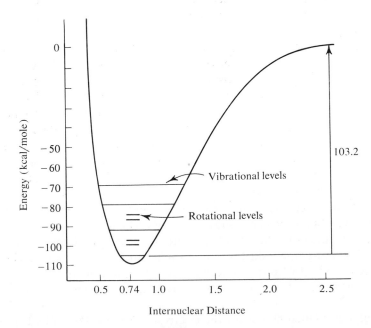

Figure 1–2

of all molecules. When polyatomic molecules are discussed, the abscissa of the curve takes into account the internuclear distances of all the nuclei, and data are much more difficult to obtain. We do know, however, that the general shape of the coulombic energy curve must be similar to that presented for hydrogen.

The fact that a molecule possesses a high energy need not make it unstable. This energy can be in the form of translational kinetic energy; a rapidly moving molecule does not necessarily react any faster than a slowly moving one. In order for a reaction to proceed, this translational energy must be absorbed inside the molecule, for increasing the internal energy does lead to a species capable of undergoing chemical change. Increasing the internal energy leads to higher energy rotational and vibrational states and even to electronic excitation. It is the high energy, large amplitude vibrations that usually lead to bond rupture and cause chemical reactions to take place. This shift of energy from translational kinetic to internal is brought about by molecular collisions. The molecules collide, the kinetic energy is absorbed internally, and the reaction may proceed. Even then, it is not generally the average molecules that react. The average molecules in a system do not have sufficient energy, and collisions between average molecules produce no chemical change. It is generally the very energetic species that undergo chemical change. Furthermore, this energy must be properly distributed. In order to react, the energy absorbed by the molecule as a result of a collision must be distributed to the pertinent atoms. The proper vibrational modes must participate, for the energy absorbed must be distributed in such a way that those portions of the molecule undergoing chemical change can use this energy. Energy that is not available to the pertinent atoms does not aid the reaction.

At any given time only a very small fraction of the total number of reacting molecules present in the system actually undergo chemical change. We assume that the concentration of molecules is sufficiently high that collisions take place frequently. This assures us that at the reaction temperature a statistical number of molecules possess enough energy, and in that case if the total number of reactant molecules in the system is N, then the number of molecules N^* possessing sufficient energy to react is given approximately by:

$$N^* = N e^{-E_{act}/RT}$$

where E_{act} is the energy of activation for the process. The fraction of molecules having sufficient energy is,

$$\frac{N^*}{N} = e^{-E_{act}/RT} \tag{1-1}$$

Assuming that the energy of activation for a reaction is 10 kcal/mole (not an unreasonable figure), then the fraction of molecules possessing enough energy at 0°C to overcome this energy of activation barrier is,

$$\frac{N^*}{N} = e^{-10/(0.001987)(273.2)}$$

$$\frac{N^*}{N} = \frac{1}{100\ 000\ 000} = 10^{-8}$$

At any given time, only a single molecule out of one hundred million possesses sufficient energy to react (a rather small fraction of the total number).

In a reaction of the type:

$$B \longrightarrow C$$

one mole of B is being converted to one mole of C. If the concentration of B in moles per liter is $[B]$, then the moles per liter of B with enough energy to react, given by $[B^*]$, is, according to Eq. (1–1):

$$[B^*] = [B]e^{-E_{act}^f/RT}$$

where E_{act}^f is the energy of activation for the forward reaction. The fraction is,

$$\frac{[B^*]}{[B]} = e^{-E_{act}^f/RT}$$

As soon as we form C, some fraction of C is energetically capable of returning to B; that fraction is,

$$\frac{[C^*]}{[C]} = e^{-E_{act}^r/RT}$$

where E_{act}^r is the energy of activation for the reverse reaction.

This leads to an interesting conclusion. As soon as we form C, some fraction of the C molecules possess enough energy to return to B. Regardless of how large E_{act} is, the exponential term is never zero, and some fraction of C always returns to B. Indicating a reaction as irreversible implies that the reversal to B is insignificant; it does not imply that reversal is strictly absent. Of course, this raises a difficulty. When is reversal significant and when isn't it? If the reversal to B can be measured, then presumably it is significant. If it cannot, reversal is probably not important.

A reaction for which reversal is not important is indicated by a single arrow:

$$B \longrightarrow C$$

A reaction for which reversal is important is generally indicated:

$$B \rightleftarrows C$$

Unfortunately, this last symbolism does not distinguish between a reaction already at equilibrium and a reaction that is approaching but has not yet reached the equilibrium position. However, the distinction can usually be inferred from context.

As B is converted to C, the concentration of C, $[C]$, increases while that of B, $[B]$, decreases. At any time, the change in the concentration of C per unit time is given by,

$$\frac{d[C]}{dt}$$

and this must equal the decrease in $[B]$:

$$\frac{d[C]}{dt} = -\frac{d[B]}{dt} \tag{1-2}$$

We already know that not all B molecules are immediately capable of forming C. First, they must have sufficient energy to undergo conversion, and this energy must be properly distributed. In addition, it is likely that only a particular conformation of B can form C and that other conformations of B, although energetically capable, do not have the proper geometry for reaction. Not all of the sufficiently energetic molecules of B have the desired geometry. In order to form C the pertinent atoms within B must collide, and this requires a particular orientation for the B molecules. The number of moles per liter actually transforming into C equals the moles per liter of B that undergo the required intramolecular collision between pertinent parts of the molecule with sufficient energy. We write this as,

$$\frac{d[C]}{dt} = [B^*]A'$$

The term $[B^*]$ represents the number of moles per liter of B having enough energy to react. The term A' indicates the likelihood that molecules with enough energy actually do react, that is, it indicates the likelihood that the desired geometry will be assumed by B and that the atoms collide.

Since,

$$[B^*] = [B]e^{-E_{act}/RT}$$

we substitute this into the original expression and obtain

$$\frac{d[C]}{dt} = Be^{-E_{act}/RT}A'$$

We represent the terms,

$$A'e^{-E_{act}/RT}$$

by the single parameter k, the specific rate constant.

$$k = A'e^{-E_{act}/RT} \tag{1-3}$$

and

$$\frac{d[C]}{dt} = k[B]$$

Furthermore, $d[C]/dt$ equals $-d[B]/dt$, and we obtain

$$-\frac{d[B]}{dt} = \frac{d[C]}{dt} = k[B]$$

The specific rate constant k is simply a constant of proportionality and indicates the susceptibility of product formation to the concentration of B, the larger the numerical value of k, the faster C is formed. The rate constant k has for this reaction the dimension, time^{-1}, and is usually expressed in reciprocal seconds (sec^{-1}). The units min^{-1} and hour^{-1} have occasionally been employed.

Equation (1–3) relating k to E_{act}, is similar to another equation, the Arrhenius equation, developed as a result of rate studies on the acid catalyzed hydrolysis of sucrose. The latter equation has the same form,

$$k = Ae^{-E_A/RT} \tag{1-4}$$

where E_A is the Arrhenius energy of activation, and A, the proportionality term, is called the Arrhenius frequency factor or simply the preexponential factor.

These equations differ theoretically. In fact, three quantities (E_{act}, E_A, and $\Delta H^{\ddagger}$) stemming from three different theories have about the same numerical value. The first of these comes from collision theory; the second was proposed by Arrhenius to explain the fact that the rate of a reaction is a function of the temperature; the third emanates from transition state theory. For reactions of interest they are related as follows,

$$E_A = E_{act} + \tfrac{1}{2}RT \tag{1-5}$$

$$\Delta H^{\ddagger} = E_A - RT = E_{act} - \tfrac{1}{2}RT \tag{1-6}$$

Since RT is usually less than one kcal/mole, the numerical values for these quantities differ by less than this amount.

These three quantities indicate essentially the same thing; the energy barrier over which reactant molecules must pass in order to be transformed into product. Naturally, it becomes important to determine these quantities experimentally. It is only necessary to evaluate one of them. The others can be obtained from the relationships just presented. From the Arrhenius equation, Eq. (1–4), we obtain,

$$\ln k = \ln A - E_A/RT$$

We assume that E_A is independent of the temperature. (This assumption that E_A is not a function of the temperature is only approximately correct.) We measure the rate of a reaction and determine k. If we measure the rate at various temperatures, we can determine how $\ln k$ varies with the temperature. The quantity $\ln k$ is then plotted against the reciprocal of the absolute temperature. The result is a straight line with slope equal to $-E_A/R$. Since R, the gas constant, is known, we have determined E_A.

$$\frac{d(\ln k)}{d\left(\frac{1}{T}\right)} = -E_A/R$$

The other quantities can be obtained once E_A has been evaluated. Alternatively, it is possible to evaluate them directly. In Eq. (1–3) derived from collision theory,

$$k = A'e^{-E_{act}/RT}$$

A' contains a temperature term $T^{1/2}$; however, it is possible to write,

$$A' = A''T^{1/2}$$

and

$$k = A''T^{1/2}e^{-E_{act}/RT}$$

We then perform the same sort of treatment for k and obtain E_{act} directly.

$$\frac{d(\ln k)}{d\left(\frac{1}{T}\right)} = -\left(\frac{E_{act}}{R} + \frac{T}{2}\right) \tag{1–7}$$

The quantity $\Delta H^{\ddagger}$ is evaluated directly from the equation,

$$\frac{d(\ln k)}{d\left(\frac{1}{T}\right)} = -\left(\frac{\Delta H^{\ddagger}}{R} + T\right) \tag{1–8}$$

1.2 ΔH and ΔH‡

Most organic reactions are conducted under isothermal conditions, that is, they are conducted at constant temperature. Therefore, heat can pass into or out of the system, but the temperature does not change.

In the reaction, $B \longrightarrow C$, one mole of B in a reaction vessel and at a fixed temperature is converted to one mole of C. If no work accompanies the conversion of B to C, then the energy change ΔE is equal to the heat that is absorbed or given off by the system. The most common type of work is pressure-volume work against the surroundings; however, organic chemical reactions are generally conducted in solution, and under these conditions pressure-volume changes are negligible.

$$\Delta E = E_C - E_B \qquad (1-9)$$

and

$$\Delta H = \Delta E + \Delta(PV) \qquad (1-10)$$

but we have assumed that the term $\Delta(PV)$ is negligible; therefore, Eq. (1-10) becomes:

$$\Delta H = \Delta E = E_C - E_B$$

In the reaction:

$$B \longrightarrow C$$

one possibility for carrying out this transformation is to convert B into its component atoms, then allow them to recombine and form C. This process requires considerable energy and is not a very desirable route for the reaction. If we plot the coulombic energy changes that occur in the decomposition of B into its atoms, we obtain a curve (Figure 1–3) similar to Figure 1–1 for hydrogen.

The curve for the formation of C from these atoms appears in Figure 1–4, and combining the two curves leads to the result presented in Figure 1–5.

Naturally, an enormous quantity of energy is required to decompose B, and it is fortunate that chemical reactions need not proceed by this route.

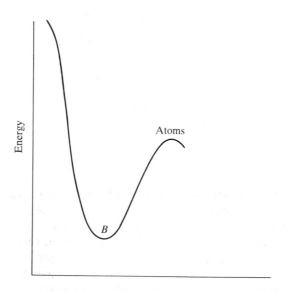

Figure 1–3

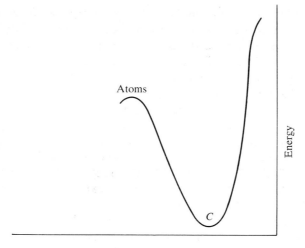

Figure 1–4

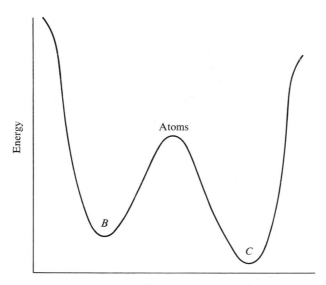

Figure 1–5

It is quite likely that starting with the proper conformation of B and distorting the pertinent bonds leads to a species capable of forming C without complete dissociation of the molecule. Even this process requires energy. The transformation requires a rearrangement of the atoms within the molecule. Bonds are being broken and new bonds formed. In addition steric factors play a role. During the reaction, certain atoms with their electrons must come very close to other atoms and their electrons, and this occurs whether or not the atoms are involved in the bond-making bond-breaking process. When the electrons and nuclei of two different atoms in the molecule are very close (internuclear distance less than the sum of the covalent radii), the interactions that result are frequently unfavorable. These interactions are usually called steric interactions although a better name would be van der Waals interactions or in some cases nonbonded interactions.

The transformation of *B* to *C* does require some energy to overcome the barrier, but if the pertinent atoms all move in the proper direction, a much smaller quantity than for complete dissociation. Of course, not all of the molecules of *B* form *C* by this lowest energy route but most of them will. Some molecules of *B*, those containing sufficient energy, are able to react by higher energy pathways. However, when discussing a reaction, we generally describe the most feasible route (the mechanism).

If we plot only the coulombic energy changes that take place during the preferred route from *B* to *C*, we get the curve illustrated in Figure 1–6.

If in the reaction *B* ⟶ *C* the energy of *C* is greater than that of *B*, we must supply energy (usually by supplying heat). A reaction that absorbs heat is endothermic. Conversely, a reaction that liberates heat is exothermic; this occurs when the energy of *C* is less than that of *B*.

In Figure 1–7, we plot the energy of the system as we proceed from one mole of *B* to one mole of *C*. The diagram on the left depicts a process which is endothermic while that on the right illustrates an exothermic reaction. In these diagrams we have assumed for the sake of simplicity that at each point

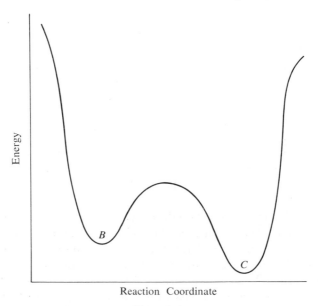

Reaction Coordinate

Figure 1–6

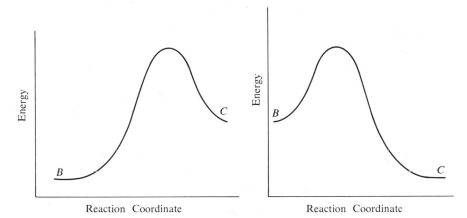

Reaction Coordinate   Reaction Coordinate

Figure 1–7

on the curve the nuclei of B and C are stationary. Electronic energies and internuclear repulsion terms are considered but vibrational and rotational energy levels have been omitted. We have plotted the coulombic energy changes that occur as we proceed from B to C along the preferred route.

The atoms of B and C are actually vibrating about their equilibrium positions, and ΔH does include terms for rotational and vibrational energy differences. Since we have plotted only coulombic energy changes, $E_C - E_B$ in these diagrams is not exactly equal to ΔH. However, the coulombic contribution to ΔH is generally the most important and we can consider that in these diagrams $E_C - E_B$ represents ΔH to a good approximation. The result is schematically illustrated in Figure 1–8.

Notice that ΔH is positive when the process is endothermic ($E_C > E_B$) and negative when the reaction is exothermic ($E_C < E_B$). Furthermore, if B is in its standard state, this energy difference becomes $\Delta H°$.

The region where the system is least stable is called the transition state. In our examples, the transition state occurs at a region intermediate between the reactant B and the product C; however, for some reactions the region of highest energy is found at an extreme.

For most reactions the region of highest energy occurs at an intermediate position, and molecules of B must pass over this energy barrier in order to form C. The difference between the energy of the transition state and the energy of B is represented by the symbol $\Delta H^{\ddagger}$[1]. If we now include the transition states and $\Delta H^{\ddagger}$ in the previous diagrams, they look as pictured in Figure 1–9.

Since the transition state for the reaction, $B \longrightarrow C$, occurs at a point intermediate between B and C, we might also expect the geometry of the

[1] The transition state lacks an internal degree of freedom in the direction of the reaction coordinate; we discuss this more fully in the penultimate section of this chapter.

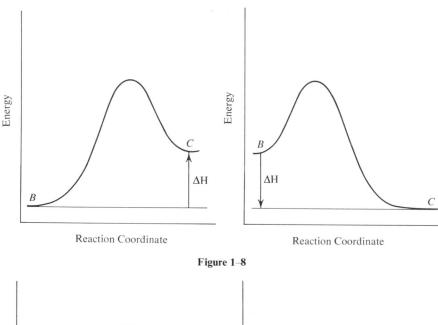

Figure 1–8

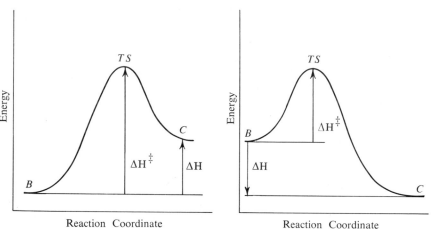

Figure 1–9

transition state (the way the transition state looks) to be intermediate between the geometry of *B* and the geometry of *C*, and this is indeed the case. For example, in the formation of *t*-butyl carbonium ion from *t*-butyl chloride, the transition state has an intermediate geometry. The carbon-chlorine bond has been stretched and has partially, but not completely, ruptured:

$$
\begin{array}{ccccc}
& CH_3 & & CH_3 & & CH_3 \\
& | & & |_{\delta+}\;_{\delta-} & & | \\
CH_3-\!\!\!&C\!-\!Cl & \longrightarrow & CH_3-\!C\!-\!-\!Cl & \longrightarrow & CH_3-\!C^+ \quad Cl^- \\
& | & & | & & | \\
& CH_3 & & CH_3 & & CH_3
\end{array}
$$

    In organic reactions we generally make the assumption that molecules pass over the energy barrier and through the transition state to form products. Quantum mechanically this need not be the case, and it is becoming more and more apparent that some reactants form products by passing through the barrier rather than over it. This phenomenon, which is called tunneling, takes place most readily when the energy barrier is both low and narrow. Ammonia undergoes inversion (see Figure 1–10) and the inversion frequency can be measured. The energy barrier is only about 6 kcal/mole, but the measured frequency is much more rapid than expected for a reaction having this barrier. Molecules of ammonia invert by passing over the barrier. However, the width of the barrier is narrow, and most of the ammonia molecules tunnel through.

    We shall assume in subsequent discussions that reactants form products primarily by passing over the barrier. With some hydrogen transfers tunneling does appear to be important.

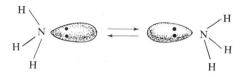

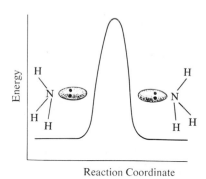

Reaction Coordinate

Figure 1–10

1.3 Forward and Reverse Reactions

Consider the endothermic reaction, $B \longrightarrow C$. Instead of forming C, let us use C as the reactant and form B. For this process we follow the reaction profile in just the opposite direction. Nothing changes, the energy of the system remains exactly the same at every point, but we travel from C to B. The result is illustrated in Figure 1–11.

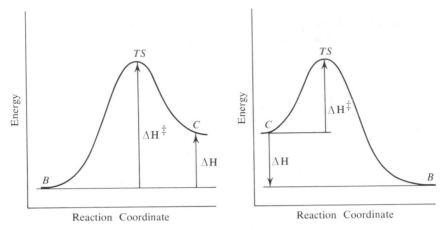

Figure 1–11

The reaction (C going to B) is now exothermic, and $\Delta H^{\ddagger}$ is much smaller. However, the transition state occurs at exactly the same position that it did in the forward reaction. It has the same energy and must have exactly the same geometry. This is an important conclusion. Forward and reverse processes have identical transition states.

In the formation of *t*-butyl chloride from *t*-butyl carbonium ion and chloride ion (the reverse of the previous example) the same transition state is involved.

$$
\underset{\underset{\text{CH}_3}{|}}{\overset{\overset{\text{CH}_3}{|}}{\text{CH}_3-\text{C}^+}} \quad \text{Cl}^- \quad \longrightarrow \quad \underset{\underset{\text{CH}_3}{|}}{\overset{\overset{\text{CH}_3}{|}}{\text{CH}_3-\overset{\delta+}{\text{C}}--\overset{\delta-}{\text{Cl}}}} \quad \longrightarrow \quad \underset{\underset{\text{CH}_3}{|}}{\overset{\overset{\text{CH}_3}{|}}{\text{CH}_3-\text{C}-\text{Cl}}}
$$

1.4 ΔG° and $\Delta G^{\ddagger}$

In the previous examples one mole of B was converted to one mole of C and we discussed the reaction in terms of the energy changes involved. In addition to the change in energy, the randomness of the system is also significant. In a reaction of the type,

$$A + B \longrightarrow C$$

two moles of reactants are converted to a single mole of product. In the reactants, the molecules of A move freely and independently of the molecules of B, but in the product these molecules are bonded and cannot move independently. The randomness of the system has decreased. The system contains more external degrees of freedom before reaction than afterwards and decreasing the number of external degrees of freedom is not a favorable process. Accordingly, in order to obtain a more complete picture of a chemical reaction, we define a quantity known as the standard Gibbs free energy of reaction $\Delta G°$.

$$\Delta G° = \Delta H° - T\Delta S°$$

The quantity $\Delta H°$ indicates the change in energy, and $\Delta S°$ is a measure of the change in the randomness of the system. The more positive $\Delta S°$, the more favorable for product formation is the change in the randomness of the system. For the reaction $A + B \longrightarrow C$, $\Delta S°$ is negative.

The importance of entropy changes ($\Delta S°$) upon the standard free energy of reaction $\Delta G°$ can be seen by considering the free energy of formation of hydrocarbons of increasing complexity from carbon as graphite and molecular hydrogen as a gas.

The reaction for methane is,

$$C_{graphite} + 2H_{2\,gas} \longrightarrow CH_{4\,gas}$$

and in the general case,

$$nC_{graphite} + (n + 1)H_{2\,gas} \longrightarrow C_nH_{2n+2\,gas}$$

The terms $\Delta H°$, $\Delta S°$, and $\Delta G°$ have been compiled at 25°C. The results are presented in Table 1–1.

Table 1–1*

Hydrocarbon (gas)	$\Delta H°$ (kcal)	$\Delta S°$ (cal/deg)	$\Delta G°$ (kcal)
Methane	−17.89	−19.3	−12.14
Ethane	−20.24	−41.5	−7.86
n-Propane	−24.80	−64.4	−5.61
n-Butane	−29.81	−87.4	−3.75
n-Pentane	−35.00	−110.8	−1.96
n-Hexane	−39.96	−134.5	+0.05
n-Heptane	−44.89	−157.6	+2.09
n-Octane	−49.82	−181.0	+4.14
n-Nonane	−54.74	−204.3	+6.18
n-Decane	−59.67	−227.7	+8.23

* The data are from Strong, L. E. and Stratton, W. J., *Chemical Energy*. New York, Reinhold, 1965, p. 101.

As the molecular complexity increases, the free energy of reaction becomes less favorable. At room temperature the larger hydrocarbons are much less stable, yet bond formation (indicated by $\Delta H°$) is favorable and becomes more favorable as the number of bonds in the molecule increases. It is the entropy term $\Delta S°$ that becomes the dominating factor with the larger molecules. The constraints (the decrease in randomness) produced by formation of the molecule simply outweigh the favorable effects of bond formation.

We also define $\Delta G^{\ddagger}$, the standard free energy of activation, as:

$$\Delta G^{\ddagger} = \Delta H^{\ddagger} - T\Delta S^{\ddagger} \qquad (1\text{--}11)$$

where $\Delta G^{\ddagger}$ is the difference between the free energy of the transition state and the free energy of the reactants.

Returning to the original example, $B \longrightarrow C$, for the forward reaction

$$\Delta G^{\circ} = G_C^{\circ} - G_B^{\circ} \qquad \text{and} \qquad \Delta G^{\ddagger} = G_{TS}^{\circ} - G_B^{\circ}$$

where the terms G_C°, G_B°, and G_{TS}° are the standard free energies of formation of the different species.

We now plot in Figure 1–12 the free energy change for the forward and reverse processes. These diagrams are not much different from the previous ones. The transition state remains the same in either direction.

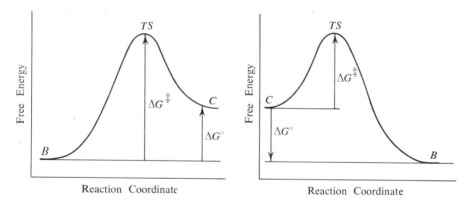

Figure 1–12

A reaction for which the products are more constrained than the reactants is accompanied by a negative ΔS°. If in passing to the products constraints are removed, ΔS° is positive. Similar arguments apply for $\Delta S^{\ddagger}$ when passing to the transition state.

Since $\Delta G^{\ddagger}$ and $\Delta S^{\ddagger}$ represent respectively the free energy and entropy differences between the transition state and the reactants, they must be related to the specific rate constant k. The rate of product formation depends upon k. Since it also depends upon $\Delta G^{\ddagger}$ and $\Delta S^{\ddagger}$, these quantities must be related.

If k for the reaction is known, it is possible to determine $\Delta H^{\ddagger}$, $\Delta G^{\ddagger}$, and $\Delta S^{\ddagger}$. We have already discussed the determination of $\Delta H^{\ddagger}$. The other two quantities are related as follows,

$$\Delta G^{\ddagger} = -RT\ln\frac{kh}{\kappa k'T} \qquad (1\text{--}12)$$

and

$$\Delta S^{\ddagger} = \frac{\Delta H^{\ddagger} - \Delta G^{\ddagger}}{T}$$

$$\Delta S^{\ddagger} = R\left(\ln \frac{kh}{\kappa k' T} - 1\right) - \frac{R}{T} \frac{d(\ln k)}{d\left(\frac{1}{T}\right)}$$

(1–13)

where k is the specific rate constant, h is Planck's constant, k' is Boltzmann's constant, and κ (the transmission coefficient) is the fraction of the transition state species, formed from reactants, that passes on to products.

We can write k as,

$$k = \frac{\kappa k' T}{h} e^{-\Delta G^{\ddagger}/RT}$$

$$k = \frac{\kappa k' T}{h} e^{\Delta S^{\ddagger}/R} e^{-\Delta H^{\ddagger}/RT}$$

This last equation has the same form as the Arrhenius equation, Eq. (1–4), and from them we can correlate the various terms. Since

$$\Delta H^{\ddagger} = E_A - RT$$

(1–14)

the last equation becomes

$$k = \frac{\kappa k' T e}{h} e^{\Delta S^{\ddagger}/R} e^{-E_A/RT}$$

and A in the Arrhenius equation is then equal to,

$$A = \frac{\kappa k' T e}{h} e^{\Delta S^{\ddagger}/R}$$

(1–15)

1.5 Rate and Equilibrium

When a reaction is at equilibrium, the concentrations of the various components remain constant, but this does not imply that the molecules are unreactive:

$$B \rightleftharpoons C$$

The product C is continuously being formed from B, but the rate of decomposition of C back to B exactly equals the rate of formation of C. Therefore, the concentrations of the various species do not change with time. This implies that the molecules constantly pass back and forth over the energy barrier separating B and C, and in that case the energy barrier is not important. Although the height of the free energy barrier is not important, the difference between the free energies of B and C is significant; the material having the lower free energy content is present in greater concentration. The free energy difference between C and B is just the free energy of reaction $\Delta G°$, and it is upon this that the position of the equilibrium depends. An equilibrium depends upon $\Delta G°$, but the value of $\Delta G^{\ddagger}$ is irrelevant. The equilibrium constant K is the ratio of concentrations,

$$K = \frac{[C]}{[B]}$$

This is related to $\Delta G°$ by the equation,

$$\Delta G° = -RT \ln K \qquad (1\text{–}16)$$

where,

$$\Delta G° = G_C^° - G_B^°$$

To measure the rate of a reaction is to measure how fast the reaction proceeds, and this rate depends upon several factors. For the case, $B \longrightarrow C$, the rate of formation of C depends upon the absolute temperature, upon the concentration of B, and upon the free energy of activation $\Delta G^{\ddagger}$. Molecules of B must pass over the free energy barrier $\Delta G^{\ddagger}$ in order to form C, and all other factors being kept constant, the higher this barrier the slower is the reaction. Any discussion of reaction rates must be in terms of $\Delta G^{\ddagger}$. One expression for this term is given by Eq. (1–11). Another involves the equilibrium constant $K^{\ddagger}$.

Let $[TS]$ represent the concentration of the transition state at any time, and let $[B]$ represent the concentration of the reactant at that same time. If the transition state is in equilibrium with the reactant, then the equilibrium constant $K^{\ddagger}$ for this process is,

$$K^{\ddagger} = \frac{[TS]}{[B]}$$

Now $\Delta G^{\ddagger}$ is given by the expression:

$$\Delta G^{\ddagger} = -RT \ln K^{\ddagger}$$

This equation relates $\Delta G^{\ddagger}$ to $K^{\ddagger}$. We can also relate $K^{\ddagger}$ to the specific rate constant k. The free energy of activation is equal to the expression just presented; it is also equal to:

$$\Delta G^{\ddagger} = -RT \ln \frac{kh}{\kappa k' T} \qquad (1\text{–}17)$$

Equating the two expressions for the free energy of activation leads to the result:

$$k = \frac{\kappa k' T}{h} K^{\ddagger}$$

It is possible to obtain this relationship by another method that perhaps provides more insight into the meaning of the various terms. We know that the rate of formation of C is given by the expression,

$$\frac{d[C]}{dt} = k[B]$$

This relationship states that the increase in the concentration of C is proportional to the concentration of B that is present. The constant of proportionality is k. Since C is formed by the decomposition of the transition state into product, $d[C]/dt$ must also be proportional to the concentration of the transition state $[TS]$. We write,

$$\frac{d[C]}{dt} = b[TS]$$

which states that the increase in C depends upon the concentration of the transition state. Since,

$$[TS] = K^{\ddagger}[B]$$

then

$$\frac{d[C]}{dt} = bK^{\ddagger}[B]$$

Therefore,

$$bK^{\ddagger} = k$$

where the k is the specific rate constant for the reaction. The constant of proportionality b, the rate constant for decomposition of the transition state, turns out to be the composite term,

$$b = \frac{\kappa k'T}{h}$$

For any reaction the position of the equilibrium depends upon ΔG° while the rate depends upon $\Delta G^{\ddagger}$.

1.6 Competitive Reactions

Consider the case of two competitive reactions where compound A may be converted to either B or C:

$$C \longleftarrow A \longrightarrow B$$

We assume that the reaction profile for these two processes looks as illustrated in Figure 1–13.

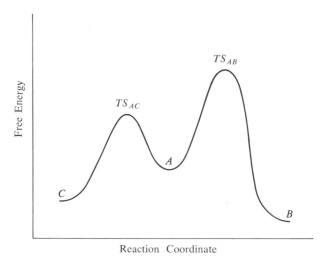

Figure 1–13

The reaction having a smaller free energy of activation proceeds more rapidly; therefore, in this case C is formed more quickly than B. Alternatively, we may speak in terms of the free energy of the transition state. The transition state for the faster reaction is more stable (in terms of free energy) than the transition state for the slower process; TS_{AC} is more favorable than TS_{AB} and C is formed faster.

We shall frequently compare reaction rates by comparing the free energies of their transition states rather than speaking in terms of $\Delta G^{\ddagger}$. The same idea is conveyed, and it is important to realize that $\Delta G^{\ddagger}$ is implied. Furthermore, by the stability of a transition state we generally mean stability in terms of its free energy content.

1.7 Kinetic and Thermodynamic Products

In the competitive reaction just discussed ($C \longleftarrow A \longrightarrow B$), the system had the reaction profile presented in Figure 1–13.

Examination of this reaction profile indicates that while C is formed more rapidly, B is more stable. The material that is formed more quickly is called the kinetic product while the more stable material is called the thermodynamic product. Usually, the compound formed most rapidly is also the most stable, but this is not necessarily true.

When the reaction is run under mild conditions, that is, at low temperatures for short periods of time, C is the major product. It is formed most readily, and under the mild conditions slower reactions such as the formation of B, although they take place, are not significant. Reversal of C to A takes place under all conditions. We can write the equation for the reaction as,

$$C \;\underset{\longrightarrow}{\overset{\longleftarrow}{}}\; A \longrightarrow B$$

or as

$$C \longleftarrow A \longrightarrow B$$

depending upon the position of the equilibrium between C and A. Even under mild conditions some B is formed and a certain fraction of these B molecules return to A; however, the extent of this return to A and in some cases even the formation B itself is negligibly small.

If the reaction is run for long periods of time, the slower reactions do become important and B can become the major product. Under these conditions the system does not contain sufficient free energy to form B quickly, yet under more vigorous conditions (higher temperatures) the system does contain enough free energy for rapid formation of B. Eventually (long periods of time or high temperatures) the system reaches equilibrium, and then B, the more stable product, is the major component of the mixture.

$$C \;\underset{\longrightarrow}{\overset{\longleftarrow}{}}\; A \rightleftarrows B$$

At equilibrium all materials are present in their equilibrium concentrations and these are related to the free energies of reaction $\Delta G°$. The free energies of the materials involved are important. The most stable material is present in the highest concentration; see Figure 1–14.

$$K_{AB} = \frac{[B]}{[A]}$$

$$K_{AC} = \frac{[C]}{[A]}$$

$$K_{CB} = \frac{[B]}{[C]} = K_{AB}K_{CA}$$

where $K_{CA} = 1/K_{AC}$

and

$$\Delta G°_{AB} = -RT \ln K_{AB}$$

$$\Delta G°_{AC} = -RT \ln K_{AC}$$

$$\Delta G°_{CB} = -RT \ln K_{AB}K_{CA}$$

These reactions also illustrate that in order to prepare B it is not necessary to use A as the reactant. If C is more readily available, we may equally well employ this to form B.

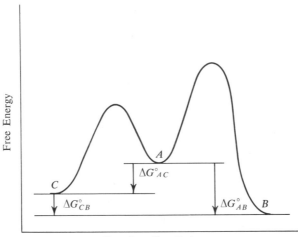

Reaction Coordinate

Figure 1–14

Another and perhaps more common type of reaction that gives rise to both kinetic and thermodynamic products is one with the reaction profile shown in Figure 1–15.

Using A as the starting material, compound B is formed quickly and is the kinetic product. Under vigorous conditions the system is also able to form C, and the latter is the thermodynamic product.

The addition of hydrogen bromide to 1,3-butadiene exemplifies a reaction yielding both kinetic and thermodynamic products.

$$CH_2=CH-CH=CH_2 + HBr \longrightarrow CH_3-CHBr-CH=CH_2$$

1,2 addition

$$+ CH_3-CH=CH-CH_2Br$$

1,4 addition

and

$$CH_3-CHBr-CH=CH_2 \xrightarrow{\Delta} CH_3-CH=CH-CH_2Br$$

The intermediate in this reaction is an allylic carbonium ion which affords both the 1,2 and the 1,4 adducts. Under mild conditions the 1,2 adduct is the chief component of the product mixture while at higher temperatures it is the 1,4 adduct that is the principal product.

1.8 The Rate Limiting Step

Another important concept is that of the rate limiting step in a reaction. Most organic reactions involve a number of reactive intermediates and the rate of

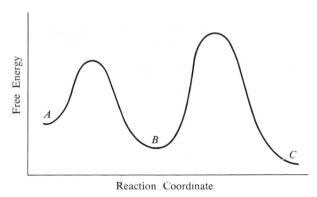

Reaction Coordinate

Figure 1–15

the process depends upon their behavior. Consider for example the reaction,

$$A \rightleftharpoons B$$

$$B \longrightarrow C$$

where C is produced from A by way of the unstable intermediate B. The rate of formation of C depends upon both steps and the behavior of B is crucial.

If B returns to A much more frequently than it passes on to C, we have a system where A and B are interconverted rapidly and only occasionally is a molecule of C produced. The second step in the reaction ($B \longrightarrow C$) is much slower than the first, and the rate of formation of C depends largely on how fast B passes on to C, the rate of the second step. This step, the "bottleneck," is the rate limiting step.

A number of reactions of this type, where the second step is rate limiting, are known. It is also possible for the first step in such a reaction, $A \longrightarrow B \longrightarrow C$, to be the rate limiting step. When the first step is rate limiting, the reactive intermediate B is transformed into C much more frequently than it returns to A. The return to A is, in fact, unimportant, and the rate of formation of C depends only on how fast B is formed.

We have presented the two extreme cases, the one where B returns to A much more frequently than it passes on to C and the other where B passes on to C much more frequently than it reverts to A. It is also possible for these two processes, return to A and conversion to C, to occur at nearly the same rate, and in such cases neither step in the reaction is truly rate limiting.

When the intermediate B forms C more readily than it reverts to A, the first step is rate limiting. When it returns to A much more frequently than it passes on to C, the second step is the important rate limiting one. If these two processes take place at nearly the same rate, neither step can be said to be truly rate limiting.

The relative heights of the free energy barriers which B must overcome is the criterion for determining the crucial step; see Figure 1–16.

In these reaction coordinate diagrams we assume that one mole of each species (A, B, and C) is present. In the third case where neither step is truly rate limiting, it is difficult to present pictorially the free energy of activation for the entire process. However, in the two extreme cases a simple picture can be given, and here the rate limiting step is the step that involves the transition state of highest energy. Thus, for the first reaction coordinate (see also Figure 1–17) the transition state TS_{AB} is the transition state of highest energy, and the first step is rate limiting.

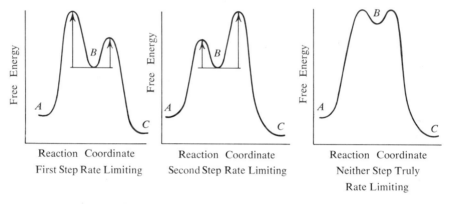

<table>
<tr><td align="center">Reaction Coordinate
First Step Rate Limiting</td><td align="center">Reaction Coordinate
Second Step Rate Limiting</td><td align="center">Reaction Coordinate
Neither Step Truly
Rate Limiting</td></tr>
</table>

Figure 1–16

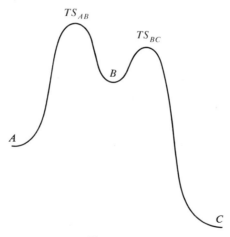

Figure 1–17

Each step in the reaction has a transition state and a free energy of activation. In the formation of C from A it is the transition state in the rate limiting step that is important, and the free energy of activation for the entire reaction, A going to C, is equal to the difference between the free energy of this transition state and that of $A(\Delta G_{AC}^{\ddagger}$ in Figure 1–18).

It is apparent from the reaction coordinate diagram that TS_{AB} is the transition state of highest energy and that the free energy of activation for the entire reaction equals the free energy of activation for the first step.

When the second step is rate limiting, the diagram becomes; see Figure 1–19.

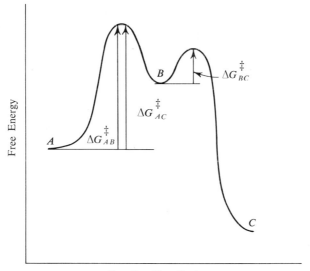

Reaction Coordinate

Figure 1–18

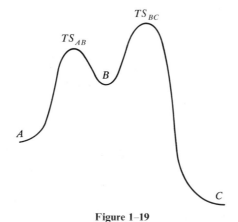

Figure 1–19

Notice again, that every reaction and every step in any reaction has a transition state; the transition state in the rate limiting step (TS_{BC} here) is the more significant one. Since TS_{BC} is the transition state of highest energy, the second step is rate limiting. In the formation of C from A, the free energy of activation for the entire process is equal to the difference between the free energy of this transition state and that of $A(\Delta G^{\ddagger}_{AC}$ in Figure 1–20).

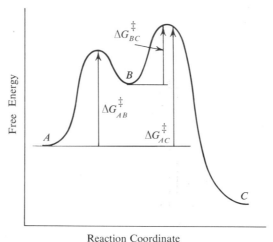

Reaction Coordinate

Figure 1–20

In a reaction involving unstable intermediates a good general rule is the following:

If in a reaction, one of the steps involves a transition state whose energy is much higher than the energies of the other transition states, then that step is rate limiting. If no single transition state has a significantly higher free energy than the others, then no single step in the reaction is truly rate limiting.

We assume in the reaction coordinates that one mole of each species is present. However, in the laboratory a reaction is not usually conducted with equal concentrations of all species. Thus, the experimentally determined rate limiting step depends upon a factor besides $\Delta G^{\ddagger}$ for the various steps. The concentrations of the various reactants influence the experimental results. Consider the more complex reaction:

$$A \; \rightleftharpoons \; B$$

$$B + C \; \longrightarrow \; D$$

where B can revert to A or react with C to form D. When the concentration of C is low, B returns most frequently to A, and the second step is rate controlling (prior equilibrium followed by slow step). However, when the concentration of C is high, B reacts with C more readily than it returns to A. The reaction then depends only upon the rate of formation of B, and the first step becomes rate limiting. Thus, the rate controlling step is dependent upon the concentration of C as well as upon $\Delta G^{\ddagger}$. Solvolysis reactions of certain alkyl halides illustrates this idea:

$$R_3C-X \rightleftharpoons R_3C^+ + X^-$$

$$R_3C^+ \xrightarrow{H_2O} R_3C-\overset{H}{\underset{+}{\overset{|}{O}}}-H$$

$$R_3C-\overset{H}{\underset{+}{\overset{|}{O}}}-H + H_2O \longrightarrow R_3COH + H_3O^+$$

Formation of the alkyl carbonium ion is rate limiting when the halide ion concentration is low. Under these conditions the carbonium ion reacts with water to form the alcohol rather than with halide ion. When the halide ion concentration is high or the water concentration low, the reversal to alkyl halide takes place more often, and the second step can become rate limiting.

1.9 The Principle of Microscopic Reversibility

The principle of microscopic reversibility states that if the mechanism and the reaction profile for any forward reaction is known, then the mechanism and reaction profile for the reverse reaction must also be known. Under the same conditions the mechanism for the reverse reaction must be just the reverse of the mechanism for the forward reaction, and the reaction profile is traversed in just the opposite direction. This is presented schematically for the conversion of A to E and its reversal (forming A from E under the same conditions):

$$A \rightleftharpoons B \rightleftharpoons C \rightleftharpoons D \rightleftharpoons E$$

We assume the reaction profile presented in Figure 1–21.

If B, C, and D are intermediates in the forward reaction, they must also be intermediates in the reverse reaction. The rate limiting step in the forward reaction is formation of D from C; the free energy of activation for the forward reaction (formation of E) is $\Delta G^{\ddagger}_{AE}$. For the reverse reaction, conversion of D into C is rate limiting and $\Delta G^{\ddagger}_{EA}$ is the free energy of activation.

We illustrate with an example. The halide interchange reaction:

$$CH_3-\underset{\underset{CH_3}{|}}{\overset{\overset{CH_3}{|}}{C}}-Cl + Br^- \rightleftharpoons CH_3-\underset{\underset{CH_3}{|}}{\overset{\overset{CH_3}{|}}{C}}-Br + Cl^-$$

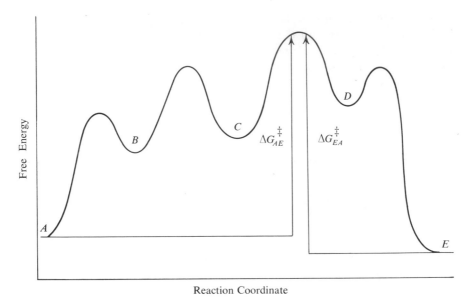

Free Energy

Reaction Coordinate

Figure 1–21

involves the *t*-butyl carbonium ion as intermediate,

$$CH_3\!-\!\underset{\underset{CH_3}{|}}{\overset{\overset{CH_3}{|}}{C}}\!-\!Cl \;\rightleftharpoons\; CH_3\!-\!\underset{\underset{CH_3}{|}}{\overset{\overset{CH_3}{|}}{C^+}} + Cl^-$$

$$CH_3\!-\!\underset{\underset{CH_3}{|}}{\overset{\overset{CH_3}{|}}{C^+}} + Br^- \;\rightleftharpoons\; CH_3\!-\!\underset{\underset{CH_3}{|}}{\overset{\overset{CH_3}{|}}{C}}\!-\!Br$$

It also involves the following transition states:

$$CH_3\!-\!\underset{\underset{CH_3}{|}}{\overset{\overset{CH_3}{|}}{\overset{\delta+}{C}}}\!-\!-\!\overset{\delta-}{Cl} \qquad\qquad CH_3\!-\!\underset{\underset{CH_3}{|}}{\overset{\overset{CH_3}{|}}{\overset{\delta+}{C}}}\!-\!-\!\overset{\delta-}{Br}$$

Now the mechanism for the formation of *t*-butyl chloride from *t*-butyl bromide is just the reverse of the mechanism for the forward process; the same intermediate and the same transition states are involved.

For any reaction, product formation proceeds by a number of different mechanisms, and more than a single reaction profile is involved. Most of the product is formed by way of the pathway with the lowest free energy of activation; however, the observed rate of product formation also depends upon the concentrations of the reactants, and changing the concentration of a reactant can cause a new mechanism and a new reaction profile to become the major route. For example, an increase in the concentration of a strong base changes the predominant mechanism for elimination reactions from *E*1 to *E*2. Furthermore, it is usually not possible to carry out a reverse reaction in good yield under exactly the same conditions as those under which the forward process proceeds favorably. A slight change in the reaction conditions does not generally change the reaction mechanism; however, if a reverse reaction only proceeds favorably under conditions that are drastically different from those employed for the forward reaction, then the reaction mechanism may well change.

The interconversion of *t*-butyl alcohol and *t*-butyl chloride is an example of reactions conducted under somewhat different conditions, yet the mechanism does not change appreciably. The forward reaction, formation of *t*-butyl alcohol, is conducted in the presence of a large excess of water while the reverse reaction proceeds most readily in concentrated hydrochloric acid, yet the mechanism that is written for one process is just the reverse of the mechanism written for the other.

$$CH_3-\underset{\underset{CH_3}{|}}{\overset{\overset{CH_3}{|}}{C}}-Cl \; \rightleftarrows \; CH_3-\underset{\underset{CH_3}{|}}{\overset{\overset{CH_3}{|}}{C^+}} + Cl^-$$

$$CH_3-\underset{\underset{CH_3}{|}}{\overset{\overset{CH_3}{|}}{C^+}} \; \underset{}{\overset{H_2O}{\rightleftarrows}} \; CH_3-\underset{\underset{CH_3}{|}}{\overset{\overset{CH_3\;\;H}{|\;\;\;|}}{C}}\!\!-\!\!\underset{+}{O}\!-\!H$$

$$CH_3-\underset{\underset{CH_3}{|}}{\overset{\overset{CH_3\;\;H}{|\;\;\;|}}{C}}\!\!-\!\!\underset{+}{O}\!-\!H \; \rightleftarrows \; CH_3-\underset{\underset{CH_3}{|}}{\overset{\overset{CH_3}{|}}{C}}-OH + H^+$$

1.10 The Role of the Catalyst

A catalyst is a material that increases the rate of a reaction without in principle affecting the position of the equilibrium. A catalyst is not consumed during the process; if the catalyzing material is consumed during the course of a reaction, the term accelerator is used.

A catalyst enters into a reaction yet is regenerated in its original form at some later stage. For a fixed concentration of reactants the rate of a reaction depends upon $\Delta G^{\ddagger}$. On the other hand, the rate can be increased without lowering the free energy of activation simply by increasing the concentrations of the reactants. No other means for rate enhancement are possible. Therefore, a rate increase due to the catalyzing agent must be accomplished either by lowering $\Delta G^{\ddagger}$ or by increasing the concentration of one or more of the reactants, or both.

One way of increasing the rate is by decreasing $\Delta G^{\ddagger}$, and this can be done by opening new pathways by which the reaction may proceed. The possibility that a substance can catalyze a reaction by opening up new pathways is illustrated by the S_N2 reaction of methyl bromide with water:

$$CH_3Br + H_2O \longrightarrow CH_3\overset{\overset{\displaystyle H}{\displaystyle |}}{\underset{+}{O}}-H + Br^-$$

$$CH_3\overset{\overset{\displaystyle H}{\displaystyle |}}{\underset{+}{O}}-H + H_2O \longrightarrow CH_3OH + H_3O^+$$

This reaction is catalyzed by the addition of a small amount of iodide ion to the mixture. The reaction now proceeds by the mechanism,

$$CH_3Br + I^- \longrightarrow CH_3I + Br^-$$

$$CH_3I + H_2O \longrightarrow CH_3\overset{\overset{\displaystyle H}{\displaystyle |}}{\underset{+}{O}}-H + I^-$$

$$CH_3\overset{\overset{\displaystyle H}{\displaystyle |}}{\underset{+}{O}}-H + H_2O \longrightarrow CH_3OH + H_3O^+$$

Since the iodide ion is regenerated in the second step, this material is effectively a catalyst. Although the catalyzed reaction involves an extra step, it still proceeds more readily than the uncatalyzed process. Iodide ion is displaced by water much more readily than bromide ion, and the first two steps in the catalyzed process take place more rapidly than the single step in the uncatalyzed reaction. The fact that iodide ion is both an effective nucleophile and an efficient leaving group makes catalysis by this anion possible.

If the reaction, $B \longrightarrow C$, is thermodynamically favorable but proceeds slowly, the product may be obtained more readily by adding a catalyst to the system. The free energy of activation is lowered, and C is formed more quickly, see Figure 1–22.

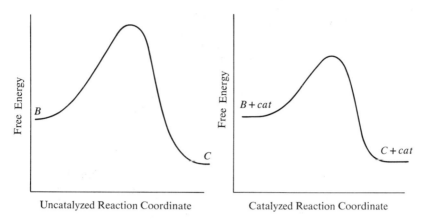

Figure 1–22

Even after a catalyst has been added to the system, the old uncatalyzed pathway for reaction still exists. However, the majority (but not all) of the reactant molecules will react by way of the lower energy catalyzed pathway.

In this example the forward reaction proceeds more readily after catalysis, yet so does the reverse reaction, $C \longrightarrow B$. The same transition state is involved in either direction, and the free energy of activation has been lowered in either direction. This result is a direct consequence of the principle of microscopic reversibility. If a catalyst lowers the free energy of activation for the forward process, it must simultaneously lower the free energy of activation for the reverse process. However, the position of the equilibrium remains unaltered; $\Delta G°$ remains unaltered.

The concept, that a catalyst influences the rate of reaction but not the equilibrium, is illustrated by the mutarotation of D-glucose. This compound is an aldohexose existing in the form of a hemiacetal. The usual crystalline material is α-D-glucose which when dissolved in water has a specific rotation of $+113°$. However, the specific rotation of an aqueous solution slowly decreases, and after some time it reaches the value of $+52.5°$. After attaining this value no further change is observed. There exists in addition to the α-isomer, a β-D-glucose, and a solution of this material has an initial specific rotation equal to $+19°$. Once again, the rotatory power of the solution slowly changes, this time increasing in value until a specific rotation of $+52.5°$ is reached. Dissolving either of these substances in water, we observe a slow change in the specific rotation until the value of $+52.5°$ is attained. After this no further change is observed.

We explain this phenomenon by assuming that in solution these materials are in equilibrium with the open form of the sugar. This open form then re-closes to form a mixture of the α- and β-isomers. We start with either the pure α or the pure β form and ultimately obtain an equilibrium mixture of the two (small amounts of other species are also present). It is this equilibrium mixture that has a specific rotation equal to $+52.5°$.

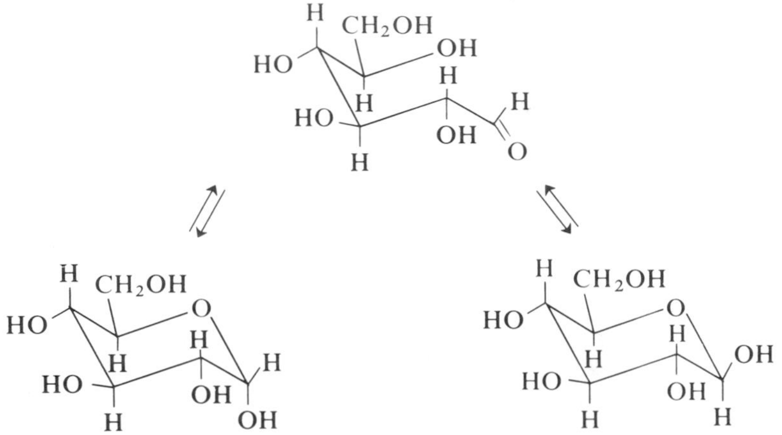

α-D-Glucose
$+113°$

β-D-Glucose
$+19°$

Starting with either pure α or pure β material and repeating this process in the presence of a small amount of added acid or base, we find that the change in specific rotation is now quite rapid. The equilibrium value of $+52.5°$ is attained much more quickly. The acid or base catalyzes the rate of reaction but leaves the position of the equilibrium unaffected.

1.11 The Transition State

An isolated atom can move through space in three independent directions, along the x, y, and z axes. A movement in any other direction is not a new motion but can be considered as a combination of these translations. For example, if an atom moves at an angle of 45° in the xy plane, this is the same as a motion in the x direction followed by a motion in the y direction. The movement at 45° is not truly different or new. These three independent movements can be regarded as the degrees of freedom. An atom has three degrees of freedom, and a molecule composed of N atoms has $3N$ degrees of freedom corresponding to the motions of the individual atoms through space. Of these $3N$ degrees of freedom, three are translations of the molecule, that is, a simultaneous movement of all of the atoms through space in the same direction constitutes a translation of the molecule as a whole. There are three independent translations, in the x, y, and z directions. For nonlinear molecules there also exist three molecular rotations about the x, y, and z axes. Thus, of the $3N$ degrees of freedom for the molecule, $(3N - 6)$ are internal vibrational degrees of freedom. These motions are called the normal modes of vibration or simply the normal vibrations.

Instead of the usual three, a linear molecule has only two rotational degrees of freedom. For example, a linear molecule with the molecular axis lying along the x axis can rotate in the xy plane (about the z axis) and in the xz plane (about the y axis), but there is no degree of freedom about the x axis. The nuclei lie on this axis. Thus a linear molecule composed of N atoms has three translational, two rotational, and $(3N - 5)$ vibrational degrees of freedom.

Consider the reaction,

$$H\bullet + H{-}H \longrightarrow H{-}H + H\bullet$$

where a hydrogen atom collides with a hydrogen molecule to form a new molecule of hydrogen and another hydrogen atom. The transition state for the reaction is,

$$H{-}{-}H{-}{-}H$$

The lowest energy for the transition state occurs when the attacking hydrogen atom is as far removed as possible from the departing hydrogen atom. Therefore, the transition state is a triatomic linear system. The reaction profile is shown in Figure 1–23.

Now if the species H_3 were a normal linear molecule, it would have $(3N - 5 = 4)$ vibrational degrees of freedom. These four vibrational degrees of freedom would be the two bending vibrations (**1** and **2**) and the two stretching vibrations (**3** and **4**) illustrated:

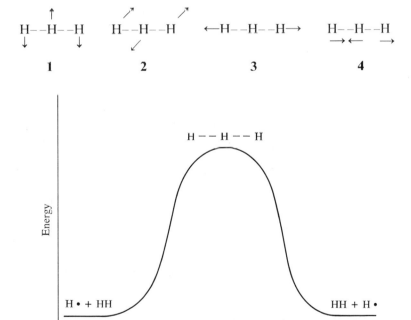

Figure 1–23

However, the transition state is not a normal molecule and one vibrational degree of freedom is missing. The unsymmetrical stretching vibration **4** is just the movement that converts the transition state into the product. Consequently, this internal degree of freedom is missing in the transition state. It becomes a translation in the direction of the reaction coordinate. The linear transition state has $(3N - 6)$ vibrational degrees of freedom instead of the usual $(3N - 5)$ present in a normal molecule. A nonlinear transition state has $(3N - 7)$ instead of the usual $(3N - 6)$ vibrational degrees of freedom.

1.12 Kinetic Isotope Effects

The electronic energy of a system is a function only of the interatomic distances and is unaffected by the masses of the nuclei, yet both vibrational and rotational energy levels depend strongly upon the atomic masses. Remember that the atoms in a molecule are in motion and the molecule is executing normal vibrations even when it is in its lowest energy state. This vibrational energy, called the zero-point energy, always exists. Since it affects the total energy of the system, replacing one atom in the system by an isotopically equivalent atom also affects the rate of a reaction. The masses are important, and the isotope effect is most pronounced when hydrogen is replaced by deuterium or tritium; here, the masses are doubled and tripled respectively. The atoms within a molecule are vibrating and replacing one atom by its isotope changes the vibrational energy levels of the molecule. Since they affect the energy of the system, changes in the vibrational energy affect the rates of reaction.

The zero-point energy for vibration of hydrogen is 6.3 kcal/mole. Thus, the reaction profile for the reaction of hydrogen atoms with hydrogen molecules in their ground state

$$\text{H} \bullet + \text{H} - \text{H} \longrightarrow \text{H} - \text{H} + \text{H} \bullet$$

actually looks as follows; see Figure 1–24.

The energy level for the lowest vibrational state is 6.3 kcal/mole above the electronic level.

The zero-point energy associated with a vibration is

$$E = \tfrac{1}{2}h\nu_0 \quad (6.3 \text{ kcal/mole for hydrogen})$$

where h is Planck's constant and ν_0 is the frequency of the vibration. This frequency is related to the masses of the vibrating atoms (m_1 and m_2) by the equation,

$$2\pi\nu_0 = (k/\mu)^{1/2} = \frac{k^{1/2}}{\left(\dfrac{m_1 m_2}{m_1 + m_2}\right)^{1/2}}$$

where k is the force constant for the vibration with the molecular bond treated

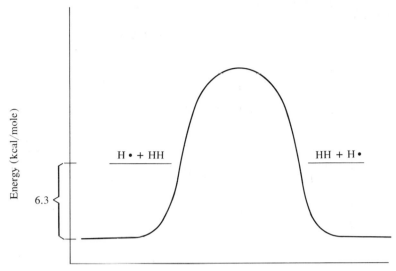

Reaction Coordinate

Figure 1–24

as a vibrating spring and μ is the reduced mass of the vibrating atoms. Substituting, we find for the energy of a vibration in terms of the masses of the participating atoms:

$$E_{12} = \frac{hk^{1/2}}{4\pi}\left(\frac{m_1 + m_2}{m_1 m_2}\right)^{1/2} \qquad (1\text{–}18)$$

If we replace m_2 by an isotope having mass m_3, the force constant k remains unaffected, and the energy for the ground state vibration of the molecule becomes,

$$E_{13} = \frac{hk^{1/2}}{4\pi}\left(\frac{m_1 + m_3}{m_1 m_3}\right)^{1/2}$$

We see that as the mass of the isotope increases, the vibrational energy of the system decreases. If we compare the ground state vibrational energies of H—H and D—H, we find that D—H is more stable,

$$E_{HH} = \frac{hk^{1/2}N^{1/2}}{4\pi}(2)^{1/2}$$

while

$$E_{DH} = \frac{hk^{1/2}N^{1/2}}{4\pi}\left(\frac{3}{2}\right)^{1/2} = \frac{hk^{1/2}N^{1/2}}{4\pi}(1.5)^{1/2}$$

where N is Avogadro's number.

For the reactions,

$$H\bullet + H-H \longrightarrow H-H + H\bullet$$

and

$$H\bullet + D-H \longrightarrow H-D + H\bullet$$

the reaction profile is presented in Figure 1–25.

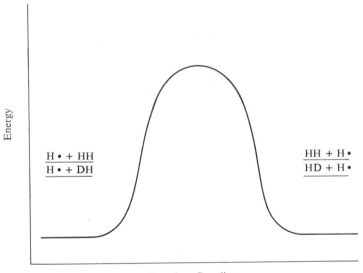

Reaction Coordinate

Figure 1–25

The reactant $D-H$ is more stable than $H-H$. In the transition state this stability difference virtually disappears. Consequently $H-H$ is expected to react more rapidly than $D-H$ and replacing hydrogen by deuterium decreases the rate of reaction. This effect of isotopic replacement upon the rate is called a primary kinetic isotope effect.

The vibrational energy is related to the frequency of the vibrations. As the isotopic mass increases, the vibrational frequency and consequently the vibrational energy decrease.

The reason that the two transition states

$$H--H--H \quad \text{and} \quad H--D--H$$

have nearly the same energy is that the unsymmetrical stretching vibration is not allowed in the transition state. The symmetrical stretching vibration does not involve a movement of the central atom. As a result, the symmetrical stretching vibrations of the two transition states do not depend upon the masses of the central atoms, and the two symmetrical stretching vibrations have the same energy. The two bending vibrations are also active, and any energy differences between the two transition states arise from differences in the bending vibrational energies; however, these energy differences are small.

In examples such as this one, bond rupture involves the isotopic atom (hydrogen or deuterium), and the kinetic isotope effect attains its maximum value, but a number of factors influence the magnitude of these effects. In the example just presented,

$$E_{\text{IIII}} - F_{\text{DII}} = 6.3 - 5.4 = 0.9 \ \text{kcal/mole}$$

and assuming that the transition states have the same energy, we find for the calculated ratio of the specific rate constants,

$$\frac{k_{\text{IIII}}}{k_{\text{DH}}} = e^{0.9/RT}$$

In the temperature range of interest the exponential term has a value of approximately five, therefore:

$$\frac{k_{\text{HH}}}{k_{\text{DH}}} = 5$$

Hydrogen transfer is calculated on this basis to be about five times as rapid as deuterium transfer. Actually this ratio is affected by the still active bending vibrations in the transition state, and tunneling effects are important. Hydrogen tunnels more effectively than deuterium. Furthermore, not all of the reactant molecules are in their ground state as we have assumed. These factors influence the measured ratio $k_{\text{HH}}/k_{\text{DH}}$.

We are most interested in reactions involving C—H and C—D bonds. When these rate constants are being compared, the measured ratio $k_{\text{CH}}/k_{\text{CD}}$ can be as high as seven or eight. For example, for the bromination of acetone, the ratio is 7.7. However, ratios of much less than this (two or three) are more common, and these smaller isotope effects can be attributed to several causes.

If a reaction is a several step process, the magnitude of the observed kinetic isotope effect will naturally depend upon the importance of the step involving bond breakage to hydrogen or deuterium. When this bond breakage step is a relatively unimportant part of the reaction, that is, when it is not the rate limiting step, smaller values for the observed kinetic isotope effect are expected, and values approaching zero can be obtained for the experimentally determined isotope effect.

Even when hydrogen or deuterium bond breakage is rate limiting, smaller values are sometimes expected. Consider the reactions:

$$X{-}H + Y\bullet \longrightarrow X\bullet + H{-}Y$$
$$X{-}D + Y\bullet \longrightarrow X\bullet + D{-}Y$$

where the transition states are,

$$X\text{-}\text{-}H\text{-}\text{-}Y \qquad X\text{-}\text{-}D\text{-}\text{-}Y$$

In these transition states the central atoms are not bonded with equal strength to the two groups X and Y. Consequently, in these transition states the central atom does move during the symmetrical stretching vibration:

$$X\text{-}\text{-}H\text{-}\text{-}Y \qquad X\text{-}\text{-}D\text{-}\text{-}Y$$
$$\leftarrow \quad \rightarrow \quad \rightarrow \qquad \leftarrow \quad \rightarrow \quad \rightarrow$$

This vibration is allowed in the transition state, the central atom moves, and the zero point vibrational energy of the transition state depends upon the masses of the central atoms. The transition state for the deuterium containing compound is the lower energy state. The reactant XD is more stable than XH, but this difference is partially offset by the difference in the stability of the transition states. The deuterium containing compound still reacts more slowly, but the ratio k_H/k_D is smaller. This is illustrated in Figure 1–26.

In the previous examples we were concerned with reactions in which hydrogen or deuterium bonds were broken. The effects associated with these reactions are called primary kinetic isotope effects. The replacement of hydrogen by deuterium also affects the rate of reactions where these bonds are not being

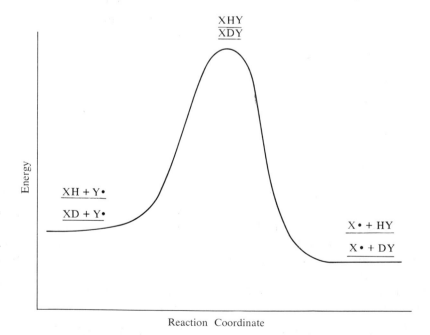

Reaction Coordinate

Figure 1–26

ruptured. These smaller secondary effects are called secondary kinetic isotope effects.

The modes of vibration of the transition state differ from those in the reactant. For example, a reaction taking place in another part of the molecule changes the stretching and bending vibrational frequencies of a carbon-hydrogen bond. This bond is not being broken, but in passing to the transition state the vibrational frequencies change. If there is a decrease in passing to the transition state, the effect is smaller in magnitude but similar to a primary effect, and replacing the hydrogen atom by deuterium causes the reaction to proceed more slowly (k_H/k_D is usually less than 1.5). On the other hand it is possible that the modes of vibration involving the hydrogen atom occur with greater frequency in the transition state than in the reactant, and in such cases where the frequencies increase in passing to the transition state, the deuterium containing compound actually reacts faster. Thus, both normal and inverse secondary isotope effects are known.

Supplementary Reading

1. Breslow, R., *Organic Reaction Mechanisms.* New York, Benjamin, 1965.
2. Dewar, M. J. S., *An Introduction to Modern Chemistry.* New York, Oxford U. P., 1965
3. Gould, E. S., *Mechanism and Structure in Organic Chemistry.* New York, Holt, 1959.
4. Hammett, L. P., *Physical Organic Chemistry.* New York, McGraw-Hill, 1940.
5. Hine, J., *Physical Organic Chemistry.* New York, McGraw-Hill, 1962.
6. Laidler, K. J., *Chemical Kinetics.* New York, McGraw-Hill, 1965.
7. Leffler, J. E., and Grunwald, E., *Rates and Equilibria of Organic Reactions.* New York, Wiley, 1963.
8. Melander, L., *Isotope Effects on Reaction Rates.* New York, Ronald, 1960.
9. Moore, W. J., *Physical Chemistry.* Englewood Cliffs, New Jersey, Prentice-Hall, 1962.
10. Strong, L. E., and Stratton, W. J., *Chemical Energy.* New York, Reinhold, 1965.
11. Wiberg, K. B., *Physical Organic Chemistry.* New York, Wiley, 1964.

Chapter 2

Chemical Kinetics

2.1 General Discussion

A study of chemical reactions requires a knowledge of chemical kinetics, the dynamic pathway by which reactions occur. The rate of any process naturally depends upon the particular reaction under investigation. Some reactions are slow; others are fast; all are temperature dependent. For a given reaction at a fixed temperature we also assume that the rate of any single step in the reaction is proportional to the concentrations of the species entering into that step. In the single step process, $B \longrightarrow C$, the rate of formation of C is proportional to the concentration of B.

At the start of the reaction ($B \longrightarrow C$) no product exists; only reactant is present. Since the concentration of B is large, we form a considerable amount of C very quickly. Towards the end of the reaction the concentration of B is small, and we form only small amounts of C. For example, more C is produced during the first second of reaction when the concentration of B is large than during the last second of reaction when the concentration of B is small. Thus, during any time interval (say, one second) the amount of C formed depends upon the average amount of B present during that interval.

As any reaction proceeds, there is a continuous increase in the concentrations of the products and a decrease in the concentrations of the starting materials. Most organic reactions also involve intermediates. These are generally unstable and therefore are present only in small amounts. The very fact that these intermediates are present to a small degree and cannot usually be detected allows us to neglect their concentrations. We generally need to know only the concentrations of reactants and products. To follow how quickly these products are formed and how rapidly the starting materials disappear, we must measure each of their concentrations at intervals throughout the duration of the reaction.

We must ascertain the concentrations of reactants and products, and to measure these concentrations various techniques exist. The determination depends upon the distinguishing physical or chemical characteristics of the material. The analytical procedure may involve gravimetric or volumetric methods. Alternatively, physical measurements can be employed. The latter include the ability of a solution to conduct electricity, a change in optical rotation for optically active substances, colorimetry, ultraviolet or infrared spectroscopy, and nuclear magnetic resonance phenomena. The choice of the analytical method depends upon the system under consideration.

If the mechanism for a reaction is known, a kinetic scheme can be written. In practice one encounters the reverse situation. A measurement of the kinetics of reaction is made, and one must then postulate a mechanism consistent with the observed kinetic picture. We next illustrate kinetic principles by using certain examples. For the reaction,

$$A \xrightarrow{k_1} B \xrightarrow{k_2} C$$

at any time the increase in the concentration of B per unit time (given by $d[B]/dt$) is equal to the difference between how fast B is formed and how quickly it decomposes. If the concentration of B is to change with time, it must be formed at a rate different from its rate of decomposition. The change in the concentration of B is equal to its rate of formation minus its rate of decomposition:

$$\frac{d[B]}{dt} = \text{rate of formation of } B - \text{rate of decomposition of } B$$

Now the rate of formation of B is proportional to the concentration of A that is present, and we can express this proportionality in mathematical terms:

$$\text{rate of formation of } B = k_1[A]$$

where k_1, the constant of proportionality, is the specific rate constant for the first step. The significance of this constant was discussed in the previous chapter.

The rate of decomposition of B is proportional to the concentration of B itself. The more B that is present, the more decomposes:

$$\text{rate of decomposition of } B = k_2[B]$$

Then the change in the concentration of B is given by,

$$\frac{d[B]}{dt} = k_1[A] - k_2[B]$$

2.2 Unimolecular First-Order Reactions

For the reaction,

$$B \xrightarrow{k} C$$

$d[C]/dt$ is equal to the difference between how fast C is formed and how quickly it decomposes. In the present example C is stable, and once formed it does not decompose extensively. Therefore,

$$\text{rate of decomposition of } C = 0$$

and

$$\frac{d[C]}{dt} = \text{rate of formation of } C$$

Now the rate of formation of C is proportional to the concentration of B. We express this as,

$$\text{rate of formation of } C = k[B]$$

Therefore,

$$\frac{d[C]}{dt} = k[B]$$

This expression, which indicates the factors influencing the increase in the concentration of product, is called a general rate expression or rate law. Here the change in the concentration of C depends upon the concentration of B and upon the specific rate constant for the reaction. These general rate expressions are sometimes integrable, but for our purposes it suffices to leave them in the unintegrated form.

We define the order of this particular reaction as equal to the number of chemical species entering into the general rate expression. The reaction just discussed is first order since only a single species B enters into the rate law. We also define the molecularity of a reaction as the number of chemical species entering into the rate limiting step, that is, the order of a general rate expression determined just for the rate limiting step. This example is a one-step reaction; therefore, this step must be rate limiting. Since the step involves one species B, the present example is also unimolecular. The reaction is a unimolecular first-order reaction.

Notice the difference between the order and the molecularity of a reaction. The idea of the order of a reaction is meaningful only when the general rate expression for product formation has the form:

$$\frac{d[\text{product}]}{dt} = k[A]^a[B]^b[C]^c$$

and the reaction is then said to be ath order in A, bth order in B, cth in C, and the overall order is $a + b + c$.

The general rate law indicates the chemical entities whose concentrations affect the rate of product formation.

2.3 Equilibria

In the equilibrium:

$$B \underset{k_{-1}}{\overset{k_1}{\rightleftarrows}} C$$

where k_1 is the specific rate constant for the forward reaction and k_{-1} the specific rate constant for the reverse reaction, the change in the concentration of C is again equal to the difference between its rate of formation and its rate of decomposition. Now, the rate of formation of C is proportional to the concentration of B while the rate of decomposition is proportional to that of C. Therefore,

$$\frac{d[C]}{dt} = k_1[B] - k_{-1}[C]$$

At equilibrium, there is no change in the concentration of C, and

$$\frac{d[C]}{dt} = 0$$

Consequently,

$$0 = k_1[B] - k_{-1}[C]$$

or

$$k_1[B] = k_{-1}[C]$$

At equilibrium the rate of formation of C equals its rate of decomposition. Furthermore, transposing this equation leads to:

$$\frac{k_1}{k_{-1}} = \frac{[C]}{[B]}$$

Since the equilibrium constant for the reaction is also defined as

$$K = \frac{[C]}{[B]}$$

We find that

$$K = \frac{k_1}{k_{-1}}$$

The equilibrium constant can be expressed as the ratio of the specific rate constants for the forward and reverse processes. When the reaction is:

$$A \underset{k_{-1}}{\overset{k_1}{\rightleftharpoons}} B \underset{k_{-2}}{\overset{k_2}{\rightleftharpoons}} C$$

the equilibrium concentrations of C and A are related as follows,

$$K = \frac{k_1 k_2}{k_{-1} k_{-2}} = K_1 K_2 = \frac{[C]}{[A]}$$

2.4 Bimolecular Second-Order Reactions

Having discussed unimolecular processes, we next consider the case of a bimolecular reaction:

$$A + B \xrightarrow{k} C$$

This reaction is a single-step process, and this step must be rate limiting. Two chemical species, A and B, enter into this rate limiting step; therefore, the reaction is bimolecular.

The increase in the concentration of C is equal to the rate of formation of this material, for C, once formed, does not decompose. The general rate expression is,

$$\frac{d[C]}{dt} = \text{rate of formation of } C$$

Since this depends upon the concentrations of both A and B, we obtain,

$$\frac{d[C]}{dt} = k[A][B]$$

Two chemical entities enter into the general rate law; the reaction is second order.

The one-step dimerization of any substance is also a second order reaction,

$$B + B \xrightarrow{k} C$$

The general rate expression is,

$$\frac{d[C]}{dt} = k[B]^2$$

The species B enters into the general rate law twice.

2.5 The Steady-State Approximation

The general rate expression for a one-step reaction can be obtained easily. If the reaction involves more than a single step, the situation becomes more complex. In the reaction,

$$A \xrightarrow{k_1} B \xrightarrow{k_2} C$$

the general rate expression is given in terms of $[B]$ by the expression,

$$\frac{d[C]}{dt} = k_2[B]$$

Now if B is an intermediate that is present in high concentrations, that is, a long-lived stable intermediate, we can either directly or indirectly determine its concentration at any time. However, if B is an unstable short-lived intermediate, the concentration of B present at any time is undetectably small. In that case, it becomes meaningless to leave the general rate expression in terms of B; instead we must express it in terms of A. To accomplish this we use the steady-state approximation.

The intermediate B is unstable and never present in large amounts. It is being formed continuously, yet it is reactive and its concentration remains small. This implies that the rate of decomposition of B must be nearly the same as its rate of formation, and this is the steady-state approximation—the rate of formation of a reactive intermediate equals its rate of decomposition.

Since the change in the concentration of B is given by,

$$\frac{d[B]}{dt} = \text{rate of formation of } B - \text{rate of decomposition of } B$$

we find that,

$$\frac{d[B]}{dt} = 0$$

and the steady-state approximation is equivalently given by the statement—there is no change in the concentration of a reactive intermediate.

This is an approximation. How well it holds, naturally depends upon how accurately it describes the given situation.

Returning to our example, $A \longrightarrow B \longrightarrow C$, we have

$$\frac{d[C]}{dt} = k_2[B]$$

Using the steady-state approximation for B,

$$0 = \frac{dB}{dt} = k_1[A] - k_2[B]$$

or

$$k_1[A] = k_2[B]$$

Substituting this result into the general rate law yields,

$$\frac{d[C]}{dt} = k_1[A]$$

This affords the general rate expression in terms of A.

Notice that the increase in the concentration of C equals the decrease in the concentration of A. This is expected. Since very little material is stored as the intermediate B, disappearance of A must be matched by appearance of C.

$$\frac{d[C]}{dt} = -\frac{d[A]}{dt} = k_1[A]$$

A reaction coordinate that satisfies the criterion that the concentration of B remain at all times small is shown in Figure 2–1.

Many carbonium ion reactions have a reaction profile with this general shape, and carbonium ion reactions are treated quite successfully using the steady-state technique.

The only requirement for satisfactory application of the steady-state assumption is that the concentration of B be very low. Thus, the reaction,

$$A \underset{k_{-1}}{\overset{k_1}{\rightleftharpoons}} B \overset{k_2}{\longrightarrow} C$$

where we consider a possible reversal of the first step, is also treated successfully by the steady-state technique when the concentration of B satisfies this requirement.

We allow B to decompose by two routes; it may return to reactant or proceed on to product. We obtain our previous result for the general rate expression in terms of B:

$$\frac{d[C]}{dt} = k_2[B]$$

Using the steady-state approach for B (rate of formation equals the rate of decomposition),

$$k_1[A] = k_{-1}[B] + k_2[B]$$

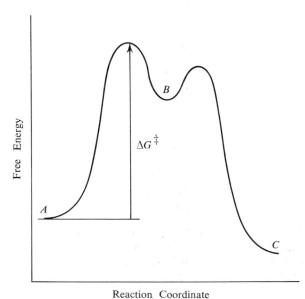

Reaction Coordinate

Figure 2-1

Here, B decomposes by two routes. Solving for $[B]$,

$$[B] = \frac{k_1[A]}{k_{-1} + k_2}$$

and substituting for $[B]$ into the original expression affords,

$$\frac{d[C]}{dt} = \frac{k_1 k_2[A]}{k_{-1} + k_2}$$

This rate expression, somewhat more complex than the previous result, can be simplified under certain circumstances. We consider two situations where simplification is possible. If the first step in this reaction is rapid and reversible and only slowly is B converted to C, then step two is rate limiting. Under these conditions B returns to A much more frequently than it decomposes to product. The major route for the decomposition of B is by reversal; then,

$$k_{-1}[B] > k_2[B]$$

or

$$k_{-1} > k_2$$

In the denominator of the general rate expression we add a large term k_{-1} and a small term k_2, and it becomes possible to neglect k_2. The rate law now becomes,

$$\frac{d[C]}{dt} = \frac{k_1 k_2[A]}{k_{-1}}$$

Using the definition for the equilibrium constant,

$$\frac{d[C]}{dt} = K_1 k_2[A]$$

A reaction coordinate consistent with this result is presented in Figure 2–2.

Some carbonium ion reactions follow this type of a reaction profile, yet these reactions are also treated successfully by the steady-state method.

We are able to simplify the rate expression when k_{-1} is much larger than k_2. The other case, k_2 much larger than k_{-1}, also results in a simplification of the rate equation. If k_2 is much larger than k_{-1}, B decomposes more readily to product and return to reactant is negligible. The term k_{-1} can then be neglected in the denominator of the rate expression which now becomes,

$$\frac{d[C]}{dt} = k_1[A] \qquad k_2 > k_{-1}$$

This is the same result as that which we obtained previously, and of course, the situation is the same. The intermediate passes on to product and return to

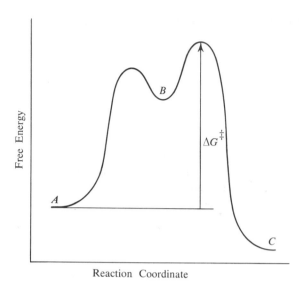

Figure 2-2

reactant can be neglected. This leads to

$$A \longrightarrow B \longrightarrow C$$

2.6 Unimolecular Second-Order Reactions

In the sequence,

$$A + B \underset{k_{-1}}{\overset{k_1}{\rightleftarrows}} C \overset{k_2}{\longrightarrow} D$$

the second step is rate limiting. Since this step involves only the intermediate C, the reaction is unimolecular. The general rate expression is obtained as follows,

$$\frac{d[D]}{dt} = k_2[C]$$

Employing a steady state treatment for C,

$$k_1[A][B] = k_{-1}[C] + k_2[C]$$

then

$$[C] = \frac{k_1[A][B]}{k_{-1} + k_2}$$

and substitution of this quantity into the rate expression yields,

$$\frac{d[D]}{dt} = \frac{k_1 k_2 [A][B]}{k_{-1} + k_2}$$

The general rate expression involves the two species A and B; therefore the reaction is second-order. Since k_{-1} is by assumption much larger than k_2, the equation may be simplified:

$$\frac{d[D]}{dt} = K_1 k_2 [A][B]$$

The rate law for this example can be written in terms of the intermediate C or in terms of the reactants A and B. This rate law indicates the materials entering into the rate limiting step, and it is actually C that is involved; however, the intermediate is formed from A and B. Therefore, we know that the transition state in the rate controlling step is composed of one molecule of A and one of B.

2.7 Fractional Exponents

In the previous general rate expressions, the exponents of the concentrations were whole numbers, that is, the expressions were of the type, $k[A][B]$ and $k[A]^2$. It is also possible to have fractional exponents. For example the reaction:

$$A \underset{k_{-1}}{\overset{k_1}{\rightleftarrows}} B + C$$

$$B + D \overset{k_2}{\longrightarrow} E$$

leads to a general rate expression that under some conditions has such exponents. For this reaction:

$$K_1 = \frac{[B][C]}{[A]}$$

and

$$\frac{d[E]}{dt} = k_2 [B][D]$$

The transition state of importance involves molecules of B and D. If this reaction is run under conditions where the only source of B and C is from A, then

$$[B] = [C]$$

and

$$K_1 = \frac{[B]^2}{[A]}$$

Therefore,

$$[B] = K_1^{1/2}[A]^{1/2}$$

and the rate law becomes,

$$\frac{d[E]}{dt} = K_1^{1/2}k_2[A]^{1/2}[D]$$

2.8 Reversible Product Formation

It is worthwhile to consider one case where the product is formed reversibly, for this serves to illustrate how one deals with these more difficult kinetic situations. We assume that the first step in the sequence is rate limiting:

$$A \xrightarrow{k_1} B$$

$$B \underset{k_{-2}}{\overset{k_2}{\rightleftharpoons}} C$$

Now the equilibrium constant for the second step is:

$$K_2 = \frac{[C]}{[B]}$$

or

$$[C] = K_2[B]$$

Then differentiating both sides of this equation with respect to t,

$$\frac{d[C]}{dt} = K_2\frac{d[B]}{dt}$$

The product is in equilibrium with its precursor, and an increase in the concentration of product is reflected by a corresponding increase in the precursor concentration.

Now an increase in the concentrations of B and C must be matched by a decrease in the concentration of A. As the concentration of B and C increases, the concentration of A must decrease by an equal amount, and we write this as,

$$\frac{d[C]}{dt} + \frac{d[B]}{dt} = -\frac{d[A]}{dt} = k_1[A]$$

Transposing,

$$\frac{d[B]}{dt} = k_1[A] - \frac{d[C]}{dt}$$

and from the general rate law,

$$\frac{d[C]}{dt} = K_2 \left(k_1[A] - \frac{d[C]}{dt} \right)$$

Solving for $d[C]/dt$:

$$\frac{d[C]}{dt} = \frac{k_1 K_2 [A]}{K_2 + 1}$$

General rate expressions can be obtained when product formation is significantly reversible, but the techniques are somewhat more complex.

2.9 Interpretation of Kinetic Data

We have shown that when the mechanism for a reaction is known, the general rate expression can always be obtained; however, one usually conducts kinetic experiments without prior knowledge of the mechanism. In fact, if the mechanism is known, kinetic measurements are not required. Having the kinetic results, it then becomes necessary to postulate a mechanism in agreement with the experimental data. This problem is far more difficult, for kinetic data can frequently be interpreted in a number of ways. Several pathways can usually be written to satisfy kinetic results, but not all are equally logical. The chemist's intuition must then come into play in order to decide which of the several possibilities is most likely. For example in Section 2.7, the reaction involving fractional exponents could have been interpreted in a number of ways. It requires some understanding of chemical principles to realize that the fractional exponent for A in the rate law implies a prior reversible dissociation of the reactant.

Kinetic results tell us nothing concerning the number of unstable intermediates involved in a reaction; for example, if we measure the rate of formation of a compound C from some compound A, and if we find that the disappearance of A is matched by the appearance of C, this still tells us nothing concerning which or how many undetectable intermediates were involved. A large number of intermediates could be involved. If each of these were present in very low concentration, the difference between the disappearance of A and the appearance of C would be immeasurably small, and to all apparent purposes the two would be equal.

$$\frac{d[C]}{dt} = -\frac{d[A]}{dt}$$

The value of the observed specific rate constant k_{obs} gives no information. Consider two possible routes for the formation of C:

$$A \xrightarrow{k} C$$

$$A \xrightarrow{k_1} B \xrightarrow{k_2} C$$

The first proposed route is a single-step sequence while the second involves an intermediate with the first step rate limiting. Possible reaction coordinates are shown in Figure 2–3.

If the first reaction is correct, $k_{obs} = k$, whereas if the second is correct, $k_{obs} = k_1$. Naturally, it is not possible to determine which of these possibilities is the proper one.

It is not even necessary that the first step for the sequence involving B be rate limiting. The second step could be rate limiting or neither could be. Other possible reaction profiles are illustrated in Figure 2–4.

If neither step is rate limiting or if the second step is, the sequence becomes,

$$A \underset{k_{-1}}{\overset{k_1}{\rightleftharpoons}} B \overset{k_2}{\longrightarrow} C$$

and when neither step is rate controlling,

$$k_{obs} = \frac{k_1 k_2}{k_{-1} + k_2}$$

while if the second step is,

$$k_{obs} = K_1 k_2$$

Here k_{obs} becomes a composite term made up of several constants.

It is not possible to distinguish between the various possibilities, unless we are able to prove in some other way that B participates in the reaction. Thus,

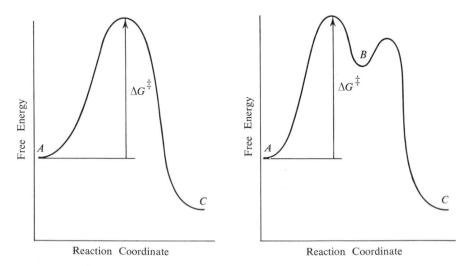

Figure 2-3

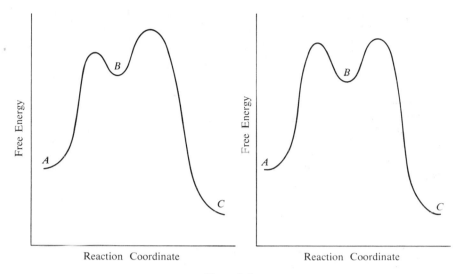

Figure 2-4

kinetic measurements yield a great deal of information, but they do not provide all the answers.

2.10 The Mass Law Effect

The exchange reaction between benzhydryl chloride and fluoride ion, which proceeds quite rapidly at the start, decreases in rate as the concentration of chloride ion increases,

$$\phi-\overset{\displaystyle H}{\underset{\displaystyle Cl}{C}}-\phi + F^- \longrightarrow \phi-\overset{\displaystyle H}{\underset{\displaystyle F}{C}}-\phi + Cl^-$$

Furthermore, addition of chloride ion to the mixture causes a marked decrease in the rate of product formation. This retardation is due to the mass-law effect of chloride ion, and the following mechanism is consistent with these observations,

$$\phi-\overset{\displaystyle H}{\underset{\displaystyle Cl}{C}}-\phi \underset{k_{-1}}{\overset{k_1}{\rightleftharpoons}} \phi-\overset{\displaystyle H}{\underset{\displaystyle +}{C}}-\phi + Cl^-$$

$$\phi-\overset{\displaystyle H}{\underset{\displaystyle +}{C}}-\phi + F^- \overset{k_2}{\longrightarrow} \phi-\overset{\displaystyle H}{\underset{\displaystyle F}{C}}-\phi$$

Chloride ion competes quite successfully with fluoride for the carbonium ion intermediate. This causes a reversal of the ionization step. When the chloride concentration is high, a smaller fraction of the carbonium ion reacts with fluoride ion, and the rate of the overall reaction decreases.

If the reversal of the first step occurs significantly more often than the second step, we have a reaction that is similar in principle to the usual S_N1 reaction yet having the second step as the rate limiting step. The reaction is then bimolecular.

Determination of the general rate law for this reaction leads to the result,

$$\frac{d\left[\begin{matrix}H\\|\\\phi-C-\phi\\|\\F\end{matrix}\right]}{dt} = \frac{k_1 k_2 \left[\begin{matrix}H\\|\\\phi-C-\phi\\|\\Cl\end{matrix}\right][F^-]}{k_{-1}[Cl^-] + k_2[F^-]}$$

Both chloride and fluoride ion concentrations enter into the rate expression. Since the term $[Cl^-]$ appears only in the denominator of this rate law, increasing the chloride ion concentration decreases the rate of reaction.

If reversal of the first step is slow, implying that the term $k_{-1}[Cl^-]$ is small, we may neglect this term in the rate expression, and obtain the first order result:

$$\frac{d\left[\begin{matrix}H\\|\\\phi-C-\phi\\|\\F\end{matrix}\right]}{dt} = k_1 \left[\begin{matrix}H\\|\\\phi-C-\phi\\|\\Cl\end{matrix}\right]$$

Thus the reaction follows first order kinetics while the chloride ion concentration is small yet deviates from this simple rate law as the chloride ion concentration increases. The mass law effect becomes important in this type of reaction whenever the term $k_{-1}[Cl^-]$ is significant.

2.11 General Acid and Base Catalysis

A reaction that is general acid catalyzed requires a molecule of the catalyzing acid HX (assumed to be a weak acid) to enter into the rate limiting step. The catalyst enters into the transition state and into the general rate expression. However, since the catalyzing acid ionizes according to the equation,

$$HX \rightleftharpoons H^+ + X^-$$

it is not possible to tell whether it is the undissociated HX that is involved or the separate species H^+ and X^-. If the reaction rate shows dependence upon HX, and if we assume that the dissociated acid is involved, then both H^+ and X^- must be included. A reaction that depends only upon H^+ is said to be specific acid catalyzed.

To illustrate the idea of general acid catalysis we return to the reaction,

$$B \xrightarrow{k} C$$

and assume that we are conducting this reaction in aqueous solution. The increase in the concentration of C for this process is given by the expression $k[B]$.

This reaction in solution appears to be uncatalyzed because the general rate expression for product formation is simply:

$$\frac{d[C]}{dt} = k[B]$$

Yet as is usually the case, a reaction proceeds more rapidly in solution than in the gas phase or in the pure solid or liquid state. Consequently the solvent must be catalyzing the process in some way. Since the solvent is in large excess, its concentration does not vary appreciably during the reaction. As a result the reaction appears to be independent of the concentration of the solvent, and solvent does not enter into the general rate expression. Although reactions in solution appear to be uncatalyzed processes, they may actually be solvent catalyzed.

In addition to this uncatalyzed (solvent catalyzed) process, let us assume that addition of a weak acid HX to the solution catalyzes the reaction according to the mechanism,

$$B + HX \xrightarrow{k_1} HB^+ + X^-$$
$$HB^+ \xrightarrow{k_2} C + H^+$$

where the first step, proton transfer, is rate limiting. The increase in the concentration of C due to the HX acid catalyzed reaction is,

$$k_1[B][HX]$$

Now in aqueous solution the acid catalyst is known to dissociate,

$$HX + H_2O \underset{}{\overset{K_a}{\rightleftharpoons}} H_3O^+ + X^-$$

Consequently, HX is not the only available source of protons. A small amount of the strong acid H_3O^+ is present, and this can also catalyze the reaction. (Once again, we assume that the first step is rate limiting.)

$$B + H_3O^+ \xrightarrow{k_1'} HB^+ + H_2O$$
$$HB^+ \xrightarrow{k_2} C + H^+$$

The change in the concentration of C resulting from this last process is given by the expression,

$$k_1'[B][H_3O^+]$$

Since C is formed simultaneously by three distinct pathways, the total increase in the concentration of C resulting from all of these processes is given by the sum of the three rate expressions.

$$\frac{d[C]}{dt} = k[B] + k_1[B][HX] + k_1'[B][H_3O^+]$$

Notice that both acids, HX and H_3O^+, enter into the rate expression. Increasing the concentration of undissociated HX increases the rate of reaction even under conditions where the concentration of H_3O^+ is kept constant (constant pH). To maintain a constant pH we simultaneously increase the concentration of HX and X^- (by adding Na^+X^-). The sodium salt buffers the solution, and the concentration of H_3O^+ remains constant.

The kinetic scheme for the entire acid catalyzed process is:

$$B + HX + H_2O \underset{}{\overset{K_a}{\rightleftharpoons}} B + H_3O^+ + X^-$$

$$\searrow k_1 \qquad\qquad k_1' \swarrow$$

$$HB^+ + X^- + H_2O$$

$$HB^+ \xrightarrow{k_2} C + H^+$$

The reaction is catalyzed by both of the acids present in the solution. If other acids were present these could also catalyze the reaction, and the rate expression would contain additional terms involving these acids. This type of reaction, where the rate depends upon the concentration of all of the acids present in the system, is an example of general acid catalysis.

In this type of general acid catalyzed reaction, proton transfer by the acid was rate limiting. Reactions can be catalyzed in an analogous fashion by bases, and in general base catalyzed processes proton abstraction by the general base is rate limiting.

We have presented one example; other mechanistic possibilities also giving rise to what is apparently general acid catalysis exist. For example, the following type of reaction also gives rise to a general rate expression containing a term for each acid, and it is therefore considered in the category of general acid and base catalysis:

$$B + HX \underset{k_{-1}}{\overset{k_1}{\rightleftharpoons}} HB^+ + X^-$$

$$HB^+ + X^- \xrightarrow{k_2} C + HX$$

In this reaction the rate limiting step is proton abstraction by the general base. Thus, any acid present in the system can transfer a proton (H_3O^+ and HX), and any base present (H_2O, X^-) can abstract a proton in the second step. Since proton transfer in the first step does not constitute the rate limiting portion of the reaction, whether the original proton source is HX or H_3O^+ is immaterial. The general rate expression is,

$$\frac{d[C]}{dt} = k[B] + k_2[HB^+][X^-] + k_2'[HB^+]$$

where the first term represents the uncatalyzed (solvent catalyzed) process, the second is for the X^- catalyzed reaction, and in the third the solvent H_2O acts as the base. In terms of the acids H_3O^+ and HX, this rate expression becomes,

$$\frac{d[C]}{dt} = k[B] + K_1 k_2[B][HX] + \frac{K_1 k_2'}{K_a}[B][H_3O^+]$$

All general acid catalyses require a molecule of the general acid in the rate limiting step. This acid can enter as HX or as H^+X^-, but it must be included in some way. The transition state must also involve HX or H^+X^-.

In the example just presented, although the reaction appears kinetically as general acid catalysis, the first step is rapid, and proton abstraction by the base is actually rate limiting. In some cases it is also possible for the first step to be rapid and essentially irreversible. In those cases the concentration of the intermediate HB^+ builds up and ultimately becomes equal to the initial concentration of B.

Certain reactions are both general acid and general base catalyzed. Examples include the mutarotation of glucose and the enolization of acetone. At moderate pH's the rate of halogenation of acetone is enhanced by both acids and bases yet is independent of the halogen concentration. The following mechanism is compatible with these experimental observations (the first step is rate limiting):

$$CH_3COCH_3 \xrightarrow{HX} CH_3\overset{\overset{\displaystyle OH}{\displaystyle |}}{C}=CH_2$$

$$CH_3\overset{\overset{\displaystyle OH}{\displaystyle |}}{C}=CH_2 + X_2 \longrightarrow CH_3COCH_2X$$

2.12 Specific Acid and Base Catalysis

A specific acid catalyzed reaction involves only the protonated reactant in the rate limiting step. The reaction rate depends upon the hydrogen ion concentration, and the transition state involves a proton but not X^-, that is, only H^+ enters into the general rate expression. A specific base catalyzed reaction involves only the deprotonated reactant in the rate limiting step.

We use the following hypothetical example to illustrate specific acid catalysis. Assume that the reaction:

$$C \xrightarrow{k} D$$

proceeds in aqueous solution and that this reaction is catalyzed by the acid HX according to the mechanism:

$$C + HX \underset{k_{-1}}{\overset{k_1}{\rightleftharpoons}} HC^+ + X^-$$

$$HC^+ \xrightarrow{k_2} HD^+$$

$$HD^+ \xrightarrow{k_3} D + H^+ \qquad (2\text{–}1)$$

where the second step is rate limiting.

In the previous examples (general acid catalysis) the rate limiting step was proton transfer to the reactant or proton abstraction by the base. In the present case the rate limiting portion of the reaction takes place after proton transfer and before proton abstraction. The rate limiting step is the conversion of the conjugate acid of the reactant HC^+ to the conjugate acid of the product HD^+. This step occurs independently of the proton source (HX or H_3O^+) and it is not pertinent which base (X^-, H_2O) abstracts the proton, for none of these enter into the rate limiting step.

The rate of product formation by the acid catalyzed pathway is given by,

$$\frac{d[D]}{dt} = k_2[HC^+]$$

The rate of reaction is proportional to the concentration of protonated reactant. Furthermore, in aqueous solution HX is in equilibrium with protonated solvent,

$$HX + H_2O \overset{K_a}{\rightleftharpoons} H_3O^+ + X^-$$

and this acid H_3O^+ can also catalyze the reaction,

$$C + H_3O^+ \underset{k'_{-1}}{\overset{k'_1}{\rightleftharpoons}} HC^+ + H_2O$$

$$HC^+ \xrightarrow{k_2} HD^+$$

$$HD^+ \xrightarrow{k_3} D + H^+ \qquad (2\text{–}2)$$

The kinetic scheme for the overall process is:

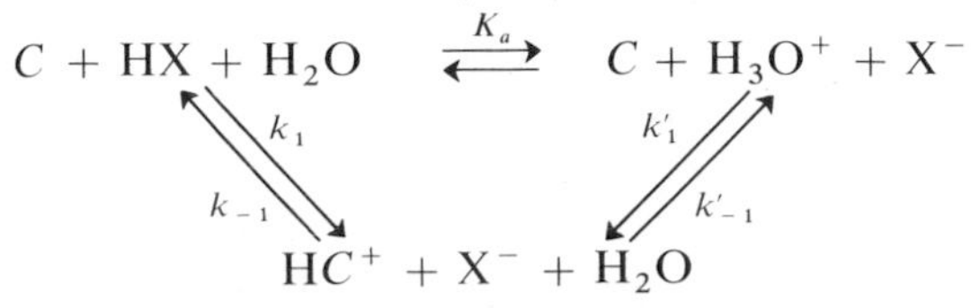

$$C + HX + H_2O \overset{K_a}{\rightleftharpoons} C + H_3O^+ + X^-$$

$$HC^+ + X^- + H_2O$$

$$HC^+ \xrightarrow{\;k_2\;} HD^+$$

$$HD^+ \xrightarrow{\;k_3\;} D + H^+$$

The reaction involves several equilibria followed by a rate limiting step, and the rate of reaction depends only upon the concentration of the acid HC^+. Any factor that increases the concentration of HC^+ increases the rate of reaction; processes not influencing this concentration do not affect the rate of reaction. Furthermore, this species is in equilibrium with the other acids (HX and H_3O^+) that are present, and the concentration of HC^+ is related to the concentrations of these other acids. It is most convenient to develop the general rate expression in terms of H_3O^+, for this concentration can be determined most readily as the pH of the solution.

To develop this rate expression we consider the reaction involving H_3O^+ and HC^+. The concentration of one is directly related to the concentration of the other by process [Eq. (2–2)], and the general rate expression is,

$$\frac{d[D]}{dt} = \frac{k_1' k_2 [C][H_3O^+]}{k_{-1}'}$$

We discover that the rate is a function of the H_3O^+ concentration and increasing this concentration increases the rate of reaction. At constant pH the rate of reaction remains constant.

We could equally well have developed the rate expression in terms of HX. The process is given by Eq. (2–1), and the rate expression is

$$\frac{d[D]}{dt} = \frac{k_1 k_2 [C]}{k_{-1}} \frac{[HX]}{[X^-]}$$

This result concurs with the previous expression. Notice again, that increasing the concentration of HX at constant H_3O^+ concentration (by simultaneously adding HX and Na^+X^-) does not increase the rate of this type of reaction, for under such conditions the ratio:

$$\frac{[HX]}{[X^-]}$$

remains constant and the rate is unaltered. Thus the rate does depend upon the concentration of protonated solvent, yet at constant pH it is independent of the concentration of any other acid. This type of reaction that depends only upon the protonated solvent is said to be specific acid catalyzed. Analogously, a reaction depending only upon the deprotonated solvent (OH^- when the solvent is H_2O) is specific base catalyzed.

A reaction proceeding by the general acid catalyzed pathway,

$$C + HX \underset{k_{-1}}{\overset{k_1}{\rightleftharpoons}} HC^+ + X^-$$

$$HC^+ + X^- \xrightarrow{\;k_2\;} D + HX$$

where HX represents any acid and where the rate limiting step is proton abstraction by the general base X$^-$, may appear to be specific acid catalyzed when the concentration of HX is low. This is seen most readily by considering the general rate expression which is,

$$\frac{d[D]}{dt} = k[C] + K_1 k_2 [C][HX] + \frac{K_1 k_2'[C][H_3O^+]}{K_a}$$

When the concentration of HX is low, the second term may not be detected experimentally, and the catalyzed reaction then appears to depend only on the concentration of H_3O^+. The reaction thus appears to be specific acid catalyzed.

This can also be seen qualitatively. When the concentration of HX is low, the concentration of X$^-$ must be low. The solvent H_2O is present in much greater concentration, and under these conditions this acts as the general base. Such a process with the solvent behaving as the general base is kinetically indistinguishable from specific acid catalysis.

Supplementary Reading

1. Frost, A. A., and Pearson, R. G., *Kinetics and Mechanism, 2nd Edition*. New York, Wiley, 1961.

2. Gould, E. S., *Mechanism and Structure in Organic Chemistry*. New York, Holt, 1959.

3. Hammett, L. P., *Physical Organic Chemistry*. New York, McGraw-Hill, 1940.

4. Hine, J., *Physical Organic Chemistry*. New York, McGraw-Hill, 1962.

5. King, E. L., *How Chemical Reactions Occur*. New York, Benjamin, 1963.

6. Laidler, K. J., *Chemical Kinetics*. New York, McGraw-Hill, 1965.

7. Latham, J. L., *Elementary Reaction Kinetics*. London, Butterworths, 1964.

Chapter 3

Acids and Bases

3.1 General Discussion

Reactions such as,

$$HSO_4^- + H_2O \rightleftharpoons H_3O^+ + SO_4^{--}$$

are acid-base reactions. The Brønsted-Lowry acid HSO_4^- loses a proton and is converted to the base SO_4^{--}. This base is called the conjugate base. Thus, SO_4^{--} is the conjugate base of HSO_4^- while the acid HSO_4^- is the conjugate acid of SO_4^{--}. The base H_2O is converted to its conjugate acid.

The acid in an acid-base reaction gives up a proton and is converted to its conjugate base; the base accepts a proton and is converted to its conjugate acid. Looking at the equilibrium in the opposite direction, SO_4^{--} accepts a proton and is converted to its conjugate acid; H_3O^+, which gives up a proton, is converted to its conjugate base.

As another example consider the equilibrium,

$$\phi COOH + OH^- \rightleftharpoons \phi COO^- + H_2O$$

In the forward direction benzoic acid reacts with hydroxide ion and is converted to its conjugate base. The hydroxide ion picks up a proton and forms its conjugate acid H_2O.

In the first example water behaves as a base; in the second it behaves as an acid. The species H_2O is the conjugate acid of OH^- and the conjugate base of H_3O^+. All materials can behave in this manner. Compounds react as either acids or bases, and their behavior depends upon the other reagents present in the system. Benzoic acid, for example, behaves as an acid in aqueous solutions, yet in the presence of the stronger acid H_2SO_4 it behaves as a base. Nitric acid behaves similarly:

$$\phi COOH + H_2O \rightleftharpoons \phi COO^- + H_3O^+$$

$$\phi COOH + H_2SO_4 \rightleftharpoons \phi - \overset{\overset{\displaystyle OH}{|}}{\underset{+}{C}} - OH + HSO_4^-$$

and

$$HNO_3 + H_2O \rightleftharpoons H_3O^+ + NO_3^-$$

$$HNO_3 + H_2SO_4 \rightleftharpoons H-\overset{\overset{\displaystyle H}{|}}{\underset{+}{O}}-NO_2 + HSO_4^-$$

Autoprotonation also takes place, and the following examples are illustrative:

$$H_2O + H_2O \rightleftharpoons H_3O^+ + OH^-$$

and

$$HNO_3 + HNO_3 \rightleftharpoons H-\overset{\overset{\displaystyle H}{|}}{\underset{+}{O}}-NO_2 + NO_3^-$$

When an acid HX reacts with water, the following equilibrium is set up,

$$HX + H_2O \rightleftharpoons H_3O^+ + X^-$$

and the stronger the acid the further to the right lies the equilibrium. For very strong acids such as HCl, HNO_3, and so forth, the ionization is virtually complete in dilute solutions. However, even strong acids such as HCl and HNO_3 are not completely ionized in very concentrated solutions. The relative strengths of various acids can be determined by measuring the degree of reaction, that is, by measuring the position of the equilibrium.

The strengths of bases Y^- can also be determined by measuring the positions of equilibria such as,

$$Y^- + H_2O \rightleftharpoons HY + OH^-$$

The relative strengths of many acids and bases can be determined in aqueous solution. There exist, however, very strong acids and bases and very weak acids and bases, and for these water is not a suitable medium. The equilibria for strong acids such as HCl, HNO_3, $HClO_4$, and for extremely strong bases (NH_2^-, $CH_3CH_2O^-$, and so forth) lie too far to the right; the reaction is virtually complete. In order to differentiate between very strong acids, a weaker base than water must be employed, while to determine the relative strengths of very strong bases a solvent that is less acidic than water is required.

For the very weak bases sulfuric acid serves as a sufficiently strong acid, and the relative strengths of these materials can be determined in this solvent. For weak acids the strong base NH_2^- in liquid ammonia is useful.

For materials that are not completely converted to products the degree of reaction can be measured in a variety of ways, and an equilibrium constant K can be calculated. For any acid-base reaction,

$$HX + Y^- \rightleftharpoons HY + X^-$$

an equilibrium constant can be calculated once the equilibrium concentrations of the various species have been determined. On the other hand, a knowledge of the equilibrium constant allows one to calculate the equilibrium concentrations:

$$K = \frac{[HY][X^-]}{[HX][Y^-]}$$

This law usually applies in dilute solutions; in concentrated solutions and for associated materials the activity coefficients must be included in the equilibrium expression. The equation becomes:

$$K' = \frac{[HY]f_{HY}[X^-]f_{X^-}}{[HX]f_{HX}[Y^-]f_Y}$$

We define a new equilibrium constant K'; the f's are the activity coefficients of the various species. Then,

$$K = K' \frac{f_{HX}f_{Y^-}}{f_{HY}f_{X^-}} = \frac{[HY][X^-]}{[HX][Y^-]}$$

The equilibrium constant K is truly constant only so long as the activity coefficients remain constant. These coefficients vary with the solvent, the concentrations, the ionic strength of the solution, and so forth.

Under conditions where the activity coefficients are nearly equal to unity (in dilute aqueous solutions) or when the activity coefficients remain constant under the experimental conditions, it is possible to work with equilibrium constants in terms of concentrations. When these coefficients are not constant over the range of concentrations being studied, they must be included explicitly in the expressions for the equilibrium constants.

In a very dilute solution of a nondissociating solute in a solvent, the solvent obeys Raoult's law while the solute follows Henry's law. As long as the solute does obey Henry's law the activity coefficient of the solute is equal to unity. An activity coefficient equal to unity implies that the molecules of the solute do not interact and that the only interactions are between molecules of solvent and the solute. Consequently, in dilute solutions the activity coefficients of various solutes approach unity, yet they deviate from this value as the concentration of solute is increased. These deviations from unity indicate that interactions between solute molecules are present, and as the concentration of solute is increased, these interactions become more pronounced.

Expressions similar to Henry's law can be developed for solutes such as NaCl and HCl that do dissociate when dissolved in a solvent, and the activity coefficients are again defined in such a way that they approach unity in very dilute aqueous solutions. In general, the activity coefficients will not be equal to unity, but by working with extremely dilute solutions in polar solvents, these coefficients will have nearly this value. Alternatively, it is possible to work under conditions where the expressions involving the activity coefficients, expressions such as,

$$\frac{f_{HY} f_{X^-}}{f_{HX} f_{Y^-}}$$

remain nearly constant. It may be necessary to keep the solution at constant ionic strength. Under the proper conditions K, the equilibrium constant in terms of concentrations, is a suitable measure of the extent of reaction.

Consider the effect of adding small amounts of an inert salt such as sodium chloride upon the equilibrium,

$$HX + Y^- \rightleftharpoons HY + X^-$$

with

$$K' = \frac{[HY][X^-]}{[HX][Y^-]} \cdot \frac{f_{HY} f_{X^-}}{f_{HX} f_{Y^-}}$$

Addition of sodium chloride to the medium stabilizes any ions that are present. The ions tend to surround themselves with other ions of opposite charge. This stabilizes them and decreases their activity coefficients. Adding sodium chloride affects the activity coefficients of the charged ions more than it affects the activity coefficients of the uncharged molecules; however, since both X^- and Y^- are charged, the position of the equilibrium is only slightly influenced.

However, in a reaction of the type,

$$HX + H_2O \rightleftharpoons H_3O^+ + X^-$$

The products are ions while the reactants are molecules. Now addition of sodium chloride stabilizes the ions and shifts the equilibrium to the right. The equilibrium constant K' for the process is given by (a_{H_2O} represents the activity of water under the experimental conditions),

$$K' = \frac{[H_3O^+][X^-]}{[HX]} \cdot \frac{f_{H_3O^+} f_{X^-}}{a_{H_2O} f_{HX}}$$

Since the activity coefficients in the numerator decrease when a salt is added and since K' remains constant, this means that the concentrations of H_3O^+ and X^- must increase. Thus, addition of sodium chloride shifts the equilibrium to the right. For this same example, addition of the less polar ethyl alcohol to the original aqueous solution of HX increases the activity coefficients of the ions H_3O^+ and X^-; the ions become less stable; and their concentration decreases. Upon addition of ethyl alcohol, the equilibrium is shifted to the left.

These facts demonstrate one point quite clearly; namely, that the strength of an acid depends to some degree upon the solvent in which it is dissolved. A solution of HCl in ethanol is a much stronger acid than a solution of HCl in water. If the solvent is a weaker base, a solution of a strong acid in that solvent is a more effective proton donor, that is, such a solution is a stronger acid.

Dissolving a weaker acid such as acetic or benzoic acid in ethanol rather than in water causes the degree of dissociation of the acid to decrease. This is due to a decrease in the stability of the ions in the less polar solvent; remember that the activity coefficients increase in value in less polar solvents:

$$RCOOH \rightleftarrows H^+ + RCOO^-$$

When comparing the strengths of a series of acids, precautions must be taken to see that the activity coefficients do not vary. Whenever possible a series of acids is studied in the same solvent at the same temperature, and to insure against salt effects, at constant ionic strength. This last measure is accomplished by adding a chemically inert salt such as sodium chloride to the medium. Addition of a moderately large concentration of the salt maintains the ionic strength at a constant value. If the concentrations of the acids being studied are varied, slightly more or less salt is introduced to compensate. This keeps the total salt effect constant. Alternatively, the salt effect may be eliminated by measuring the acid strengths in terms of concentrations at various ionic strengths and extrapolating to zero ionic strength.

When the strengths of various acids can be compared by measuring the degree of dissociation in dilute aqueous solution, the equilibrium is:

$$HX + H_2O \rightleftarrows H_3O^+ + X^-$$

or simply,

$$HX \rightleftarrows H^+ + X^-$$

and the larger the value of K_a, the equilibrium constant for the dissociation, the stronger is the acid:

$$K_a = \frac{[H^+][X^-]}{[HX]}$$

A similar expression can be written for the reaction of the conjugate base X^- with water:

$$X^- + H_2O \rightleftarrows HX + OH^-$$

and

$$K_b = \frac{[HX][OH^-]}{[X^-]}$$

These two expressions can be combined to yield,

$$K_a \cdot K_b = \frac{[H^+][X^-]}{[HX]} \cdot \frac{[HX][OH^-]}{[X^-]}$$

$$K_a \cdot K_b = [H^+][OH^-] = K_w$$

where K_w is given by,

$$H_2O \rightleftharpoons H^+ + OH^-$$

$$K_w = [H^+][OH^-]$$

Since K_w is constant under a given set of conditions and

$$K_w = K_a K_b$$

we find that the stronger the acid, the weaker is its conjugate base.

Just as the hydrogen ion concentration $[H^+]$ or $[H_3O^+]$ is related to the pH,

$$pH = -\log[H^+]$$

or

$$pH = -\log[H_3O^+]$$

the equilibrium constant K_a can be related to a quantity the pK_a, which we define as,

$$pK_a = -\log K_a$$

$$pK_a = -\log\frac{[H^+][X^-]}{[HX]}$$

It is possible to rewrite the expression for the pK_a as,

$$pK_a = -\log[H^+] - \log\frac{[X^-]}{[HX]}$$

$$pK_a = pH - \log\frac{[X^-]}{[HX]}$$

We also define a pK_b:

$$pK_b = -\log K_b$$

and

$$pK_a + pK_b = pK_w$$

If the acid and base strengths are measured in a solvent other than water, then

$$K_a K_b = K_s$$

where K_s is the autoprotolysis constant for the solvent. For example, for methanol:

$$CH_3OH + CH_3OH \rightleftharpoons CH_3OH_2^+ + CH_3O^-$$

or simply

$$CH_3OH \rightleftharpoons H^+ + CH_3O^-$$

$$K_s - [H^+][CH_3O^-]$$

and at 25°C,

$$pK_s = 16.7$$

The values of K_s have been determined for a number of solvents. These values vary with the temperature. The value of K_w at various temperatures has been determined from measurements of the conductivity of pure water; see Table 3–1. This conductivity is due to the presence of the ions H^+ and OH^-.

Table 3–1

T	K_w
0°C	0.12×10^{-14}
25°C	1.04×10^{-14}
50°C	5.66×10^{-14}

3.2 Acidity Functions and Acidity Scales

In dilute aqueous solutions where it is not necessary to consider the activity coefficients explicitly, the K_a for an acid can be expressed in terms of concentrations and the pH indicates the hydrogen ion concentration.

$$K_a = \frac{[H^+][X^-]}{[HX]}$$

and

$$pK_a = pH - \log\frac{[X^-]}{[HX]}$$

where

$$pH = -\log[H^+]$$

These functions are perfectly good in dilute aqueous solutions; however, under other conditions the activity coefficients must also be included. The expression becomes,

$$K_a = \frac{[H^+][X^-]}{[HX]}\frac{f_{H^+} f_{X^-}}{f_{HX}}$$

Then,

$$pK_a = -\log\left([H^+]\frac{f_{H^+}f_{X^-}}{f_{HX}}\right) - \log\frac{[X^-]}{[HX]}$$

The first term approaches the pH as the activity coefficients approach unity. When these coefficients are not equal to unity and must be considered, we can define new functions h_- and H_- as,

$$h_- = [H^+]\frac{f_{H^+}f_{X^-}}{f_{HX}}$$

and

$$H_- = -\log\left([H^+]\frac{f_{H^+}f_{X^-}}{f_{HX}}\right)$$

$$H_- = -\log h_-$$

The expression for the pK_a becomes equal to,

$$pK_a = H_- - \log\frac{[X^-]}{[HX]}$$

We have made no assumptions and the functions h_- and H_- are perfectly valid; however, they are not very general. Since the terms f_{X^-} and f_{HX} enter into these expressions, these functions might be expected to depend upon the nature of X^- and its conjugate acid HX. It turns out that under some conditions the ratio,

$$\frac{f_{X^-}}{f_{HX}}$$

has the same value for several related bases X^-, and as long as this ratio remains the same for different bases the functions h_- and H_- are general functions, independent of the base, and similar in nature to $[H^+]$ and the pH.

All of the bases in question must be negatively charged. Naturally this ratio is not expected to be the same for negatively charged bases and for neutral bases. When neutral bases such as H_2O, ROH, and RNH_2 are employed in the reaction, we must define new Hammett functions h_0 and H_0. These functions are employed when the reactions involve neutral bases Y.

$$h_0 = [H^+]\frac{f_{H^+}f_Y}{f_{HY^+}}$$

and

$$H_0 = -\log h_0$$

The functions h_0 and h_- are useful in elucidating reaction mechanisms. Consider a reaction of the type,

$$Y + H^+ \underset{}{\overset{K}{\rightleftarrows}} HY^+$$

$$HY^+ \overset{k}{\longrightarrow} \text{products}$$

where the rate limiting step of the reaction is the unimolecular decomposition of the conjugate acid HY^+ into the products. According to the theory of reaction rates, the change in the concentration of products $d[P]/dt$ is given by,

$$\frac{d[P]}{dt} = k[HY^+]$$

If the reaction is being conducted under conditions where the activity coefficients deviate significantly from unity, these coefficients must be included in the rate expression. The rate law becomes,

$$\frac{d[P]}{dt} = k[HY^+] \frac{f_{HY^+}}{f^{\ddagger}_{HY^+}}$$

where f_{HY^+} is the activity coefficient of the intermediate and $f^{\ddagger}_{HY^+}$ is the activity coefficient of the transition state.

Now the equilibrium constant for the reversible step is equal to,

$$K = \frac{[HY^+]}{[Y][H^+]} \frac{f_{HY^+}}{f_{H^+} f_Y}$$

and substituting for $[HY^+]f_{HY^+}$ into the rate expression affords,

$$\frac{d[P]}{dt} = kK[Y][H^+] \frac{f_{H^+} f_Y}{f^{\ddagger}_{HY^+}}$$

Since the transition state and the reactant Y differ in composition by a proton, the ratio $f_Y/f^{\ddagger}_{HY^+}$ is expected to vary in the same manner as f_Y/f_{HY^+}. Therefore, the term

$$[H^+] \frac{f_{H^+} f_Y}{f^{\ddagger}_{HY^+}}$$

is proportional to the function h_0, and the general rate expression becomes,

$$\frac{d[P]}{dt} = k_{obs}[Y]h_0$$

The rates of reactions of this type are proportional to the function h_0, and this proportionality serves as a criterion of mechanism. When the reaction rate varies linearly with the function h_0, we can usually assume a mechanism in which the transition state differs in composition from the reactant by a proton.

Unfortunately, caution must be exercised when equilibria and rates are discussed using h_0 as a criterion of mechanism. The definition of h_0, which includes the ratio f_Y/f_{HY^+}, is general only as long as this ratio of activity coefficients remains constant. Yet not all neutral bases Y and their conjugate acids HY^+ are expected to afford the same ratio. A series of structurally similar primary amines affords one ratio; a series of tertiary amines can afford another. Thus, there is a change in the activity coefficients even when passing from one neutral base to another. Only when a series of very similar bases Y is being compared, can the ratio f_Y/f_{HY^+} be expected to be about the same throughout the series. Another difficulty is that few reactions follow h_0 exactly. Thus interpretation of the data becomes difficult. Despite obvious shortcomings, h_0 and h_- are useful.

Functions such as h_0 and H_0, h_- and H_- are extremely useful; the former are employed in conjunction with neutral bases and the latter with negatively charged bases. They can even be used in nonaqueous solvents, and two different acidic solutions with the same value of H_0 are equally efficient at protonating a neutral base. Still another acidity function H_R has been defined for work in connection with reactions such as,

$$\phi - \overset{\displaystyle \phi}{\underset{\displaystyle \phi}{\overset{|}{\underset{|}{C}}}} - OH + H^+ \quad \rightleftharpoons \quad \phi - \overset{\displaystyle \phi}{\underset{\displaystyle \phi}{\overset{|}{\underset{|}{C^+}}}} + H_2O$$

In these carbonium ion forming reactions a molecule of water is produced along with the acid $\phi_3 C^+$. The reaction is an acid-base reaction but is not expected to correlate well with H_0; consequently, another acidity function has been defined.

Other acidity functions and acidity scales have been proposed for acid-base reactions. Some involve more than a single parameter. One of these acidity scales, the Grunwald scale, involves an adjustable parameter designated as f_{H^+}. This parameter f_{H^+} is defined in such a way that it can be interpreted as the activity coefficient of the proton in various organic solvents and aqueous-organic mixtures. Most of the work has been done in ethanol-water mixtures. The function f_{H^+} indicates the stability of the proton in the solvent, and the larger the value of f_{H^+} the less stable is the proton. Of course, as the proton becomes less stable, there is a greater tendency for it to be donated. Therefore the values of f_{H^+} for a particular solvent composition indicate the ability of that mixture to donate a proton to a base. For example, for a 50% ethanol-water mixture $f_{H^+} = 1.8$, and this implies that a solution of a strong acid in a 50–50 mixture of ethanol and water is 1.8 times as effective a proton donor as a solution of that same acid in pure water. Since the values of f_{H^+} in a particular solvent do not depend upon whether the original acid is positively charged such as anilinium ion or neutral such as acetic acid, the values of f_{H^+} appear to be independent of the acid that originally supplies the proton and the base that accepts it, and this makes f_{H^+} an interesting function (h_0 and h_- do depend upon the base accepting the proton).

3.3 The Behavior of Ions in Solution

A solution of an acid HX in water contains in addition to unionized HX the hydrated and solvated ions H^+ and X^-. Separation of these ions requires the separation of oppositely charged species, and since the attraction between these two decreases rather slowly as they move farther apart, some association still exists between them even when they are separated by a rather large distance. Furthermore, the rates of ionization of molecules and the rates of recombination of ions to form molecules are extremely rapid. Thus few ions in a solution can be considered to move freely and independently of other ions that are present, and the most likely processes for ions after they are formed is to recombine or to reassociate as ionic aggregates. These phenomena become increasingly important as the ionic concentration increases.

The formation of ionic aggregates held together by coulombic attraction occurs readily at higher ionic concentrations and in less polar solvents. The ionic radii are also important, and the smaller the ionic radii, the greater the degree of association as ionic aggregates. Two oppositely charged ions held together in this manner are called an ion pair, three ions ($+ - +$ or $- + -$) electrostatically held are triplets, and so forth. Such association into ionic aggregates lowers the value of the ionic activity coefficients.

When calculating the degree of dissociation of an acid, the K_a, the formation of ion pairs, triplets, and so forth must be considered. Ionic aggregates do not behave as free ions, and some of their physical properties may be intermediate between those of the undissociated molecule and those of the free ions. Therefore the degree of dissociation of an acid when calculated from conductance measurements or from measurements of the osmotic pressure may have a different value from that obtained from spectroscopic data. The spectroscopic behavior of an ionic aggregate is similar to that of the free ions. Consequently this method indicates the total concentration of the ionic species, both the free ions and the ionic aggregates. Absorption in the visible region occurs for some ions; ultraviolet spectroscopy and the Raman spectra also serve to measure the concentrations of the species present. For example, the dissociation constant for HNO_3, calculated from the Raman spectra of concentrated solutions, is found to equal 21.4 at 25° ($K_a = 21.4$). Occasionally x-ray studies of concentrated ionic mixtures are possible, and these give direct information concerning ionic association.

Not only can ionic association influence the values for K_a, but hydrogen bonding also affects the equilibrium. Triethylamine reacts with excess acetic acid in carbon tetrachloride to form the ion pair $(CH_3CH_2)_3NH^{+\,-}OOCCH_3$, and this ion pair is solvated by hydrogen bonding with another molecule of acetic acid. Thus ionic association and hydrogen bonding may interfer with the determination of acid strengths. Such difficulties can sometimes be overcome by adding a large excess of an inert salt to the medium. The salt effect keeps the ionic strength and the ionic environment in the solution constant.

3.4 The Leveling Effect

Another factor that must be considered when determining the relative strengths of acids is the leveling effect of the solvent. All of the acids HI, HNO_3, $HClO_4$ appear to be equally strong in dilute aqueous solutions. The ionization

$$HX + H_2O \rightleftharpoons H_3O^+ + X^-$$

occurs to such an extent under these conditions that the concentration of unionized HX is immeasurably low. As a result it is not possible to ascertain which is the stronger acid; the ionization is virtually complete for all of them. Using a weaker base than water does make it possible to distinguish between these acids. Acetic acid is such a substance; a much weaker base than water, when these acids are dissolved in acetic acid, differences in acid strength are noticeable. The equilibrium:

$$HX + CH_3COOH \rightleftharpoons CH_3\overset{OH}{\underset{+}{C}}{-}OH + X^-$$

is less favorable than the previous one, and in acetic acid it becomes possible to determine the relative strengths of the acids. For example, using the same molar concentrations of $HClO_4$ and HNO_3 in acetic acid, the equivalent conductivity of the $HClO_4$ solution is much greater than the conductivity of the HNO_3 solution. This conductivity indicates and is related to the concentrations of ions that are present. The greater conductivity of $HClO_4$ demonstrates that it is the stronger acid. Employing the weaker base acetic acid allows us to differentiate between the acids while the leveling effect of a stronger base like water prevents us from making such a discrimination.

In order to determine the relative strengths of a series of acids it is necessary to react these acids with some base, when possible, a common base and under the same conditions. These reactions should not be too favorable for then all of the acids appear to be equally strong. Nor should the reactions be too unfavorable, for if none of the acids in the series reacts appreciably with the base, then all of them appear to be equally weak. The same concepts apply in the determination of relative base strengths.

3.5 Acids

The relative strengths of moderately strong water soluble acids can be determined by measuring their degree of dissociation in aqueous solution. The strengths of very strong acids such as HNO_3 and $HClO_4$ can be compared in nonaqueous solvents. Thus, in water HI, $HClO_4$, and HNO_3 are all strong acids. In methanol and in ethanol HI and $HClO_4$ are still strong, yet HNO_3 is weak. In acetone even HI is a weak acid while $HClO_4$ remains a strong acid. Thus the order of acid strengths is,

$$HClO_4 > HI > HNO_3$$

Carboxylic acids RCOOH appear to be strong acids when reacting with the strong base NH_3. In aqueous solution their dissociation is incomplete, and they behave as weaker acids. When treated with HCl or H_2SO_4, these carboxylic acids behave as bases.

Both HCOOH and HCl behave as strong acids when treated with NH_3. With water, HCOOH no longer dissociates completely while HCl still behaves as a strong acid. When HCl is dissolved in HCOOH, HCl behaves as a moderately strong acid and HCOOH becomes the base. The first ionization of H_2SO_4 is virtually complete even in formic acid solution. The order of acid strengths in this series becomes,

$$H_2SO_4 > HCl > HCOOH$$

By making comparisons such as these, the relative strengths of the stronger acids can be determined. Very weak acids require a stronger base than OH^- and nonaqueous solvents must be employed. Liquid ammonia containing the amide ion NH_2^- (in the form of KNH_2 or $NaNH_2$) serves moderately well in this capacity. The reaction of a weak acid with amide ion is represented by the equilibrium,

$$HX + NH_2^- \rightleftharpoons NH_3 + X^-$$

For extremely weak acids still stronger bases must be employed. Grignard reagents or other organometallic compounds in ethereal solution serve for this purpose:

$$RH + R'MgX \rightleftharpoons R'H + RMgX$$

By studying related equilibria the relative strengths of many organic acids have been established, and similar techniques are employed for bases.

3.6 Bases

The strengths of various bases can also be correlated. This can be accomplished either by studying the reactions of the bases or by making use of available data concerning their conjugate acids. When comparing base strengths, use is made of the fact that the strength of a base is related to the strength of its conjugate acid. The equation,

$$K_a K_b = K_s$$

relates these two, as do the expressions K_a and $1/K_a$. Since the value of K_a

indicates the degree of dissociation of the conjugate acid HY into H^+ and Y^-,

$$K_a = \frac{[H^+][Y^-]}{[HY]}$$

the value of the expression $1/K_a$ indicates the ability of the base Y^- to abstract protons. Thus use is made, when comparing base strengths, of knowledge concerning the strengths of the conjugate acids; the stronger the conjugate acid, the weaker the base.

   If data on the conjugate acid are not available, the reactions of the base can be studied. The results of such studies indicate not only the strength of the base but also furnish information concerning the strength of the conjugate acid. Consequently, the same procedures that are used for determining acid strengths are employed for establishing base strengths. If a base is soluble in water and reacts measurably but not completely with H_2O or H_3O^+, the equilibrium constant can be determined:

$$Y^- + H_2O \;\rightleftharpoons\; HY + OH^-$$

or

$$Y^- + H_3O^+ \;\rightleftharpoons\; HY + H_2O$$

   The extent of reaction can be measured in several ways. If ions are created or destroyed in the process, the conductivity of the solution serves as an indicator of the degree of reaction. Alternatively, spectroscopic analyses can be employed to measure the concentrations of HY and Y^-. Another possibility involves the use of indicators which can be introduced into the solution, and the color changes of these indicators serve to measure the pH.

   A variety of experimental techniques are available. For example, the ionization of HCOOH is virtually complete in NH_3 yet incomplete in H_2O. Consequently, NH_3 is a stronger base than H_2O. Furthermore, NH_3 reacts with H_2O, and the reaction between these two materials can be represented by the equilibrium,

$$H_2O + NH_3 \;\rightleftharpoons\; NH_4^+ + OH^-$$

   The strengths of many bases can be determined by measuring the extent of reaction of the base with water. However this reaction of the base with water is not suitable for comparing very strong or very weak bases. For the former the process is essentially complete while for the latter the extent of conversion of the weak bases to their conjugate acids is in all cases immeasurably small. For such bases solvents other than water must be employed. Very strong bases must be reacted with extremely weak acids. The reactions of these bases in liquid ammonia or with hydrocarbons in ether serve to correlate their strengths. Very weak bases on the other hand require a strong acid, and solutions of these weak bases in H_2SO_4 are useful.

An interesting technique exists for measuring base strengths in sulfuric acid. Sulfuric acid freezes at a temperature of 10.5°. When a solute is dissolved, the freezing point is lowered. The behavior is analogous to that of other solvents; for example, the freezing point of water is also depressed when solutes are dissolved in it. A nondissociating solute lowers the freezing point of sulfuric acid 6°/mole/1000 g of H_2SO_4, that is, the introduction of one mole of a non-dissociating solute into 1000 g of sulfuric acid lowers the freezing point by 6°. When solutes that do dissociate are added to sulfuric acid, the lowering of the freezing point indicates the degree of dissociation. Thus the introduction of salts such as $NaHSO_4$ and $KHSO_4$, which are completely dissociated in solution, is expected to depress the freezing point by twice the previously specified value. Two species are present in solution (for example, K^+ and HSO_4^-), and a freezing point depression equal to 12°/mole/1000 g of H_2SO_4 is expected. Materials that are only partially dissociated lower the freezing point by an intermediate value, and the decrease in the freezing point is directly proportional to the degree of dissociation.

Now, sulfuric acid reacts with weak neutral bases Y according to the equation,

$$Y + H_2SO_4 \rightleftharpoons HY^+ + HSO_4^-$$

If the ionization is complete, a molal freezing point depression of 12° is expected. When ionization fails to take place, a 6° lowering is observed. Partial reaction affords an intermediate value. These cryoscopic measurements are extremely useful for determining base strengths. Thus, acetic acid and chloroacetic acid are completely converted to their conjugate acids when dissolved in sulfuric acid. For dichloroacetic acid a molal freezing point depression between 6° and 12° is observed, and this indicates that dichloroacetic acid is only partially protonated under these conditions. Trichloroacetic acid is not significantly converted to its conjugate acid. The carboxylic acids become progressively weaker bases as more chlorine is introduced into the organic system. Such behavior is expected and can be attributed to the inductive effect of the halogen:

$$CH_3COOH + H_2SO_4 \rightleftharpoons CH_3\underset{+}{C}(OH)_2 + HSO_4^-$$

$$CH_2ClCOOH + H_2SO_4 \rightleftharpoons CH_2Cl\underset{+}{C}(OH)_2 + HSO_4^-$$

$$CHCl_2COOH + H_2SO_4 \rightleftharpoons CHCl_2\underset{+}{C}(OH)_2 + HSO_4^-$$

$$CCl_3COOH + H_2SO_4 \rightleftharpoons CCl_3\underset{+}{C}(OH)_2 + HSO_4^-$$

Many organic compounds are soluble in sulfuric acid. Although complications do exist, a large number of bases have been studied, and extensive correlations of base strengths have been made.

A variety of experimental procedures are available, and using these techniques enables us to correlate acid and base strengths. However, a simple empirical correlation is not adequate. It is not sufficient to know that one acid is stronger than another. We must also understand why various acids behave differently. It is the job of the chemist to draw conclusions from the experimental data. It is our task to evaluate the experimental results and from the data gain some theoretical insight into the behavior of acids and bases, and in the following chapter we discuss how changes in structure influence acid-base behavior.

Supplementary Reading

1. Bell, R. P., *The Proton in Chemistry*. Ithaca, New York, Cornell U.P., 1959.

2. Brown, H. C., McDaniel, D. H., and Häfliger, O., *Determination of Organic Structures by Physical Methods,* (eds.) E. A. Braude and F. C. Nachod. New York, Academic, 1955.

3. Gould, E. S., *Mechanism and Structure in Organic Chemistry*. New York, Holt, 1959.

4. Hammett, L. P., *Physical Organic Chemistry*. New York, McGraw-Hill, 1940.

5. Hine, J., *Physical Organic Chemistry*. New York, McGraw-Hill, 1962.

6. Ingold, C. K., *Structure and Mechanism in Organic Chemistry*. Ithaca, New York, Cornell U.P., 1953.

7. Leffler, J. E., and Grunwald, E., *Rates and Equilibria of Organic Reactions*. New York, Wiley, 1963.

Chapter 4

Structure-Reactivity Relationships

4.1 Introduction

Using techniques such as the freezing point depression of sulfuric acid, or spectroscopic procedures, or performing conductivity measurements has led to the evaluation of relative acid and base strengths. Having evaluated the relative strengths of a series of acids or bases, it then becomes the task of the chemist to interpret their behavior in terms of simple chemical principles such as the inductive effect, resonance effect, steric effects, and so forth. Unfortunately, an interpretation of acid-base behavior in terms of any single concept is certainly an oversimplification of the problem. When comparing two acids or two bases, we are comparing two entirely different systems, and it is unlikely that only a single factor changes. For example, the difference between the basicity of methylamine and that of ammonia is not entirely due to the inductive effect of the methyl group. The inductive effect certainly plays a role. However, many factors are involved, and a complete analysis ought to consider differences in hydrogen bonding, and other solvent effects as well as a variety of other phenomena. Of course, an exact analysis of the situation is not possible. It does give some insight into chemical behavior to assume that it is chiefly the inductive effect that is responsible for the observed difference in basicity. It must be remembered, however, that the problem is far more complex. Since we cannot make a complete analysis of any reaction but usually assume that a single factor is largely responsible, it may later turn out that a previously neglected factor is far more important.

The base strength of ammonia is indicated by the extent of its reaction with an acid HX, and this base strength is expressed by the value of the equilibrium constant for the reaction,

$$NH_3 + HX \rightleftharpoons NH_4^+ + X^-$$

where

$$K = \frac{[NH_4^+][X^-]}{[NH_3][HX]}$$

The equilibrium constant is related to the $\Delta G°$ for the process by the equation,

$$\Delta G° = -RT \ln K$$

Thus an acid-base reaction depends upon the $\Delta G°$ for the reaction, and differences in base strength are caused by differences in $\Delta G°$ (for example, $\Delta G°_{CH_3NH_2} - \Delta G°_{NH_3}$). Now $\Delta G°$ is a complex function containing many terms, and to assume that differences in $\Delta G°$ are due largely to a single cause such as the inductive effect is an oversimplification. It turns out that for a series of very closely related acids, variations in some $\Delta G°$'s can be attributed to a single factor; however, the problem is generally far too complex for so simple an analysis.

Despite the fact that interpreting differences in $\Delta G°$ on the basis of a single factor is not generally warranted, making such an interpretation for a series of related acids or bases does provide some insight into chemical behavior. We next discuss how structural changes (for example, replacing H by CH_3 or ϕ) can influence chemical behavior. Since acid-base reactions depend upon $\Delta G°$, we must consider both the products and the reactants in order to determine how a structural change affects the free energy of the system. We shall interpret the influence of changes in structure upon the free energy in terms of a single concept such as the inductive effect, the resonance effect, and so forth, yet we must remember that other factors are also involved. Since $\Delta G°$ for the dissociation of an acid is given by the expression,

$$\Delta G° = -RT \ln K_a$$

$$\Delta G° = -2.3 RT \log K_a$$

and since the pK_a is given by,

$$pK_a = -\log K_a$$

the quantity pK_a is directly proportional to $\Delta G°$.

$$pK_a = \frac{\Delta G°}{2.3 RT}$$

Consequently, it is possible to discuss acid-base behavior equally well in terms of the pK_a or in terms of $\Delta G°$.

4.2 The Inductive Effect

The effect of a change in structure upon the acid or base strength of an organic compound depends upon the nature of the group being introduced. If one group in an organic acid or base is replaced by another of different electronegativity, the acid or base strength changes. The introduction of electron withdrawing substituents increases the strength of an acid and decreases the strength of a base; the introduction of electron donating groups has the opposite effect.

The base strength of the carboxylic acids— CH_3COOH, CH_2ClOOH, $CHCl_2COOH$, CCl_3COOH — decreases as more halogens are introduced into the system. The inductive effect of chlorine causes $\Delta G°$ for the reaction of these materials as bases to become less favorable.

Of course, these materials normally react as acids, and in this case the inductive effect of chlorine causes the acidity to increase. The reaction is,

$$CH_3COOH \rightleftharpoons CH_3COO^- + H^+$$

$$CH_2ClCOOH \rightleftharpoons CH_2ClCOO^- + H^+$$

$$CHCl_2COOH \rightleftharpoons CHCl_2COO^- + H^+$$

$$CCl_3COOH \rightleftharpoons CCl_3COO^- + H^+$$

Both the $\Delta G°$ and the pK_a for dissociation become more favorable as we proceed along the series. This is presented schematically in Figure 4–1.

The pK_a's are:

	CH_3COOH	$CH_2ClCOOH$	$CHCl_2COOH$	CCl_3COOH
pK_a	4.76	2.86	1.29	0.65

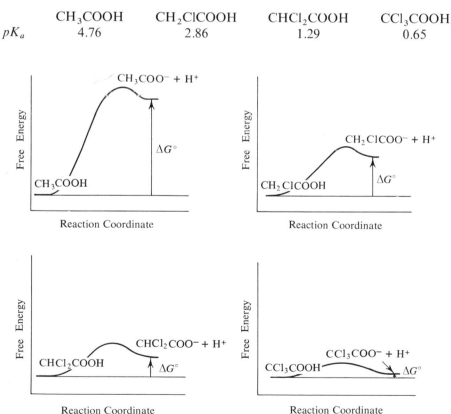

Figure 4–1

The strengths of the anions RCOO⁻ reacting as bases is obtained by considering the reaction profile in the opposite direction.

4.3 The Resonance Effect

Aliphatic alcohols have their pK_a's in the region 16–20, yet phenol is much more acidic having a pK_a equal to about 10. This marked difference in the acidity is due to the presence of the aromatic ring; see Figure 4–2.

Since the acidity of phenol depends upon the $\Delta G°$ for dissociation, we must consider both the products and the reactant. This enhanced acidity is due to resonance stabilization, yet both phenol and the phenoxide ion are resonance stabilized. In both cases the π electrons are delocalized over the entire system:

OH   ⁺OH   ⁺OH   ⁺OH

and

O⁻   O   O   O

However, electronic delocalization in phenol requires the separation of opposite charges. Such charge separation, which is unfavorable, does not occur with the phenoxide ion. Consequently, the resonance stabilization of the anion is greater than that of phenol itself. The energy of both phenol and its anion is decreased by resonance, but the energy of the anion is lowered to a greater extent. The $\Delta G°$ and the pK_a for dissociation are smaller; therefore, dissociation

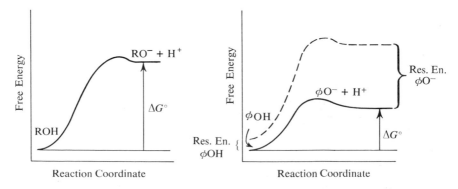

Figure 4–2

is more favorable for phenol than for aliphatic alcohols where such resonance stabilization does not occur.

A similar relationship exists between aniline and the aliphatic amines. Aniline is stabilized by π electronic delocalization, and such delocalization is not possible for the aliphatic amines.

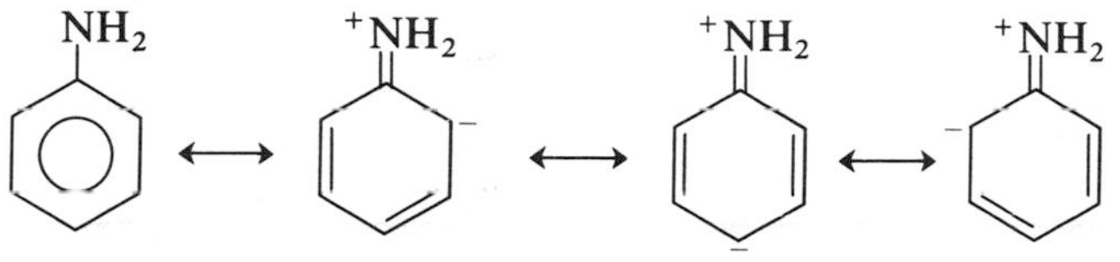

Aniline is stabilized by resonance involving the nitrogen; its conjugate acid, on the other hand, is not stabilized in this manner. Protonation of aniline destroys this resonance stabilization. Structures of the type,

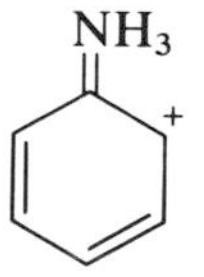

place ten elections (five bonds) about the nitrogen; therefore, such structures are unimportant. We expect aniline to be protonated less readily than aliphatic amines which are not stabilized. This makes aniline a weaker base than aliphatic amines. If aniline is a weaker base, its conjugate acid must be a stronger acid. The acid ϕNH_3^+ must be stronger than acids of the type RNH_3^+. This behavior is observed; aniline is a weaker base, and its conjugate acid is a stronger acid. The pK_b, which indicates base strength is equal to 9.4 for aniline yet has a value between 3–5 for simple aliphatic amines. The higher value of pK_b implies that aniline is indeed a weaker base.

$$K_b = \frac{[RNH_3^+][OH^-]}{[RNH_2]}$$

and

$$pK_b = -\log K_b$$

Acid and base strengths are usually expressed in terms of the pK_a which indicates the acid strength of the conjugate acid. The pK_b for aniline in water at 25°C is equal to 9.4, and the pK_w for water at 25° is about 14. Now,

$$pK_a + pK_b = pK_w$$

therefore the pK_a for ϕNH_3^+ is equal to 4.6 while the pK_a's for aliphatic cases lie between 9–11; see Figure 4–3.

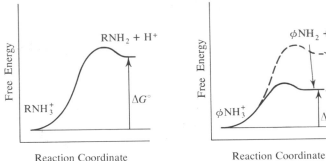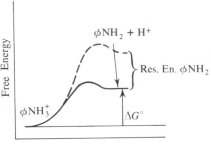

Figure 4–3

Resonance stabilization makes aniline a weaker base than aliphatic amines. Since the introduction of a single phenyl group decreases the basicity, the introduction of a second ought to lower the base strength still further. Thus, diphenylamine is expected, and is found, to be a weaker base than aniline; triphenylamine is still weaker. Under ordinary conditions this last material is not even considered to be basic:

$$\phi NH_2 > \phi_2 NH > \phi_3 N$$
$$\underrightarrow{\text{Decreasing Basicity}}$$

4.4 Steric Inhibition of Resonance

In order for π electronic delocalization and resonance stabilization to take place, the nitrogen atom in aniline and substituted anilines must be sp^2 hybridized (or nearly so), and the remaining p orbital must overlap with the p orbital of the carbon atom on the aromatic ring. Orbital overlap is required for resonance stabilization,

Bending the nitrogen atom out of the plane of the benzene ring or rotating the amino group decreases the resonance stabilization, for under these circumstances orbital overlap decreases:

bent amino group   partially rotated amino group

The presence of large *ortho* substituents on the aromatic ring may force such bending or such a rotation; the resonance stabilization of the aromatic amine then decreases; and the aromatic amine becomes a stronger base. When the presence of large groups prevents resonance stabilization from taking place, the phenomenon is appropriately called steric inhibition of resonance.

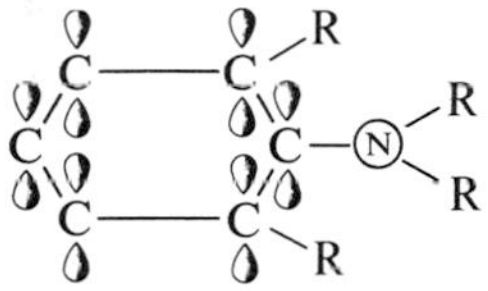

rotation and steric inhibition of resonance

Steric inhibition of resonance has been observed in a number of cases. For example, 2,4,6-trinitroaniline **1** is an extremely weak base. The N,N-dimethyl compound **2** is thousands of times as strong. The former is resonance stabilized while the introduction of the two methyl groups prevents such stabilization in **2**. The NH_2 group is small; π electronic delocalization and resonance stabilization are possible. Since the $N(CH_3)_2$ group is large, steric interactions between the methyl groups and the *ortho* nitro groups inhibit resonance stabilization, and the base strength increases.

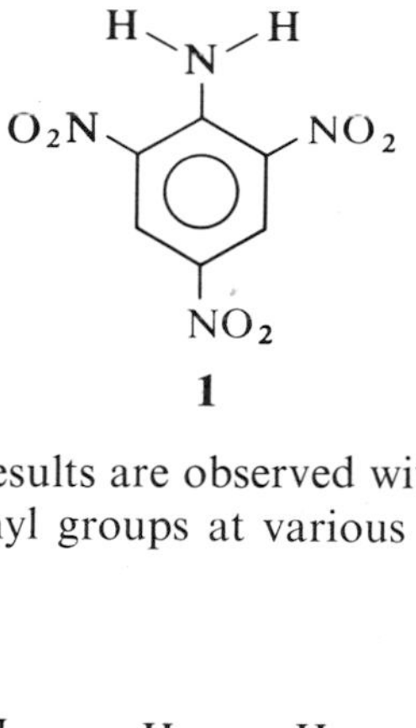

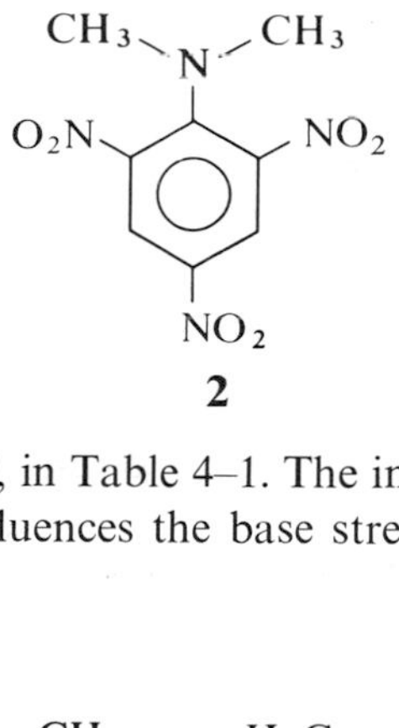

Similar results are observed with **3, 4**, and **5**, in Table 4–1. The introduction of the methyl groups at various positions influences the base strengths. The

Table 4–1

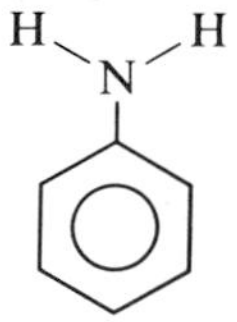

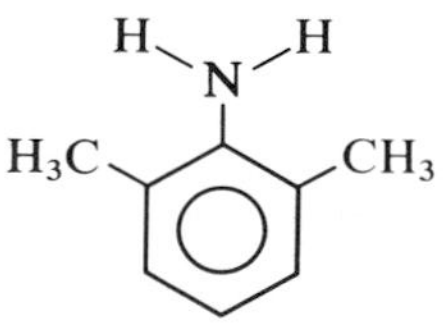

	3	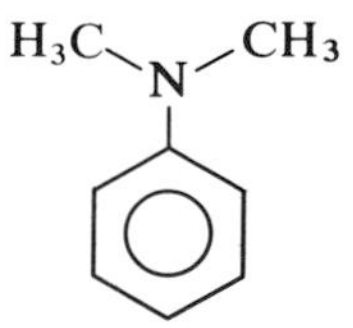	**4**	**5**
pK_a	4.25	3.42	4.26	4.69
μ	1.5D	1.6D	1.6D	0.9D

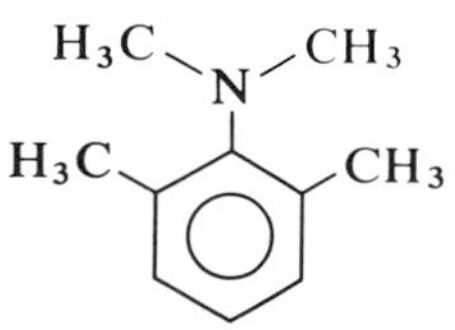

pK_a's in terms of concentrations for the conjugate acids in 50% aqueous ethanol at 25° are given. The dipole moments in benzene solution are also presented.

Steric inhibition of resonance causes an increase in the base strength of **5**.

Other properties that depend upon electronic delocalization are also influenced; for example, the dipole moment and the rate of electrophilic aromatic substitution of **5** are affected. Resonance stabilization of aromatic amines involves structures such as:

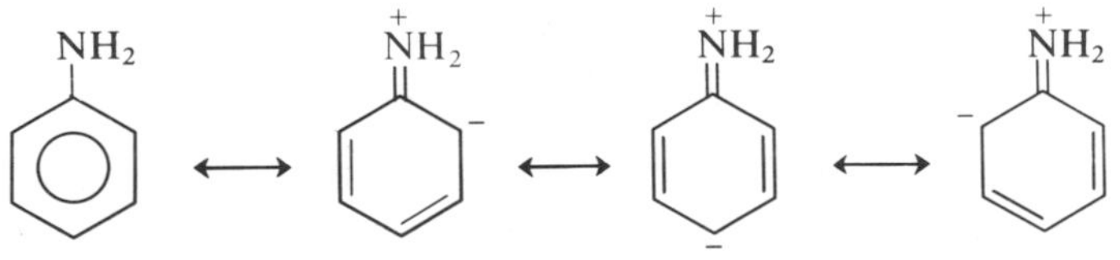

The effect of these structures is to increase the magnitude and to alter the direction of the dipole moment of aromatic amines. Inhibition of resonance is expected to reduce the observed dipole moment, and this decrease is observed in **5**.

Steric inhibition of resonance also affects the rate of electrophilic aromatic substitutions. Compound **4** reacts readily with the phenyldiazonium cation ϕN_2^+. Azo-coupling takes place as expected, and *ortho-para* products predominate. Under the same conditions compound **5** does not suffer coupling. Although both *ortho* positions are blocked, the *para* position is available, and the failure of **5** to react with ϕN_2^+ can be attributed to steric inhibition of resonance in the transition state for this electrophilic aromatic substitution:

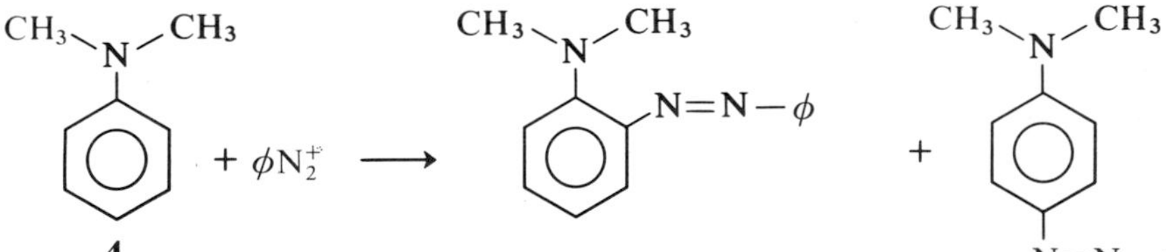

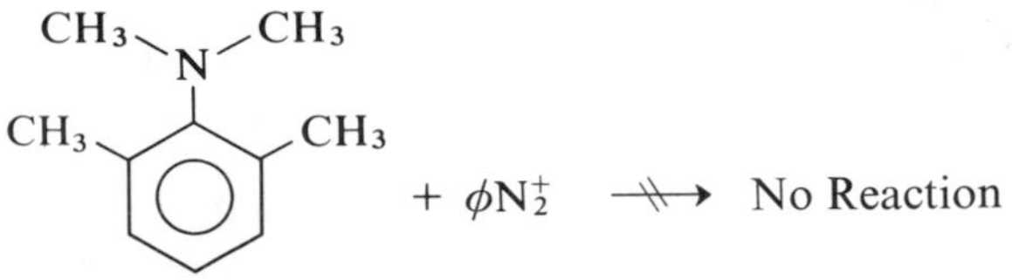

4.5 Steric Effects

The two bases, triethylamine **6** and quinuclidine **7**, have nearly the same pK_b values, and this indicates that the equilibria,

$$(CH_3CH_2)_3N + H^+ \rightleftharpoons (CH_3CH_2)_3NH^+$$
6

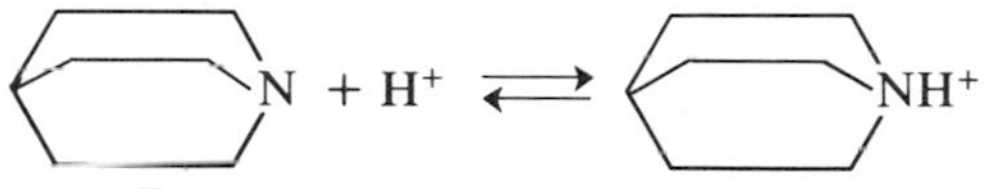

7

occur to about the same extent. However, when these bases are reacted with the Lewis acid $B(CH_3)_3$, the equilibrium involving **6** is much less favorable than that involving **7**:

$$(CH_3CH_2)_3N + B(CH_3)_3 \rightleftharpoons (CH_3CH_2)_3\overset{+}{N} - \overset{-}{B}(CH_3)_3$$
6

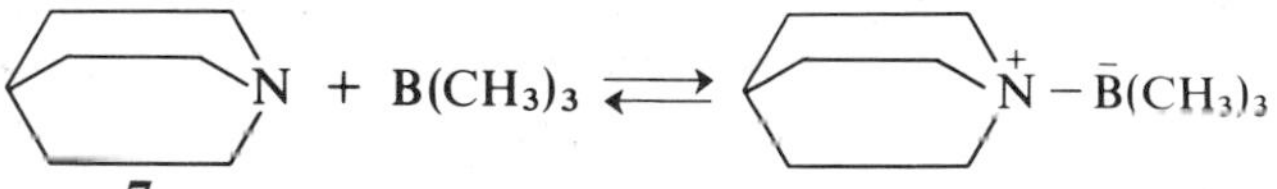

7

The term steric effects or steric interactions implies changes in hybridization caused by large groups as well as restricted vibrations and restricted rotations caused by nonbonded interactions. Such steric interactions raise the free energy of the complex formed from **6**. This complex is less stable, and the equilibrium is less favorable. In the complex formed from **7** the alkyl groups of the amine are held back and away; steric interactions are less pronounced; the complex is more stable.

The reactions of nitrogenous bases (amines) with alkylborons have been studied extensively, and steric effects have been found in a number of cases. Thus, $(CH_3)_3N$ forms a less stable complex with $B(CH_3)_3$ than does $(CH_3)_2NH$, and this decrease in stability is due to steric factors.

4.6 Solvent Effects

We have already discussed how changing from one solvent to another affects the activity coefficients of the various species. Thus carboxylic acids dissociate to a much greater extent in water than in ethanol, for the activity coefficients of the ions are much larger in ethanol. This implies that the ions are less stable.

$$RCOOH \rightleftharpoons RCOO^- + H^+$$

The dissociation of ammonium ions is also influenced by changing from one solvent to another. However, both the products and the reactant are charged in these cases; therefore, a change in solvent has a lesser effect upon the position of the equilibrium:

$$RNH_3^+ \rightleftharpoons RNH_2 + H^+$$

Changing solvents can affect not only the degree of dissociation of an acid, it can alter the very order of acid or base strengths. Thus, in aqueous solution the values listed in Table 4–2 have been determined for the pK_b's of various amines.

Table 4–2

	NH_3	CH_3NH_2	$(CH_3)_2NH$	$(CH_3)_3N$
pK_b	4.8	3.4	3.2	4.2

	NH_3	$C_2H_5NH_2$	$(C_2H_5)_2NH$	$(C_2H_5)_3N$
pK_b	4.8	3.3	3.1	3.1

	NH_3	$C_4H_9NH_2$	$(C_4H_9)_2NH$	$(C_4H_9)_3N$
pK_b	4.8	3.4	2.7	4.1

Remember that the larger the value of the pK_b, the weaker the base. The replacement of hydrogen by an alkyl group is expected to increase the base strength of an amine because of the electron releasing ability of the alkyl group. In the reactions,

$$RNH_2 + H_3O^+ \rightleftharpoons RNH_3^+ + H_2O$$

$$R_2NH + H_3O^+ \rightleftharpoons R_2NH_2^+ + H_2O$$

$$R_3N + H_3O^+ \rightleftharpoons R_3NH^+ + H_2O$$

the alkyl groups, which are electron releasing, are better able to delocalize the positive charge in the conjugate acids. This stabilizes the conjugate acids. Consequently, the amine becomes a progressively stronger base as more alkyl groups are introduced. The inductive effect of the alkyl groups serves to increase the base strength of the amine except for tertiary amines. These are weaker bases than the corresponding secondary amines, and this decrease in base strength in passing on to tertiary amines can be attributed to the solvent effect.

The base NH_3 reacts with H_3O^+ to form the acid NH_4^+. All of the species are solvated, particularly the acids H_3O^+ and NH_4^+. In water, solvation includes the formation of hydrogen bonds between these acids and the solvent. The primary amine RNH_2 reacts with H_3O^+ to form RNH_3^+. The acid H_3O^+ remains solvated just as before. Now the species RNH_3^+ is less highly solvated by hydrogen bonding than is NH_4^+. The replacement of H by R has increased the base strength, but this effect is partially nullified by a decrease in hydrogen bonding. This decrease somewhat reduces the stability of the conjugate acid RNH_3^+. Extending this idea, continued replacement of H by R progressively reduces the hydrogen bonding of the conjugate acids. The conjugate acid

R_3NH^+ with only a single hydrogen available for hydrogen bonding is much less stabilized in this manner than the other acids. The tertiary amine is less basic than expected because its conjugate acid R_3NH^+ is not stabilized by hydrogen bonding to the same extent as the other acids. The introduction of the third alkyl group does not compensate for the large reduction in hydrogen bonding.

Proof that these ideas are correct comes from a study of the relative base strengths of various amines in a solvent that is not capable of behaving in this fashion. When the relative base strengths of the butylamines are determined in a nonhydrogen-bonding solvent, the base strengths follow the expected order:

$$(C_4H_9)_3N > (C_4H_9)_2NH > C_4H_9NH_2$$

Decreasing Basicity ⟶

4.7 Hydrogen Bonding

Hydrogen bonding can affect acid and base strengths in several ways. For example, in the hydroxybenzoic acid series:

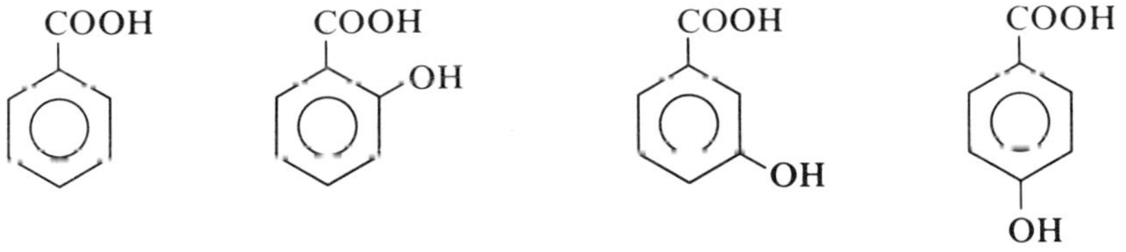

COOH	COOH—OH	COOH—OH	COOH—OH
pK_a 4.2	3.0	4.1	4.6

The acidities of all but the *ortho* substituted benzoic acid can be explained by the fact that the OH group is inductively electron withdrawing (from the *meta* position) but an electron donor by resonance (from the *para* position).

The acidity of the *ortho* substituted acid is surprisingly high. This acid turns out to be somewhat stronger than benzoic acid although by the resonance effect it is expected to be weaker than the unsubstituted acid. The high acidity of *ortho* hydroxybenzoic acid is due to intramolecular hydrogen bonding.

The *ortho* acid is hydrogen bonded in the following way.

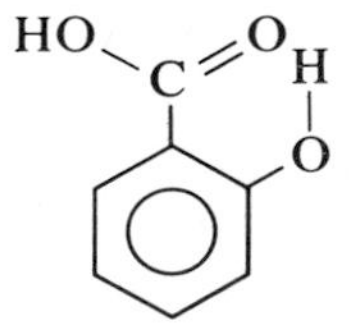

The OH hydrogen is hydrogen bonded to the oxygen atom of the carboxylic acid. While this stabilizes the acid, upon ionization the oxygen atom becomes more negative and hydrogen bonding increases:

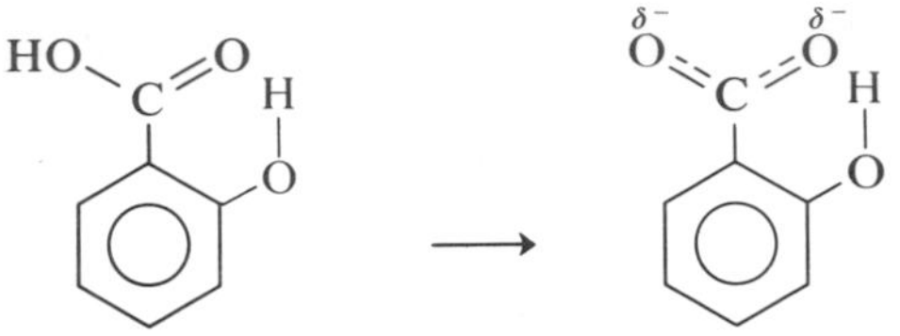

Thus the dissociation of the acid is aided because the process is accompanied by an increase in intramolecular hydrogen bonding. Both the carboxylic acid and its anion are stabilized by hydrogen bonding, but the anion is stabilized to a greater degree. The free energy for ionization decreases, and the acid is stronger.

4.8 Hybridization Effects

Acetylene is a stronger acid than ethylene, and the latter is in turn a stronger acid than ethane. We may represent these acidities as:

$$HC\equiv CH \rightleftharpoons HC\equiv C:^- + H^+$$

$$CH_2=CH_2 \rightleftharpoons CH_2=CH:^- + H^+$$

$$CH_3CH_3 \rightleftharpoons CH_3CH_2:^- + H^+$$

and

$$HC\equiv CH > CH_2=CH_2 > CH_3CH_3$$

Decreasing Acidity
$\longrightarrow$

Since the $2s$ orbital of carbon is more stable than the $2p$ orbital of that atom, the more s character in a hybridized orbital the greater is the stability of that orbital. Thus, the two electrons in the conjugate base of acetylene occupy an sp hybridized orbital ($\frac{1}{2}$ s). These electrons are more stable than the two in the conjugate base of ethylene. The latter occupy an sp^2 orbital ($\frac{1}{3}$ s). An sp^3 hybridized orbital ($\frac{1}{4}$ s) is occupied by the two electrons in the conjugate base of ethane. The relative acidities of these hydrocarbons can be explained on this basis.

The same hybridization effects are present but to a lesser degree in the hydrocarbons themselves. The two electrons in the C—H bond of the hydrocarbons can be found some of the time near carbon and some of the time near hydrogen. In the carbanions these electrons spend all of their time about carbon. Therefore, changes in the hybridization of carbon have a greater effect upon the energy of the electrons in the carbanions than in the hydrocarbons.

A similar situation is found in a series such as R_3N, C_5H_5N, RCN. Aliphatic tertiary amines exhibit pK_b's in the region 3–5. Pyridine, C_5H_5N, is a tertiary amine, yet has a pK_b equal to 9.0. Nitriles are not usually considered bases.

In aliphatic tertiary amines the unshared electrons are in an sp^3 orbital, in pyridine they are in an sp^2 orbital, and in nitriles they occupy an sp hybridized orbital. The basicity of the material decreases as the stability of the orbital occupied by the nonbonded electrons increases.

Changes in hybridization influence the acidity and basicity in a number of cases, because these changes alter the free energy of reaction.

4.9 The Hammett Equation

We have previously discussed in a qualitative way how changes in structure can affect the reactivity of an acid or base. In certain special cases it is possible to discuss structure-reactivity relationships in a more quantitative manner. These linear free energy relationships, as such relationships are sometimes called, are not confined to acid-base reactions but extend to other processes as well.

An acid such as *meta* nitrobenzoic acid is a stronger acid than benzoic acid, and this increase in acid strength is due to the electron withdrawing effect of the nitro group. Furthermore, the acid strengths of benzoic acid and *meta* nitro-benzoic acid are indicated by the equilibrium constants for dissociation (K_a); these are related to the free energies for dissociation by the equations:

$$\Delta G^\circ_{NO_2} = -RT \ln K_{NO_2} = -2.3\, RT \log K_{NO_2}$$

and

$$\Delta G^\circ_{H} = -RT \ln K_H = -2.3\, RT \log K_H$$

Thus, the influence of the nitro group is reflected in the free energy change for dissociation, that is, the free energy of reaction is related to the electron with-drawing effect of the nitro group.

The Hammett equation, which we develop here, is applicable to a large number of reactions. In this equation we indicate the electron donating or electron withdrawing ability of a group Z by the symbol σ_Z, and we assume that this quantity remains invarient. We assign to a group such as the *meta* nitro group in the previous example a certain value for σ_{metaNO_2} (this is deter-mined experimentally), and we naturally wish to use the same value for σ_{metaNO_2} whenever a *meta* nitro group is present in the system. In an analogous fashion, values for σ are assigned to all groups.

Consider two acids,

$$Z-\langle\bigcirc\rangle-COOH \;\rightleftharpoons\; Z-\langle\bigcirc\rangle-COO^- + H^+$$

and

The Hammett equation shows how *meta* or *para* substituents on the aromatic
ring affect the reactions of a side chain attached to that ring. In this example the
aromatic side chain is the carboxyl group, and the group Z is a substituent on the
aromatic ring. We assume that the difference in acid strengths between *para*-Z-
benzoic acid and benzoic acid is due to the effect exerted by Z. If Z is an electron
donor, the substituted acid is a weaker acid than benzoic acid. If Z is an electron
withdrawer, the substituted acid is stronger. The effect exerted by Z influences
ΔG_Z°.

The difference between ΔG_Z° and ΔG_H° is proportional to the electron donating
or electron withdrawing ability of Z. We write this proportionality as

$$\Delta G_Z^\circ - \Delta G_H^\circ = -2.3\,RT\rho\sigma_Z$$

where σ_Z is a measure of the electron donating or electron withdrawing ability
of the group Z. The actual constant of proportionality is ρ; the terms $-2.3\,RT$
have been included for convenience.

The quantities $\rho\sigma_Z$ may be interpreted as follows. In this example the aromatic
side chain is carboxyl, and we proceed from the neutral carboxylic acid to the
negatively charged carboxylate anion. If we assume that Z exerts the same
effect in other reactions where other side chains are involved, then it is quite
reasonable that σ_Z should have the same value in each of these reactions. We
assume that the electron donating or electron withdrawing ability of a group
is a fixed quantity that depends only upon the particular group and which does
not depend upon how electron deficient or how electron rich the aromatic side
chain becomes during the course of a reaction. Of course, the effect due to Z
becomes more or less important as the electron density on the side chain varies.
We may then consider ρ as indicating the sensitivity of a particular reaction to
electron donation or electron withdrawal by Z. Thus, one possible interpretation
is to consider that a given group exerts a fixed electronic effect indicated by the
value of σ and that ρ measures how important this effect is in a reaction.

Actually the electron donating or electron withdrawing ability of Z does vary.
The more electron deficient the side chain becomes during a reaction the more
effectively electrons are withdrawn from Z. However, we may still interpret
$\rho\sigma_Z$ as a measure of the electronic effect of Z. The quantity σ_Z indicates the
effect due to Z for some standard reaction (for example, the ionization of benzoic
acids), and ρ is then a multiplier that modifies the effect of Z as it becomes larger
or smaller than the standard value. Another interpretation considers σ_Z as an
indication of the electronic effect due to Z for the ionization of benzoic acids.
The term ρ is a corrective modifier to adjust for changes in this effect in different
reactions.

We see in a simple way why expressions of the type,

$$\Delta G_Z^\circ - \Delta G_H^\circ = -2.3\, RT\rho\sigma_Z$$

are called linear free energy relationships. A plot of ΔG_Z° against σ_Z for various groups Z results in a straight line with slope equal to $-2.3\, RT\rho$ and an intercept equal to ΔG_H°.

This equation can be modified

$$\Delta G^\circ = -2.3\, RT \log K$$

we obtain:

$$\log K_Z - \log K_H = \rho\sigma_Z$$

or

$$\log \frac{K_Z}{K_H} = \rho\sigma_Z$$

The terms K_Z and K_H are the equilibrium constants for dissociation of the acids. We have related the equilibrium constant for dissociation of a substituted benzoic acid to the electron donating or electron withdrawing ability of that substituent.

The ideas just developed need not be restricted to acid-base reactions. Other equilibria also ought to obey this equation (the K's will no longer be dissociation constants). Furthermore, the rates of various reactions can be expected to follow a similar equation. Here we deal with $\Delta G_Z^\ddagger$ and $\Delta G_H^\ddagger$ and obtain the expression:

$$\log \frac{k_Z}{k_H} = \rho\sigma_Z$$

where k_Z and k_H are the specific rate constants for a reaction. We assume here that the difference in rates depends only upon the electronic effect exerted by the group Z.

The Hammett equation can be used in connection with any series of reactions where the various groups Z exert the same sort of influence throughout the series. If in another series of reactions the type of influence exerted by the various Z's changes, the equation can still be used; however, different values must be employed for the σ_Z's.

This equation can be used to predict the rates of reaction of certain compounds, the positions of equilibria, the rate limiting step in reactions, and so forth. It is also helpful in elucidating the mechanism of reactions.

We can obtain the values of K_Z and K_H (or k_Z and k_H) for various compounds; however, to use the Hammett equation we must also know the values of ρ or σ. We have a single equation containing two unknown variables. For the equation to be useful we must know the values of these two quantities, and we determine them in the following fashion.

The Hammett equation is,

$$\log \frac{K_Z}{K_H} = \rho \sigma_Z$$

For the ionization of benzoic acids in water at 25° we arbitrarily set ρ equal to unity, and for this reaction the equation becomes,

$$\log \frac{K_Z}{K_H} = \sigma_Z$$

and

$$\rho = 1.00$$

In order to obtain a single equation having only a single unknown we set ρ equal to unity. We then measure the degree of dissociation of benzoic acid as well as that of various *meta* and *para* substituted benzoic acids and obtain the values of K_H and of K_Z for different groups Z. Substituting the data into the equation affords values for σ_Z. Some of these are listed in Table 4–3.

Table 4–3. σ-Values

	CH_3	CH_3CH_2	$(CH_3)_3C$	NO_2	NH_2	OH	OCH_3
σ_{meta}	−0.07	−0.07	−0.10	+0.71	−0.16	+0.12	+0.12
σ_{para}	−0.17	−0.15	−0.20	+0.78	−0.66	−0.37	−0.27

Since σ_Z is determined experimentally, we can always obtain values for this parameter. However, the values obtained from one reaction need not be satisfactory values for this quantity when employed in another reaction. The values listed in Table 4–3 for such groups as *para* amino, *para* methoxy, and so forth, include in addition to the inductive effects of these groups, contributions to σ_Z due to resonance. Consequently, these values of σ_Z are not satisfactory for use in other reactions where resonance is either not involved or where resonance effects are much more pronounced than they are here.

We can assign values for σ_Z by studying one reaction. The same values can be used in other reactions only if the effect exerted by Z is nearly the same in all of these reactions. This serves as a criterion of mechanism. If in two different reactions the values of σ_Z differ, the influence of Z in these two reactions must be different.

We see from Table 4–3 that electron withdrawers have positive σ values whereas electron donors have negative values. This result is a direct consequence of the equation relating σ to log K_Z/K_H. When the group Z is an electron withdrawer, the substituted benzoic acid is a stronger acid than benzoic acid itself. Consequently, K_Z is larger than K_H, and the ratio K_Z/K_H is greater than unity. The log of a number larger than unity is positive. On the other hand, if the group Z is an electron donor, K_Z is smaller numerically than K_H, and the ratio K_Z/K_H is less than unity. The log of a number smaller than unity is negative.

Having found the values for σ_Z and knowing the value for ρ for the dissociation of benzoic acids, we then look at other reactions. For a given substituent Z exerting the same sort of effect in a number of different reactions the values of σ_Z remain the same. The values of ρ, indicating the importance of this effect in a reaction, change. We measure the rates of other reactions and obtain the values of k_Z and k_H (K_Z and K_H for equilibria), and knowing the values for σ_Z, we determine the ρ's for these other reactions. Some of these are listed in Table 4–4.

Table 4–4. ρ Values

Reaction	Solvent	Temp. (°C)	ρ
	Equilibria		
Dissociation of: ArCOOH	H_2O	25	+1.00
ArOH	H_2O	25	+2.11
ArNH$_3^+$	H_2O	25	+2.77
ArNH$_3^+$	20% Dioxane	25	+3.26
	Rates		
Basic hydrolysis of methyl benzoates	60% Acetone	0	+2.46
HCN + ArCHO	95% Ethanol	20	+2.33
ArNH$_2$ + ϕCOCl	Benzene	25	−2.78
ArN(CH$_3$)$_2$ + CH$_3$I	90% Acetone	35	−3.30

Again from the equation,

$$\log \frac{k_Z}{k_H} = \rho\sigma_Z$$

we see that reactions with positive ρ's are enhanced by electron withdrawers (positive σ_Z) and made less favorable by electron donors. Reactions with negative ρ's proceed less readily when electron withdrawers are present, more readily when electron donors are present. Thus a knowledge of ρ may give insight into the changes in electron density that occur during reactions at the aromatic side chain.

Having established the values of some σ's and some ρ's, it is possible to extend the list by studying new and different reactions.

There is an alternative way of writing the Hammett equation. Since by definition,

$$\log \frac{K_Z}{K_H} = \sigma_Z$$

for the dissociation of benzoic acids, we may substitute this expression for σ_Z into the Hammett equation and obtain,

$$\log \frac{k_Z}{k_H} = \rho \log \frac{K_Z}{K_H}$$

where k_Z and k_H are the specific rate constants for another reaction that also obeys the Hammett equation. For some other equilibrium we obtain,

$$\log \frac{K'_Z}{K'_H} = \rho \log \frac{K_Z}{K_H}$$

Here K'_Z and K'_H are the equilibrium constants for the other reaction.

A substituent Z can exert both a resonance effect and an inductive effect. We include in the term inductive effect, in addition to the usual inductive effect that works only along the σ bond framework of the molecule, the following effect which is at least partially a resonance effect.

In *meta* substituted benzoic acids such as *meta* nitrobenzoic acid and *meta* aminobenzoic acid there are no direct resonance interactions between the meta substituents and the carboxy group. There are, however, resonance interactions which change the electron density at the *ortho* and *para* positions. Thus for *meta* aminobenzoic acid, resonance interactions such as the following:

COOH   COOH

$\longleftrightarrow$ $\longleftrightarrow$

NH$_2$ $\overset{+}{N}H_2$

COOH   COOH

$\longleftrightarrow$

$\overset{+}{N}H_2$ $\overset{+}{N}H_2$

tend to increase the electron density at the *ortho* and *para* positions.

Now this increase in electron density at the *ortho* and *para* carbon atoms can be transmitted to the carboxy group inductively. Consequently, this effect alters the acid strength of the molecule. The acid strength is altered, yet there are no direct resonance interactions between the amino group and the carboxy group. Therefore, we include this effect as part of the overall inductive effect of the *meta* amino group. Similar effects occur with the other *meta* substituents. While direct resonance interactions between *meta* oriented groups are not possible, this effect, which is partially a resonance effect and partially an inductive effect, does take place and is included as part of the overall inductive effect of *meta* substituents. Effects such as the field effect and the polarizability of electrons are also placed in this category of the inductive effect. Other effects such as solvation effects are not usually considered explicitly.

The Hammett equation, which we have developed here, is applicable to a large number of reactions. In this equation we indicate the electron donating or electron withdrawing ability of a group Z by the symbol σ_Z, and we assume that this quantity σ_Z remains invarient. We assign to a group such as the *meta* amino group in the previous example a certain value for σ_{metaNH_2}, and we naturally wish to use the same value for σ_{metaNH_2} whenever a *meta* amino group is present in the system. In an analogous fashion values for σ are assigned to all groups.

Now, if we determine σ_Z for some group Z in a reaction where the major influence of Z upon the reaction is an inductive influence, we cannot then expect the same value of σ_Z to hold in other reactions where Z exerts a large resonance effect in addition to the inductive effect. Conversely, if we determine the value of σ_Z in a reaction where Z influences the reaction by resonance as well as inductively, we should not attempt to use this value of σ_Z in a reaction where the only contribution of Z is an inductive one. Thus, we use different values for σ_Z; one value for reactions where Z exerts primarily an inductive effect and others when Z is also involved in resonance.

We assume in the Hammett equation that Z exerts the same sort of effect in a number of different reactions. Consequently, *meta* and some *para* substituted aromatic systems follow this, but we cannot expect *ortho* substituted aromatic systems to obey this assumption.

COOH

Ortho substituents exert a steric effect in addition to the resonance and inductive effects, and changing from one group Z to another alters both the electronic effect and the steric requirements. In such cases, where steric effects are also present, the problem becomes more complex. In addition, while *meta* substituents may be considered to have only an inductive influence upon the reaction, *para* substituents can exert a direct resonance effect as well. Naturally, this also complicates the situation. The Hammett equation only works well for *para* substituents when their resonance effects are small. The Hammett equation can also be developed for use in reactions where Z exerts a large resonance effect in addition to the inductive effect; however, such cases should be considered separately.

The Hammett equation can be employed in a simple manner to predict the positions of equilibria or the values for specific rate constants. It can also be used for more sophisticated problems such as indicating differences in mechanism or changes in the rate limiting step of a reaction. To illustrate a simple use we consider the equilibria:

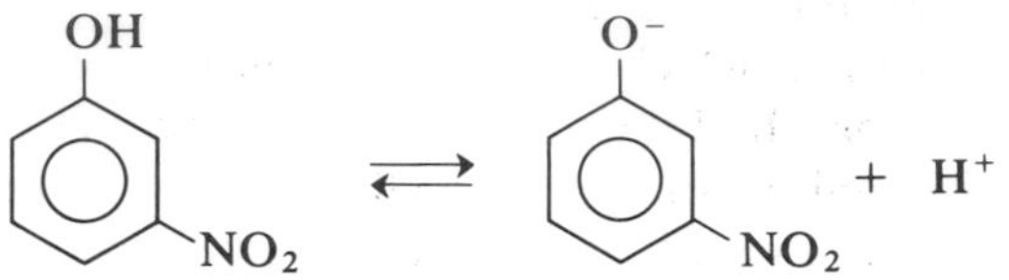

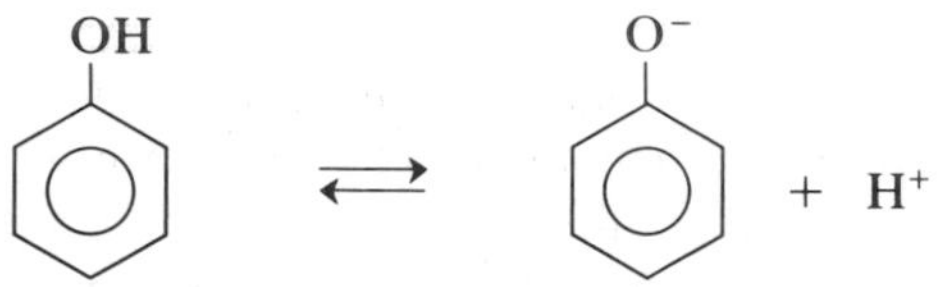

Knowing the pK_a for phenol and the values for ρ and σ_{metaNO_2}, we are able to find the pK_a of *meta* nitrophenol.

According to the Hammett equation,

$$\log \frac{K_{metaNO_2}}{K_H} = \rho\sigma_{metaNO_2}$$

or

$$\log K_{metaNO_2} - \log K_H = \rho\sigma_{metaNO_2}$$

Then

$$-\log K_{metaNO_2} = -\log K_H - \rho\sigma_{metaNO_2}$$

From the definition of pK_a,

$$pK_{metaNO_2} = -\log K_{metaNO_2}$$

and we obtain

$$pK_{metaNO_2} = pK_H - \rho\sigma_{metaNO_2}$$

Substituting the appropriate values for pK_H (10.0), ρ (2.11), and σ_{metaNO_2} (0.71) into this expression, leads to:

$$pK_{metaNO_2} = 10.0 - 1.50$$

$$pK_{metaNO_2} = 8.5$$

We find 8.5 for the pK_a of *meta* nitrophenol; the experimental value is 8.4. Thus, the Hammett equation affords us a value quite close to the actual acidity of this substituted phenol.

For anilines,

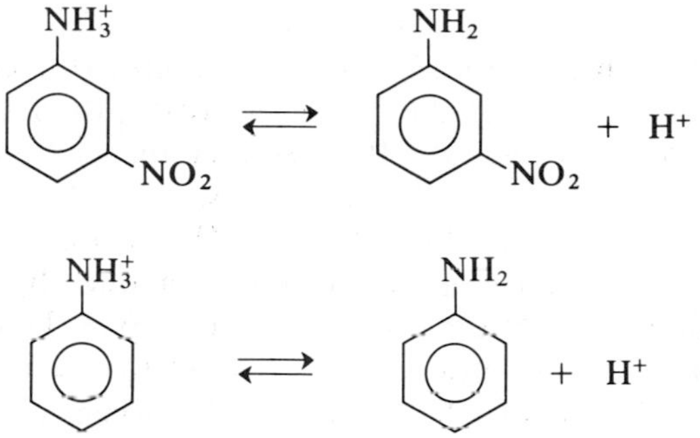

Again,

$$pK_{metaNO_2} = pK_H - \rho\sigma_{metaNO_2}$$

Here

$$pK_H = 4.6$$

$$\rho = 2.77$$

$$\sigma_{metaNO_2} = 0.71$$

The pK_a of *meta* nitroaniline is found to be 2.6; the actual value is 2.4.

The Hammett equation finds use in other ways. This equation can be written as,

$$\log k_Z = \rho\sigma_Z + \log k_H$$

and plots of $\log k_Z$ against σ_Z should result in a straight line with a slope equal to ρ. Such Hammett plots have aided investigations of the mechanism of semicarbazone formation **9**:

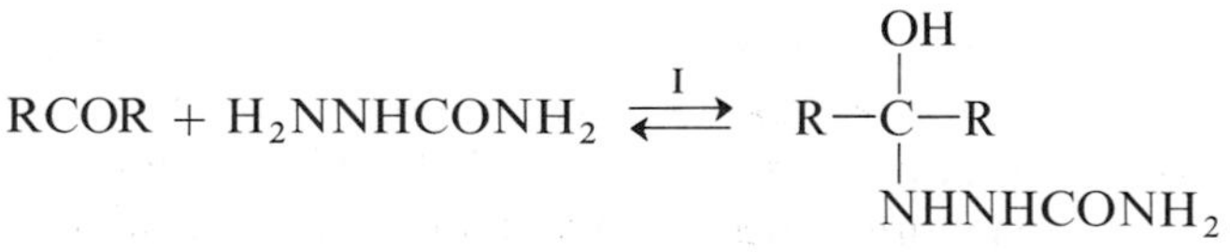

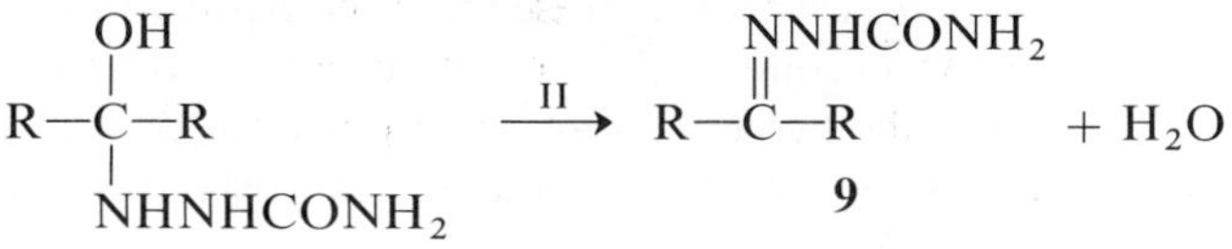

This reaction is a two-step process involving the formation and decomposition of the intermediate **8**. The product **9** serves as a derivative of carbonyl compounds.

The rate of semicarbazone formation is a function of the pH. Lowering the pH from slightly alkaline to slightly acidic increases the rate of reaction. A further lowering decreases the rate. It is assumed that this change is due to a change in the rate limiting step. At slightly alkaline pH's the acid catalyzed dehydration step is rate limiting. Lowering the pH increases the rate of this step. Further lowering causes attack of the carbonyl compound by semicarbazide to become rate limiting. The rate of step I depends upon the concentration of semicarbazide, and in acid solution this is converted to its conjugate acid. Thus, a lowering of the pH decreases the rate of reaction when step I is rate limiting because more of the amine is converted to its conjugate acid. Confirmatory evidence comes from Hammett plots.

For a series of substituted benzaldehydes reacting with semicarbazide, the reaction is:

$$\text{ArCHO} + \text{H}_2\text{NNHCONH}_2 \underset{k_{-1}}{\overset{k_1}{\rightleftharpoons}} \begin{matrix} \text{OH} \\ | \\ \text{ArCH} \\ | \\ \text{NHNHCONH}_2 \\ \mathbf{10} \end{matrix}$$

$$\begin{matrix} \text{OH} \\ | \\ \text{ArCH} \\ | \\ \text{NHNHCONH}_2 \\ \mathbf{10} \end{matrix} \overset{k_2}{\longrightarrow} \text{ArCH}=\text{NNHCONH}_2 + \text{H}_2\text{O}$$

At low pH's where the rate limiting step is attack by the amine we expect electron withdrawing substituents on the aldehyde to increase the rate of reaction and electron donors to decrease it. The overall specific rate constant k_{obs} is equal to k_1, and we expect a plot of log k_{obs} to correlate nicely with σ_Z. Figure 4–4 is a plot of log k_{obs} against σ for the rate of semicarbazone formation in 25% ethanol at pH $= 1.75$.[1] We see that such a correlation is observed.

A ρ value equal to 0.91 demonstrates that the reaction under these conditions has about the same substituent sensitivity as the ionization of benzoic acids.

In neutral solution the rate limiting step in semicarbazone formation is the acid catalyzed dehydration step, and $k_{obs} = K_1 k_2$. Under these conditions the rate of semicarbazone formation depends upon both the equilibrium concentration of the intermediate **10** and its rate of decomposition. Now the concentration of **10** is increased by the presence of electron withdrawing groups, but the acid catalyzed decomposition of **10** is enhanced by electron donating substituents. Since the two effects are in opposition, the rate of semicarbazone formation under these conditions should be insensitive to changes in σ. A plot

[1] Figures 4–4, 4–5, and 4–6 are from Jencks, W. P., *Progress in Physical Organic Chemistry*. New York, Interscience, 1964, vol. 2 pp. 73–5.

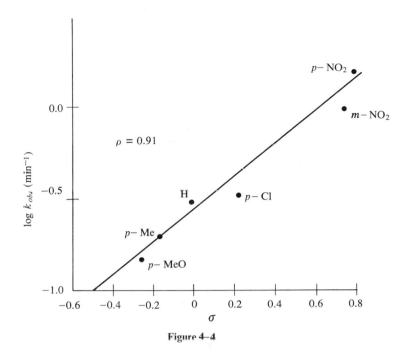

Figure 4-4

of $\log k_{obs}$ against σ should exhibit a small value for ρ, thus indicating the insensitivity of the reaction in neutral solution to substituent effects. A nearly horizontal line indicates a small ρ value. Just such a line is observed ($\rho = 0.07$) in Figure 4-5 for semicarbazone formation in 25% ethanol at neutral pH.

Further evidence in favor of this mechanism and a change in the rate limiting step with changes in the pH comes from a Hammett plot at intermediate pH (pH = 3.9).

Since the addition step is made more difficult, and the dehydration step is facilitated by the presence of electron donors (negative σ's), at intermediate pH's, the rate limiting step for these aldehydes is the addition step ($k_{obs} = k_1$ and large ρ value). For aldehydes bearing electron withdrawing substituents (positive σ's), the addition is favorable, and the dehydration is difficult. Consequently, for these aldehydes at intermediate pH's the second step is rate limiting ($k_{obs} = K_1 k_2$ and small ρ value). Thus a Hammett plot of $\log k_{obs}$ versus σ is expected to show one value for ρ with aldehydes having electron donating substituents and another value for ρ with aldehydes bearing electron withdrawing substituents. We expect a break in the Hammett plot at about $\sigma = 0$. In the region of negative σ's we should obtain a linear correlation with a large ρ value while in the region of positive σ's a line with a small value for ρ is expected, and this is exactly what is found. Figure 4-6 is a plot of $\log k_{obs}$ for semicarbazone formation against σ in 25% ethanol at a pH of 3.9.

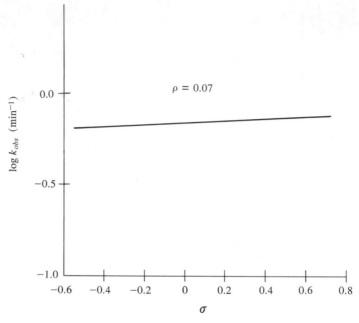

Figure 4–5

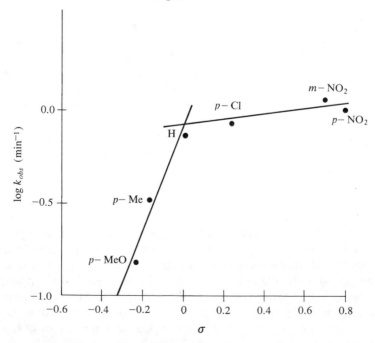

Figure 4–6

The evidence is certainly in favor of the mechanism proposed for semicarbazone formation and agrees with the idea of the rate limiting step being a function of the pH.

The plots just presented clearly show the effect of substituents upon the rate of reaction and the sensitivity of the reaction rate to substituent changes. It would have been most difficult to evaluate the experimental data without resorting to these plots. We see here the usefulness of the Hammett equation.

4.10 Discussion of the Hammett Equation

For the dissociation of *para* Z-benzoic acid,

$$Z-\!\!\left\langle\bigcirc\right\rangle\!\!-COOH \;\rightleftarrows\; Z-\!\!\left\langle\bigcirc\right\rangle\!\!-COO^- + H^+$$

ΔG_Z° is equal to the difference between the free energy of the products and the free energy of the reactant.

$$\Delta G_Z^\circ = G_{Z-C_6H_4-COO^-}^\circ + G_{H^+}^\circ - G_{Z-C_6H_4-COOH}^\circ$$

Since these reactions are carried out in solution, solvation effects must also be considered, and these are included implicitly in the free energy terms.

Similarly for ΔG_H°,

$$\Delta G_H^\circ = G_{H-C_6H_4-COO^-}^\circ + G_{H^+}^\circ - G_{H-C_6H_4-COOH}^\circ$$

We assume that the total free energies of species such as *para* Z-benzoic acid and benzoic acid are separable into components, that is, the free energy of *para* Z-benzoic acid equals the sum of the free energies of Z, the aromatic system, the carboxyl group, plus terms for the free energies of interaction between the various groups:

$$G_{Z-C_6H_4-COOH}^\circ = G_Z + G_{C_6H_4} + G_{COOH} + G_{Z-C_6H_4} + G_{C_6H_4-COOH} + G_{Z-COOH}$$

where the last three terms represent changes in the free energy due to interactions between the groups.

For $G_{Z-C_6H_4-COO^-}^\circ$ we obtain:

$$G_{Z-C_6H_4-COO^-}^\circ = G_Z + G_{C_6H_4} + G_{COO^-} + G_{Z-C_6H_4} + G_{C_6H_4-COO^-} + G_{Z-COO^-}$$

and for ΔG_Z° we find

$$\Delta G_Z^\circ = G_{H^+}^\circ + G_{COO^-} + G_{C_6H_4-COO^-} + G_{Z-COO^-}$$
$$- G_{COOH} - G_{C_6H_4-COOH} - G_{Z-COOH}$$

(This assumes the constancy of the terms G_Z, $G_{C_6H_4}$, and $G_{Z-C_6H_4}$ in both the product and the reactant).

Carrying out the same separation of terms for benzoic acid and its conjugate base affords for ΔG_H°:

$$\Delta G_H^\circ = G_{H^+}^\circ + G_{COO^-} + G_{C_6H_4-COO^-} + G_{H-COO^-}$$
$$- G_{COOH} - G_{C_6H_4-COOH} - G_{H-COOH}$$

Subtracting ΔG_H° from ΔG_Z° yields,

$$\Delta G_Z^\circ - \Delta G_H^\circ = (G_{Z-COO^-} - G_{Z-COOH}) - (G_{H-COO^-} - G_{H-COOH})$$

We find that the only terms that remain in the expression, $\Delta G_Z^\circ - \Delta G_H^\circ$, are terms due to interactions between the substituents on the aromatic ring.

The effect of interactions between the groups Z and COO^- upon the free energy is represented by the term G_{Z-COO^-}. If we assume that the only interaction between these groups is due to the inductive effect of Z, we may separate the term G_{Z-COO^-} into two variables. One of these variables σ_Z measures the contribution of Z to the term G_{Z-COO^-}, and the other F_{COO^-} indicates the contribution of COO^- to the term G_{Z-COO^-}. We assume

$$G_{Z-COO^-} = \sigma_Z F_{COO^-}$$

Similarly,

$$G_{Z-COOH} = \sigma_Z F_{COOH}$$
$$G_{H-COO^-} = \sigma_H F_{COO^-}$$
$$G_{H-COOH} = \sigma_H F_{COOH}$$

Substitution of these expressions into the previous equation and rearrangement of the terms leads to,

$$\Delta G_Z^\circ - \Delta G_H^\circ = (\sigma_Z - \sigma_H)(F_{COO^-} - F_{COOH})$$

Carrying out a similar analysis for the ionization of phenols leads to the equation (for phenols),

$$\Delta G_Z^\circ - \Delta G_H^\circ = (\sigma_Z - \sigma_H)(F_{O^-} - F_{OH})$$

and analogously for anilines,

$$\Delta G_Z^\circ - \Delta G_H^\circ = (\sigma_Z - \sigma_H)(F_{NH_2} - F_{NH_3^+})$$

The value of $(\sigma_Z - \sigma_H)$ is the same for all reactions. It is independent of the reaction under consideration. Thus, the terms inside the first parentheses are a function only of the group Z, changing Z changes the value of $(\sigma_Z - \sigma_H)$. The term σ_H is a constant which we can set equal to zero if we wish.

The value of the terms inside the second parentheses is a constant for any given reaction. Thus, when comparing dissociation constants for a series of benzoic acids, the term $(F_{COO^-} - F_{COOH})$ remains invarient throughout the series. However this function $(F_{X^-} - F_{HX})$ varies from reaction to reaction. This function like ρ depends upon the reaction but remains constant for any given reaction.

Setting σ_H equal to zero,

$$\sigma_H = 0$$

and expressing the function $(F_{X^-} - F_{HX})$ in terms of the parameter ρ:

$$F_{X^-} - F_{HX} = -2.3\,RT\rho$$

affords the Hammett equation:

$$\Delta G_Z^\circ - \Delta G_H^\circ = -2.3\,RT\rho\sigma_Z$$

In deriving the Hammett relationship we assumed that the only influence of Z was an inductive effect. It is possible (and likely) that two groups on the aromatic ring interact in more than one way. Perhaps Z exerts a resonance effect as well as an inductive effect, or a steric effect in addition to the inductive effect, or all three. In these more complex cases it may no longer be satisfactory to separate terms such as G_{Z-COO^-} into only two variables. Additional parameters are necessary to account for the extra interactions. We see, therefore, why the Hammett equation can fail; we have assumed that the interactions between substituents on the aromatic ring can be expressed in terms of two parameters. When this is not possible, the Hammett equation cannot hold.

We can equally well derive linear free energy relationships for cases where the substituents interact in more than one way, for example, inductive and resonance or inductive and steric interactions. The problem is especially simple if we assume that these interactions operate independently. We assume that one of these interactions, for example the inductive effect, operates independently of the other, for example the resonance effect. Returning to the equation,

$$\Delta G_Z^\circ - \Delta G_X^\circ = (G_{Z-COO^-} - G_{Z-COOH}) - (G_{X-COO^-} - G_{X-COOH})$$

(the reference compound need not be the unsubstituted acid) we assume that we can treat these two effects, inductive and resonance, independently, and we may then separate terms such as G_{Z-COO^-} as follows:

$$G_{Z-COO^-} = \sigma_Z F_{COO^-} + \sigma'_Z F'_{COO^-}$$

where the first set of variables represents the contribution to G_{Z-COO^-} caused by the inductive effect, and the second set the contribution due to resonance effects. We treat the other interaction terms in a similar manner and substitute the results into the original equation. This yields,

$$\Delta G_Z^\circ - \Delta G_X^\circ = (\sigma_Z - \sigma_X)(F_{COO^-} - F_{COOH}) + (\sigma'_Z - \sigma'_X)(F'_{COO^-} - F'_{COOH})$$

Upon the proper choice of standard states, we obtain an equation similar to the

Hammett equation:

$$\log \frac{K_Z}{K_X} = \rho\sigma_Z + \rho'\sigma'_Z$$

If in the above equation we multiply the second term by ρ/ρ and factor out ρ, we obtain

$$\log \frac{K_Z}{K_X} = \rho\left(\sigma_Z + \frac{\rho'}{\rho}\sigma'_Z\right)$$

Representing the composite expression by the single variable σ''_Z,

$$\sigma''_Z = \left(\sigma_Z + \frac{\rho'}{\rho}\sigma'_Z\right)$$

we obtain an expression analogous in form to the Hammett equation:

$$\log \frac{K_Z}{K_X} = \rho\sigma''_Z$$

As long as the composite term σ'' can be treated as a single parameter, the Hammett equation will work even when both inductive and resonance effects are operative.

4.11 Other Linear Free Energy Relationships

There exist, besides the Hammett equation, a number of other linear free energy relationships. All of these can be derived by treatments similar to that employed for the Hammett equation. There are three broad methods by which two groups can interact (inductive, resonance, steric). If we assume that each of these interactions takes place independently, we can by the proper choice of standard states obtain the equation,

$$\log \frac{k_Z}{k_X} = \rho\sigma + \rho'\sigma' + \rho''\sigma''$$

where Z is the substituent, X is the reference compound, and where the first set of parameters indicates the contribution due to inductive effects, the second the contribution from resonance effects, and the third that due to steric effects.

Now we must choose standard reactions to evaluate as many of the parameters as possible. Since we cannot evaluate all of them, simplifying assumptions are necessary. The hydrolyses of esters are chosen as our standard reactions, and the reference compound is CH_3COOR (X = CH_3). The rate of hydrolysis of this compound is compared with the rates of hydrolysis of other esters ZCOOR (where Z is any other group). In this manner the term $\log k_Z/k_X$ can be evaluated.

We measure the rates of hydrolysis of a series of esters under both acidic and basic conditions, and this leads to the equations (*B* refers to hydrolysis under basic conditions, A to acidic conditions),

$$\log\left(\frac{k_Z}{k_X}\right)_B = \rho_B\sigma_B + \rho_B'\sigma_B' + \sigma_B''\sigma_B''$$

and

$$\log\left(\frac{k_Z}{k_X}\right)_A = \rho_A\sigma_A + \rho_A'\sigma_A' + \rho_A''\sigma_A''$$

If we assume that steric factors are the same under both sets of conditions, then the term $\rho_B''\sigma_B''$ is equal to $\rho_A''\sigma_A''$, and subtracting the second of the previous equations from the first leads to,

$$\log\left(\frac{k_Z}{k_X}\right)_B - \log\left(\frac{k_Z}{k_X}\right)_A \doteq (\rho_B\sigma_B - \rho_A\sigma_A) + (\rho_B'\sigma_B' - \rho_A'\sigma_A')$$

If we further assume that resonance effects are negligible in these reactions, or if we assume that resonance effects are the same under both sets of conditions, or that these effects differ in the two series by a constant amount, then we can neglect the term $(\rho_B'\sigma_B' - \rho_A'\sigma_A')$. Our equation reduces to,

$$\log\left(\frac{k_Z}{k_X}\right)_B - \log\left(\frac{k_Z}{k_X}\right)_A = (\rho_B\sigma_B - \rho_A\sigma_A)$$

To the extent that the previous assumptions are correct, they allow us to express our equation in terms of parameters involving only the inductive effects of the various groups. We have assumed that differences between $\log(k_Z/k_X)_B$ and $\log(k_Z/k_X)_A$ are due entirely to a difference in the inductive effect under the different conditions. We can compare these reactions with other reactions involving only inductive effects and obtain values for σ's and ρ's.

Multiplying the second term in the last equation by ρ_B/ρ_B and factoring ρ_B affords,

$$\log\left(\frac{k_Z}{k_X}\right)_B - \log\left(\frac{k_Z}{k_X}\right)_A = \rho_B\left(\sigma_B - \frac{\rho_A}{\rho_B}\sigma_A\right)$$

We further simplify the equation by representing the composite term by the single parameter σ^*:

$$\sigma^* = \left(\sigma_B - \frac{\rho_A}{\rho_B}\sigma_A\right)$$

This last assumption is quite good. It turns out experimentally that electronic effects are far more important for hydrolyses conducted under basic conditions and that hydrolyses conducted under acidic conditions are quite insensitive to electronic effects. Therefore ρ_A is much smaller than ρ_B, and the ratio ρ_A/ρ_B is much less than unity. Since σ_A is a small number, the term $(\rho_A \sigma_A / \rho_B)$ has a value close to zero. Consequently, σ^* is approximately equal to σ_B. Since,

$$\frac{\rho_A}{\rho_B} \sigma_A \simeq 0$$

therefore,

$$\sigma^* \simeq \sigma_B$$

Representing the composite term by a single parameter is a satisfactory assumption. The equation becomes:

$$\log\left(\frac{k_Z}{k_X}\right)_B - \log\left(\frac{k_Z}{k_X}\right)_A = \rho\sigma^*$$

We could set ρ equal to unity and use the values of $\log(k_Z/k_X)_B - \log(k_Z/k_X)_A$ to determine σ^*. However, it is desirable to keep the values of σ^* obtained by this equation similar to the values of σ in the Hammett equation. Since the difference in logs affords larger values than desired, we define a new function ρ^* as

$$\rho = 2.48 \; \rho^*$$

and obtain the equation

$$\frac{1}{2.48}\left[\log\left(\frac{k_Z}{k_X}\right)_B - \log\left(\frac{k_Z}{k_X}\right)_A\right] = \rho^*\sigma^*$$

The division by 2.48 is purely arbitrary. It keeps the values of σ^* about the same as the values for σ in the Hammett equation. Now setting ρ^* equal to unity, we use the rates of hydrolysis of various esters to determine values for σ^*.

$$\frac{1}{2.48}\left[\log\left(\frac{k_Z}{k_X}\right)_B - \log\left(\frac{k_Z}{k_X}\right)_A\right] = \sigma^*$$

These σ^* values are assumed to indicate the inductive effect of Z as compared to that of X. Other reactions where changing the substituents alters only the inductive effect should also be related to σ^* (with other values for ρ^*). Therefore, if we determine the specific rate constants k_Z and k_X for some other reaction where Z and X exert only an inductive effect, the term $\log k_Z/k_X$ as evaluated for this other reaction should be proportional to σ^*. Thus,

$$\log\frac{k_Z}{k_X} = \rho^*\sigma^*$$

We evaluate $\log k_Z/k_X$ for various other reactions, and knowing σ^* we determine ρ^* for these reactions.

This is the Taft equation.

Other linear free energy relationships include the Brown equation:

$$\log \frac{f_p}{f_m} = (1 - \sigma_m^+/\sigma_p^+) \log f_p$$

intended for use in aromatic substitution, the Swain equation:

$$\log \frac{k_N}{k_O} = sn + s'e$$

for use in connection with nucleophilic substitution, and the Brønsted catalysis law:

$$\log k_A = \alpha \log K_a + A$$

or

$$\log k_B = \beta \log K_b + B$$

The Brønsted catalysis equations assume that for acid or base catalyzed reactions the ability of an acid or a base to catalyze a reaction is related to the strength of that acid or base (as indicated by the ionization constant K_a or K_b). It seems reasonable to assume that the greater the ability of an acid to donate a proton or of a base to abstract one, the more effective it ought to be as a catalyst. Therefore, the free energy of activation $\Delta G^{\ddagger}$ for the catalyzed reaction ought to be proportional to $\Delta G°$ for ionization of the catalyst,

$$\Delta G^{\ddagger} - c\Delta G° + C$$

This assumption leads directly to the two equations just presented.

Since the pK_a is defined as

$$pK_a = -\log K_a$$

and

$$pK_b = -\log K_b$$

we can rewrite the equations as,

$$\log k_A = -\alpha(pK_a) + A$$

$$\log k_B = -\beta(pK_b) + B$$

Plots of $\log k_A$ against the pK_a of the acid catalyst ought to be linear with slopes equal to $-\alpha$. Similarly, basic catalysts ought to afford straight lines having slopes equal to $-\beta$. The values of α and β like ρ are constant within a given series of reactions but vary from one series of reactions to another.

Many other free energy relationships are known. All of them involve parameters that must be evaluated experimentally, and we have seen how useful these structure-reactivity relationships can be.

Supplementary Reading

1. Bell, R. P., *The Proton in Chemistry*. Ithaca, New York, Cornell U.P., 1959.

2. Brown, H. C., McDaniel, D. H., and Häfliger, O., *Determination of Organic Structures by Physical Methods*, (eds.) E. A. Braude and F. C. Nachod, New York, Academic, 1955.

3. Ehrenson, S., *Progress in Physical Organic Chemistry*, Vol. 2, (eds) S. G. Cohen, A. Streitwieser, Jr., R. W. Taft. New York, Interscience, 1964.

4. Gould, E. S., *Mechanism and Structure in Organic Chemistry*. New York, Holt, 1959.

5. Hammett, L. P., *Physical Organic Chemistry*. New York, McGraw-Hill, 1940.

6. Hine, J., *Physical Organic Chemistry*. New York, McGraw-Hill, 1962.

7. Jaffé, H. H., *Chem. Rev.*, **53**, 191 (1953).

8. Leffler, J. E., and Grunwald, E., *Rates and Equilibria of Organic Reactions*. New York, Wiley, 1963.

9. Ritchie, C. D., and Sager, W. F., *Progress in Physical Organic Chemistry*, Vol. 2, (eds.) S. G. Cohen, A. Streitwieser, Jr., R. W. Taft. New York, Interscience, 1964.

10. Taft, R. W., Jr., *Steric Effects in Organic Chemistry*, (ed.) M. S. Newman. New York, Wiley, 1956.

11. Wiberg, K. B., *Physical Organic Chemistry*. New York, Wiley, 1964.

Chapter 5

Quantum Chemistry

5.1 Wave-Particle Duality

The modern theory of wave mechanics developed by Schrödinger is based upon de Broglie's postulate of wave-particle duality. It had been known for several years that light, usually regarded as a wave, also displayed particlelike properties. Under some conditions light exhibited wavelike behavior, yet under others light behaved as if it were composed of particles (photons). Light, then, displayed wave-particle duality. De Broglie reasoned that if light were capable of such behavior why couldn't this be true of all substances? Why couldn't we associate with any particle a wave? A substance could manifest itself as a particle under some conditions and as a wave under other conditions. The properties of a material would depend upon the experimental conditions. With this idea in mind de Broglie searched for an equation that would relate the properties of a particle to the properties of a wave. Characteristic of a particle is its momentum, and characteristic of a wave is its wavelength. De Broglie succeeded in relating these two. In 1924, he postulated that a particle moving with a linear momentum p had associated with it a wave having wavelength λ, and these two quantities were related by the expression,

$$\lambda = \frac{h}{p} \qquad (5\text{--}1)$$

where h, a constant of proportionality, is Planck's constant. A particle of mass m moving with linear velocity v has linear momentum p,

$$p = mv$$

and associated with it a wave of wavelength λ.

$$\lambda = \frac{h}{p}$$

$$\lambda = \frac{h}{mv}$$

5.2 Energy

The total energy of a system of several particles is equal to the total kinetic energy of the system plus the total potential energy of the system,

$$E = T + U \tag{5-2}$$

where E is the total energy of the system, T is the total kinetic energy, and U is the total potential energy of the system.

If the system is composed of only a single particle,

$$E = T + U$$

where T is the kinetic energy and U the potential energy of that particle.

The kinetic energy of a particle is usually expressed as $mv^2/2$. However, multiplying both numerator and denominator of this expression by m, leads to the result,

$$T = \frac{mv^2}{2} = \frac{mv^2}{2} \cdot \frac{m}{m} = \frac{m^2v^2}{2m} = \frac{p^2}{2m} \tag{5-3}$$

Equation (5–3) gives an alternative expression for the kinetic energy of a particle in terms of its linear momentum.

The potential energy U of a particle depends upon its environment. We shall be dealing with atoms and molecules and in these systems shall consider only the electrostatic interactions between charged particles. The potentials associated with such interactions are called coulombic potentials and the potential energies, coulombic potential energies. The coulombic potential energy between two charged particles is given by the expression,

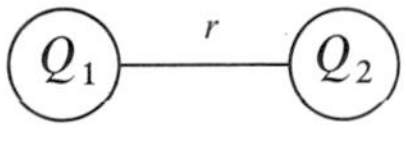

$$Q_1 \underset{}{\overset{r}{\text{———}}} Q_2$$

$$U = \frac{Q_1 Q_2}{r} \tag{5-4}$$

where Q_1 is the charge of particle one, Q_2 the charge of particle two, and r is the distance between them.

If the charge of an electron is $-e$ and the charge of a proton is $+e$, then the potential energy of attraction between a proton and an electron is given by,

$$U = \frac{(+e)(-e)}{r} = -\frac{e^2}{r} \tag{5-5}$$

where r is the distance separating them.

The potential energy of repulsion between two electrons is,

$$U = \frac{(-e)(-e)}{r} = \frac{e^2}{r}$$

The potential energy of attraction between a lithium nucleus ($Q = +3e$) and an electron is given by the expression,

$$U = \frac{(+3e)(-e)}{r} = -\frac{3e^2}{r}$$

while the repulsion between two alpha particles (helium nuclei) is equal to,

$$U = \frac{(+2e)(+2e)}{r} = \frac{4e^2}{r}$$

Notice that all attractive potential energies (between oppositely charged particles) are negative while all repulsive potential energies (between similarly charged species) are positive.

The total kinetic energy for a system of two particles equals the sum of the kinetic energies of the individual particles.

$$T = \frac{p_1^2}{2m_1} + \frac{p_2^2}{2m_2}$$

The first term refers to the kinetic energy of particle one, the second to that of particle two.

If the system of two particles happens to be composed of two electrons, the energy of the system is equal to,

$$E = \frac{p_1^2}{2m} + \frac{p_2^2}{2m} + \frac{e^2}{r}$$

where e^2/r is the potential energy of repulsion between the two electrons. These electrons have the same mass, but their velocities and their linear momenta may be different.

We shall assume in this discussion that when dealing with atoms and molecules, all the nuclei are stationary; their kinetic energy is therefore zero. Consequently, if the system of two particles is a hydrogen atom which is composed of a proton and an electron, the energy of this system equals,

$$E = \frac{p^2}{2m} - \frac{e^2}{r}$$

The first term represents the kinetic energy of the electron and the second, the potential energy of the system.

For this system to be stable, that is, for the hydrogen atom to be stable, the electron must remain bound to the proton. The two particles remain together only if the attractive potential holding the electron is greater than its kinetic energy. When this is not true, the electron possesses sufficient kinetic energy to leave, and the hydrogen atom dissociates into a proton and an electron. Stability implies that the potential energy term $-e^2/r$ must be greater in magnitude than the term $p^2/2m$. Since the potential energy term is the larger and since it is negative, E must be negative for stable systems.

The total energy for a system of three electrons is,

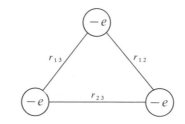

$$E = \frac{p_1^2}{2m} + \frac{p_2^2}{2m} + \frac{p_3^2}{2m} + \frac{e^2}{r_{12}} + \frac{e^2}{r_{13}} + \frac{e^2}{r_{23}}$$

5.3 The Hamiltonian

Consider a system of several particles in motion. It is desirable to describe the motion of these particles, and to do this requires a function (the Hamiltonian) involving their positions, their momenta, and the time. The equations of motion of the system are expressed in classical mechanics in terms of the Hamiltonian which usually is a complicated function. However, the Hamiltonian, H, for a system whose total energy remains constant is simply equal to that total energy:

$$H = E$$

For such a system the classical Hamiltonian is equal to the sum of the total kinetic energy and the total potential energy.

$$H = E = T + U \tag{5–6}$$

The Hamiltonian for a single particle is,

$$H = E = \frac{p^2}{2m} + U$$

For the hydrogen atom,

$$H = \frac{p^2}{2m} - \frac{e^2}{r}$$

while for the helium atom,

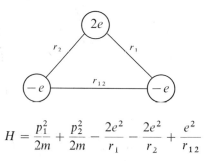

$$H = \frac{p_1^2}{2m} + \frac{p_2^2}{2m} - \frac{2e^2}{r_1} - \frac{2e^2}{r_2} + \frac{e^2}{r_{12}}$$

The first two terms in the Hamiltonian for helium represent the kinetic energies of electrons one and two, $-2e^2/r_1$ is the attraction of electron one for the nucleus, $-2e^2/r_2$ the attraction of electron two, and e^2/r_{12} represents the repulsion between the electrons.

The Hamiltonian for the lithium atom takes the form,

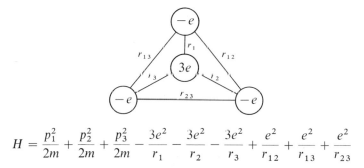

$$H = \frac{p_1^2}{2m} + \frac{p_2^2}{2m} + \frac{p_3^2}{2m} - \frac{3e^2}{r_1} - \frac{3e^2}{r_2} - \frac{3e^2}{r_3} + \frac{e^2}{r_{12}} + \frac{e^2}{r_{13}} + \frac{e^2}{r_{23}}$$

5.4 Standing Waves

A sine wave is described by the equation,

$$\psi = A \sin \frac{2\pi}{\lambda} x \qquad (5\text{–}7)$$

where A is the amplitude of the wave (the maximum value of ψ), and λ is the wavelength of the wave.

That Eq. (5–7) does describe a sine wave can be seen from Figure 5–1. According to this diagram, if we start at the origin and travel along the x axis a distance equal to one wavelength λ, the value of ψ at this point equals the sine of 2π. At the point where x is equal to $\lambda/2$, ψ is equal to the sine of π. Notice that ψ takes on positive values in some regions and negative values in others; from the origin to π, ψ is positive, but between π and 2π, ψ is negative.

In Figure 5–2 we construct a coordinate system and assume that we have an electron with constant kinetic energy and constant potential energy traveling

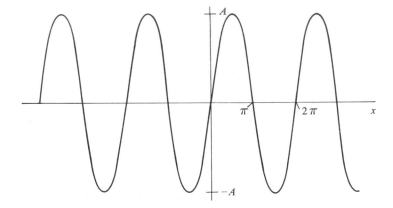

Figure 5–1

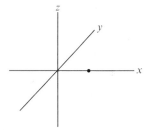

Figure 5–2

along the x axis of that coordinate system. We allow the electron to move along the x axis but do not give it freedom in the y and z directions.

The motion of the electron is restricted to the x axis of the coordinate system, and according to de Broglie this electron has a wave associated with it. To describe the electron we need only describe this associated wave; the concept of wave-particle duality allows us to treat the electron in terms of this wave. Let us further assume that we have restricted the motion of the electron in such a way that the wave associated with it is the sine wave just discussed, Eq. (5–7). We have an electron traveling along a region of the x axis, and associated with this electron is the sine wave, $\psi = A \sin 2\pi x/\lambda$. This wave is the orbital of the electron, that is, we have an electron occupying the very simple orbital ψ.

The usual problem is to determine the total energy of the electron and to discover the regions along the x axis where it is likely to be found. Since the sine wave describes our electron, a point where the value of ψ is large represents a point where the electron is likely to be found. Thus, the electron is most likely to be found at points such as $\pi/2$, $3\pi/2$ and $5\pi/2$ for ψ is large in a positive sense at $\pi/2$ and $5\pi/2$ and large in a negative sense at $3\pi/2$.

A point where the value of ψ is zero is a point where the electron cannot be found; the electron will not be found at the points π or 2π.

We relate the value of ψ to the probability of finding the electron. Regions where ψ is large (either positively or negatively large) represent regions where the electron is likely to be found, while regions where ψ is small are regions of low probability. Furthermore, we relate the momentum of the electron to the wavelength of its associated wave. Since,

$$\lambda = \frac{h}{p}$$

we are able to replace λ in Eq. (5–7) by its equivalent h/p.

$$\psi = A \sin \frac{2\pi p}{h} x \qquad\qquad (5\text{–}8)$$

5.5 The One-Dimensional Schrödinger Equation

We present in this section the Schrödinger equation for a single particle moving in one dimension. In the preceding sections we discussed the idea of wave-particle duality and the concept of the Hamiltonian. The Schrödinger equation is a differential equation that incorporates both of these ideas. We have an electron (or for that matter any particle); this electron has a certain energy and has associated with it a wave. The usual problem to confront us is to find the energy E of the particle and the wave ψ (orbital) associated with it. A knowledge of these quantities is all we can hope to obtain. These quantities E and ψ are obtained by solving the Schrödinger equation. A solution affords the energy and indicates where the particle is likely to be found. Large values of ψ represent regions of high probability of finding the electron (alternatively, regions of high electron density).

In the last section we restricted the motion of the electron in such a way that we could assign to it the sine wave given by Eq. (5–8). However, the wave associated with a particle need not be the simple sine wave that we have described; far more complex expressions for ψ are possible.

One sets up the Schrödinger equation and when possible solves it for E and ψ. When the equation is too complex for an exact solution, one can still construct an approximate function for ψ and using this function, solve for E. Naturally, the better the choice for ψ, the closer is the calculated value of E to the experimental value. At this time it suffices to assume that ψ is given by Eq. (5–8). Using this ψ we develop the Schrödinger equation.

Once again, we restrict an electron of constant kinetic energy and constant potential energy to the x axis. We restrict the motion of the electron to the x axis but do not allow it to move in the y and z directions. Consequently, the Schrödinger equation that we develop in this section will involve x but not y and z. Such an equation, which involves only one of the three dimensions of space, is called a one-dimensional equation.

To obtain the Schrödinger equation for the electron we carry out the following transformation:

1. Set up the classical Hamiltonian $(T + U)$ for the problem and equate this expression to the total energy of the electron.
2. Multiply this equation by ψ which for our electron is given by Eq. (5–8).
3. Convert to quantum mechanics by replacing the term $p^2 \psi$ that results from these operations by a more complex expression.

This procedure affords the Schrödinger equation for the electron.

The Hamiltonian for the electron or for any single particle is given by Eq. (5–6) as,

$$H = \frac{p^2}{2m} + U \tag{5–9}$$

and this expression equals the total energy of the electron.
Therefore,

$$\frac{p^2}{2m} + U = E$$

This gives the energy (operation one). The wave associated with the electron is, from Eq. (5–8),

$$\psi = A \sin \frac{2\pi p}{h} x$$

and multiplication of Eq. (5–9) by ψ affords,

$$\frac{p^2}{2m}\psi + U\psi = E\psi \tag{5–10}$$

or

$$\frac{p^2}{2m}\left(A \sin \frac{2\pi p}{h} x\right) + U\left(A \sin \frac{2\pi p}{h} x\right) = E\left(A \sin \frac{2\pi p}{h} x\right)$$

We have carried out the first two steps of the procedure. To obtain the appropriate expression for $p^2\psi$, we differentiate ψ twice with respect to x:

$$\psi = A \sin \frac{2\pi p}{h} x$$

$$\frac{d\psi}{dx} = \frac{2\pi p}{h} A \cos \frac{2\pi p}{h} x$$

$$\frac{d^2\psi}{dx^2} = -\frac{4\pi^2 p^2}{h^2} A \sin \frac{2\pi p}{h} x$$

The term

$$A \sin \frac{2\pi p}{h} x$$

in the expression for the second derivative is just ψ, and we obtain,

$$\frac{d^2\psi}{dx^2} = -\frac{4\pi^2 p^2}{h^2} \psi$$

Transposing and solving for $p^2\psi$,

$$p^2\psi = -\frac{h^2}{4\pi^2} \frac{d^2\psi}{dx^2} \tag{5-11}$$

This is the desired expression. We convert to quantum mechanics by replacing the term $p^2\psi$ in Eq. (5–10) by the more complex expression given by Eq. (5–11). Making this substitution yields the Schrödinger equation for a single particle traveling along the x axis. Replacing $p^2\psi$ affords,

$$-\frac{h^2}{8\pi^2 m} \frac{d^2\psi}{dx^2} + U\psi = E\psi \tag{5-12}$$

This is the Schrödinger equation. We already know that ψ for the electron is given by Eq. (5–8). If we did not know this, we could solve the differential Eq. (5–12) for ψ and E and obtain both the energy of the electron and the wave associated with it.

The Hamiltonian for a single particle is given by Eq. (5–9), and the corresponding Schrödinger equation is given by Eq. (5–12). The procedure used to obtain this result is a general one and works for any one-dimensional problem. We first set up the expression for the classical Hamiltonian of the system; we next multiply this expression by ψ; we then obtain the Schrödinger equation for the problem by replacing $p^2\psi$ wherever it occurs by Eq. (5–11).

We are able to rewrite the Schrödinger equation in the following manner:

$$\left[-\frac{h^2}{8\pi^2 m} \frac{d^2}{dx^2} + U \right] \psi = E\psi \tag{5-13}$$

Although we have rewritten this equation, its significance is unchanged. This is still the Schrödinger equation for the electron; factoring ψ to obtain an expression of this type is merely a form of mathematical shorthand or symbolism. Comparison of Eqs. (5–13) and (5–9) shows that H has been replaced by an operator equivalent. In quantum mechanics the Hamiltonian is an operator:

$$H = -\frac{h^2}{8\pi^2 m}\frac{d^2}{dx^2} + U \tag{5–14}$$

We can write the Schrödinger equation in terms of this Hamiltonian operator as,

$$H\psi = E\psi \tag{5–15}$$

where the symbol H is now given by Eq. (5–14). This operator H is the one-dimensional Hamiltonian operator.

Equations (5–12), (5–13), and (5–14) all represent the same equation. They are merely three different ways of writing this equation. Solving the Schrödinger equation affords the energy E of the electron and the wave ψ associated with it. When one solves such an equation for E, this energy is frequently called the eigenvalue and ψ is called the eigenfunction; these are mathematical terms.

Equation (5–12) was obtained for an electron having constant kinetic as well as constant potential energy, yet this equation is actually valid for any particle whose total energy remains constant. The only restriction on Eq. (5–12) is that E be constant; T and U may vary. However, since

$$E = T + U$$

in order for E to remain constant, a decrease in T must be accompanied by an increase in U.

Starting with a knowledge of ψ, we were able to obtain the Schrödinger equation. In general, neither ψ nor E is known. Even without a knowledge of ψ, we can still set up the Schrödinger equation for any problem. Solving the differential equation for ψ and E yields both the wave associated with the particle (eigenfunction, orbital) and its energy (eigenvalue).

A solution to the Schrödinger equation depends upon the particle under consideration. Usually, more than a single solution is possible. A whole series of eigenfunctions (ψ's) can be obtained and associated with each ψ is an energy. For the electron, one possible solution is the sine wave given by Eq. (5–8); however, this is not the only possible wave that we could associate with the electron. Other possibilities include

$$\psi_2 = A \cos \frac{2\pi p}{h}x$$

and

$$\psi_3 = A \sin \frac{2\pi p'}{h}x$$

The term p' in ψ_3 represents an electron moving with a different linear momentum. Which wave we associate with the electron depends upon the restrictions imposed upon it and its energy. For example, an electron described by the functions ψ_2 or ψ_3 could well have a different total energy from the electron described by Eq. (5–8). Furthermore, the functions need not be sine and cosine waves; more difficult problems give rise to more complex solutions. However, in all cases, regions where ψ is large represent regions of high probability of finding the electron (regions of high electron density).

5.6 The Three-Dimensional Schrödinger Equation

We obtained the one-dimensional Schrödinger equation by setting up the Hamiltonian for the system, multiplying the expression by ψ, and replacing $p^2\psi$ by the expression given in Eq. (5–11). The same procedure is followed to obtain the three-dimensional Schrödinger equation. The electron is no longer restricted to the x axis, and since it can move in any direction, the three-dimensional equivalent to Eq. (5–11) contains additional terms involving y and z.

For the one-dimensional problem we found,

$$p^2\psi = -\frac{h^2}{4\pi^2}\frac{d^2\psi}{dx^2}$$

In three dimensions the expression for $p^2\psi$ becomes,

$$p^2\psi = -\frac{h^2}{4\pi^2}\frac{\partial^2\psi}{\partial x^2} - \frac{h^2}{4\pi^2}\frac{\partial^2\psi}{\partial y^2} - \frac{h^2}{4\pi^2}\frac{\partial^2\psi}{\partial z^2} \qquad (5\text{–}16)$$

Of course, in this case ψ is no longer given by Eq. (5–8). The function ψ has become more complex and so has the expression for $p^2\psi$, but the Hamiltonian for the electron remains unaltered. We obtain the three-dimensional Schrödinger equation by substituting Eq. (5–16) for $p^2\psi$ into Eq. (5–10). Substitution yields,

$$-\frac{h^2}{8\pi^2 m}\frac{\partial^2\psi}{\partial x^2} - \frac{h^2}{8\pi^2 m}\frac{\partial^2\psi}{\partial y^2} - \frac{h^2}{8\pi^2 m}\frac{\partial^2\psi}{\partial z^2} + U\psi = E\psi \qquad (5\text{–}17)$$

This is the three-dimensional Schrödinger equation. Solving this equation for ψ and E gives the energy of the electron and the wave associated with it.

Factoring ψ once again, it is possible to rewrite the left side of Eq. (5–17) as,

$$\left[-\frac{h^2}{8\pi^2 m}\frac{\partial^2}{\partial x^2} - \frac{h^2}{8\pi^2 m}\frac{\partial^2}{\partial y^2} - \frac{h^2}{8\pi^2 m}\frac{\partial^2}{\partial z^2} + U\right]\psi = E\psi \qquad (5\text{–}18)$$

Comparing Eq. (5–18) with Eq. (5–9) indicates that H has again been replaced by an operator equivalent:

$$H = -\frac{h^2}{8\pi^2 m}\left(\frac{\partial^2}{\partial x^2} + \frac{\partial^2}{\partial y^2} + \frac{\partial^2}{\partial z^2}\right) + U \qquad (5\text{–}19)$$

This operator is called the three-dimensional Hamiltonian operator, and in terms of this operator we are still able to write the Schrödinger equation as,

$$H\psi = E\psi \tag{5-20}$$

where H is now given by Eq. (5–19). The energy of the electron is still called the eigenvalue and the wave is still the eigenfunction. The eigenfunctions ψ resulting from three-dimensional problems involve x, y, and z (or in polar coordinates r, θ, ϕ). Furthermore, these functions are the orbitals which are familiar to all chemists. Equation (5–20) states that an electron in orbital ψ has energy E. If the electron is in the $1s$ atomic orbital of hydrogen, the Schrödinger equation becomes,

$$H(1s_H) = E_{1s}(1s_H)$$

where $1s_H$ represents the $1s$ atomic orbital occupied by the electron, and E_{1s} indicates the energy of an electron occupying that orbital. If the electron is in the $2s$ orbital of carbon, Eq. (5–20) becomes,

$$H(2s_C) = E_{2s}(2s_C)$$

where E_{2s} is now the energy of an electron in the $2s$ orbital of carbon. For an electron in a p atomic orbital of carbon we have,

$$H(p_C) = E_p(p_C)$$

and E_p is the energy of the electron in that p orbital.

5.7 Probability and Normalization

In Section 5.4 the idea was presented that the probability of finding the electron is related to the value of ψ. When ψ is large, the probability is high whereas regions where the value of ψ is small are regions where the probability of finding the electron is low.

Probability varies between the limits zero and unity. Zero implies no probability of finding the electron, that is, certainty of its absence, whereas a value of unity implies a certainty of finding the electron. A probability equal to 0.7 indicates a seventy per cent chance of finding the electron; 0.1 implies a ten per cent chance, and so forth. The probability is always positive.

In Section 5.4 the wave associated with the electron was the sine wave,

$$\psi = A \sin \frac{2\pi p}{h} x$$

This wave is positive in some regions and negative in others. Therefore, ψ cannot be a direct measure of the probability because it takes on both positive and negative values, and we require a quantity that is always positive. The choice of ψ^2 as a probability appears reasonable, for the square of any real number is always positive. Thus, the probability of finding the electron in some region is related to the value of ψ^2 for that region.

For a one-dimensional problem where we restrict the motion of the electron to the x axis, the probability of finding the electron in the region between x and $x + dx$ is given by the value of $\psi^2\,dx$ for that region. If the value of $\psi^2\,dx$ is large, there is a good chance of finding the electron in the region between x and $x + dx$. If the value is small, the chance of finding the electron is poor. Naturally the larger we make dx, the greater the probability of finding the electron.

An alternative explanation is to consider the value of $\psi^2\,dx$ as the electron density in the region between x and $x + dx$. We shall use these ideas of electron probability and electron density interchangeably.

If the probability of finding the electron in some small region is given by $\psi^2\,dx$, then the total probability of finding the electron on the entire x axis is given by the integral of this quantity:

$$\int_{-\infty}^{\infty} \psi^2\,dx$$

Since for our one-dimensional problem our initial assumption restricted the electron to the x axis, we are certain of finding the electron here, and

$$\int_{-\infty}^{\infty} \psi^2\,dx = 1 \qquad (5\text{–}21)$$

The requirement that Eq. (5–21) be equal to unity is called the normalization requirement for a one-dimensional problem. For a three-dimensional problem where the electron is also able to move in the y and z directions, the normalization requirement becomes,

$$\int_{-\infty}^{\infty}\int_{-\infty}^{\infty}\int_{-\infty}^{\infty} \psi^2\,dxdydz = 1 \qquad (5\text{–}22)$$

For convenience we rewrite this expression as,

$$\int \psi^2\,dv = 1 \qquad (5\text{–}23)$$

where dv is the volume element $dxdydz$ and the limits of integration are implicit.

Thus, if we have a set of functions $\psi_1, \psi_2, \psi_3, \ldots \psi_n$, each member of this set should obey Eq. (5–23).

$$\int \psi_1\psi_1\,dv = 1$$

$$\int \psi_2\psi_2\,dv = 1$$

$$\int \psi_3\psi_3\,dv = 1$$

For any function ψ_A,

$$\int \psi_A \psi_A \, dv = 1 \qquad (5\text{--}24)$$

Since the functions ψ are the orbitals with which we are already familiar, these orbitals are mathematical functions which must obey Eq. (5–24). For example in the $1s$, $2s$, and $2p_z$ orbitals for the hydrogen atom :

$$\int (1s)(1s) \, dv = 1$$

$$\int (2s)(2s) \, dv = 1$$

$$\int (2p_z)(2p_z) \, dv = 1$$

Diagrams such as Figure 5–3 which are usually associated with these orbitals ($1s, 2s, 2p_z$) represent regions where an electron occupying one of these orbitals is likely to be found.

The sphere associated with the $1s$ orbital represents a region of high probability of finding the electron, that is, a region of high electron density. In all cases these diagrams indicate only the regions where the probability of finding the electron is high.

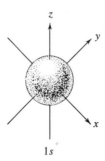

$1s$

Figure 5–3

5.8 Orthogonality

Consider the orbitals associated with a hydrogen atom. These are the $1s$, $2s$, $2p_z$, and so forth. Now there is no net overlap between the $1s$ and the $2s$ or between either of these and the p orbitals. To indicate this fact we say that these orbitals are orthogonal. The $1s$ orbital is orthogonal to the $2s$, and so forth. Two different atomic orbitals associated with the same atom are orthogonal.

Similarly, different molecular orbitals associated with the same molecule are orthogonal. A set of molecular orbitals $\psi_1, \psi_2, \psi_3, \ldots \psi_n$ belonging to the same molecule is orthogonal; there is no net overlap between any two of these molecular orbitals.

Mathematically, the idea of orbital overlap between any two orbitals ψ_1 and ψ_2 is given by the expression,

$$\int \psi_1 \psi_2 \, dv$$

and the requirement that there be no net overlap between them is expressed by setting this integral equal to zero:

$$\int \psi_1 \psi_2 \, dv = 0 \qquad (5\text{--}25)$$

In the hydrogen atom,

$$\int (1s)(2s) \, dv = 0$$

$$\int (1s)(2p_z) \, dv = 0$$

A set of molecular orbitals is also orthogonal; as,

$$\int \psi_1 \psi_2 \, dv = 0$$

$$\int \psi_2 \psi_3 \, dv = 0$$

For any two orbitals ψ_A and ψ_B,

$$\int \psi_A \psi_B \, dv = 0 \qquad (5\text{--}26)$$

As set of functions $\psi_1, \psi_2, \psi_3, \ldots \psi_n$, both normalized and orthogonal, that is, a set of functions obeying both Eqs. (5–24) and (5–26) is called an orthonormal set. We can express an orthonormal set in the following way:

$$\int \psi_A \psi_B \, dv = \begin{cases} 1 & A = B \\ 0 & A \neq B \end{cases} \qquad (5\text{--}27)$$

To prove that two orbitals ψ_A and ψ_B are orthogonal, let these two orbitals be two different orbitals on the same molecule. An electron in orbital ψ_A has energy E_A, and an electron in ψ_B has energy E_B. Then according to the Schrödinger equation:

$$H\psi_A = E_A \psi_A$$

$$H\psi_B = E_B \psi_B$$

Multiply the first of these equations by ψ_B and the second by ψ_A:

$$\psi_B H \psi_A = \psi_B E_A \psi_A$$

$$\psi_A H \psi_B = \psi_A E_B \psi_B$$

Integration of both equations yields:

$$\int \psi_B H \psi_A \, dv = \int \psi_B E_A \psi_A \, dv$$

$$\int \psi_A H \psi_B \, dv = \int \psi_A E_B \psi_B \, dv$$

Now, E_A and E_B are numbers representing the energy of an electron in these two orbitals. Since they are numbers, it is possible to place them before the integral sign:

$$\int \psi_B H \psi_A \, dv = E_A \int \psi_B \psi_A \, dv$$

$$\int \psi_A H \psi_B \, dv = E_B \int \psi_A \psi_B \, dv$$

(5–28)

The integrals on the left side of these two equations must have the same value:

$$\int \psi_B H \psi_A \, dv = \int \psi_A H \psi_B \, dv$$

also,

$$\int \psi_B \psi_A \, dv = \int \psi_A \psi_B \, dv$$

Returning to Eqs. (5–28), we subtract the second equation from the first one. This gives:

$$0 = (E_A - E_B) \int \psi_A \psi_B \, dv$$

Now E_A is not in general equal to E_B, and the term $(E_A - E_B)$ does not equal zero. Therefore, in order for this equation to be valid, the integral must equal zero:

$$\int \psi_A \psi_B \, dv = 0 \qquad E_A - E_B \neq 0$$

This illustrates the orthogonality of the ψ's. The assumption that E_A does not equal E_B is unnecessary. It can be shown that all ψ's are orthogonal even in cases where E_A is equal to E_B.

5.9 Degeneracy

Different orbitals corresponding to the same energy are said to be degenerate. The p atomic orbitals serve as an example. An electron in the p_x orbital has the same energy as an electron in the p_y or p_z orbitals. The Schrödinger equations for this situation are,

$$Hp_x = E_x p_x$$

$$Hp_y = E_y p_y$$

$$Hp_z = E_z p_z$$

where $E_x = E_y = E_z$.

Two different molecular orbitals ψ_A and ψ_B are degenerate if:

$$H\psi_A = E_A \psi_A$$

$$H\psi_B = E_B \psi_B$$

yet

$$E_A = E_B$$

Supplementary Reading

1. Cartmell, E., and Fowles, G. W. A., *Valency and Molecular Structure*. London, Butterworths, 1961.

2. Coulson, C. A., *Valence*, 2nd Ed. London, Oxford U. P., 1961.

3. Daudel, R., Lefebvre, R., and Moser, C., *Quantum Chemistry*. New York, Interscience, 1959.

4. Liberles, A., *Introduction to Molecular Orbital Theory*. New York, Holt, 1966.

5. Linnett, W. L., *Wave Mechanics and Valency*. London, Methuen, 1960.

6. Moore, W. J., *Physical Chemistry*. Englewood Cliffs, New Jersey, Prentice-Hall, 1962.

7. Pullman, B., *The Modern Theory of Molecular Structure*. New York, Dover, 1962.

8. Wiberg, K. B., *Physical Organic Chemistry*. New York, Wiley, 1964.

Chapter 6

Molecular Orbital Theory

6.1 General Discussion

The Schrödinger equation for a system is given by the expression:

$$H\psi = E\psi$$

If the system contains one electron, ψ is the orbital occupied by that electron; the Hamiltonian operator is obtained from the one electron Hamiltonian, and E is the energy of that electron. The only problem that can be solved exactly by quantum mechanics is that of the hydrogen atom. For more complicated systems only approximate solutions to the Schrödinger equation can be obtained, and several methods do exist which give approximate solutions.

We are interested in the total energy of a system containing several electrons. We assume that the nuclei are stationary and substitute fixed values for the internuclear distances. The problem reduces to finding the energy of all of the electrons in the system. The Schrödinger equation for a system composed of several electrons is still given by the above expression. In this case ψ represents the orbitals of all the electrons in the system, the Hamiltonian operator is obtained from a many-electron Hamiltonian, and E is the total energy of all the electrons. A solution to the appropriate Schrödinger equation gives the energy of these electrons; however, we are unable to obtain an exact solution.

Let us multiply both sides of the Schrödinger equation by ψ and integrate:

$$\int \psi H\psi \, dv = \int \psi E\psi \, dv = E \int \psi\psi \, dv$$

Since E is a number representing the total energy of all the electrons, it can be placed before the integral sign. Solving for E yields,

$$E = \frac{\int \psi H\psi \, dv}{\int \psi\psi \, dv} \tag{6-1}$$

We have an expression giving the energy of the electrons. If the eigenfunctions are normalized, the denominator is equal to unity and Eq. (6–1) becomes,

$$E = \int \psi H\psi \, dv \tag{6-2}$$

126

The energy of the electrons is given in the general case by Eq. (6–1) and in those cases where ψ is normalized by Eq. (6–2). The approximate methods which we shall consider do not assume that ψ is normalized. These methods make use of Eq. (6–1) to find the energy of the system, and ψ is normalized only after the energy of the electrons has been found.

We should like to apply the principles of wave mechanics to the more difficult molecular problems where we cannot obtain an exact solution to Eq. (6–1). For these cases, the usual procedure is to arbitrarily select some function ψ and assume that this ψ is the solution to the Schrödinger equation. Since ψ is not exact, we obtain only approximate values for E. Naturally, for our choice of ψ we want a function that describes reasonably well the probable positions of the electrons in the molecule. A wise choice for ψ leads to values for E which are in good accord with the experimentally determined values. A poor choice for ψ leads to poor values for E. The calculated values for E will be higher than the actual energy of the molecule. In molecular problems we do not know ψ exactly, and consequently, we cannot obtain the exact values for E. In fact, an approximate knowledge of ψ is still insufficient. The expression for H in Eq. (6–1) is also quite complex, and even with a good choice for ψ it may be extremely difficult to obtain a solution to Eq. (6–1); however, we can solve Eq. (6–1) in terms of certain parameters which involve both H and ψ. We must then go into the laboratory and evaluate these parameters experimentally. The actual techniques are illustrated in subsequent sections of this chapter.

In this chapter and the next, we consider two approximate methods for solving molecular problems. The first of these, the molecular orbital method, involves the parameters α and β. The second technique, the valence-bond approach, is also developed in terms of two parameters, Q and J.

The molecular orbital technique is less familiar to the organic chemist than is the valence-bond method, but it is simpler to develop mathematically, and for this reason we consider it first.

6.2 Molecular Orbitals

We assume in the molecular orbital method that an electron is not restricted to just one particular region but that it is able to travel over the entire molecule. The orbital ψ associated with this electron then encompasses the entire molecule. We construct a molecular orbital ψ which describes reasonably well the positions of a single electron traveling over the entire molecule.

The molecular orbital theory presented in this text is the Hückel method, and the molecular orbitals that are used in the Hückel theory obey all the rules of atomic orbitals. The Aufbau procedure is followed exactly. We construct a set of molecular orbitals $\psi_1, \psi_2, \psi_3, \ldots \psi_n$; we calculate the energy of an electron in each of these molecular orbitals; we next arrange these orbitals in order of increasing energy. Each molecular orbital can then accommodate two electrons of opposite spin.

Assume that we have constructed a set of five molecular orbitals. The technique employed for their construction is presented in Section 6.3 (five atomic orbitals must be used to construct a set of five molecular orbitals). We calculate the energy of an electron in each of these molecular orbitals and arrange them as in Figure 6–1, in order of increasing energy.

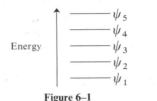

Figure 6–1

Here ψ_1 is the most stable molecular orbital and ψ_5 the least stable. Each of these molecular orbitals can accommodate two electrons of opposite spin. When dealing with four electrons, two of them are placed in ψ_1 and two in ψ_2 while ψ_3, ψ_4, and ψ_5 remain empty. This is illustrated in Figure 6–2.

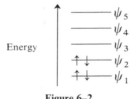

Figure 6–2

In Figure 6–3 we add a fifth electron to the system, this last electron must enter ψ_3.

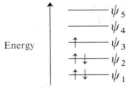

Figure 6–3

A sixth electron can also enter ψ_3 with antiparallel spin to that of the electron already present. This is pictured in Figure 6–4.

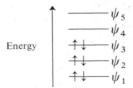

Figure 6–4

If degenerate molecular orbitals are present, one electron with parallel spin goes into each degenerate orbital until all of these are half filled. Any remaining electrons are used to fill the degenerate orbitals. Assume once again that we have five molecular orbitals, this time with the energy sequence presented in Figure 6–5.

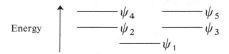

Figure 6 5

In this situation, ψ_2 and ψ_3 are degenerate (both correspond to the same energy), and ψ_4 and ψ_5 are also degenerate.

We have arranged the orbitals in order of increasing energy. If this system contains four electrons, we place two of them in ψ_1, one in ψ_2, and one electron with parallel spin in ψ_3; see Figure 6 6.

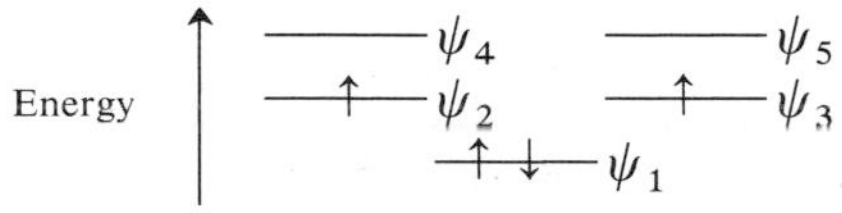

Figure 6–6

Figure 6–7 illustrates that a fifth electron enters ψ_2 while a sixth must be placed in ψ_3.

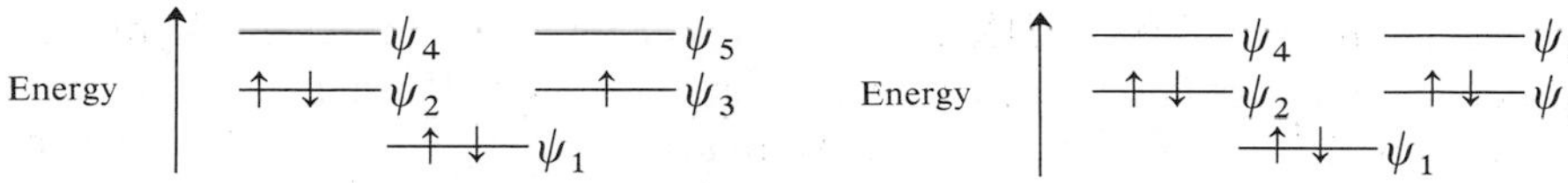

Figure 6–7

Electronic excitation involves the transition of an electron from one orbital to another of higher energy. In the case just discussed where the system contains six electrons, the system can absorb energy and use this energy to promote an electron from a lower energy molecular orbital to a higher energy orbital; in Figure 6–8 for example, from ψ_3 to ψ_4.

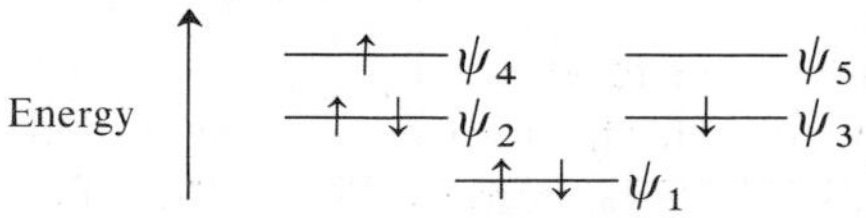

Excited Singlet State

Figure 6–8

We are now able to place the electrons into a set of molecular orbitals but are still unable to construct these orbitals or to calculate their energies. In the next section we discuss how these molecular orbitals are constructed.

6.3 The Linear Combination of Atomic Orbitals Method

Consider two functions ψ_1 and ψ_2; for example,

$$\psi_1 = \sin \frac{2\pi p}{h} x$$

$$\psi_2 = \cos \frac{2\pi p}{h} x$$

Multiplying ψ_1 by a constant a_1 and ψ_2 by a constant a_2 and adding the resulting expressions leads to,

$$a_1 \sin \frac{2\pi p}{h} x + a_2 \cos \frac{2\pi p}{h} x$$

or

$$a_1\psi_1 + a_2\psi_2$$
$$\psi = a_1\psi_1 + a_2\psi_2 \tag{6-3}$$

Such a combination of ψ_1 and ψ_2 is called a linear combination of these two functions.

Molecular orbitals are usually constructed in just this manner, as a linear combination of atomic orbitals. For example, according to molecular orbital theory, in a hydrogen molecule the bond joining the two hydrogen atoms is a molecular orbital. This molecular orbital encompasses the entire hydrogen molecule and contains two electrons of opposite spin. If we are to construct such a molecular orbital, we must do so in such a way that it describes reasonably well the probable positions of the two electrons. To generate the molecular orbital for hydrogen, we assume that the molecule is formed by the overlap of two $1s$ atomic orbitals, one from each hydrogen atom. Consequently, a good but not exact description of the bond in the hydrogen molecule is obtained by expressing this molecular orbital as a linear combination of these two $1s$ atomic orbitals:

$$H_1 - H_2$$

$$\psi_{HH} = a_1 s_1 + a_2 s_2$$

The subscripts 1 and 2 refer to atoms 1 and 2.

The molecular orbital in the molecule is generated by combining the $1s$ atomic orbital of H_1 with the $1s$ atomic orbital of H_2. Two entire atomic orbitals are not required for the construction of a single molecular orbital. Only a fraction of each atomic orbital is needed. Since the probability of finding the electron is given by ψ^2, the squares of the coefficients (a_1^2 and a_2^2) represent the fraction of atomic orbital used. Thus, a_1^2 is the fraction of atomic orbital s_1 and a_2^2 the fraction of atomic orbital s_2 used in the construction of the molecular orbital. The values of a_1 and a_2 will always be less than unity. This method of constructing molecular orbitals is the method employed in the Hückel theory.

If inner-shell electrons are present, we can simplify the problem by assuming that these make no contribution to bond formation. As an example, consider the Li_2 molecule. Each lithium atom contains three electrons, two at the $1s$ level and one in the $2s$ orbital. A discussion of the Li_2 molecule should involve all six electrons. We ought to construct three molecular orbitals to accommodate these six electrons. However, to a good approximation we can assume that bond formation involves only the valence electrons. The bond in the Li_2 molecule can be regarded as a single molecular orbital involving only the electrons from the $2s$ orbital of each lithium atom. The molecular orbital is constructed as a linear combination of the $2s$ atomic orbitals:

$$Li_1 - Li_2$$

$$\psi_{LiLi} = a_1 s_1 + a_2 s_2$$

The terms s_1 and s_2 represent the $2s$ atomic orbitals associated with each lithium atom.

Similarly, in the hydrogen chloride molecule the bond holding the two atoms together is a molecular orbital formed from the $1s$ atomic orbital of hydrogen and the $3p$ atomic orbital of chlorine.

$$H - Cl$$

$$\psi_{HCl} = a_1 s + a_2 p$$

The molecular orbital is formed as a linear combination of these two atomic orbitals, and all other electrons occupy the same orbitals in the molecule that they occupy in the chlorine atom.

Chlorine in this example is much more electronegative than hydrogen; in the ground state the two electrons in the hydrogen-chlorine bond are more likely to be found in the chlorine portion of the molecule. (The electron density due to the two electrons is greater at chlorine.) Since the molecular orbital must indicate the probable positions of the electrons, we construct this orbital in such a way that the electron density is greater at chlorine. To accomplish this, we make the coefficient a_2 greater than a_1. We construct our molecular orbital for the ground state by using a greater fraction of the orbital from chlorine and a smaller fraction of the orbital from hydrogen.

Thus far, all of the molecular systems have been diatomic. In a more complex system such as methane CH_4, the molecular orbitals should still encompass the entire molecule. Such molecular orbitals would include all four $1s$ atomic orbitals, one from each of the four hydrogen atoms, as well as the $2s$, $2p_x$, $2p_y$, and $2p_z$ atomic orbitals of carbon. However, these molecular orbitals can be simplified since σ bonds can usually be treated individually. Thus, each carbon-hydrogen bond is regarded as a separate molecular orbital involving the $1s$ atomic orbital of hydrogen and an sp^3 hybridized orbital of carbon. The eight electrons occupy four molecular orbitals of this type;

$$\begin{array}{c} H \\ | \\ H-C-H \\ | \\ H \end{array}$$

$$\psi_{CH} = a_1 s + a_2 sp^3$$

In ethane, the carbon-hydrogen bond is again composed of the $1s$ atomic orbital of hydrogen and an sp^3 orbital of carbon. The constituents of the carbon-carbon bond are both sp^3 orbitals:

$$\begin{array}{cc} H & H \\ | & | \\ H-C_1-C_2-H \\ | & | \\ H & H \end{array}$$

$$\psi_{CH} = a_1 s + a_2 sp^3$$

$$\psi_{CC} = a_1 sp^3{}_1 + a_2 sp^3{}_2$$

For molecules such as ethylene and for most other systems containing both σ and π electrons, we make the assumption that these electrons can be treated separately, and we construct the following molecular orbitals,

$$\begin{array}{c} H \diagdown\ \ \ \diagup H \\ C_1-C_2 \\ H \diagup\ \ \ \diagdown H \end{array}$$

$$\psi_{CH} = a_1 s + a_2 sp^2$$

$$\psi_{CC}(\sigma) = a_1 sp^2{}_1 + a_2 sp^2{}_2$$

$$\psi_{CC}(\pi) = a_1 p_1 + a_2 p_2$$

With alkenes such as ethylene there exists between the carbon atoms a rather diffuse region of electron density (electron probability):

One way of describing this region is illustrated in Figure 6–9 where we consider the inner portion as a σ bond and the other portion as a π bond. This is really a rather arbitrary choice and other methods of describing the electron density are discussed in Chapter 8. In this chapter we describe the alkenes in the usual manner.

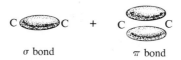

σ bond π bond

Figure 6–9

In butadiene there are nine σ bonds containing 18 electrons and four electrons that must be placed in π molecular orbitals. A π molecular orbital, which encompasses all four carbon atoms, is formed as a linear combination of p atomic orbitals, one from each carbon atom:

$$C_1-C_2-C_3-C_4$$

$$\psi(\pi) = a_1p_1 + a_2p_2 + a_3p_3 + a_4p_4$$

Butadiene contains four π electrons; since each molecular orbital can hold only two of these electrons, we place these four electrons in two different π molecular orbitals, each having the form

$$\psi = a_1p_1 + a_2p_2 + a_3p_3 + a_4p_4$$

The values of the coefficients (a_1, a_2, a_3, and a_4) are not the same for these two orbitals nor is their energy.

We calculate in this chapter the π electronic energies of systems containing two and three carbon atoms. For ethylene the electrons in the π bond occupy a molecular orbital given by the expression,

$$\psi = a_1p_1 + a_2p_2 \tag{6–4}$$

The molecular orbital is constructed by combining p atomic orbitals, one from each carbon atom. We shall also consider the allylic system. A π electron in this system occupies an orbital described as:

$$C_1-C_2-C_3$$

$$\psi = a_1p_1 + a_2p_2 + a_3p_3$$

To generate the molecular orbital, we again combine the p atomic orbitals. In the cyclopropenyl system a π bond molecular orbital is also expressed as,

$$\psi = a_1 p_1 + a_2 p_2 + a_3 p_3$$

The molecular orbitals that we have constructed are formed as linear combinations of atomic orbitals. Remember, however, that this is an assumption; we could have constructed these molecular orbitals in some other way. We form ψ and substitute this expression for ψ into Eq. (6–1). The coefficients $a_1, a_2, \ldots, a_n$ remain undetermined, and the calculated energy of an electron depends upon the values assigned to these coefficients. We want those values of the coefficients that minimize the energy E of the electron.

The proper values of E and of the coefficients are obtained by taking the derivative of E with respect to each coefficient and setting that derivative equal to zero:

$$\frac{\partial E}{\partial a_1} = 0$$

$$\frac{\partial E}{\partial a_2} = 0 \qquad \text{and so forth.}$$

This process, called a variational procedure, not only enables us to obtain the coefficients, it also affords the allowed energies of an electron.

One more point must be considered. We have the expression for ψ and can find the desired values of the coefficients, yet it is still not possible to calculate, except for very simple systems, the numerical value for the energy of the electron because it is not possible to evaluate numerically all of the integrals appearing in Eq. (6–1). On the other hand, it is possible to perform certain laboratory experiments, and the results of such experiments indicate the numerical values that should be assigned to these integrals. Equation (6–1) is developed in terms of the two parameters α and β, which are then evaluated in the laboratory.

6.4 The Parameters α and β

An electron in the π bond of ethylene occupies the orbital described by Eq. (6–4).

$$\psi = a_1 p_1 + a_2 p_2$$

This molecular orbital, as are all π bond molecular orbitals in the Hückel theory, is expressed in terms of p atomic orbitals. We shall assume that these p atomic orbitals form an orthonormal set, that is, we shall assume that they obey Eq. (5–27):

$$\int p_1 p_1 \, dv = 1$$

$$\int p_2 p_2 \, dv = 1$$

$$\int p_1 p_2 \, dv = 0$$

$$\int p_2 p_1 \, dv = 0$$

and in general,

$$\int p_A p_B \, dv = \begin{cases} 1 & A = B \\ 0 & A \neq B \end{cases}$$

If we consider a molecule of ethylene, the electron prior to formation of the π bond occupies a p atomic orbital. After formation of the π bond it occupies the molecular orbital given previously. Prior to π bond formation, if the electron is in p_1, the p atomic orbital associated with carbon atom 1, the energy of this electron is given by Eq. (6–1). The orbital associated with the electron is p_1 and the energy of the electron is given by the expression,

$$E = \frac{\int p_1 H p_1 \, dv}{\int p_1 p_1 \, dv}$$

Since the p atomic orbitals are normalized, the denominator is equal to unity and,

$$E = \int p_1 H p_1 \, dv \qquad (6\text{–}5)$$

this integral represents the energy of an electron in the $2p$ atomic orbital of carbon. Such an integral is too difficult to evaluate directly, and we assign the value H_{11} or simply α to it. If we wish to obtain a numerical value for α, we must do so experimentally. We do know that the value of this integral is negative. The electron is attracted to the carbon nucleus and its negative potential energy must be greater in magnitude then its positive kinetic energy (see Section 5.2).

Similarly, if the electron occupies the orbital p_2, the energy of the electron is given by,

$$E = \int p_2 H p_2 \, dv = H_{22} = \alpha \qquad (6\text{--}6)$$

The energy of an electron in the orbital p_2 must be the same as the energy of an electron in p_1. We arbitrarily assign to this integral the symbol H_{22} or α.

The other parameter β represents the energy of an electron associated with both orbitals:

$$\int p_1 H p_2 \, dv = H_{12} = \beta \qquad (6\text{--}7)$$

$$\int p_2 H p_1 \, dv = H_{21} = \beta \qquad (6\text{--}8)$$

The value of these integrals is also negative, and a numerical value can be obtained experimentally.

The integrals

$$\int p_A p_B \, dv$$

also appear in Hückel calculations. These are represented by the symbol S_{AB}. We already know the values assigned to them:

$$\int p_A p_B \, dv = \begin{cases} 1 & A = B \\ 0 & A \neq B \end{cases}$$

Thus, the Hückel molecular orbital calculation for ethylene involves the integrals

$$\int p_A H p_A \, dv = H_{AA} = \alpha$$

$$\int p_A H p_B \, dv = H_{AB} = \beta$$

$$\int p_A p_A \, dv = S_{AA} = 1$$

$$\int p_A p_B \, dv = S_{AB} = 0$$

Similar terms occur in all Hückel calculations.

For systems that are more complex than ethylene, we must look more closely at the term H_{AB}. This symbol represents the value of the integral,

$$\int p_A H p_B \, dv$$

and this value depends upon the proximity of the orbital p_A to the orbital p_B. If these two orbitals p_A and p_B are on adjacent carbon atoms, that is, if the carbon atoms are also σ bonded, the value of the integral is equal to β. Therefore, for ethylene, where carbon atoms 1 and 2 are adjacent, Eqs. (6–7) and (6–8) apply. For more complex systems the value of H_{AB} is still β when the orbitals are on adjacent atoms. For example, a molecular orbital calculation for the allylic system involves the terms:

$$\int p_1 H p_2 \, dv = H_{12} = \beta$$

$$\int p_2 H p_1 \, dv = H_{21} = \beta$$

$$\int p_2 H p_3 \, dv = H_{23} = \beta$$

$$\int p_3 H p_2 \, dv = H_{32} = \beta$$

However, such a calculation also involves the terms,

$$\int p_1 H p_3 \, dv = H_{13}$$

$$\int p_3 H p_1 \, dv = II_{31}$$

Here the orbitals in question are not on adjacent atoms. These orbitals are widely separated, and the value of terms such as these is zero:

$$\int p_1 H p_3 \, dv = H_{13} = 0 \tag{6–9}$$

$$\int p_3 H p_1 \, dv = H_{31} = 0 \tag{6–10}$$

A summary of the values assigned to the terms occurring in Hückel calculations follows:

$$H_{AA} = \alpha$$

$$H_{AB} = \begin{cases} \beta & \text{if carbon atoms } A \text{ and } B \text{ are also } \sigma \text{ bonded} \\ 0 & \text{if carbon atoms } A \text{ and } B \text{ are not } \sigma \text{ bonded} \end{cases}$$

$$S_{AA} = 1$$

$$S_{AB} = 0$$

We have made no attempt to assign numerical values to the parameters α and β. While it is unnecessary, it is certainly possible to assign such values. We are interested in the resonance energy of a system, and resonance energies are expressed in terms of β. The value of α is not pertinent to such a discussion. Therefore, we shall not assign a numerical value to this parameter. The value assigned to β depends upon the system under consideration and the assumptions made in the evaluation. In chapter 7 we shall discuss the resonance energy of benzene and shall present two possible values. They are 36 kcal/mole and 63 kcal/mole. A molecular orbital calculation of the resonance energy of benzene assigns to this molecule the value -2β. Equating -2β to these numerical values, we find two possible values for β.

$$-2\beta = 36$$

$$\beta = -18 \text{ kcal/mole}$$

or

$$-2\beta = 63$$

$$\beta = -32 \text{ kcal/mole}$$

We see immediately the difficulty in evaluating the parameters α and β. Since we are not certain of the resonance energy of benzene, we cannot assign an exact numerical value to β. In our calculations we shall leave the resonance energy of a molecule in terms of β since for our purposes numerical evaluation is unnecessary.

6.5 Bonding, Nonbonding, and Antibonding Molecular Orbitals

The energy of an electron in a p atomic orbital of carbon is α. If an electron in a molecular orbital is more stable than this, then ψ is a bonding molecular orbital. If the energy associated with ψ is α, ψ is nonbonding. An energy greater than α makes ψ an antibonding molecular orbital.

The energy of an electron in a molecular orbital is expressed in terms of the two parameters α and β. Since β is negative, an electron having energy $\alpha + \beta$ contains less energy and is therefore more stable than an electron with energy α. Therefore, if the energy associated with ψ is $\alpha + \beta$, ψ is a bonding molecular orbital.

In Section 6.8, we carry out the calculation for the allylic system and shall find that there are three possible molecular orbitals for an electron in the allylic system. The energy associated with these orbitals is $\alpha + \sqrt{2}\beta$, α, $\alpha - \sqrt{2}\beta$. Consequently the first of these, ψ_1 with energy $\alpha + \sqrt{2}\beta$, is a bonding molecular orbital; the second ψ_2 is nonbonding, and the third ψ_3 is antibonding. Naturally, when placing electrons into these orbitals, we begin with that of lowest energy.

6.6 The Secular Equation

Consider one of the electrons in the π bond of ethylene. The molecular orbital occupied by that electron is given by Eq. (6–4):

$$\psi = a_1 p_1 + a_2 p_2$$

To find the energy associated with an electron occupying this orbital we substitute this expression into Eq. (6–1):

$$E = \frac{\int (a_1 p_1 + a_2 p_2) H (a_1 p_1 + a_2 p_2)\, dv}{\int (a_1 p_1 + a_2 p_2)(a_1 p_1 + a_2 p_2)\, dv}$$

Expansion of this equation leads to:

$$E = \frac{a_1^2 \int p_1 H p_1\, dv + a_1 a_2 \int p_1 H p_2\, dv + a_2 a_1 \int p_2 H p_1\, dv + a_2^2 \int p_2 H p_2\, dv}{a_1^2 \int p_1 p_1\, dv + a_1 a_2 \int p_1 p_2\, dv + a_2 a_1 \int p_2 p_1\, dv + a_2^2 \int p_2 p_2\, dv}$$

Substitution of the symbols $H_{11}, H_{12}, S_{11}, S_{12}$ into this equation yields,

$$E = \frac{a_1^2 H_{11} + a_1 a_2 H_{12} + a_2 a_1 H_{21} + a_2^2 H_{22}}{a_1^2 S_{11} + a_1 a_2 S_{12} + a_2 a_1 S_{21} + a_2^2 S_{22}}$$

The only unknown quantities in this equation are the coefficients a_1 and a_2, and we want those values of a_1 and a_2 that minimize the energy of the electron. To obtain the desired values of a_1 and a_2, we differentiate this quotient first with respect to a_1 and set the derivative equal to zero; we then differentiate the expression with respect to a_2 and again set the derivative equal to zero.

$$\frac{\partial E}{\partial a_1} = 0$$

$$\frac{\partial E}{\partial a_2} = 0$$

Carrying out the differentiation with respect to a_1 results in the following equation:[1]

$$a_1 (H_{11} - S_{11} E) + a_2 (H_{12} - S_{12} E) = 0$$

where the symbols have their usual significance and E is still the energy of the

[1] The mathematical manipulations that give rise to this equation can be found in several of the books listed at the end of this chapter.

electron. Repeating this operation with respect to a_2 affords a second such equation.

$$a_1(H_{21} - S_{21}E) + a_2(H_{22} - S_{22}E) = 0$$

Solving these two simultaneous equations gives rise to two different values for the energy, E_1 and E_2. Associated with each value of E is a molecular orbital. There are then two possible π molecular orbitals which an electron in the π bond of ethylene can occupy, ψ_1 and ψ_2. An electron in ψ_1 has energy E_1, while in ψ_2, the electron has energy E_2. We solve these two equations for E, and each value of E corresponds to the energy of an electron in a different molecular orbital of ethylene. The molecular orbitals are arranged in order of increasing energy, and the two π electrons are placed in the lower energy molecular orbital.

Using these equations we not only obtain the values of E, we are also able to obtain the desired values of the coefficients.

The equations can be simplified. Multiply the first equation by the term,

$$a_2(H_{22} - S_{22}E)$$

and the second equation by the term,

$$a_2(H_{12} - S_{12}E)$$

This leads to the expressions,

$$a_1a_2(H_{11} - S_{11}E)(H_{22} - S_{22}E) + a_2{}^2(H_{12} - S_{12}E)(H_{22} - S_{22}E) = 0$$

$$a_1a_2(H_{12} - S_{12}E)(H_{21} - S_{21}E) + a_2{}^2(H_{12} - S_{12}E)(H_{22} - S_{22}E) = 0$$

Subtracting the second of these expressions from the first affords the single equation,

$$a_1a_2(H_{11} - S_{11}E)(H_{22} - S_{22}E) - a_1a_2(H_{12} - S_{12}E)(H_{21} - S_{21}E) = 0$$

Factoring out a_1 and a_2,

$$a_1a_2[(H_{11} - S_{11}E)(H_{22} - S_{22}E) - (H_{12} - S_{12}E)(H_{21} - S_{21}E)] = 0 \quad (6\text{--}11)$$

We now have a single equation to satisfy. It is possible to simplify this still further, for a_1 and a_2 are constants and do not equal zero. Therefore, for this equation to hold, since the product $a_1a_2 \neq 0$, the expression inside the brackets must equal zero:

$$[(H_{11} - S_{11}E)(H_{22} - S_{22}E) - (H_{12} - S_{12}E)(H_{21} - S_{21}E)] = 0$$

Furthermore, the expression inside the brackets can be written as a second order determinant:

$$\begin{vmatrix} H_{11} - S_{11}E & H_{12} - S_{12}E \\ H_{21} - S_{21}E & H_{22} - H_{22}E \end{vmatrix} = \begin{aligned} &[(H_{11} - S_{11}E)(H_{22} - S_{22}E) \\ &-(H_{12} - S_{12}E)(H_{21} - S_{21}E)] = 0 \end{aligned} \quad (6\text{--}12)$$

The determinant is called the secular determinant for ethylene. We arrive at Eq. (6–12) which is the secular equation for ethylene. Solving this equation yields the permissible values of E, and each value of E corresponds to the energy of a molecular orbital.

We began with two equations,

$$a_1(H_{11} - S_{11}E) + a_2(H_{12} - S_{12}E) = 0$$
$$a_1(H_{21} - S_{21}E) + a_2(H_{22} - S_{22}E) = 0 \qquad (6\text{–}13)$$

and arrive at the result that a solution for E can be obtained if the secular determinant equals zero.

$$\begin{vmatrix} H_{11} - S_{11}E & H_{12} - S_{12}E \\ H_{21} - S_{21}E & H_{22} - S_{22}E \end{vmatrix} = 0 \qquad (6\text{–}14)$$

Analogously, in the allylic system where there are three carbon atoms each with a p orbital, the molecular orbital ψ is given by the expression,

$$\psi = a_1 p_1 + a_2 p_2 + a_3 p_3 \qquad (6\text{–}15)$$

To find the permissible energies of the electron in the allylic system we substitute this expression for ψ into Eq. (6–1). We now differentiate with respect to the three coefficients a_1, a_2, a_3. This results in three equations having the form,

$$a_1(H_{11} - S_{11}E) + a_2(H_{12} - S_{12}E) + a_3(H_{13} - S_{13}E) = 0$$
$$a_1(H_{21} - S_{21}E) + a_2(H_{22} - S_{22}E) + a_3(H_{23} - S_{23}E) = 0 \qquad (6\text{–}16)$$
$$a_1(H_{31} - S_{31}E) + a_2(H_{32} - S_{32}E) + a_3(H_{33} - S_{33}E) = 0$$

To solve for E and the coefficients a_1, a_2, a_3, it is only necessary that the third order determinant equal zero:

$$\begin{vmatrix} H_{11} - S_{11}E & H_{12} - S_{12}E & H_{13} - S_{13}E \\ H_{21} - S_{21}E & H_{22} - S_{22}E & H_{23} - S_{23}E \\ H_{31} - S_{31}E & H_{32} - S_{32}E & H_{33} - S_{33}E \end{vmatrix} = 0 \qquad (6\text{–}17)$$

Solving this secular equation for E gives the energies of an electron in the various π molecular orbitals of the allylic system. The cyclopropenyl system also contains three carbon atoms, and ψ again takes the form of Eq. (6–15). Substitution of this expression into Eq. (6–1) and repeating the previous operations yields three equations having exactly the same form as Eqs. (6–16), and the secular equation again takes the form given in Eq. (6–17). However, C_1 and C_3

are bonded in the cyclopropenyl system; $H_{13} = H_{31} = \beta$:

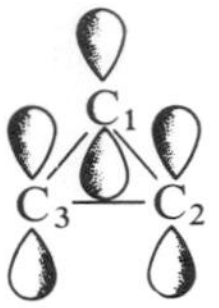

If our system contains n carbon atoms each with a p orbital, ψ is given by,

$$\psi = a_1 p_1 + a_2 p_2 + a_3 p_3 + \cdots + a_n p_n$$

The simultaneous equations become,

$$a_1(H_{11} - S_{11}E) + a_2(H_{12} - S_{12}E) + \cdots + a_n(H_{1n} - S_{1n}E) = 0$$
$$a_1(H_{21} - S_{21}E) + a_2(H_{22} - S_{22}E) + \cdots + a_n(H_{2n} - S_{2n}E) = 0$$
$$a_1(H_{31} - S_{31}E) + a_2(H_{32} - S_{32}E) + \cdots + a_n(H_{3n} - S_{3n}E) = 0$$
$$\vdots \qquad\qquad \vdots \qquad\qquad \vdots \qquad\qquad \vdots$$
$$a_1(H_{n1} - S_{n1}E) + a_2(H_{n2} - S_{n2}E) + \cdots + a_n(H_{nn} - S_{nn}E) = 0$$

and the secular equation for the system becomes,

$$
\begin{vmatrix}
H_{11} - S_{11}E & H_{12} - S_{12}E & \cdots & H_{1n} - S_{1n}E \\
H_{21} - S_{21}E & H_{22} - S_{22}E & \cdots & H_{2n} - S_{2n}E \\
H_{31} - S_{31}E & H_{32} - S_{32}E & \cdots & H_{3n} - S_{3n}E \\
\vdots & \vdots & \cdots & \vdots \\
H_{n1} - S_{n1}E & H_{n2} - S_{n2}E & \cdots & H_{nn} - S_{nn}E
\end{vmatrix} = 0
$$

6.7 Ethylene

We are interested in calculating the allowed energies for a π electron in ethylene. To obtain these energies we must solve the secular equation Eq. (6–14):

$$
\begin{vmatrix}
H_{11} - S_{11}E & H_{12} - S_{12}E \\
H_{21} - S_{21}E & H_{22} - S_{22}E
\end{vmatrix} = 0
$$

where

$$H_{11} = H_{22} = \alpha$$
$$H_{12} = H_{21} = \beta$$
$$S_{11} = S_{22} = 1$$
$$S_{12} = S_{21} = 0$$

Upon substitution of these values, Eq. (6–14) becomes,

$$\begin{vmatrix} \alpha - E & \beta \\ \beta & \alpha - E \end{vmatrix} = 0$$

It is possible to rewrite this equation as:

$$\begin{vmatrix} \dfrac{\alpha - E}{\beta} & 1 \\ 1 & \dfrac{\alpha - E}{\beta} \end{vmatrix} = 0$$

We now make the substitution,

$$x = \frac{\alpha - E}{\beta}$$

and this leads to,

$$\begin{vmatrix} x & 1 \\ 1 & x \end{vmatrix} = 0$$

Solving this equation for x yields,

$$x^2 - 1 = 0$$

or

$$x = 1$$

$$x = -1$$

There are two different values for x. Replacing x by its equivalent $(\alpha - E)/\beta$,

$$\frac{\alpha - E_1}{\beta} = -1$$

$$E_1 = \alpha + \beta$$

We find that the energy associated with ψ_1 is $\alpha + \beta$. Solving for E_2,

$$\frac{\alpha - E_2}{\beta} = 1$$

then

$$E_2 = \alpha - \beta$$

There are two allowed energy levels for the electron in ethylene. There is a bonding molecular orbital ψ_1 with energy $(\alpha + \beta)$ and an antibonding molecular orbital ψ_2 having energy $(\alpha - \beta)$. There are two π electrons in ethylene, and both of these are placed in ψ_1. The total energy of these two π electrons is, $2E_1 = 2\alpha + 2\beta$. This is represented schematically in Figure 6–10.

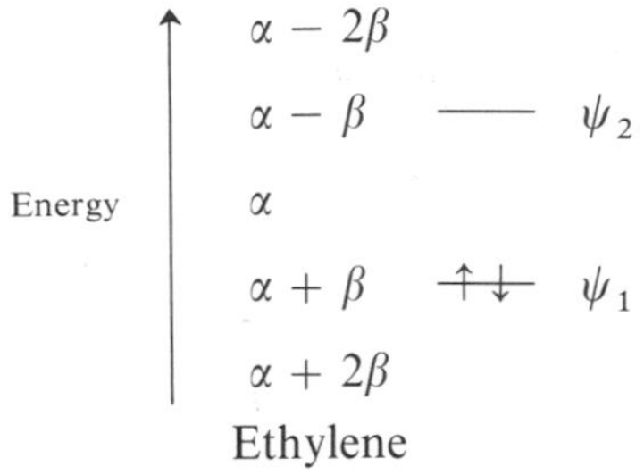

$$\alpha - 2\beta$$
$$\alpha - \beta \quad \text{———} \quad \psi_2$$
Energy $\quad \alpha$
$$\alpha + \beta \quad \uparrow\downarrow \quad \psi_1$$
$$\alpha + 2\beta$$
Ethylene

Figure 6–10

6.8 The Allylic System

The secular equation for the allylic system is Eq. (6–17).

$$\begin{vmatrix} H_{11} - S_{11}E & H_{12} - S_{12}E & H_{13} - S_{13}E \\ H_{21} - S_{21}E & H_{22} - S_{22}E & H_{23} - S_{23}E \\ H_{31} - S_{31}E & H_{32} - S_{32}E & H_{33} - S_{33}E \end{vmatrix} = 0$$

Substituting the appropriate values for these terms affords the result,

$$\begin{vmatrix} \alpha - E & \beta & 0 \\ \beta & \alpha - E & \beta \\ 0 & \beta & \alpha - E \end{vmatrix} = 0$$

This leads to

$$\begin{vmatrix} \dfrac{\alpha - E}{\beta} & 1 & 0 \\ 1 & \dfrac{\alpha - E}{\beta} & 1 \\ 0 & 1 & \dfrac{\alpha - E}{\beta} \end{vmatrix} = 0$$

Making the substitution $x = (\alpha - E)/\beta$ gives rise to,

$$\begin{vmatrix} x & 1 & 0 \\ 1 & x & 1 \\ 0 & 1 & x \end{vmatrix} = 0$$

and expansion of this determinant affords the polynomial equation,

$$x^3 - 2x = 0$$

This equation has the solutions,

$$x = -\sqrt{2}$$
$$x = 0$$
$$x = \sqrt{2}$$

Solving for the energies,

$$E_1 = \alpha + \sqrt{2}\beta$$
$$E_2 = \alpha$$
$$E_3 = \alpha - \sqrt{2}\beta$$

Since there is a molecular orbital associated with each value of E, we find three permissible molecular orbitals and three permissible energies for the electron; see Figure 6–11.

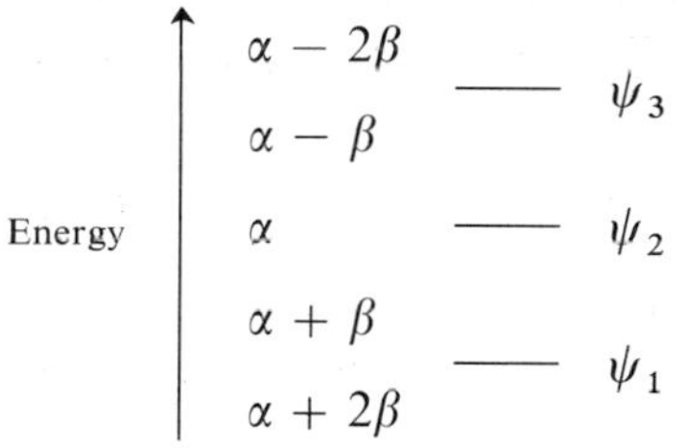

Energy

$$\alpha - 2\beta$$
$$\alpha - \beta \qquad\qquad \overline{}\ \psi_3$$
$$\alpha \qquad\qquad \overline{}\ \psi_2$$
$$\alpha + \beta \qquad\qquad \overline{}\ \psi_1$$
$$\alpha + 2\beta$$

Figure 6–11

The two π electrons present in the allylic carbonium ion are both placed in ψ_1. The allylic radical contains three electrons. This third π electron must enter ψ_2. In the allylic carbanion with four electrons, two are placed in ψ_1 and two in ψ_2. The results are presented in Figure 6–12.

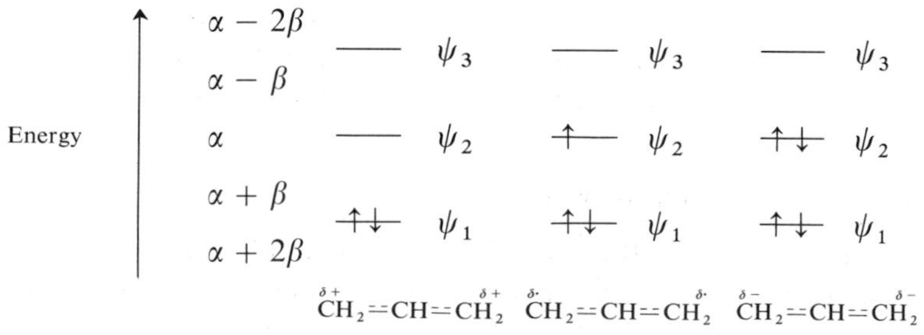

Energy

$$\alpha - 2\beta$$
$$\alpha - \beta$$
$$\alpha$$
$$\alpha + \beta$$
$$\alpha + 2\beta$$

$$\overset{\overset{\delta+}{C}H_2{=}CH{=}\overset{\delta+}{C}H_2}{} \qquad \overset{\overset{\delta\cdot}{C}H_2{=}CH{=}\overset{\delta\cdot}{C}H_2}{} \qquad \overset{\overset{\delta-}{C}H_2{=}CH{=}\overset{\delta-}{C}H_2}{}$$

Figure 6–12

The energy of the two π electrons in the allylic carbonium ion is,

$$2(\alpha + \sqrt{2}\beta) = 2\alpha + 2\sqrt{2}\beta$$

while the π electronic energy of the radical is,

$$2(\alpha + \sqrt{2}\beta) + \alpha = 3\alpha + 2\sqrt{2}\beta$$

The π electronic energy of the carbanion with two electrons in ψ_1 and two in ψ_2 is calculated to be,

$$2(\alpha + \sqrt{2}\beta) + 2\alpha = 4\alpha + 2\sqrt{2}\beta$$

We are also interested in the resonance energies of these systems. The resonance energy of the allylic carbonium ion is the difference between the energy of the classical structure,

$$CH_2{=}CH{-}\overset{+}{C}H_2$$

and the energy of the actual ion. In the classical structure the two π electrons are localized in an ethylenic linkage with energy $(2\alpha + 2\beta)$. The calculated resonance energy is the difference between the energy of the electrons in this structure and their energy in the actual ion, and this difference turns out to be,

$$R.E. = 2\alpha + 2\beta - (2\alpha + 2\sqrt{2}\beta) = -0.8\beta$$

The resonance energy of the radical and that of the carbanion are obtained in similar fashion. The classical structure for the radical is,

$$CH_2{=}CH{-}\overset{\cdot}{C}H_2$$

where we have two of the π electrons in an ethylenic linkage and the third electron in an isolated p atomic orbital with energy α. The resonance energy is calculated to be,

$$R.E. = 3\alpha + 2\beta - (3\alpha + 2\sqrt{2}\beta) = -0.8\beta$$

A calculation of the resonance energy of the carbanion also leads to the result -0.8β. According to the Hückel theory, all three of these species have a large resonance energy and are expected to be quite stable, a result which has been verified experimentally.

6.9 The Cyclopropenyl System

The secular equation for the cyclopropenyl system also involves a third order determinant. However, in this system C_1 and C_3 are bonded; this results in:

$$H_{13} = H_{31} = \beta$$

In terms of x the secular equation becomes,

$$\begin{vmatrix} x & 1 & 1 \\ 1 & x & 1 \\ 1 & 1 & x \end{vmatrix} = 0$$

where

$$x = \frac{\alpha - E}{\beta}$$

Expanding this determinant and solving the resulting polynomial equation:

$$x = -2$$
$$x = 1$$
$$x = 1$$

We find three molecular orbitals having the following energies,

$$E_1 = \alpha + 2\beta$$
$$E_2 = \alpha - \beta$$
$$E_3 = \alpha - \beta$$

Here we encounter degenerate molecular orbitals for the first time. In the cyclopropenyl system ψ_2 and ψ_3 are degenerate, for the energy associated with each is $(\alpha - \beta)$. The cyclopropenyl carbonium ion with two electrons in ψ_1 has a π electronic energy equal to $(2\alpha + 4\beta)$ and a resonance energy equal to -2β. The total energy of the carbanion is $(4\alpha + 2\beta)$, and the resonance energy of this species is zero. We find that the carbonium ion is predicted to be very stable whereas the carbanion has no resonance stabilization. Figure 6–13 is an energy level diagram for this series.

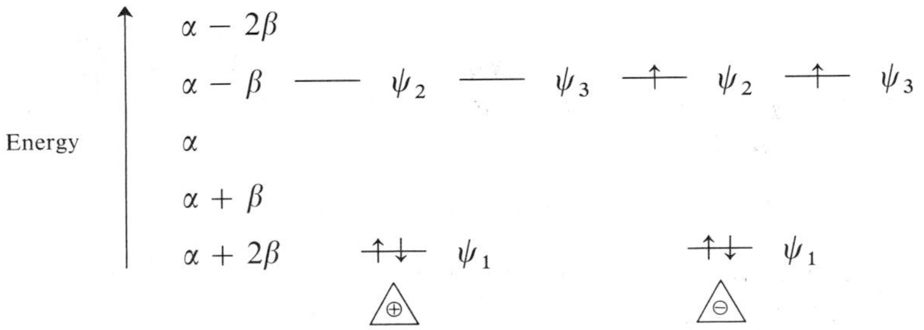

Figure 6–13

6.10 The Coefficients

In the previous sections we calculated the π electronic energies of several systems, yet the coefficients a_1, a_2, a_3 were not evaluated. Having calculated the energies of the various molecular orbitals, we are now able to determine the values of these coefficients.

All molecular orbitals obey Eq. (5–27). This equation must be employed in order to calculate the values of the coefficients. Since the p atomic orbitals are also assumed to form an orthonormal set, we have the two equations,

$$\int \psi_A \psi_B \, dv = \begin{cases} 1 & A = B \\ 0 & A \neq B \end{cases}$$

and

$$\int p_A p_B \, dv = \begin{cases} 1 & A = B \\ 0 & A \neq B \end{cases}$$

There are two allowable molecular orbitals for ethylene (ψ_1 and ψ_2), and both of these have the form,

$$\psi = a_1 p_1 + a_2 p_2$$

However, the values of a_1 and a_2 are not the same for these two molecular orbitals.

Normalization requires that,

$$\int \psi_1 \psi_1 \, dv = 1$$

$$\int \psi_2 \psi_2 \, dv = 1$$

Substitution of the appropriate expressions for ψ_1 and ψ_2 into the normalization requirement yields the result that for both molecular orbitals,

$$a_1{}^2 + a_2{}^2 = 1$$

We have one equation relating the coefficients for ethylene. Each of the three molecular orbitals in the allylic system is also formed as a linear combination of the p atomic orbitals.

$$\psi = a_1 p_1 + a_2 p_2 + a_3 p_3$$

Substitution of this expression affords the result that for all three molecular orbitals in the allylic system,

$$a_1{}^2 + a_2{}^2 + a_3{}^2 = 1$$

For the cyclopropenyl system we again obtain the equation,

$$a_1{}^2 + a_2{}^2 + a_3{}^2 = 1$$

The homogeneous Eqs. (6–13) and (6–16) also relate the coefficients.

Let us determine the values of a_1 and a_2 for the molecular orbitals in ethylene. The homogeneous equations are,

$$a_1(H_{11} - S_{11}E) + a_2(H_{12} - S_{12}E) = 0$$
$$a_1(H_{21} - S_{21}E) + a_2(H_{22} - S_{22}E) = 0$$

When written in terms of x, these equations become,

$$a_1 x + a_2 = 0$$
$$a_1 + a_2 x = 0$$

where $x = (\alpha - E)/\beta$.

We have the normalization requirement, these two equations, and we know the allowed values for x. This information enables us to determine the values of a_1 and a_2. For ethylene, the allowed values of x are -1 and 1. The value of x for the bonding molecular orbital ψ_1 is -1. The energy associated with ψ_1 is $(\alpha + \beta)$, and this value of E is obtained when $x = -1$.

Substituting $x = -1$ into these equations, we find that

$$a_1 = a_2$$

from the normalization requirement,

$$a_1{}^2 + a_2{}^2 = 1$$

Since $a_1 = a_2$, we obtain,

$$a_1 = \frac{1}{\sqrt{2}}$$

$$a_2 = \frac{1}{\sqrt{2}}$$

For ψ_2, x takes on the value 1. We substitute this value for x into the homogeneous equations and find that for ψ_2,

$$a_2 = -a_1$$

and from the normalization requirement,

$$a_1 = \frac{1}{\sqrt{2}}$$

Since $a_2 = -a_1$,

$$a_2 = -\frac{1}{\sqrt{2}}$$

The two orthonormal molecular orbitals for ethylene are,

$$\psi_1 = \frac{1}{\sqrt{2}} p_1 + \frac{1}{\sqrt{2}} p_2$$

$$\psi_2 = \frac{1}{\sqrt{2}} p_1 - \frac{1}{\sqrt{2}} p_2$$

The coefficients in the allylic system are evaluated in similar fashion. Equations (6–16) when written in terms of x become,

$$a_1 x + a_2 \qquad\qquad = 0$$

$$a_1 + a_2 x + a_3 = 0$$

$$a_2 + a_3 x = 0$$

Here x takes on the values $-\sqrt{2}, 0,$ and $\sqrt{2}$. When $x = -\sqrt{2}$ we find that,

$$a_2 = \sqrt{2} a_1$$

$$a_3 = a_1$$

The normalization requirement enables us to solve for a_1:

$$a_1 = 1/2$$

$$a_2 = \frac{\sqrt{2}}{2}$$

$$a_3 = 1/2$$

These are the coefficients for ψ_1. Substitution of $x = 0$ affords the appropriate values for ψ_2. The coefficients for ψ_3 are obtained upon substitution of the $\sqrt{2}$ for x into these equations. The three molecular orbitals in the allylic system are,

$$\psi_1 = \frac{1}{2} p_1 + \frac{\sqrt{2}}{2} p_2 + \frac{1}{2} p_3$$

$$\psi_2 = \frac{1}{\sqrt{2}} p_1 - \frac{1}{\sqrt{2}} p_3$$

$$\psi_3 = \frac{1}{2} p_1 - \frac{\sqrt{2}}{2} p_2 + \frac{1}{2} p_3$$

We are also able to determine the coefficients for the molecular orbitals in the cyclopropenyl system:

$$\psi_1 = \frac{1}{\sqrt{3}}p_1 + \frac{1}{\sqrt{3}}p_2 + \frac{1}{\sqrt{3}}p_3$$

$$\psi_2 = \frac{1}{\sqrt{2}}p_1 - \frac{1}{\sqrt{2}}p_3$$

$$\psi_3 = \frac{1}{\sqrt{6}}p_1 - \frac{2}{\sqrt{6}}p_2 + \frac{1}{\sqrt{6}}p_3$$

6.11 The Concept of Aromaticity

The notion of aromaticity implies a π molecular system possessing exceptional stability. Such a molecular system contains less energy, is formed more readily, and is less reactive than expected. According to molecular orbital theory, this idea of exceptional stability and chemical inertness in certain organic systems containing π electrons can be attributed to two factors. All bonding and non-bonding orbitals must be complete, and the system should possess a large resonance energy.

A requirement for aromaticity is that all bonding and nonbonding molecular orbitals be complete, that is, all should contain two electrons. All antibonding orbitals should be empty. In the cyclopropenyl system (Figure 6–14) there is a single bonding molecular orbital; there are no nonbonding orbitals. The bonding orbital is complete in the carbonium ion, and therefore, the cyclopropenyl carbonium ion satisfies this criterion. The carbanion, on the other hand, does not and is not aromatic.

The other criterion, and the one that appears to be the least important in the Hückel molecular orbital theory, is probably the more familiar; namely, that the system possess a large resonance energy. The cyclopropenyl carbonium ion with a calculated resonance energy of -2β also satisfies this requirement, and we predict aromaticity for this system.

A less stringent requirement for stability is that the π system possess a closed-shell configuration. The inert gases possess such a configuration. In helium the

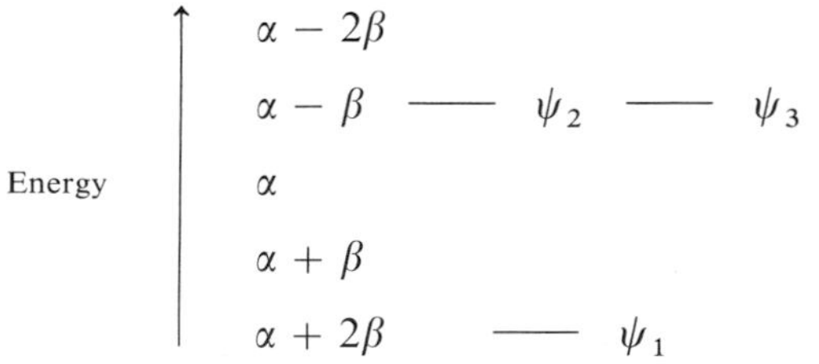

Energy

$$\alpha - 2\beta$$

$$\alpha - \beta \quad —— \quad \psi_2 \quad —— \quad \psi_3$$

$$\alpha$$

$$\alpha + \beta$$

$$\alpha + 2\beta \quad —— \quad \psi_1$$

Figure 6–14

first energy level, the 1s orbital, is completely occupied. In neon the first and second shells are full; the 1s, 2s, and 2p orbitals are all complete. Only when a similar requirement in terms of molecular orbitals is satisfied can a molecule possess exceptional stability. In the cyclopropenyl system, as pictured in Figure 6–14, there are two energy levels; ψ_1 at the first level, ψ_2 and ψ_3 both occupying the second level.

The cyclopropenyl carbonium ion has two π electrons, and this system possesses a closed-shell configuration; the first energy shell containing ψ_1 is full. The cyclopropenyl carbanion with four electrons does not possess such a configuration; here ψ_2 and ψ_3 each contain only one electron. This last system cannot be aromatic.

According to molecular orbital theory there are two criteria for exceptional stability, complete bonding and nonbonding orbitals and a large resonance energy. A system that satisfies these is aromatic.

Some of these ideas were recognized by Hückel as early as 1931 and were formulated in what is known today as Hückel's rule. According to this rule a monocyclic system (a system containing a single ring) is aromatic if every carbon atom in the ring contributes a p orbital and if that system contains $(4n + 2)\pi$ electrons; n can have the values 0, 1, 2, and so forth. According to this empirical rule, monocyclic systems containing 2, 6, 10, and so forth π electrons are aromatic. Thus, the cyclopropenyl carbonium ion with two π electrons, the cyclopentadienyl carbanion with six, and benzene with six are all aromatic. Cyclobutadiene with four and cyclooctatetraene with eight π electrons are not aromatic.

A simple empirical method for determining the aromaticity of a system is to see if it obeys Hückel's rule. A more satisfactory method is to carry out a molecular orbital calculation and ascertain whether or not the system satisfies the requirements presented earlier. Of course, the most satisfactory test for aromaticity, and also the most difficult, is to prepare the molecule in the laboratory and study its properties.

Supplementary Reading

1. Coulson, C. A., *Valence,* 2nd Ed. London, Oxford U. P., 1961.

2. Daudel, R., Lefebvre, R., and Moser, C., *Quantum Chemistry.* New York, Interscience, 1959.

3. Gray, H. B., *Electrons and Chemical Bonding.* New York, Benjamin, 1964.

4. Liberles, A., *Introduction to Molecular Orbital Theory.* New York, Holt, 1966.

5. Pullman, A., and Pullman, B., *Les Théories Electroniques de la Chimie Organique.* Paris, Masson, 1952.

6. Roberts, J. D., *Notes on Molecular Orbital Calculations.* New York, Benjamin, 1961.

7. Streitwieser, A., Jr., *Molecular Orbital Theory for Organic Chemists.* New York, Wiley, 1961.

8. Wheland, G. W., *Resonance in Organic Chemistry.* New York, Wiley, 1955.

9. Wiberg, K. B., *Physical Organic Chemistry.* New York, Wiley, 1964.

Chapter 7

The Valence-Bond Method

7.1 Introduction

The valence-bond approach to molecular structure is closely related to the usual ideas of bond formation. According to this method the positions of an electron in a molecule are adequately described by atomic orbitals. For example in the hydrogen molecule, which is composed of two protons H_1 and H_2 and two electrons e_1 and e_2, we assume that when an electron is near proton one H_1, it occupies the $1s$ atomic orbital of H_1. When an electron is near H_2, we assume that it occupies the $1s$ atomic orbital of H_2. In this chapter we discuss probable positions for the electrons in terms of atomic orbitals and not in terms of molecular orbitals.

In the molecular orbital method we were working with one-electron molecular orbitals and the Hamiltonian operators were obtained from one-electron Hamiltonians. The functions ψ in the valence-bond method represent the orbitals for several electrons, and the Hamiltonian operators are obtained from many-electron Hamiltonians.

Mathematical evaluation of the various terms that occur in molecular orbital theory was not possible. The terms occurring in the valence-bond treatment are still more difficult to evaluate. Consequently this theory is also developed in terms of two parameters Q and J with resonance energies expressed in terms of the latter.

7.2 The Covalent Bond

The usual picture of the covalent bond is based upon the assumption that this bond is formed from orbital overlap. Figure 7–1 shows the bond in the hydrogen molecule resulting from the overlap of two $1s$ atomic orbitals, one from each hydrogen atom. The covalent bond contains two electrons of opposite spin.

The bond in the hydrogen chloride molecule results from overlap of the $1s$ atomic orbital of hydrogen with the $3p$ atomic orbital of chlorine, pictured in Figure 7–2.

Similarly, in methane (Figure 7–3) four hydrogen atoms, each using a $1s$ atomic orbital, overlap with the four sp^3 hybridized orbitals of carbon.

Figure 7–1

Figure 7–2

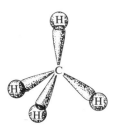

Figure 7–3

In ethylene there are both σ and π bonds. Figure 7–4 illustrates the situation. The carbon-hydrogen bonds are formed by overlap of the $1s$ atomic orbitals of hydrogen with sp^2 hybridized orbitals of carbon. The two carbon-carbon bonds result, the one from sp^2-sp^2 endwise orbital overlap and the other from p-p sidewise overlap.

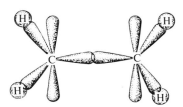

Figure 7–4

Bond formation in each case results from orbital overlap; each bond contains two electrons of opposite spin.

These simple pictures give us a qualitative idea of the phenomenon of covalent bond formation, but they give no indication of the distribution of electrons in these bonds. A somewhat more detailed description of molecular structure involves the ideas of valence bond theory.

7.3 The Hydrogen Molecule

The hydrogen molecule is composed of two protons H_1 and H_2 and two electrons e_1 and e_2. To describe this molecule, we assume that e_1 occupies the $1s$ orbital of hydrogen atom 1 and that e_2 occupies the $1s$ orbital of hydrogen atom 2. We designate the $1s$ orbital of hydrogen atom 1 simply as s_1 and the $1s$ orbital of hydrogen atom 2 as s_2. Then the function ψ_1 that describes the positions of these two electrons in structure **1** is given by,

$$
\begin{array}{cc}
e_1 & e_2 \\
\cdot & \cdot \\
H_1 & H_2
\end{array}
$$

1

$$\psi_1 = s_1(1)s_2(2)$$

where the symbol $s_1(1)$ refers to the fact that e_1 is in the orbital s_1. An analogous interpretation is given to the symbol $s_2(2)$. Notice that ψ_1 here represents the orbitals of both the electrons and that such a two-electron function is formed as the product of the one-electron functions.

This is just one possible description of the hydrogen molecule. Since the electrons are physically indistinguishable, it is possible to exchange the positions of the electrons. An equally good description of the hydrogen molecule is given by structure **2**,

$$
\begin{array}{cc}
e_2 & e_1 \\
\cdot & \cdot \\
H_1 & H_2
\end{array}
$$

2

$$\psi_2 = s_1(2)s_2(1)$$

This second description is just as good a representation of the hydrogen molecule as the first, and of course, neither description is adequate. We obtain a better picture of the molecule by taking into account both structures **1** and **2**. The function ψ that describes the positions of two electrons is then formed as a linear combination of ψ_1 and ψ_2:

$$\psi = a_1\psi_1 + a_2\psi_2$$
$$\psi = a_1[s_1(1)s_2(2)] + a_2[s_1(2)s_2(1)]$$

It is this function ψ that is usually implied when one represents the hydrogen molecule by the simple covalent structure,

$$H_1 - H_2$$

and ψ describes the two electrons in this covalent structure.

This function for ψ was used by Heitler and London in 1927. They substituted ψ into Eq. (6–1) and calculated the energy of the hydrogen molecule.

Substitution of ψ into Eq. (6–1) and employing the same variational procedure described previously leads to the secular equation,

$$\begin{vmatrix} H_{11} - S_{11}E & H_{12} - S_{12}E \\ H_{21} - S_{21}E & H_{22} - S_{22}E \end{vmatrix} = 0$$

where

$$H_{11} = \int s_1(1)s_2(2)Hs_1(1)s_2(2)\,dq = Q$$

$$H_{22} = \int s_1(2)s_2(1)Hs_1(2)s_2(1)\,dq = Q$$

$$H_{12} = \int s_1(1)s_2(2)Hs_1(2)s_2(1)\,dq = J$$

$$H_{21} = \int s_1(2)s_2(1)Hs_1(1)s_2(2)\,dq = J$$

$$S_{11} = S_{22} = 1$$

$$S_{12} = \int s_1(1)s_2(2)s_1(2)s_2(1)\,dq = S$$

$$S_{21} = \int s_1(2)s_2(1)s_1(1)s_2(2)\,dq = S$$

and ultimately to the values for E given by ($S_{12} = S_{21} = S$ is not set equal to zero in this calculation),

$$E_1 = \frac{Q + J}{1 + S}$$

$$E_2 = \frac{Q - J}{1 - S}$$

Although the Heitler-London treatment was somewhat different, it leads to the same equations for E_1 and E_2. In the case of the hydrogen molecule, the various integrals can be evaluated. The Heitler-London calculation represents the first valence-bond calculation. They found that the energy of bond formation in the hydrogen molecule was -72 kcal/mole. The experimental value for the energy is -109.5 kcal/mole. This experimental value is the negative of the bond dissociation energy when the zero-point energy is not included.

The procedure just indicated gives a reasonably good description of the hydrogen molecule, yet a somewhat better picture can be obtained. We have neglected the possibility that both electrons can be near the same nucleus. A better picture of the hydrogen molecule results if we also take into account structures such as **3** and **4**:

$$e_1 \cdot \overset{\overset{\displaystyle e_2}{\displaystyle \cdot}}{H_1} \; H_2$$

3

$$\psi_3 = s_1(1)s_1(2)$$

$$H_1 \; \overset{\overset{\displaystyle e_1}{\displaystyle \cdot}}{H_2} \cdot e_2$$

4

$$\psi_4 = s_2(1)s_2(2)$$

These structures correspond to the simple ionic pictures,

$$H_1 : {}^- H_2^+ \qquad H_1^+ \; :H_2^-$$

3   **4**

Such contributors represent higher energy structures, and the contribution that they make to the actual molecule is small; however, they should not be neglected. We form a new function ψ that includes all four structures. This new function that now describes the hydrogen molecule is formed as a linear combination of the four functions ψ_1, ψ_2, ψ_3, ψ_4:

$$\psi = a_1\psi_1 + a_2\psi_2 + a_3\psi_3 + a_4\psi_4$$

Substitution of this expression for ψ into Eq. (6–1) leads to a different value for the energy of the hydrogen molecule. According to this calculation, the energy of bond formation is equal to about -92 kcal/mole. This result is closer to the actual value. We approach the actual energy for bond formation as we include more valence-bond contributors in the calculation. Naturally the calculation becomes more difficult. Thus we see that including more valence-bond contributors in the calculation gives a more accurate description of the molecule.

As a further example, we consider the case of hydrogen chloride. We assume that the bond in the molecule is formed by overlap of the $1s$ atomic orbital of hydrogen (designated simply as s) with the $3p$ atomic orbital of chlorine (designated as p). We do not in this discussion consider any of the other electrons that are associated with the chlorine atom.

A possible description of the hydrogen chloride molecule is given by **A**,

$$e_1 \quad e_2$$
$$\overset{\cdot}{\text{H}} \quad \overset{\cdot}{\text{Cl}}$$

A

$$\psi_A = s(1)p(2)$$

and an equally good description of the molecule is given by **B**,

$$e_2 \quad e_1$$
$$\overset{\cdot}{\text{H}} \quad \overset{\cdot}{\text{Cl}}$$

B

$$\psi_B = s(2)p(1)$$

The ψ that describes these two electrons in the actual molecule is formed as a linear combination of ψ_A and ψ_B.

$$\text{H—Cl}$$

$$\psi = a_A\psi_A + a_B\psi_B$$

Once again, a better description of the molecule results when we also consider ionic structures such as **C**:

$$e_1$$
$$\text{H} \quad \overset{\cdot}{\text{Cl}} \cdot e_2$$

C

$$\psi_C = p(1)p(2)$$

Because of the electronegativity of chlorine, this structure with both electrons in the $3p$ atomic orbital of chlorine is much more important than the corresponding structures in the hydrogen molecule. We may also include a structure such as **D**:

$$e_2$$
$$e_1 \cdot \overset{\cdot}{\text{H}} \quad \text{Cl}$$

D

$$\psi_D = s(1)s(2)$$

Structure **D** represents a very high energy valence-bond contributor, but a more accurate description of hydrogen chloride is obtained if **D** is taken into account.

Considering structures **A**, **B**, **C** and **D** leads to an expression for ψ given by,

$$\psi = a_A\psi_A + a_B\psi_B + a_C\psi_C + a_D\psi_D$$

The first two terms represent the usual covalent structure,

$$H—Cl$$

the third term represents the ionic structure,

$$H^+ :Cl^-$$

while the last describes the high energy contributor,

$$H:^- Cl^+$$

The ideas that we have presented thus far should be familiar. A qualitative presentation of these same concepts is called resonance theory. In the previous discussions no mention was made of electronic spin. It is implicitly assumed in resonance theory that all of the bonds in a molecule contain two electrons of opposite spin. For example in the ground state of the hydrogen molecule, the bond holding the atoms together contains two electrons of opposite spin. We wish to describe this bond; consequently, all acceptable valence-bond structures for the ground state must also contain two electrons of opposite spin. Thus, if we represent the hydrogen molecule by the structures:

$$
\begin{array}{cccc}
\overset{\overset{e_1}{\bullet}\;\;\overset{e_2}{\bullet}}{H_1 \;\; H_2} & \overset{\overset{e_2}{\bullet}\;\;\overset{e_1}{\bullet}}{H_1 \;\; H_2} & \overset{e_2}{\overset{\bullet}{e_1 \cdot H_1 \;\; H_2}} & \overset{e_1}{\overset{\bullet}{H_1 \;\; H_2 \cdot e_2}} \\
\mathbf{1} & \mathbf{2} & \mathbf{3} & \mathbf{4}
\end{array}
$$

we assume that in each structure the two electrons have opposite spin. A structure such as **5**,

$$
\overset{e_1\uparrow \;\; e_2\uparrow}{\overset{\bullet\;\;\;\;\bullet}{H_1 \;\; H_2}}
$$
$$\mathbf{5}$$

which contains two electrons having parallel spin, is not an acceptable contributor; it does not describe the bond.

We may also represent **5** simply as,

$$H_1 \cdot \;\; \cdot H_2$$

where we assume that the two dots represent two electrons with parallel spins.

7.4 Resonance Theory

We discuss in this section resonance theory and consider as an example the molecule of hydrogen chloride.

The two atoms (H and Cl) in the hydrogen chloride molecule are constantly moving back and forth; we assume that these two atoms are stationary at their equilibrium positions. The distance separating the atoms is then just the equilibrium bond length 1.28 Å. We also assume that bond formation involves only a $3p$ atomic orbital of chlorine and the $1s$ atomic orbital of hydrogen. All other electrons are assumed to occupy the same orbitals in the hydrogen chloride molecule that they occupy in the chlorine atom. We can now consider the bond in the hydrogen chloride molecule to be formed by overlap of the $1s$ atomic orbital of hydrogen with a $3p$ atomic orbital of chlorine, and we can represent this molecule by the simple structure,

$$H-Cl$$

6

This structure, as we know, does not adequately represent the hydrogen chloride molecule. Since chlorine is more electronegative than hydrogen, the bond in the molecule is a polar-covalent bond. The most probable positions for the electrons are near the chlorine atom, and this structure does not take sufficient account of the polar nature of the molecule.

Alternatively, we could represent the hydrogen chloride molecule by the structure,

$$H^+ :Cl^-$$

7

Here both of the electrons are in the $3p$ atomic orbital of chlorine (the internuclear distance is still 1.28 Å). However, this picture overemphasizes the polar nature of the molecule and is an even poorer description of hydrogen chloride than the first structure. We consider that the actual molecule is not adequately represented by either of these classical structures. The actual molecule is intermediate in nature between these two extreme forms, and the hydrogen chloride molecule is then said to be a resonance hybrid receiving contributions from these two resonance (valence-bond) contributors:

$$H-Cl \longleftrightarrow H^+ :Cl^-$$

6   **7**

Remember that we always assume two electrons of opposite spin.

7.5 The Requirements for Resonance

We indicated in Section 7.4 that the hydrogen chloride molecule is a resonance hybrid receiving contributions from the valence-bond structures **6** and **7**. These two structures are not the only possible valence-bond contributors. We have not taken into account possibilities such as **8**. Here both electrons occupy the $1s$ orbital of hydrogen:

$$H:^- Cl^+$$

8

Structure **8** represents a high energy contributor, and therefore, such a valence-bond structure is not as important as the other two. However, a better description of the molecule is obtained if we also include this possibility:

$$H-Cl \longleftrightarrow H^+:Cl^- \longleftrightarrow H:^-Cl^+$$

$$\textbf{6} \qquad\qquad \textbf{7} \qquad\qquad \textbf{8}$$

As we have already seen, this is a general phenomenon. The inclusion of more valence-bond contributors affords a better description of any molecule.

While the inclusion of more contributors gives a more accurate representation of any molecule, not all possible valence-bond contributors are acceptable. There are certain requirements that must be met by these valence-bond contributors in order that they may be considered acceptable.

The number of unpaired electrons must be the same in all structures. For example, the bond in hydrogen chloride contains two electrons of opposite spin. Consequently, in all acceptable valence-bond contributors, there must be two electrons having opposite spin. Thus, the hydrogen chloride molecule may be considered as a resonance hybrid of **6**, **7** and **8** since all of these contain two electrons of opposite spin, but structure **9** cannot contribute to the ground state since the two electrons here have parallel spins:

$$H-Cl \longleftrightarrow H^+:Cl^- \longleftrightarrow H:^-Cl^+ \longleftrightarrow\!\!\!|\!\!\!\longrightarrow H\cdot\ \cdot Cl$$

$$\textbf{6} \qquad\qquad \textbf{7} \qquad\qquad \textbf{8} \qquad\qquad \textbf{9}$$

Secondly, the electrons and the nuclei must occupy almost the same positions in all resonance contributors. This prevents isomers from being considered as resonance contributors.

Finally, if resonance is to be large, each of the various contributing structures should have approximately the same energy. High energy structures such as **8** contribute little to the hybrid.

These are the requirements for resonance. Valence-bond structures that do not satisfy these requirements are not acceptable resonance contributors.

7.6 The Resonance Energy

We do not consider a molecule to be adequately described by any one valence-bond structure. More than a single such structure is necessary to accurately describe the molecule, and as we shall see, the actual molecule is more stable than any of these valence-bond contributors. The difference between the energy of the most stable valence-bond structure and the energy of the actual molecule is defined as the resonance energy for that molecule. For hydrogen chloride, the difference between the energy of structure **6** and the energy of the actual molecule represents the resonance energy of hydrogen chloride. For benzene, which we assume to be a hybrid of the two Kekulé structures, the resonance energy is defined as the difference between the energy of one of these (**10** or **11**) and the energy of the actual molecule **12**:

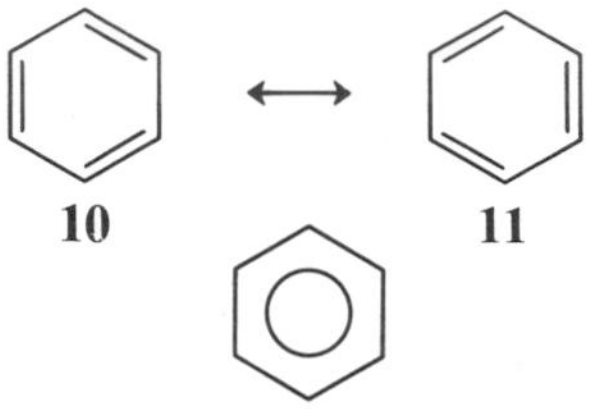

10   **11**

12

Resonance Energy = energy of **10** − energy of **12**

Resonance energies are always positive. Numerical evaluation of the resonance energy of any molecule depends upon the system under consideration, the technique used, and the assumptions made. The difficulty in the case of benzene arises because it is impossible to determine accurately the energy of the hypothetical molecule represented by Kekulé structure **10**, and without this knowledge it is not possible to determine the resonance energy of benzene. It is almost always possible to determine experimentally the energy of an actual molecule. It is never possible to determine experimentally nor even to calculate reasonably well the energy of the most stable valence-bond contributor. Since we cannot determine the exact energy of the hypothetical molecule, only approximate values for the resonance energy can be obtained.

Consider, for example, the thermodynamic evaluation of the resonance energy of benzene. We are attempting to determine the difference between the energy of the Kekulé structure **10** and the energy of the actual benzene molecule **12**. The following heats of hydrogenation have been determined experimentally,

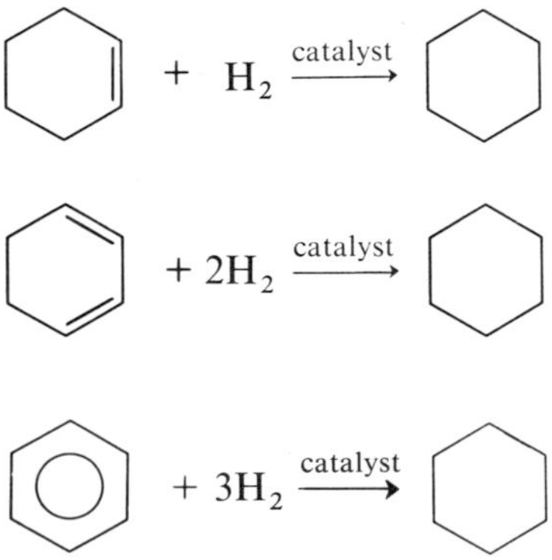

$\Delta H = -28.6 \text{ kcal/mole}$

$\Delta H = -55.4 \text{ kcal/mole}$

$\Delta H = -49.8 \text{ kcal/mole}$

Cyclohexadiene has two double bonds and might be expected to have a heat of hydrogenation equal to twice that of cyclohexene. The hypothetical molecule represented by Kekulé structure **10** contains three double bonds. This might then be expected to have a heat of hydrogenation equal to three times that of cyclohexene,

$$2 \times -28.6 = -57.2 \, \text{kcal/mole}$$

$$3 \times -28.6 = -85.8 \, \text{kcal/mole}$$

The experimentally determined values are less than these. Cyclohexadiene is 1.8 kcal/mole more stable and benzene 36.0 kcal/mole more stable than expected.

$$57.2 - 55.4 = 1.8 \, \text{kcal/mole}$$

$$85.8 - 49.8 = 36.0 \, \text{kcal/mole}$$

The two compounds are more stable than expected, and this extra stability is usually assumed to equal the resonance energy of these molecules. The results are illustrated in Figure 7–5.

The resonance energy of benzene is determined to be 36.0 kcal/mole, yet in the previous discussion many assumptions have tacitly been made. To assume that structure **10** ought to have a heat of hydrogenation equal to three times that of cyclohexene is a gross oversimplification of the problem. The heat of hydrogenation is an experimental quantity that indicates energy differences. This includes differences in zero-point energy as well as differences in molecular vibrations and molecular rotations. We have not taken these differences into account and, in fact, assume when discussing resonance energies that the nuclei are stationary. We are required to neglect the vibrational and rotational contribution to the observed heat of hydrogenation. Furthermore, changes in bond lengths and bond angles must also be considered. The approximate length of the double bond in cyclohexene is 1.33 Å, and the heat of hydrogenation is −28.6 kcal/mole. If structure **10** is expected to have a heat of hydrogenation equal to three times this value, then we have tacitly assumed that structure **10** contains three double bonds each having a length of 1.33 Å. In the previous discussion structure **10** was assumed to be a molecule with three double bonds of length 1.33 Å and three single bonds each having a length of approximately 1.50 Å,

$$1.33 \, \text{Å} \longrightarrow \bigcirc \longleftarrow 1.50 \, \text{Å}$$

10A

We have calculated that benzene is more stable than this hypothetical molecule by 36.0 kcal/mole:

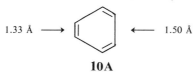

10A

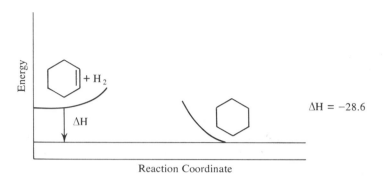

$$\Delta H = -28.6$$

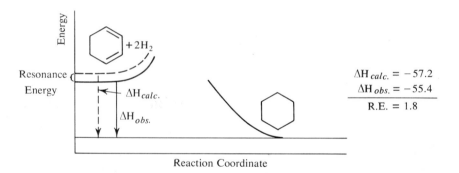

$$\Delta H_{calc.} = -57.2$$
$$\underline{\Delta H_{obs.} = -55.4}$$
$$R.E. = 1.8$$

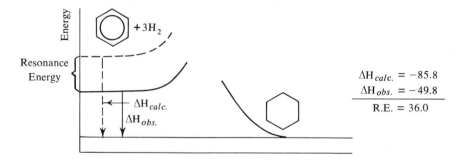

$$\Delta H_{calc.} = -85.8$$
$$\underline{\Delta H_{obs.} = -49.8}$$
$$R.E. = 36.0$$

Figure 7–5

Now the bond lengths in structure **10** should be the same as the bond lengths in benzene (1.39 Å), and these are not the same as the bond lengths in cyclohexene. We must modify structure **10A** so that it conforms to our requirements. We see the difficulty in obtaining the resonance energy of benzene.

In benzene the carbon-carbon bond lengths are all equivalent and equal to 1.39 Å. Consequently these bond lengths in structure **10** should also equal 1.39 Å. The hypothetical structure **10A** used in the previous discussion is not a good valence-bond contributor; we must modify the bond lengths. If we compress the carbon-carbon single bonds and stretch the double bonds in **10A** until all bond lengths equal 1.39 Å, we obtain the desired Kekulé structure **10**.

We have a hypothetical molecule with localized double bonds yet having the same carbon-carbon bond distances as those found in benzene. This process of modifying the bond lengths from their normal values makes the hypothetical molecule still less stable than before. The various carbon-carbon single and double bonds are distorted from their normal lengths. It has been calculated that the process of distorting these bond distances requires 27 kcal/mole.

The vertical resonance energy is then defined as the difference between the energy of this structure, which is assumed to represent structure **10**, and the energy of the actual benzene molecule. The vertical resonance energy is calculated to be 63 kcal/mole:

Vertical Resonance Energy = 36 + 27 = 63 kcal/mole

Changing the definition of resonance energy leads to a different value for the calculated resonance energy of benzene; even this calculation of the vertical resonance energy involves many assumptions. In discussions involving the resonance energy of various molecules we shall always speak in terms of the vertical resonance energy, that is, we shall always compare systems where the internuclear distances are the same.

We have discussed certain ideas concerning the resonance energy. A theoretical development of these ideas is embodied in the valence-bond approach.

7.7 The Valence-Bond Approach to the Resonance Energy of Benzene

The ideas of resonance and resonance energy are intimately involved in a valence-bond picture of molecular structure. Let us again consider the hydrogen chloride molecule where we wish to describe the probable positions of the two electrons that make up the bond. Hydrogen chloride is assumed to be a resonance hybrid receiving contributions from the valence-bond structures **6** and **7**:

$$H—Cl \longleftrightarrow H^+ :Cl^-$$

$$\textbf{6} \qquad\qquad \textbf{7}$$

If we describe the two electrons in structure **6** by the function ψ_6 and the two electrons in structure **7** by ψ_7, then the two electrons in the actual molecule are described by ψ where ψ is formed as a linear combination of ψ_6 and ψ_7:

$$\psi = a_6\psi_6 + a_7\psi_7$$

If we also include structure **8** in our description and represent the electrons in **8** by ψ_8, then ψ is formed as a linear combination of all three of these functions:

$$H:^- Cl^+$$

$$\textbf{8}$$

and

$$\psi = a_6\psi_6 + a_7\psi_7 + a_8\psi_8$$

The coefficients a_1, a_2, a_3 remain to be determined, and these can be evaluated using the variational procedure presented in Chapter 6.

Similarly, if we describe the six π electrons in Kekulé structure **10** by ψ_{10} and the six π electrons in structure **11** by ψ_{11},

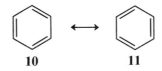

$$\textbf{10} \qquad\qquad \textbf{11}$$

then the function ψ that describes the six π electrons in the actual benzene molecule **12** is made up as a linear combination of ψ_{10} and ψ_{11}:

$$\textbf{12}$$

$$\psi = a_{10}\psi_{10} + a_{11}\psi_{11}$$

We assume here that the π electrons can be treated separately. We then substitute this expression for ψ into Eq. (6–1) and find the energy of the six π electrons and the values for the coefficients a_{10} and a_{11}. Notice that ψ describes the positions of all six π electrons and that the Hamiltonian operator must be obtained from a six-electron Hamiltonian. The technique employed to determine the values of E and a_{10} and a_{11} is the same as that described in Chapter 6. Minimizing the energy with respect to the two coefficients results in two equations having the same form as Eq. (6–13):

$$\frac{\partial E}{\partial a_{10}} = 0$$

and

$$\frac{\partial E}{\partial a_{11}} = 0$$

This leads to the result,

$$a_{10}(H_{AA} - S_{AA}E) + a_{11}(H_{AB} - S_{AB}E) = 0$$
$$a_{10}(H_{BA} - S_{BA}E) + a_{11}(H_{BB} - S_{BB}E) = 0$$

where

$$H_{AA} = \int \psi_{10}H\psi_{10}\,dq$$

$$H_{BB} = \int \psi_{11}H\psi_{11}\,dq$$

$$H_{AB} = \int \psi_{10}H\psi_{11}\,dq$$

$$H_{BA} = \int \psi_{11}H\psi_{10}\,dq \quad \text{and so forth.}$$

These integrals involve six-electron functions.

We can solve for E, the energy of the six π electrons, by setting the secular determinant equal to zero:

$$\begin{vmatrix} H_{AA} - S_{AA}E & H_{AB} - S_{AB}E \\ H_{BA} - S_{BA}E & H_{BB} - S_{BB}E \end{vmatrix} = 0$$

This secular equation can only be solved in terms of the two parameters Q and J. The integrals are too difficult for numerical evaluation. The term H_{AA} is just the energy of the six π electrons in Kekulé structure **10** while the term H_{BB} represents the energy of these six electrons in structure **11**. Consequently,

$$H_{AA} = H_{BB}$$

and from the normalization requirement,

$$S_{AA} = S_{BB} = 1$$

In terms of the parameters Q and J, the terms H_{AA} and H_{BB} are equal to Q, plus a term J for adjacent atoms joined by a double bond, minus a term $0.5 J$ for adjacent atoms not connected by double bonds. In structure **10**, there are three pairs of adjacent atoms connected by double bonds and three pairs of adjacent atoms not joined by double bonds; therefore,

$$H_{AA} = Q + 3.0 J - 1.5 J$$
$$H_{AA} = Q + 1.5 J$$

and we obtain the same result for H_{BB},

$$H_{BB} = Q + 1.5 J$$

Evaluation of the mixed terms $(H_{AB} - S_{AB}E)$ and $(H_{BA} - S_{BA}E)$ is somewhat more difficult. In terms of the parameters Q and J, these terms become,

$$H_{AB} - S_{AB}E = 0.25 Q + 1.5 J - 0.25 E$$
$$H_{BA} - S_{BA}E = 0.25 Q + 1.5 J - 0.25 E$$

and the secular equation becomes,

$$\begin{vmatrix} Q + 1.5 J - E & 0.25 Q + 1.5 J - 0.25 E \\ 0.25 Q + 1.5 J - 0.25 E & Q + 1.5 J - E \end{vmatrix} = 0$$

Dividing by J and setting $(Q - E)/J$ equal to x leads to,

$$\begin{vmatrix} x + 1.5 & 0.25 x + 1.5 \\ 0.25 x + 1.5 & x + 1.5 \end{vmatrix} = 0$$

where $x = (Q - E)/J$.

Expanding this determinant leads to the result,

$$(x + 1.5)^2 - (0.25 x + 1.5)^2 = 0$$

and to the two solutions,

$$x + 1.5 = -(0.25 x + 1.5)$$
$$x + 1.5 = +(0.25 x + 1.5)$$

with the following values for x,

$$x = -2.4$$
$$x = 0$$

Replacing x by its equivalent affords,

$$E_1 = Q + 2.4 J$$

$$E_2 = Q$$

where E_1 and E_2 are possible energies for the six π electrons. Since J is negative, the energy of these electrons in the ground state of benzene is given by E_1.

The resonance energy of benzene is the difference between the energy of Kekulé structure **10** and the energy of the actual molecule represented by structure **12**. The only difference between the energies of these two is that in **10** the motion of the π electrons is restricted while in **12** they are delocalized. Thus the resonance energy of benzene is the difference between the energy of the six π electrons in **10** (this is equal to H_{AA}, $Q + 1.5 J$) and their energy in **12** ($Q + 2.4 J$). All other factors remain constant. Accordingly the resonance energy is calculated to be,

$$R.E. = Q + 1.5 J - (Q + 2.4 J)$$

$$R.E. = -0.9 J$$

Here again, we could evaluate J by equating this calculated resonance energy to either the thermodynamic resonance energy of benzene (36.0 kcal/mole) or to the vertical resonance energy (63 kcal/mole). However, this is unnecessary, and we leave the calculation in terms of J.

The inclusion of more valence-bond contributors in the calculation affords a better picture of the benzene molecule. If we include the Dewar structures in our description of benzene, ψ becomes a linear combination involving the five functions ψ_{10} through ψ_{15}. The two dots in the Dewar structures (**13, 14** and **15**) represent two electrons of opposite spin:

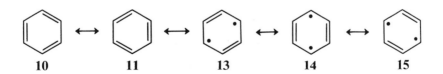

| **10** | **11** | **13** | **14** | **15** |

and

$$\psi = a_{10}\psi_{10} + a_{11}\psi_{11} + a_{13}\psi_{13} + a_{14}\psi_{14} + a_{15}\psi_{15}$$

Just as in the cases of hydrogen and hydrogen chloride, the inclusion of more valence-bond contributors gives a more accurate description of the molecule. We can now substitute this expression for ψ into Eq. (6–1) and again calculate the energy of the benzene molecule. This time we minimize E with respect to all five coefficients. The resulting secular equation is,

$$
\begin{vmatrix}
H_{AA} - S_{AA}E & H_{AB} - S_{AB}E & H_{AC} - S_{AC}E & H_{AD} - S_{AD}E & H_{AE} - S_{AE}E \\
H_{BA} - S_{BA}E & H_{BB} - S_{BB}E & H_{BC} - S_{BC}E & H_{BD} - S_{BD}E & H_{BE} - S_{BE}E \\
H_{CA} - S_{CA}E & H_{CB} - S_{CB}E & H_{CC} - S_{CC}E & H_{CD} - S_{CD}E & H_{CE} - S_{CE}E \\
H_{DA} - S_{DA}E & H_{DB} - S_{DB}E & H_{DC} - S_{DC}E & H_{DD} - S_{DD}E & H_{DE} - S_{DE}E \\
H_{EA} - S_{EA}E & H_{EB} - S_{EB}E & H_{EC} - S_{EC}E & H_{ED} - S_{ED}E & H_{EE} - S_{EE}E
\end{vmatrix} = 0
$$

Solving this secular equation in terms of the parameters Q and J leads to a different calculated value for the energy of the six π electrons. The values of E resulting from this equation are,

$$E_1 = Q + 2.6\,J$$

$$E_2 = Q$$

$$E_3 = Q - 2.0\,J$$

$$E_4 = Q - 2.0\,J$$

$$E_5 = Q - 4.6\,J$$

In the ground state the energy of the six π electrons is given by E_1, and the resonance energy is now calculated to be,

$$R.E. = Q + 1.5\,J - (Q + 2.6\,J)$$

$$R.E. = -1.1\,J$$

We find that the resonance energy of benzene is calculated to be larger when we include more valence bond contributors in the calculation. This is a general result. The calculation becomes more difficult, but the inclusion of more contributors in a calculation yields a better description of the molecule and leads to larger values for the calculated resonance energy.

Supplementary Reading

1. Coulson, C. A., *Valence,* 2nd Ed. London, Oxford U. P., 1961.
2. Pauling, L., *Nature of the Chemical Bond,* 3rd Ed. Ithaca, New York, Cornell U. P., 1960.
3. Pullman, B., *The Modern Theory of Molecular Structure.* New York, Dover, 1962.
4. Wheland, G. W., *Resonance in Organic Chemistry.* New York, Wiley, 1955.

Chapter 8

Molecular Structure

8.1 Introduction

We consider a molecule in its ground state and assume that the atoms which are continuously vibrating back and forth are in their equilibrium positions. This molecule has a certain conformation; methane, for example, is tetrahedral and boron trifluoride planar. When discussing molecular structure, it is customary to assume that the molecule is in its lowest energy state, the ground state, and also to assume that a unique conformation can be associated with this ground state. Occasionally the energy difference between ground-state spacial arrange ments is small; then more than a single such arrangement is possible. Cyclohexane, for example, exists in both the chair and boat forms:

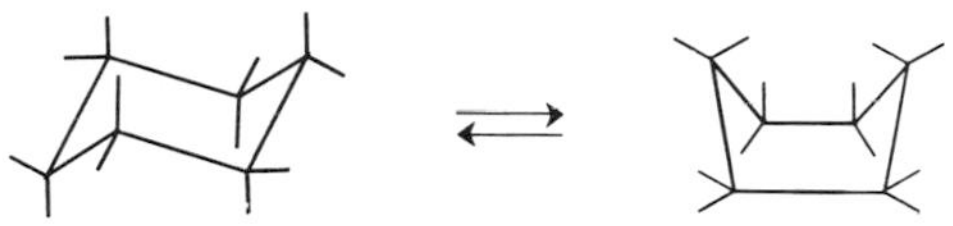

In the ground state the molecule possesses as little energy as it can possibly have, and under such conditions a molecule assumes the conformation that gives it minimum energy. If we excite the molecule in some way, the system possesses more energy and different geometries become possible. For example, acetylene in its ground state is a linear molecule with *sp* hybridized carbon atoms. Excitation of acetylene to the lowest energy singlet excited state not only promotes an electron from one orbital to another of higher energy, the hybridization of the entire molecule changes. The excited state is best described as sp^2 hybridized with a *trans*-geometry,

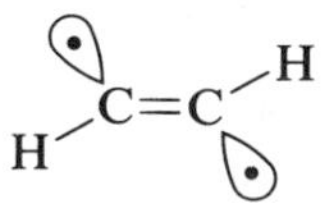

| ground state | excited state |

The behavior of ethylene upon excitation also illustrates the idea that the geometry of a molecule varies with its energy. In the ground state, ethylene is a planar molecule with sp^2 hybridized carbon atoms; in the excited triplet state the methylene groups are perpendicular (some change in hybridization may accompany the process):

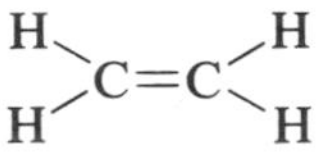

ground state 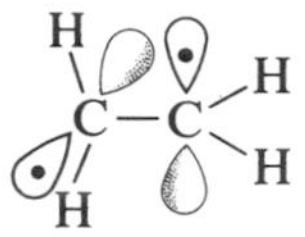   excited state

When discussing molecular geometry it is generally assumed that the molecule is in its electronic ground state, and even when in its ground state the factors that govern molecular structure are varied and complex. It is necessary to consider orbital overlap, internuclear and interelectronic repulsion, as well as coulombic attraction between nuclei and electrons. All of these play a role; no single factor is responsible for a particular conformation. In the following sections we discuss in a qualitative manner the effect of changes in structure upon molecular geometry.

8.2 Hybridization

We have indicated that the four carbon-hydrogen bonds in methane can be treated as four separate molecular orbitals where each bond is formed as a linear combination of the $1s$ orbital from hydrogen and an sp^3 orbital from carbon:

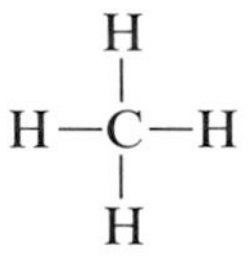

$$
\begin{array}{c}
H \\
| \\
H-C-H \\
| \\
H
\end{array}
$$

$$\psi_{CH} = a_1 s + a_2 sp^3$$

The sp^3 orbitals are themselves formed as linear combinations of atomic orbitals. The carbon atom in methane has associated with it the $2s$, $2p_x$, $2p_y$, and $2p_z$ orbitals, and such a carbon atom can form four sp^3 hybridized orbitals by combining linearly the appropriate atomic orbitals:

$$sp^3 = a_1 s_C + a_2 p_x + a_3 p_y + a_4 p_z$$

The term s_C refers to the $2s$ atomic orbital of carbon.

A carbon atom that is sp^3 hybridized has four orbitals of this type associated with it. Naturally the coefficients a_1, a_2, a_3, and a_4 differ for each hybridized orbital. One possible set of sp^3 hybridized orbitals is given by,

$$sp^3{}_1 = 1/2s_C + 1/2p_x + 1/2p_y + 1/2p_z$$
$$sp^3{}_2 = 1/2s_C - 1/2p_x + 1/2p_y - 1/2p_z$$
$$sp^3{}_3 = 1/2s_C - 1/2p_x - 1/2p_y + 1/2p_z$$
$$sp^3{}_4 = 1/2s_C + 1/2p_x - 1/2p_y - 1/2p_z$$

Such an sp^3 orbital is pictured in Figure 8–1.

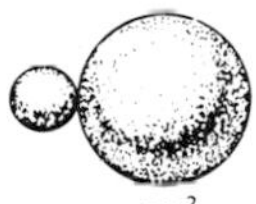

sp^3

Figure 8–1

The fraction of s orbital used in forming an sp^3 orbital is equal to,

$$a_1{}^2 = (1/2)^2 = 1/4$$

The fraction of p orbital in such a hybridized orbital is given by,

$$a_2{}^2 + a_3{}^2 + a_4{}^2 = 3/4$$

In all cases the fraction of p atomic orbital is equal to 3/4, and such an orbital which is 1/4 s and 3/4 p is said to be sp^3 hybridized.

Since the s_C and p atomic orbitals of carbon form an orthonormal set (see Eq. (5–27)), the four sp^3 hybridized orbitals also form an orthonormal set:

$$\int s_C s_C \, dv = 1$$

$$\int p_A p_B \, dv = \begin{cases} 1 & A = B \\ 0 & A \neq B \end{cases}$$

$$\int s_C p_A \, dv = 0$$

Therefore,

$$\int sp^3{}_A sp^3{}_B \, dv = \begin{cases} 1 & A = B \\ 0 & A \neq B \end{cases}$$

A description of the four bonds in methane is given by the expression,

$$\psi_1 = a_1 s + a_2(1/2s_C + 1/2p_x + 1/2p_y + 1/2p_z)$$
$$\psi_2 = a_1 s + a_2(1/2s_C - 1/2p_x + 1/2p_y - 1/2p_z)$$
$$\psi_3 = a_1 s + a_2(1/2s_C - 1/2p_x - 1/2p_y + 1/2p_z)$$
$$\psi_4 = a_1 s + a_2(1/2s_C + 1/2p_x - 1/2p_y - 1/2p_z)$$

A carbon atom that is sp^2 hybridized has three orbitals of the form,

$$sp^2 = a_1 s_C + a_2 p_x + a_3 p_y$$

and a single p atomic orbital that is not involved in hybridization (see Figure 8–2). This orbital, usually the p_z atomic orbital is chosen, remains unaltered.

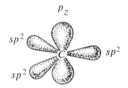

Figure 8–2

A possible set of sp^2 orbitals is given by,

$$sp^2{}_1 = \frac{1}{\sqrt{3}}s_C + \frac{\sqrt{2}}{\sqrt{3}}p_x$$

$$sp^2{}_2 = \frac{1}{\sqrt{3}}s_C - \frac{1}{\sqrt{6}}p_x + \frac{1}{\sqrt{2}}p_y$$

$$sp^2{}_3 = \frac{1}{\sqrt{3}}s_C - \frac{1}{\sqrt{6}}p_x - \frac{1}{\sqrt{2}}p_y$$

These sp^2 orbitals are $1/3$ s in character and $2/3$ p.

Orbitals that are sp hybridized are formed as a linear combination involving a single p atomic orbital as well as the s_C orbital:

$$sp = a_1 s_C + a_2 p_x$$

There are two orbitals of this type and two p atomic orbitals not involved in hybridization:

$$sp_1 = \frac{1}{\sqrt{2}}s_C + \frac{1}{\sqrt{2}}p_x$$

$$sp_2 = \frac{1}{\sqrt{2}}s_C - \frac{1}{\sqrt{2}}p_x$$

We have used for convenience the p_x orbital; however, the choice is arbitrary.

8.3 Bond Angles and Hybridized Orbitals

Bonds are actually orbitals. In order to discuss bond angles one assumes that an orbital can be represented by a straight line. As shown in Figure 8–3 the angle between these lines is then the bond angle.

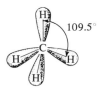

Figure 8–3

The usual assumption that a carbon atom bonded by four σ bonds to other atoms has bond angles of 109.5° is an oversimplification of the problem. The carbon atom in methyl chloride is bonded by four σ bonds, yet the bond angles here are not equal to 109.5°. In the ground state, a molecule has that geometry which gives it minimum energy, and only if four equivalent groups are bonded to a carbon atom, can one expect the true tetrahedral bond angles. In such cases as methane and for the central carbon atom in neopentane, the tetrahedral bond angle is expected:

$$
\begin{array}{ccc}
\text{H} & & \text{CH}_3 \\
\overset{|}{\underset{C}{\curvearrowright}}\ 109.5° & & \overset{|}{\underset{C}{\curvearrowright}}\ 109.5° \\
\text{H}\diagdown\ |\ \diagdown\text{H} & & \text{CH}_3\diagdown\ |\ \diagdown\text{CH}_3 \\
\text{H} & & \text{CH}_3
\end{array}
$$

These are however the special cases. In the general case where the groups attached to a carbon atom are not equivalent one should not expect nor does one find bond angles of 109.5°, nor is the hybridization at carbon in these cases really sp^3. The deviations are slight, and one can generalize the idea of sp^3 hybridization and consider a carbon atom to be sp^3 hybridized as long as it forms four σ bonds; the bond angles need not be the true tetrahedral angle. The carbon atom in methyl chloride, the nitrogen atom in ammonia, and the oxygen atom in water can all be assumed to use sp^3 hybridization although, as we shall see, none of these have bond angles equal to 109.5°.

One possible description of the ammonia and water molecules considers them to be sp^3 hybridized, yet while methane has bond angles equal to the tetrahedral angle, this angle in ammonia is 107.3° and in water it is only 104.5°. Figure 8–4 illustrates.

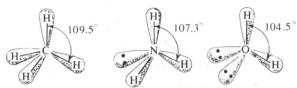

Figure 8–4

Methane is most stable when the bond angles are equal to 109.5°. As was pointed out at the beginning of this chapter the actual factors that must enter into a discussion of molecular geometry are varied and complex. No single factor causes this particular molecular geometry. Several plausible explanations for the observed structure of methane have been advanced. The idea that the carbon atom uses sp^3 hybridized orbitals has become accepted. Maximum overlap can now occur between the hydrogen atoms with their $1s$ orbitals and these sp^3 orbitals. The structure of methane can be explained on this basis. Alternatively, the hydrogen nuclei, which repel each other, are as far apart as possible in a tetrahedral arrangement. Furthermore, each orbital contains an electron pair, and these electron pairs are as widely separated as possible when the bond angles are 109.5°. All of these facts are in agreement with the observed bond angles for methane; it is not possible to say with certainty which factor is most important.

In ammonia the angle between N—H bonds is 107.3°, and once again several explanations have been advanced. One theory considers the nitrogen to be sp^3 hybridized. The molecule then has three N—H bonds and one sp^3 orbital containing a nonbonded electron pair. This theory assumes that the geometry of a molecule depends only upon the repulsion between the four electron pairs occupying these orbitals. There are eight electrons, two in each orbital, and minimizing the repulsion between the electrons pairs is sufficient to determine the molecular structure.

The electrons in an N—H bond occupy an orbital that is narrower than the sp^3 orbital occupied by the nonbonded electrons. This is shown in Figure 8–5.

Figure 8–5

The ammonia molecule contains three narrow orbitals for the N—H bonds and a broad orbital for the nonbonded electrons. The repulsion between electron pairs is minimized when the N—H bonds are brought closer together, and the smaller bond angles in ammonia can be explained on this basis.

The observed bond angle for water, 104.5°, can be explained in similar fashion. In the water molecule the nonbonded electrons occupy broad orbitals, and contraction of the bond angle minimizes the interelectronic repulsion.

These examples illustrate that while a system can be considered as sp^3 hybridized, it need not have bond angles of 109.5°. Methyl chloride also exemplifies this idea:

$$\begin{array}{c} \text{H} \\ 111° \quad \text{C} \overset{108°}{-} \text{Cl} \\ \text{H} \quad \text{H} \end{array}$$

The H—C—Cl bond angle in this molecule is only 108° while the angle between C—H bonds has increased to 111°. Although it is usually stated that this molecule is sp^3 hybridized, the bond angles do not have the exact tetrahedral value.

The change in bond angles can be attributed to the electronegativity of the halogen. An *s* orbital is more stable than a *p* orbital, yet since the electrons in the carbon-halogen bond are more likely to be found near the halogen, the carbon atom can put more *p* character into the orbital it uses for this bond without increasing significantly the energy of the two electrons. Since it has put more *p* character into the carbon-halogen bond, the carbon atom can put more *s* character into the remaining bonds, and this stabilizes considerably the other electrons.

An explanation in terms of interelectronic repulsion can also be given. The electrons in the carbon-halogen bond are found most often near chlorine. The repulsion between these electrons and the six other bonding electrons is decreased. The three other bonds which in methane are held back and away from this fourth bond can, in methyl chloride, move forward and farther apart. In the actual molecule many factors contribute to determine the spacial arrangement and which, if either, of the preceeding is most important is, of course, uncertain.

8.4 *sp²* and *sp* Hybridized Systems

A carbon atom that is sp^3 hybridized need not have bond angles equal to 109.5°. This idea can be extended to sp^2 hybridized systems. In certain systems an sp^2 hybridized carbon atom is expected to have bond angles of 120°, whereas for other systems deviations from this value would not be surprising. The methyl carbonium ion should be planar and have bond angles equal to this value, and the true trigonal angles should also be found in the *t*-butyl carbonium ion:

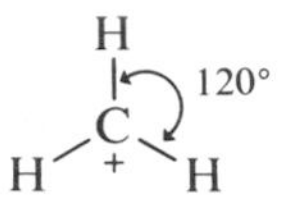

methyl carbonium ion 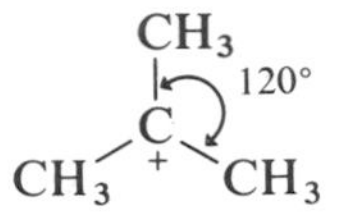   *t*-butyl carbonium ion

Boron uses sp^2 hybridization in some molecules. Boron trifluoride and boron trichloride are both planar molecules having the expected bond angles:

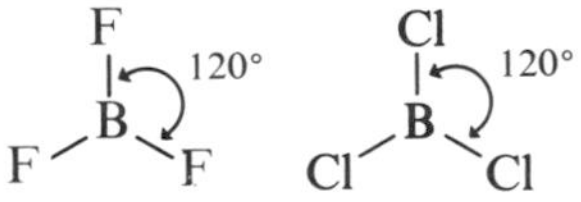

Once again, these are the special cases. The sp^2 hybridized carbon atoms in ethylene and in most other alkenes do not have the true trigonal angle. The angle between C—H bonds in ethylene is smaller while the H—C—C angle is slightly larger:

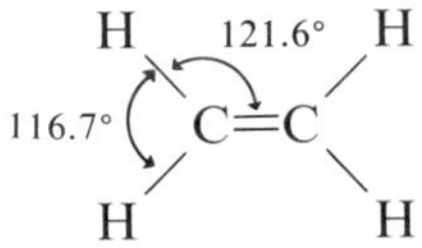

Carbon uses sp^3 hybridization; it also uses sp^2. A third possibility is the use of sp hybridized orbitals. Carbon can form two σ bonds with these hybridized orbitals and two π bonds with the remaining *p* orbitals. The bond angles are 180°. Thus in acetylene:

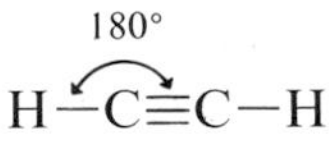

Beryllium dichloride exhibits no dipole moment in solution; consequently, the molecule under these conditions must be linear.

Beryllium difluoride is also a linear molecule, and the use of sp hybridized orbitals by the beryllium explains these facts:

A fact not apparent from a simple orbital picture of alkynes like acetylene is that the electron density in the triple bond of such a molecule has cylindrical symmetry; see Figure 8–6.

Figure 8–7 is a simple orbital picture of acetylene.

Figure 8–6

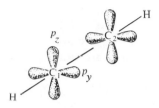

Figure 8–7

Here π bond formation results from overlap of the p_y and p_z orbitals of carbon atom 1 with the p_y and p_z orbitals of carbon atom 2. In this picture there appear to be regions between the p_y and p_z orbitals where there is little likelihood of finding an electron. We have stated that the electron density is cylindrically symmetrical, and the apparent anomaly between the picture and this fact can be readily resolved.

Remember that when we represent an orbital pictorially, only regions of high electron density (high probability) are indicated. There is always a small but finite probability of finding the electron outside the region pictured. The fact that cylindrical symmetry does exist between the carbon atoms in acetylene can be seen from the following qualitative discussion. In Figure 8–8, we look only at carbon atom 1.

We are interested in the electron density in the yz plane at a distance r from the carbon nucleus. The electron density there due to the electron in the p_y orbital is given by the value of p_y^2. Similarly, the electron density for an electron

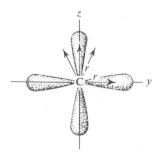

Figure 8–8

in the p_z orbital is given by the value of p_z^2. Since we cannot distinguish between electrons, the total electron density due to both electrons is given by,

$$p_y^2 + p_z^2$$

At a distance r from the carbon nucleus and on the y axis, the value of p_y^2 is large, but there is no electron density for the p_z electron at a point on the y axis. There the value of p_z^2 is zero, and the total electron density is given by the value of p_y^2. Similarly, at a point on the z axis the electron density is given by p_z^2. At a distance r at some point intermediate between these two axes, both p_y^2 and p_z^2 are small. However, we are adding the two numbers and their sum, $p_y^2 + p_z^2$, is not small. In fact, this sum is exactly equal to the value that we find for p_y^2 for the electron on the y axis and also equal to the value of p_z^2 for the electron on the z axis. The electron density in the yz plane at a distance r from the carbon nucleus is exactly the same for all points on the plane. Thus, as in Figure 8–9, it is symmetrical about the nucleus.

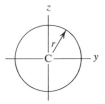

Figure 8–9

A simple mathematical discussion also illustrates the idea of symmetry about the nucleus. If we assume the distance r to be a constant as we do here, then a mathematical description of the p_z orbital is given by the expression,

$$p_z = A \cos \theta$$

where A is a constant and θ is the angle indicated in Figure 8–10.

A description of the p_y orbital is given by,

$$p_y = A \sin \theta$$

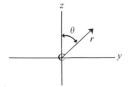

Figure 8–10

and the electron density due to the two electrons by the expression,

$$A^2 \cos^2\theta + A^2 \sin^2\theta$$

or simply,

$$A^2 (\cos^2\theta + \sin^2\theta) = A^2$$

The electron density at a distance r from the nucleus is independent of the value of θ and is equal to a constant.

In acetylene this results in a cylinder of electron density about the carbon atoms. Furthermore, since we have symmetry about the molecular axis just as we do in a carbon-carbon single bond, there can be free rotation about a triple bond.

8.5 An Equivalent Description of Ethylene; The τ Bond

The usual description of ethylene considers each carbon atom to be sp^2 hybridized. The two bonds joining these carbon atoms are then a σ bond formed by combining sp^2 orbitals and a π bond which is formed by combining p_z orbitals:

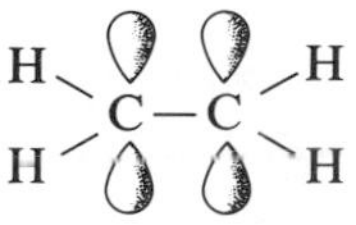

There is an equivalent description that one may give for the C—C bonds in ethylene. According to molecular orbital theory, this alternative description is mathematically exactly the same as the usual formulation, and any apparent difference in picturing the bonds is due to the fact that only regions of high electron density are illustrated.

In alkenes such as ethylene there exists between the carbon atoms a diffuse region of electron density. This is illustrated in Figure 8–11.

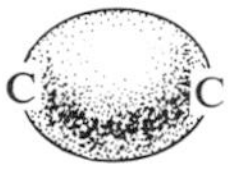

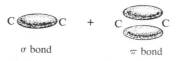

Figure 8–11

It is customary to describe the inner portion of this region as a σ bond, formed by combining sp^2 orbitals, and the outer portion as a π bond. This is shown in Figure 8–12.

C ⬭ C   +   C ⬭ C

σ bond π bond

Figure 8–12

However, this description is arbitrary, and other methods for describing this region of electron density exist. We consider only the carbon-carbon bonds; the carbon-hydrogen bonds remain unaltered. Each carbon atom uses an sp^2 orbital and a p orbital for the carbon-carbon bonds:

However, we can form a new hybridized orbital ψ_A on carbon atom 1 as a linear combination involving the sp^2 orbital and the p orbital of this atom:

$$\psi_A = a_1 sp^2 + a_2 p$$

Determination of the values for a_1 and a_2 leads to,

$$a_1 = a_2 = \frac{1}{\sqrt{2}}$$

and

$$\psi_A = \frac{1}{\sqrt{2}} sp^2 + \frac{1}{\sqrt{2}} p$$

A second such orbital ψ_B is also possible:

$$\psi_B = \frac{1}{\sqrt{2}} sp^2 - \frac{1}{\sqrt{2}} p$$

These new orbitals may be depicted as,

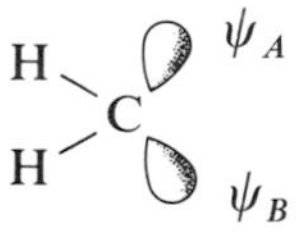

These orbitals are also hybridized orbitals intermediate in character between sp^2 and p. Since the square of the coefficient indicates the fraction of each, these orbitals are $1/2\ sp^2$ and $1/2\ p$. Furthermore, the sp^2 orbital is itself $1/3\ s$ and $2/3\ p$. Therefore, the amount of s character in ψ_A or ψ_B is equal to, .

$$1/2(1/3\ s) = 1/6\ s$$

while the amount of p character is,

$$1/2(2/3\ p) + 1/2\ p = 5/6\ p$$

Since the total amount of p character is $5/6\ p$, these new orbitals ψ_A and ψ_B are sp^5 hybridized orbitals.

We have two new hybridized orbitals at carbon atom 1, and we may construct such a set at carbon atom 2; see Figure 8–13.

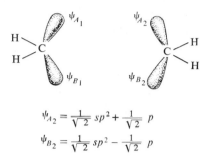

$$\psi_{A_2} = \frac{1}{\sqrt{2}} sp^2 + \frac{1}{\sqrt{2}} p$$

$$\psi_{B_2} = \frac{1}{\sqrt{2}} sp^2 - \frac{1}{\sqrt{2}} p$$

Figure 8–13

It is now possible to form a bond in ethylene by combining ψ_{A_1}, with ψ_{A_2}. The second bond is formed by combining ψ_{B_1} with ψ_{B_2}. These new bonds, which are given the name τ bonds, appear in Figure 8–14.

$$\tau_1 = \frac{1}{\sqrt{2}}\psi_{A_1} + \frac{1}{\sqrt{2}}\psi_{A_2}$$

$$\tau_2 = \frac{1}{\sqrt{2}}\psi_{B_1} + \frac{1}{\sqrt{2}}\psi_{B_2}$$

The four electrons bonding the carbon atoms are placed in these orbitals. There are also two antibonding τ* orbitals that do not contain electrons:

$$\tau_1^* = \frac{1}{\sqrt{2}}\psi_{A_1} - \frac{1}{\sqrt{2}}\psi_{A_2}$$

$$\tau_2^* = \frac{1}{\sqrt{2}}\psi_{B_1} - \frac{1}{\sqrt{2}}\psi_{B_2}$$

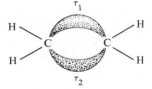

Figure 8–14

8.6 Cyclopropane

The carbon atoms in cyclopropane are at the corners of an equilateral triangle. Connecting these atoms by straight lines, and assuming that these lines represent the orbitals joining the carbon atoms, leads to the conclusion that the angle between bonds is the equilateral angle 60°:

H   H
  \ /
   C
H   H
 \ 60° /
  C———C
 /   \
H   H

However, bringing the electron pair in one carbon-carbon bond close to the electrons in a second carbon-carbon bond increases the repulsion between such electron pairs. Consequently, this molecule is most stable when each carbon atom uses orbitals that are farther apart than 60°, and the bonds joining the atoms cannot be represented adequately as straight lines. A more adequate picture may be that shown in Figure 8–15.

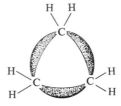

Figure 8–15

8.7 Bond Lengths and Hybridized Orbitals

Thus far the discussion has been devoted entirely to the effect of hybridization upon the bond angles in a molecule and no mention of bond lengths has been made. There is a simple general rule that explains, at least qualitatively, the variation in bond lengths with a change in hybridization.

The bond between carbon and some other atom is formed by combining the hybridized orbital of carbon with the atomic orbital of the other atom; for example, a carbon-hydrogen bond is formed by combining a hybridized orbital of carbon with the $1s$ atomic orbital of hydrogen. One finds that such bonds between carbon and other atoms are shorter the more s character there is in the hybridized orbital. A carbon-hydrogen bond in acetylene, where carbon uses sp hybridization, is shorter than the carbon-hydrogen bond in ethylene; here carbon uses sp^2 hybridized orbitals. This bond is in turn shorter than the carbon-hydrogen bond in ethane. This phenomenon also occurs with carbon-carbon bonds. Increasing the amount of s character in such bonds shortens them. These data are presented in Table 8–1.

Table 8–1

Compound	Bond Type	Bond Length
CH_3CH_3	$C-H\ sp^3-s$	1.10 Å
$CH_2=CH_2$	$C-H\ sp^2-s$	1.08 Å
$HC\equiv CH$	$C-H\ sp-s$	1.06 Å
CH_3CH_3	$C-C\ sp^3-sp^3$	1.54 Å
$CH_3CH=CH_2$	$C-C\ sp^3-sp^2$	1.51 Å*
$CH_3C\equiv CH$	$C-C\ sp^3-sp$	1.46 Å*

* This bond shortening is in part due to increased s character, and in part it may be due to hyperconjugation.

Increasing the s character in a bond not only shortens that bond, but since an electron in the $2s$ atomic orbital of carbon is more stable than an electron in a $2p$ atomic orbital of such an atom, increasing the s character also makes that bond more stable. This is indicated by the data in Table 8–2.

Table 8–2

Compound	Bond Type	Bond Energy (kcal/mole)
CH_3CH_3	$C-H\ sp^3-s$	98
$CH_2=CH_2$	$C-H\ sp^2-s$	~106
$HC\equiv CH$	$C-H\ sp-s$	~121
CH_3CH_3	$C-C\ sp^3-sp^3$	83
$CH_3CH=CH_2$	$C-C\ sp^3-sp^2$	109*

* Some of this increased stability may be due to hyperconjugation.

Supplementary Reading

1. Cartmell, E. and Fowles, G. W. A., *Valency and Molecular Structure*. London, Butterworths, 1961.
2. Coulson, C. A., *Valence*, 2nd Ed. London, Oxford U. P., 1961.
3. Dewar, M. J. S., *Hyperconjugation*. New York, Ronald Press, 1962.
4. Mislow, K., *Introduction to Stereochemistry*. New York, Benjamin, 1965.
5. Pauling, L., *Nature of the Chemical Bond*. Ithaca, New York, Cornell U. P., 1960.
6. Pitzer, K. S., *Quantum Chemistry*. Englewood Cliffs, New Jersey, Prentice-Hall, 1953.
7. Pullman, B., *The Modern Theory of Molecular Structure*. New York, Dover, 1962.
8. Roberts, J. D. and Caserio, M. C., *Basic Principles of Organic Chemistry*. New York, Benjamin, 1964.
9. Wiberg, K. B., *Physical Organic Chemistry*. New York, Wiley, 1964.

Chapter 9

Dipole Moments and Carbonium Ion, Olefinic and Free Radical Stability

9.1 Dipole Moments

A diatomic molecule such as hydrogen has a covalent bond which contains two electrons of opposite spin. Two hydrogen atoms, each with a single electron, combine to form this bond. Since each hydrogen atom contributes one electron, a neutral hydrogen atom must have an electron density equal to unity. The two electrons in the covalent bond are shared equally, the electron density is the same at each atom (unity), and the molecule is nonpolar:

$$H\text{—}H$$

In a molecule such as hydrogen chloride the two electrons are not shared equally. The electron density at hydrogen is less than unity while the electron density at chlorine is greater. In this molecule there exists a region which is relatively positive and a region that is relatively negative; such a molecule is a polar molecule:

$$\overset{\delta^+}{H}\text{—}\overset{\delta^-}{Cl}$$
$$\longrightarrow$$

In a molecule containing atoms of different electronegativity there are regions of high electron density and regions of low electron density. The electron density is greater near highly electronegative atoms and lower near the less electronegative atoms. While the molecule as a whole is neutral, there are, within the molecule, regions which are relatively positive and regions that are relatively negative. It is possible to speak of a point within the molecule about which the positive charge centers (center of positive charge) and a point about which the negative charge centers (center of negative charge). If these two centers, the center of positive charge and the center of negative charge, do not coincide, the molecule has an electric dipole moment.

Although it is possible to speak of regions of positive and negative charge, it is simpler to speak in terms of point charges. Thus we assume that within a

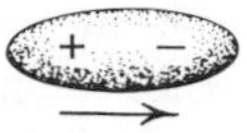

Figure 9–1

molecule all of the positive charge is localized at a single point, the center of positive charge, while all of the negative charge is localized at the center of negative charge. For example, in hydrogen chloride we can assume that the center of positive charge is the hydrogen nucleus and the center of negative charge the chlorine nucleus (see Figure 9–1).

If at the center of positive charge of a molecule the charge is $+q$, then at the center of negative charge the charge must be $-q$ (the molecule as a whole must be neutral), and the electric dipole moment $\mathbf{\mu}$ is defined as $\mathbf{\mu} = q\mathbf{d}$ (Figure 9–2).

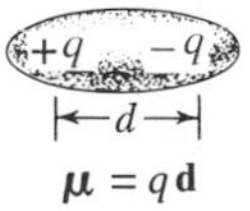

$$\mu = q\,\mathbf{d}$$

Figure 9–2

Here q is the magnitude of charge at either end of the dipole, and $\mathbf{d}$ is the distance between the centers of positive and negative charge. The dipole moment is a vector quantity; associated with it is both magnitude and direction (in this text towards the center of negative charge).

Dipole moments have the dimensions of charge × distance (esu-cm). Since the charge is on the order of 1×10^{-10} esu and the distances involved are on the order of 1 Å (10^{-8} cm), the order of magnitude for dipole moments is,

$$\mathbf{\mu} = (1 \times 10^{-10})(10^{-8}) \text{ esu-cm}$$

$$\mathbf{\mu} = 1 \times 10^{-18} \text{ esu-cm}$$

The dipole moment is expressed in Debyes where

$$1\text{D} = 1 \times 10^{-18} \text{ esu-cm}$$

According to molecular orbital theory, the electrons in a molecule are able to travel over the entire molecule, yet we can usually treat these electrons as if they were restricted to just a portion of the molecule. We can then speak of a bond in the molecule, and to each bond we can assign a bond dipole moment (bond moment).

We measure the dipole moment of a molecule and on this basis should like to say something concerning molecular structure. The difficulty here is that while the dipole moment of the entire molecule is measurable, the individual bond moments are not. We attempt to resolve the molecular moment, which is measurable, into the component bond moments, which are not. Consequently, we have no way of knowing whether such a resolution into components is correct. However, we generally assume that in the absence of strong resonance interactions we can discuss molecular structure in terms of the usual localized σ bonds, and the dipole moment of the entire molecule is then just the vectorial sum of the individual bond moments.

There are virtually no resonance interactions in methane. Therefore, we can treat this molecule in terms of the usual four C—H bonds. To predict the moment of the molecule, we assign to each C—H bond a bond moment, we add these four bond moments vectorially, and we find that the molecule is not expected to exhibit a dipole moment ($\mu = 0$). This prediction is confirmed experimentally. One assumption then is to consider that within a molecule there are localized bonds and that to these bonds can be assigned a bond moment.

Other assumptions are frequently made. If the electrons in a given bond are not involved in resonance, we usually assume that the dipole moment associated with such a bond is invariant from molecule to molecule. For example, associated with an O—H bond is a bond moment directed towards oxygen; this is represented as:

$$\text{H}\!-\!\text{O}$$
$$\longrightarrow$$

We generally assume that as long as there are no resonance interactions involving the electrons in this bond, the bond moment has the same value in every compound containing an O—H bond.

Such an assumption is not correct. We should not expect the same O—H bond moment in all molecules; we should not expect the same O—H bond moment for water and for phenol:

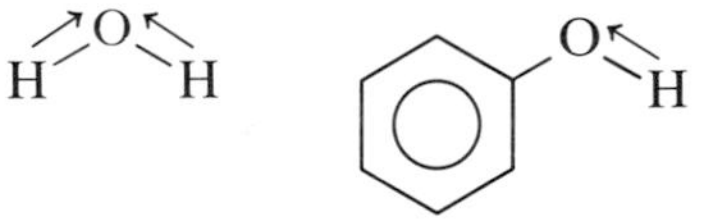

The electrons in the O—H bond of phenol are in a completely different coulombic environment from the electrons in the O—H bond of water, and a different value ought to be assigned to the bond moment. For qualitative discussions the idea of invariance of bond moments is simple and useful; however, there is no rigorous justification for such an assumption. In fact, from molecular moments there is good evidence to the contrary, that bond moments do vary in proceeding from one compound to another. When assuming constant bond moments, one employs an average value obtained from measurements on a large number of different molecules.

Although the ideas of localized bonds and invariant bond moments are assumptions, they are useful, for they have helped to elucidate the structures of a large number of molecules.

9.2 Bond Moments

We have represented the methane molecule in Figure 9–3,

Figure 9–3

with each C—H bond corresponding to a molecular orbital formed as a linear combination of an sp^3 hybridized orbital and a $1s$ atomic orbital.

$$\psi_{CH} = a_1s + a_2sp^3$$

However, this is just one possible representation of the molecule. Various equivalent representations of methane exist. According to molecular orbital theory the eight electrons in these bonds are delocalized over the entire molecule. Thus, we could equally well represent the positions of the electrons by molecular orbitals that do not correspond to the usual C—H bonds, but which are linear combinations of these bonds. For example, a bond could be represented by Figure 9–4.

Figure 9–4

This molecular orbital involves an orbital from carbon that does not overlap well with any single $1s$ atomic orbital of hydrogen but which does overlap with three of these $1s$ orbitals. Such a molecular orbital accommodates two electrons.

Accordingly, we could describe the methane molecule in terms of new molecular orbitals. The energy of methane as well as other properties such as the dipole moment of the molecule have exactly the same value according to this new description as they do according to the usual description. It is simpler, of course, to discuss methane in terms of familiar pictures, but this is not necessary. The dipole moment of methane would be calculated as zero regardless of which representation of the molecule is used. All equivalent representations give the same values for the electron density. The centers of positive and negative charge are the same in all representations, and the dipole moment is calculated to be the same.

We should like to discuss the structure of methane in terms of the usual C—H bonds. This is certainly possible, but it must be remembered that the usual description is just one possibility out of an infinite number of entirely equivalent ways of describing the molecule. As long as there are no strong resonance effects we can discuss molecular structure in terms of localized bonds, yet whenever resonance effects are present, this picture of localized electrons and localized molecular orbitals (which is only a choice of convenience in any event) breaks down.

9.3 Molecular Moments

Assuming then that resonance effects are not present, we can speak of localized bonds within molecules. We assign to each bond a bond moment, and the dipole moment of the entire molecule is just the vectorial sum of these individual bond moments.

Symmetrical diatomic molecules such as hydrogen, bromine, and nitrogen do not have a dipole moment whereas unsymmetrical diatomic molecules do:

$$H—H \qquad Br—Br \qquad N≡N$$

$$\mu = 0 \qquad \mu = 0 \qquad \mu = 0$$

$$H—F \qquad H—Cl \qquad H—I$$

$$\mu = 1.75 \qquad \mu = 1.03 \qquad \mu = 0.38$$

Carbon tetrachloride has four polar C—Cl bonds, yet these are tetrahedrally arranged and their vectorial sum is zero:

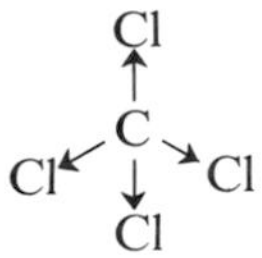

$$\mu = 0$$

The other chloromethanes all exhibit moments with chlorine at the negative end of the dipole:

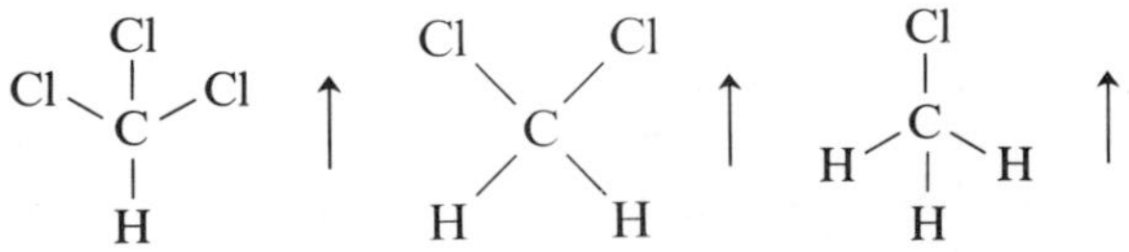

$$\mu = 1.01 \qquad \mu = 1.59 \qquad \mu = 1.87$$

In practice it is the molecular moment that is obtained experimentally, and the magnitude of this moment frequently affords information concerning molecular structure. For example, neither beryllium dichloride (in solution) nor carbon dioxide exhibit dipole moments. Consequently, a linear structure is assigned to these compounds:

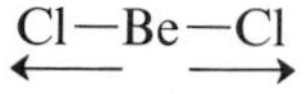

$$Cl-Be-Cl \qquad\qquad O=C=O$$

$$\mu = 0 \qquad\qquad\qquad \mu = 0$$

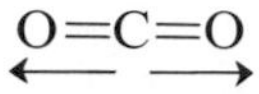

Water, on the other hand, does have a dipole moment and cannot be a linear molecule:

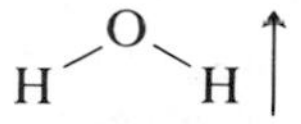

$$H \overset{O}{\diagdown} H \uparrow$$

$$\mu = 1.84$$

Alcohols and ethers also have dipole moments; in the dialkyl ethers these moments are directed away from the alkyl groups:

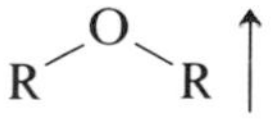

$$R \overset{O}{\diagdown} R \uparrow$$

From the fact that boron trifluoride exhibits no dipole moment, we can deduce that this is a planar molecule with bond angles equal to 120°. The compound NF_3, which does have a molecular moment, cannot be planar:

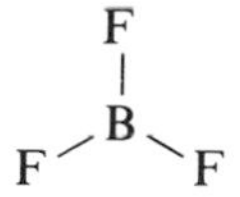

$$\begin{array}{c} F \\ | \\ F-B-F \end{array} \qquad\qquad \begin{array}{c} N \\ F-|-F \\ F \end{array}$$

$$\mu = 0 \qquad\qquad\qquad \mu = 0.2$$

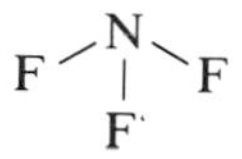

Compounds such as *cis-* and *trans-*1,2-dichloroethylene can be characterized by the difference in their molecular moments:

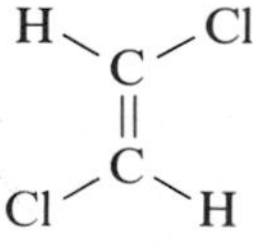

$$\begin{array}{cc} H\diagdown\diagup Cl \\ C \\ || \\ C \\ Cl\diagup\diagdown H \end{array} \qquad\qquad \begin{array}{cc} H\diagdown\diagup Cl \\ C \\ || \\ C \\ H\diagup\diagdown Cl \end{array}$$

$$\mu = 0 \qquad\qquad\qquad \mu = 1.89$$

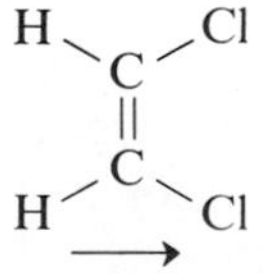

As in the previous example, it is usually possible to deduce from considerations of molecular symmetry whether a molecule will or will not display a dipole moment. Thus, regardless of the direction of the C—H bond moment, compounds such as methane, ethylene, benzene, and acetylene cannot have a dipole moment:

$$
\begin{array}{c}
\text{H} \\
| \\
\text{H} - \underset{|}{\text{C}} - \text{H} \\
\text{H}
\end{array}
\qquad
\begin{array}{c}
\text{H} \\ \diagdown \\ \text{C} = \text{C} \\ \diagup \qquad \diagdown \\ \text{H} \qquad\qquad \text{H}
\end{array}
\begin{array}{c}
\text{H} \\ \diagup \\ \\ \diagdown \\ \text{H}
\end{array}
\qquad
\bigcirc\!\!\!\!\bigcirc
\qquad
\text{H} - \text{C} \equiv \text{C} - \text{H}
$$

9.4 The Direction of the Carbon–Hydrogen Bond Moment

One of the most controversial topics in organic chemistry is that of the direction of the C—H bond moment. It is not yet certain whether this bond moment is directed towards hydrogen or towards carbon.

$$
\begin{array}{cc}
\text{H} \uparrow & \text{H} \\
| \uparrow & | \\
\text{C} | & \text{C} \downarrow
\end{array}
\quad \text{or} \quad
$$

Experimental evidence has not answered the question and theoretical calculations give varying results. An exact theoretical calculation has not been possible; all approximate calculations involve assumptions of one kind or another. The results of any approximate calculation may be questioned if one questions these underlying assumptions.

The direction of the C—H bond moment does not depend only upon the relative electronegativities of the individual atoms. Several other factors are important. Carbon, for example, can use sp^3 hybridized orbitals, and these are directed in space as shown in Figure 9–5.

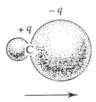

Figure 9–5

The center of negative charge for an electron in such an sp^3 hybridized orbital does not occur at the carbon nucleus but at some distance from it.

We can associate with an electron in an sp^3 orbital a dipole moment oriented in the same direction as the orbital, and the bond moment for a C—H bond depends to some extent upon this. For this and other reasons, we shall assume that the C—H bond moment is directed towards hydrogen.

$$
\begin{array}{c}
\text{H} \uparrow \\
| \uparrow \\
\text{C} |
\end{array}
$$

In proceeding from an sp^3 hybridized orbital to an sp^2 orbital the amount of s character increases. Since an electron in the $2s$ orbital of carbon is more stable than an electron in a $2p$ orbital of that atom, increasing the amount of s character stabilizes the electrons. Effectively, the carbon atom appears more electronegative. In addition, an sp^2 orbital is not so well directed in space as an sp^3 orbital. We assume that this bond moment is still directed towards hydrogen, but we naturally expect the magnitude of the C—H bond moment to be smaller when the carbon atom is sp^2 hybridized.

In acetylene, where the carbon atoms are sp hybridized, we continue to assume that the orientation of the C—H bond moment is towards hydrogen. Naturally, we expect the magnitude of this moment to be even smaller than the other C—H bond moments:

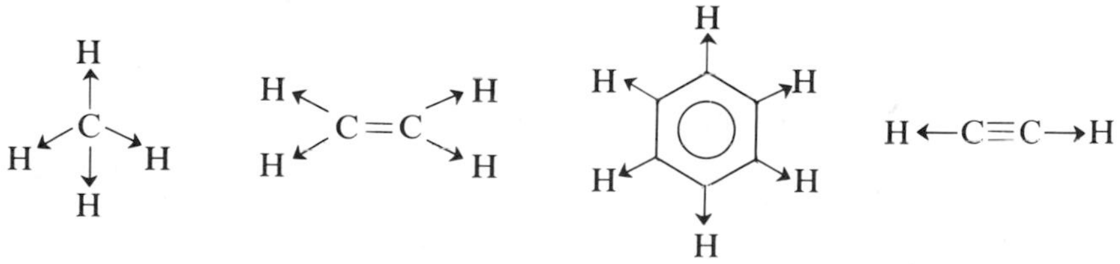

9.5 The Effect of Nonbonded Electrons Upon the Molecular Moment

We have previously stated that it is possible to associate a dipole moment with an electron in an sp^3 hybridized orbital. In the water molecule, where we have four electrons in the two O—H bonds and four electrons in sp^3 hybridized orbitals, the dipole moment arises not only from the two bond moments but also from the four electrons in the nonbonded sp^3 orbitals:

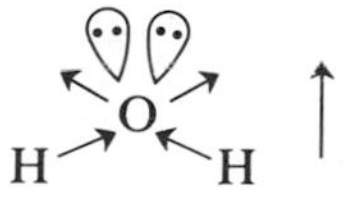

$$\mu = 1.84$$

When discussing molecular moments, we must consider the effect of nonbonded electrons. If these electrons are in orbitals which are directed in space, then such electrons contribute to the total dipole moment of the molecule.

This effect is found in nitrogen-containing compounds where the electrons in the sp^3 orbital of the nitrogen atom contribute to the molecular moment:

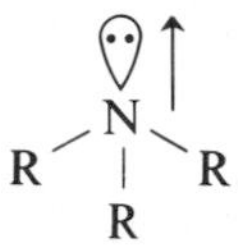

If the nitrogen atom is sp^3 hybridized, there is a moment associated with the two nonbonded electrons, and this moment is directed away from the nitrogen nucleus. Thus, ammonia has an appreciable dipole moment (1.5) while the compound NF_3 has a much smaller dipole moment (0.2):

$$\mu = 1.5 \qquad\qquad\qquad \mu = 0.2$$

In ammonia the moment due to the nonbonded electrons operates in the same direction as the N—H bond moments. In NF_3, it is oriented in opposition to the nitrogen-fluorine moments. The result is a larger molecular moment for ammonia.[1]

9.6 Hybridization and Dipole Moments

We have seen that the dipole moment of a molecule is influenced by the presence of nonbonded electrons. We have also seen that the magnitude of the C—H bond moment depends upon the hybridization of carbon. These are general phenomena. The hybridization of the various atoms in a molecule affects the dipole moment. For example, the carbon atoms in cyclopropane do not use four equivalent sp^3 hybridized orbitals. The C—C bonds in this molecule contain more than the usual amount of p character, and the C—H bonds contain more s character than usual. Therefore, while most alkyl chlorides have dipole moments in the region of 2.0, cyclopropyl chloride has a dipole moment equal to only 1.76. The smaller dipole moment of the latter can be attributed to the fact that the hybridized orbital used by carbon for the C—Cl bond contains more than the usual amount of s character. This, in effect, increases the electronegativity of the carbon atom, decreases the length of the C—Cl bond, and decreases the dipole moment of the molecule.

The effect of changes in hybridization upon the dipole moment of a molecule is further illustrated by the following examples. Neither CH_4 nor CF_4 have dipole moments. This implies that in methane the vectorial sum of three C—H bond moments must result in a single moment which is equal in magnitude yet opposite in direction to the fourth C—H bond moment; the vectorial sum of three C—H moments is equal in magnitude to a single C—H moment,

$$\mu = 0$$

[1] A slightly different explanation but along these same lines can be found in E. Cartmell and G. W. A. Fowles, *Valency and Molecular Structure*. Butterworths, London, 1961, p. 163.

In CF_4 this implies that the resultant of three C—F moments is equal in magnitude and opposite in direction to the fourth C—F moment:

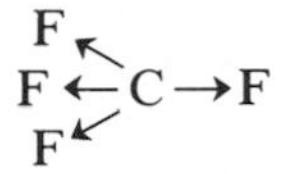

$$F \leftarrow C \rightarrow F$$

(with F groups above and below)

$$\mu = 0$$

If the hybridization and the bond lengths in both CH_3F and CHF_3 were the same, these two molecules would have the same dipole moment. In CH_3F, it is possible to replace the three C—H bond moments by a single resultant moment which is equal in magnitude to a single C—H bond moment yet exactly opposite to the direction of the C—F moment.

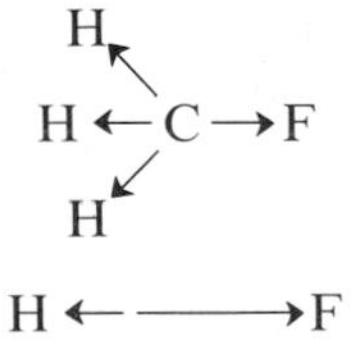

$$H \leftarrow C \rightarrow F$$

$$H \leftarrow\!\!\longrightarrow F$$

Similarly, the three C—F moments in CHF_3 can be replaced by a moment which is equal in magnitude to a single C—F moment:

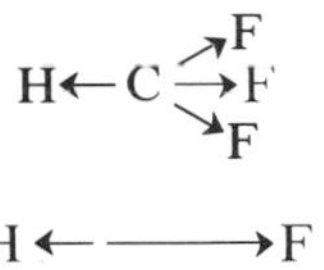

$$H \leftarrow C \rightarrow F$$

$$H \leftarrow\!\!\longrightarrow F$$

For each of these molecules, the dipole moment of the entire molecule equals the sum of two colinear bond moments, a C—H and a C—F moment. Therefore, the two might be expected to have identical dipole moments, yet this is not the case. The molecule CH_3F has a molecular moment equal to 1.81, whereas the CHF_3 moment is only 1.61. The hybridization of carbon must be slightly different in the two molecules, and a change in the hybridization of one atom affects the hybridization of all the other atoms in the molecule. Thus, the hybridization of fluorine and even of hydrogen must also differ (for hydrogen this difference is probably small).

This result also illustrates the idea that the invariance of bond moments is only approximately correct.

9.7 Interpretation of Dipole Moments

Since the dipole moment μ is defined as,

$$\mu = q\mathbf{d}$$

a large value for μ can be interpreted as resulting either from a large charge q

at the ends of the dipole or from a large value for **d**, the distance separating the ends of the dipole. Either interpretation is correct.

Consider the series:

$$\overrightarrow{H-I} \qquad \overrightarrow{H-Cl} \qquad CH_3I$$

$$\mu = 0.38 \qquad \mu = 1.03 \qquad \mu = 1.64$$

The fact that the dipole moment of hydrogen chloride is greater than that of hydrogen iodide is due to the greater electronegativity of the chlorine. However, this can be interpreted in two ways. We assume that the center of negative charge for the two electrons in the H—Cl bond is quite close to the halogen and far from the center of positive charge. In hydrogen iodide, the center of negative charge for the two electrons lies quite close to the center of positive charge. This leads to the conclusion that the larger dipole moment of hydrogen chloride is due to a larger value for **d**. Alternatively, we can fix the centers of positive and negative charge by assuming that the former coincides with the hydrogen nucleus and the latter with the halogen nucleus. This fixes **d**, which becomes equal to the internuclear distances of hydrogen chloride and hydrogen iodide. The larger dipole moment of the chloride must now result from a larger value for q. We see that the interpretation of dipole moments depends to a large measure upon our approach to the problem. (This qualitative discussion is confirmed by a simple mathematical analysis.)

The dipole moment of methyl iodide is even larger than that of hydrogen chloride. Again, we may interpret this result in terms of q or **d**; we are free to choose. Since methyl iodide contains no highly electronegative atoms, it is more attractive to the chemist to attribute the large moment of this molecule to a large value for **d**.

9.8 The Effect of Conformational Changes

For simple compounds such as hydrogen chloride, the dipole moment is a constant and does not vary with changes in temperature. However, the dipole moment of a more complex compound may indeed be temperature dependent and such variations depend upon several factors. For example, the dipole moment of 1,2-dichloroethane varies. This variation is due to the fact that different conformations are possible. At room temperature the compound exists largely in the *trans* form **1**, but the *skew* form **2** is also possible; these are in equilibrium:

The energy of the *trans* form is slightly lower than that of the *skew*, and at moderate temperatures it is the former that predominates. As the temperature is increased, the concentration of the *skew* conformation increases while that of the *trans* decreases.

The *trans* form is expected to show little or no dipole moment, but the *skew* form should show a significant moment. Thus, as the temperature is increased, we expect the observed dipole moment to increase, and this is exactly what occurs. The dipole moment of 1,2-dichloroethane increases with increasing temperature. At extremely high temperatures other effects become important, and the problem becomes more complex.

9.9 Resonance and Dipole Moments

In those cases where resonance interactions are present, the molecular dipole moment can no longer be inferred by the process of addition of bond moments (steric effects can also cause deviations). When resonance effects are present, the usual idea of bond moments breaks down, and we can see why if we consider a molecule such as acrolein, with the structure,

$$CH_2=CH-CH=O$$

$$\mu = 3.0$$

From the data:

$$\mu = 0 \qquad\qquad\qquad \mu = 2.3$$

we can attempt to predict the dipole moment of the acrolein molecule. If the ideas of localized bond moments and invariance of bond moments were applicable in this case, the predicted moment for this molecule would be the same as the dipole moment of formaldehyde itself. Yet the actual dipole moment of acrolein is larger than the predicted moment. This increase in the dipole moment of acrolein over the predicted value is due in part to changes in the σ electron system, and in part it is due to the electrons in the π system. The inductive effect operating along the σ framework increases the dipole moment of acrolein. It has been suggested that this accounts for about half of the observed increase. Furthermore, the electrons in the σ bond system of this molecule may be treated as if they were in localized molecular orbitals, yet the electrons in the π system cannot be so considered. The π electrons, which in ethylene and formaldehyde are restricted to two atoms, are able to travel over all four atoms in acrolein. To obtain the dipole moment of acrolein by vectorial addition of bond moments cannot possibly give the correct result, for this process does not properly consider the delocalization of the π electrons. This is indicated by:

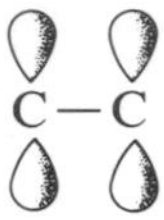

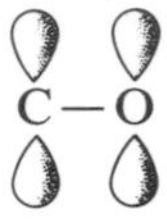

$$C-C \qquad C-O$$

$$\psi(\pi) = a_1 p_1 + a_2 p_2 \qquad \psi(\pi) = a_O p_O + a_C p_C$$

Yet for acrolein,

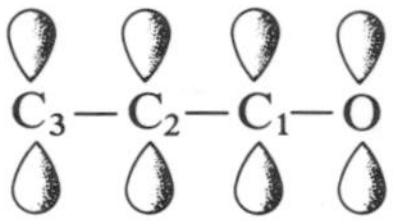

$$C_3-C_2-C_1-O$$

$$\psi(\pi) = a_O p_O + a_1 p_1 + a_2 p_2 + a_3 p_3$$

where p_O is the $2p$ atomic orbital of oxygen.

It is also worthwhile to look at a valence-bond description of acrolein. The most stable valence-bond contributor has the structure,

$$CH_2=CH-CH=O$$

3

yet in order to discuss the dipole moment we must also consider structures such as:

$$CH_2=CH-\overset{+}{C}H-\overset{-}{O} \quad \text{and} \quad \overset{+}{C}H_2-CH=CH-\overset{-}{O}$$

4   **5**

The actual molecule is then a hybrid receiving contributions from these valence-bond structures.

$$CH_2=CH-CH=O \longleftrightarrow CH_2=CH-\overset{+}{C}H-\overset{-}{O} \longleftrightarrow$$

3   **4**

$$\overset{+}{C}H_2-CH=CH-\overset{-}{O}$$

5

The actual dipole moment of the molecule depends upon structures **4** and **5**. If we consider ethylene and formaldehyde and attempt to predict the dipole moment of acrolein on this basis, we do not take into account the effect of **5** upon the dipole moment.

A structure such as **5** is not possible in the model compounds:

$$\text{H}\diagdown\text{C}=\text{C}\diagup\text{H}$$
$$\text{H}\diagup\qquad\diagdown\text{H}$$

$$
\underset{\text{H}\diagup^{\overset{\displaystyle\text{O}}{\|}}\text{C}\diagdown_{\text{H}}}{}
\quad\longleftrightarrow\quad
\underset{\text{H}\diagup^{\overset{\displaystyle\text{O}^-}{|}}\overset{+}{\text{C}}\diagdown_{\text{H}}}{}
$$

The effect of this valence-bond contributor **5** is to increase both the charge q and the distance **d**, thereby increasing the dipole moment of acrolein.

Similar effects occur with the substituted benzenes. For these molecules, vectorial addition of bond moments and group moments does not adequately consider resonance effects, and attempts to predict the dipole moment of substituted benzenes on the basis of vectorial addition of bond moments generally fail.

Another instance in which π electronic delocalization affects the dipole moment can be seen by considering the sequence,

$$\text{CH}_3\text{CH}_2-\text{Cl}\qquad\qquad \text{CH}_2=\text{CH}-\text{Cl}\qquad\qquad \text{CH}\equiv\text{C}-\text{Cl}$$
$$\longrightarrow\qquad\qquad\qquad\longrightarrow\qquad\qquad\qquad\longrightarrow$$
$$\mu = 2.05\qquad\qquad\qquad \mu = 1.44 \qquad\qquad\qquad \mu = 0.44$$

In proceeding from chloroethane to chloroacetylene the molecular moment decreases. The hybridization of carbon changes from sp^3 to sp in proceeding along the sequence, and this change is undoubtedly responsible for some of the observed decrease. In addition, there is the possibility of resonance interactions.

In chloroethylene this resonance involves the electrons in the p_z orbitals of the molecule. Since the π resonance gives rise to a dipole moment in opposition to the σ moment, such resonance decreases the total dipole moment of the molecule. In chloroacetylene resonance is even more pronounced since both the p_y and p_z orbitals are involved.
For chloroethylene,

$$\text{C}-\text{C}-\text{Cl}$$

From a valence-bond point of view,

$$\text{CH}_2=\text{CH}-\text{Cl}\quad\longleftrightarrow\quad\overset{-}{\text{C}}\text{H}_2-\text{CH}=\overset{+}{\text{Cl}}$$

For chloroacetylene,

9.10 The Dipole Moment of Propylene

Methane, ethylene and benzene display no dipole moment, yet propylene and toluene each have a moment that is surprisingly large. Alkanes have little or no moment; alkenes do have a dipole moment. Both propylene and toluene exhibit a dipole moment equal to 0.4, and this moment is assumed to be directed away from the methyl group. Furthermore, propyne has a dipole moment equal to 0.7, an extremely large moment for a hydrocarbon:

$$CH_3CH{=}CH_2 \qquad CH_3{-}\!\bigcirc \qquad CH_3{-}C{\equiv}C{-}H$$
$$\longrightarrow \qquad\qquad \longrightarrow \qquad\qquad \longrightarrow$$
$$\mu = 0.4 \qquad\qquad \mu = 0.4 \qquad\qquad \mu = 0.7$$

Several theories, which venture to explain these facts, have been advanced. To state simply that a methyl group is electron releasing without offering an explanation for this electron release is not satisfactory. The statement is certainly reasonable, but a proper explanation of these dipole moments must also indicate why the methyl group is electron releasing. The assumption of electron release by methyl accounts for both the existence of a dipole moment and its orientation. We present in this section two theories that have been put forth in order to explain the observed dipole moments. Both of these lead to the conclusion that a methyl group is electron donating compared to hydrogen, yet the theoretical basis for this result is quite different. We use propylene as an example; the results are, of course, equally applicable to toluene and propyne.

Ethylene has no dipole moment; propylene does, and it is assumed that this moment is directed away from the methyl group. In proceeding from ethylene to propylene, a hydrogen is replaced by a methyl group; this substitution gives rise to a molecular moment.

$$CH_2{=}CH_2 \qquad\qquad CH_3CH{=}CH_2$$
$$\longrightarrow$$
$$\mu = 0 \qquad\qquad\qquad \mu = 0.7$$

Theories have been advanced to account for this electron release.
One of these, the theory of hyperconjugation, is best illustrated using valence-bond theory. Although we write for propylene the structure **6**, this is only one valence-bond contributor. To obtain a better description of the molecule we

include structures such as **7**, **8** and **9**.

$$H-\overset{\overset{\displaystyle H}{|}}{\underset{\underset{\displaystyle H}{|}}{C}}-CH{=}CH_2 \longleftrightarrow H-\overset{\overset{\displaystyle \dot{H}}{|}}{\underset{\underset{\displaystyle H}{|}}{C}}{=}CH-\dot{C}H_2 \longleftrightarrow$$

$$\qquad\qquad\qquad 6 \qquad\qquad\qquad\qquad 7$$

$$H-\overset{\overset{\displaystyle H^{+}}{|}}{\underset{\underset{\displaystyle H}{|}}{\overset{..}{\underset{}{C}}{}^{-}}}-CH-CH_2 \longleftrightarrow H\quad \overset{\overset{\displaystyle H^{+}}{|}}{\underset{\underset{\displaystyle H}{|}}{C}}{=}CH-\overset{..}{C}H_2^{-}$$

$$\qquad\qquad\qquad 8 \qquad\qquad\qquad\qquad 9$$

The two dots in structure **7** represent two electrons of opposite spin. A structure such as **7** having two electrons of parallel spin is not an acceptable valence-bond contributor. Furthermore, we have involved only a single hydrogen in resonance. It is obvious that structures similar to **7**, **8** and **9** can be written which involve the other two hydrogens of the methyl group.

If we describe the positions of the electrons in structure **6** by the function ψ_6, the positions of the electrons in **7** by ψ_7, the electrons in **8** by ψ_8, and the positions of the electrons in **9** by ψ_9, then the function ψ that describes the positions of the electrons in the actual propylene molecule is formed as a linear combination of these four functions:

$$\psi = a_6\psi_6 + a_7\psi_7 + a_8\psi_8 + a_9\psi_9$$

A structure such as **9** is the valence-bond way of stating that the electrons in the methyl group are not restricted to that group but are actually delocalized to other parts of the molecule. The effect of such structures is to reduce the electron density in the methyl group and to increase the electron density at the methylene group, and this seems to explain the observed dipole moment of propylene.

There is no doubt that structures such as **7**, **8** and **9** are acceptable valence-bond contributors, nor is there any question concerning the possible delocalization of the electrons in the methyl group to other parts of the molecule. Molecular orbital theory also assumes that the electrons in the methyl group can be found in other parts of the molecule. In fact, this is the basic assumption, and hyperconjugation can be developed equally well using molecular orbital theory.

The shortcoming, if there is one, to the theory of hyperconjugation lies in the fact that structures such as **10** and **11** are considered to represent high energy valence-bond contributors which make little contribution to the actual propylene molecule:

$$H-\overset{\overset{\displaystyle \ddot{H}^-}{|}}{\underset{\displaystyle H}{C^+}}-CH=CH_2 \quad \longleftrightarrow \quad H-\overset{\overset{\displaystyle \ddot{H}^-}{|}}{\underset{\displaystyle H}{C}}=CH-\overset{+}{C}H_2$$

$$\textbf{10} \qquad\qquad\qquad\qquad\qquad \textbf{11}$$

These structures lead to the prediction of a dipole moment that is oriented in just the reverse of the normally accepted direction, that is, they lead to the conclusion that the dipole moment of propylene is directed towards the methyl group.

$$\underset{\longleftarrow}{CH_3CH=CH_2}$$

Thus, if hyperconjugation is to give the desired direction to the dipole moment, structures such as **10** and **11** must be assumed to be high energy structures, and it is this point that is controversial. There exists no conclusive evidence that **10** and **11** do represent high energy structures.

If we accept the assumption that **10** and **11** are unimportant and do not make a significant contribution to the propylene molecule, then the ideas of hyperconjugation explain the dipole moment of the molecule. The methyl group is electron releasing compared to hydrogen because the electrons in the C—H bonds of the methyl group can be redistributed to other parts of the molecule.

Alternatively, another suggestion that does not involve these C—H bonds has been proposed. This second proposal is essentially an inductive type argument and is based upon the assumption that an electron withdrawing group is able to withdraw electrons more effectively from carbon than from hydrogen. This proposal is also based upon a controversial point since it is not generally agreed that an electron withdrawer is more effective with carbon than with hydrogen. However, if we accept this idea, then the arguments of hyperconjugation appear weak while this alternative proposal explains satisfactorily the observed dipole moment of propylene.

To obtain the dipole moment of propylene we first set up the various bond moments for the molecule. All the C—H bond moments are assumed to be oriented towards hydrogen. Furthermore, the C—C single bond in propylene is an sp^3-sp^2 bond, and since an sp^2 orbital is more stable than an sp^3 orbital, the electron density is greater in the sp^2 portion of the bond. This implies that we can associate with an sp^3-sp^2 C—C bond a dipole moment directed towards the sp^2 hybridized atom. The sp^2 orbital is also less well-directed in space than the sp^3 orbital and this adds to the C—C moment:

Since methane has no dipole moment, the vectorial sum of three C—H bond moments in methane must yield a resultant moment that is equal in magnitude yet opposite in direction to the fourth C—H bond moment:

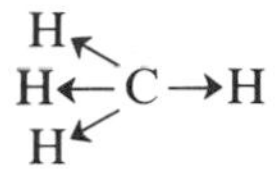

$$H \leftarrow C \rightarrow H$$

$$\mu = 0$$

Similarly, the three C—H moments in the methyl group of propylene can be replaced by a single moment oriented in the proper direction:

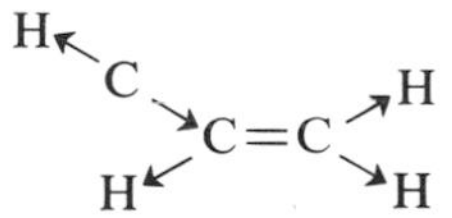

$$C=C$$

The bond moments due to the *trans*-hydrogens cancel, and the effective moments in the molecule are,

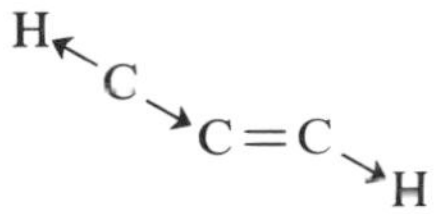

$$C=C$$

We are left with three moments, an sp^3-s C—H moment, an sp^2-s C—H moment, and an sp^3-sp^2 C—C moment. Unfortunately, the two C—H moments do not cancel, for as was stated in Section 9-4, the sp^3-s moment is larger than the sp^2-s moment. The sp^2 hybridized carbon atom withdraws electrons from hydrogen more effectively than does the sp^3 hybridized carbon atom, and the difference between these two C—H moments is a small moment directed towards the methyl group:

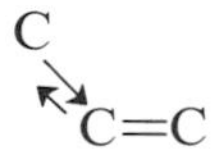

$$C=C$$

This small moment is a measure of the extra ability of an sp^2 hybridized carbon atom to withdraw electrons from hydrogen. Opposing this moment is the C—C moment which measures the ability of an sp^2 hybridized atom to withdraw electrons from carbon. We have assumed previously that electrons can be withdrawn more readily from carbon than from hydrogen. Therefore, the C—C moment is the larger of the two. There results then a net moment directed towards the sp^2 hybridized atom and away from the methyl group:

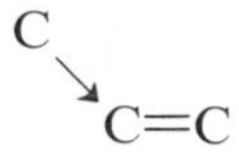

$$C=C$$

This net moment is small, and it may be too small to account for the entire dipole moment of propylene. However, a small moment such as this may induce polarization of other electrons in the molecule and thereby account for the dipole moment of propylene.

We have presented two different theories which attempt to explain the dipole moment of propylene. Both of these theories lead to the conclusion that replacement of hydrogen by methyl gives rise to electron donation by the methyl group. The first theory, that of hyperconjugation, attributes electron release to the electrons in the C—H bonds of the methyl group while the second theory, the inductive argument, attributes electron release to the idea that an sp^2 hybridized carbon atom can withdraw electrons more effectively from sp^3 hybridized carbon than from hydrogen.

These same two theories can be used to explain the dipole moment of toluene. The larger dipole moment of propyne is also readily explained by both. In propyne, according to the theory of hyperconjugation, resonance becomes more pronounced because electrons can now be delocalized into both p_y and p_z orbitals. According to the inductive theory, electrons can be released even more readily by the methyl group because the carbon atom to which this group is attached is now sp hybridized:

$$CH_3 \overset{\frown}{-} C \equiv C \overset{\frown}{-} H$$

$$sp^3\text{-}sp \qquad\qquad sp\text{-}s$$

This type of hybridization is more effective for withdrawing electrons than the sp^2 hybridized carbon atom in propylene.

These theories also explain the observed order of carbonium ion stability and olefin stability. We discuss these topics in the following sections.

9.11 The Structure of Carbonium Ions

We begin our discussion by first considering the structure of carbonium ions; the simplest of which is the methyl carbonium ion:

$$120° \quad \overset{\displaystyle H}{\underset{H \qquad H}{\diagdown C^+}}$$

The carbon atom in this species is sp^2 hybridized, which leads to a planar ion having bond angles of 120°. The six electrons used in the three C—H bonds occupy three orbitals each one of which is formed from an sp^2 orbital of carbon and an s orbital of hydrogen. The remaining orbital of carbon, a p orbital, is empty:

$$\overset{H}{\underset{H}{\diagdown}} C^+ {-} H$$

An empty orbital is just an empty region of space. The significance of this empty orbital is that when the carbon atom does begin to form a bond with an approaching nucleophile, it uses this orbital to do so. Thus an attacking nucleophile $Y:^-$ approaches preferentially from directly above or directly below the carbon atom. This is shown in Figure 9-6.

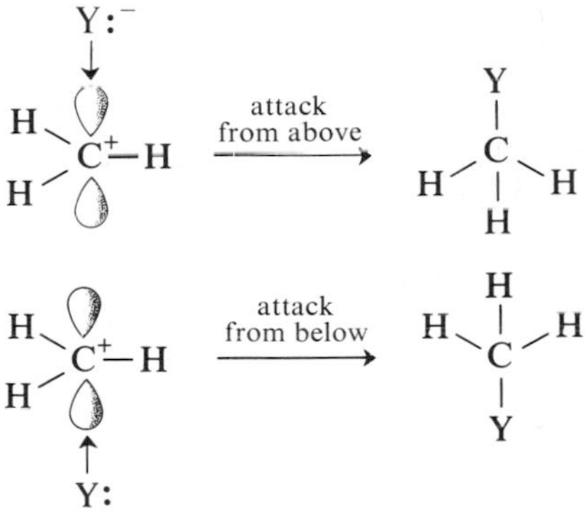

Figure 9-6

In carbonium ions the carbon atom bearing the positive charge is generally sp^2 hybridized. Thus the central carbon atom in the t-butyl carbonium ion is also sp^2 hybridized:

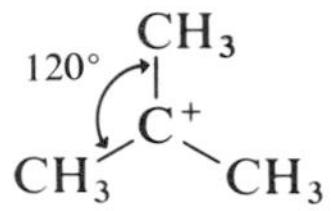

12

However, although we generally represent the t-butyl carbonium ion by this single structure, the positive charge does not reside entirely on the central carbon atom. It is delocalized over the entire molecule, and we could write structure **13** to indicate charge delocalization:

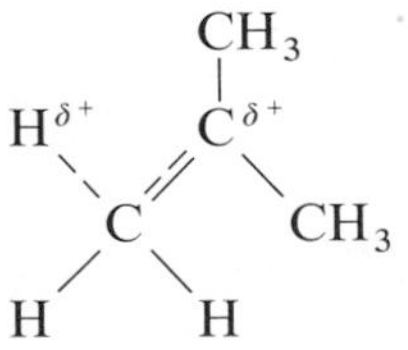

13

We have indicated the participation of the electrons in one C—H bond. Since all nine C—H bonds are equivalent, it is obvious that the electrons in the other bonds behave in a similar fashion. In terms of valence-bond structures charge delocalization is indicated in the following way,

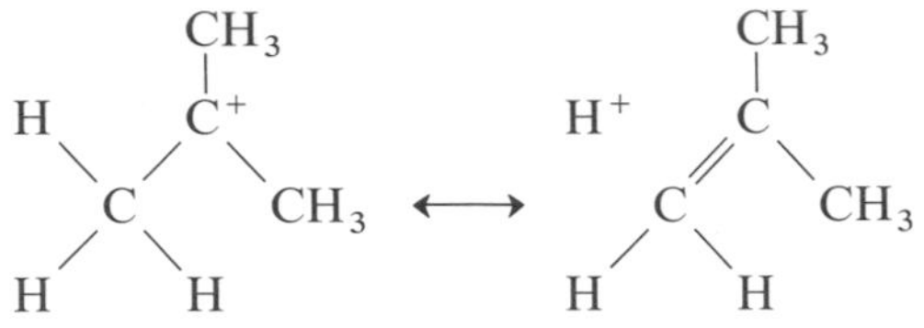

14   **15**

There are nine structures equivalent to **15**.

While we generally represent the *t*-butyl carbonium ion by structure **14**, it must be remembered that this is only a single valence-bond contributor and that other structures (for example, **15**) are necessary for a more complete description of the cation. In structure **14**, all of the positive charge does reside on the central carbon atom which is sp^2 hybridized and has an empty p orbital. In the actual carbonium ion, the charge is delocalized, and the p orbital is not truly empty. This is due to the influence of structures such as **15**. Addition to a cationic system occurs most readily when an approaching nucleophile attacks from directly above or directly below this central atom.

9.12 The Nonclassical Carbonium Ion

We have stated that although we usually represent a carbonium ion by a classical structure such as **14**, that this is just one valence-bond contributor, other valence-bond structures being necessary for a more complete description of the system.

This is illustrated, as we saw in the previous section, by the *t*-butyl carbonium ion which is described by contributors such as:

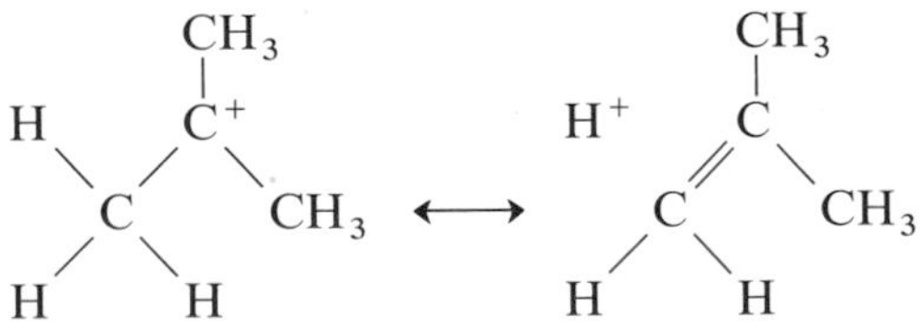

14   **15**

The classical structure **14** is the major contributor to the actual molecule, but the other nine structures (**15** and its equivalent forms) should also be considered.

We have also presented the idea that an alternative method of indicating delocalization of the positive charge is to represent this cation by structures such as **13**.

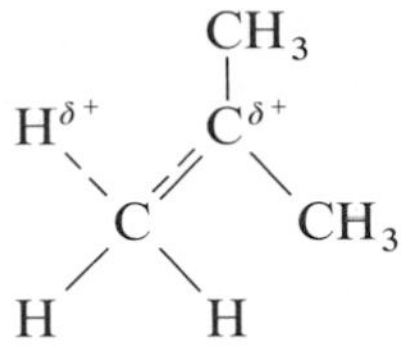

13

The idea has been advanced that in certain special cases it is no longer accurate to represent a carbonium ion by a classical structure such as **14** and that in these cases structures analogous to **13** give a better description of the carbonium ions. In other words, in these special cases, charge delocalization is so important that structures like **14** no longer give a good description of the actual carbonium ion, and the other valence-bond contributors become increasingly important. When we represent a carbonium ion by the classical structure **14**, we usually imply that this representation gives us a good but not exact description of the system. When we represent a carbonium ion by a nonclassical structure such as **13**, we imply that charge delocalization is extremely important and that the classical structure does not give a good description of the actual carbonium ion.

The compound, *exo* norbornyl chloride **16**, reacts with nucleophilic solvents more rapidly than the corresponding *endo* norbornyl chloride **17**, and it has been suggested that the nonclassical carbonium ion **18** may be involved in this reaction. It has been argued that charge delocalization in the transition state resulting from **16** (similar to the charge delocalization in **18**) stabilizes this transition state and leads to a faster solvolysis rate for the *exo* isomer,

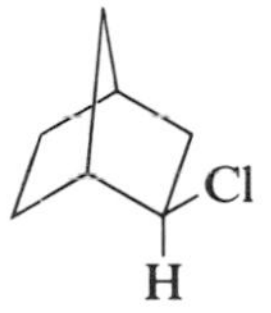

16 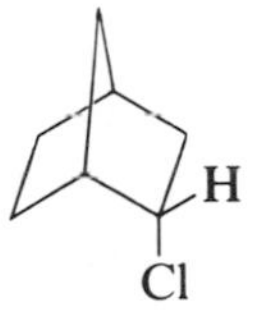   **17**

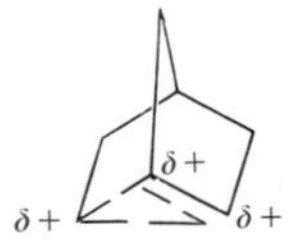

18

Describing **18** from a valence-bond viewpoint,

The previous example illustrates one reaction where a nonclassical intermediate has been postulated, other examples exist. The basis for such a postulation is kinetic and stereochemical in nature. While the evidence is good, it is far from conclusive. It is possible that the observed rate differences and isomer distributions are due to other causes; solvent and steric effects may account for the experimental observations. Nonclassical structures are certainly possible, and the idea is not unreasonable, but we must wait for additional evidence before coming to a definite conclusion. This problem is discussed more fully in Chapter 18.

9.13 Carbonium Ion Stability

A carbonium ion is always generated as the result of some reaction. The addition of a proton to an alkene, the treatment of an alcohol with acid, or simply the dissociation of an alkyl halide, all can generate carbonium ions.

$$\begin{array}{c}R\\\diagdown\\\diagup\\R\end{array}C=C\begin{array}{c}R\\\diagup\\\diagdown\\R\end{array} + H^+ \longrightarrow R-\underset{\underset{H}{|}}{\overset{\overset{R}{|}}{C}}-\underset{+}{\overset{\overset{R}{|}}{C}}-R$$

$$ROH + H^+ \longrightarrow R^+ + HOH$$

$$RCl \longrightarrow R^+ + Cl^-$$

Now by the statement that one carbonium ion is more stable than another, we do not generally refer to the total free energy content of the two carbonium ions. Instead we usually infer from this statement that the $\Delta G°$ for carbonium ion formation is more favorable for one carbonium ion than for another. For example, we usually state that *t*-butyl carbonium ion is more stable than methyl carbonium ion, and by this we imply only that $\Delta G°$ for generation of *t*-butyl carbonium ion by some process is more favorable than $\Delta G°$ for the generation of methyl carbonium ion by that same process. We do not actually compare the total free energy content of these two cations; see Figure 9–7.

Only when comparing isomeric carbonium ions would a comparison of the total free energy content be meaningful. For comparisons of stability of non-isomeric cations, we really must use the $\Delta G°$ for formation of the cations from reactants. If we assume that the two reactants have the same free energy, we can then speak of the two cationic products as if we were comparing their total free energy. It is simpler to compare two cationic systems if we always assume that the reactants leading to these two systems have the same free energy; actually, we are discussing $\Delta G°$.

We attribute the difference in stability of two carbonium ions to certain factors (in the previous example, we compare the effect of hydrogen and methyl); these same factors are usually present in the reactants, but the effects are more pronounced in the products. When making comparisons of carbonium ion

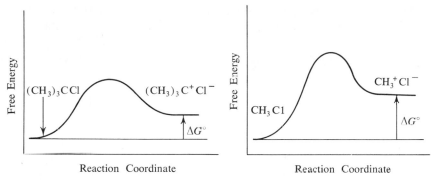

Reaction Coordinate   Reaction Coordinate

Figure 9–7

stability, we assume that the free energy of the reactants is the same. Furthermore, the factors to which we attribute stability are also present in the reactants
but are more pronounced in the products.

We compare $\Delta G°$ for carbonium ion formation which is given by the equation,

$$\Delta G° = \Delta H° - T\Delta S°$$

and we generally assume that $\Delta H°$ is more significant. Steric factors (rehydridiza-
tion and restricted rotations and restricted vibrations resulting from nonbonded
interactions) sometimes influence the stability of very crowded cations, however,
we do not consider steric factors at this time. There is one overriding factor
which alone seems to account for carbonium ion stability, and we develop this
idea in the following way.

There is a problem in quantum mechanics called the *particle in a box* (Figure
9–8) that consists of placing a particle in a box of length L and calculating its
energy. The solution to this problem indicates that the energy of the particle
depends among other things upon the length of the box, and increasing the
length of the box stabilizes the particle.

Figure 9–8

If we assume that our particle is a charged particle, this implies that spreading out the charge is a stabilizing factor. Delocalization of charge stabilizes the system, and we can see readily why carbonium ions such as the allylic and benzylic carbonium ions are stable. The positive charge is effectively delocalized in these systems:

$$CH_2=CH-\overset{+}{C}H_2 \longleftrightarrow \overset{+}{C}H_2-CH=CH_2$$

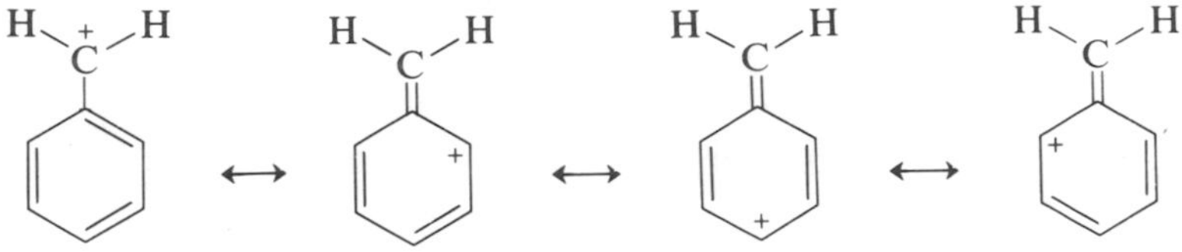

These two carbonium ions are extremely stable; others are less stable. The *t*-butyl carbonium ion is less stable than these yet more stable than the methyl carbonium ion. For these two carbonium ions, the *t*-butyl and the methyl, it is less apparent just how the positive charge is delocalized. However, the ideas that we developed in the previous sections are also applicable here.

In proceeding from the methyl to the *t*-butyl carbonium ion, we replace hydrogen by methyl. The methyl group releases electrons more readily than hydrogen, the positive charge is more effectively delocalized in the case of the *t*-butyl carbonium ion, and this ion is more stable.

Both the theory of hyperconjugation and the inductive theory predict the following order of stability for carbonium ions:

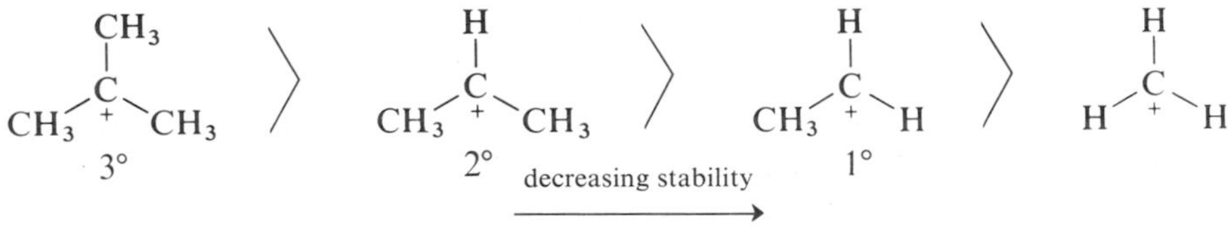

While the two theories agree on the general order of carbonium ion stability, they do not concur on all points. According to the inductive argument, replacing hydrogen by methyl always stabilizes the carbonium ion regardless of which hydrogen is being replaced. Consequently, this theory predicts for primary carbonium ions the following order of stability,

decreasing stability according to inductive argument

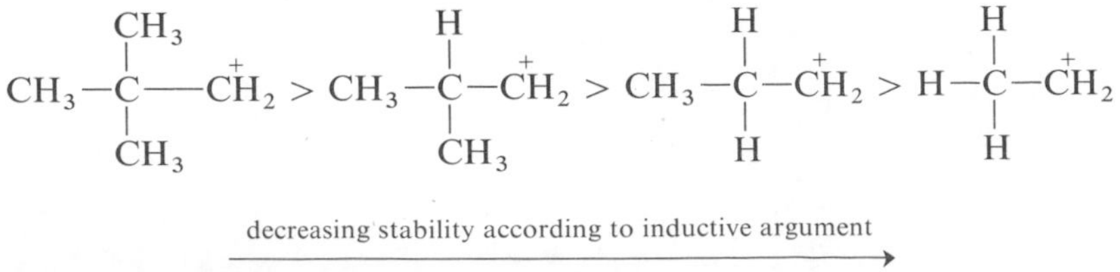

The theory of hyperconjugation, on the other hand, does not predict this order of stability. It also leads to the conclusion that primary carbonium ions are generally less stable than secondary or tertiary, but within each class, this theory predicts just the reverse order for cationic stability.

$$
\begin{array}{cccc}
\text{H} & \text{H} & \text{H} & \text{CH}_3 \\
| & | & | & | \\
\text{H}-\overset{}{\underset{|}{\text{C}}}-\overset{+}{\text{CH}}_2 > \text{CH}_3-\overset{}{\underset{|}{\text{C}}}-\overset{+}{\text{CH}}_2 > \text{CH}_3-\overset{}{\underset{|}{\text{C}}}-\overset{+}{\text{CH}}_2 > \text{CH}_3-\overset{}{\underset{|}{\text{C}}}-\overset{+}{\text{CH}}_2 \\
\text{H} & \text{H} & \text{CH}_3 & \text{CH}_3
\end{array}
$$

decreasing stability according to hyperconjugation
$\longrightarrow$

To see why this reversal arises in the theory of hyperconjugation we consider the first two cations in the series, the ethyl and the *n*-propyl carbonium ions. According to the ideas of hyperconjugation, we are able to write the following valence-bond contributors for the ethyl cation,

$$
\begin{array}{cccc}
\text{H}\ \text{H} & \text{H}^+\ \text{H} & \text{H}\ \text{H} & \text{H}\ \text{H} \\
|\ \ | & |\ \ | & |\ \ | & |\ \ | \\
\text{H}-\text{C}-\text{C}^+ \longleftrightarrow \text{H}-\text{C}=\text{C} \longleftrightarrow \text{H}^+\ \text{C}=\text{C} \longleftrightarrow \text{H}-\text{C}=\text{C} \\
|\ \ | & |\ \ | & |\ \ | & |\ \ | \\
\text{H}\ \text{H} & \text{H}\ \text{H} & \text{H}\ \text{H} & \text{H}^+\ \text{H}
\end{array}
$$

while for the *n*-propyl carbonium ion,

$$
\begin{array}{cc}
\text{H}\ \text{H} & \text{H}^+\ \text{H} \\
|\ \ | & |\ \ | \\
\text{CH}_3-\text{C}-\text{C}^+ \longleftrightarrow \text{CH}_3-\text{C}=\text{C} \longleftrightarrow \\
|\ \ | & |\ \ | \\
\text{H}\ \text{H} & \text{H}\ \text{H} \\
\textbf{19} & \textbf{20}
\end{array}
$$

$$
\begin{array}{cc}
\text{H}\ \text{H} & \text{H}\ \text{H} \\
|\ \ | & |\ \ | \\
\overset{+}{\text{CH}}_3\ \ \text{C}=\text{C} \longleftrightarrow \text{CH}_3-\text{C}=\text{C} \\
|\ \ | & |\ \ | \\
\text{H}\ \text{H} & \text{H}^+\ \text{H} \\
\textbf{21} & \textbf{22}
\end{array}
$$

According to this theory, structure **21** which places a positive charge on carbon is a high energy valence-bond contributor and is therefore less significant. The ethyl carbonium ion has no high energy contributing structure analogous to **21** and is therefore more stable. Naturally, we can extend these ideas to the other carbonium ions in the sequence. These two theories do not concur on the order of stability of secondary carbonium ions; nor do they agree on the order for tertiary carbonium ions. In principle, it is therefore possible to distinguish between these two concepts, the inductive argument and that of hyperconjugation. Unfortunately, experimental results depend upon many factors. Since these differences in stability are expected to be small, experimental results are contradictory and lead to no definite conclusion.

According to the theory of hyperconjugation, we can predict the stability of a carbonium ion simply by counting the number of hydrogens on the carbon atoms adjacent to the positively charged atom (β-hydrogens). Thus, the ethyl carbonium ion with three hydrogens on the adjacent carbon atom is predicted to be more stable than the *n*-propyl cation which has only two,

$$CH_3CH_2^+ \qquad CH_3CH_2CH_2^+$$

and the carbonium ion with five β-hydrogens:

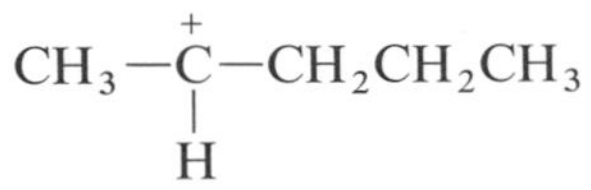

$$CH_3 - \overset{+}{\underset{\underset{H}{|}}{C}} - CH_2CH_2CH_3$$

is expected to be more stable than the isomeric,

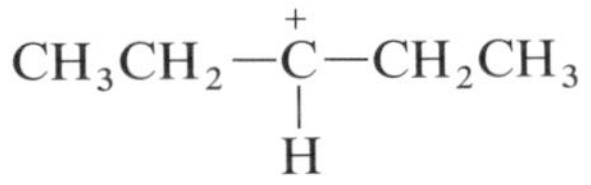

$$CH_3CH_2 - \overset{+}{\underset{\underset{H}{|}}{C}} - CH_2CH_3$$

which has only four such hydrogen atoms.

It might be worthwhile to mention briefly at this time some of the difficulties encountered when attempting to assess the importance of hyperconjugation. We use isotopic labeling experiments and secondary deuterium isotope effects to illustrate.

Consider the *t*-amyl cation,

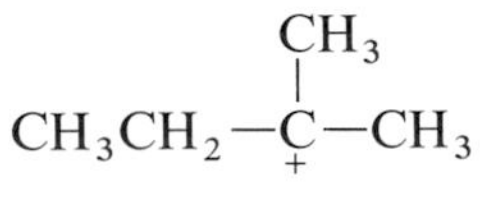

$$\overset{\overset{\displaystyle CH_3}{|}}{CH_3CH_2 - \underset{+}{C} - CH_3}$$

which receives contributions from structures of the type,

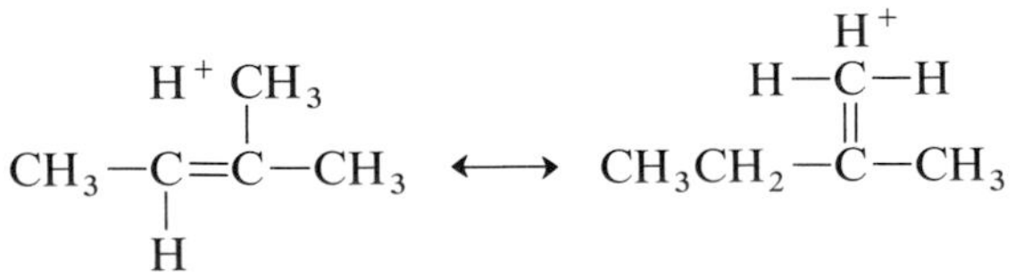

$$CH_3 - \overset{\overset{\displaystyle H^+\ CH_3}{\underset{\displaystyle |}{}}}{\underset{\underset{\displaystyle H}{|}}{C}} = C - CH_3 \quad \longleftrightarrow \quad CH_3CH_2 - \overset{\overset{\displaystyle H^+}{\overset{\displaystyle H-C-H}{\|}}}{C} - CH_3$$

These contributors are expected to decrease the frequencies of the C—H vibrational modes and to weaken the pertinent C—H bonds. As a result, the cations

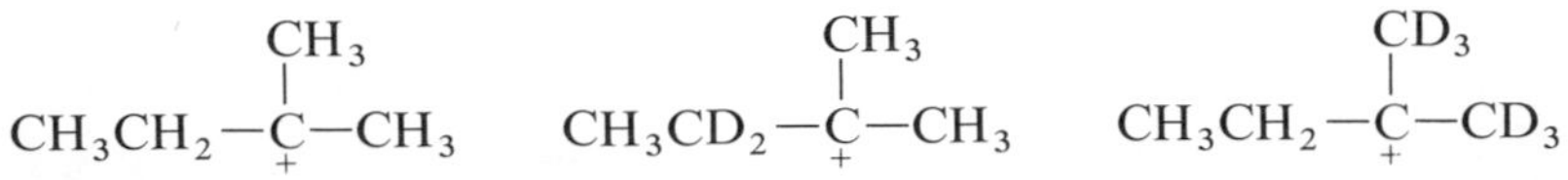

$$\overset{\overset{\displaystyle CH_3}{|}}{CH_3CH_2 - \underset{+}{C} - CH_3} \qquad \overset{\overset{\displaystyle CH_3}{|}}{CH_3CD_2 - \underset{+}{C} - CH_3} \qquad \overset{\overset{\displaystyle CD_3}{|}}{CH_3CH_2 - \underset{+}{C} - CD_3}$$

ought to approach each other in stability, the deuterated cations still being slightly more stable than the nondeuterated analogue. However, the alkyl chlorides that give rise to these carbonium ions differ in stability to a greater degree, for hyperconjugation is less important here. The deuterated halides are more stable, but this difference in stability somewhat decreases in passing to the cations and would also be expected to decrease in the transition states for solvolysis. The nondeuterated chloride, which is less stable, is more reactive. The rates of solvolysis of these halides have been measured in 80% aqueous ethanol with the results:

$$CH_3CH_2-\underset{\underset{Cl}{|}}{\overset{\overset{CH_3}{|}}{C}}-CH_3 \qquad CH_3CD_2-\underset{\underset{Cl}{|}}{\overset{\overset{CH_3}{|}}{C}}-CH_3 \qquad CH_3CH_2-\underset{\underset{Cl}{|}}{\overset{\overset{CD_3}{|}}{C}}-CD_3$$

$$\frac{k_H}{k} = \qquad 1.0 \qquad\qquad\qquad 1.4 \qquad\qquad\qquad 1.8$$

The theory of hyperconjugation predicts that replacing β-hydrogens by deuterium should decrease the rate of solvolysis and such a decrease is observed. Unfortunately, the conclusions that can be drawn from the experimental observations are not straightforward, for cyclopentyl tosylates such as,

also solvolyze at different rates. Replacing the α-hydrogen by deuterium decreases the rate of solvolysis, yet this hydrogen cannot participate in hyperconjugation. Some other explanation must be advanced. It is possible that replacing β-hydrogens decreases the rate because of hyperconjugation while replacing α-hydrogens decreases the solvolysis rate for some other reason. However, we cannot be certain of this, and it is reasonable to assume that the same factor operates in both cases. Interpreting the experimental findings becomes difficult, and we cannot be certain of the importance of hyperconjugation.

Both the inductive theory and the theory of hyperconjugation agree that replacement of hydrogen by methyl stabilizes the carbonium ion; however, they do not agree on the effect caused by replacing a methyl group by some other alkyl group. One theory predicts that replacing the methyl group in a carbonium ion by ethyl, isopropyl, t-butyl, and so forth stabilizes that cation while the other theory predicts that this type of a substitution destablizes the carbonium ion. The same arguments presented here for carbonium ion stability are also important in discussing olefinic stability, for the same ideas are involved.

9.14 Olefinic Stability

We base our discussion of olefinic stability upon data concerning heats of hydrogenation. This is essentially a discussion in terms of ΔH for the reaction,

$$
\begin{array}{c}
\text{R} \qquad \text{R} \\
\diagdown \qquad \diagup \\
\text{C=C} \qquad + \text{ H}_2 \longrightarrow \\
\diagup \qquad \diagdown \\
\text{R} \qquad \text{R}
\end{array}
\qquad
\begin{array}{c}
\text{R} \quad \text{R} \\
| \quad | \\
\text{R}-\text{C}-\text{C}-\text{R} \\
| \quad | \\
\text{H} \quad \text{H}
\end{array}
\qquad \Delta H \simeq -30 \, \text{kcal/mole}
$$

The reaction is exothermic, and we assume that the less exothermic the reaction the more stable is the olefin. Naturally, a discussion in terms of ΔH for the reaction should involve not only the energy of the reactants but also that of the product. Consequently, differences in ΔH are not a quantitative measure of olefinic stability, yet the trend is certainly in the expected direction. Replacement of hydrogen by methyl does appear to stabilize the olefin (see Table 9–1). We find that olefin stability decreases in the order,

$$
\underset{\text{CH}_3}{\overset{\text{CH}_3}{>}}\text{C=C}\underset{\text{CH}_3}{\overset{\text{CH}_3}{<}}
\; \Big\rangle \;
\underset{\text{CH}_3}{\overset{\text{CH}_3}{>}}\text{C=C}\underset{\text{CH}_3}{\overset{\text{H}}{<}}
\; \Big\rangle \;
\underset{\text{H}}{\overset{\text{CH}_3}{>}}\text{C=C}\underset{\text{CH}_3}{\overset{\text{H}}{<}}
\; \Big\rangle
$$

decreasing stability →

$$
\underset{\text{H}}{\overset{\text{CH}_3}{>}}\text{C=C}\underset{\text{H}}{\overset{\text{CH}_3}{<}}
\; \Big\rangle \;
\underset{\text{H}}{\overset{\text{CH}_3}{>}}\text{C=C}\underset{\text{H}}{\overset{\text{H}}{<}}
\; \Big\rangle \;
\underset{\text{H}}{\overset{\text{H}}{>}}\text{C=C}\underset{\text{H}}{\overset{\text{H}}{<}}
$$

decreasing stability →

Table 9–1   Heats of Hydrogenation of Olefins

Compound	Heat of Hydrogenation (kcal/mole)
$CH_2=CH_2$	32.82
$CH_3CH=CH_2$	30.12
$CH_3CH_2CH=CH_2$	30.34
$(CH_3)_2CHCH=CH_2$	30.33
$(CH_3)_3CCH=CH_2$	30.34
$CH_3(CH_2)_4CH=CH_2$	30.14
cis-$CH_3CH=CHCH_3$	28.57
trans-$CH_3CH=CHCH_3$	27.62
$(CH_3)_2C=CHCH_3$	26.92
$(CH_3)_2C=C(CH_3)_2$	26.63

The greater stability of *trans*-2-butene compared with *cis*-2-butene is attributed to interaction between the two methyl groups in the *cis*-isomer.

The data are not clearcut concerning the effect caused by replacement of methyl by another alkyl group. For the sequence,

$$(CH_3)_3CCH=CH_2 \quad (CH_3)_2CHCH=CH_2 \quad CH_3CH_2CH=CH_2$$

$$CH_3CH=CH_2 \quad CH_3(CH_2)_4CH=CH_2$$

no definite conclusion can be reached. The first three alkenes in this sequence exhibit the same heat of hydrogenation and so do the last two. Furthermore, the small differences that are observed can be attributed to other factors.

The most highly substituted alkene is generally the most stable. Introducing more alkyl groups about the olefinic linkage increases olefinic stability:

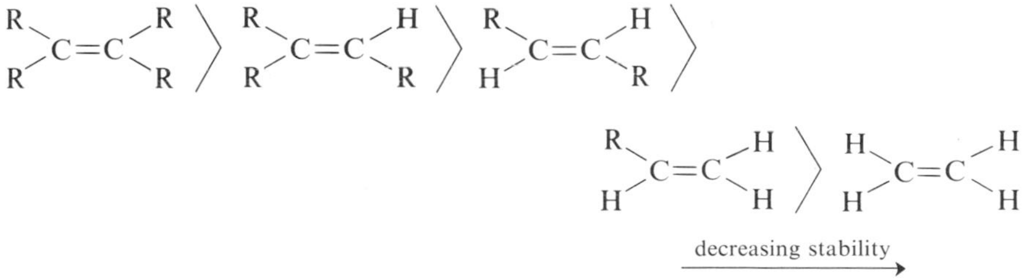

decreasing stability

There are, however, exceptions to this general rule. When the alkyl groups become excessively large, steric factors become more important, and in such cases the less highly substituted alkene is occasionally the most stable.

To determine the effect of increasing size upon the product distribution, a series of alkyl bromides having the general structure **23** was reacted under conditions favoring the formation of the corresponding alkyl carbonium ion:

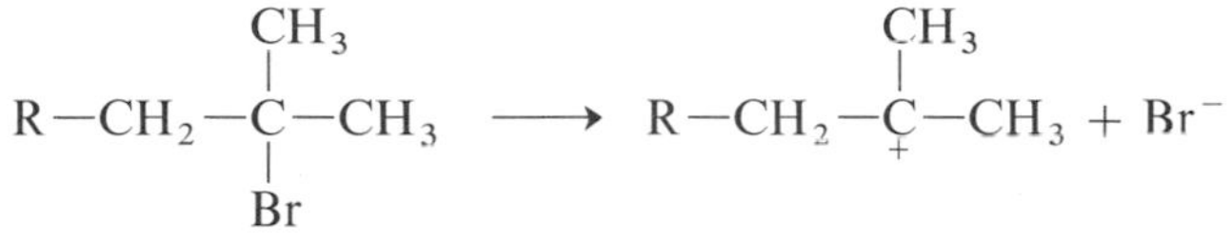

23

This carbonium ion reacts with solvent to yield both substituted products and olefinic products. Furthermore, two olefinic materials are possible:

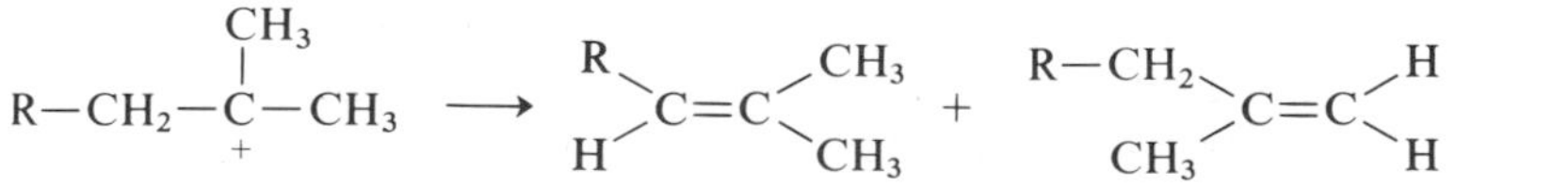

The rate of reaction of **23** is nearly the same when R is methyl, ethyl, or iso-propyl, but it increases sharply when R is *t*-butyl. In addition, both the olefinic fraction of the product and the yield of **25** in this olefinic fraction increase with increasing size of R, results being most dramatic when R is *t*-butyl. The data are presented in Table 9–2.

Table 9–2

| R | Yield of Olefin (%) | Composition of Olefin (%) | | $k(hr^{-1})$ |
		24	25	
CH_3-	27	79	21	0.387
CH_3CH_2-	32	71	29	0.297
$(CH_3)_2CH-$	46	59	41	0.697
$(CH_3)_3C-$	57	19	81	4.71

Loss of hydrogen bromide from the alkyl halides **23** leads to a mixture of olefinic products, and the less highly substituted alkene **25** is the major component of the mixture when R is *t*-butyl. Steric interactions in the more highly substituted olefin **24** and in the transition state leading to it explain this observation.

9.15 The Structure and Stability of Free Radicals

Information concerning the structure of organic free radicals comes from electron spin resonance experiments. Information concerning their stability can be gathered from the ΔH for bond breakage. This ΔH, the bond dissociation energy, is the negative of the bond strength.

An electron has intrinsic angular momentum or spin, and a spinning electron has associated with it a magnetic moment. In a molecule the magnetic moments of all the spin-paired electrons cancel, but each unpaired electron present in a free radical gives rise to a permanent magnetic moment. The presence of such a magnetic moment causes the radical to be paramagnetic, that is, causes the radical to be drawn into a magnetic field. Magnetic susceptibility measurements make use of the property, but such measurements, while indicating the presence and the concentrations of radicals, give no information concerning their structure. Electron spin resonance spectroscopy, on the other hand, does provide information concerning the structure of radicals, and this method is more useful to the organic chemist.[1]

The hyperfine splitting that can be observed in the electron spin resonance spectra of many organic radicals does provide information concerning structure. The spin vector **S** of an unpaired electron has a z component S_z that lines up parallel or antiparallel to an external magnetic field **H** in the z direction:

$$\mathbf{H}\uparrow \quad \downarrow \quad S_z = -1/2 \qquad \mathbf{H}\uparrow \quad \uparrow \quad S_z = +1/2$$

lower energy orientation

higher energy orientation

[1] Electron spin resonance is discussed more fully in Section 10.6.

The antiparallel orientation of S_z constitutes the lower energy state, but an electron in this state can absorb energy and enter the higher energy state.[2] In electron spin resonance experiments one determines the external field strength at which the electronic spin flips.

Although C^{12} does not have a nuclear magnetic moment, other nuclei (C^{13}, H, and others) present in organic compounds do have such moments. Because of interactions between the unpaired electron and the nuclei possessing magnetic moments, the field strength for spin inversion varies slightly from radical to radical.

The magnetic moments of the nuclei are oriented in a number of different directions. Some are oriented in such a way as to add to the external field while the magnetic moments of other nuclei are oriented in opposition to the external field.

As for the electron, m_z for a nucleus is parallel or antiparallel to the field. For example, in the methyl radical each hydrogen nucleus has a magnetic moment. Possibilities for the three nuclear spins are,

$$+1/2 + 1/2 + 1/2$$

$$+1/2 + 1/2 - 1/2 \qquad +1/2 - 1/2 + 1/2 \qquad -1/2 + 1/2 + 1/2$$

$$+1/2 - 1/2 - 1/2 \qquad 1/2 - 1/2 + 1/2 \qquad -1/2 + 1/2 - 1/2$$

$$-1/2 - 1/2 - 1/2$$

Each hydrogen nucleus has a magnetic moment. The z components of some of these nuclear magnetic moments line up parallel to the external field; others are aligned in an antiparallel manner. In passing from one methyl radical to another the alignment varies.

In methyl radicals the unpaired electron interacts with the nuclear field as well as with the external field, and not all of the electrons experience the same nuclear field. As a result the transition to the excited state takes place at slightly different external magnetic field strengths. These interactions between the unpaired electron and the nuclei give rise to hyperfine splitting, and an examination of the number of peaks in the spectrum and their relative intensity provides information about the structure of the radical.

Studies are frequently made by generating the radical inside a glass at low temperatures. The radical is generated, but it is trapped in the holes of the glass where it is unable to react. Matrices of a solid rare gas (krypton, xenon) have also been used to contain the radical. Other techniques that enable one to examine radicals generated in liquids have recently been developed. In addition to electron spin resonance spectroscopy (ESR), infrared and ultraviolet

---

[2] In contrast to the proton, the magnetic moment vector **m** for an electron is antiparallel to the spin vector **S**. In the lower energy state m_z is parallel to **H** but S_z is antiparallel. The converse holds for the higher energy state.

spectroscopic measurements have been employed. The methyl radical has been studied extensively. The ESR spectrum of $C^{12}H_3\cdot$ displays the $1:3:3:1$ pattern characteristic of an unpaired electron interacting with three equivalent hydrogen nuclei. The spectrum shows that the three hydrogen nuclei are equivalent but fails to distinguish between a truly planar methyl radical (sp^2 hybridization and the electron in a p orbital) and a conformation in which the hybridization is intermediate between sp^3 and sp^2.

The ESR spectrum of $C^{13}H_3\cdot$ has been examined and provides more information concerning the structure. The observed hyperfine splitting is consistent with a planar model and any deviation from planarity is calculated to be less than 5°. Thus, methyl radical is planar. The radicals $H_2NCOCHF\cdot$ and $H_2NCOCF_2\cdot$ have also been studied. These were single crystal experiments. A single large crystal of the precursor is grown and the radical generated inside the crystal. Their ESR spectra are consistent with and favor a planar geometry.

While these radicals are planar or nearly so, not all radicals are. The fluorinated methyl radicals, $CF_3\cdot$, $CHF_2\cdot$, and $CH_2F\cdot$ have also been investigated. The first two are nonplanar, the deviation from planarity θ being 17.8° for $CF_3\cdot$ and 12.7° for $CHF_2\cdot$,

Thus trifluoromethyl radical can be described as sp^3 hybridized (the F—C—F angle is approximately 111°), and difluoromethyl is intermediate. (Since the designations sp^3, sp^2, and so forth are only approximate, we can also consider $CHF_2\cdot$ to be sp^3 hybridized.) Calculations for the $CH_2F\cdot$ predict a nonplanar geometry for this radical, yet the ESR spectrum shows that θ is less than 5°.

Other less direct evidence concerning the structure of radicals comes from a study of the reactions of bicyclic systems. In bicyclic systems of the type

the bridgehead carbon atoms cannot become sp^2 hybridized without causing extensive strain in the system. Therefore, it is difficult to form a carbonium ion in these systems (either because of strain or because a carbonium ion that is not really sp^2 hybridized is involved). Actually, both factors contribute, and in any case the transition state leading to the cationic intermediate is of high energy. Consequently, the solvolyses reactions of these bridgehead halides proceed slowly. If the preferred geometry of the radical were similar to that of the carbonium ion (sp^2 hybridization), free radical reactions at a bridgehead also ought to proceed slowly. On the other hand, if the preferred geometry for a radical is a nonplanar geometry, less difficulty should be encountered in forming it:

Studies involving bridgehead radicals have been made, and it appears that while these radicals are somewhat more reactive, they are formed at about the normal rate. The transition states leading to these bridgehead radicals are not unduly energetic and therefore it seems that these systems are not excessively strained. The data favor the idea that some radicals are planar or nearly so while others neither require nor prefer a planar geometry.

Drawing conclusions about an intermediate on the basis of the geometry of the transition state is not always reliable, but much evidence is available to show that bridgehead radicals can be formed. Although only two bridgehead tertiary hydrogens are available while twelve secondary hydrogens are, the following chlorination affords a large percentage of bridgehead product:

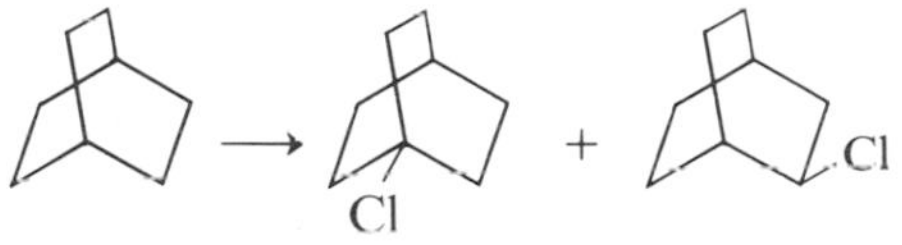

It is significant, however, that norbornane yields no bridgehead material:

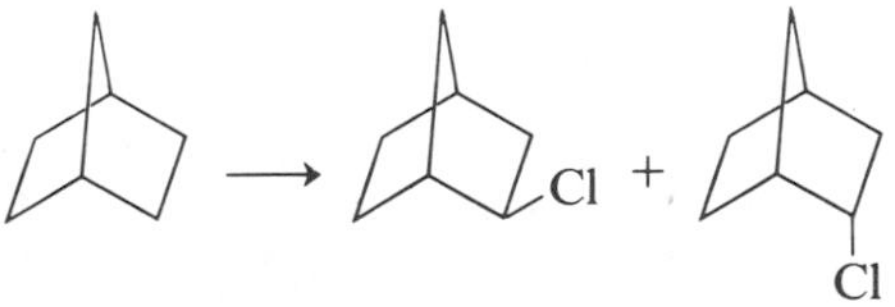

This last result can be explained by the fact that the hybridization of the bridgehead radical does approach sp^2 and that even this strain is excessive in the transition state for the norbornane system. Bridgehead norbornyl radicals are formed as intermediates in other reactions.

In systems such as the allylic system and the benzylic system where π electronic delocalization is possible, the carbon atom is generally considered to be sp^2 hybridized with the unpaired electron delocalized over the entire π system.

According to the Hückel molecular orbital theory, the odd electron in these systems occupies a nonbonding molecular orbital, and the electron density is nonzero at alternant positions. It is possible to calculate the electron density at the various positions; the results are,

$$\overset{1/2}{CH_2} == CH == \overset{1/2}{CH_2}$$

In the allylic system the two methylene positions are equivalent, while in the benzylic system only 4/7 of the electron density due to the unpaired electron is found at the methylene position, the remaining 3/7 being found at the ortho and para positions.[3]

These radicals, where the electron is more effectively delocalized, have greater stability than the saturated radicals discussed previously.

Experimental techniques are available for evaluating radical stability. One possibility is to compare for a series of hydrocarbons the rates of a reaction where hydrogen atom abstraction is the rate limiting step. The results obtained in this way compare favorably with the ΔH for homolytic bond breakage of the carbon-hydrogen bond. While difficulties arise when interpreting the bond dissociation energy in a quantitative manner, for a simple qualitative discussion ΔH for dissociation is certainly an adequate means of expressing radical stability. The more positive ΔH is for the reaction, the less stable is the radical. This is demonstrated in Table 9–3.

Table 9–3

			ΔH(kcal/mole)
$H-H$	$\longrightarrow$	$H\cdot + H\cdot$	104.2
CH_3-H	$\longrightarrow$	$CH_3\cdot + H\cdot$	102
CH_3CH_2-H	$\longrightarrow$	$CH_3CH_2\cdot + H\cdot$	96
$CH_3CH_2CH_2-H$	$\longrightarrow$	$CH_3CH_2CH_2\cdot + H\cdot$	100
$(CH_3)_2CH-H$	$\longrightarrow$	$(CH_3)_2CH\cdot + H\cdot$	94
$CH_3CH_2CH_2CH_2-H$	$\longrightarrow$	$CH_3CH_2CH_2CH_2\cdot + H\cdot$	101
$(CH_3)_3C-H$	$\longrightarrow$	$(CH_3)_3C\cdot + H\cdot$	89
$CH_2{=}CHCH_2-H$	$\longrightarrow$	$\overset{\delta\cdot}{CH_2}{=}CH{=}\overset{\delta\cdot}{CH_2} + H\cdot$	76
ϕCH_2-H	$\longrightarrow$	$\phi CH_2\cdot + H\cdot$	78

[3] Electron spin resonance spectra indicate that the Hückel theory is only approximately correct. Some spin density does exist at the central carbon atom of the allyl radical and at the meta positions in the benzylic system. The observed hyperfine splittings further demonstrate that the assumption of noninteracting σ and π electrons is not strictly correct.

As the bond dissociation energies indicate, radical stability follows the same order as carbonium ion stability (Section 9–13); however, the differences in stability between primary, secondary and tertiary radicals are less pronounced:

$$3° > 2° > 1° > CH_3•$$

decreasing stability →

The benzylic and allylic radicals are more stable than the saturated systems. Since introducing a single phenyl group stabilizes the radical, introducing a second and third ought to stabilize the system still more:

$$\phi_3C• > \phi_2CH• > \phi CH_2•$$

decreasing stability →

This expectation is confirmed and leads to rather interesting results. When the appropriate groups are introduced, the radical becomes more stable than the corresponding dimer. Thus although radicals usually dimerize according to the equation:

$$R• + R• \longrightarrow R - R$$

when the radical is sufficiently stable, this dimerization does not take place. Materials have been prepared that exist as radicals even in the solid state. The substance

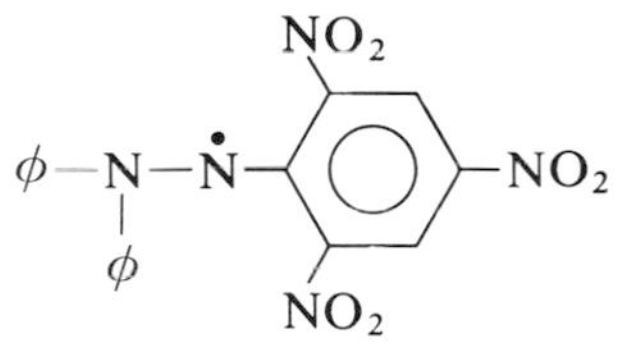

is such a material, existing entirely in the radical form. (Admittedly, steric interactions destabilize the dimeric species.) Hexaphenylethane dissociates in solution to form triphenylmethyl radicals:

$$\phi_3C - C\phi_3 \rightleftarrows 2\phi_3C•$$

The low value for the bond dissociation energy of hexaphenylethane (11 kcal/mole) can be attributed to delocalization of the unpaired electron in the radical and steric interactions in the dimer.

One might assume because radicals are electrically neutral that they would be insensitive to the polar nature of the solvent and to substituent changes in the system. This appears to be the case for most radical reactions, but some do display a marked sensitivity to substituent effects and solvent effects.

A study of the reaction

$$Cl-\langle\bigcirc\rangle-\overset{\overset{O}{\|}}{C}-O-O\cdot \; + \; H-\overset{\overset{O}{\|}}{C}-\langle\bigcirc\rangle-Z \; \longrightarrow$$

$$Cl-\langle\bigcirc\rangle-\overset{\overset{O}{\|}}{C}-O-OH \; + \; \cdot\overset{\overset{O}{\|}}{C}-\langle\bigcirc\rangle-Z$$

for a series of *meta* and *para* substituted benzaldehydes indicates that this reaction is extremely sensitive to changes in the substituent Z. The rate of reaction is increased by electron donors and decreased by electron withdrawers, that is, the reaction is characterized by a negative ρ ($\rho = -1.67$). This necessitates a transition state in which the aldehyde has become electron deficient and this reaction is more sensitive to changes in the substituent than is the ionization of benzoic acids. Cumene hydroperoxide is frequently used as a free radical initiator, and the rate of decomposition of this material varies with the solvent.

As a rule radical reactions are insensitive to polar solvents, and di-*t*-butyl peroxide decomposes at the same rate under a variety of conditions. The half-life of this peroxide is 200 hours at 100° and 2 hours at 140°, and the fact that the half life is the same in the gas phase and in different solvents indicates that the transition state for the decomposition is not polar:

$$CH_3-\underset{\underset{CH_3}{|}}{\overset{\overset{CH_3}{|}}{C}}-O-O-\underset{\underset{CH_3}{|}}{\overset{\overset{CH_3}{|}}{C}}-CH_3 \; \longrightarrow \; 2CH_3-\underset{\underset{CH_3}{|}}{\overset{\overset{CH_3}{|}}{C}}-O\cdot$$

The rate of decomposition of azonitriles is similarly insensitive to changes in the solvent:

$$R-\underset{\underset{CN}{|}}{\overset{\overset{R}{|}}{C}}-N{=}N-\underset{\underset{CN}{|}}{\overset{\overset{R}{|}}{C}}-R \; \underset{\Delta}{\longrightarrow} \; 2R-\underset{\underset{CN}{|}}{\overset{\overset{R}{|}}{C}}\cdot + N_2$$

Free radical reactions play an important role in organic chemistry. The reactions effected are much the same as those brought about under ionic conditions (substitutions, additions, and molecular rearrangements). We discuss some of these in Chapter 20.

Supplementary Reading

1. Baker, J. W., *Electronic Theories of Organic Chemistry*. London, Oxford U. P., 1958.

2. Cartmell, E. and Fowles, G. W. A., *Valency and Molecular Structure*. London, Butterworths, 1961.

3. Coulson, C. A., *Valence*, 2nd Ed. London, Oxford U. P., 1961.

4. Dewar, M. J. S., *Hyperconjugation*. New York, Ronald Press, 1962.

5. Ferguson, L. N., *The Modern Structural Theory of Organic Chemistry*. Englewood Cliffs, New Jersey, Prentice-Hall, 1963.

6. Gould, E. S., *Mechanism and Structure in Organic Chemistry*. New York, Holt, 1959.

7. Hine, J., *Physical Organic Chemistry*. New York, McGraw Hill, 1962.

8. Moore, W. J., *Physical Chemistry*. Englewood Cliffs, New Jersey, Prentice-Hall, 1962.

9. Pitzer, K. S., *Quantum Chemistry*. Englewood Cliffs, New Jersey, Prentice-Hall, 1953.

10. Streitwieser, A., Jr., *Molecular Orbital Theory for Organic Chemists*. New York, Wiley, 1961.

11. Wheland, G. W., *Resonance in Organic Chemistry*. New York, Wiley, 1955.

Chapter 10

Chemical Spectroscopy

10.1 General Discussion

A molecule absorbs electromagnetic radiation (for example, light) and proceeds from a lower energy state to a higher energy state. If the absorbed light is in the ultraviolet region or, for some molecules, in the visible region, the transition is an electronic one. An electron is promoted from a lower energy molecular orbital to one of higher energy. Of course, an electronic transition may be accompanied by vibrational and rotational changes.

Absorption of radiation in the infrared region does not lead to electronic excitation but to changes in vibrational energy. Electromagnetic radiation in the infrared region contains only low energy components, and absorption of such radiation does not impart sufficient energy to a molecule to cause electronic transitions. When radiation in the infrared region is employed, only vibrational and rotational changes can be observed. The latter appear as the fine structure in the vibrational spectrum.

Electromagnetic radiation in the far infrared or in the microwave region causes rotational transitions whereby a molecule absorbs radiation and enters a higher energy rotational state. In all cases (electronic, vibrational and rotational transitions), the gain in energy by the molecule equals the energy of the radiation absorbed. The wavelengths of the absorbed radiation can be measured experimentally, and the spectra resulting from such processes are the absorption spectra frequently used to characterize organic compounds. In addition, a material previously excited by some process and existing in an excited state can emit electromagnetic radiation and enter a lower energy state. These processes give rise to emission spectra.

10.2 The Franck-Condon Principle

Before discussing in detail the ideas that were just presented, we present the Franck-Condon principle. This principle, similar to the Born-Oppenheimer approximation encountered in quantum mechanics, states that electronic excitation occurs so rapidly that the nuclei do not have time to change their positions or their momenta during the transition. Thus, if a hydrogen molecule in its ground electronic, vibrational, and rotational state is excited, this principle states that the excitation will occur before the nuclei can rearrange themselves. Therefore, if the nuclei are at their equilibrium distance 0.74 Å when the excitation occurs, they will also be at this distance immediately after the excitation.

The nuclei do not move during a Franck-Condon transition. Excitation of a molecule in its ground electronic, vibrational, and rotational state can lead to an excited state that is electronically, vibrationally, and rotationally excited. Another transition that is mentioned frequently is the 0-0 transition. This is a transition between ground vibrational states. These are shown in Figure 10–1.

When a molecule is in its ground vibrational state, the most probable positions for the nuclei are their equilibrium positions; however, this is not true for excited vibrational states where the most probable positions of the nuclei are towards the extremes of the vibration.

Excitation of a molecule can lead to dissociation even in cases where a metastable excited state exists. This occurs when the Franck-Condon transition leads to a vibrational level that is above the dissociation energy of the excited state; see Figure 10–2.

10.3 Transition Probabilities and the Einstein Coefficients

The irradiation of an organic compound with electromagnetic radiation of appropriate frequency v causes that compound to absorb radiation and enter into a higher energy state. The probability that the event takes place can be calculated, and the change in energy that accompanies the process is equal to hv:

$$\Delta E = hv = \frac{hc}{\lambda}$$

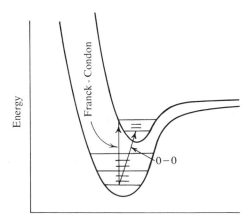

Figure 10–1

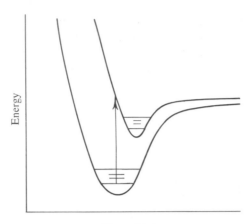

Figure 10–2

A molecule acted upon by electromagnetic radiation absorbs energy equal to $E_n - E_m$ and makes a transition from a lower energy state E_m to a state of higher energy E_n. The electromagnetic radiation acts as a small perturbation, and using time dependent perturbation theory, it is possible to calculate the probability per unit time that this perturbation actually causes such a transition. This quantity is called the transition rate for absorption R_{mn} and has the same meaning as a specific rate constant in chemical kinetics. Thus the rate of passage of molecules from E_m to E_n equals $R_{mn}N_m$, where N_m is the number of molecules having energy E_m.

Related to the probability of excitation is the probability of emission. A molecule in an excited state with energy E_n eventually makes a "spontaneous" transition from that state to some state of lower energy E_m, and accompanying this process is the emission of electromagnetic radiation with energy $E_n - E_m$. The probability per unit time that this transition will take place is called the transition rate for spontaneous emission S_{nm}. Even spontaneous emission requires a perturbation of some sort, and this type of emission is treated most successfully using quantum electrodynamics.

In addition, a third quantity, the transition rate for induced emission R_{nm}, must be considered. This quantity can also be evaluated using perturbation theory. It turns out that the the transition rate for induced emission equals that for absorption:

$$R_{nm} = R_{mn}$$

The process of spontaneous emission is not the same as induced emission. The latter depends upon the electromagnetic radiation applied to the molecule; however, spontaneous emission depends only upon the particular molecule, and the rate for the spontaneous process is not proportional to the applied radiation.

The quantities R_{mn}, R_{nm}, and S_{nm} can be considered the specific rate constants for the various processes.

$$\frac{dN_n}{dt} = R_{mn}N_m - R_{nm}N_n - S_{nm}N_n$$

If in addition to the transitions between E_m and E_n other transitions take place, these must also be included in the general rate expression, which becomes a summation:

$$\frac{dN_n}{dt} = \sum_i (R_{in} + S_{in})N_i - \sum_i (R_{ni} + S_{ni})N_n$$

Furthermore, we have considered only those transitions accompanied by absorption or emission of electromagnetic radiation. Other energy transfers also take place.

It is possible to relate all three quantities R_{mn}, R_{nm}, and S_{nm} by using a statistical treatment developed by Einstein. We assume that a number of molecules of the same type are being irradiated and that the system is in equilibrium under these conditions. Thus, the number of molecules entering an energy state E_n is equal to the number of molecules leaving that state. We do not assume that the electromagnetic radiation incident upon these molecules contains only a single frequency; instead we assume that at the temperature T the radiation has the spectral distribution characteristic of a black body at that same temperature. A black body heated to a temperature T emits light, and we assume that it is this light that is used to irradiate the molecules. It is convenient to speak of the energy content per unit volume of this radiation (designated as ρ). This energy density for photons of frequency v is equal to the energy of a single photon (hv), times the number of photons having that energy (n), divided by the volume occupied by them (V):

$$\rho = \frac{nhv}{V}$$

For a black body it turns out that the energy density is

$$\rho = \frac{8\pi hv^3}{c^3} \frac{1}{e^{hv/kT} - 1}$$

where h is Planck's constant, k is Boltzmann's constant, and c is the velocity of light.

Now the rate of passage of molecules from a lower energy state to a higher energy state N_{mn} is equal to the transition rate for a single molecule R_{mn} times the number of molecules in the lower energy state N_m:

$$N_{mn} = R_{mn}N_m$$

The probability R_{mn} is proportional to the energy density of the radiation ρ.

$$R_{mn} = B_{mn}\rho$$

Where B_{mn} is a constant of proportionality known as Einstein's coefficient of absorption.

Then

$$N_{mn} = B_{mn}\rho N_m$$

At equilibrium this must equal the rate of transitions from the higher energy state to the lower energy state N_{nm}.

$$N_{nm} = N_{mn}$$

Furthermore, the rate of transitions from the high to the low energy state is equal to the number of molecules in the high energy state N_n times the probability that a single molecule will make either an induced emission or a spontaneous emission $(R_{nm} + S_{nm})$:

$$N_{nm} = (R_{nm} + S_{nm})N_n$$

The spontaneous emissions are independent of the energy density of the electromagnetic radiation, but the induced probability is proportional to ρ:

$$R_{nm} = B_{nm}\rho$$

Where B_{nm} is a constant of proportionality known as Einstein's coefficient of induced emission.

Since $R_{nm} = R_{mn}$ we find that,

$$B_{nm} = B_{mn}$$

Making the appropriate substitutions leads to the expression,

$$B_{mn}\rho N_m = (B_{nm}\rho + S_{nm})N_n$$

For the sake of conformity we set the term S_{nm} equal to a new term A_{nm} called Einstein's coefficient of spontaneous emission. The equation can now be transformed to read:

$$\frac{N_n}{N_m} = \frac{B_{mn}\rho}{B_{nm}\rho + A_{nm}}$$

Since these molecules obey Boltzmann's distribution law, at the temperature T the probability that a molecule has energy E_n is given by $Ae^{-E_n/kT}$ while the probability that the molecule has energy E_m is equal to $Ae^{-E_m/kT}$. The ratio of the number of molecules in the higher energy state to the number of molecules in the lower energy state is given by,

$$\frac{N_n}{N_m} = \frac{e^{-E_n/kT}}{e^{-E_m/kT}} = e^{-(E_n - E_m)/kT}$$

Since the difference between these energy states equals hv, this becomes,

$$\frac{N_n}{N_m} = e^{-hv/kT}$$

In terms of the Einstein coefficients and ρ,

$$e^{-hv/kT} = \frac{B_{mn}\rho}{B_{nm}\rho + A_{nm}}$$

Multiplying both sides of this expression by $e^{hv/kT}$ and solving for ρ yields,

$$\rho = \frac{A_{nm}}{B_{mn}e^{hv/kT} - B_{nm}}$$

Finally equating ρ to the black body expression,

$$\frac{8\pi hv^3}{c^3} \frac{1}{e^{hv/kT} - 1} = \frac{A_{nm}}{B_{mn}e^{hv/kT} - B_{nm}}$$

Since $B_{mn} = B_{nm}$, we find

$$A_{nm} = \frac{8\pi hv^3}{c^3} B_{nm}$$

We have succeeded in relating the various coefficients.

$$A_{nm} = \frac{8\pi hv^3}{c^3} B_{nm}$$

$$B_{mn} = B_{nm}$$

For the transition rate constants,

$$S_{nm} = A_{nm} = \frac{8\pi hv^3}{c^3} B_{nm}$$

$$R_{nm} = B_{nm}\rho$$

$$R_{mn} = B_{mn}\rho = B_{nm}\rho$$

Since S_{nm} is equal to A_{nm}, we find that the probability of a spontaneous emission by an excited molecule is related to the cube of the frequency (energy) of the emitted radiation.

In order to obtain the transition moment for radiation we proceed further. Every molecule has a center of positive charge and a center of negative charge. If these coincide, the molecule has no dipole moment. When they do not coincide, a permanent electric dipole moment μ exists. We now construct a coordinate system so that the origin of this system is the center of positive charge of the molecule. The dipole moment for the molecule is then given by

$$\mu = \sum_i e\mathbf{r}_i$$

where $\mathbf{r}_i$ is the position vector for electron i, and the summation is over all the electrons in the molecule.

According to classical physics, absorption or emission of radiation can take place when the charge distribution within a molecule changes with time. We assume that this charge distribution is indicated by the electric dipole moment. (Magnetic interactions also cause transitions. We do not consider factors such as the electric quadrupole moment or the magnetic dipole moment, and so forth.) Thus, absorption or emission of radiation requires a changing dipole moment. If the dipole moment of the molecule is not a function of the time, the molecule can neither absorb nor radiate. We describe a molecule by a function ψ which includes not only the electronic positions but also the vibrational and rotational states of the molecule,

$$\psi = \psi_e \psi_v \psi_r$$

and

$$E = E_e + E_v + E_r$$

and as long as the molecule is described by the same ψ, neither absorption nor emission is possible. Under these circumstances there is no change in the dipole moment.

Classically an electron i has a certain position within the molecule, and as long as μ_i is constant, there is no emission of radiation. However, if its position oscillates with time, electromagnetic waves can be emitted with frequency equal to that of the oscillation. Quantum mechanically, this implies that there must be a mixing of ψ's, which leads to an oscillating probability density.

Prior to radiation the molecule has energy E_n, and the system is described by ψ_n. After emission the molecule has energy E_m, and the system is described by ψ_m. The transition must be accompanied by a change in the dipole moment μ. These ideas are expressed quantum mechanically by the fact that if the transition is to take place, the transition moment μ_{nm} cannot equal zero:

$$\mu_{nm} = \int \psi_n \mu \psi_m \, d\tau$$

Notice that μ is in the integrand of the equation for the transition moment. Therefore, this μ is not the dipole moment of the molecule either before or after radiation but its moment during radiation. During the transition the molecule is described neither by ψ_n alone nor by ψ_m alone, but by a linear combination of these two functions.

The transition moment is naturally expected to be related to the coefficients and transition rates discussed earlier; such a relationship does exist. As in most quantum mechanical relationships, it is the square of the transition moment that is physically significant. The relationships for the Einstein coefficients are,

$$B_{nm} = \frac{8\pi^3}{3h^2} |\mu_{nm}|^2$$

$$B_{mn} = \frac{8\pi^3}{3h^2} |\mu_{mn}|^2$$

$$A_{nm} = \frac{64\pi^4 v^3}{3hc^3} |\mu_{nm}|^2$$

$|\mu_{nm}|$ refers to absolute value. For the transition rate constants,

$$R_{nm} = \rho \frac{8\pi^3}{3h^2} |\mu_{nm}|^2$$

$$R_{mn} = \rho \frac{8\pi^3}{3h^2} |\mu_{mn}|^2$$

$$S_{nm} = \frac{64\pi^4 v^3}{3hc^3} |\mu_{nm}|^2$$

The transition probabilities depend in a very definite way upon the transition moment; the larger the moment, the greater the likelihood of a transition per unit time. The probability of a molecule making a transition depends not only upon the initial state but also upon the final state, for both of these quantities (ψ_m and ψ_n) enter into the transition moment.

We have developed expressions for transitions that involve only the electric dipole moment. We have not considered either the electric quadrupole or the magnetic dipole moments. These can also change because of interactions of the molecule with the electromagnetic radiation, and even when strong transitions are forbidden because the electric dipole transition moment equals zero, weaker transitions due to these other interactions may be possible.

Consider a molecule in an excited state. The decay of this excited species in the absence of induced emission is a first order process depending only on the value of the spontaneous emission rate constant S_{nm}. If a number of decay routes are available, the total probability per unit time that an excited molecule decay by any one of these routes is,

$$\sum_i S_{ni}$$

where the i states are the states of lower energy than n into which the molecule can enter after radiating. If N molecules are in the state n, then the total number of transitions per unit time is,

$$N \sum_i S_{ni}$$

This is a first order process. The decrease in the number of excited molecules is proportional to the number of molecules actually in the excited state. The constants of proportionality, the specific rate constants, are the S_{ni}:

$$-\frac{dN}{dt} = N \sum_i S_{ni}$$

or

$$-\frac{dN}{N} = \sum_i S_{ni} \, dt$$

Integrating between the limits 0 and t affords the usual first order result,

$$N = N_0 \, e^{-\Sigma_i S_{ni} t}$$

The number of molecules decaying into lower energy states follows an exponential rate law.

We can obtain the average lifetime of an excited molecule by using the theorem of the mean which states that the following equality holds,

$$\tau \int_0^\infty N \, dt = \int_0^\infty t N \, dt$$

where τ is the average lifetime, that is, the average time spent by a molecule in the excited state. Substituting our previous result this becomes,

$$\tau = \frac{\displaystyle\int_0^\infty t \, e^{-\Sigma_i S_{ni} t} \, dt}{\displaystyle\int_0^\infty e^{-\Sigma_i S_{ni} t} \, dt}$$

This equation can be evaluated and the result is,

$$\tau = \frac{1}{\displaystyle\sum_i S_{ni}}$$

As expected, the lifetime of an excited molecule is inversely proportional to the probability for decay. When decay is rapid, the lifetime is short; when decay is slow, the average lifetime is long.

It is also possible to develop relationships between the lifetime of the excited molecules and the absorption of radiation which allows lower energy molecules to enter that excited state. When the absorption is strong, the lifetime is short, and when the absorption is weak, the lifetime of the excited state is long. This idea follows quite naturally from the discussions of the transition moment, the Einstein coefficients, and the transition probability rates. A relationship also exists between the lifetime of a state and the width of the spectral lines arising from transitions into and out of that state. Consider transitions between the ground state and an excited state. The width of the spectral line can be measured, and the width Δv at half the maximum peak height (see Figure 10–3) is related to the lifetime of the excited state by the equation,

$$\tau = \frac{1}{2\pi \Delta v} = \frac{h}{2\pi \Gamma}$$

where $\Gamma = h\Delta v$.

The lifetime of the excited state is inversely proportional to the width of the band. If efficient modes of deactivating the excited molecule exist, the band is broad. If only ineffective means are available, a narrow spectral band is observed. Band broadening and band narrowing can be due to a number of sources, but the fact that the relationship exists at all can be traced back to the uncertainty principle:

$$\Delta E \, \Delta t \simeq \frac{h}{2\pi}$$

The uncertainty in the time for a transition into a lower energy state must be at least of the same order of magnitude as the lifetime of the species,

$$\Delta t \simeq \tau$$

The uncertainty in the energy is related to the uncertainty in the frequency Δv by the equation, $\Delta E = h\Delta v$, and ΔE is therefore related to the width of the

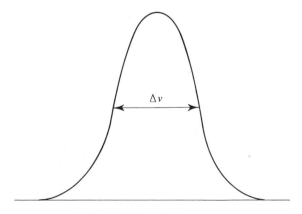

Figure 10–3

spectral line. Substitution into the uncertainty relationship affords the desired result.

There exist in chemical spectroscopy certain selection rules which indicate whether a transition from one state to another is allowed or forbidden. All of these rules are founded upon the idea that if a transition from one energy state to another is to take place, the transition moment μ_{nm} cannot equal zero. If it does, the transition probabilities equal zero. Naturally, the larger the value of μ_{nm}, the greater the likelihood of transitions into and out of a state. We have already noted one requirement, that a change in the dipole moment must accompany the transition. We present others in the following sections.

10.4 Ultraviolet Spectroscopy

In ultraviolet spectroscopy we are concerned with electronic transitions, that is, transitions involving changes in ψ_e. An electron is promoted from one molecular orbital to another having higher energy. Changes in vibrational and rotational states can also take place, and a molecule in the state ψ_m where

$$\psi_m = \psi_e \psi_v \psi_r$$

can be excited to the state ψ_n

$$\psi_n = \psi'_e \psi'_v \psi'_r$$

However, energy differences between the various vibrational and rotational states are small. Consequently, the excitations,

$$\psi_m \longrightarrow \psi_n \quad \text{and} \quad \psi_m \longrightarrow \psi'_n,$$

$$\psi'_n = \psi'_e \psi''_v \psi''_r$$

where the same electronic state ψ'_e is involved but different vibrational and rotational energy levels, differ in their energy requirement to only a small degree. As a result, absorption of radiation for these two excitations takes place in the same region of the ultraviolet.

We assume that in passing from one electronic state to another, only a single electron in the molecule changes its orbital. Two electron changes are possible, but such transitions have much lower probabilities.

An electron is promoted from one molecular orbital to another of higher energy. Ethylene has two π molecular orbitals, ψ_1 designated here as π and ψ_2 designated as π^*. In the ground state, π contains two electrons of opposite spin while π^* is empty. Excitation of σ electrons is possible, and promotion to σ^* orbitals is conceivable; however, most organic applications involve only the π and π^* molecular orbitals of an alkene. Such a transition from a bonding π molecular orbital of an alkene to an antibonding π^* molecular orbital is appropriately termed a π-π^* transition.

In carbonyl systems there are in addition to the π electrons, the nonbonding electrons about the oxygen. These electrons occupy sp^2 hybridized nonbonding orbitals designated as n. Excitation of a carbonyl compound can involve not only π-π^* transitions, but also n-π^* transitions whereby one of these nonbonding electrons is promoted into the π^* orbital.

In ultraviolet spectroscopy radiation is absorbed by a molecule and an electron is promoted. The geometry of the excited state can differ from that of the ground state, for a change in hybridization may accompany the excitation.

In the ground state of ethylene each bond contains two electrons of opposite spin. Such a system containing only paired electrons is called a singlet state. In the excited state one of the π electrons has been promoted into the π^* orbital. Both the π and π^* orbitals contain a single electron, and these may have parallel or antiparallel spin. If spins are paired (antiparallel), the state is an excited singlet state; unpaired spins lead to an excited triplet state. Thus, both singlet and triplet excited states are possible.

One of the more important selection rules in ultraviolet spectroscopy is that no change occurs in the spin multiplicity during a transition, that is, singlet-singlet and triplet-triplet transitions are allowed, while singlet-triplet and triplet-singlet transitions are said to be spin forbidden. This selection rule is, of course, a generalization based upon an approximate transition moment and some exceptions do occur.

If the excited state is a singlet state, it may return readily to the ground state since singlet-singlet transitions are allowed. A return not involving emission of radiation is called internal conversion; return accompanied by emission is called fluorescence. A transition between states having different spin multiplicity is termed intersystem crossing when it is not accompanied by emission of radiation and phosphorescence when the change in spin multiplicity is accompanied by emission of radiation.

We have presented the idea that transitions between different spin states are forbidden, and the origin of this selection rule comes from the fact that if a transition is to take place, the transition moment must exist.

We assume that ψ_m describes the molecule when it has energy E_m and ψ_n describes the molecule in the state with energy E_n. We further assume in this discussion that ψ_m contains a factor σ_m that describes the spin states of all the electrons when the molecule has energy E_m. Analogously, the function ψ_n contains a term σ_n describing the electronic spins when the molecule is in the state with energy E_n. We write

$$\psi_m = \phi_m \sigma_m$$

$$\psi_n = \phi_n \sigma_n$$

where φ_m describes the spacial electronic, vibrational, and rotational states, and σ_m the spin state when the molecule has energy E_m. A similar interpretation is given to φ_n and σ_n. In terms of these functions the transition moment becomes,

$$\boldsymbol{\mu}_{mn} = \int \phi_m \boldsymbol{\mu} \phi_n \sigma_m \sigma_n \, d\tau$$

The spin functions σ_m and σ_n form an orthonormal set. When σ_m and σ_n describe the same spin state, the integral exists. When σ_m and σ_n represent different spin states, the integral equals zero because of the orthogonality of these spin functions. Thus singlet-triplet and triplet-singlet transitions are forbidden because the integral equals zero in such cases.

Actually exceptions to this requirement occur but with diminished intensity. With atoms of higher atomic number and with some molecules, the spin and orbital angular momenta become mixed. This mixing called $L \cdot S$ or spin-orbital coupling mixes singlet and triplet states and allows these "forbidden" transitions to take place.

Ultraviolet spectroscopy serves as a tool in two broad areas. The various electronic transitions can be investigated by examining the spectra of compounds of known structure, and in this way the different transitions and their energy requirements can be studied. In the other broad area, ultraviolet spectra serve as an aid in structural elucidations. By comparing the spectra of materials of unknown structure with the spectra of known compounds, information concerning the unknowns is obtained. A set of empirical rules developed by Dr. R. B. Woodward is useful for this type of work.

Examination of the spectra of a number of known compounds has lead to the establishment of a set of empirical rules. Employing these rules in conjunction with the spectra of materials of unknown structure gives some information concerning the nature of the unknown materials. Solvent effects have been considered, for an absorption spectrum is somewhat solvent dependant, and corrections must be made when more than a single solvent is employed. However, steric effects are not treated explicitly, and deviations can occur when bulky groups are introduced. The steroid testosterone **1**,

1

contains the chromophore:

$$C=C-C=O$$

to which various substituents have been added. The ultraviolet spectrum of testosterone has been examined in a number of solvents; the results are tabulated in Table 10–1. These results demonstrate clearly that the polarity of the solvent does influence the position of λ_{max}. The extinction coefficient ε is virtually unaffected.

Table 10–1

Solvent	$\lambda_{max}(m\mu)$
Hexane	230
Ether	234
Ethanol	241

The empirical rules, Woodward's rules, which were mentioned previously are used with α,β-unsaturated ketones and with conjugated dienes. Simple alkenes generally absorb in the region below 200 mμ, and difficulties due to absorption by the solvent arise at these shorter λ. In the region between 200 mμ and 400 mμ measurements can be performed readily, and compounds that absorb in this region of the ultraviolet have been studied extensively. For carbonyl compounds the parent chromophore is the α,β-unsaturated system:

$$\overset{\beta}{C}=\overset{\alpha}{C}-C=O$$

which is assumed to have a λ_{max} in ethanol at 215 mμ. The introduction of an alkyl substituent at the α or β position causes a shift in λ_{max} to longer wavelengths, a bathochromic shift. The introduction of an α substituent causes a shift of 10 mμ while a β-alkyl group causes a shift of 12 mμ. These terms must be added to the base value of 215 mμ in order to obtain the total value when such substituents are present. In addition, 5 mμ must be added when the double bond is exocyclic to a ring. Thus the system **2**,

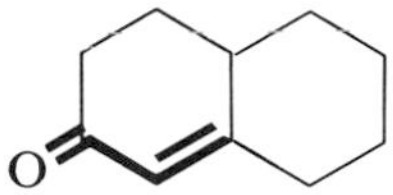

2

contains no α-alkyl substituents, two β-alkyl substituents, and the olefinic linkage is exocyclic to a six membered ring. In ethanol this compound is predicted to absorb at

$$215 + 2(12) + 5 = 244 \; m\mu$$

Testosterone **1** and corticosterone **3** have this chromophore. The value determined experimentally for corticosterone is 240 mμ.

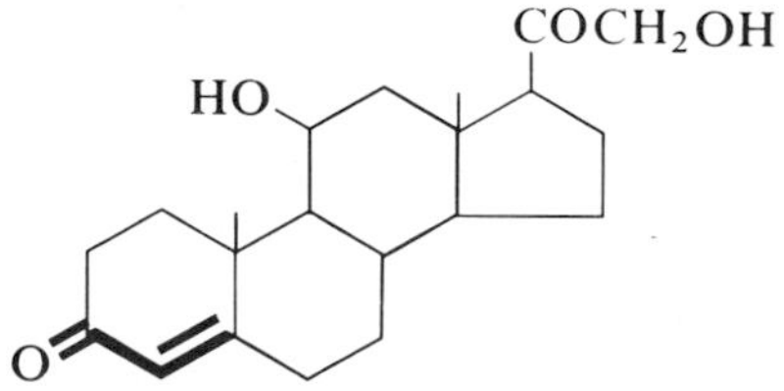

3

Predicted values generally correlate well with observed values. The steroid cholest-1-en-3-one (**4**) is predicted to absorb at 227 mμ; the observed value is 230 mμ:

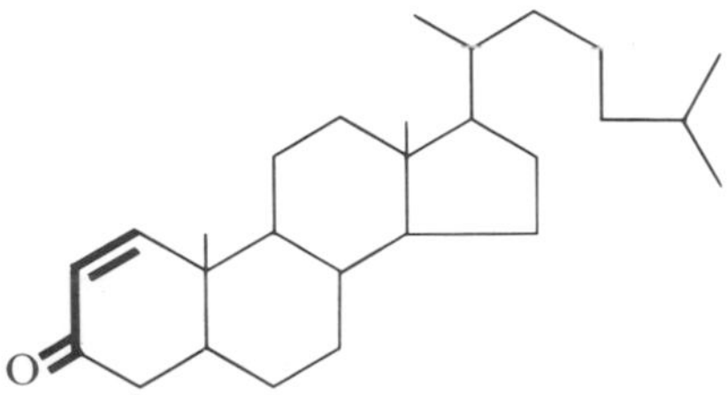

4

predicted value = 215 + 12 = 227 mμ

The steroid **5** has a predicted value for λ_{max} equal to 249 mμ; that observed experimentally is 252 mμ:

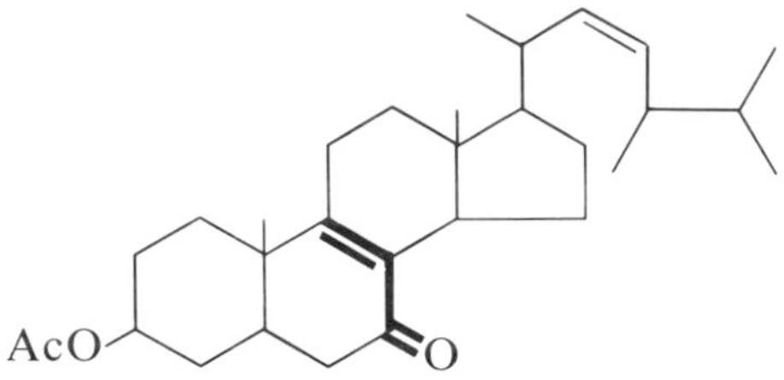

5

predicted value = 215 + 10 + 2(12) = 249 mμ

When the chromophore contains an additional double bond in conjugation,

$$\overset{\delta}{C}=\overset{\gamma}{C}-\overset{\beta}{C}=\overset{\alpha}{C}-C=O$$

another 30 mμ must be added, and the introduction of alkyl substituents at the γ and δ positions increases λ_{max} by 18 mμ for each group.

Thus **6**, which is calculated to absorb at 280 mμ, actually has a λ_{max} at 283 mμ:

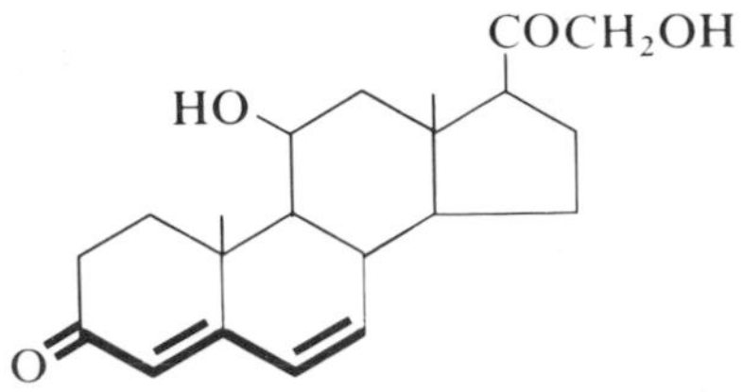

6

Dienes are treated in similar fashion. A diene such as butadiene absorbs at 217 mμ in hexane. If one measures λ_{max} for a large number of dienes and then determines the average value, 214 mμ is obtained for the chromophore,

$$C=C-C=C$$

when the two double bonds are in different rings (hetroannular dienes),

7 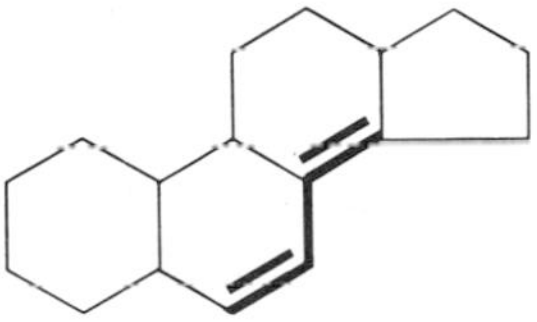   **8**

Alkyl substituents cause a bathochromic shift equal to 5 mμ; an exocyclic double bond also has this effect (5 mμ). In contrast to the solvent effects observed for α,β-unsaturated carbonyl compounds, no such shifts are observed when dienes are studied. The value of λ_{max} for dienes is independent of the solvent.

A diene such as **7** has a predicted absorption spectrum having λ_{max} at 234 mμ:

$$214 + 3(5) + 5 = 234 \text{ m}\mu$$

The steroid cholesta-3,5-diene **9**, which does have this chromophore, absorbs at exactly this value:

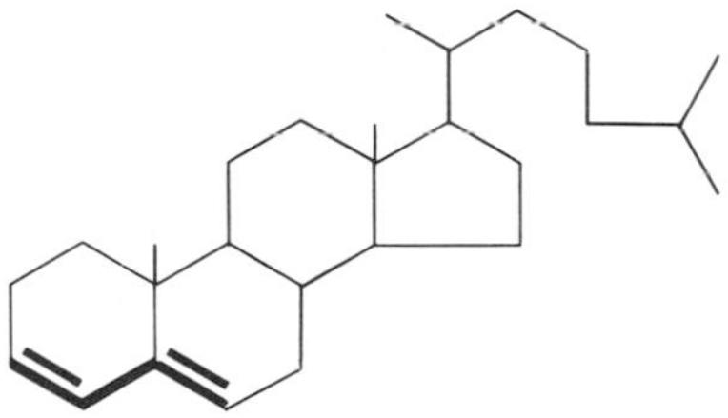

9

Homoannular dienes have both double bonds in the same ring, that is, they have the chromophore,

In systems of this type, λ_{max} for the parent chromophoric system is 253 mμ. The steroid ergosterol **10** contains a homoannular diene. Since alkyl groups and exocyclic double bonds exert the same influence in both cases, ergosterol has a

predicted λ_{max} at 283 mμ. The value observed for this steroid is 280 mμ:

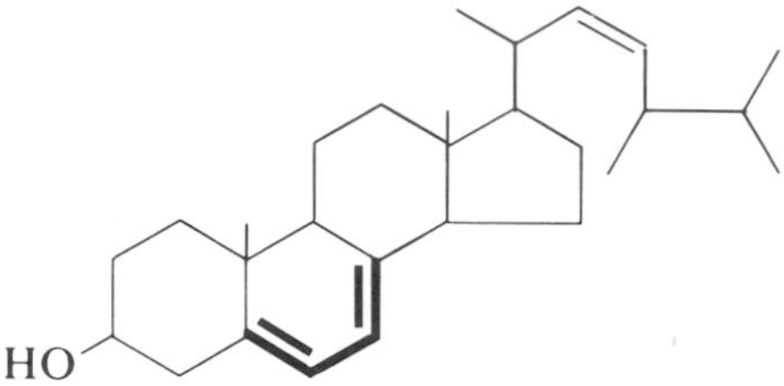

10

predicted value = 253 + 4(5) + 2(5) = 283 mμ

We see how useful these rules are. Taking the ultraviolet spectrum of a compound gives information concerning its structure. Of course, additional evidence is necessary, and a variety of other instrumental methods are available. The infrared spectrum affords information concerning functional groups while the nuclear magnetic resonance spectrum (NMR) indicates the types of hydrogen atoms present in the system and their environment. Instrumental methods simplify enormously the task of the organic chemist. Evidence that would require years to obtain using ordinary synthetic or degradative procedures is obtained in a matter of minutes with modern instruments.

In this discussion we have considered only the near ultraviolet because it is in this region that most of the research has been conducted. Absorption also takes place in the far ultraviolet (the region under 200 mμ); however, studies in this region must be made with special equipment. Consequently, research in this area is more difficult. Less is known concerning the behavior of organic systems when irradiated with electromagnetic radiation of shorter wavelengths.

One requirement that was not mentioned previously is that the extinction coefficient must have a reasonable value. This extinction coefficient ε indicates the intensity of the absorption. Thus while simple nonconjugated carbonyl compounds such as acetone do absorb in the near ultraviolet, ε is extremely small (~ 16 for acetone). Therefore, these compounds are not studied conveniently in the ultraviolet. They can, however, be investigated by using infrared spectroscopy. Simple ketones such as acetone show weak absorption in the region between 270-285 mμ. This band is due to the "forbidden" n-π^* transition. Since this transition is forbidden, its intensity is weak. Strong absorption does take place for these systems in the region between 185-195 mμ. The transition is an allowed π-π^* transition and the extinction coefficient is moderately large ($\varepsilon \simeq 1000$). However, spectroscopic studies in this region are difficult, and more work is necessary. The energy changes for the transitions are shown in Figure 10–4.

Simple alkenes such as ethylene also show strong absorption. For ethylene, the allowed π-π^* transition occurs at 175 mμ with $\varepsilon \simeq 5000$. Again, this is beyond the range of most instruments.

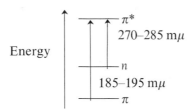

Figure 10–4. Carbonyl absorption for nonconjugated systems.

10.5 Infrared Spectroscopy

A molecule absorbs radiation in the infrared region and undergoes a transition from one vibrational or rotational state to another. Now the infrared range is arbitrarily divided into near and far regions, and absorption in the near ($\lambda = 1\,\mu$ to $25\,\mu$, where $1\,\mu = 10^4\,\text{Å} = 10^{-4}\,\text{cm}$) causes vibrational changes with rotational changes appearing as fine structure in the vibrational spectrum. Absorption in the far infrared ($25\,\mu$ to $1\,\text{mm}$) causes rotational excitation. Absorption in this far region or in the microwave range affords rotational spectra, for the energy gained as a result of the absorption is not sufficient for vibrational excitation. Thus, in the near infrared we are generally concerned with vibrational transitions,

$$\psi_v \longrightarrow \psi'_v$$

while measurements in the far infrared region involve rotational changes:

$$\psi_r \longrightarrow \psi'_r$$

This separation of the infrared range into near and far regions (above and below $25\,\mu$) is, of course, arbitrary and is based upon the theoretical considerations just discussed. Rotational and vibrational transitions are shown in Figure 10–5.

After a vibrational transition, the amplitude of the vibration has increased, while a rotational transition leads to a more rapidly rotating molecule. A change in the dipole moment vector must take place during either transition.

Consider a molecule of hydrogen chloride. The nuclei are vibrating back and forth, and the vibrational energy of such a system is given by,

$$E_v = (n + 1/2)hv \qquad n = 0, 1, 2, \cdots$$

where v is the frequency of the vibration, and n is the vibrational quantum number. If radiation having the same frequency v with which the molecule vibrates is incident upon that molecule, radiation may be absorbed by the system, and the hydrogen chloride molecule then enters a higher energy state. If as a result of the transition, a hydrogen chloride molecule initially in its ground state with only zero-point energy ($n = 0$) enters the first excited vibrational

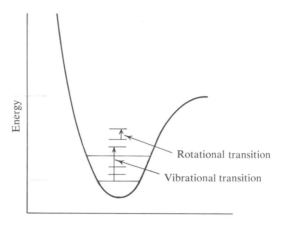

Energy

Rotational transition

Vibrational transition

Figure 10–5

state ($n = 1$), the change in energy is,

$$\Delta E_v = 3/2hv - 1/2hv = hv$$

The molecule absorbs radiation of frequency v and gains energy equal to hv. Absorption in the infrared is expressed in terms of the wavelengths or in terms of the wave numbers $\bar{v}$ of the absorbed radiation, these are related as follows,

$$\bar{v} = \frac{1}{\lambda}$$

Since the energy change ΔE_v resulting from a transition is related to the frequency v and the wavelength λ of the absorbed radiation, using the previous equation, it is also possible to relate ΔE_v to $\bar{v}$. This relationship is given by the equation,

$$\Delta E_v = hv = h\frac{c}{\lambda} = hc\bar{v}$$

We have mentioned that $\bar{v}$ is just the reciprocal of λ when the two have the proper units. However, since λ is usually expressed in μ (10^{-4} cm) and $\bar{v}$ in reciprocal centimeters (cm^{-1}), a conversion factor of 10^4 must be employed to convert wavelengths in μ to wave numbers in cm^{-1}.

$$\bar{v}(\text{cm}^{-1}) = \frac{10^4}{\lambda(\mu)}$$

In order to discuss the phenomenon of absorption in the near infrared more fully we must first consider explicitly the modes of vibration of a molecule. A nonlinear molecule composed of N atoms has $3N - 6$ internal vibrational degrees of freedom. These degrees of freedom are called the normal modes of vibration. A linear molecule has $3N - 5$ normal vibrational modes. Thus a diatomic molecule such as hydrogen chloride has only a single mode of vibration, the stretching vibration.

$$\leftarrow H - Cl \rightarrow$$

A molecule of hydrogen chloride vibrates with frequency v. If radiation of this same frequency is incident upon the molecule, radiation may be absorbed, and the molecule enters a vibrationally excited state in which the amplitude of the vibration increases:

$$\psi_v \longrightarrow \psi'_v$$

and

$$\Delta E_v = hv$$

During the vibration, the internuclear distance between two dissimilar nuclei changes. This changes the dipole moment. If a vibrational mode gives rise to a change in the dipole moment, then that vibrational mode is active in the near infrared. Since the dipole moment does change during the stretching vibration of hydrogen chloride, this molecule is active.

The frequency of the vibration equals the frequency of the absorbed radiation, and it is possible to relate this to the reduced mass μ by considering a molecule of hydrogen chloride as a vibrating spring (harmonic oscillator). The equation relating μ and v is,

$$2\pi v = \left(\frac{k}{\mu}\right)^{1/2}$$

where k is the force constant for the vibration and μ is the reduced mass $(m_1 m_2/m_1 + m_2)$. The force constant k indicates the ease or difficulty of distortion of the bond, that is, it indicates the stiffness of the spring.

Force constants can be calculated once $\bar{v}$ has been measured:

$$2\pi v = \left(\frac{k}{\mu}\right)^{1/2}$$

and

$$v = \frac{c}{\lambda} = c\bar{v}$$

therefore

$$2\pi c\bar{v} = \left(\frac{k}{\mu}\right)^{1/2}$$

and

$$k = 4\pi^2 c^2 \bar{v}^2 \mu$$

The value of $\bar{\nu}$ for monomeric hydrogen chloride (HCl^{35}) in the gas phase is 2886 cm^{-1}, and this affords for the force constant,

$$k = 5 \times 10^5 \text{ dyne/cm}$$

Although hydrogen chloride has only a single vibrational mode, the compound absorbs at more than a single wavelength in the near infrared, and there are a number of reasons why the infrared spectrum of a molecule contains more than a single sharp absorption peak.

Hydrogen chloride in its ground state is characterized by the vibrational quantum number $n = 0$. Excitation of the molecule to the state $n = 1$ is called the fundamental transition; the peak is the fundamental absorption band. This occurs for hydrogen chloride in the gas phase at about 2886 cm^{-1}.

The chief selection rule for absorption or emission of radiation by a vibrating system is,

$$\Delta n = \pm 1$$

But the assumption that hydrogen chloride executes simple harmonic motion is only approximately correct, and "forbidden" transitions do occur although with diminished intensity. Thus in addition to the fundamental transition, transitions also take place from the ground state to the second excited state ($n = 0$ to $n = 2$), from the ground state to the third excited state ($\Delta n = 3$), and so forth. The peak intensity decreases rapidly, however, as Δn increases (the transition probability decreases). The transition from $n = 0$ to $n = 2$ is called the first overtone, that from $n = 0$ to $n = 3$, the second overtone. Since the first overtone requires approximately twice the energy of the fundamental transition, we expect a peak at twice the wave number. The actual value is 5668 cm^{-1}. The second overtone appears at 8347 cm^{-1}, slightly less than three times the wave number of the fundamental.

The spectrum of hydrogen chloride also depends upon its concentration, its environment, and the resolution of the instrument. If an absorption band is examined under high resolution using a low concentration of the gas, the fine structure associated with each peak appears.

Hydrogen chloride molecules exist in a number of rotational states prior to excitation and enter different rotational states after excitation. Thus a molecule in the ground vibrational and first excited rotational state ($n = 0, J = 1$) can undergo a fundamental transition to either the state ($n = 1, J = 0$) or the state ($n = 1, J = 2$). These transitions are,

$$\Delta n = +1 \qquad \Delta n = +1$$

$$\Delta J = -1 \qquad \Delta J = +1$$

Both transitions are allowed, yet they obviously have different energy requirements. Therefore, these transitions occur at slightly different wave numbers. A number of fine structure components of this type make up each absorption peak, and under the proper conditions these can be resolved.

The fact that chlorine is present as two naturally occurring isotopes also influences the fine structure spectrum. Their ratio is about $3:1$, and in a high resolution spectrum each fine structure component appears as a doublet with this relative intensity.

Finally the spectrum is influenced by the environment in which the absorbing molecule finds itself. As a gas phase monomer, the fundamental for hydrogen chloride occurs at 2886 cm^{-1}. As a solid or in solvents the absorption band is shifted. For example, in the organic solvent mesitylene, absorption takes place at 2712 cm^{-1}, while in ether it occurs at 2393 cm^{-1}. Since hydrogen chloride forms complexes in solution, a change in the spectrum is not unexpected. Changes in pressure influence the spectrum of the gas phase and changes in temperature alter the liquid phase spectra.

The fundamental under medium and high resolution appears in Figure 10–6.

We show the effect of environmental changes on the first overtone (Figure 10–7).[1]

A molecule generally has a number of modes of vibration, and corresponding to each mode there is a vibrational energy and a vibrational quantum number n. When each of the vibrational quantum numbers is equal to zero, the molecule is in its ground state. If it absorbs electromagnetic radiation so that one mode of vibration is excited to the state $n - 1$ while the other modes are still characterized by $n = 0$, the molecule has undergone a fundamental transition. If this mode is doubly excited, the transition is called the first overtone, that is, a transition from $n = 0$ to $n = 2$. If the mode is triply excited (to $n = 3$), the

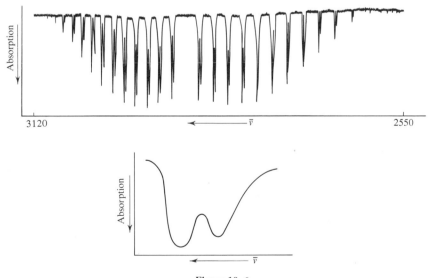

Figure 10–6

[1] W. Brügel, *An Introduction to Infrared Spectroscopy*. London, Methuen, (1962), p. 94.

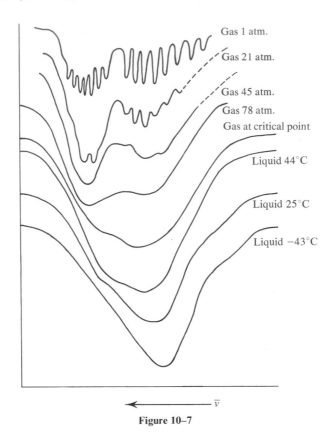

Gas 1 atm.

Gas 21 atm.

Gas 45 atm.

Gas 78 atm.

Gas at critical point

Liquid 44°C

Liquid 25°C

Liquid −43°C

$\bar{\nu}$

Figure 10–7

transition is the second overtone. Of course, each mode of vibration is capable of fundamental transitions and overtones. When two or more modes are excited simultaneously, the absorption band produced is called a combination band; the transition is a combination. These processes produce much of the absorption spectrum of a molecule, but other factors also contribute.

Even when the same initial and final vibrational states are involved for a mode of vibration, not all molecules are in the same initial rotational state, nor do they all enter the same final rotational state after absorption. Thus, small differences occur even in the same region of the spectrum and make up the fine structure of each peak.

Another phenomenon that introduces changes in absorption spectra is Fermi resonance. The chief selection rule is,

$$\Delta n = \pm 1$$

Allowed transitions are those that change the vibrational quantum number by only a single unit, and others are forbidden transitions that occur with diminished intensity. However, when an overtone or a combination has a frequency close to that of the fundamental of another vibrational mode, the two excited states have nearly the same energy. In such cases there can be an interaction between the excited states. A mixing of states occurs, the overtone acquires some fundamental character, and the intensity of the overtone band increases. This mixing also shifts the wave numbers at which absorption takes place.

We mentioned previously that a change in the dipole moment must be associated with a particular mode of vibration in order for that mode to be active in the infrared. Consequently, not all of the vibrational modes of a molecule need absorb. For water all vibrational modes are active, but for carbon dioxide this is not the case. Water has 3 atoms and $3N - 6 = 3$ normal vibrational modes. These are,

The three normal modes for water are a symmetrical stretch v_1, a bend v_2, and an unsymmetrical stretch v_3. All three modes give rise to a changing dipole moment, and all are active in the infrared. The first absorbs at 3652 cm^{-1}, the second at 1595 cm^{-1}, and the third at 3756 cm^{-1}. These are the fundamental transitions. We see that the stretching vibrations require radiation having larger wave numbers (more energy) than the bending vibration, and this is a general result. A molecule is deformed more readily by bending than by stretching, and k, the force constant, is smaller for bending modes.

Carbon dioxide is also a triatomic molecule; however, this is a linear system with $3N - 5 = 4$ vibrational modes. The four modes for this molecule are,

The symmetrical stretching vibration v_1 does not produce a changing dipole moment and is inactive in the infrared. The two bending modes v_{2a} and v_{2b} are degenerate. As a result both vibrate with the same frequency and produce only a single band in the infrared. This occurs at 667 cm^{-1}. The unsymmetrical stretching vibration v_3 is also active in the infrared, absorbing at 2350 cm^{-1}.

Not all vibrational modes are active. While the others absorb in the infrared, the symmetrical stretching mode for carbon dioxide is inactive. Of course, molecules more complex than hydrogen chloride, water, and carbon dioxide behave similarly to these simpler systems, and applying infrared spectroscopy to problems encountered in organic chemistry has simplified considerably the task of identifying these organic compounds. The vibrational modes of organic systems are considerably more complex than those of the simple compounds just discussed. However, the principles are the same. If a vibrational mode gives rise to a changing dipole moment, that mode is active in the near infrared. Since the vibrational modes differ in passing from one molecule to the next, it is not obvious that different molecules should absorb in the same region of the infrared. However, it turns out that the various organic systems do absorb in the same region and that compounds having structural similarities actually absorb at very nearly the same wave number. Thus all C—H bonds appear in the region near 3000 cm^{-1} and all carbonyl systems at approximately 1700 cm^{-1}, and it is this behavior of organic systems that has proven useful to the chemist. Examination of the infrared spectrum of an organic compound of unknown structure yields a great deal of information concerning its chemical make-up.

The absorption of radiation by organic compounds in the region near 3000 cm^{-1} arises from the activity of C—H stretching modes. It has been shown that this absorption occurs at nearly the same wave number for a large number of compounds and is virtually independent of the structure of the rest of the molecule. Aliphatic C—H bonds do absorb at a position slightly different from the aromatics. In addition to the stretching absorption, there is absorption due to C—H bending modes. As was mentioned previously, bending motions absorb at lower wave numbers than stretching motions, and in this case the peak occurs at approximately 1460 cm^{-1}. The other bonds and groups in an organic compound also give rise to definite absorption patterns, and careful examination of an infrared spectrum affords much useful information. Of course, the amount of material gleaned depends upon the experience of the examiner.

A number of generalizations have been made correlating structure and absorption in the infrared. The effect of factors such as conjugation, ring strain, and hydrogen bonding upon infrared spectra has been studied, and the results generally confirm our expectations based on considerations of bond strength. Conjugation causes olefinic absorption to take place at lower wave numbers; an exocyclic double bond absorbs at higher wave numbers as the ring becomes smaller; and so forth. Thus butanone **11** absorbs at 1720 cm^{-1} and 1-butene **12** at 1647 cm^{-1}, yet methyl vinyl ketone **13** has carbonyl absorption at 1685 cm^{-1} and olefinic absorption at only 1623 cm^{-1}. Because of conjugation the absorption peaks are found at lower wave numbers:

$$
\begin{array}{ccc}
\overset{\displaystyle O}{\overset{\displaystyle \|}{CH_3CCH_2CH_3}} & CH_3CH_2CH{=}CH_2 & \overset{\displaystyle O}{\overset{\displaystyle \|}{CH_3CCH{=}CH_2}}
\end{array}
$$

$$\bar{v}(CO) = 1720 \text{ cm}^{-1} \qquad \bar{v}(C{=}C) = 1647 \text{ cm}^{-1}$$

$$\bar{v}(CO) = 1685 \text{ cm}^{-1}$$
$$\bar{v}(C{=}C) = 1623 \text{ cm}^{-1}$$

11   **12**   **13**

The positions at which absorption takes place for a compound vary to some extent with the medium. Thus, acetone exhibits carbonyl absorption at $1742\ cm^{-1}$ in the vapor phase, yet solutions of this compound in various solvents absorb in the range between $1728\ cm^{-1}$ and $1718\ cm^{-1}$. The solvent does play a role and must be considered.

A molecule vibrates and these vibrations give rise to absorption in the near infrared. In addition, a molecule may rotate about its center of mass (center of gravity), and the rotational frequency (approximately 10^{11} cycles/sec) is the same as the frequency of radiation in the far infrared. It is rotational excitation that causes the absorption peaks in the far infrared and microwave regions.

In the near infrared we treat bonds to a fair approximation as vibrating springs. This treatment works reasonably well for the lower vibrational states characterized by small values for the vibrational quantum numbers. In rotational studies the bonds are considered to be rigid, and a molecule becomes a rigid rotor rotating about its center of mass. Again, the rigid-rotor approximation works best for low values of the rotational quantum number J and fails at higher rotational energies.

The rotational spectra of simple molecules such as hydrogen chloride provide considerable useful information. For more complex systems a simple rotational spectrum is frequently insufficient, and gives little structural information. The information must be supplemented by other data such as x-ray or electron diffraction. Alternatively, isotopic substitution provides additional information. One takes the rotational spectrum of a compound that contains first one isotope and then repeats using the same compound but replacing the first isotope by another. These techniques provide data from which bond lengths and bond angles can be calculated. Furthermore, rotational spectra change in the presence of an external electric field (the Stark effect), and these changes provide information for determining the molecular dipole moment. The hyperfine structure of rotational spectra provide information concerning nuclear spin. Thus rotational spectra are useful in a number of ways. Naturally, the less complex molecules are investigated most readily.

A molecule rotates about its center of mass; it is the moment of inertia I that is important in molecular rotations. This quantity is defined for a rigid body as,

$$I = \sum_i m_i r_i^2 \qquad (10\text{--}1)$$

where m_i is the mass of atom i and r_i is its distance from the center of mass. For a diatomic molecule with internuclear distance r,

where

$$r_1 + r_2 = r$$

the moment of inertia equals,

$$I = m_1 r_1^2 + m_2 r_2^2$$

It turns out for a diatomic molecule that the center of mass is located at the point where,

$$m_1 r_1 = m_2 r_2 \qquad (10\text{–}2)$$

Since

$$r_2 = r - r_1$$

substitution into Eq. (10–2) leads to,

$$m_1 r_1 = m_2 r - m_2 r_1$$

or

$$r_1 = \frac{m_2 r}{m_1 + m_2}$$

Similarly we find for r_2,

$$r_2 = \frac{m_1 r}{m_1 + m_2}$$

Introducing these expressions for r_1 and r_2 into the original Eq. (10–1) affords,

$$I = \frac{m_1 m_2}{m_1 + m_2} r^2$$

$$I = \mu r^2$$

where μ is the reduced mass of the system.

When the three axes of inertia are the x, y, and z axes which pass through the center of mass as in Figure 10–8, we are able to define moments of inertia I_x, I_y and I_z about these x, y, and z axes:

$$I_x = \sum_i m_i(y_i^2 + z_i^2)$$

$$I_y = \sum_i m_i(x_i^2 + z_i^2)$$

$$I_z = \sum_i m_i(x_i^2 + y_i^2)$$

where x_i, y_i, z_i are the coordinates of atom i and $x_i^2 + y_i^2 + z_i^2 = r_i^2$.

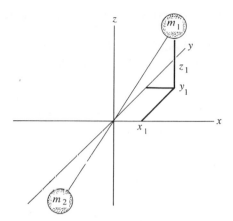

Figure 10–8

Molecules are frequently classified according to their moments of inertia about the principal axes (in the general case the a, b, and c axes). Thus, linear molecules **14** where the molecular axis is the a axis have moments of inertia about the b and c axes but not about the a axis, that is, I_b and I_c have a nonzero value but not I_a:

$$I_a = 0$$

$$I_b = I_c$$

A linear molecule such as nitric oxide is an exception. Furthermore, only molecular rotations, not nuclear spins, are considered.

Certain molecules such as methane and carbon tetrachloride are known as spherical tops **15**. For these,

$$I_a = I_b = I_c$$

There also exist symmetrical tops. Molecules in this class are the methyl halides, methyl cyanide, boron trifluoride, and benzene. The class of symmetrical tops is subdivided further. There are the prolates **16** and the oblates **17**. For all symmetrical tops, two moments of inertia are equal and differ from the third. Thus, if

$$I_b = I_c$$

yet

$$I_b = I_c > I_a$$

we have the prolate series which includes the methyl halides, methyl cyanide, and so forth. If for a molecule,

$$I_a = I_b < I_c$$

the molecule is in the oblate series, and this series includes boron trifluoride and benzene.

Finally there are the asymmetrical tops **18**, and most molecules fall into this class. For these none of the principal moments are equal:

$$I_a \neq I_b \neq I_c$$

Examples of asymmetrical tops include water, formaldehyde, methylene chloride, ethylene oxide.

linear molecule	spherical top	prolate symmetrical top	oblate symmetrical top	asymmetrical top
14	**15**	**16**	**17**	**18**

Of course, a quantum mechanical calculation of the rotational energy of these systems becomes more complicated as the molecule becomes more complex. The linear molecule is treated most easily, and the energy levels for a diatomic molecule such as hydrogen chloride treated as a linear rigid rotor are given by,

$$E_r = \frac{h^2 J(J+1)}{8\pi^2 I} \qquad J = 0, 1, 2, \cdots$$

where J is the rotational quantum number and I is the moment of inertia.

This equation holds for low rotational energies. At higher rotational energies the assumption that the bond is rigid, that the internuclear distance is fixed, fails and correction factors must be added to E_r.

Transitions in the far infrared are also accompanied by an energy change equal to $h\nu$ where ν is the frequency of the absorbed radiation.

$$\Delta E_r = h\nu$$

The selection rule that allows the transition moment to exist is,

$$\Delta J = \pm 1$$

In rotational spectroscopy J can take on the value zero, and absorption leads to an increase in J, emission to a decrease. In certain cases, it is possible for ΔJ to equal zero, but for diatomic molecules this is unusual.

For nonlinear molecules, a moment of inertia is possible about each of the principal axes and the situation becomes more complex. In these cases, the selection rule for J becomes,

$$\Delta J = 0, \pm 1$$

However, changes in J do not give the complete picture and other restrictions must be considered for nonlinear systems.

We have mentioned previously that rotational spectra are found in the far infrared and in the microwave region and that the hyperfine structure of rotational spectra provides information concerning nuclear spin. A more exact picture of molecular rotations must consider not only the molecular angular momentum but also that due to nuclear spin. Nuclear spin not only plays a role in rotational transitions, it also influences electron spin resonance spectra and nuclear magnetic resonance spectra; we discuss these next.

In electron spin resonance spectroscopy (ESR) and nuclear magnetic resonance spectroscopy (NMR), transitions are studied that result from absorption of electromagnetic radiation in the presence of an external magnetic field **H**. In electron spin resonance, the spin of an odd electron in an organic free radical is oriented either parallel or antiparallel to the external field, and an electron in the lower energy state is able to absorb radiation and pass from that to the higher energy state. Investigation of the spectra resulting from such transitions gives rise to much information concerning the structure of organic radicals.

In nuclear magnetic resonance spectroscopy, nuclear spin is considered, and again, only certain spin orientations of the nuclei with respect to the external field are allowed. Absorption of radiation allows a nucleus to change its spin orientation and enter a higher energy state. It is this absorption in the presence of a magnetic field which causes a change in nuclear orientation and affords the spectrum.

10.6 Electron Spin Resonance Spectroscopy

In this section we are concerned chiefly with the detection and structure of free radicals, and the technique commonly employed, electron spin resonance, depends upon the fact that an organic free radical, which contains an unpaired electron, has a magnetic moment due to the spin of that odd electron. An electron has intrinsic angular momentum or spin, and a spinning electron has associated with it a magnetic moment **m**. One may consider an electron as a small magnet, that is, as a magnetic dipole with north and south poles, and in the presence of an external magnetic field **H**, there is an interaction between the field and **m**.

The magnetic moment vector **m** has a z component $\mathbf{m}_z$, and in the presence of an external field **H** in the z direction, $\mathbf{m}_z$ can have only two possible orientations, parallel or antiparallel to the external field.

H ↑ ↑ $\mathbf{m}_z$ parallel   H ↑ ↓ $\mathbf{m}_z$ antiparallel

The magnetic moment vector is related to the spin vector **S** by the equation,

$$\mathbf{m} = -g\beta\mathbf{S} \qquad (10\text{--}3)$$

where g is called the spectroscopic splitting factor and for our purposes is simply a constant. The value of g for a free electron is 2.0023. The term β is also a constant known as the Bohr magneton.

An electron in a radical is not a free electron. It has intrinsic angular momentum or spin. In addition it may have orbital angular momentum due to motion about the nuclei. This orbital angular momentum influences the values of g and **m** for the electron. Thus, a deviation of the g value from that for a free electron sometimes provides useful information about the radical. However, for organic radicals g is approximately equal to 2.0023, the value for a free electron, and this indicates that little coupling occurs between spin and orbital motion. Since g is nearly the same for organic radicals (a few exceptions are known), a determination of g generally provides no information concerning structure, and some other property must be studied.

If we assume that **H** is in the z direction, we are then interested in the z components, $\mathbf{m}_z$ and $\mathbf{S}_z$, related by the equation:

$$\mathbf{m}_z = -g\beta\mathbf{S}_z$$

Notice that $\mathbf{m}_z$ and $\mathbf{S}_z$ are antiparallel; a parallel orientation between $\mathbf{m}_z$ and the field indicates an antiparallel orientation of $\mathbf{S}_z$. The potential energy of a free electron in a magnetic field depends upon the field strength H (magnitude of **H**) and upon $m_z (m_z = -g\beta S_z)$:

$$U = -m_z H$$

In terms of the spin S_z, this becomes,

$$U = g\beta H S_z$$

The potential energy of an electron in the presence of a magnetic field depends upon the strength of the field H and upon the value of S_z ($-1/2$ or $+1/2$). The electron has a lower potential energy when S_z equals $-1/2$ and a higher potential energy when S_z equals $+1/2$:

$$\mathbf{H}\uparrow \quad \downarrow \atop \mathbf{S}_z = -1/2 \qquad\qquad \mathbf{H}\uparrow \quad \uparrow \atop \mathbf{S}_z = +1/2$$

lower energy
orientation   higher energy
orientation

An electron in the first state has potential energy,

$$U_1 = -1/2 g\beta H$$

while in the higher energy state U_2 equals,

$$U_2 = 1/2 g\beta H$$

Associated with each spin orientation of the electron is a potential energy U. The value of the potential energy in each orientation depends upon both the external field strength H, and the value of S_z. The negative value of U_1 indicates the lower and favorable potential energy of the former alignment.

In passing from the more stable orientation to the other, the change in energy ΔE equals ΔU:

$$\Delta E = U_2 - U_1 = g\beta H$$

An electron in the state U_1 may absorb energy (electromagnetic radiation) and enter U_2. An electron in U_2 can emit radiation and enter U_1. The same energy change is involved in both processes ($g\beta H$).

The change in the potential energy of the electron when passing from one state to the other must equal the energy of the radiation absorbed or emitted:

$$\Delta E = h\nu$$

and

$$h\nu = g\beta H \tag{10-4}$$

An electron with spin $-1/2$ absorbs radiation of frequency ν, changes its spin orientation, and gains energy equal to $h\nu$. An electron with spin $+1/2$ can emit radiation with frequency ν. The transitions are presented in Figure 10–9.

We have obtained Eq. (10–4) which relates the frequency of the radiation to the magnetic field strength; ν is proportional to H. It is advantageous in studies of this type to use powerful magnetic fields (3000 gauss to over 10,000 gauss), and this corresponds to radiation in the microwave region (1 cm to 4 cm for λ). In some cases studies can be made using radiation in the radio frequency region.

In electron spin resonance spectroscopy a source of microwave radiation of constant frequency ν is employed, and the external field strength H is varied. The radiation must be in the plane perpendicular to the direction of H, say in the x direction. In these studies we fix the energy change for the transition at $h\nu$ and measure the external field strength at which this energy change occurs. Absorption or emission takes place only when Eq. (10–4) is satisfied. For example, an electron in the lower energy state can absorb radiation and gain energy $h\nu$ only when the field strength has its proper value. Measuring the field strength at which transitions take place gives rise to a spectrum. A peak is observed as in Figure 10–10 at the field strength where the transition from one spin orientation to the other is allowed.

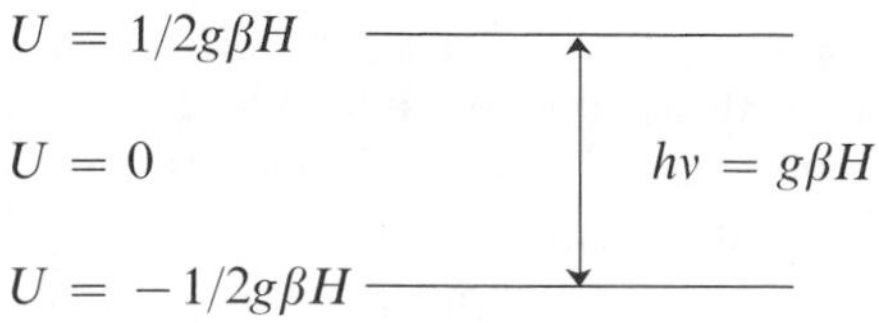

$$U = 1/2g\beta H$$
$$U = 0 \qquad\qquad h\nu = g\beta H$$
$$U = -1/2g\beta H$$

Figure 10–9

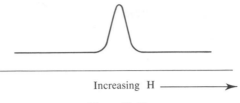

Increasing H ⟶

Figure 10–10

For a given frequency, transitions occur at nearly the same field strength for all organic radicals; however, the hyperfine structure of the spectrum varies, and this provides useful data. The hyperfine splitting that is found in the electron spin resonance spectra of many organic radicals comes from the inter-action of the nuclei with the electronic magnetic moment. Many nuclei, like the electron, also have a spin associated with them, and this spin $\mathbf{I}$ gives rise to a nuclear magnetic moment $\mathbf{m}$. The equations relating $\mathbf{I}$ and $\mathbf{m}$ have the same form as the previous ones. For a proton they are,

$$\mathbf{m} = g_n \beta_n \mathbf{I}$$

and

$$\mathbf{m}_z = g_n \beta_n \mathbf{I}_z$$

where g_n is the nuclear g factor, and β_n the nuclear magneton. These equations differ from the previous ones because the proton has a larger mass than the electron and opposite charge, factors that must be considered. Notice therefore that $\mathbf{m}_z$ and $\mathbf{I}_z$ are parallel for the proton.

The potential energy of a proton in the presence of a magnetic field is (when $\mathbf{H}$ is in the z direction),

$$U = -g_n \beta_n H I_z$$

The proton also has spin values of $+1/2$ and $-1/2$, the lower energy state being $I_z = +1/2$.

$$U_1 = -1/2 g_n \beta_n H$$

$$U_2 = 1/2 g_n \beta_n H$$

Interaction between the magnetic moments of a proton and an electron takes place in two general ways. One is dipolar interaction between two magnets, each with a north and south pole. This interaction is important when the ESR spectra of solids are considered but averages to zero when the molecules are rotating rapidly and randomly. Thus, in the spectra of radicals generated in liquids, the peak positions and intensities do not depend upon dipolar coupling. The other, contact interaction (isotropic coupling), is a quantum mechanical phenomenon. A spinning electron gives rise to electric currents and a magnetic field at the nucleus. Contact interaction represents the energy due to the proton's magnetic moment in this magnetic field and takes place only when the electron exists at the nucleus (when electron density exists at the nucleus). Thus, electrons in s orbitals and in hybridized orbitals with s character give rise to contact interaction. Electrons in p orbitals also interact but by indirect methods.

Free electrons give rise to a single ESR peak. In atomic hydrogen, where we have an electron interacting with a single hydrogen nucleus, the ESR spectrum consists of two peaks of equal intensity. The splitting arises from contact interaction, and we write the contact energy as,

$$aI_zS_z$$

where a, the coupling constant, may be considered as a constant of proportionality. The terms I_z and S_z are the spin values ($+1/2$, $-1/2$) for the proton and electron.

The magnetic energy of a hydrogen atom in the presence of a magnetic field equals the energy of the electron ($g\beta HS_z$), plus the energy of the proton ($-g_n\beta_n HI_z$), plus the contact interaction energy (aS_zI_z).

$$E = g\beta HS_z - g_n\beta_n HI_z + aS_zI_z$$

Thus in the presence of a magnetic field, four states exist,

$$
\mathrm{II} \uparrow \atop \underset{S_z\,I_z}{\;} \qquad
\downarrow \uparrow \atop \underset{S_z\,I_z}{\;} \qquad
\downarrow \downarrow \atop \underset{S_z\,I_z}{\;} \qquad
\uparrow \uparrow \atop \underset{S_z\,I_z}{\;} \qquad
\uparrow \downarrow \atop \underset{S_z\,I_z}{\;}
$$

The energy associated with each state is,

$$E_1 = -1/2g\beta H - 1/2g_n\beta_n H - a/4$$

$$E_2 = -1/2g\beta H + 1/2g_n\beta_n H + a/4$$

$$E_3 = +1/2g\beta H - 1/2g_n\beta_n H + a/4$$

$$E_4 = +1/2g\beta H + 1/2g_n\beta_n H - a/4$$

A hydrogen atom with energy E_1 can absorb radiation. The electron's spin inverts, and the system enters the state E_3. Similarly, a hydrogen atom in state E_2 absorbs energy and enters E_4. In electron spin resonance experiments the electronic spin inverts while the nuclear spin remains unaltered. Transitions which invert both the electronic and nuclear spins are forbidden and occur with diminished intensity. The energy changes for these processes are,

$$E_3 - E_1 = g\beta H + a/2$$

$$E_4 - E_2 = g\beta H - a/2$$

and this must in both cases equal $h\nu$.

$$h\nu = g\beta H + a/2$$

$$h\nu = g\beta H - a/2$$

The magnetic fields at which the transitions occur are,

$$H_1 = \frac{(h\nu - a/2)}{g\beta}$$

$$H_2 = \frac{(h\nu + a/2)}{g\beta}$$

For a free electron,

$$h\nu = g\beta H$$

and the resonance peak occurs at

$$H = h\nu/g\beta$$

For hydrogen atoms, two resonance peaks of equal intensity are found (the transitions are equally probable):

$$H_1 = \frac{(h\nu - a/2)}{g\beta}$$

$$H_2 = \frac{(h\nu + a/2)}{g\beta}$$

The presence of a proton has split the resonance peak. The difference $(H_2 - H_1)$ equals,

$$H_2 - H_1 = \frac{a}{g\beta}$$

Therefore the magnitude of the splitting is a direct measure of the coupling constant. The difference $(H_2 - H_1)$ allows one to evaluate the magnitude of a. The spectrum appears in Figure 10–11.

In the absence of nuclear interactions, transitions occur at H. After nuclear interaction is considered, the peak is split into two components. Transitions occur at slightly lower external field strengths for the first example $H_1(E_3 - E_1)$ than for the second $H_2(E_4 - E_2)$. In this example the coupling constant a is positive; however, a need not be positive and negative values for coupling constants are known.

The splitting is a direct measure of the interaction between a hydrogen nucleus and the unpaired electron. Thus, it gives information concerning the delocalization of the electron into the region about the hydrogen nucleus. Organic radicals contain carbon and most contain hydrogen. Now C^{12} does not have a nuclear moment, but C^{13} does. Chlorine and fluorine also interact. Thus all types of organic radicals provide spectra. Furthermore, not only is

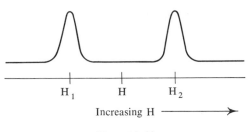

$$H_1 \qquad H \qquad H_2$$

Increasing H ⟶

Figure 10–11

the number of peaks and their relative intensity important, the magnitude and sign of the coupling constant provide data of importance.

Contact interaction depends upon the unpaired electron's existence at the nucleus. Naturally this is related to the unpaired spin density (electron density) in the orbital about the nucleus. When the electron is restricted to a single $1s$ orbital as in the hydrogen atom, the splitting and therefore the coupling constant are large. If the unpaired electron is delocalized over several hydrogen atoms, the spin density in a particular $1s$ orbital is smaller, contact interaction with a particular nucleus is less pronounced, and the coupling constant decreases in magnitude. Thus, for the hydrogen atom the coupling constant has a value (in gauss) of 507 gauss while for t-butyl radical, the coupling constant is 23 gauss.

Since the methyl hydrogens in the t-butyl radical cause splitting, the unpaired electron must be delocalized into the $1s$ orbitals of these hydrogens and this provides evidence for the existence of hyperconjugation. It does not imply, however, that hyperconjugation is responsible for differing radical stabilities.

The energy for a system of two equivalent protons interacting with a single electron is given by,

$$E = g\beta H S_z - g_n\beta_n H I_{z_1} - g_n\beta_n H I_{z_2} + aS_z I_{z_1} + aS_z I_{z_2}$$

Spin states are, for $S_z = -1/2$,

$$\downarrow \qquad \uparrow\uparrow \qquad \uparrow\downarrow \qquad \downarrow\uparrow \qquad \downarrow\downarrow$$

$-1/2$ nuclear spins

while for $S_z = +1/2$,

$$\uparrow \qquad \uparrow\uparrow \qquad \uparrow\downarrow \qquad \downarrow\uparrow \qquad \downarrow\downarrow$$

$+1/2$ nuclear spins

Transitions take place only between states for which the nuclear spin remains unaltered.

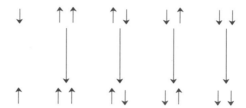

We find four allowed transitions, all equally probable. Notice also that the central two transitions are degenerate, that is, both occur at the same field strength H.

A single hydrogen nucleus splits the peak into two components. If the odd electron interacts with two chemically equivalent protons, the spectrum becomes still more complex. The problem of determining nuclear spin orientations is like that of throwing heads or tails with a coin. The spectrum that results in this case is shown in Figure 10–12.

The relative peak intensities are $1 : 2 : 1$. Of course, if the hydrogen nuclei are not seen by the electron as equivalent, that is, if the coupling constants a_1 and a_2 are not equal, the degeneracy is removed and a four-peak spectrum results. This is shown in Figure 10–13.

For a radical like the methyl radical, where the unpaired electron interacts with three equivalent nuclei, the spectrum has the appearance (for $C^{12}H_3 \cdot$) indicated in Figure 10–14.

The peak intensities have the distribution $1:3:3:1$.

One may, in general, determine relative peak intensities by using Pascal's triangle; see Figure 10–15.

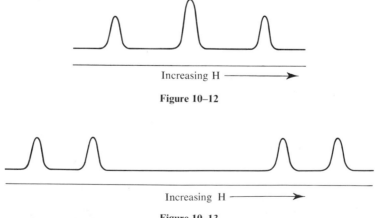

Increasing H ⟶

Figure 10–12

Increasing H ⟶

Figure 10–13

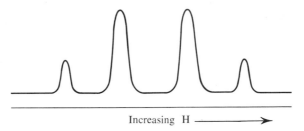

Increasing H ⟶

Figure 10–14

```
0                    1
1                 1     1
2              1    2    1
3           1    3    3   1
4        1    4   6    4   1
5     1   5  10  10   5   1
```

Pascal's Triangle

Figure 10–15

In Figure 10–15 the equivalent hydrogen nuclei are on the left. The relative intensities make up the triangle. The first and last terms in each row are unity, and the other terms are obtained by adding the numbers that appear to the left and right in the row above. Thus the splitting produced by six equivalent protons can be determined as follows.

The first peak has an intensity of unity, the second peak intensity is obtained by adding one and five. The third peak is obtained by adding five and ten, the fourth by adding ten and ten, the fifth by adding five and ten, and so forth. The result for splitting by six equivalent hydrogen nuclei is,

$$1:6:15:20:15:6:1$$

An example illustrating the splitting of spectra because of nuclear interactions is found with the electron spin resonance spectra of *para* benzosemiquinone anions. The parent compounds have the structural formula **19**, and these add an electron to form the radical anions **20**:

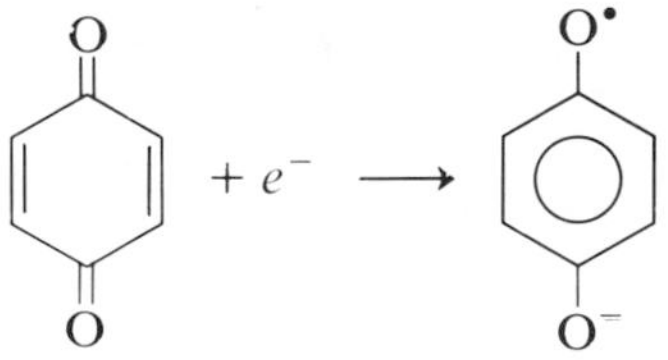

19   **20**

The compounds studied were,

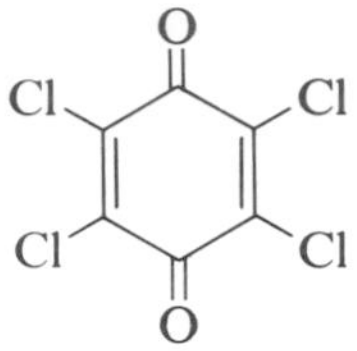

21 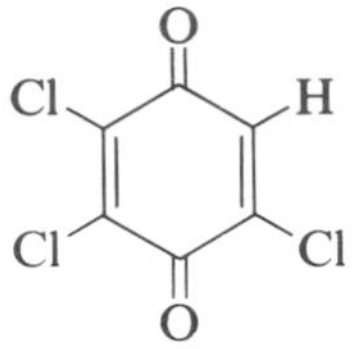   22 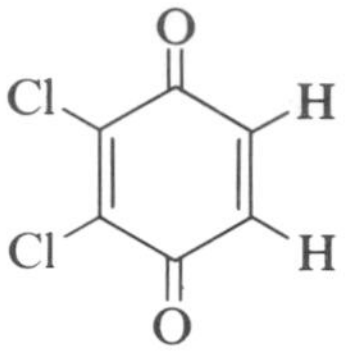   23

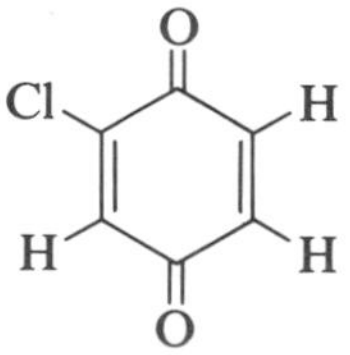

24 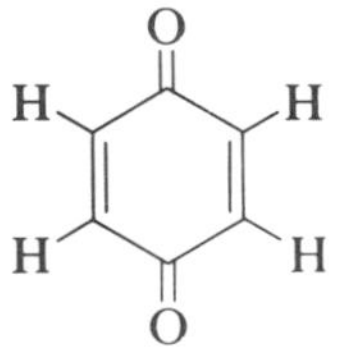   25

The odd electron in the radicals is delocalized over the entire π system. Splitting is caused by interactions with the protons, but the interaction with chlorine is small and is not considered. The spectra showed the expected splittings. In **21** no splitting is observed; in **25** the spectrum has the expected 1:4:6:4:1 ratio for peak intensities. The four hydrogens are equivalent and split the peak into components. The results are presented in Table 10–2.

Examination of the hyperfine structure of a spectrum enables us in many cases to detect the number of hydrogens and their environment. The data are useful for elucidating the structures of unknown radicals that may be formed during a reaction as well as yielding information concerning the delocalization of the odd electron. The magnitude and sign of the coupling constant afford data concerning the molecular orbital occupied by the electron.

The methyl radical is planar with the unpaired electron generally considered to be in a p orbital. The *para* benzosemiquinone anions are also planar with the unpaired electron in a delocalized π molecular orbital. Yet the hydrogens present in these systems cause splitting, and this requires unpaired spin density in the hydrogen $1s$ orbitals. Consequently, there must be interaction between the unpaired electron and these hydrogen nuclei. The mechanism for the interaction is an indirect one involving the electrons in the C—H σ bonds. Consider the methyl radical,

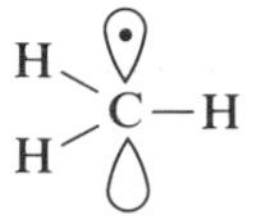

Table 10–2

Radical	Relative Peak Intensities
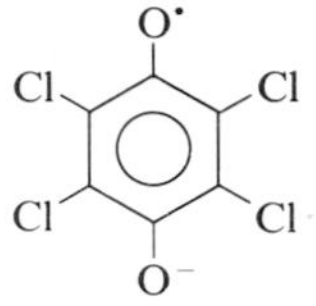	1
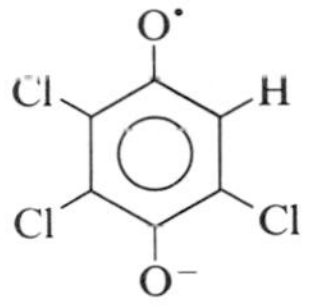	1:1
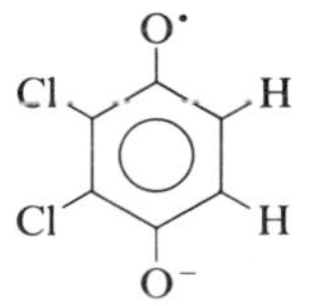	1:2:1
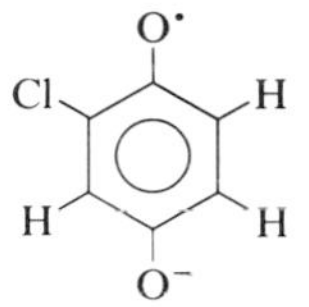	1:3:3:1
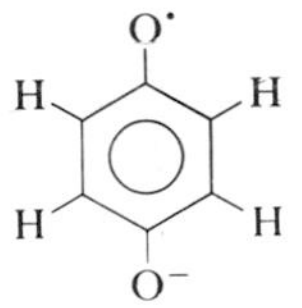	1:4:6:4:1

The two electrons in a C—H bond have opposite spin and assuming that the unpaired electron has a spin of $-1/2$, two structures can be written,

If, as is frequently assumed, there were no interactions between σ and π electrons, these two structures would have the same energy. However, some interaction does exist and causes the first structure to become slightly more stable. A parallel spin orientation is preferred for the two electrons near carbon, and this requires an antiparallel orientation for the electron near hydrogen. Thus a spin of $-1/2$ in the p orbital causes a spin of $+1/2$ near the hydrogen atom. The unpaired electron generates unpaired spin density at the hydrogen atom. Furthermore, the spin density at the hydrogen atom is opposite to that in the π system, and this leads to a negative value for the coupling constant ($a = -23$ gauss for the methyl radical). When the unpaired π electron is delocalized over several carbon atoms as it is in the *para* benzosemiquinone anions, the splitting caused by any single hydrogen is naturally expected to be smaller. An equation has been developed relating the spin density at carbon to the coupling constant:

$$a = Q\rho$$

This equation, known as McConnell's equation, states that the coupling constant is proportional to the spin density ρ on the carbon atom. The term Q is a constant of proportionality. Since ρ for the methyl radical is equal to unity while a equals -23 gauss, Q has a value of approximately -23 gauss.

Using this value for Q, it is possible to predict the value of the coupling constant. The predicted results generally correlate well with the experimental findings. For example, the odd electron in the cyclopentadienyl radical is delocalized over five carbon atoms. Consequently, the spin density at any single carbon atom is $1/5$, and the coupling constant has a calculated value of,

$$a = 1/5(-23) = -4.6 \text{ gauss}$$

The experimental value is -6 gauss.

The magnitude and sign of the coupling constant depend upon how well the electron is restricted to the region near the nucleus. Electrons restricted to the $1s$ orbitals of hydrogen atoms absorb at field strengths differing by about 507 gauss, an extremely large splitting of peaks. However if the electron is delocalized the magnitude of the splitting is reduced. Splittings of 50 to 100 gauss have been observed. In methyl radical the splitting is approximately 23 gauss and in other radicals it can be 1 to 10 gauss or less.

The use of electron spin resonance is not restricted to organic radicals. In fact, inorganic compounds were studied first. The unpaired electrons in the d and f orbitals of the transition metals also afford spectra; use can be made of this when studying the behavior of organometallic systems. Copper complexes as well as silver and gold complexes absorb when these central atoms are in the divalent state, and several systems of this type have been studied. Certain biological processes can also be investigated using this technique, since they generate or consume radicals.

When alcohols such as 2-propanol containing a trace of hydrogen peroxide are cooled to 110°K, and the solid that results irradiated with ultraviolet light, radicals are formed. The ultraviolet radiation decomposes the hydrogen peroxide which abstracts a hydrogen atom from the 2-propanol:

$$H_2O_2 \xrightarrow{hv} 2HO\cdot$$

$$\underset{\underset{H}{|}}{\overset{\overset{OH}{|}}{CH_3CCH_3}} + \cdot OH \longrightarrow H_2O + \underset{}{\overset{\overset{OH}{|}}{CH_3\overset{.}{C}CH_3}}$$

The radical that is generated is immobile and unreactive under these conditions and can be studied. At 110°K, the interaction with the hydroxyl hydrogen is not observed but splitting with the six equivalent methyl hydrogens does occur and affords the expected seven-line spectrum. As the temperature is lowered, the spectrum changes. This is probably due to restricted rotations of the methyl groups and the fact that splitting with the hydroxyl hydrogen becomes effective. A study of this type yields valuable information concerning the interaction of the various hydrogens with the odd electron as well as illustrating the behavior of organic systems at low temperatures.

Solid state studies similar to this one have also been performed on polymers. Irradiation of polymers with gamma rays generates radicals. Since these radicals are held as part of rigid systems, they cannot react readily.

The free radicals were generated; the electron spin resonance spectra examined. Polyethylene gave a seven-line spectrum, polystyrene a three-line spectrum, and teflon an eight-line spectrum (fluorine interacts with the odd electron). Results such as these provide evidence for the conformations of polymers and the reactive sites on the polymer chain.

The major limitation of electron spin resonance spectroscopy is that the organic system to be studied must have an unpaired electron. Organic systems not having an odd electron do not afford spectra, and systems that do have an unpaired electron are generally unstable. The triphenylmethyl radical 26 and the diphenylpicrylhydrazyl radical 27 can be studied with ease, but these are the exceptions:

$$\begin{array}{cc} \textbf{26} & \textbf{27} \end{array}$$

If a reaction does involve a radical intermediate, its concentration is generally low and its average lifetime short. This makes an investigation difficult. The special conditions under which the radical is formed in high yield yet remains unreactive cannot always be found. Work in the solid state has been successful, and new techniques are being developed. The bombardment of organic molecules with high energy electrons has recently been introduced as a means of generating radicals. There are shortcomings, but the tool is useful. The data help both the structural organic chemist and the theoretician.

10.7 Nuclear Magnetic Resonance Spectroscopy

The phenomenon of nuclear magnetic resonance has a theoretical basis similar to electron spin resonance. However, changes in nuclear spin orientation are considered instead. Most of the work has been done on proton magnetic resonance, and we discuss this case first.

In the presence of an external field the proton spin may be oriented with or against the external field. A parallel orientation constitutes the lower energy state, the other the state of higher energy; however, radiation may be absorbed and the spin reversed. A nucleus in the lower energy state absorbs radiation, reverses its spin, and enters the higher state. The energy change accompanying the process is $h\nu$. The energies involved are much smaller than for the electron, and absorption takes place largely in the radio frequency range. The equation relating the energy change to the external field strength has the same form as Eq. (10–4):

$$h\nu = g_n\beta_n H$$

where g_n is the nuclear g factor and β_n the nuclear magneton.

This discussion suggests that a free proton in the presence of a magnetic field ought to absorb radiation and give a single sharp absorption line; however, the hydrogen nuclei in organic compounds are not free. Within a molecule the environment about a nucleus affects both the position at which absorption occurs and the type of spectrum that results. This environment influences the actual magnetic field seen by the nucleus, and different hydrogen nuclei in a molecule absorb at slightly different field strengths. The intensity of each absorption peak indicates the number of hydrogens of that type, and the position at which the peak is observed indicates to some extent the nuclear environment.

Crystalline materials, pure liquids, and solutions containing absorbing solutes all afford nuclear magnetic resonance spectra, but the information obtained is not the same for solid and liquid phase spectra. Liquids afford much narrower NMR peaks, and from these, chemical shifts and coupling constants are determined. Solid phase spectra proved information concerning crystalline structure; here internuclear distances and nuclear orientations can be evaluated.

An organic liquid may afford a nuclear magnetic resonance spectrum, but the actual magnetic field experienced by a hydrogen nucleus within a molecule does not equal the external field. One factor is that electronic currents in the molecule alter the field, which becomes, at the nucleus,

$$(1 - \sigma)H$$

where σ is the screening or shielding constant.

The potential energy of a proton in the magnetic field becomes,

$$U = -g_n\beta_n(1 - \sigma)HI_z$$

where I_z equals $+1/2$ when the z component of the spin vector is parallel to the magnetic field and $-1/2$ when the z component is antiparallel. The two allowed states are:

$$-1/2g_n\beta_n(1 - \sigma)H$$

$$+1/2g_n\beta_n(1 - \sigma)H$$

The resonance equation becomes,

$$hv = g_n\beta_n(1 - \sigma)H$$

which indicates that more highly shielded protons absorb at higher external field strengths.

Since σ differs for chemically different protons, spin inversion takes place at different field strengths. A positive shielding constant indicates that the nucleus experiences a field weaker than the external field, $(1 - \sigma)$ is less than unity. A negative screening constant implies that a stronger field exists at the nucleus. For protons σ is positive, yet both positive and negative screening constants have been determined for fluorine nuclei.

Several factors contribute to the value of the screening constant, and σ is actually a composite term which we consider as a sum of individual screening constants.

$$\sigma = \sigma_1 + \sigma_2 + \sigma_3$$

Within a molecule there exists an electron density in the $1s$ orbital of any hydrogen atom. Circulation of these $1s$ electrons generates a weak magnetic field $\sigma_1 H$ opposed to the external field yet proportional to it. A hydrogen nucleus within the molecule experiences in addition to the external field, this weak secondary field in the opposite direction. In the absence of other effects the actual field at the nucleus is therefore the combination of these:

$$H - \sigma_1 H = (1 - \sigma_1)H$$

Since the strength of this secondary field depends upon the electron density in the hydrogen $1s$ orbital, the greater the electron density, the greater the shielding. Therefore, hydrogens near electronegative elements are deshielded relative to hydrogens farther away and absorb at lower external magnetic field strengths.

This factor, at least to some extent, accounts for the position at which absorption is observed. Decreasing the electron density causes a hydrogen nucleus to experience more fully the external field H (deshields the nucleus), thus causing hydrogen nuclei near highly electronegative atoms to absorb at slightly lower external field strengths. Typical examples are ethanol and the ethyl halides. Low resolution spectra of these materials appear in Figure 10–16.

For ethanol, the peak intensities, which are in the ratio $3:2:1$, indicate the relative number of each type of hydrogen, and the fact that three peaks are found demonstrates that three different types of hydrogen atoms are present. The low field position of the hydroxyl hydrogen is in part due to hydrogen bonding, and if the spectrum is taken in dilute solution in a solvent such as carbon tetrachloride, the peak moves farther upfield. This finding demonstrates that factors other than electron density are also involved. We have not shown in these low resolution spectra the fine structure which splits each peak into several components.

Another factor influencing peak position is hydrogen bonding. The peak position of a hydrogen-bonded proton depends upon the electron density and upon the degree of hydrogen bonding, since the electrostatic interactions that give rise to hydrogen bonding make a contribution to the total screening constant σ.

The electron density about a hydrogen nucleus is one factor influencing the position of absorption, hydrogen bonding plays a role, and other factors must also be considered. If π electrons are present in the molecule, the orbital motion of these electrons gives rise to a magnetic field that either opposes or adds to the external magnetic field depending upon the position of a nucleus within this induced field. If, at the hydrogen nucleus, the induced field opposes the external field, that proton experiences a weaker field and that proton is shielded; it absorbs at higher external field strengths. If, on the other hand, the field generated by the electrons is seen by the proton to be in the same direction as

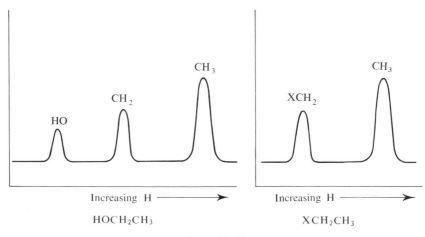

Figure 10–16

the external field, the nucleus experiences a somewhat stronger field (deshielding), and absorption occurs at lower external field strengths. Both possibilities are conceivable and both have been observed. This last effect can be important.

Aromatic hydrogens, for example those in benzene, appear at relatively low field. When the molecule is perpendicular to the external field, the induced field at the proton due to π electronic motion is parallel to the external field as in Figure 10–17. There is no such induced field when the benzene molecule is parallel to the external field. Averaging over all orientations, there results at the nuclei a field in the same direction as the external field. This generates a stronger field at the nuclei and causes the resonance peak to appear downfield.

Hydrogens inside the ring current, that is, within the ring, are expected on this basis to be under the influence of a field opposed to **H** and absorb at higher field strengths. This has been verified for molecules such as,

where the protons above the ring absorb at higher fields.

The important observation that similar hydrogen atoms absorb in the same region but that hydrogen atoms in different environments absorb at different field strengths is useful to the chemist. Aromatic hydrogens absorb in one region, aliphatic in another, and so forth. Thus, in compounds of unknown structure it is possible to determine the types of hydrogens present. Furthermore, the relative intensities of the various peaks indicate the relative number of each type of hydrogen, and a knowledge of the type and relative number of hydrogens is useful information.

The positions at which absorption takes place can be correlated most readily by establishing a scale. Tetramethylsilane $(CH_3)_4Si$ is chosen as the standard because it affords a peak at very high field strengths, other compounds generally absorbing downfield. Since silicon is less electronegative than carbon, the

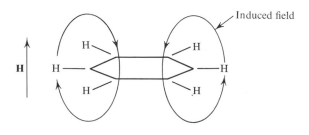

Figure 10–17

electron density is greater at the hydrogen atoms of this compound. The increased shielding that results causes this material to absorb upfield. The hydrogens in most organic compounds display peaks at lower fields than the standard, and a scale of chemical shifts δ can be established. This chemical shift δ in parts per million (ppm) is defined by the equation,

$$\delta = \frac{\text{shift} \times 10^6}{60 \times 10^6}$$

The term shift in the numerator refers to the measured difference between the tetramethylsilane peak and the sample peak. This measured shift, which is in cycles per second, is multiplied by 10^6 and divided by the frequency at which the instrument operates. Since 60 megacycle (60×10^6 cycles per second) frequencies are most common, we have placed this value in the denominator. Thus, if using a 60 megacycle instrument, a hydrogen atom affords a peak 240 cycles per second (cps) downfield from the standard, this atom has a δ value equal to 4.00 ppm (the secondary hydrogen of isopropyl bromide gives a signal in this region).

$$\delta = \frac{240 \times 10^6}{60 \times 10^6} = 4.0 \text{ ppm}$$

Aromatic hydrogens give a signal at very low fields. The observed shift for benzene is about 436 cps, which corresponds to δ equal to 7.27.

In addition to δ values, τ values have been employed. These are defined as

$$\tau = 10.00 - \delta$$

Of course, either scale affords the same information.

We place a small amount of the standard in a sample tube together with the material whose NMR spectrum we are taking. We measure the positions at which peaks occur, and determine δ. This yields information concerning the structure. The spectrum for toluene is given in Figure 10–18 and that for ethyl bromide in Figure 10–19.

In both cases the position of the signal gives some information concerning the types of hydrogen in the compound, and the ratio of the areas under the peaks indicates the ratio of these hydrogens. For example, in the ethyl bromide spectrum, the area under the methylene peak is two-thirds of the area under the methyl peak. The area under the peak due to the standard, of course, depends upon how much of the standard is introduced.

The spectra that we have presented thus far are low resolution spectra that do not show fine structure. High resolution spectra are considerably more complex; each peak is split into components. The process is called spin-spin coupling, and such fine structure gives additional information about the structure of a compound.

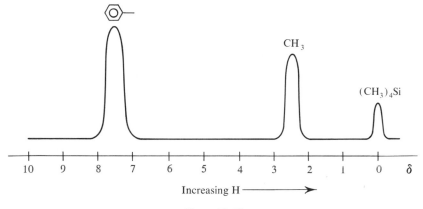

Increasing H ⟶

Figure 10–18

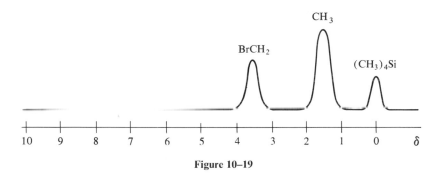

Figure 10–19

The low resolution spectrum of ethanol has the appearance shown in Figure 10 20.

While a higher resolution spectrum is presented in Figure 10–21.

Just as the magnetic field seen by the odd electron in a radical is influenced by the spins of the hydrogen nuclei, the magnetic field seen by one nucleus is influenced by the spin of another. In solids, where molecules are aligned, the major interaction is a direct nucleus-nucleus interaction analogous to the interaction between two magnets. Consider a proton interacting with one other proton. A proton can have spin parallel or antiparallel to the external field. If the spin of the first proton adds to the external field, the second proton experiences a stronger field, and the peak occurs at lower external field strengths. If the first proton has a spin orientation that detracts from the external field, the second proton sees a weaker field and the peak due to that second proton is found at higher external field strengths.

The factor just discussed is of prime importance when the NMR spectra of solids are being studied. In solids this effect is large; however, in liquids (and

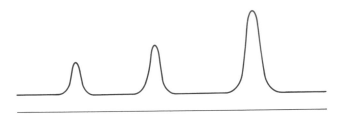

Figure 10–20

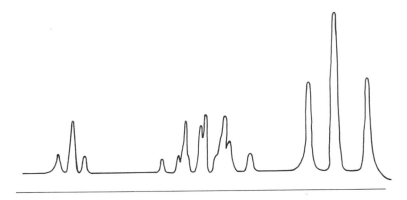

Figure 10–21

gases) where the molecules are not constrained but may move about and rotate more freely, any such direct interactions between nuclei tend to average out. Splitting of smaller magnitude is found even in the NMR spectra of liquids, but the pathway is indirect involving the electrons in the molecule. In liquids, spin-spin interactions between protons are complex and due to a number of causes (by way of the electrons).

In the presence of a magnetic field of strength H in the z direction, the Zeeman energy of a single hydrogen nucleus is,

$$E = -g_n \beta_n (1 - \sigma) H I_z$$

If two hydrogen nuclei, whose screening constants are different, are present in the molecule, the energy becomes,

$$E = -g_n \beta_n (1 - \sigma_1) H I_{z1} - g_n \beta_n (1 - \sigma_2) H I_{z2} + J I_{z1} I_{z2}$$

where the last term is due to coupling between the nuclei and J is the coupling constant, assumed to be small relative to $(\sigma_1 - \sigma_2)$.

Possible spin orientations for the nuclei and the energy associated with each orientation are,

$$\uparrow \quad \uparrow$$

$$E_1 = -1/2g_n\beta_n(1 - \sigma_1)H - 1/2g_n\beta_n(1 - \sigma_2)H + J/4$$

$$\uparrow \quad \downarrow$$

$$E_2 = -1/2g_n\beta_n(1 - \sigma_1)H + 1/2g_n\beta_n(1 - \sigma_2)H - J/4$$

$$\downarrow \quad \uparrow$$

$$E_3 = +1/2g_n\beta_n(1 - \sigma_1)H - 1/2g_n\beta_n(1 - \sigma_2)H - J/4$$

$$\downarrow \quad \downarrow$$

$$E_4 = +1/2g_n\beta_n(1 - \sigma_1)H + 1/2g_n\beta_n(1 - \sigma_2)H + J/4$$

The allowed transitions are those for which only a single nucleus inverts its spin. Therefore two transitions are allowed for the first proton (between states E_1 and E_3 and between E_2 and F_4). The energy change is,

$$E_3 - E_1 = h\nu = g_n\beta_n(1 - \sigma_1)H - J/2$$
$$E_4 - E_2 = h\nu = g_n\beta_n(1 - \sigma_1)H + J/2$$

For the other proton, the allowed transitions are between E_1 and E_2, E_3 and E_4.

$$E_2 - E_1 = h\nu = g_n\beta_n(1 - \sigma_2)H - J/2$$
$$E_4 - E_3 = h\nu = g_n\beta_n(1 - \sigma_2)H + J/2$$

In the absence of nuclear coupling each proton affords a single NMR peak. However, when coupling is considered, we find two allowed transitions for each proton. This results in a pair of doublets of equal intensity (Figure 10–22), the separation between components being related to the magnitude of the coupling constant J (J is generally expressed in cycles per second). Furthermore, the sign of J can be either positive or negative.

A proton interacts with another proton, and the peak due to each is split into a doublet. The mechanisms by which interaction takes place involve the electrons in the molecule, and most important is contact interaction.

A hydrogen nucleus with spin oriented in a certain direction tends to cause an electron at that nucleus to orient its spin. Furthermore, since electrons in bonds must have antiparallel spins, this in turn orients the spins of other electrons in the molecule, and these other electrons cause other hydrogen

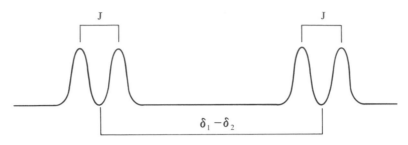

Figure 10–22

nuclei to orient their spin. As a result, the spin of one hydrogen nucleus influences by way of the electrons the spins of other hydrogen nuclei. The closer the hydrogen nuclei to each other, the more effective this contact coupling interaction. Its magnitude is indicated by the coupling constant J, expressed in cycles per second.

Thus we see how spin-spin interactions operate in liquids. Such interactions cause a peak to be split into components, transitions occurring at slightly different external field strengths.

Another factor influencing the magnitude of the spin-spin coupling constant J is an interaction due to electronic orbital motion. A nuclear magnetic moment induces electronic currents in the molecule, and these generate a small magnetic field seen by the other nuclei. Thus, two nuclei in a molecule interact by way of electronic currents as well as by way of contact interaction and direct coupling.

Indirect pathways involving the electrons in a molecule enable one hydrogen nucleus to experience an effect due to the spins of the other hydrogen nuclei. Thus, for a compound such as ethyl chloride whose low resolution spectrum appears in Figure 10–23, at higher resolutions each peak is split into several components (Figure 10–24). The methylene hydrogens interact with the methyl hydrogens and the methyl with the methylene, thereby splitting the peaks.

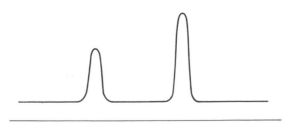

Figure 10–23

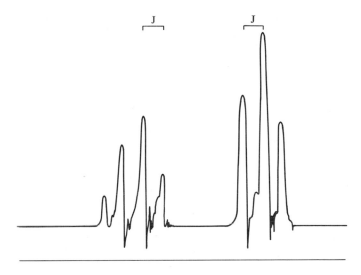

Figure 10–24

The number of fine structure components and their relative intensities can be obtained by using Pascal's triangle (Figure 10–15). One proton interacts with the spin of a second, and this alters the external field strengths at which a peak occurs. The peak due to a proton interacting with one other proton is split into a doublet with equal intensities. If a proton is influenced by the spins of two other equivalent protons, the peak is a triplet with relative intensities $1:2:1$. A proton peak split by interactions with three equivalent protons becomes four peaks having relative intensities of $1:3:3:1$, and so forth.

The high resolution spectrum of ethyl chloride exhibits this type of splitting. A methylene hydrogen interacts with the spins of the three methyl hydrogens, and the methylene peak is split into four components with relative intensities equal to $1:3:3:1$. Both methylene hydrogens appear at the same position, for the two are equivalent. For the methyl hydrogens, a triplet results with ratios $1:2:1$. These methyl hydrogens are split by the two methylene hydrogens.

We have considered examples where the chemical shift is much larger than the coupling constant. When this is not the case, the spectra become more complex.

One may well wonder about the influence of the other nuclei in a molecule upon NMR spectra. The most common element other than hydrogen is carbon, and C^{12} has no spin. Therefore, this nucleus does not influence NMR spectra. Other nuclei may indeed exert an influence. We have discussed in detail the behavior of hydrogen nuclei in the NMR. While these nuclei are most important to the organic chemist, they are not the only active ones, and many others afford NMR spectra. Nitrogen (N^{14} and N^{15}) has a small moment, and F^{19} and

P^{31} are particularly suitable. Deuterium also has a moment, and NMR studies of this isotope have been reported. The spectra of compounds containing these elements afford much information concerning structure. Two very common isotopes C^{12} and O^{16} cannot be studied, for they have no spin. It is, of course, possible to overcome this difficulty by using other isotopes of carbon and oxygen (C^{13} and O^{17}) which are suitable, but the natural abundance of these materials is small and samples enriched in these isotopes less readily available. Thus, only in certain special cases is it possible to employ elements such as C^{13}, O^{17}, or N^{15}. Many of these other nuclei afford more complex spectra than hydrogen. Deuterium, for example, has a spin of 1, and when spin-spin coupling is considered, this produces more complex results. Although these other nuclei can be studied in the NMR, they generally afford peaks at magnetic field strengths quite different from the range at which proton resonance occurs, and it is necessary to have an instrument capable of operating at diverse field strengths. Several of these nuclei do cause splitting of proton peaks, and this provides interesting and useful information.

The behavior of compounds in the NMR provides data concerning structure, yet this is not the only use for the instrument. A number of reactions can be followed by employing this technique and the rates and rate constants determined. When a product and reactant produce distinguishably different peaks, it becomes possible to follow the disappearance of starting material or the appearance of product quite conveniently by changes in peak intensity. Deuterium exchange studies are particularly convenient, for in these cases the peak simply decreases in intensity as a particular hydrogen is being replaced. Of course, other instrumental methods can also be used for this end. The appearance and disappearance of peaks in the infrared or ultraviolet afford data of a similar nature. The introduction of instrumental methods has simplified considerably the task of the chemist, and still newer methods are becoming available.

Supplementary Reading

1. Barrow, G. M., *Introduction to Molecular Spectroscopy*. New York, McGraw-Hill, 1962.

2. Bellamy, L. J., *The Infrared Spectra of Complex Molecules*. New York, Wiley, 1954.

3. Brand, J. C. R. and Speakman, J. C., *Molecular Structure: The Physical Approach*. London, Edward Arnold Ltd., 1960

4. Carrington, A. and McLachlan, A. D., *Introduction to Magnetic Resonance*. New York, Harper, 1967.

5. Fieser, L. F. and Fieser, M., *Natural Products Related to Phenanthrene*, 3rd Ed. New York, Reinhold, 1949.

6. Flett, M. St.C., *Physical Aids to the Organic Chemist*. New York, Elsevier, 1962.

7. Ingram, D. J. E., *Free Radicals as Studied by Electron Spin Resonance*. London, Butterworths, 1959.

8. Jackman, L. M., *Applications of Nuclear Magnetic Resonance Spectroscopy in Organic Chemistry*. New York, Macmillan, 1959.

9. King, G. W., *Spectroscopy and Molecular Structure*. New York, Holt, 1964.

10. Meloan, C. E., *Elementary Infrared Spectroscopy*. New York, Macmillan, 1963.

11. Morrison, R. T. and Boyd, R. N., *Organic Chemistry*, 2nd Ed. Boston, Allyn, 1966.

12. Pople, J. A., Schneider, W. G. and Bernstein, H. J., *High-resolution Nuclear Magnetic Resonance*. New York, McGraw-Hill, 1959.

13. Roberts, J. D., *Nuclear Magnetic Resonance*. New York, McGraw-Hill, 1959.

14. Roberts, J. D., *An Introduction to the Analysis of Spin-Spin Splitting in High-Resolution Nuclear Magnetic Resonance Spectra*. New York, Benjamin, 1962.

15. Silverstein, R. M. and Bassler, G. C., *Spectrometric Identification of Organic Compounds*, 2nd Ed. New York, 1967.

16. Varian Associates, compiled by N. S. Bhacca, L. F. Johnson and J. N. Shoolery, *NMR Spectra*, 2 vols. Palo Alto, California, 1962.

Chapter 11

Aliphatic Nucleophilic Substitution

11.1 Introduction

We wish to carry out the conversion,

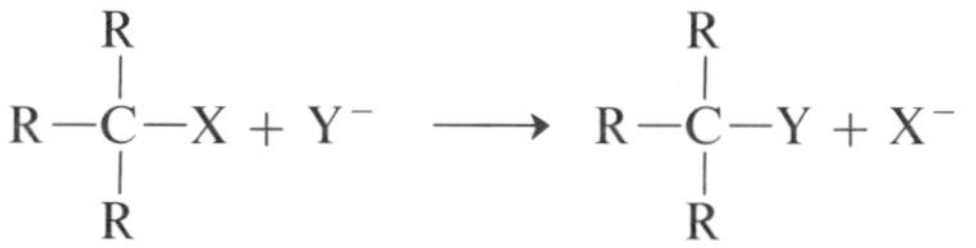

$$\begin{array}{ccc} \text{R} & & \text{R} \\ | & & | \\ \text{R}-\text{C}-\text{X} + \text{Y}^- & \longrightarrow & \text{R}-\text{C}-\text{Y} + \text{X}^- \\ | & & | \\ \text{R} & & \text{R} \end{array}$$

where R is hydrogen, alkyl, or aryl and X is a good leaving group, usually halogen. There are various mechanisms by which this transformation occurs, and various side reactions are possible. Certain compounds R_3CX react preferentially by mechanisms involving carbonium ions; others react by pathways that do not involve carbonium ion intermediates. For simple alkyl halides we know that the order of reactivity by the S_N1 pathway is,

$$3° > 2° > 1° > CH_3X$$

Decreasing Reactivity by S_N1 →

while the order of reactivity by the S_N2 pathway is just the reverse:

$$CH_3X > 1° > 2° > 3°$$

Decreasing Reactivity by S_N2 →

If R is complex or contains olefinic groups or if we choose to effect the conversion R_3CX to R_3CY using certain special reagents, still other mechanistic possibilities arise. Consequently, the mechanism by which the transformation occurs depends upon a number of factors including the nature of the reactant, the reagent used to introduce the group Y, and the reaction conditions.

278

11.2 The Carbonium Ion Reaction

In one process by which the group Y is substituted for the group X a carbonium ion participates, and reactions that have been effected by this pathway include,

$$R_3CX + H_2O \longrightarrow R_3COH$$
$$+ C_2H_5OH \longrightarrow R_3COC_2H_5$$
$$+ CH_3COOH \longrightarrow R_3COOCCH_3$$
$$+ I^- \longrightarrow R_3CI$$

The nucleophile may be negatively charged or neutral, and in those cases where the solvent itself acts as the nucleophilic reagent, the reaction is called a solvolysis reaction.

We present at this time a very simple mechanistic picture for the reaction and discuss the process in greater detail in subsequent sections:

$$R_3CX \underset{k_{-1}}{\overset{k_1}{\rightleftarrows}} R_3C^+X^-$$
$$R_3C^+X^- \overset{k_2}{\longrightarrow} R_3C^+ + X^-$$
$$R_3C^+ + Y^- \overset{k_3}{\longrightarrow} R_3CY \qquad (11\text{--}1)$$

This mechanism does not consider solvation of the various participants. The first step is formation of an ion pair with the oppositely charged species held together by electrostatic attraction. This ion pair can either recombine and regenerate the reactant or dissociate to form a freer carbonium ion and X^-. It is quite likely that in some reactions the nucleophile Y^- attacks this intimate ion pair directly, before it has a chance to dissociate and form a freer carbonium ion. This is certainly possible during some solvolysis reactions. We have assumed, however, that the reaction is being conducted under conditions where ion pair formation is reversible and where this intermediate does dissociate before the nucleophile attacks.

The reaction is pictured here as a three-step process where the first step is a reversible formation of the ion pair. Naturally, this is not the only step where reversal is possible. Any of these steps or all of them can be reversed, for reversibility depends upon the relative concentrations and reactivities of X^- and Y^- and upon the stability of the product under the reaction conditions.

Although the steps in Eq. (11–1) may be reversible, the transformation can also be conducted under conditions where none of them are. The carbonium ion reaction is a unimolecular process as long as either the first or second step is rate limiting, and the reaction is then called an S_N1 reaction. In some reactions of this type the first two steps are reversible, and the last step then becomes rate limiting. Such reactions, where the third step attack by Y^- is rate limiting, are not S_N1 processes, for the reaction is not unimolecular (it is bimolecular in these cases).

If the reaction follows the scheme presented in Eq. (11–1), formation of the carbonium ion from the ion pair is rate limiting. The reaction under these conditions is unimolecular and follows first order kinetics. The general rate expression can be written in terms of the concentration of the ion pair intermediate as,

$$\frac{d[R_3CY]}{dt} = k_2[R_3C^+X^-]$$

and factors increasing the concentration of the ion pair increase the rate of reaction. In terms of the reactant the general rate law becomes,

$$\frac{d[R_3CY]}{dt} = \frac{k_1 k_2}{k_{-1} + k_2}[R_3CX]$$

A simplified picture of the reaction coordinate is shown in Figure 11–1.

The concentration of the nucleophile Y^- plays a large role in determining which step is rate limiting.

The first and last of the transition states have the appearance:

$$\left[\begin{array}{c} R \\ | {\scriptstyle \delta+} \quad {\scriptstyle \delta-} \\ R{-}C{-}{-}X \\ | \\ R \end{array} \right] \left[\begin{array}{c} R \\ | {\scriptstyle \delta+} \quad {\scriptstyle \delta-} \\ R{-}C{-}{-}Y \\ | \\ R \end{array} \right]$$

The C—X bond has partially ruptured in the first and the C—Y bond has partially formed in the last. The carbon atom is partially positive and the nucleophile has a partial negative charge in both transition states.

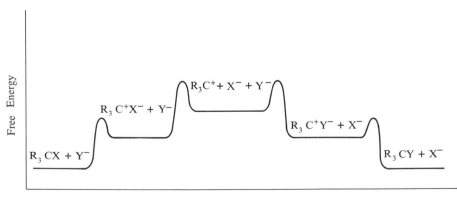

Reaction Coordinate

Figure 11–1

We have assumed that the reaction is being conducted under conditions where the rate limiting step is carbonium ion formation from the ion pair. To effect a change in the rate of the S_N1 reaction we must alter the rate of this step.

11.3 The Importance of the Solvent

Since alkyl halides do not ionize readily by themselves yet do react when placed in polar solvents, a polar solvent must promote the dissociation of the reactant. After all, the ionization of an alkyl halide involves heterolytic bond breakage and the separation of positive and negative charges. We should not expect this process to proceed readily unless some compensating factors were present.

We start with the reactant, pass through the first transition state and end up with oppositely charged ions. These ions then pass through another transition state and separate into freer species:

$$R_3CX \longrightarrow R_3\overset{\delta+}{C}\text{--}\overset{\delta-}{X} \longrightarrow R_3C^+X^- \longrightarrow R_3C^+ + X^-$$

1

The reactant is dissolved in a polar solvent and interactions exist between them; both van der Waals forces and dipole-dipole interactions are present. The reactant is surrounded by molecules of solvent, and this solvation increases in going to the transition state **1**. Here the carbon atom has become more positive, the leaving group more negative. Accompanying this buildup of charge is an increased orientation of molecules of solvent about the transition state. Solvent molecules, which previously were relatively free to move about or constrained only by hydrogen bonding, are attracted by the charges in the transition state. Such electrostatic attractions stabilize the transition state but generally cause the molecules of solvent to have less freedom of motion. We picture the solvated transition state using the solvent ethanol as an example:

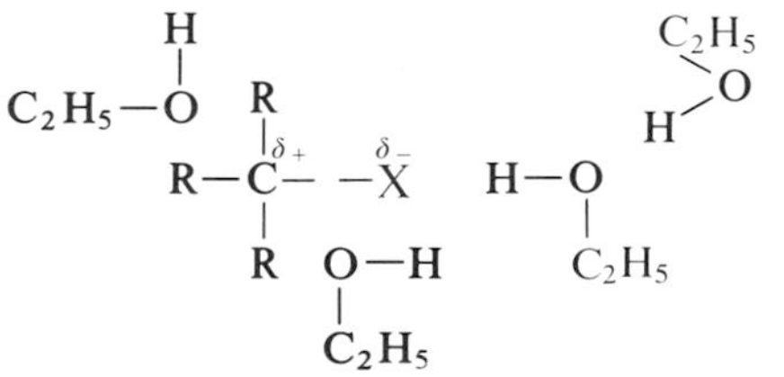

Due to coulombic interactions, the hydroxyl hydrogen of ethanol is attracted to the negatively charged leaving group (the oxygen atom is repelled), while the oxygen atom of the solvent is oriented about the positively charged portion of the transition state.

In proceeding from the reactant through the transition state to the ion pair and then to the carbonium ion and X^-, charge buildup increases and so does solvation.

In passing from the reactant through the transition state **1** to the products, solvation becomes increasingly important. At the instant of their formation the carbonium ion and the leaving group are no longer bonded, yet these two are surrounded by the solvent and held together by coulombic attraction. These two oppositely charged ions, $R_3C^+X^-$, do not move independently of each other, and under the appropriate conditions this ion pair may recombine to reform the reactant. On the other hand, if the carbonium ion is sufficiently long-lived and the solvent sufficiently polar, they may separate from each other and become freer ions in solution.

Of course, a large number of different types of ion pairs are possible. These vary in the distance separating the oppositely charged ions and in the orientation of the solvent.

Finally, a carbonium ion either as part of an intimate ion pair or as a freer ion in solution can react with a nucleophile and yield substituted products. The nucleophilic agent can be either an added nucleophile or the solvent itself. If a charged nucleophile Y^- reacts with the carbonium ion, this step is just the reverse of the ionization process, and solvation decreases in proceeding from the carbonium ion to the substituted product.

$$R_3C^+ + Y^- \longrightarrow R_3CY$$

If an uncharged nucleophilic agent such as the solvent reacts with the carbonium ion, charge dispersal occurs in passing through the transition state to the product, and once again, solvation of the organic system decreases.

In a carbonium ion reaction, molecules of the solvent surround the charged ions. The attraction is largely electrostatic; however, since the central carbon atom of the carbonium ion has a nearly empty p orbital, some covalent bonding may also occur.

When a solvent molecule acts as the attacking nucleophile, the process is necessarily complex. Many molecules of solvent are involved in the process of product formation, for we start with a large number of these solvent molecules about the carbonium ion, yet end up with a single molecule of solvent covalently bonded.

11.4 The Effect of Solvent upon the Rate of Reaction

Assuming that the second step, ion pair forming carbonium ion plus X^-, is rate limiting Eq. (11–1), the rate of reaction depends upon the difference between the free energy of the transition state for this step and that of the reactant R_3CX. We have not been explicit about the transition state for this second step, nor is it necessary to be explicit. This transition state must be more highly charged and more highly solvated than the reactant, and this fact alone suffices to explain the effect of changes in solvent upon the rate of an S_N1 reaction of this type.

The free energy of Y^- is not altered in passing from the reactants to the transition state, and the nucleophile need not be considered in a discussion of the rate of reaction; only the alkyl halide participates in the rate limiting portion of the reaction.

The products resulting from the second step have full positive and negative charges and are highly solvated. If this process to form ions from the reactant occurs readily, the free energy of activation cannot be inhibitively large. The free energy of activation is given by the equation,

$$\Delta G^{\ddagger} = \Delta H^{\ddagger} - T\Delta S^{\ddagger}$$

and the effect of increased solvation is twofold; both the terms $\Delta H^{\ddagger}$ and $\Delta S^{\ddagger}$ are influenced.

First of all, a polar solvent stabilizes the charged transition state more than it stabilizes the reactant, and it is this stabilization of the transition state by the solvent that makes the reaction possible. The $C-X$ bond must be broken and the oppositely charged ions separated. The energy required for these processes is somewhat offset by coulombic interactions between the charged transition state and the polar solvent. These coulombic interactions stabilize the transition state and have a favorable influence upon $\Delta H^{\ddagger}$.

Secondly, the transition state is more highly solvated than the reactant, and the effect of this solvation is generally to restrict the motion of the solvent molecules. Solvent molecules are held more tightly and are generally more highly oriented in the transition state. Consequently, they are less free to move, and this results in an unfavorable value for $\Delta S^{\ddagger}$. However, $\Delta H^{\ddagger}$ has a reasonable value, and this term is the more significant.

In proceeding from a less polar solvent to a more polar solvent the rate of ionization increases. The $S_N 1$ reaction occurs more readily in more polar solvents. Two explanations have been advanced to account for this rate increase. The first of these attributes this increase to a more favorable $\Delta H^{\ddagger}$. It is argued that the more polar solvents are better able to stabilize the charges that are present in the transition state. This leads to a smaller value for $\Delta H^{\ddagger}$ and a faster rate of reaction.

The second theory argues that it is the term $\Delta S^{\ddagger}$ which is more important. Although ionization in any solvent depends mostly upon $\Delta H^{\ddagger}$, in proceeding from one solvent to another, it is argued that this term remains relatively constant, and it is due to changes in $\Delta S^{\ddagger}$ that the rate varies.

According to this second theory, since a less polar solvent molecule cannot stabilize charges as effectively as a more polar solvent molecule, a nearly constant value for $\Delta H^{\ddagger}$ requires more molecules of the less polar solvent to participate in solvating the transition state. This leads to an increasingly negative value for $\Delta S^{\ddagger}$ as the polarity of the solvent is decreased. Thus the rate decreases in passing to a less polar solvent.

Furthermore, a less polar solvent is quite free to move about, yet in stabilizing the transition state it becomes tightly held, and this leads to a very negative value for $\Delta S^{\ddagger}$. A more polar solvent is held together by intermolecular attractions between solvent molecules. Attractive forces such as hydrogen bonding hold the molecules of the solvent together, and even the pure solvent molecules do not move freely. In stabilizing the transition state these molecules give up one type of restricted motion for another. The term $\Delta S^{\ddagger}$ is usually negative even for very polar solvents, but less negative. It should be pointed out that for a very highly oriented solvent such as water, positive values for $\Delta S^{\ddagger}$ can sometimes be obtained. Here solvation disrupts the solvent structure. The results reported for the solvolysis of *t*-butyl chloride in solvents of different polarity are tabulated in Table 11–1.

Table 11–1

Solvent (25°)	$\Delta H^{\ddagger}$ (kcal)	$\Delta S^{\ddagger}$ (cal/deg)
Water	23.2	+ 12.2
Methanol	24.9	− 3.1
Ethanol	26.1	− 3.2
90% Acetone	21.8	− 16.8
90% Dioxene	21.6	− 18.5

It is also of interest to look at a single case in detail. This is presented in Table 11–2.

Table 11–2

Ethanol—H_2O (vol %)	$\Delta H^{\ddagger}$ (kcal)	$\Delta S^{\ddagger}$ (cal/deg)
100	26.1	− 3.2
98	24.5	− 7.2
95	23.6	− 8.3
90	22.8	− 8.7
80	22.3	− 6.6
70	21.9	− 5.4
60	21.7	− 3.7
50	21.6	− 1.4
40	20.3	− 3.3
30	20.6	− 0.1
20	22.0	+ 6.3
10	23.3	+ 11.7

According to this second theory, $\Delta S^{\ddagger}$ is more negative when less polar solvents are employed for the reaction, and this results in a decrease in the rate of reaction.

A polar solvent also stabilizes localized charges more effectively than delocalized charges. Therefore, switching to a more polar solvent increases the rates of those reactions where charges are generated or more highly localized in the transition state than in the reactants. This switch decreases the rate of a reaction when the transition state is less highly charged or when the charge is spread out in the transition state.

The rates of certain unimolecular dissociations decrease in a more polar solvent; these reactions are actually promoted by less polar solvents. Such a decrease is observed in a number of cases and would be expected for any reaction where the positive charge is delocalized in proceeding to the transition state.

We have discussed the role of the solvent in an S_N1 reaction. Increasing the polarity of the solvent generally increases the rate. A rate increase can also be obtained by adding salts such as NaCl to the reaction mixture. The presence of these ions in the medium increases the rate of reaction, for they also stabilize charges. Thus t-butyl bromide hydrolyzes more rapidly when salts such as LiBr and LiCl are added to the solution. The data in Table 11–3 are from the reaction in 90% acetone-water at 50°; k and k_0 are the initial rate constants; k_0 is the initial rate constant in the absence of added salts.

Table 11–3

Salt	Molarity	k/k_0	$k \cdot 10^5$ (sec^{-1})
None	—	1.00	19.0
LiBr	0.1065	1.44	27.5
LiCl	0.1005	1.39	26.3
NaN$_3$	0.1000	1.40	26.5

The rate constant for a solvolysis reaction of this type (hydrolysis of t-butyl bromide) will frequently increase as the reaction proceeds. The reaction proceeds, ions are produced, and these cause rate enhancement. Also the usual first order log plots will not be linear except at the initial stages of reaction.

Naturally if the rate limiting step is not carbonium ion formation but decomposition of the carbonium ion, the general rate expression for the reaction becomes more complex (see, for example, Section 2–10). In such cases a discussion of the effect of a change in solvent upon the rate becomes more involved. These reactions, as was mentioned previously, are not S_N1 processes, for the rate limiting step is bimolecular.

11.5 The Stereochemistry of the S_N1 Reaction

We carry out the transformation,

$$\underset{\underset{R}{|}}{\overset{\overset{R}{|}}{R-C}}-X + Y^- \longrightarrow \underset{\underset{R}{|}}{\overset{\overset{R}{|}}{R-C}}-Y + X^-$$

and we wish to discover what stereochemical changes are involved. Consider, for example, the following enantiomeric reactants:

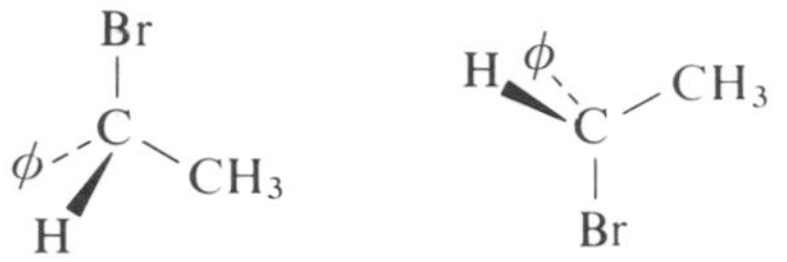

If a free carbonium ion is involved in the process, both of these reactants yield the same ionic intermediates:

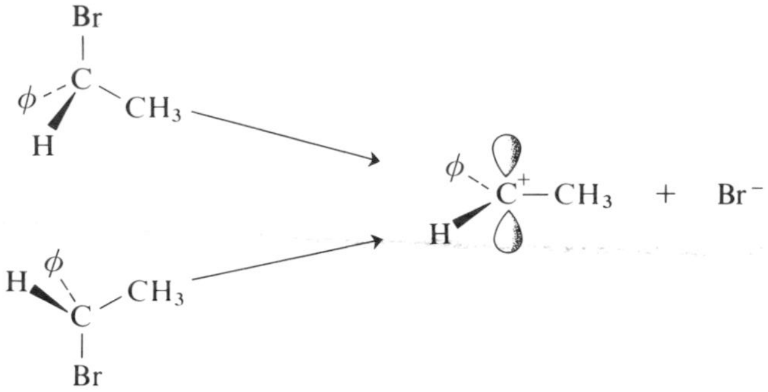

Two reactants differing only in their geometry about the central atom form the same carbonium ion.

Now the central carbon atom in the carbonium ion is sp^2 hybridized and an approaching nucleophile can attack from either above or below:

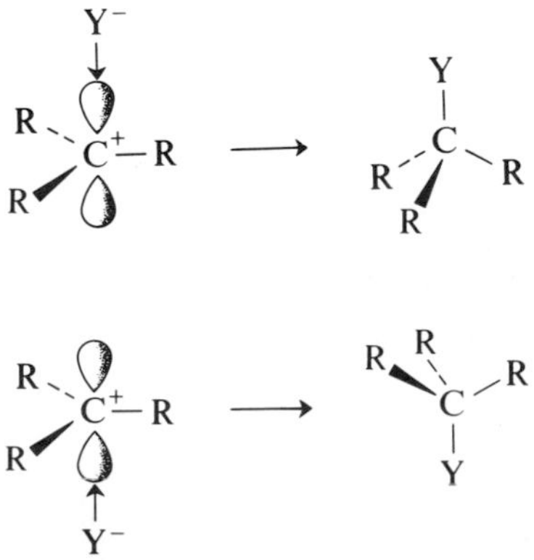

Considering again our enantiomeric example, from one of the enantiomeric pair we obtain,

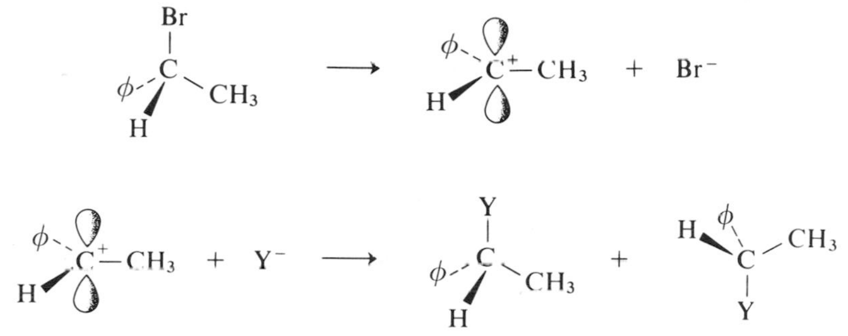

while from the other,

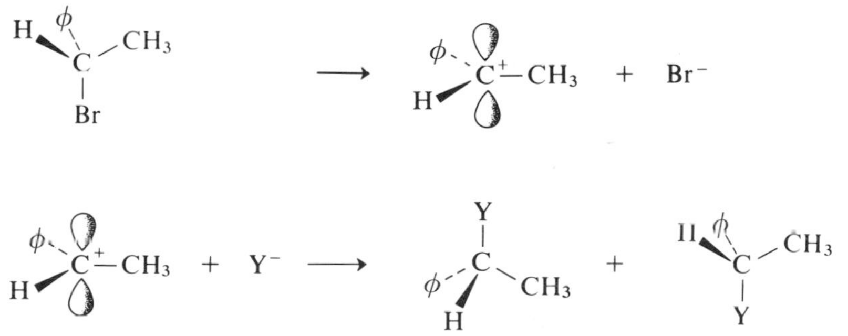

Thus, if the reaction involves a free carbonium ion, we expect racemized products even if the reactant is optically active.

On the other hand, if the reaction does not involve a free carbonium ion but if an ion pair is the intermediate, we do not expect racemization. The reactant forms an ion pair, and the nucleophile attacks more effectively from the side opposite the leaving group. The leaving group X^- partially shields and protects the carbonium ion:

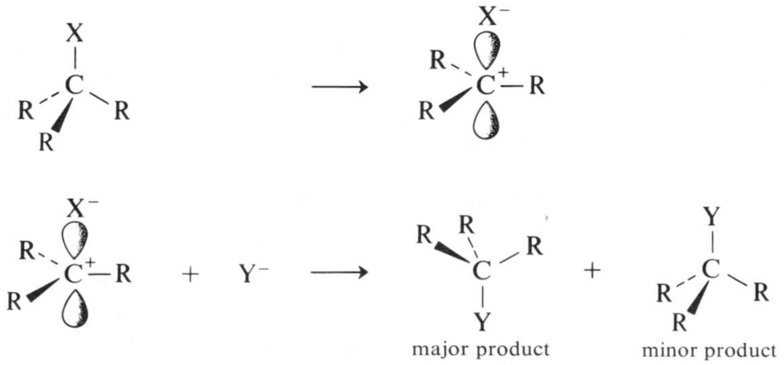

major product   minor product

Returning to our enantiomeric example we find that if an ion pair is the intermediate we obtain from one of the mirror images,

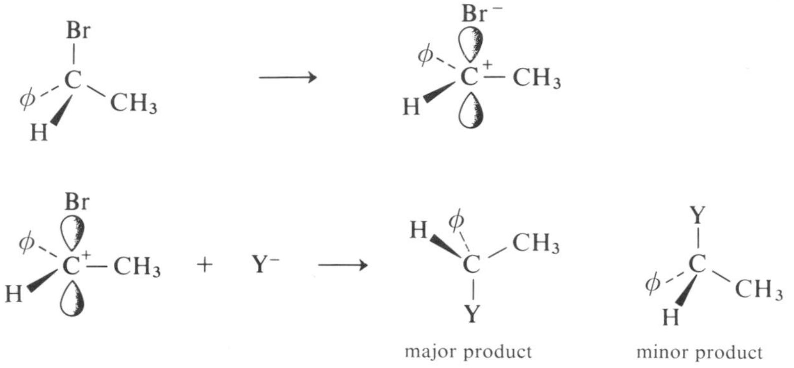

major product   minor product

and from the other,

major product   minor product

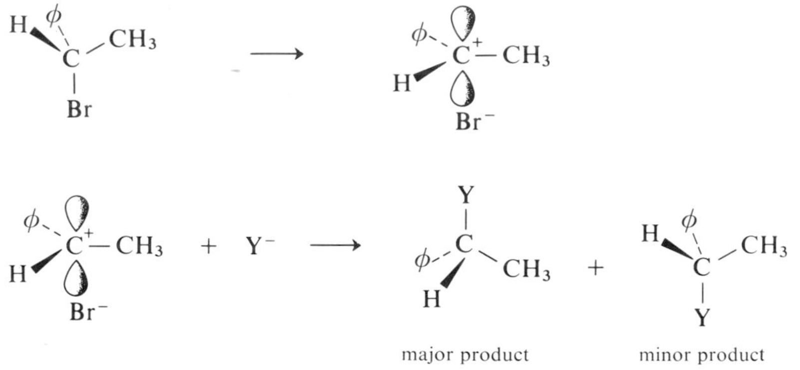

In both cases the major product is formed with inversion of configuration. Thus, when an ion pair is the intermediate in the S_N1 reaction, we expect some racemization to occur, but formation of the major product is accompanied by inversion of configuration. When starting with an optically active reactant, the product should then have some optical activity. Naturally, the extent to which racemization occurs depends upon how tightly the ion pair is held together. The closer the leaving group to the carbonium ion, the more effectively it shields the carbonium ion from attack on that side.

11.6 The Effect of the Leaving Group upon the Rate

Assuming once again that the rate limiting step is the decomposition of the ion pair into a freer carbonium ion and X^-, we may discuss the rate of reaction in terms of the free energy of activation for the process. Alternatively, since the general rate law for product formation can be expressed in terms of the concentration of the ion pair, we may discuss the rate in terms of this inter-mediate:

$$\frac{d[R_3CY]}{dt} = k_2[R_3C^+X^-]$$

The latter approach is in this case the simpler. We consider the effect of various leaving groups X upon the concentration of the ion pair, factors increasing the concentration of the ion pair increase the rate of reaction.

Any group that readily accommodates a negative charge is a good leaving group, for in the ion pair the leaving group has acquired such a charge. The better the ability of X^- to bear that charge, the greater the concentration of the ion pair and the faster the reaction. Therefore, in a rough way, we expect the reaction rate to parallel the acidity of HX. This expectation is fulfilled, and for a number of related reactions the best leaving group is the one forming the weakest conjugate base X^-. Among the halogens the following order of reactivity has been found:

$$R_3CI > R_3CBr > R_3CCl > R_3CF$$

$$\xrightarrow{\text{Decreasing Reactivity}}$$

Now X is usually a halogen atom, but various other good leaving groups are known. The anions of *para* toluenesulfonic acid **2** (the tosylate anion) and *para* bromobenzenesulfonic acid **3** (the brosylate anion) are very stable. The negative charge in each of these anions is effectively delocalized. These anions are stable and therefore excellent leaving groups:

$$^-O-SO_2-\!\!\!\left\langle\bigcirc\right\rangle\!\!\!-CH_3 \qquad\qquad ^-O-SO_2-\!\!\!\left\langle\bigcirc\right\rangle\!\!\!-Br$$

$$\textbf{2} \qquad\qquad\qquad\qquad\qquad \textbf{3}$$

Other good leaving groups are:

$$^-O-\overset{\overset{O}{\|}}{C}-\!\!\!\left\langle\bigcirc\right\rangle\!\!\!-NO_2 \qquad\qquad ^-O-\overset{\overset{O}{\|}}{C}-\!\!\!\left\langle\bigcirc\right\rangle$$

11.7 The Electronic Influence of R upon the Rate

Not only do changes in X affect the rate of the S_N1 reaction, changing the R group also exerts an influence. The more stable the negative charge, the higher the concentration of the ion pair, and by similar reasoning, the more stable the positive charge, the greater is the concentration of this intermediate. More effective delocalization of the positive charge in the ion pair intermediate stabilizes this intermediate and increases the rate of reaction.

The central carbon atom is positively charged, and delocalization of this charge exerts a favorable influence. Consequently, compounds such as allyl chloride and benzyl chloride react rapidly under S_N1 conditions:

$$\overset{\delta+}{CH_2} == CH == \overset{\delta+}{CH_2}$$
$$Cl^-$$

$$\overset{+}{CH_2} \ Cl^-$$

Somewhat less reactive are the simple aliphatic chlorides which show the following order of reactivity,

$$(CH_3)_3CCl > (CH_3)_2CHCl > CH_3CH_2Cl > CH_3Cl$$

Decreasing Reactivity by S_N1 →

11.8 Steric Effects

Changes in hybridization caused by large groups as well as restricted vibrations and restricted rotations arising from nonbonded interactions are steric effects. We wish to ascertain the effect of increasing the size of the alkyl group R upon the rate of the S_N1 reaction. Unfortunately, it is not possible to measure this effect independently of other factors, for when we replace one alkyl group by another, other factors also change. Not all R groups donate electrons equally well, and in changing R we also alter the ability of that group to donate electrons. Furthermore, small ions are more highly solvated than large ones, and changing the size of R changes solvation. Therefore, when we measure experimentally the effect of varying the size of R, we do not measure steric effects alone; these other effects, solvation and electron donating ability, are also varied. While a quantitative measurement of steric effects is not possible, we can certainly discuss in a qualitative way the effect of increasing the size of R.

In the reactant the angle between carbon-alkyl bonds is approximately equal to 109.5°; in the carbonium ion this angle is 120°. Consequently in passing from the reactant to the ion pair the alkyl groups move farther apart:

$$109.5° \overset{R}{\underset{R}{\overset{R}{C}}} - X \longrightarrow 120° \overset{R}{\underset{R}{\overset{R}{C^+}}} X^-$$

The alkyl groups are closer together in the reactant than in the ion pair and separating large groups is a favorable process. Thus, as the alkyl groups become larger, we expect the concentration of the ion pair to increase and the S_N1 reaction to proceed more rapidly.

Experimentally it has been found that increasing the size of the alkyl groups does not markedly change the rate of reaction until R becomes very large. When R is extremely large and bulky, then rate increases do occur. The alkyl chloride **4** reacts 600 times as rapidly as *t*-butyl chloride **5** in 80% aqueous ethanol:

$$(CH_3)_3C-\underset{\underset{Cl}{|}}{\overset{\overset{C(CH_3)_3}{|}}{C}}-C(CH_3)_3 \qquad CH_3-\underset{\underset{Cl}{|}}{\overset{\overset{CH_3}{|}}{C}}-CH_3$$

$$\textbf{4} \qquad\qquad\qquad \textbf{5}$$

Not all of this rate increase can be attributed to steric effects, for **4** undergoes rearrangement during the reaction. If we postulate a concerted mechanism for the rearrangement process, then this accounts for part of the rate increase.[1]

Of course, the other effects that were mentioned must also be considered.

While we cannot discuss steric effects in a quantitative manner, we can say with certainty that steric interactions due to large R groups will be more pronounced in the reactant than in the ion pair, and such interactions will raise the free energy of the reactant more than they raise the free energy of the ion pair. The concentration of the latter increases when steric interactions are present, and the S_N1 reaction proceeds more rapidly.

11.9 Side Reactions and Rearrangements

We have not thus far considered explicitly the possibility of side reactions and rearrangements. When the reaction involves a carbonium ion intermediate, two pathways exist for reaction. This intermediate can react with a nucleophile to form substituted products (S_N1) or lose a proton to yield olefinic products (*E*1). We can vary reaction conditions to favor the one or the other of these processes, yet these are two competitive reactions, and both occur. In addition, if the nucleophilic reagent is present in moderately high concentration, the S_N2 and the *E*2 pathways may also become competitive.

In certain cases the possibility for substitution exists and the possibility for elimination does not (with benzyl halides, for example), yet whenever both pathways are open, both reactions always occur. The product of an S_N1 reaction is accompanied by olefinic impurities, and conversely, when an alkene is formed by way of an *E*1 reaction, substituted products are also formed. For example, under solvolysis conditions *t*-butyl chloride forms a carbonium ion

---

[1] If we assume that the rearrangement of **4** does occur by way of a concerted mechanism, then the alkyl chlorides **4** and **5** are reacting by different pathways. Furthermore, the free energy of activation for the concerted process must be smaller than the free energy of activation for simple ionization; otherwise the concerted mechanism would not occur. Therefore, part of the rate increase is due to the fact that **4** reacts by the concerted pathway and part is due to steric interactions.

intermediate which yields both substituted and olefinic products:

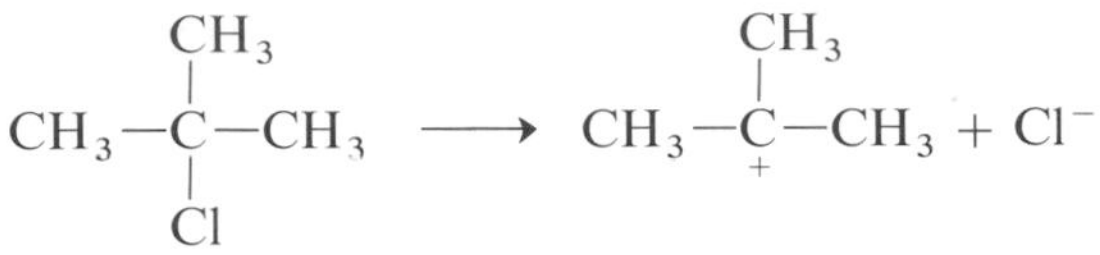

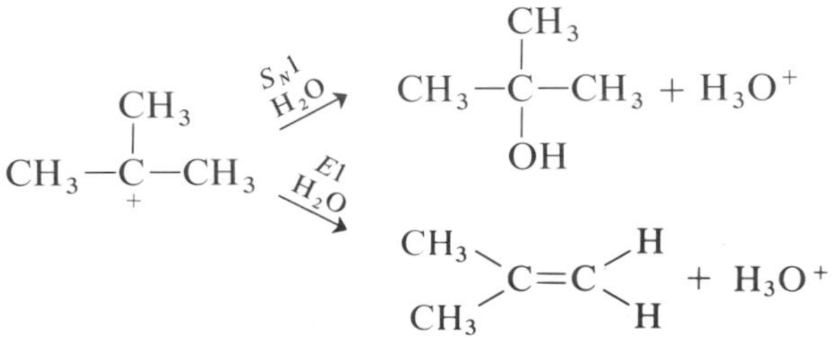

$$CH_3-\underset{\underset{Cl}{|}}{\overset{\overset{CH_3}{|}}{C}}-CH_3 \longrightarrow CH_3-\underset{+}{\overset{\overset{CH_3}{|}}{C}}-CH_3 + Cl^-$$

$$CH_3-\underset{+}{\overset{\overset{CH_3}{|}}{C}}-CH_3 \xrightarrow[\overset{S_N1}{H_2O}]{} CH_3-\underset{\underset{OH}{|}}{\overset{\overset{CH_3}{|}}{C}}-CH_3 + H_3O^+$$

$$\xrightarrow[\overset{E1}{H_2O}]{} \underset{CH_3}{\overset{CH_3}{>}}C=C\underset{H}{\overset{H}{<}} + H_3O^+$$

Rearrangements are also possible whenever a reaction involves a carbonium ion. We know that tertiary carbonium ions are more stable than secondary, and these secondary cations are more stable than primary carbonium ions. The less stable system rearranges to the more stable carbonium ion, and we must always consider the possibility of such rearrangements.

Illustrative of this is the reaction of neopentyl bromide with weak nucleophiles such as water and alcohol. The reaction proceeds through a carbonium ion pathway and only rearranged products are formed:

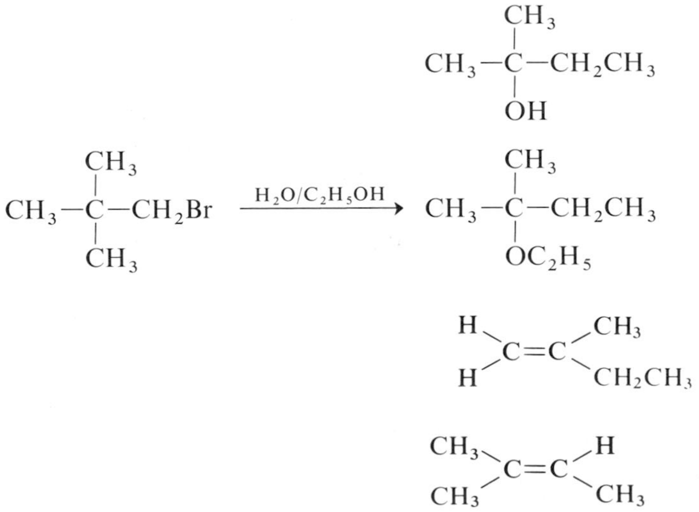

$$CH_3-\underset{\underset{CH_3}{|}}{\overset{\overset{CH_3}{|}}{C}}-CH_2Br \xrightarrow{H_2O/C_2H_5OH}$$

$$CH_3-\underset{\underset{OH}{|}}{\overset{\overset{CH_3}{|}}{C}}-CH_2CH_3$$

$$CH_3-\underset{\underset{OC_2H_5}{|}}{\overset{\overset{CH_3}{|}}{C}}-CH_2CH_3$$

$$\underset{H}{\overset{H}{>}}C=C\underset{CH_2CH_3}{\overset{CH_3}{<}}$$

$$\underset{CH_3}{\overset{CH_3}{>}}C=C\underset{CH_3}{\overset{H}{<}}$$

Two different mechanisms may be postulated for this rearrangement. The first is a stepwise mechanism involving both the neopentyl and the *t*-amyl carbonium ions:

$$CH_3-\underset{\underset{\displaystyle CH_3}{|}}{\overset{\overset{\displaystyle CH_3}{|}}{C}}-CH_2Br \longrightarrow CH_3-\underset{\underset{\displaystyle CH_3}{|}}{\overset{\overset{\displaystyle CH_3}{|}}{C}}-CH_2^+ + Br^-$$

$$CH_3-\underset{\underset{\displaystyle CH_3}{|}}{\overset{\overset{\displaystyle CH_3}{|}}{C}}-CH_2^+ \rightleftharpoons CH_3-\underset{+}{\overset{\overset{\displaystyle CH_3}{|}}{C}}-CH_2CH_3$$

$$CH_3-\underset{+}{\overset{\overset{\displaystyle CH_3}{|}}{C}}-CH_2CH_3 \xrightarrow{H_2O/C_2H_5OH} products$$

The second is a concerted mechanism with the methyl group migrating as the bromide leaves. There is at present no evidence that allows us to distinguish between them. We assume that dissociation of the reactant is rate limiting under these conditions, and the concerted mechanism is (**6** is the transition state):

$$CH_3-\underset{\underset{\displaystyle CH_3}{|}}{\overset{\overset{\displaystyle CH_3}{|}}{C}}-CH_2Br \longrightarrow \underset{\underset{\displaystyle CH_3}{|}}{\overset{\overset{\displaystyle CH_3}{|}}{C}H_3-C} \overset{\delta}{=\!=} CH_2\text{-}\text{-}\overset{\delta}{Br} \longrightarrow$$

6

$$CH_3-\underset{+}{\overset{\overset{\displaystyle CH_3}{|}}{C}}-CH_2CH_3 + Br^-$$

$$CH_3-\underset{+}{\overset{\overset{\displaystyle CH_3}{|}}{C}}-CH_2CH_3 \xrightarrow{H_2O/C_2H_5OH} products$$

In the stepwise mechanism the neopentyl carbonium ion rearranges to the more stable *t*-amyl carbonium ion. Yet both carbonium ions are present, and both of them could react with alcohol and water to form substituted products. The *t*-amyl carbonium ion is present in much higher concentration, and if the reaction proceeds by this mechanism, this must be the deciding factor, for only rearranged products are found. It is also possible that the reaction proceeds by way of the concerted mechanism.

The behavior of neopentyl bromide is typical of reactions involving carbonium ion intermediates. Not only does the reaction involve a rearrangement, but both substituted and olefinic products are observed.

11.10 Other Carbonium Ion Reactions

One type of carbonium ion reaction involves the ionization of an alkyl halide or an alkyl ester to yield a carbonium ion and some leaving group X⁻. There are, in addition to these ionizations, other substitutions that proceed by way of a carbonium ion intermediate. The reaction of *t*-butyl alcohol with concentrated hydrochloric acid proceeds by this pathway. The following mechanism is postulated for the transformation:

$$
\begin{array}{c}
\text{CH}_3 \\
| \\
\text{CH}_3\text{—C—CH}_3 + \text{H}^+ \\
| \\
\text{OH}
\end{array}
\rightleftharpoons
\begin{array}{c}
\text{CH}_3 \\
| \\
\text{CH}_3\text{—C—CH}_3 \\
| \\
\overset{+}{\text{O}} \\
\diagup \diagdown \\
\text{H} \quad \text{H}
\end{array}
$$

$$
\begin{array}{c}
\text{CH}_3 \\
| \\
\text{CH}_3\text{—C—CH}_3 \\
| \\
\overset{+}{\text{O}} \\
\diagup \diagdown \\
\text{H} \quad \text{H}
\end{array}
\longrightarrow
\begin{array}{c}
\text{CH}_3 \\
| \\
\text{CH}_3\text{—}\overset{+}{\text{C}}\text{—CH}_3 + \text{H}_2\text{O}
\end{array}
$$

$$
\begin{array}{c}
\text{CH}_3 \\
| \\
\text{CH}_3\text{—}\overset{+}{\text{C}}\text{—CH}_3 + \text{Cl}^-
\end{array}
\longrightarrow
\begin{array}{c}
\text{CH}_3 \\
| \\
\text{CH}_3\text{—C—CH}_3 \\
| \\
\text{Cl}
\end{array}
$$

The rate limiting step depends upon the reaction conditions. When the second step is rate limiting, the process is an S_N1 reaction. We effect a substitution using the nucleophile Cl⁻, and the slow step involves a single species (protonated alcohol).

A substitution related to this, is the reaction of *t*-butylacetate with concentrated hydrochloric acid. The products are *t*-butyl chloride and acetic acid, and this reaction proceeds by a mechanism analogous to that just presented:

$$
\begin{array}{c}
\text{CH}_3 \ \text{O} \\
| \quad\ || \\
\text{CH}_3\text{—C—OCCH}_3 + \text{HCl} \\
| \\
\text{CH}_3
\end{array}
\longrightarrow
\begin{array}{c}
\text{CH}_3 \\
| \\
\text{CH}_3\text{—C—Cl} + \text{CH}_3\text{COOH} \\
| \\
\text{CH}_3
\end{array}
$$

Still another related reaction is the cleavage of di-*t*-butyl ether using hydroiodic acid. Alkyl ethers when treated with hydroiodic acid yield alkyl iodides. Depending upon the reactant, the reaction proceeds either by an S_N2 or an S_N1 mechanism. Naturally, with di-*t*-butyl ether the latter pathway is more probable.

$$CH_3-\underset{\underset{\displaystyle CH_3}{|}}{\overset{\overset{\displaystyle CH_3}{|}}{C}}-O-\underset{\underset{\displaystyle CH_3}{|}}{\overset{\overset{\displaystyle CH_3}{|}}{C}}-CH_3 + 2HI \longrightarrow 2CH_3-\underset{\underset{\displaystyle CH_3}{|}}{\overset{\overset{\displaystyle CH_3}{|}}{C}}-I + H_2O$$

In this section we have discussed one pathway by which nucleophilic substitution is effected. Naturally, if we wish to effect nucleophilic substitution, we choose conditions that promote the desired reaction, that is, we choose conditions that are favorable for the substitution. Thus, we react *t*-butyl chloride under conditions that are favorable for carbonium ion formation since a tertiary halide usually undergoes nucleophilic substitution by this route. Since primary halides generally react more readily by the S_N2 pathway, for ethyl chloride we choose conditions that favor the S_N2 reaction. We discuss in the following sections the effects of solvent and structure upon the S_N2 mechanism of nucleophilic substitution.

11.11 The S_N2 Reaction

The S_N2 pathway is another means of bringing about nucleophilic substitution. This reaction, involving a single step, is accompanied by inversion of configuration and as the name implies, is bimolecular; it usually follows second order kinetics:

$$Y^- + \overset{\displaystyle R}{\underset{\displaystyle R}{\overset{|}{C}}}\!\!-X \longrightarrow \overset{\displaystyle R}{\underset{\displaystyle R}{Y\cdots \overset{|}{C}\cdots X}} \longrightarrow Y-\overset{\displaystyle R}{\underset{\displaystyle R}{C}} + X^-$$

and

$$\frac{d[R_3CY]}{dt} = k[R_3CX][Y^-]$$

R may be either hydrogen, alkyl or aryl. In the transition state the central carbon atom is sp^2 hybridized, and the remaining p orbital is used to form partial bonds with both the entering nucleophile and the leaving group.

The angles between R groups are approximately 120° while the p orbital is oriented at an angle of 90° to these three C—R bonds,

$$\underset{\underset{\displaystyle R}{90°\,|\,90°}}{\overset{\overset{\displaystyle R\;\xleftrightarrow{120°}\;R}{}}{Y-C-X}}$$

Thus, during the course of the S_N2 reaction, the central carbon atom changes its hybridization from sp^3 to sp^2 and then back to sp^3 again, the process being accompanied by inversion of configuration. The S_N2 process occurs quite readily; a large variety of attacking nucleophiles and leaving groups are known; the following examples are typical:

$$CH_3I + OH^- \longrightarrow CH_3OH + I^-$$

$$CH_3I + NH_3 \longrightarrow CH_3NH_3^+I^-$$

$$CH_3I + C_2H_5O^- \longrightarrow CH_3OC_2H_5 + I^-$$

$$CH_3\overset{+}{-}S(CH_3)_2 + OH^- \longrightarrow CH_3OH + (CH_3)_2S$$

$$CH_3\overset{+}{-}S(CH_3)_2 + N(CH_3)_3 \longrightarrow CH_3\overset{+}{N}(CH_3)_3 + (CH_3)_2S$$

The examples presented represent just a few of many S_N2 reactions. Certain more complex processes also fall into this category. The reaction of ethanol with hydrogen bromide is a bimolecular process in which the protonated alcohol and bromide ion participate. The conversion of *n*-butyl alcohol to *n*-butyl bromide is a standard laboratory preparation proceeding by the same mechanism. This second process cannot involve a carbonium ion for the unrearranged product is isolated,

$$CH_3CH_2OH + HBr \rightleftarrows CH_3CH_2\overset{H}{\underset{+}{-O}}-H + Br^-$$

$$CH_3CH_2\overset{H}{\underset{+}{-O}}-H + Br^- \longrightarrow CH_3CH_2Br + H_2O$$

and

$$CH_3CH_2CH_2CH_2OH + NaBr + H_2SO_4 \longrightarrow$$

$$CH_3CH_2CH_2CH_2Br + H_2O + NaHSO_4$$

The cleavage of dimethyl ether by hydroiodic acid affords methyl iodide, and this reaction presumably proceeds by the S_N2 pathway. The protonated ether reacts directly with iodide ion:

$$CH_3OCH_3 + 2HI \longrightarrow 2CH_3I + H_2O$$

The mechanism is probably the following,

$$CH_3OCH_3 + HI \rightleftarrows CH_3\overset{H}{\underset{+}{-O}}-CH_3 + I^-$$

$$CH_3\overset{H}{\underset{+}{-O}}-CH_3 + I^- \longrightarrow CH_3I + CH_3OH$$

Then

$$CH_3OH + HI \longrightarrow CH_3I + H_2O$$

11.12 Steric Effects upon the Rate of the S_N2 Reaction

The reactant R_3CX reacts with the nucleophile Y^- and is converted to R_3CY:

$$R_3CX + Y^- \longrightarrow R_3CY + X^-$$

The rate of reaction depends upon solvation, steric effects, and electronic effects; replacing one R group by another changes all of these. For most S_N2 processes steric interactions are of prime importance, and increased crowding about the central carbon atom raises the free energy of the transition state; this lowers the rate of reaction. Large R groups differ from small R groups in their ability to donate electrons, but in the S_N2 process this effect is secondary. Steric effects are the main consideration.

The R groups, which are separated by bond angles of about 109.5° in the reactant, move still farther apart in proceeding to the transition state (the bond angles between alkyl groups is 120° in the transition state). Thus steric interactions between R groups actually decrease. On the other hand, the angle between these R groups and the leaving group is reduced from a value near 109.5° in the reactant to 90° in the transition state. In addition, the entering nucleophile Y^-, which is not bonded initially, becomes partially bonded in the transition state; the angle again being approximately 90°. In proceeding from the reactant to the transition state the R groups approach the two groups X and Y and this is the major factor in determining the ease of reaction by way of the S_N2 mechanism:

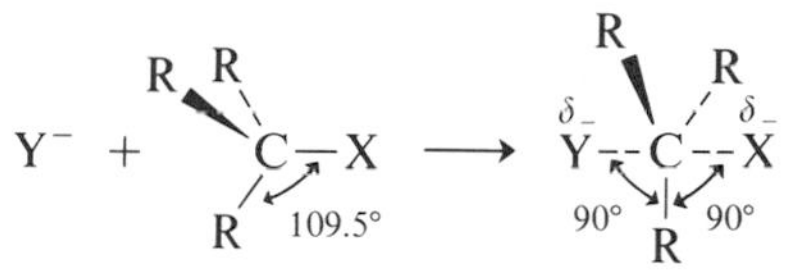

In the reaction of CH_3X little or no steric interactions are present; however, in CH_3CH_2X, where we have replaced a hydrogen atom by the larger methyl group, some steric interactions are present in the transition state and its free energy increases,

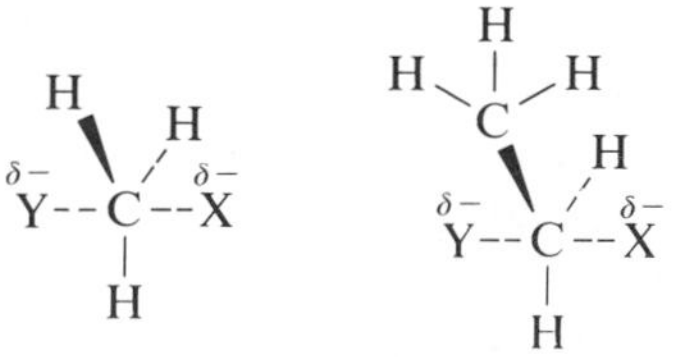

Interactions between the methyl group and the groups X and Y raise the free energy of this transition state. Since such crowding is not present in the

reactant, the free energy of activation for the process increases when methyl is introduced, and the rate of the S_N2 reaction decreases.

In proceeding along the sequence to $(CH_3)_2CHX$ and $(CH_3)_3CX$, we continue to replace hydrogen by methyl. Crowding becomes still more pronounced in the transition state, and the rate of reaction continues to decrease. As a result, we find the following order of reactivity for reaction by the S_N2 pathway:

$$CH_3X > RCH_2X > R_2CHX > R_3CX$$

Decreasing Reactivity by S_N2 →

We also consider the sequence CH_3X, CH_3CH_2X, $CH_3CH_2CH_2X$, $(CH_3)_2CHCH_2X$, $(CH_3)_3CCH_2X$ where we replace a hydrogen first by methyl then by ethyl, isopropyl, and *t*-butyl. All of these, except the first, are primary halides, yet the size of the alkyl group is again increased as we proceed along the sequence. This increase in the size of R again retards the rate of the S_N2 reaction:

$$CH_3X > CH_3CH_2X > CH_3CH_2CH_2X > (CH_3)_2CHCH_2X > (CH_3)_3CCH_2X$$

Decreasing Reactivity →

Steric effects are even more significant in this sequence than in the previous one, and neopentyl halides, although primary halides, react very slowly under S_N2 conditions. For neopentyl halides, the transition state is,

$$
\begin{array}{c}
CH_3 \\
CH_3 \diagdown \mid \diagup CH_3 \\
C \\
\diagdown \quad H \\
\overset{\delta^-}{Y} \text{--} \underset{\mid}{C} \text{--} \overset{\delta^-}{X} \\
H
\end{array}
$$

The nonbonded interactions that result from increasing the size of R restrict rotations and vibrations and raise the free energy of the system. Changes in hybridization must also be considered. Both $\Delta S^{\ddagger}$ and $\Delta H^{\ddagger}$ are affected.

As the R groups become progressively larger, steric interactions between X, Y, and these R groups become increasingly important in the transition state. These interactions raise the free energy of the transition state. Steric interactions are less pronounced in the reactant. Consequently the free energy of activation for the process increases, and the reaction proceeds more slowly.

As R increases in size, the rate of the S_N2 reaction decreases, and naturally, very large nucleophiles and very large leaving groups exert a similar influence. Increasing the size of the entering nucleophile and that of the leaving group does not affect the rate of reaction unless these two are extremely large. With very large groups the rate of reaction does decrease.

Having discussed some aspects of the S_N1 and S_N2 reactions, it becomes worthwhile to compare these two processes in a more quantitative manner. The general rate expression for hydrolysis of an alkyl halide can be written as,

$$\frac{d[\text{ROH}]}{dt} = k_1[\text{RX}] + k_2[\text{RX}][\text{OH}^-]$$

where the first term is due to hydrolysis by the S_N1 process, the second for the direct reaction with hydroxide ion. (The S_N2 reaction with water, which would be incorporated into k_1, is negligible.)

For nucleophilic substitution in aqueous ethanol (80% by volume) containing hydroxide ion, the values of the first order and second order rate constants have been obtained at 55°. The results are presented in Table 11–4.

Table 11–4*

RX	$k_1 \cdot 10^5$ (sec^{-1})	$k_2 \cdot 10^5$ (liter mole^{-1} sec^{-1})
CH_3Br	—	2140
CH_3CH_2Br	—	170
$(CH_3)_2CHBr$	0.24	4.7
$(CH_3)_3CBr$	1010	—

* Ingold, C. K., *Structure and Mechanism in Organic Chemistry*. Ithaca, New York, Cornell U.P., 1953, p. 318.

We see that under these conditions, only isopropyl bromide suffers substitution to a significant degree by both routes, the major mechanism for the secondary halide depending upon the hydroxide ion concentration.

These results do not indicate that the other routes are not significant for primary or tertiary halides. They are, but under other conditions.

We also present the second order rate constants for the reaction of various primary alkyl bromides with sodium ethoxide (55°). The expected steric retardations are confirmed (Table 11–5):

$$\text{RBr} + \text{NaOC}_2\text{H}_5 \xrightarrow{\text{C}_2\text{H}_5\text{OH}} \text{ROC}_2\text{H}_5$$

Table 11–5*

RBr	$k \cdot 10^3$ (liter mole^{-1} sec^{-1})
CH_3Br	34.4
CH_3CH_2Br	1.95
$CH_3CH_2CH_2Br$	0.547
$(CH_3)_2CHCH_2Br$	0.058
$(CH_3)_3CCH_2Br$	0.00000826

* Ingold, C. K., *Structure and Mechanism in Organic Chemistry*. Ithaca, New York, Cornell U.P., 1953, p. 408.

11.13 The Effect of Solvent upon the S_N2 Reaction

Some typical S_N2 processes were presented in Section 11.11. All of these reactions represented S_N2 conversions, yet in some cases the reactants were positively or negatively charged while in others they were neutral. The reaction of methyl iodide with sodium hydroxide represents a reaction between neutral and charged reactants while the reaction of methyl iodide with ammonia typifies an S_N2 process between uncharged reactants:

$$CH_3I + OH^- \longrightarrow CH_3OH + I^- \qquad\qquad 1$$

$$CH_3I + NH_3 \longrightarrow CH_3NH_3^+I^- \qquad\qquad 2$$

Two more possibilities exist, they are:

$$CH_3-\overset{+}{S}(CH_3)_2 + OH^- \longrightarrow CH_3OH + (CH_3)_2S \qquad\qquad 3$$

and

$$CH_3-\overset{+}{S}(CH_3)_2 + N(CH_3)_3 \longrightarrow CH_3-\overset{+}{N}(CH_3)_3 + (CH_3)S \qquad\qquad 4$$

Remember that materials in which the positive or negative charge is localized rather than delocalized are more highly solvated and that charged materials are more highly solvated than uncharged materials.

These four S_N2 reactions proceed by way of the transition states:

$$
\begin{array}{cccc}
\text{H} & \text{H} & \text{H} & \text{H} \\
\overset{\delta-}{HO}--\overset{\displaystyle|}{C}--\overset{\delta-}{I} & H_3\overset{\delta+}{N}--\overset{\displaystyle|}{C}--\overset{\delta-}{I} & \overset{\delta-}{HO}--\overset{\displaystyle|}{C}--\overset{\delta+}{S}\overset{CH_3}{<_{CH_3}} & (CH_3)_3\overset{\delta+}{N}--\overset{\displaystyle|}{C}--\overset{\delta+}{S}\overset{CH_3}{<_{CH_3}} \\
\text{H} & \text{H} & \text{H} & \text{H} \\
\\
1 & 2 & 3 & 4
\end{array}
$$

In three of these processes (cases **1**, **3**, and **4**), charge is either destroyed or delocalized upon passing from the reactants to the corresponding transition state. Consequently in each of these cases the reactants are more highly solvated than the transition state. In the second reaction, charge is generated; the transition state for this reaction is more highly charged and more highly solvated than are the reactants.

In all cases, changing from a less polar to a more polar solvent affects the rate of reaction; however, a more polar solvent decreases the rate of **1**, **3** and **4** while it increases the rate of **2**.

According to one argument a more polar solvent stabilizes the charged reactants in cases **1**, **3**, and **4** more than it stabilizes the corresponding transition states. This increases the free energy of activation and decreases the rate of reaction for these processes. In case **2**, according to this argument, the polar solvent stabilizes the charged transition state more than it stabilizes the uncharged reactants. Thus, in this case a more polar solvent increases the rate of reaction.

This theory assumes that a change in solvent influences the term $\Delta H^{\ddagger}$. Alternatively, we may assume that the term $\Delta H^{\ddagger}$ remains relatively constant and that changing to a more polar solvent influences the entropy of activation $\Delta S^{\ddagger}$.

For cases **1**, **3**, and **4** solvation decreases in passing to the transition state. The molecules of solvent become less highly oriented. They possess more freedom to move, and this has a favorable influence upon $\Delta S^{\ddagger}$. The molecules of a very polar solvent are never very free to move, and intermolecular attractions still restrict their motion in the transition state. For a less polar solvent intermolecular attractions are not so important. In proceeding to the transition state the freedom of molecules of the less polar solvent increases considerably. The term $\Delta S^{\ddagger}$ is more favorable for the less polar solvent, and these S_N2 reactions proceed more rapidly under less polar conditions. This argument is just the reverse of the effect of solvent upon the rate of the S_N1 ionization. In that case we were generating charge; here we delocalize or destroy charge.

In case **2** we do generate charge in passing to the transition state, and for this case the ideas are the same as for the S_N1 reaction. This reaction proceeds more readily in a more polar solvent.

The effect of solvent upon the S_N2 process depends upon the particular S_N2 reaction under consideration. A more polar solvent increases the rate of those S_N2 reactions where charge is generated and decreases the rate of those S_N2 reactions in which charge is either being destroyed or delocalized. Of course, the decrease in rate is more pronounced when charge is destroyed than when charge is only being delocalized.

Nucleophilic substitution by means of the bimolecular pathway depends upon steric crowding in the transition state and upon the choice of solvent. In addition, the transition state involves partial bond formation with the entering nucleophile and partial bond rupture with the leaving group. Consequently, the ability of the nucleophilic agent to form a bond to carbon is important. Good nucleophiles are those materials that readily form bonds with carbon, good leaving groups are those which suffer bond breakage readily.

There are one or two more points that should be mentioned in conjunction with the S_N2 reaction. While tertiary halides do not generally undergo substitution by way of the S_N2 mechanism, in certain special cases where the attacking agent is a good nucleophile but a poor base, substitutions are able to compete to some extent with other reactions. Iodide anion is such an attacking agent and to some degree bimolecular substitutions on tertiary halides can be effected using this nucleophile. The reaction is slow and the yield very small. If the attacking nucleophile is also a strong base, then the bimolecular elimination reaction (*E2*) occurs. Thus *t*-butyl chloride when treated with sodium ethoxide does not undergo nucleophilic substitution. Elimination by way of the $E2$ mechanism occurs instead. Virtually no substituted product is obtained:

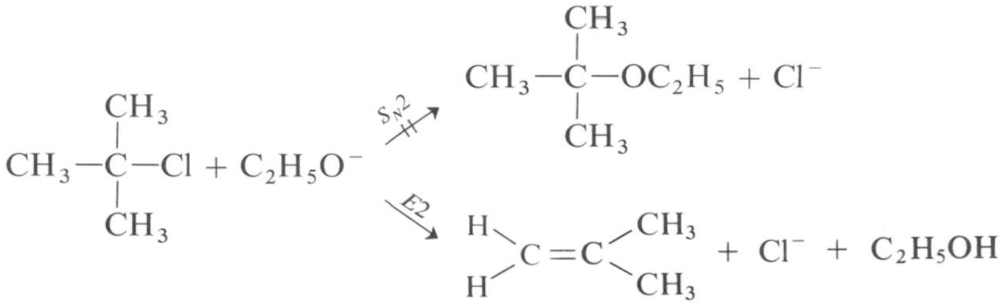

$$\begin{array}{c} CH_3 \\ | \\ CH_3-\underset{\underset{CH_3}{|}}{C}-Cl + C_2H_5O^- \end{array} \quad \overset{S_N2}{\underset{E2}{\nearrow\!\!\!\diagdown}} \quad \begin{array}{c} CH_3 \\ | \\ CH_3-\underset{\underset{CH_3}{|}}{C}-OC_2H_5 + Cl^- \\[1em] \underset{H}{\overset{H}{\diagdown}}C=C\underset{CH_3}{\overset{CH_3}{\diagup}} + Cl^- + C_2H_5OH \end{array}$$

These two reactions, the S_N2 and the $E2$ are competitive. Both occur; which predominates depends upon the reaction conditions, the nucleophilic reagent, and the starting alkyl halide. Tertiary halides suffer elimination with strong bases such as hydroxide and alkoxide. Secondary and primary halides may undergo substitution, and here the reaction conditions are important. The more polar solvent favors substitution while elimination occurs preferentially in less polar solvents. Whenever we desire to effect an S_N2 reaction, we should also consider the $E2$ process which accompanies it.

Benzyl halides and acyl halides,

suffer nucleophilic displacement readily by the S_N2 process. The rapid reactions of the first imply that in the transition state the carbon atom being attacked is charged and this charge is delocalized. The reactivity of the second may be due to partial bonding of the nucleophile to the carbonyl group in the transition state. This also delocalizes charge and accelerates the rate.

11.14 Reaction at Bridgehead Carbon Atoms

Compounds such as **7**, **8**, and **9** in which the halogen is attached to a bridgehead carbon atom are extremely unreactive:

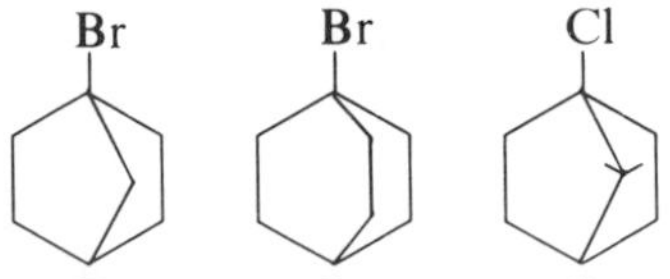

These materials do not react under S_N2 conditions nor do they react under the usual S_N1 conditions. Compound **9** undergoes neither substitution nor elimination even when treated with hot potassium hydroxide for 24 hours. Compounds **7** and **8** react very slowly with aqueous silver nitrate (these are conditions favoring carbonium ion formation) while **9** is still unreacted after treatment with silver nitrate for 48 hours.

These materials do not react readily even under strenuous conditions. Their failure to react under S_N2 conditions is due to the fact that the usual bimolecular process is accompanied by inversion of configuration, and such inversion is impossible at bridgehead carbon atoms. A bimolecular substitution involving *cis* attack is conceivable but that process would require much more energy.

Furthermore, since the carbon atom in an olefinic linkage is sp^2 hybridized, the groups attached to this carbon atom must be coplanar:

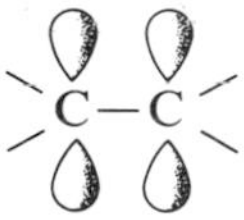

Consequently, $E1$ and $E2$ reactions are also forbidden in these bicyclic systems. Such reactions would require placing a double bond at the bridgehead position, thereby straining the system considerably.

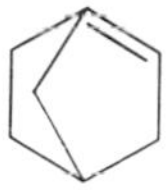

The idea that one cannot place a double bond at most bridgehead positions is well known and has been called Bredt's rule. However, we modify Bredt's rule to say that a bridgehead carbon atom cannot usually become sp^2 hybridized. Not only are double bonds at bridgehead positions unlikely, but carbonium ions are also sp^2 hybridized and their formation at bridgehead positions is also unlikely. A strained carbonium ion (not truly sp^2 hybridized) may form at a bridgehead, but even this requires extra energy.

Exceptions to this rule are known; for example, systems such as **10** have been prepared:

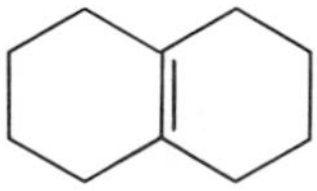

10

However, exceptions of this type are expected, for here the introduction of a double bond does not seriously strain the system. It is only in cases where sp^2 hybridization of the carbon atom would be difficult that Bredt's rule applies.

The S_N2, $E1$ and $E2$ processes do not occur for most bridgehead halides. Nor does the S_N1 reaction proceed readily, for the usual sp^2 hybridized carbonium ion is not expected to form at a bridgehead position. Although a strained carbonium ion is probably involved in the reactions of **7** and **8** with silver nitrate, it is more difficult to form this strained intermediate, and such a process involving a nonplanar carbonium ion proceeds slowly.

The usual reactions of alkyl halides do not occur when the halogen is bonded to a bridgehead carbon atom, and we may assume that any reaction requiring such a carbon atom to become sp^2 hybridized either does not occur at all or proceeds extremely slowly.

11.15 The S_Ni Reaction

Nucleophilic substitutions are effected by processes besides the direct S_N1 and S_N2 reactions. When certain special reagents are employed, other pathways become possible.

The conversion of alcohols to alkyl halides by treating them with hydrogen halides has already been discussed. The transformation is a nucleophilic substitution proceeding either through the carbonium ion or by way of the bimolecular process. The conversion of alcohols to alkyl halides is also effected using reagents such as PCl_3, PBr_3, PCl_5, $SOCl_2$, and SO_2Cl_2, and again the transformation involves nucleophilic substitution. In these reactions an intermediate ester is formed first; this ester is then converted to the alkyl halide. Thus, PCl_3 and $SOCl_2$ react to yield intermediates of the type,

$$R{-}\underset{\underset{R}{|}}{\overset{\overset{R}{|}}{C}}{-}OH + PCl_3 \longrightarrow R{-}\underset{\underset{R}{|}}{\overset{\overset{R}{|}}{C}}{-}O{-}\underset{\underset{Cl}{|}}{\overset{\overset{Cl}{|}}{P}}{-}Cl + HCl$$

and

$$R{-}\underset{\underset{R}{|}}{\overset{\overset{R}{|}}{C}}{-}OH + SOCl_2 \longrightarrow R{-}\underset{\underset{R}{|}}{\overset{\overset{R}{|}}{C}}{-}O{-}\overset{\overset{O}{\|}}{S}{-}Cl + HCl$$

11

These reactive intermediates then yield the alkyl halide. The mechanism by which the conversion to alkyl halide occurs depends upon the reaction conditions, and with $SOCl_2$ a rather interesting internal rearrangement is possible. The intermediate chlorosulfinic ester **11** breaks down to yield the alkyl chloride and sulfur dioxide:

$$\underset{R}{\overset{R}{>}}\underset{R}{\overset{}{}}C{\overset{\displaystyle{-}O}{\diagdown}}\underset{\diagdown}{\underset{Cl}{S=O}} \longrightarrow \underset{R}{\overset{R}{>}}C{-}Cl + SO_2$$

The chloride, which in the ester is bonded to the sulfur atom, enters from the same side as the leaving group, and the process is accompanied by retention of configuration. The reaction is an example of internal nucleophilic substitution (S$_N$i).

Thus, optically active α-phenylethanol, when treated with SOCl$_2$, yields the corresponding chloride with retention of configuration:

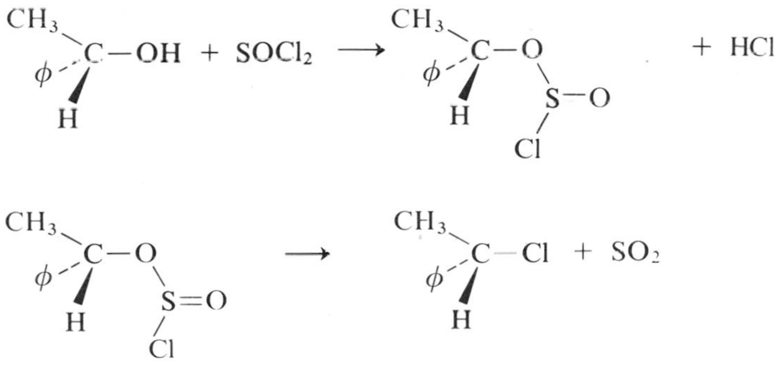

The reaction of an alcohol with SOCl$_2$ is simply a nucleophilic attack by the oxygen atom of the alcohol; the chlorosulfinic ester **11** results. This intermediate decomposes to form the product, a reaction whose rate increases with the polarity of the solvent and the stability of the carbonium ion. These facts require a charged transition state and support the participation of charged intermediates. The intermediate **11** decomposes into chloride ion, a carbonium ion **12**, and sulfur dioxide:

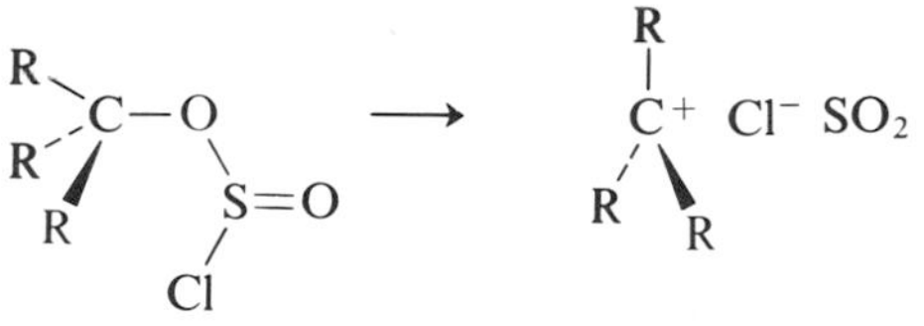

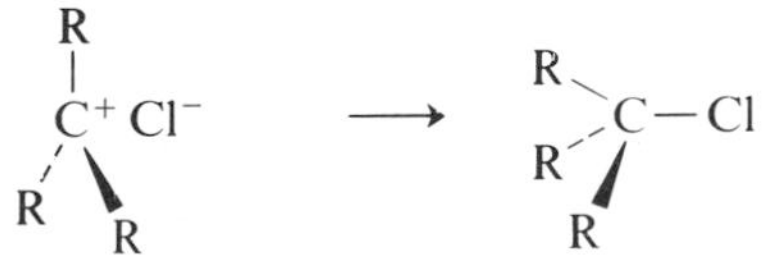

The ionic products are held together by electrostatic attraction (ion pair) and by the solvent cage. Therefore when the chloride ion attacks the carbonium ion, attack occurs most readily from the side leading to retention of configuration.

The S_N1 reaction yields chiefly racemixed products with some inversion of configuration due to shielding by the leaving group. The S_N2 reaction proceeds with inversion of configuration, and this rather interesting process, the S_Ni reaction, proceeds with retention. Each mechanism gives rise to a different stereochemical result.

When an alcohol is treated with $SOCl_2$ in the presence of pyridine, another alkyl halide is produced. This time inversion of configuration accompanies the process,

$$\begin{array}{c} R \\ R' \end{array}\!\!C\!-\!OH \; + \; SOCl_2 \; \xrightarrow[\text{N}]{\bigcirc} \; Cl\!-\!C\!\!\begin{array}{c} R \\ R \\ R \end{array}$$

The function of the pyridine is ostensibly to remove the hydrogen chloride formed along with the intermediate **11**; but by doing so, it converts the hydrogen chloride to chloride ion which attacks **11** from the rear (S_N2). The reaction now proceeds by the pathway,

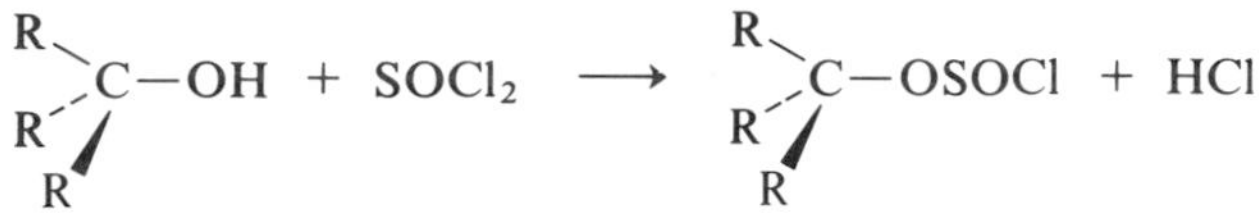

$$\begin{array}{c} R \\ R' \\ R \end{array}\!\!C\!-\!OH \; + \; SOCl_2 \; \longrightarrow \; \begin{array}{c} R \\ R' \\ R \end{array}\!\!C\!-\!OSOCl \; + \; HCl$$

11

but

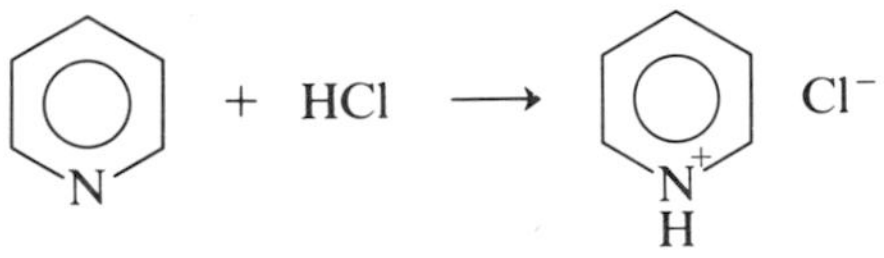

$$\bigcirc_{N} \; + \; HCl \; \longrightarrow \; \bigcirc_{\overset{+}{N}H} \; Cl^-$$

and

$$Cl^- \; + \; \begin{array}{c} R \\ R' \\ R \end{array}\!\!C\!-\!OSOCl \; \longrightarrow \; Cl\!-\!C\!\!\begin{array}{c} R \\ R \\ R \end{array} \; + \; SO_2 \; + \; Cl^-$$

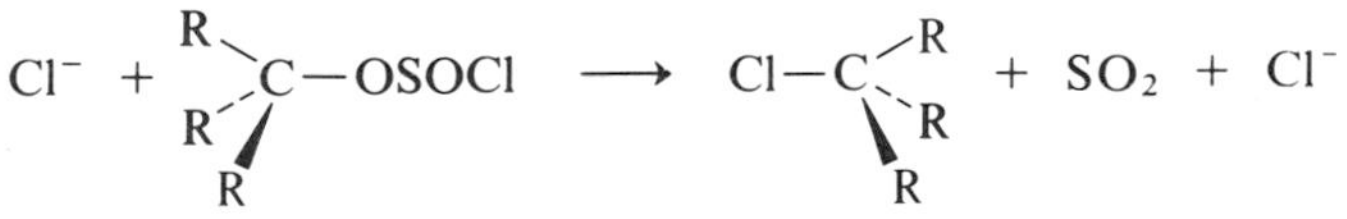

11.16 The S_N1' Reaction

We consider the system,

$$CH_2{=}CH{-}C^{14}H_2X$$

where X is a good leaving group and the halogen bearing carbon atom is labeled as C^{14}. This labeling technique permits us to distinguish between the two terminal positions in the allylic system.

Effecting nucleophilic substitution under conditions favorable to carbonium ion formation, leads to the system,

$$CH_2{=}CH{-}C^{14}H_2X \longrightarrow \overset{\delta+}{C}H_2{=}CH{=}\overset{\delta+}{C}{}^{14}H_2 + X^-$$

The positive charge in the intermediate allylic carbonium ion is delocalized, and an attacking nucleophile Y^- can attack at either of the terminal positions:

$$\overset{\delta+}{C}H_2{=}CH{=}\overset{\delta+}{C}{}^{14}H_2 \quad \begin{array}{c} \xrightarrow{\;S_N1\;} \\[4pt] \xrightarrow{\;S_N1'\;} \end{array} \quad \begin{array}{l} CH_2{=}CH{-}C^{14}H_2Y \\[10pt] YCH_2{-}CH{=}C^{14}H_2 \end{array}$$

The valence bond structures are,

$$CH_2{=}CH{-}\overset{+}{C}{}^{14}H_2 \longleftrightarrow \overset{+}{C}H_2{-}CH{=}C^{14}H_2$$

Both of the terminal carbon atoms are partially positive, and the nucleophile Y^- can add at either end of the system. If Y^- adds at C^{14}, the substitution is a simple replacement of X by Y, and the reaction is an S_N1 process. If the nucleophile adds at the other end of the allylic system, substitution is accompanied by migration of the double bond. An allylic shift has taken place, and this process is designated as an S_N1' reaction. Substitutions in allylic systems are frequently accompanied by this type of rearrangement.

The reaction of **13** with acetate ion yields such a mixture of rearranged products:

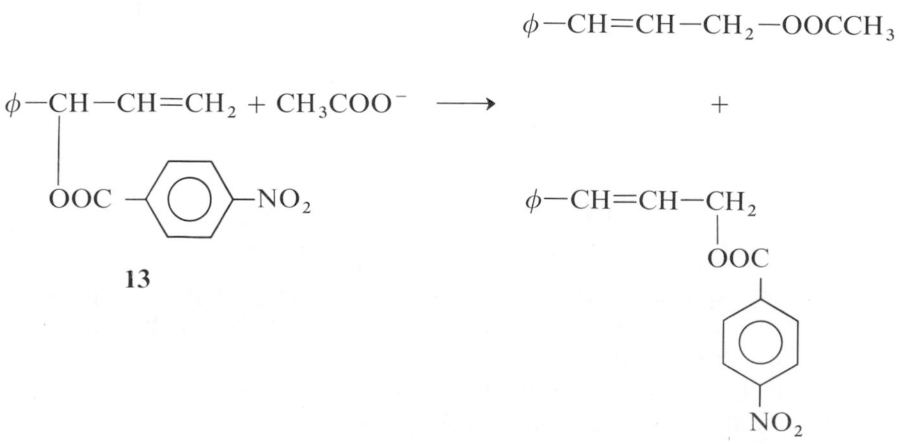

$$\phi{-}CH{=}CH{-}CH_2{-}OOCCH_3$$

$$\phi{-}CH{-}CH{=}CH_2 + CH_3COO^- \longrightarrow \qquad\qquad +$$

$$\underset{\displaystyle \text{OOC}{-}\underset{\textstyle\text{NO}_2}{\bigcirc}}{\big|}$$

13

$$\phi{-}CH{=}CH{-}CH_2$$
$$\big|$$
$$\text{OOC}$$
$$\bigcirc$$
$$\text{NO}_2$$

The isomeric chlorides **14** and **15** both yield the same products when reacted in ethanol and the reaction kept neutral with sodium ethoxide:

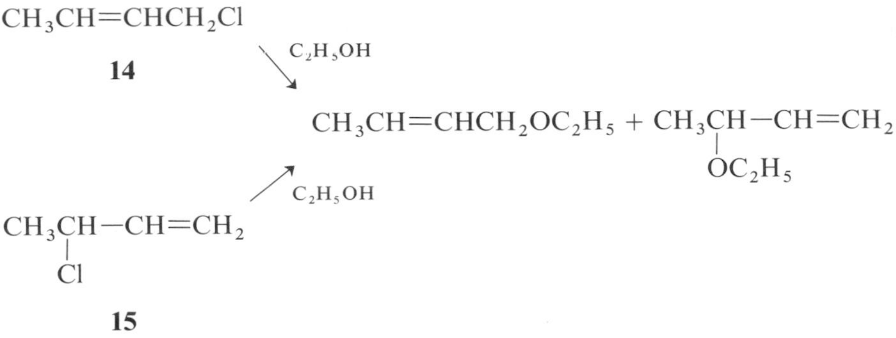

$CH_3CH=CHCH_2Cl$

    14 $\searrow$ C_2H_5OH

                           $CH_3CH=CHCH_2OC_2H_5 + CH_3CH-CH=CH_2$

                                                     OC_2H_5

     $\nearrow$ C_2H_5OH

$CH_3CH-CH=CH_2$
   |
   Cl

    15

Each reaction follows first order kinetics. These results are consistent with the idea that a common intermediate such as the carbonium ion participates.

Unfortunately, this reaction is not so straightforward as it might at first appear. A product spread is generally observed in these solvolyses reactions. Thus the following observation has been made:

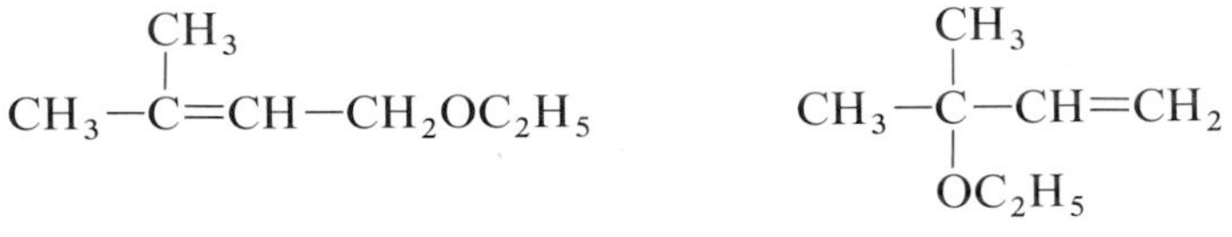

        CH_3 CH_3

        | |

$CH_3-C=CH-CH_2OC_2H_5$ $CH_3-C-CH=CH_2$

                                                   OC_2H_5

                  A   **B**

                                                A   **B**

        CH_3

        |

$CH_3-C-CH=CH_2$ $\xrightarrow{C_2H_5OH}$ 30%   70%

        |

        Cl

        CH_3

        |

$CH_3-C=CH-CH_2Cl$ $\xrightarrow{C_2H_5OH}$ 40%   60%

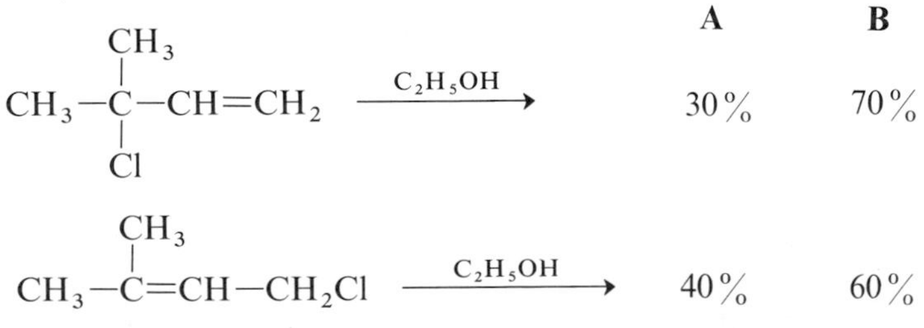

The simplest explanation that accounts for the slight variation in product distribution assumes that a small amount of product is also formed by a direct S_N2 displacement by the solvent.

Occasionally the entering nucleophile in S_N1' reactions is chemically identical to the leaving group, and in these cases the reaction is simply an isomerization:

$$\phi-CH-CH=CH_2 \longrightarrow \phi-CH=CH-CH_2-OOC-\langle\bigcirc\rangle-NO_2$$

$$\overset{|}{OOC}-\langle\bigcirc\rangle-NO_2$$

and

$$CH_2=CH-\overset{\overset{\displaystyle CH_3}{|}}{\underset{\underset{\displaystyle Cl}{|}}{C}}-CH_3 \longrightarrow ClCH_2-CH=\overset{\overset{\displaystyle CH_3}{|}}{C}-CH_3$$

The mechanism for these isomerizations involves the formation of an allylic cation followed by reentry of the leaving group:

$$CH_2=CH-\overset{\overset{\displaystyle CH_3}{|}}{\underset{\underset{\displaystyle Cl}{|}}{C}}-CH_3 \rightleftharpoons \overset{\delta+}{CH_2}=\!\!=CH \overset{\delta+}{=\!\!=} \overset{\overset{\displaystyle CH_3}{|}}{C}-CH_3$$
$$\overset{}{Cl^-}$$

$$\overset{\delta+}{CH_2}=\!\!=CH\overset{\delta+}{=\!\!=}\overset{\overset{\displaystyle CH_3}{|}}{C}-CH_3 \longrightarrow ClCH_2-CH=\overset{\overset{\displaystyle CH_3}{|}}{C}-CH_3$$
$$\overset{}{Cl^-}$$

The reaction is shown in Figure 11 2.

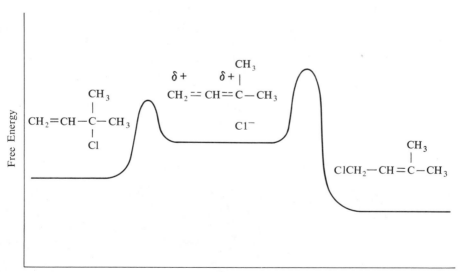

Reaction Coordinate

Figure 11–2

The S_N1' reaction occurs because both terminal positions of the allylic system are positively charged, and an entering nucleophile is able to attack at either end. If substituents are present as in the previous cases, attack does not occur equally readily at these allylic positions. Thus in systems such as

$$CH_3-\overset{\overset{\displaystyle CH_3}{|}}{\underset{\delta+}{C}}=CH=\overset{\delta+}{CH_2} \qquad CH_3-\overset{\overset{\displaystyle H}{|}}{\underset{\delta+}{C}}=CH=\overset{\delta+}{CH_2}$$

attack at the methylene positions leads to more stable products (thermodynic products), but attack at the other position occurs more readily (kinetic products). The problem is related to 1,2- and 1,4-addition to conjugated dienes.

When the isomerization of **16** is conducted in the presence of added radioactive chloride ion,

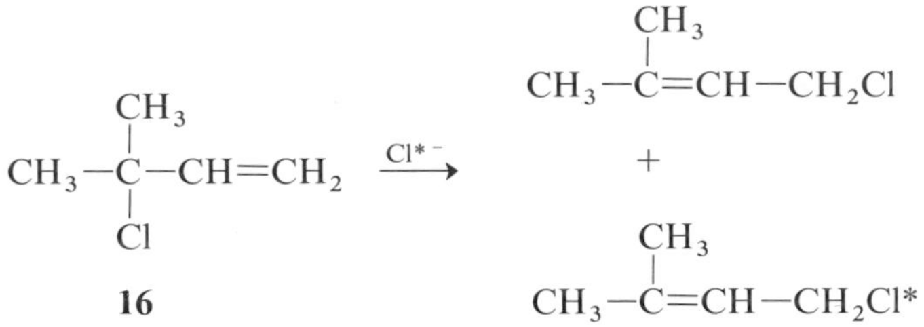

$$CH_3-\overset{\overset{\displaystyle CH_3}{|}}{\underset{\underset{\displaystyle Cl}{|}}{C}}-CH=CH_2 \xrightarrow{\;Cl^{*-}\;}$$

16

$$CH_3-\overset{\overset{\displaystyle CH_3}{|}}{C}=CH-CH_2Cl$$

$$+$$

$$CH_3-\overset{\overset{\displaystyle CH_3}{|}}{C}=CH-CH_2Cl^*$$

the isomerization occurs more quickly than does incorporation of radioactive chloride. Consequently, the leaving chloride rather than the external chloride reenters preferentially. Why the same chloride that leaves should return, is readily explained if we remember that the carbonium ion is not a free ion but part of an ion pair, and it is the chloride ion that is the partner in this ion pair that enters most easily. This process, called internal return, also occurs in nonallylic systems.

The bicyclic system **17** undergoes racemization more rapidly than it reacts with nucleophilic solvents to undergo solvolysis, and this result is also attributable to internal return of brosylate ion:

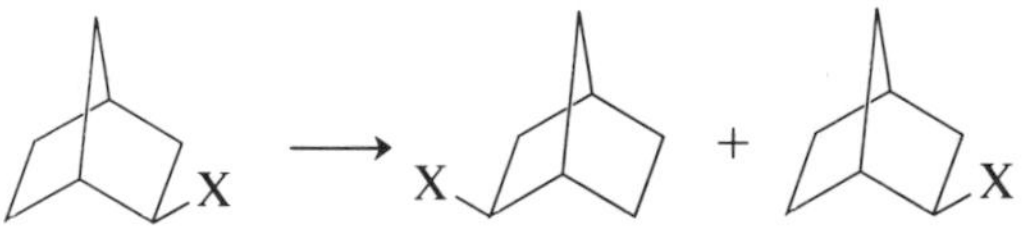

17

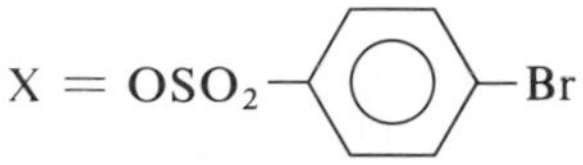

$$X = OSO_2-\!\!\left\langle\!\bigcirc\!\right\rangle\!-Br$$

The intermediates are either rapidly equilibrating classical structures,

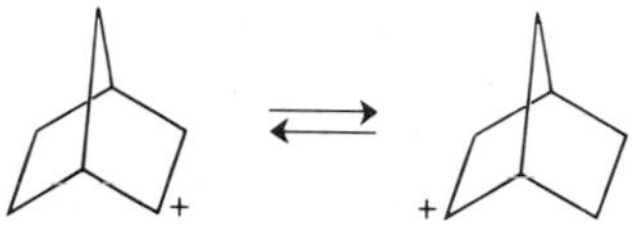

or nonclassical structures.

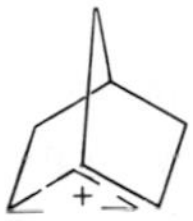

The problem is discussed more fully in Chapter 18.

The extent to which internal return takes place varies with the leaving group and the solvent. Thus in the isomerization of the chloride **16** the original chloride ion returns. In the isomerization of **18** in acetic acid containing perchloric acid, the isomerized product does not contain the original acetate group. This, of course, does not preclude a very intimate pair which can only collapse to reform reactant:

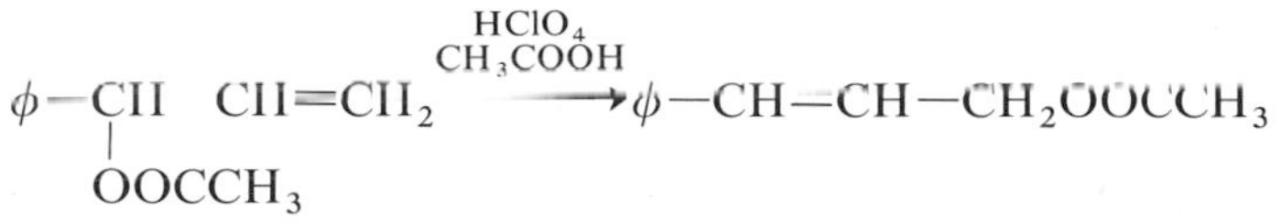

$$\phi-\text{CH}\quad\text{CH}=\text{CH}_2 \xrightarrow[\text{CH}_3\text{COOH}]{\text{HClO}_4} \phi-\text{CH}-\text{CH}-\text{CH}_2\text{OOCCH}_3$$
$$\underset{\text{OOCCH}_3}{|}$$

18

When *cis*- and *trans*-3-methylallyl chlorides are reacted with aqueous silver nitrate, it appears from the alcoholic products that the allylic cations **19** and **20** that participate maintain their stereochemical integrity:

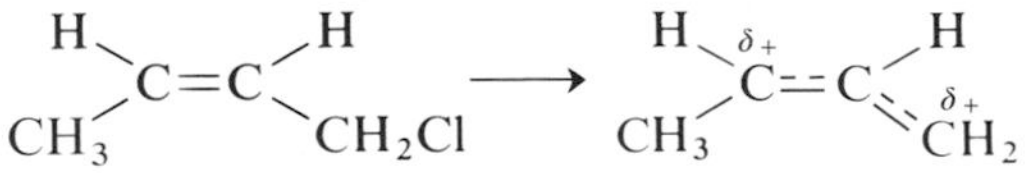

19

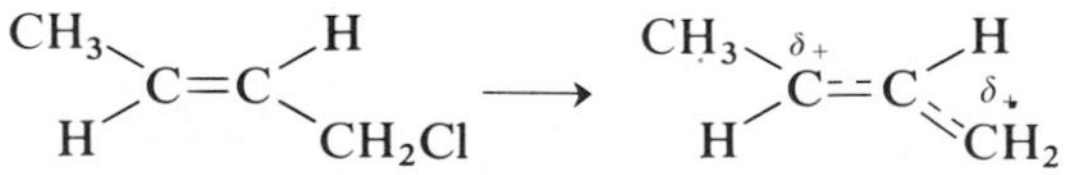

20

The fact that **19** and **20** do not isomerize is consistent with the idea of charge delocalization in these systems. Isomerization of **19** into **20** requires rotation about the central C—C bond. Such a rotation is expected to be a high energy process since orbital overlap is destroyed:

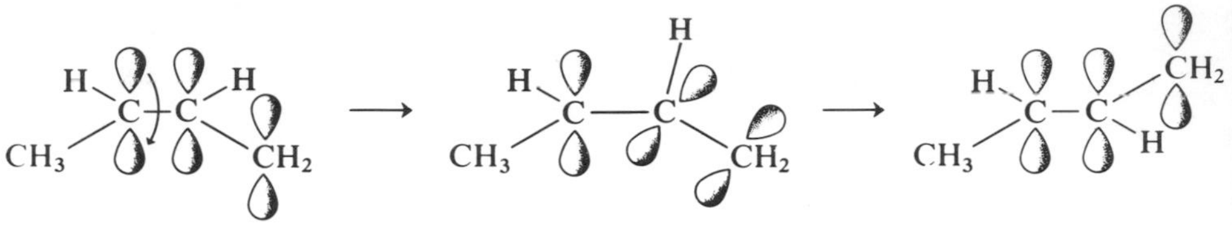

A rather interesting and novel analogy to allylic reactions occurs in the conversion of cholesteryl chloride **21** to its acetate. The chloride **21** yields the corresponding acetate with retention of configuration. The tosylate **22** also behaves in this manner, and except for a salt effect, the rate of this reaction is independent of the concentration of acetate ion:

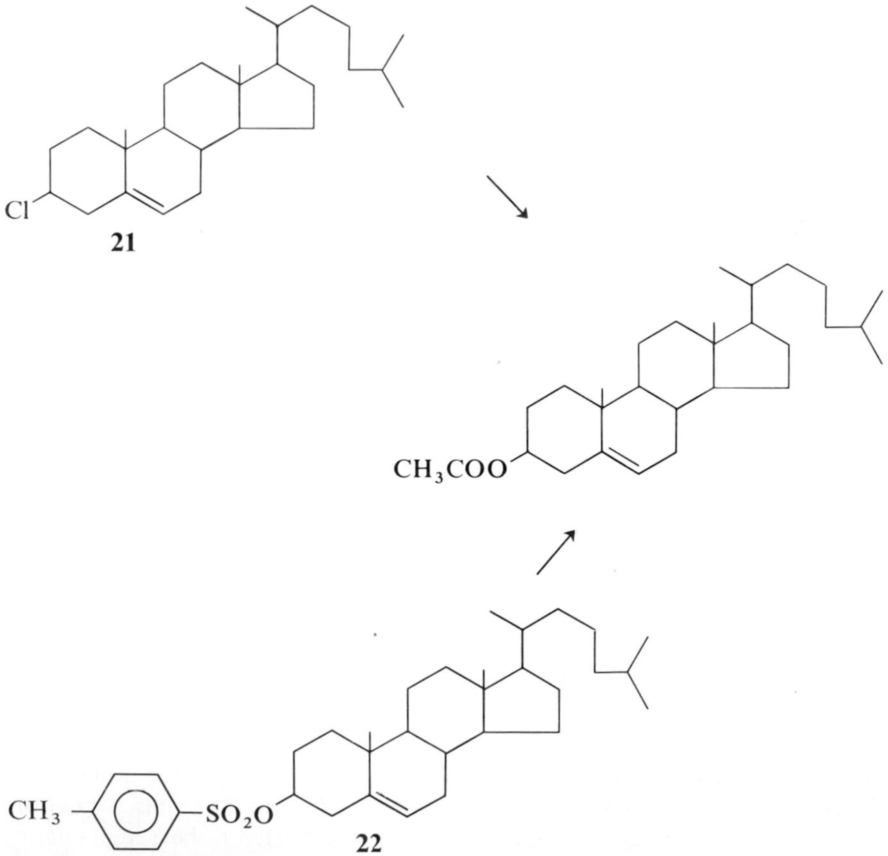

It has been argued that the intermediate in these cases is a homoallylic carbonium ion having the structure,

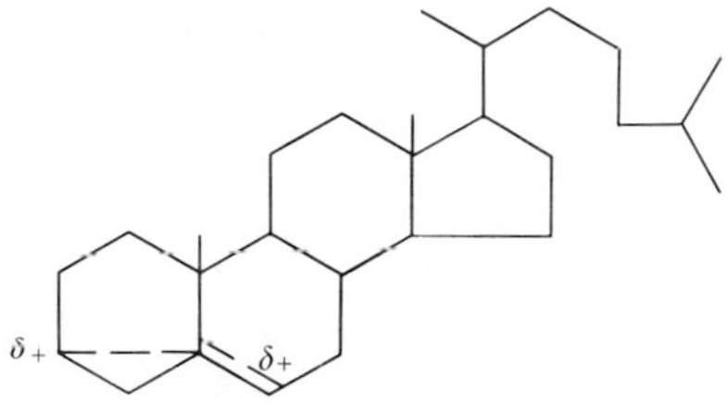

where the π electrons of the double bond have been used to delocalize the positive charge. This intermediate has a spacial geometry that permits the approaching nucleophile to enter preferentially from one side, the side previously occupied by the leaving groups, chloride and tosylate.

11.17 The S_N2' Reaction

The S_N1' reaction was discovered relatively early, and it was years later before the S_N2' process became known. The S_N2 reaction is generally much more rapid than the S_N2'; consequently, it is difficult to observe the latter. It is only when a direct S_N2 reaction is prevented or when this process does not generate new products that the S_N2' reaction can be studied. For example, the reaction of the allylic bromide **23** with bromide ions under reaction conditions favoring bimolecular substitution enables us to observe the desired reaction and to measure its rate as the rate of isomerization. The S_N2 process also occurs here and in fact, much more rapidly, but this direct substitution does not lead to new products:

$$CH_3CHBr-CH=CH_2 + Br^- \longrightarrow CH_3-CH=CH-CH_2Br + Br^-$$

$$\text{23} \qquad\qquad\qquad\qquad\qquad\qquad \text{24}$$

The transition state for the S_N2' reaction is one in which the attacking nucleophile and the leaving group are *cis* oriented. This transition state for the formation of **24** appears as follows:

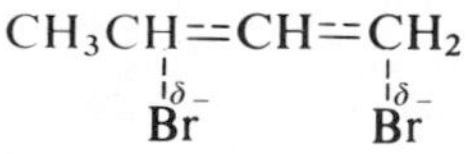

$$CH_3\underset{\underset{\text{Br}}{|}}{\overset{}{C}H}=CH=\underset{\underset{\text{Br}}{|}}{\overset{}{C}H_2}$$

Evidence for this *cis* orientation in the transition state comes from the following reaction where the geometries of the reactant and product were established:

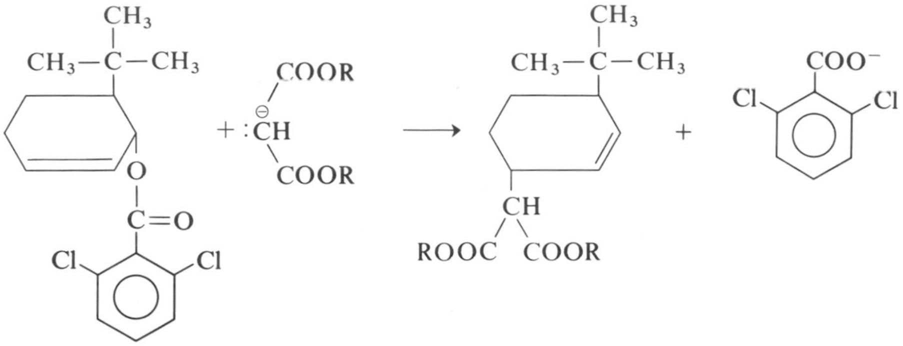

In this example the direct S_N2 reaction as well as attack at the ester linkage are sterically hindered. The *t*-butyl group occupies an equatorial position in the transition state and does not interfere with the S_N2' reaction. In fact, increasing the size of the alkyl group from methyl to *t*-butyl increases slightly the rate of reaction.

Other examples of the S_N2' reaction exist, and it has been suggested that the rearranged product in the following reaction is also formed by this mechanism:

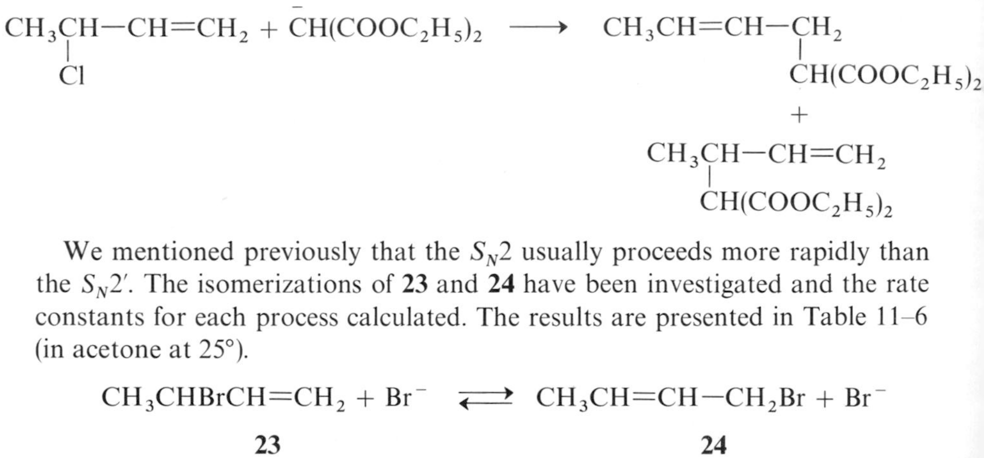

$$CH_3CH-CH=CH_2 + \bar{C}H(COOC_2H_5)_2 \longrightarrow CH_3CH=CH-CH_2$$
$$\underset{Cl}{|} \qquad\qquad\qquad\qquad\qquad\qquad\qquad\qquad \underset{CH(COOC_2H_5)_2}{|}$$
$$+$$
$$CH_3CH-CH=CH_2$$
$$\underset{CH(COOC_2H_5)_2}{|}$$

We mentioned previously that the S_N2 usually proceeds more rapidly than the S_N2'. The isomerizations of **23** and **24** have been investigated and the rate constants for each process calculated. The results are presented in Table 11–6 (in acetone at 25°).

$$CH_3CHBrCH=CH_2 + Br^- \rightleftarrows CH_3CH=CH-CH_2Br + Br^-$$

23   **24**

Table 11–6

	Mechanism	$k \times 10^7$ (liter mole^{-1} sec^{-1})
23	S_N2	87.9
23	S_N2'	1.5
24	S_N2	14100.0
24	S_N2'	0.5

The bromide **23** suffers S_N2 displacement about 60 times as rapidly as it undergoes the S_N2' reaction. The bromide **24**, which is expected to undergo the S_N2 reaction more readily and the S_N2' reaction less readily than **23**, reacts by way of the S_N2 pathway nearly 30,000 times as fast as by the S_N2'.

We also see from Table 11–6 that attack at the primary carbon atom takes place approximately 10,000 times as rapidly when an S_N2 displacement is being effected. The ratio of rate constants is about 175 for attack at the secondary position.

11.18 The S_Ni' Reaction

There is an S_N1 and an S_N1' reaction, an S_N2 reaction and an S_N2' reaction. Since there is also an S_Ni reaction, we naturally expect the corresponding S_Ni' process to occur. This process does exist and takes place with the following systems,

$$CH_3CH_2CH=CH-CH_2OH + SOCl_2 \longrightarrow CH_3CH_2CHCl-CH=CH_2$$

and

$$CH_3CH_2CHOHCH=CH_2 + SOCl_2 \longrightarrow CH_3CH_2CH=CH-CH_2Cl$$

As in the S_Ni reaction, the intermediates appear to be esters of the type,

$$CH_3CH_2CH=CH-CH_2OSOCl \qquad CH_3CH_2\underset{\underset{OSOCl}{|}}{CH}-CH=CH_2$$

which decompose to form the products. The rearrangement probably proceeds through a cyclic transition state:

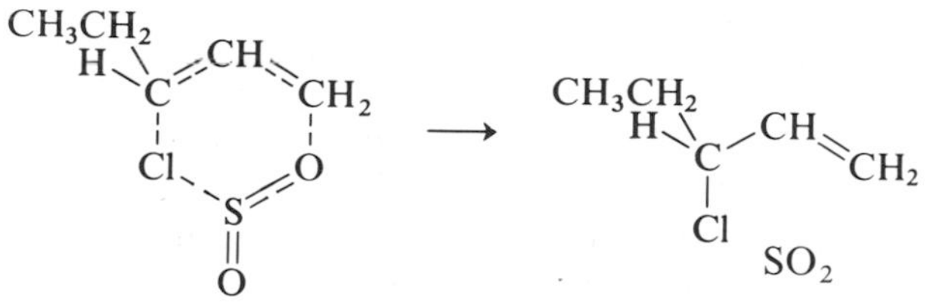

and

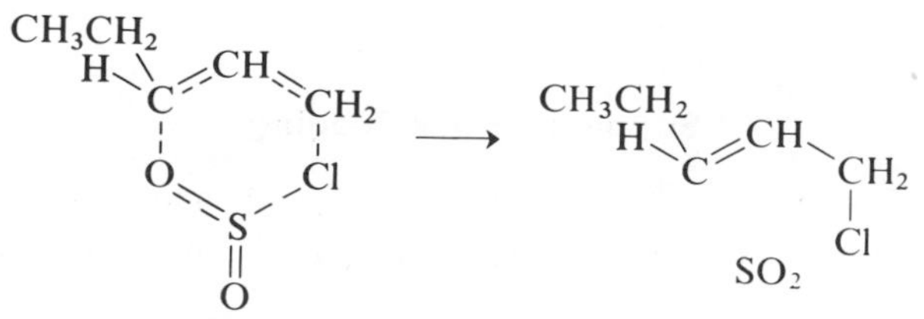

Although we have not indicated the charge distribution in the transition state, the evidence supports the idea that considerable ionic character is present.

In allylic systems such as these, where both the S_Ni and the S_Ni' are possible, the data indicate that the S_Ni' proceeds more readily, and under the proper conditions the reaction yields almost exclusively the product of the S_Ni' reaction.

A somewhat unexpected feature of these S_Ni' reactions becomes evident from stereochemical considerations.

The alcohol **25** in optically active form reacts with $SOCl_2$ to yield the chloro-sulfinic ester **26**:

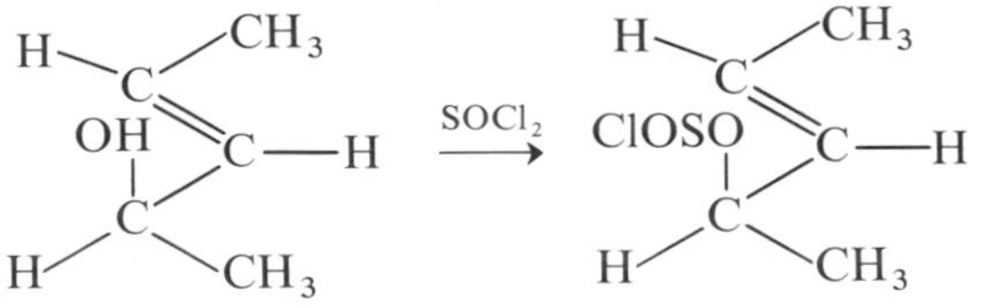

25   **26**

Because of steric interactions in the transition state, the decomposition product of **26** has the structure **27** and is also optically active:

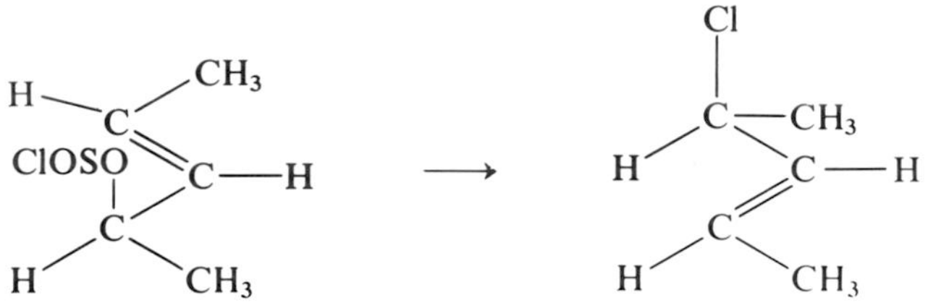

26   **27**

Nucleophilic substitution is effected under a variety of conditions and using a variety of reagents, and the mechanism by which these transformations take place depends upon the system under consideration, the solvent, and the nucleophilic agent used for the substitution. Nonallylic systems may react by way of the S_N1, S_N2, and S_Ni mechanisms. Allylic systems also react by these pathways and in addition, can react through the S_N1', S_N2', and S_Ni' mechanisms.

Supplementary Reading

1. Baker, J. W., *Electronic Theories of Organic Chemistry.* London, Oxford U.P., 1958.

2. Bunton, C. A., *Nucleophilic Substitution at a Saturated Carbon Atom.* London, Elsevier, 1963.

3. de la Mare, P. B. D., *Molecular Rearrangements*, Vol. 1, (ed.) P. de Mayo. New York, Interscience, 1963.

4. Frost, A. A. and Pearson, R. G., *Kinetics and Mechanism*, 2nd ed. New York, Wiley, 1961.

5. Gould, E. S., *Mechanism and Structure in Organic Chemistry*. New York, Holt, 1959.

6. Hammett, L. P., *Physical Organic Chemistry*. New York, McGraw-Hill, 1940.

7. Hine, J., *Physical Organic Chemistry*. New York, McGraw-Hill, 1962.

8. Ingold, C. K., *Structure and Mechanism in Organic Chemistry*. Ithaca, New York, Cornell U.P., 1953.

9. Leffler, J. E., *The Reactive Intermediates of Organic Chemistry*. New York, Interscience, 1956.

10. Saunders, W. H., Jr., *Ionic Aliphatic Reactions*. Englewood Cliffs, New Jersey, Prentice-Hall, 1965.

11. Streitwieser, A., Jr., *Solvolytic Displacement Reactions*. New York, McGraw-Hill, 1962.

Chapter 12

Elimination Reactions

12.1 Introduction

Although other eliminations are known, the group of reactions referred to as eliminations frequently consists of those processes by which an alkene is prepared from reactants of the type,

$$
\begin{array}{c}
\quad\ \text{R}\quad\ \text{R} \\
\quad\ | \quad\ \ | \\
\text{R}-\text{C}-\text{C}-\text{R} \\
\quad\ | \quad\ \ | \\
\quad\ \text{H}\quad\ \text{X}
\end{array}
$$

where X is a good leaving group. Elimination of HX from reactants of this sort affords the alkene.

These processes are more properly called 1,2-eliminations or α,β-eliminations because H and X occupy adjacent positions. Other 1,2-eliminations as well as 1,1-eliminations are known. We discuss some of these in this chapter.

A 1,2-elimination may be unimolecular involving either a carbonium ion intermediate ($E1$) or a thermal elimination. Alternatively, the reaction can be conducted under conditions favoring bimolecular elimination ($E2$). Here an added base promotes the elimination. Still another possibility involves the second order unimolecular pathway ($E1cB$) which proceeds by the two-step mechanism:

$$
\begin{array}{c}
\quad\ \text{R}\quad\ \text{R} \\
\quad\ | \quad\ \ | \\
\text{R}-\text{C}-\text{C}-\text{R} + \text{Y}^- \\
\quad\ | \quad\ \ | \\
\quad\ \text{H}\quad\ \text{X}
\end{array}
\rightleftarrows
\begin{array}{c}
\quad\ \text{R}\quad\ \text{R} \\
\quad\ | \quad\ \ | \\
\text{R}-\overset{..}{\text{C}}{}^{\!-}\text{C}-\text{R} + \text{HY} \\
\quad\quad\ \ | \\
\quad\quad\ \ \text{X}
\end{array}
$$

$$
\begin{array}{c}
\quad\ \text{R}\quad\ \text{R} \\
\quad\ | \quad\ \ | \\
\text{R}-\overset{..}{\text{C}}{}^{\!-}\text{C}-\text{R} \\
\quad\quad\ \ | \\
\quad\quad\ \ \text{X}
\end{array}
\longrightarrow
\begin{array}{c}
\text{R}\quad\quad\ \ \text{R} \\
\ \ \diagdown\quad\ \diagup \\
\quad\text{C}=\text{C} \\
\ \ \diagup\quad\ \diagdown \\
\text{R}\quad\quad\ \ \text{R}
\end{array}
+ \ \text{X}^-
$$

Only for certain substituents R is this last scheme a possibility.

These are the most common 1,2-eliminations.

318

12.2 The *E*1 Reaction

The *E*1 reaction, as the name implies, is a unimolecular elimination. The process proceeds by way of a carbonium ion, and the rate limiting step is the formation of this cationic intermediate.

 Consider the ionization of *t*-butyl chloride which dissociates in polar solvents to form an intimate ion pair and under some conditions a relatively free carbonium ion. Now if the solvent is a good nucleophile or if a good nucleophile has been added to the solution, the preferred route of reaction for this carbonium ion is to combine with the nucleophile (S_N1). However, if a good nucleophile is not present, a less favorable process, loss of a proton to the solvent, occurs (*E*1). Actually, the two reactions are competitive and both take place. The elimination is accompanied by nucleophilic substitution, and varying the reaction conditions favors one process or the other. Both reactions have the same rate limiting step, carbonium ion formation.

$$\begin{array}{ccc} & CH_3 & & CH_3 \\ & | & & | \\ CH_3-C-CH_3 & \longrightarrow & CH_3-C-CH_3 + Cl^- \\ & | & & + \\ & Cl & & \end{array}$$

$$\begin{array}{c} CH_3 \\ | \\ CH_3-C-CH_3 + H_3O^+ \\ | \\ OH \end{array}$$

$$\begin{array}{c} CH_3 \\ | \\ CH_3-\underset{+}{C}-CH_3 \end{array} \quad \xrightarrow[H_2O]{S_N1} \quad \xrightarrow[H_2O]{E1} \quad \begin{array}{c} CH_3 \\ \diagdown \\ C=C \diagdown \\ CH_3 \diagup \quad \diagdown H \end{array}^H + H_3O^+$$

We have not, in the previous example, indicated the total role played by the solvent. Remember that the various species are solvated and that such solvation is required for these processes to occur. The proton that is lost in the terminal step of the elimination is covalently bonded and highly solvated.

 When the solvent acts as the proton acceptor in the elimination, the first step, carbonium ion formation, is essentially irreversible and therefore rate limiting. When the solvent is a poor base or when some added reagent present in lower concentration plays the role of base, reversal of the steps leading to the carbonium ion is possible, and loss of the proton by the carbonium ion can then become rate limiting.

 The carbonium ion in the unimolecular elimination loses a proton to the solvent or to an added base. This proton loss occurs in several stages. Intermediates called π complexes, where the proton is loosely bound to the electrons of the incipient alkene, are involved in the expulsion of the proton; several such π complexes may participate. Structures **1** and **2** represent possible intermediates for the final stages of the elimination. Y^- is, for simplicity, an added base.

$$\begin{array}{cc}
\underset{R}{\overset{R}{\diagdown}}C\overset{\overset{\displaystyle H}{\substack{\cdots\cdots}}}{\underset{+}{=\!=\!=}}C\overset{\diagup R}{\diagdown R}
&
\underset{R}{\overset{R}{\diagdown}}C\overset{\overset{\displaystyle Y^{\delta-}}{\mid}\,\overset{\displaystyle H}{\substack{\cdots\cdots}}}{\underset{\delta+}{=\!=\!=}}C\overset{\diagup R}{\diagdown R}
\\[6pt]
\mathbf{1} & \mathbf{2}
\end{array}$$

It is also possible that **2** represents a transition state.

With arenes, materials such as **2** have been shown to be actual intermediates (for example, benzene plus hydrogen chloride and benzene-bromine complexes) and these may participate actively in aromatic substitution.

In π complexes leading to unsymmetrical alkenes the proton being lost is not bonded equally to both carbon atoms. For example, the π complex analogous to **1** for loss of a proton by the *t*-butyl carbonium ion has the structure,

$$\underset{CH_3}{\overset{CH_3}{\diagdown}}C\overset{\overset{\displaystyle H}{\diagup\;\substack{+}\;\diagdown}}{=\!=\!=}C\overset{\diagup H}{\diagdown H}$$

where the proton is bonded more strongly to the primary carbon atom.

A picture of the reaction coordinate for the elimination appears approximately as shown in Figure 12–1 (we also include that of the S_N1).

The reaction is much more complex and involves an even larger number of intermediates than we have indicated (additional ion pairs, for example). It is generally the solvent rather than an added base Y^- (which we have employed for the sake of simplicity) that acts as the proton acceptor. Consequently,

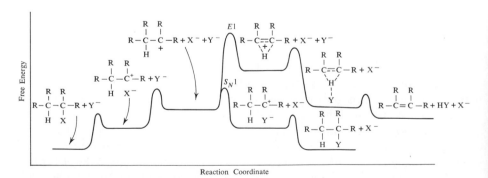

Reaction Coordinate

Figure 12–1

we write the overall mechanism for the elimination simply as,

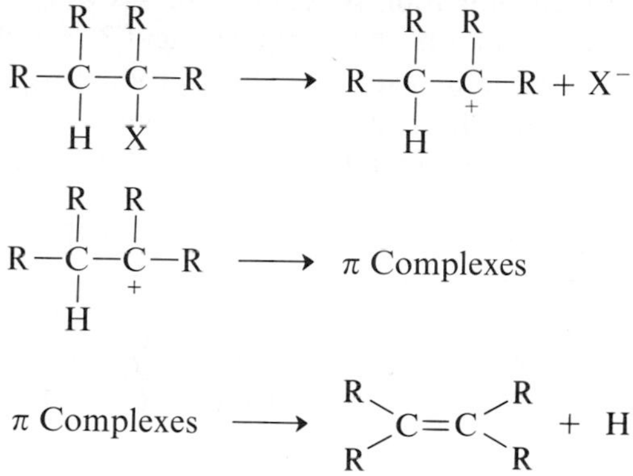

$$\begin{array}{ccc} \underset{\underset{H}{|}}{\overset{\overset{R}{|}}{R-C}}-\underset{\underset{X}{|}}{\overset{\overset{R}{|}}{C}}-R & \longrightarrow & \underset{\underset{H}{|}}{\overset{\overset{R}{|}}{R-C}}-\underset{\overset{+}{|}}{\overset{\overset{R}{|}}{C}}-R + X^- \end{array}$$

$$\underset{\underset{H}{|}}{\overset{\overset{R}{|}}{R-C}}-\underset{\overset{+}{|}}{\overset{\overset{R}{|}}{C}}-R \longrightarrow \pi \text{ Complexes}$$

$$\pi \text{ Complexes} \longrightarrow \overset{R}{\underset{R}{}}{>}C{=}C{<}\overset{R}{\underset{R}{}} + H^+$$

where we assume that the proton formed in the last step is bonded to the solvent.

The treatment of alcohols with concentrated sulfuric acid, a reaction that results in the formation of alkenes, generally proceeds by way of a carbonium ion:

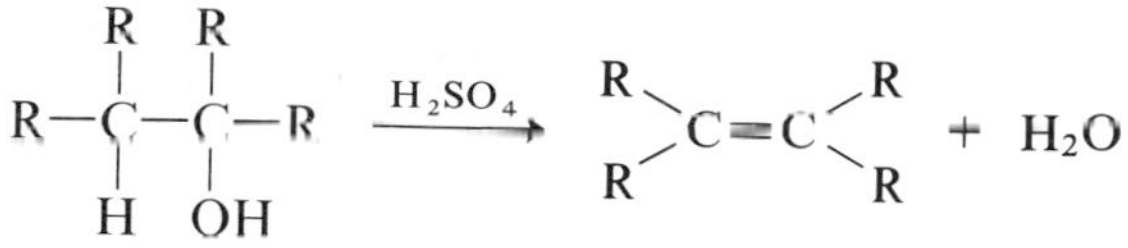

$$\underset{\underset{H}{|}}{\overset{\overset{R}{|}}{R-C}}-\underset{\underset{OH}{|}}{\overset{\overset{R}{|}}{C}}-R \xrightarrow{H_2SO_4} \overset{R}{\underset{R}{}}{>}C{=}C{<}\overset{R}{\underset{R}{}} + H_2O$$

The mechanism is similar to that just presented:

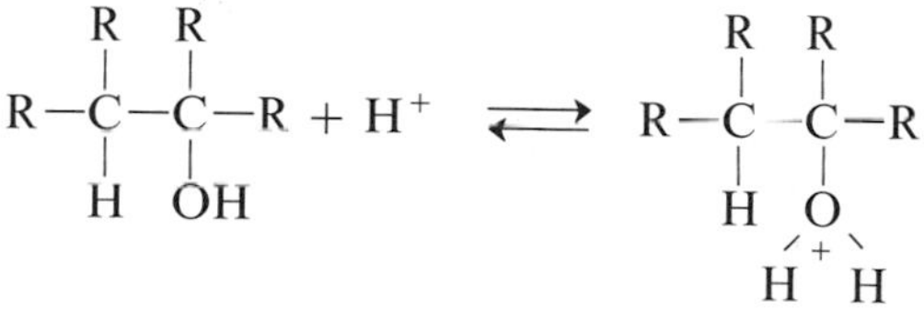

$$\underset{\underset{OH}{|}}{\overset{\overset{R}{|}}{R-C}}-\underset{\underset{OH}{|}}{\overset{\overset{R}{|}}{C}}-R + H^+ \rightleftarrows R-\underset{\underset{H}{|}}{\overset{\overset{R}{|}}{C}} \quad \underset{\underset{\overset{+}{O}}{|}}{\overset{\overset{R}{|}}{C}}-R$$
$$\overset{}{\underset{H \quad H}{}}$$

3

$$R-\underset{\underset{H \; O}{|}}{\overset{\overset{R}{|}}{C}}-\underset{}{\overset{\overset{R}{|}}{C}}-R \longrightarrow \underset{\underset{H}{|}}{\overset{\overset{R}{|}}{R-C}}-\underset{\overset{+}{|}}{\overset{\overset{R}{|}}{C}}-R + H_2O$$
$$\overset{}{\underset{H \quad H}{}}$$

$$R-\underset{\underset{H}{|}}{\overset{\overset{R}{|}}{C}}-\underset{\overset{+}{|}}{\overset{\overset{R}{|}}{C}}-R \longrightarrow \overset{R}{\underset{R}{}}{>}C{=}C{<}\overset{R}{\underset{R}{}} + H^+$$

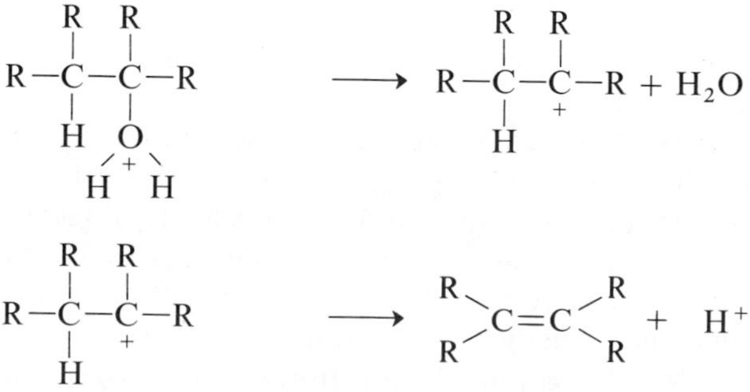

Weaker acids than sulfuric acid can also effect eliminations of this type; however, the rate of the elimination process decreases when weaker acids are used because the concentration of the conjugate acid **3** then decreases.

In reactions where more than a single olefinic product is possible, the most stable alkene is the major product. The more highly substituted alkene is generally the more stable. Occasionally steric interactions become important, and in such cases the less highly substituted alkene predominates. The ionization of *t*-amyl bromide leads to the carbonium ion **4**, which suffers both nucleophilic substitution and elimination:

$$CH_3CH_2-\underset{\underset{Br}{|}}{\overset{\overset{CH_3}{|}}{C}}-CH_3 \longrightarrow CH_3CH_2-\underset{+}{\overset{\overset{CH_3}{|}}{C}}-CH_3 + Br^-$$

4

The yield of olefinic material is only 27%, with two olefinic products being formed. In this case steric effects are less important than the position of the double bond, and the more highly substituted product predominates. The olefinic portion of the product has the distribution,

$$\underset{H}{\overset{CH_3}{}}C=C\underset{CH_3}{\overset{CH_3}{}} \qquad \underset{CH_3}{\overset{CH_3CH_2}{}}C=C\underset{H}{\overset{H}{}}$$

79 %   21 %

In this case the more highly substituted alkene is the major product. However, as the groups become increasingly large, steric factors become increasingly important, and in the series:

$$RCH_2-\underset{\underset{Br}{|}}{\overset{\overset{CH_3}{|}}{C}}-CH_3$$

5

the less highly substituted alkene is the major component of the olefinic portion of the product when R is *t*-butyl.

The unimolecular elimination reactions of a series of alkyl bromides having the general structure **5** were investigated. The reactivity of the halide as well as the olefinic product distribution were determined. The rates of reaction of **5** show no clearcut trend and are nearly the same when R is methyl, ethyl, or isopropyl, yet the rate increases when R is *t*-butyl. We see from Table 12–1 that as R becomes increasingly large, the total yield of olefinic product increases from 27% to 57%. The less highly substituted alkene forms an increasingly large percentage of this olefinic material, becoming the major product when R is *t*-butyl.

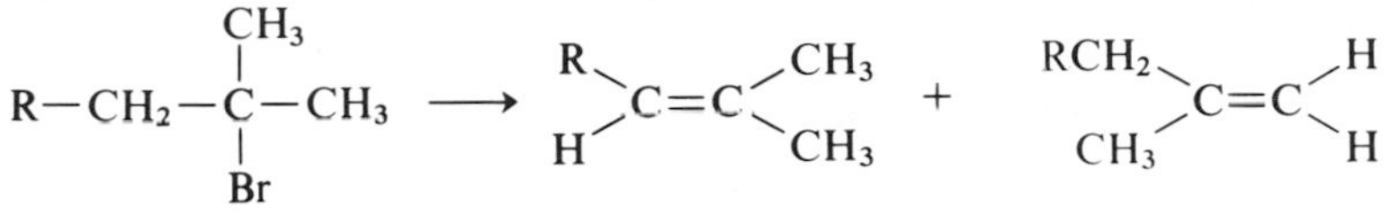

$$R-CH_2-\underset{\underset{Br}{|}}{\overset{\overset{CH_3}{|}}{C}}-CH_3 \longrightarrow \underset{H}{\overset{R}{>}}C=C\overset{CH_3}{\underset{CH_3}{<}} + \underset{CH_3}{\overset{RCH_2}{>}}C=C\overset{H}{\underset{H}{<}}$$

5   6   7

Table 12–1

| R | Yield of Olefin (%) | Composition of Olefin (%) | | k (hr^{-1}) |
		6	7	
CH_3-	27	79	21	0.387
CH_3CH_2-	32	71	29	0.297
$(CH_3)_2CH-$	46	59	41	0.697
$(CH_3)C-$	57	19	81	4.71

The rate increase when R is *t*-butyl can be attributed to a decrease in steric interactions upon passing to the transition state. Steric factors increase the rate of formation of the carbonium ion. The carbonium ion is then partitioned, and steric factors in the transition states leading to products help to determine the product distribution.

In the previous example the carbonium ion intermediate lost a proton and formed a mixture of two isomeric alkenes. When the 2-pentyl cation loses a proton, three isomeric alkenes are formed. It is *trans*-2-pentene that is the most stable of these alkenes, and this is the major product:

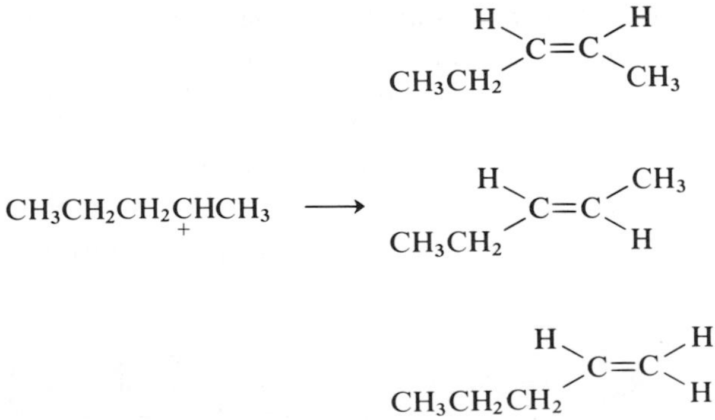

$$\underset{CH_3CH_2}{\overset{H}{>}}C=C\overset{H}{\underset{CH_3}{<}}$$

$$CH_3CH_2CH_2\overset{+}{C}HCH_3 \longrightarrow \underset{CH_3CH_2}{\overset{H}{>}}C=C\overset{CH_3}{\underset{H}{<}}$$

$$\underset{CH_3CH_2CH_2}{\overset{H}{>}}C=C\overset{H}{\underset{H}{<}}$$

We discussed in connection with the S_N1 reaction the ionization and rearrangement of neopentyl bromide. Since carbonium ions are involved in the $E1$ process, rearrangements are also observed here. When the ionization of neopentyl bromide is conducted under conditions favoring the elimination, rearrangement is observed and two olefinic products are obtained. Again, either a stepwise mechanism or a concerted process may be postulated:

$$CH_3-\underset{\underset{CH_3}{|}}{\overset{\overset{CH_3}{|}}{C}}-CH_2Br \longrightarrow CH_3-\underset{\underset{CH_3}{|}}{\overset{\overset{CH_3}{|}}{C}}-CH_2CH_3 + Br^-$$

$$CH_3-\underset{+}{\underset{\underset{CH_3}{|}}{\overset{\overset{CH_3}{|}}{C}}}-CH_2CH_3 \longrightarrow \underset{H}{\overset{CH_3}{}}C=C\underset{CH_3}{\overset{CH_3}{}} + \underset{CH_3}{\overset{CH_3CH_2}{}}C=C\underset{H}{\overset{H}{}}$$

Protons as well as alkyl groups migrate during elimination reactions, and the following examples are illustrative:

$$CH_3CH_2-\underset{\underset{H}{|}}{\overset{\overset{CH_3}{|}}{C}}-CH_2OH \xrightarrow{H^+} \underset{H}{\overset{CH_3}{}}C=C\underset{CH_3}{\overset{CH_3}{}} + \underset{CH_3}{\overset{CH_3CH_2}{}}C=C\underset{H}{\overset{H}{}}$$

$$CH_3-\underset{\underset{CH_3}{|}}{\overset{\overset{CH_3}{|}}{C}}-CHOHCH_3 \xrightarrow{H^+} \underset{CH_3}{\overset{CH_3}{}}C=C\underset{CH_3}{\overset{CH_3}{}} + \underset{CH_3}{\overset{(CH_3)_2CH}{}}C=C\underset{H}{\overset{H}{}}$$

A general rule for predicting the major product is that it is the most stable alkene formed from the most stable possible carbonium ion. The system forms the most stable carbonium ion which loses a proton to form the most stable alkene (this is usually the most highly substituted alkene).

An organic compound loses HX. The reverse reaction is also of interest. An alkene is able to add HX, and the mechanism usually postulated for the addition is just the reverse of that presented for the *E*1 reaction. The reaction profile presented previously is traversed in the opposite direction.

The addition reaction,

$$\underset{R}{\overset{R}{}}C=C\underset{R}{\overset{R}{}} + HX \longrightarrow R-\underset{\underset{H}{|}}{\overset{\overset{R}{|}}{C}}-\underset{\underset{X}{|}}{\overset{\overset{R}{|}}{C}}-R$$

occurs by several routes. One route involves a carbonium ion intermediate, and the mechanism is the reverse of that for the $E1$ reaction:

$$\underset{R}{\overset{R}{\diagup}}C=C\underset{R}{\overset{R}{\diagdown}} \quad + \quad H^+ \quad \longrightarrow \quad \pi \text{ Complexes}$$

$$\pi \text{ Complexes} \quad \longrightarrow \quad R-\overset{\overset{\displaystyle R}{|}}{\underset{\underset{\displaystyle H}{|}}{C}}-\overset{\overset{\displaystyle R}{|}}{\underset{+}{C}}-R$$

$$R-\overset{\overset{\displaystyle R}{|}}{\underset{\underset{\displaystyle H}{|}}{C}}-\overset{\overset{\displaystyle R}{|}}{\underset{+}{C}}-R + X^- \quad \longrightarrow \quad R-\overset{\overset{\displaystyle R}{|}}{\underset{\underset{\displaystyle H}{|}}{C}}-\overset{\overset{\displaystyle R}{|}}{\underset{\underset{\displaystyle X}{|}}{C}}-R$$

That this mechanism should be just the reverse of that for elimination is reasonable, and when the forward and reverse processes are conducted under the same conditions, the principle of microscopic reversibility states that this must be the case.

$$R-\overset{\overset{\displaystyle R}{|}}{\underset{\underset{\displaystyle H}{|}}{C}}-\overset{\overset{\displaystyle R}{|}}{\underset{\underset{\displaystyle X}{|}}{C}}-R \quad \rightleftharpoons \quad \underset{R}{\overset{R}{\diagup}}C=C\underset{R}{\overset{R}{\diagdown}} \quad | \quad IIX$$

The unimolecular elimination discussed in this section involves a carbonium ion intermediate, and the rate of reaction is independent of the concentration of added base. A second unimolecular process that does depend upon the base is the $E1cB$ reaction discussed in the next section.

12.3 The *E1cB* Reaction

In principle, elimination could proceed by way of a two-step mechanism of the type:

$$R-\overset{\overset{\displaystyle R}{|}}{\underset{\underset{\displaystyle H}{|}}{C}}-\overset{\overset{\displaystyle R}{|}}{\underset{\underset{\displaystyle X}{|}}{C}}-R + Y^- \quad \rightleftharpoons \quad R-\overset{\overset{\displaystyle R}{|}}{\underset{\underset{\displaystyle X}{|}}{\overset{..}{C}}}-\overset{\overset{\displaystyle R}{|}}{C}-R + HY$$

$$R-\overset{\overset{\displaystyle R}{|}}{\underset{\underset{\displaystyle X}{|}}{\overset{..}{C}}}-\overset{\overset{\displaystyle R}{|}}{C}-R \quad \longrightarrow \quad \underset{R}{\overset{R}{\diagup}}C=C\underset{R}{\overset{R}{\diagdown}} \quad + \quad X^-$$

If the first step is reversible, the second step is rate limiting and the reaction is a unimolecular second order process. Eliminations of this type can occur when the proton to be abstracted is unusually acidic. The compound R_2CHCXR_2 behaves as an acid in the first step, and the material $R_2CCXR_2^-$ is its conjugate base. The reaction is unimolecular involving only the conjugate base in the rate limiting step and is designated as an *E1cB* process (*cB* refers to conjugate base).

The *E1cB* process would be expected to occur when the electrons in the conjugate base were stabilized either by an inductive effect or by resonance, and the reaction is observed in connection with certain 1,1-eliminations. These are discussed more fully in Section 12.6.

Treatment of chloroform with a strong base affords dichlorocarbene by way of the *E1cB* mechanism:

$$\underset{\underset{Cl}{|}}{\overset{\overset{Cl}{|}}{Cl-C-H}} + Y^- \rightleftharpoons \underset{\underset{Cl}{|}}{\overset{\overset{Cl}{|}}{Cl-C:^-}} + HY$$

$$\underset{\underset{Cl}{|}}{\overset{\overset{Cl}{|}}{Cl-C:^-}} \longrightarrow \underset{\underset{Cl}{|}}{\overset{\overset{Cl}{|}}{Cl-C:}} + Cl^-$$

If the reaction is conducted in the presence of D_2O, deuterium exchange takes place, and this supports the mechanism just presented.

Other examples of the *E1cB* mechanism have been reported. Treatment of trichloroethylene with a strong base yields dichloroacetylene, and the loss of HCl occurs in two distinct steps. Again, the evidence stems from deuterium exchange studies:

$$\underset{Cl}{\overset{H}{>}}C=C\underset{Cl}{\overset{Cl}{<}} + OH^- \rightleftharpoons \underset{Cl}{\overset{\cdot\cdot}{>}}C=C\underset{Cl}{\overset{Cl}{<}} + H_2O$$

$$\underset{Cl}{\overset{\cdot\cdot}{>}}C=C\underset{Cl}{\overset{Cl}{<}} \longrightarrow Cl-C\equiv C-Cl + Cl^-$$

Eliminations of the type,

$$R-\overset{\overset{O}{\parallel}}{C}CH_2-\underset{\underset{X}{|}}{CHR} + Y^- \longrightarrow R-\overset{\overset{O}{\parallel}}{C}-CH=CHR + HY + X^-$$

probably take place by the *E1cB* mechanism. The reaction is the reverse of Michael addition, and an example is the formation of acrylonitrile from

$$\phi OCH_2CH_2CN \xrightarrow{\ Y^-\ } CH_2{=}CHCN$$

8

A two-step mechanism involving the conjugate base of the reactant has also been suggested for the formation of phenylcyclopropane. Upon treatment of the starting material with amide ion (NH_2^-) the carbanion can be formed:

$$\phi CH_2CH_2CH_2{-}\overset{+}{N}(CH_3)_3 + NH_2^- \longrightarrow \phi{-}\overset{-}{\underset{..}{C}}HCH_2CH_2{-}\overset{+}{N}(CH_3)_3$$

$$\phi{-}\overset{-}{\underset{..}{C}}HCH_2CH_2{-}\overset{+}{N}(CH_3)_3 \longrightarrow \phi{-}\triangleleft + N(CH_3)_3$$

The mechanism presented here has not been definitely established. It is possible that the leaving group $N^+(CH_3)_3$ begins its departure while the base abstracts the proton rather than afterwards.

The *E1cB* process occurs only rarely in conjunction with 1,2-eliminations. Instead abstraction of a proton by the base Y^- occurs simultaneously with the departure of the leaving group X:

$$\begin{array}{c} Y^{\delta-} \\ \vdots \\ H \\ \vdots \\ R{-}C \\ \diagdown \\ R{-}C \\ \diagup \\ X^{\delta-} \end{array}$$

The process is concerted, and the elimination is bimolecular (*E2*).

12.4 The *E2* Reaction

When we treat an alkyl halide with a nucleophile that is also a strong base such as hydroxide ion or ethoxide ion, we effect both bimolecular substitution (S_N2) and bimolecular elimination (*E2*). These two reactions are competitive. In fact, if the concentration of nucleophile is low or if the *E2* and S_N2 reactions are slow, the *E1* and S_N1 may also occur, and all four processes then proceed simultaneously. Of course, under the appropriate conditions (high concentration of the nucleophilic reagent) the bimolecular processes are generally much more rapid.

Since the S_N2 and *E2* are competitive, the treatment of alkyl halides with strong bases affords both substituted and eliminated products. An example of this is the Williamson ether synthesis. An alkyl halide is treated with alkoxide ion and the ether that results contains olefinic impurities:

$$CH_3CH_2Br + C_2H_5O^- \begin{array}{c} \xrightarrow{\ S_N2\ } CH_3CH_2OCH_2CH_3 + Br^- \\ \xrightarrow{\ E2\ } CH_2{=}CH_2 + C_2H_5OH + Br^- \end{array}$$

The reaction of ethylsulfonium ion with ethoxide ion affords an analogous result:

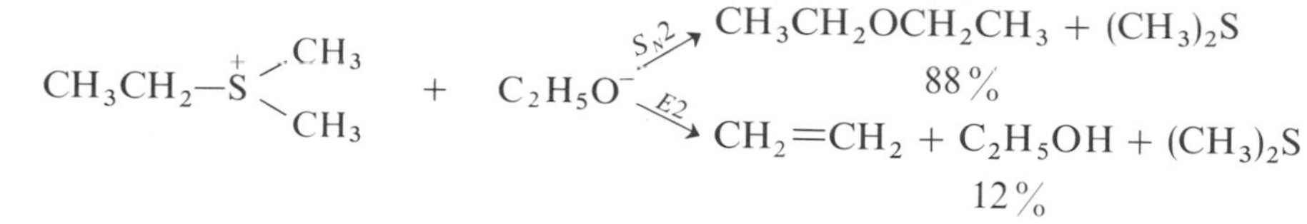

$$CH_3CH_2-\overset{+}{\underset{\underset{CH_3}{|}}{S}} \diagdown \overset{CH_3}{} \quad + \quad C_2H_5O^- \quad \overset{S_N2}{\underset{E2}{}} \quad \begin{array}{c} CH_3CH_2OCH_2CH_3 + (CH_3)_2S \\ 88\% \\ CH_2{=}CH_2 + C_2H_5OH + (CH_3)_2S \\ 12\% \end{array}$$

In these reactions the substituted material is the major product, but the reaction of isopropylsulfonium ion yields the alkene as the major product:

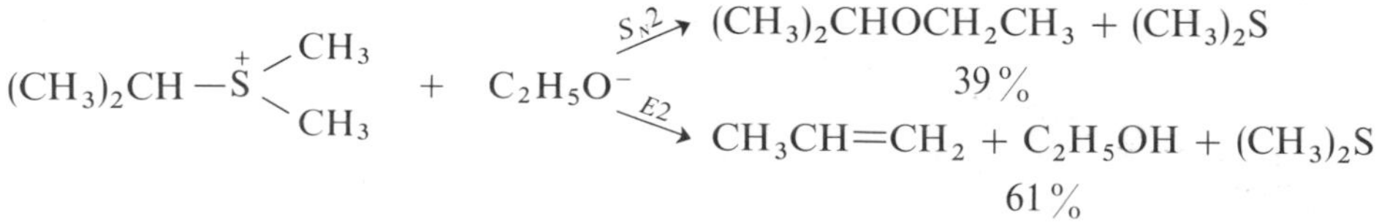

$$(CH_3)_2CH-\overset{+}{\underset{\underset{CH_3}{|}}{S}} \diagdown \overset{CH_3}{} \quad + \quad C_2H_5O^- \quad \overset{S_N2}{\underset{E2}{}} \quad \begin{array}{c} (CH_3)_2CHOCH_2CH_3 + (CH_3)_2S \\ 39\% \\ CH_3CH{=}CH_2 + C_2H_5OH + (CH_3)_2S \\ 61\% \end{array}$$

Both the ethyl and the isopropyl systems yield a mixture of substituted and olefinic products with more alkene formed by the latter. The reaction of *t*-butylsulfonium ion with ethoxide yields virtually no substituted product, and essentially only the *E*2 reaction occurs:

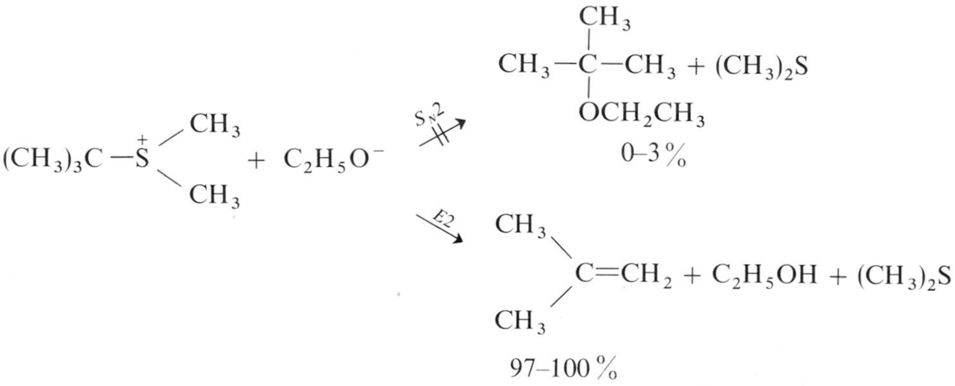

$$(CH_3)_3C-\overset{+}{\underset{\underset{CH_3}{|}}{S}} \diagdown \overset{CH_3}{} \quad + \quad C_2H_5O^- \quad \begin{array}{c} \overset{S_N2}{\diagup\!\!\!\diagup} \quad \begin{array}{c} CH_3 \\ | \\ CH_3{-}C{-}CH_3 + (CH_3)_2S \\ | \\ OCH_2CH_3 \\ 0{-}3\% \end{array} \\ \\ \overset{E2}{\searrow} \quad \begin{array}{c} CH_3 \diagdown \\ C{=}CH_2 + C_2H_5OH + (CH_3)_2S \\ CH_3 \diagup \\ 97{-}100\% \end{array} \end{array}$$

Analogous results are obtained when the corresponding alkyl bromides are treated with sodium ethoxide. In the case of ethyl bromide the major product is the substituted material (99%). With isopropyl bromide the olefin predominates (79%), and in the reaction of *t*-butyl bromide with sodium ethoxide only olefinic material is found (~100%). The rate constants are presented in Table 12–2.

Table 12-2

Compound	$k \cdot 10^5$ (liter mole^{-1} sec^{-1})*	
	S_N2	$E2$
CH_3CH_2Br	118.2	1.2
$(CH_3)_2CHBr$	2.1	7.6
$(CH_3)_3CBr$	small	50.

* Ethanol at 55°.

Ingold, C. K., *Structure and Mechanism in Organic Chemistry*, Cornell U.P., Ithaca, New York, 1953, p. 439.

In proceeding from ethyl bromide, to isopropyl bromide, and finally to *t*-butyl bromide the S_N2 process becomes increasingly difficult while the $E2$ occurs more readily. These $E2$ reactions proceed as follows:

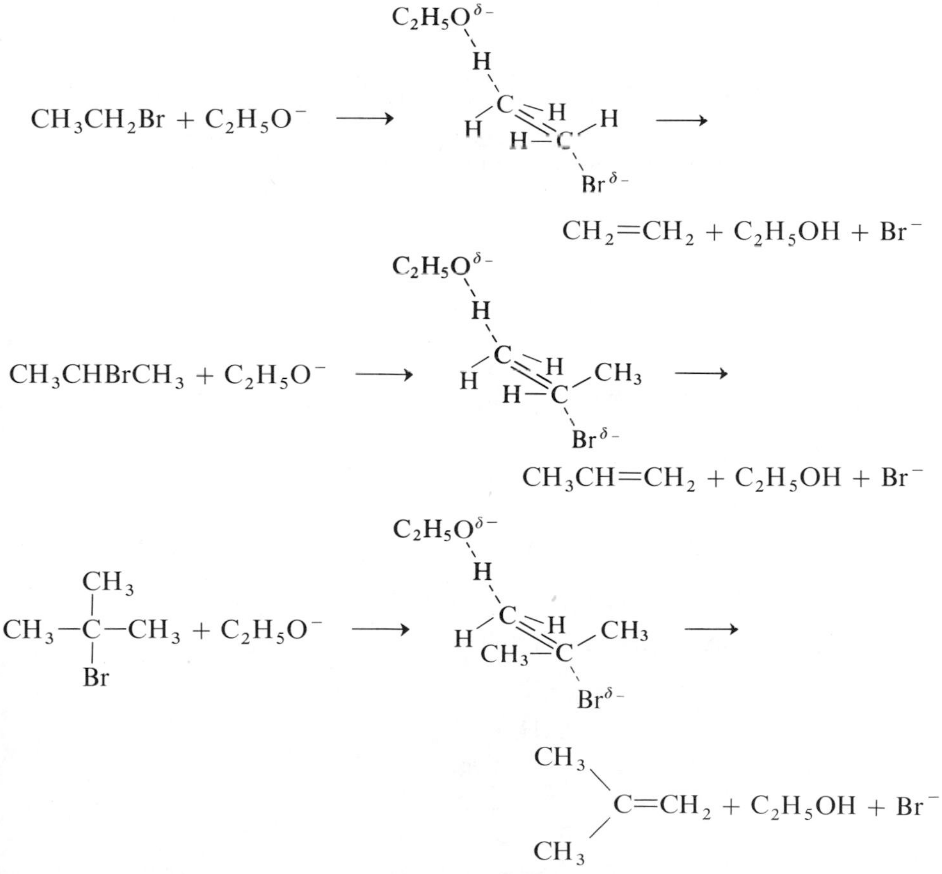

$$CH_3CH_2Br + C_2H_5O^- \longrightarrow$$

$$CH_2{=}CH_2 + C_2H_5OH + Br^-$$

$$CH_3CHBrCH_3 + C_2H_5O^- \longrightarrow$$

$$CH_3CH{=}CH_2 + C_2H_5OH + Br^-$$

$$CH_3{-}\underset{\underset{Br}{|}}{\overset{\overset{CH_3}{|}}{C}}{-}CH_3 + C_2H_5O^- \longrightarrow$$

$$\underset{CH_3}{\overset{CH_3}{>}}C{=}CH_2 + C_2H_5OH + Br^-$$

Thus we see why the *E2* reaction increases in rate as we proceed along the sequence. The transition states have olefinic character, and the more stable alkene is formed more readily.

Bimolecular eliminations also occur in cyclic systems as the reaction of cyclohexyl bromide illustrates,

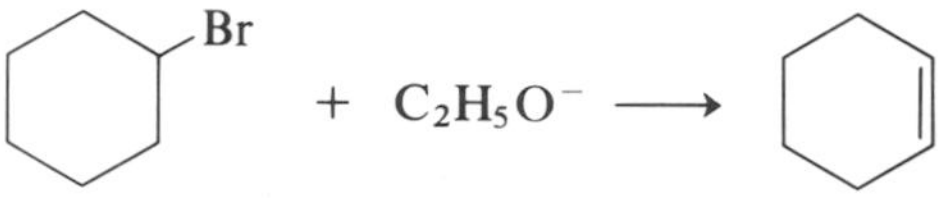

$$\text{(cyclohexyl bromide with Br)} + C_2H_5O^- \longrightarrow \text{(cyclohexene)}$$

Hofmann eliminations are usually bimolecular processes, and the following reactions are typical,

$$CH_3CH_2\overset{+}{N}(CH_3)_3OH^- \xrightarrow{\Delta} CH_2=CH_2 + (CH_3)_3N + H_2O$$

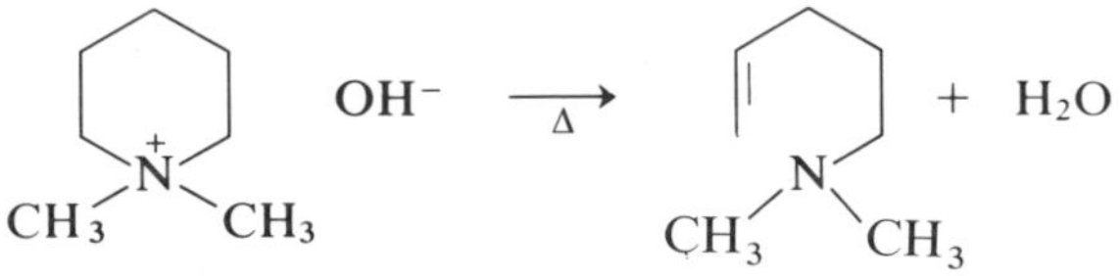

$$\text{(piperidinium ring)} + OH^- \xrightarrow{\Delta} \text{(ring)} + H_2O$$

Elimination of HX is also observed in the preparation of acetylenic systems:

$$KOOC-CH-CH-COOK + 2KOH \longrightarrow KOOC-C{\equiv}C-COOK$$
$$\qquad\quad | \qquad |$$
$$\qquad\quad Br \quad\ Br$$

$$\phi-CH=CHBr + KOH \longrightarrow \phi-C{\equiv}CH$$

and,

$$CH_3(CH_2)_7CBr=CH_2 + NaNH_2 \longrightarrow CH_3(CH_2)_7C{\equiv}CH$$

The *E2* reaction

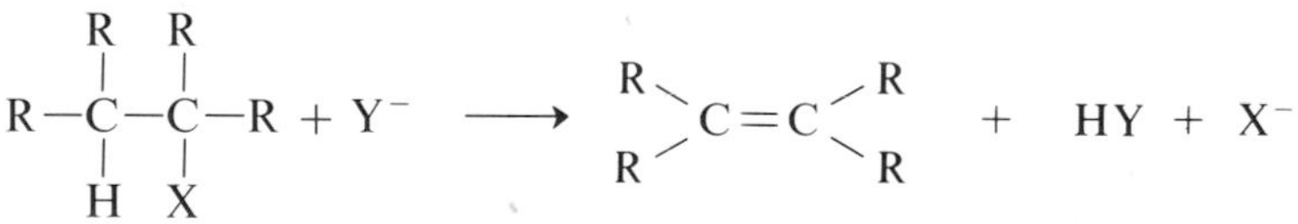

$$
\begin{array}{cc}
R & R \\
| & | \\
R-C-C-R + Y^- \\
| & | \\
H & X
\end{array}
\longrightarrow
\begin{array}{c}
R \\ \diagdown \\
\quad C=C \\
R \diagup
\end{array}
\begin{array}{c}
R \\ \diagup \\
\diagdown R
\end{array}
+ \quad HY + X^-
$$

is a single-step reaction having the following transition state:

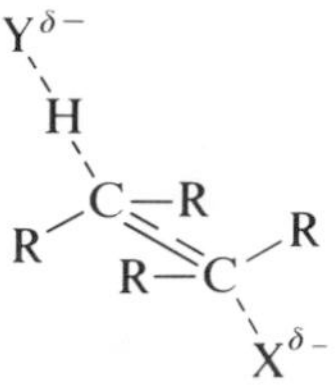

$$
\begin{array}{c}
Y^{\delta-} \\
\vdots \\
H \\
\vdots \\
R-\underset{R=C}{\overset{C=R}{|}}-R \\
\vdots \\
X^{\delta-}
\end{array}
$$

In the transition state the atoms H and X are trans oriented, the four atoms H—C—C—X are in the same plane (coplanar), and the olefinic bond is partially formed. The transition state for the E2 process has olefinic character, and this influences its free energy. The reaction is also sensitive to steric interactions and these two factors, olefin stability and steric factors, determine the nature of the products.

When the groups R, Y, or X are large and bulky, steric interactions determine the course of the E2 process. The reaction proceeds through the least crowded transition state where the base abstracts the most accessible hydrogen atom, and the olefinic product need not be the most highly substituted olefin. On the other hand, when steric interactions are less important, the position of the double bond is the determining factor, and in these cases bimolecular elimination affords the most highly substituted alkene.

Eliminations that yield the most stable olefin are called Saytzeff eliminations, whereas those in which steric factors determine the course of the reaction are called Hofmann eliminations.

The following are typical examples of Saytzeff eliminations where the most stable olefin is the major product. We present only the composition of the olefinic portion of the product. Remember that substitution also occurs:

$$CH_3CH_2CHBrCH_3 \xrightarrow{C_2H_5O^-} CH_3CH=CHCH_3 \quad CH_3CH_2CH=CH_2$$
$$81\% \qquad\qquad 19\%$$

$$CH_3CH_2CH_2CHBrCH_3 \xrightarrow{C_2H_5O^-}$$
$$CH_3CH_2CH=CHCH_3 + CH_3CH_2CH_2CH=CH_2$$
$$69\% \qquad\qquad\qquad 31\%$$

$$
\begin{array}{c}
\quad\;\; CH_3 \\
\;\; | \\
CH_3CH_2-C-CH_3 \\
\;\; | \\
\quad\;\; Br
\end{array}
\xrightarrow{C_2H_5O^-}
CH_3CH=C(CH_3)_2 +
\begin{array}{c}
CH_3 \\
| \\
CH_3CH_2C=CH_2
\end{array}
$$
$$69\% \qquad\qquad 31\%$$

In all of these reactions both the leaving group and the attacking base are small; steric factors are less important than olefin stability; the transition state leading to the most stable olefin is preferred; and the most stable olefin predominates.

Examples of Hofmann type eliminations include,

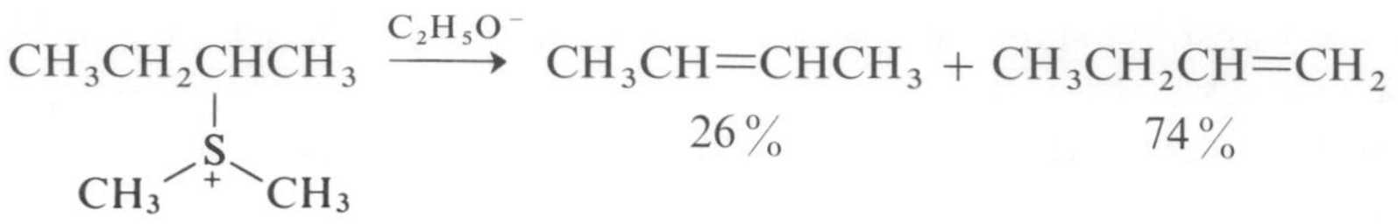

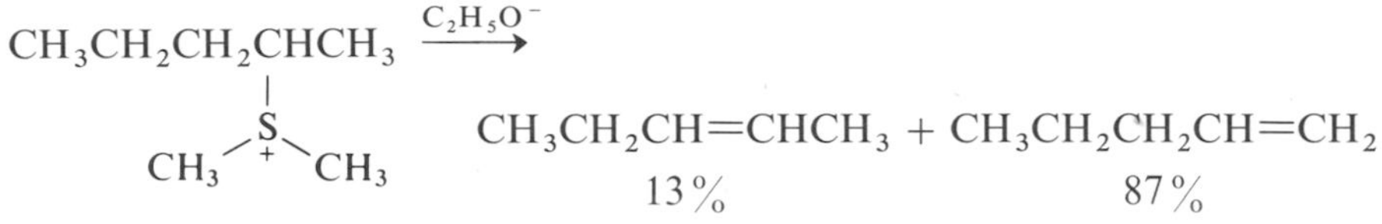

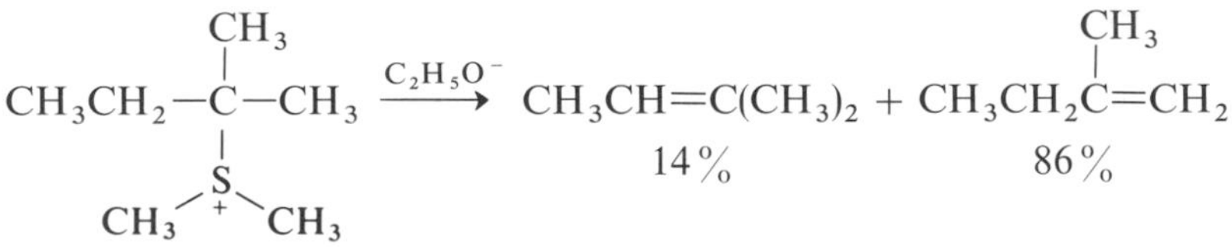

$$CH_3CH_2CHCH_3 \xrightarrow{C_2H_5O^-} CH_3CH=CHCH_3 + CH_3CH_2CH=CH_2$$

with $\overset{+}{S}(CH_3)_2$ leaving group:

26%   74%

$$CH_3CH_2CH_2CHCH_3 \xrightarrow{C_2H_5O^-}$$

$$CH_3CH_2CH=CHCH_3 + CH_3CH_2CH_2CH=CH_2$$

13%   87%

$$CH_3CH_2-\overset{\overset{\displaystyle CH_3}{|}}{\underset{\underset{\displaystyle S^+(CH_3)_2}{|}}{C}}-CH_3 \xrightarrow{C_2H_5O^-} CH_3CH=C(CH_3)_2 + CH_3CH_2\overset{\overset{\displaystyle CH_3}{|}}{C}=CH_2$$

14%   86%

In these examples the leaving group is large, steric factors are more influential than olefin stability, the reaction proceeds through the least crowded transition state, and Hofmann elimination predominates.

Changing the leaving group from Br to $S^+(CH_3)_2$ causes the pathway to change from a Saytzeff to a Hofmann elimination.

In the previous examples we altered the leaving group. We may also change the attacking base, and as the data clearly indicate, steric crowding in the transition state caused either by a large leaving group or a large base gives rise to Hofmann elimination; see Table 12–3. The absence of extremely large groups promotes Saytzeff elimination.

Table 12–3

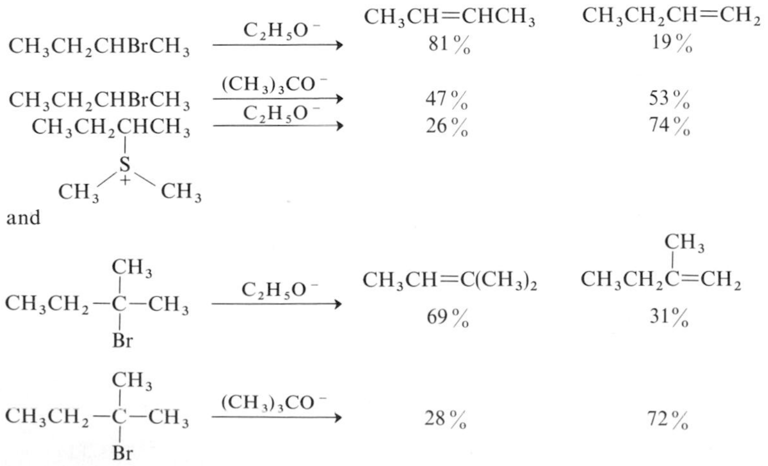

		$CH_3CH=CHCH_3$	$CH_3CH_2CH=CH_2$
$CH_3CH_2CHBrCH_3$	$\xrightarrow{C_2H_5O^-}$	81%	19%
$CH_3CH_2CHBrCH_3$	$\xrightarrow{(CH_3)_3CO^-}$	47%	53%
$CH_3CH_2CHCH_3$ with $S^+(CH_3)_2$	$\xrightarrow{C_2H_5O^-}$	26%	74%

and

		$CH_3CH=C(CH_3)_2$	$CH_3CH_2\overset{CH_3}{\underset{|}{C}}=CH_2$
$CH_3CH_2-\overset{CH_3}{\underset{Br}{C}}-CH_3$	$\xrightarrow{C_2H_5O^-}$	69%	31%
$CH_3CH_2-\overset{CH_3}{\underset{Br}{C}}-CH_3$	$\xrightarrow{(CH_3)_3CO^-}$	28%	72%

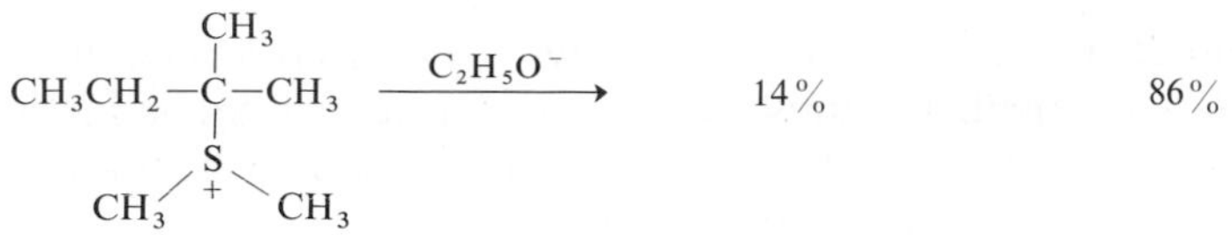

$$CH_3CH_2-\overset{\overset{\displaystyle CH_3}{|}}{\underset{\overset{\displaystyle S}{\underset{\displaystyle CH_3\overset{+}{\diagup}\diagdown CH_3}{|}}}{C}}-CH_3 \xrightarrow{\ C_2H_5O^-\ } \qquad 14\% \qquad\qquad 86\%$$

Transition states for the processes presented in Table 12–3 are (for the *t*-amyl derivatives),

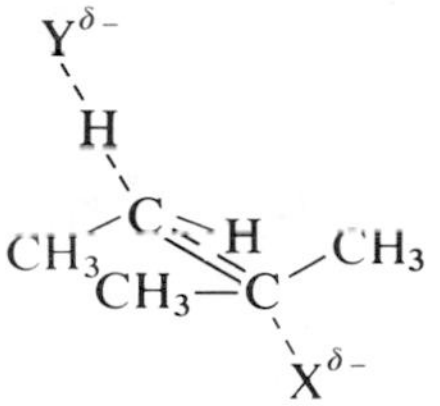

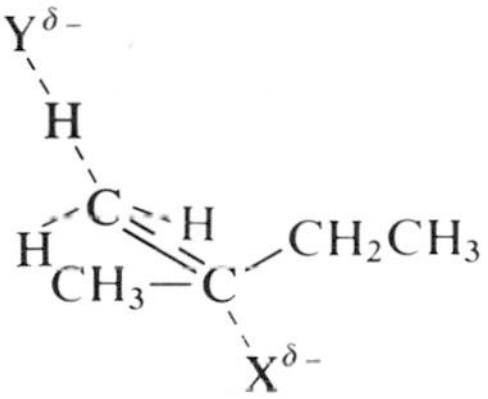

where transition state **8** gives rise to 2-methyl-2-butene (the more stable olefin) and transition state **9** gives rise to 2-methyl-1-butene (the less stable olefin). The difference in the free energy of these two transition states is small and both of them are formed; however, the reaction proceeds most readily by way of the transition state with the lower free energy. If transition state **8** is the more stable, 2-methyl-2-butene is the major product, while if transition state **9** is the more stable, 2-methyl-1-butene is the major product. In the absence of large groups, olefin stability is the overriding factor. Under these conditions **8** is more stable than **9** and Saytzeff elimination occurs. This is the situation when the leaving group is bromide and the attacking base is ethoxide. When X or Y is large, steric interactions become the significant consideration. Under these conditions **9** is more stable than **8**, and 2-methyl-1-butene becomes the major product.

The 2-*n*-butyl system was also presented in Table 12–3, and for this system three different transition states must be considered, that leading to *trans*-2-butene, the one leading to *cis*-2-butene, and that leading to 1-butene. The transition state for the reaction leading to *cis*-2-butene is the following,

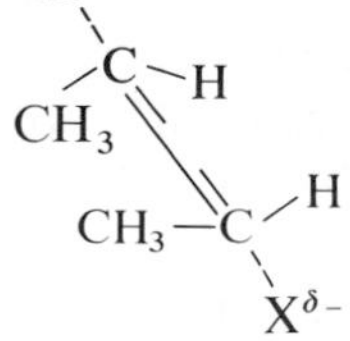

10

The *cis*-product is not formed as readily as the *trans*-isomer for in this transition state the methyl groups are already *cis* oriented. Steric factors play a role even in Saytzeff eliminations. The interactions between these two *cis* methyl groups raise the free energy of **10**.

Λ similar situation occurs with **11** and **12**. These systems yield *trans*-2-pentene, *cis*-2-pentene, and 1-pentene, the *cis*-2-pentene being formed in lowest yield.

Both Hofmann and Saytzeff eliminations afford *cis*-2-pentene as the minor component of the product mixture:

$$CH_3CH_2CH_2CHBrCH_3 \qquad\qquad CH_3CH_2CH_2CHCH_3$$

11

$$\overset{\displaystyle CH_3CH_2CH_2CHCH_3}{\underset{\overset{\displaystyle \mid}{\underset{\displaystyle CH_3 \overset{+}{S} CH_3}{}}}{}}$$

12

$$\underset{CH_3CH_2}{\overset{H}{\diagdown}}C = C\underset{\diagdown H}{\overset{\diagup CH_3}{}} \qquad \underset{CH_3CH_2}{\overset{H}{\diagdown}}C = C\underset{\diagdown CH_3}{\overset{\diagup H}{}} \qquad \underset{CH_3CH_2CH_2}{\overset{H}{\diagdown}}C = C\underset{\diagdown H}{\overset{\diagup H}{}}$$

11 $\xrightarrow{C_2H_5O^-}$ 51%   18%   31%

12 $\xrightarrow{C_2H_5O^-}$ 8%   5%   87%

Factors such as the polarity of the solvent also influence the *E*2 reaction. The effect of a change in solvent upon the rate of an *E*2 reaction is exactly as expected. A more polar solvent increases the rate of those bimolecular eliminations where charge is generated in proceeding from the reactants to the transition state and decreases the rate of processes where charge is destroyed or delocalized in proceeding to the transition state. The decrease is most pronounced when charge is destroyed.

Another point that should be considered is that the preferred orientation for the hydrogen atom being abstracted is *trans* to, yet coplanar with the leaving group. Other orientations are possible but require more energy. The free energy of the transition state is lower when these two groups are *trans*. Elimination still occurs even when such an orientation is impossible, but these other eliminations are less favorable and proceed more slowly.

Many examples exist which illustrate quite convincingly that a *trans*-orientation of these two groups is preferred. Particularly good evidence comes from a consideration of the reactions of stilbene dibromides. In the presence of hydroxide ion the *meso* compound affords *cis*-bromostilbene while a racemic mixture of the D, L- material yields the *trans*-product:

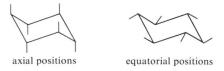

meso   racemic mixture of D and L

This evidence illustrates fairly convincingly that the *trans* orientation is indeed preferred. It is difficult to explain the experimental results on any other basis. Incidentally, we expect the *meso* reactant to undergo elimination more slowly than the D, L- pair, for in the former the two large phenyl groups are *cis* oriented in the transition state, whereas in the latter a *trans*-orientation of these two groups occurs.

The fact that a *trans*-coplanar transition state is the one having lowest energy plays an important role in the behavior of cyclic compounds during bimolecular eliminations. There are six axial and six equatorial positions in the chair form of cyclohexane,

axial positions   equatorial positions

and the most stable conformation of substituted cyclohexanes is generally that having the substituent in an equatorial position **13**. However, conformation **13** is not favorable for an E2 reaction. A hydrogen atom on the adjacent position is *trans* but not coplanar. Such coplanarity is desirable and is attained in the less stable conformation **14** where the leaving group occupies an axial position. Here the two atoms (H and X) to be eliminated both occupy axial positions. These are *trans* and coplanar, and it is in this conformation that cyclohexyl derivatives react with strong bases to undergo elimination:

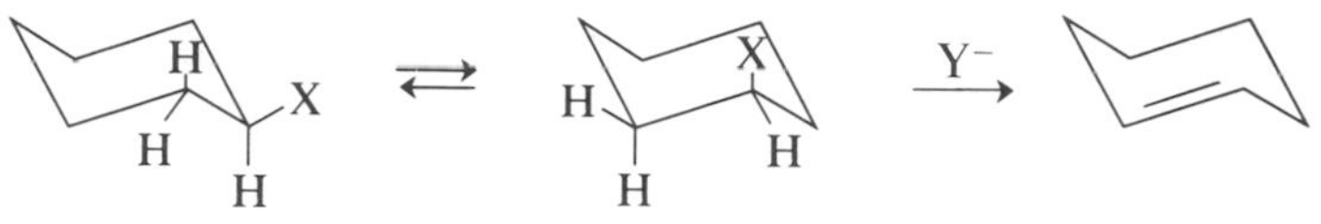

13   **14**

An example of this type of a reaction is cyclohexyl bromide reacting with sodium ethoxide to yield cyclohexene:

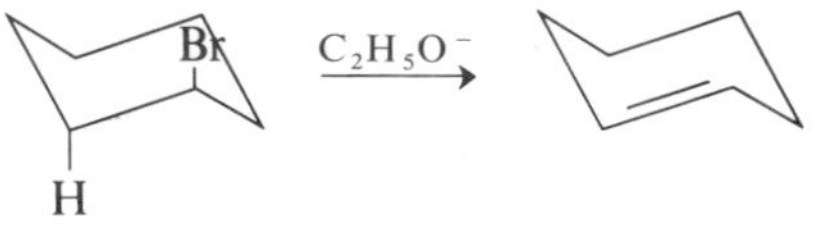

The elimination takes place most readily with the hydrogen and the leaving group both occupying axial positions, for this conformation leads to the transition state having the proper geometry. Interesting results are sometimes obtained because of this requirement. For example, compound **15** in which the isopropyl group is *trans* to the chlorine atom cannot form the more stable olefin by way of a *trans*-elimination. The isopropyl group occupies this position. It can form the more stable olefin by way of a *cis*-elimination or undergo a *trans*-elimination to form a less stable alkene **16**. Reaction of **15** with ethoxide ion yields only the less stable isomer **16**. Thus, bimolecular eliminations in cyclohexyl derivatives proceed most readily by way of the diaxial *trans*-conformation in the transition state even when this leads to a less stable alkene:

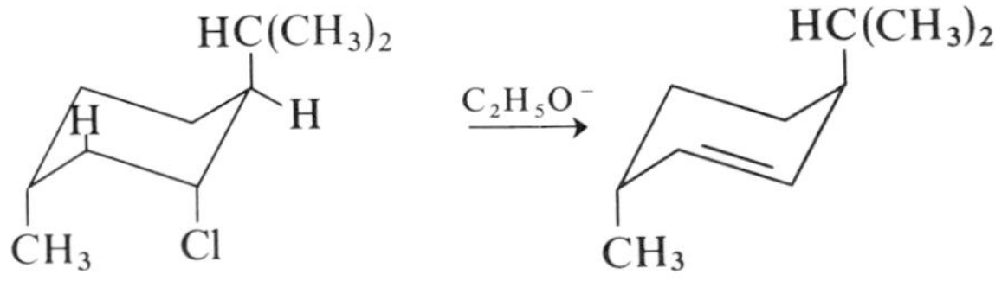

15   **16**

Materials such as **17** and **18** can react with ethoxide to yield either of two olefinic products. Thus **17** in which the R group and the chloride atom are *cis* has two axial hydrogens, and from **17** we expect a mixture of olefinic materials with a preponderance of the more stable isomer. Compound **18** has only a single axial hydrogen available; the other axial position is occupied by R. From **18** we expect only a single olefinic product; the less stable alkene:

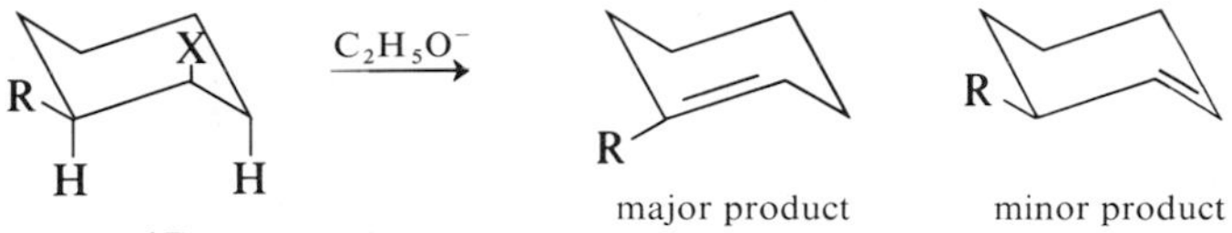

major product   minor product

17

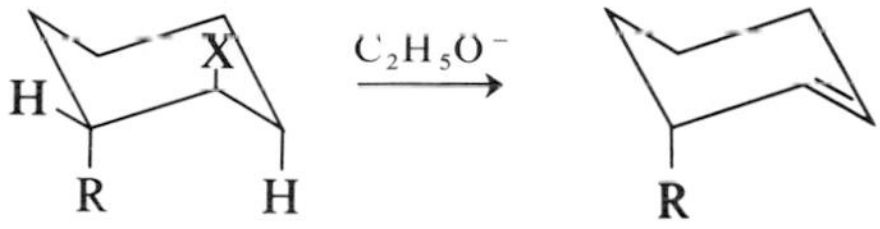

18

In certain cases, acid catalyzed dehydrations are *E2* processes. When this occurs in cyclohexyl systems, an axial position is also expected for the leaving group in the transition state of these reactions:

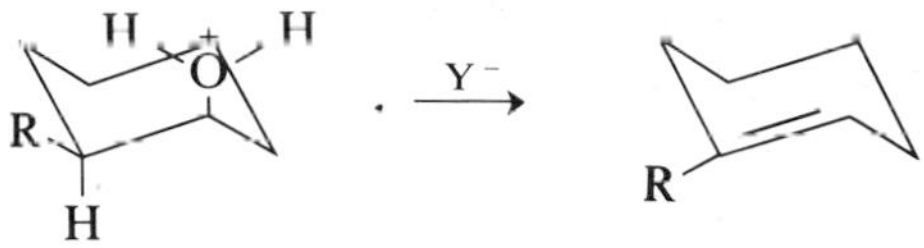

Bimolecular eliminations do occur when diaxial conformations cannot exist, but these processes require more energy. It has recently been shown that *exo* norbornyl derivatives undergo a *cis-E2* elimination:

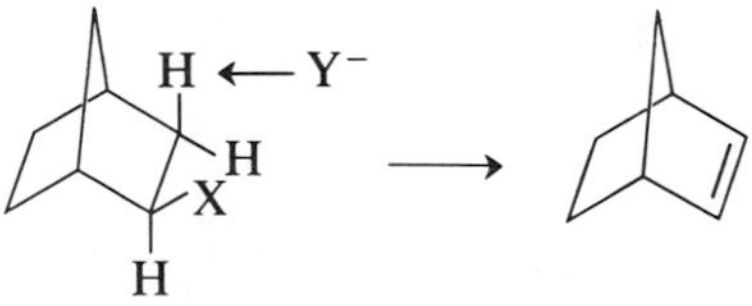

The *endo* isomers behave as expected.

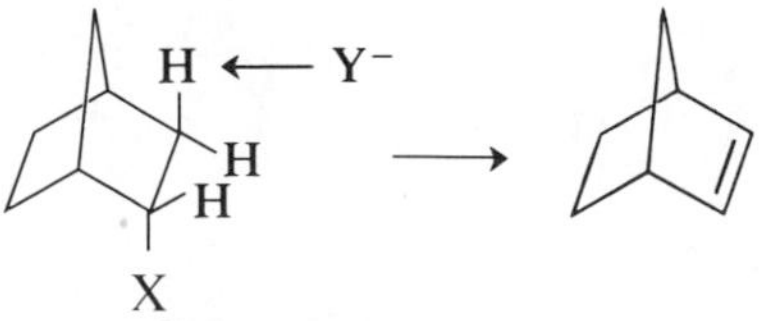

The decomposition of quarternary ammonium hydroxides at elevated temperatures yields alkenes, and this particular elimination is called the Hofmann exhaustive methylation in honor of its discoverer:

$$
R-\underset{\underset{H}{|}}{\overset{\overset{R}{|}}{C}}-\underset{\underset{NH_2}{|}}{\overset{\overset{R}{|}}{C}}-R \xrightarrow{CH_3I} R-\underset{\underset{H}{|}}{\overset{\overset{R}{|}}{C}}-\underset{\underset{\overset{+}{N(CH_3)_3}I^-}{|}}{\overset{\overset{R}{|}}{C}}-R \xrightarrow[Ag_2O]{H_2O} R-\underset{\underset{H}{|}}{\overset{\overset{R}{|}}{C}}-\underset{\underset{\overset{+}{N(CH_3)_3}OH^-}{|}}{\overset{\overset{R}{|}}{C}}-R
$$

$$
R-\underset{\underset{H}{|}}{\overset{\overset{R}{|}}{C}}-\underset{\underset{\overset{+}{N(CH_3)_3}OH^-}{|}}{\overset{\overset{R}{|}}{C}}-R \xrightarrow{\Delta} \underset{R}{\overset{R}{\diagdown}}C=C\underset{\diagdown R}{\overset{\diagup R}{}}
$$

We have presented the idea that the elimination in the last step is an *E*2 process. The reaction of **19** with phenyllithium also gives rise to an olefinic product. The reaction appears to be related to the Hofmann exhaustive methylation, yet the mechanism postulated for this decomposition is somewhat different. It has been suggested that the first step is a halide exchange to yield the ylid **20** and that this ylid then decomposes by way of a cyclic transition state to form the alkene:

$$
CH_3-\underset{\underset{CH_3}{|}}{\overset{\overset{H}{|}}{C}}-\overset{+}{\underset{\underset{CH_2I}{|}}{N}}-CH_3 \xrightarrow{\phi Li} CH_3-\underset{\underset{CH_3}{|}}{\overset{\overset{H}{|}}{C}}-\overset{+}{\underset{\underset{CH_2^-}{|}}{N}}-CH_3
$$

$$
\mathbf{19} \qquad\qquad\qquad \mathbf{20}
$$

$$
CH_3-\underset{\underset{\overset{H}{\diagup}\overset{|}{C}\diagdown H}{|}}{\overset{\overset{H}{|}}{C}}-\overset{+}{\underset{\underset{CH_2^-}{\diagdown}}{N}}-CH_3 \longrightarrow \underset{\underset{H}{\diagup}\overset{\diagup CH_3}{C}\underset{\diagdown H}{\overset{\diagdown H}{}}}{\overset{\overset{CH_3}{\diagdown}/\overset{H}{}}{\underset{||}{C}}} + \underset{\underset{CH_3}{|}}{\overset{\overset{CH_3}{|}}{N}}-CH_3
$$

This reaction appears to proceed through a cyclic transition state, and in some cases Hofmann exhaustive methylations may proceed in similar fashion:

$$
\begin{array}{c}
\text{R} \quad \text{R} \\
| \quad | \\
\text{R}-\text{C}-\text{C}-\text{R} \quad \text{OH}^- \\
| \quad | \\
\text{H} \;\; {}^+\text{N(CH}_3)_2 \\
| \\
\text{CH}_3
\end{array}
\longrightarrow
\begin{array}{c}
\text{R} \quad \text{R} \\
| \quad | \\
\text{R}-\text{C}-\text{C}-\text{R} \\
| \quad | \\
\text{H} \;\; {}^+\text{N(CH}_3)_2 \\
\quad \diagup \\
:\!\ddot{\text{C}}\text{H}_2^-
\end{array}
$$

$$
\begin{array}{c}
\text{R} \quad\quad \text{R} \\
| \quad\quad | \\
\text{R}-\text{C}{-}{-}\text{C}-\text{R} \\
|\nearrow \quad\searrow_+ \\
\text{H} \quad\quad \text{N(CH}_3)_2 \\
\quad\quad\quad \diagup \\
\quad\quad :\text{CH}_2^-
\end{array}
\longrightarrow
\begin{array}{c}
\text{R} \diagdown \quad\quad \diagup \text{R} \\
\quad \text{C}=\text{C} \\
\text{R} \diagup \quad\quad \diagdown \text{R}
\end{array}
+ \quad \text{N(CH}_3)_3
$$

The mechanism for decompositions of this type involves a *cis*-orientation in the transition state. A number of eliminations proceed by way of similar transition states, and we discuss these in the next section.

12.5 *Cis*-Eliminations

Tertiary amines when treated with hydrogen peroxide or peroxyacids are oxidized to compounds known as amine oxides:

$$
\begin{array}{c}
\text{R} \\
| \\
\text{R}-\text{N}-\text{R}
\end{array}
\xrightarrow{\text{H}_2\text{O}_2 \text{ or } \text{R}\overset{\text{O}}{\overset{\|}{\text{C}}}\text{OOH}}
\begin{array}{c}
\text{R} \\
| \\
\text{R}-\overset{+}{\text{N}}-\text{R} \\
| \\
\text{O}^-
\end{array}
$$

and

$$
\begin{array}{c}
\text{R} \quad \text{R} \\
| \quad | \\
\text{R}-\text{C}-\text{C}-\text{R} \\
| \quad | \\
\text{H} \quad \text{N(CH}_3)_2
\end{array}
\xrightarrow{\text{H}_2\text{O}_2 \text{ or } \text{R}\overset{\text{O}}{\overset{\|}{\text{C}}}\text{OOH}}
\begin{array}{c}
\text{R} \quad \text{R} \\
| \quad | \\
\text{R}-\text{C}-\text{C}-\text{R} \\
| \quad |_+ \\
\text{H} \quad \text{N(CH}_3)_2 \\
\quad\quad \diagup \\
\quad\quad \overset{-}{\text{O}}
\end{array}
$$

Thermal decomposition of these amine oxides yields olefins and derivatives of hydroxylamine:

$$
\begin{array}{c}
\text{R} \quad\quad \text{R} \\
| \quad\quad | \\
\text{R}-\text{C}{-}{-}\text{C}-\text{R} \\
|\nearrow \quad\searrow_+ \\
\text{H} \quad\quad \text{N(CH}_3)_2 \\
\quad\quad\quad \diagup \\
\quad\quad \overset{-}{\text{O}}
\end{array}
\xrightarrow{\Delta}
\begin{array}{c}
\text{R} \diagdown \quad\quad \diagup \text{R} \\
\quad \text{C}=\text{C} \\
\text{R} \diagup \quad\quad \diagdown \text{R}
\end{array}
+ \quad \text{HON(CH}_3)_2
$$

The mechanism for the decomposition is similar to that presented at the close of the previous section; a cyclic transition state is involved. The transition state is

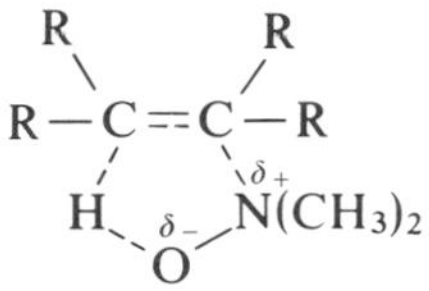

$$
\begin{array}{ccc}
R & & R \\
\backslash & & / \\
R-C & = & C-R \\
/ & & \backslash^{\delta+} \\
H & \searrow & \overset{}{N}(CH_3)_2 \\
& \overset{\delta-}{O} &
\end{array}
$$

Notice that the hydrogen being abstracted and the leaving group are *cis*-oriented in the transition state for these cyclic eliminations.

The thermal decomposition of amine oxides is a good preparative method for alkenes, and 1,4-pentadiene has been prepared in this manner:

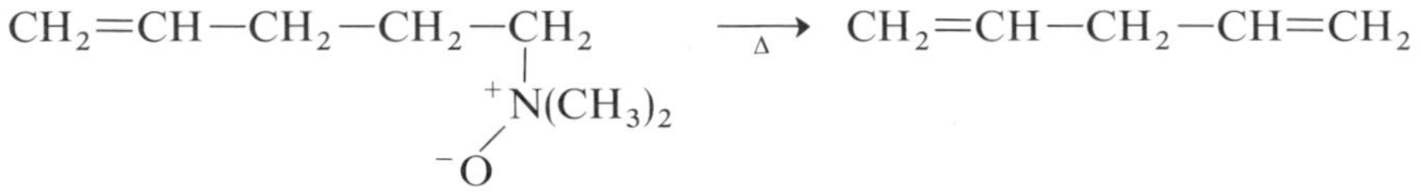

$$
\begin{array}{c}
CH_2{=}CH{-}CH_2{-}CH_2{-}CH_2 \\
\underset{\overset{/}{-O}}{\overset{|}{{}^{+}N(CH_3)_2}}
\end{array}
\xrightarrow{\Delta} CH_2{=}CH{-}CH_2{-}CH{=}CH_2
$$

Other *cis*-eliminations are known. The usual method of converting alcohols to alkenes is to treat the corresponding alcohol with concentrated sulfuric acid; however, another method for bringing about this conversion is known, the Chugaev reaction. This method involves thermal decomposition of the xanthate ester which is prepared from the alcohol:

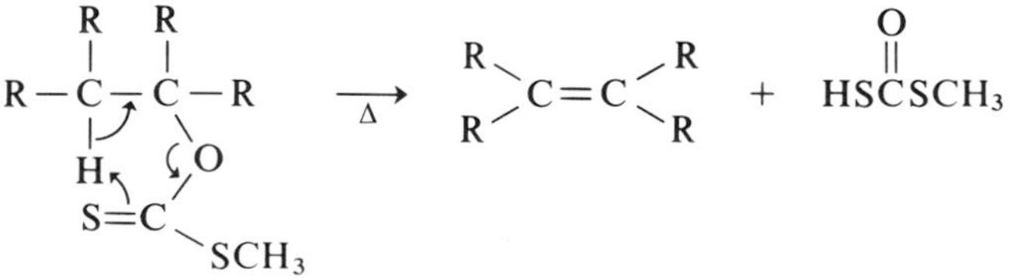

$$
\begin{array}{c}
\overset{R}{\underset{}{\overset{|}{R-C}}}\overset{R}{\underset{}{\overset{|}{{-}C{-}R}}} \\
\underset{S{=}C}{\overset{|}{H}}\overset{}{\underset{\diagdown SCH_3}{\overset{\diagup O}{}}}
\end{array}
\xrightarrow{\Delta}
\begin{array}{c}
R\diagdown \quad \diagup R \\
C{=}C \\
R\diagup \quad \diagdown R
\end{array}
+ \; HS\overset{\overset{O}{\parallel}}{C}SCH_3
$$

For the most part the reaction proceeds through a cyclic transition state and leads to *cis*-elimination. The acid HSCOSCH$_3$ that is formed initially subsequently decomposes:

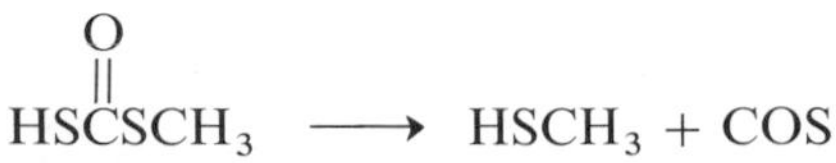

$$
HS\overset{\overset{O}{\parallel}}{C}SCH_3 \longrightarrow HSCH_3 + COS
$$

The xanthate ester is prepared from the alcohol in the following manner:

$$\begin{array}{c} \text{R} \quad \text{R} \\ | \quad | \\ \text{R}-\text{C}-\text{C}-\text{R} \\ | \quad | \\ \text{H} \quad \text{OH} \end{array} + \text{NaOH} \rightleftharpoons \begin{array}{c} \text{R} \quad \text{R} \\ | \quad | \\ \text{R}-\text{C}-\text{C}-\text{R} \\ | \quad | \\ \text{H} \quad \text{O}^-\text{Na}^+ \end{array} + \text{H}_2\text{O}$$

$$\begin{array}{c} \text{R} \quad \text{R} \\ | \quad | \\ \text{R}-\text{C}-\text{C}-\text{R} \\ | \quad | \\ \text{H} \quad \text{O}^-\text{Na}^+ \end{array} + \text{CS}_2 \longrightarrow \begin{array}{c} \text{R} \quad \text{R} \\ | \quad | \\ \text{R}-\text{C}-\text{C}-\text{R} \\ | \quad | \\ \text{H} \quad \text{O} \\ \quad\quad | \\ \quad\quad \text{S}=\text{C} \\ \quad\quad\quad\quad \backslash \\ \quad\quad\quad\quad\quad \text{S}^-\text{Na}^+ \end{array}$$

$$\begin{array}{c} \text{R} \quad \text{R} \\ | \quad | \\ \text{R}-\text{C}-\text{C}-\text{R} \\ | \quad \backslash \\ \text{H} \quad \text{O} \\ \text{S}=\text{C} \\ \quad\quad \backslash \\ \quad\quad \text{S}^-\text{Na}^+ \end{array} + \text{CH}_3\text{I} \longrightarrow \begin{array}{c} \text{R} \quad \text{R} \\ | \quad | \\ \text{R}-\text{C}-\text{C}-\text{R} \\ | \quad \backslash \\ \text{H} \quad \text{O} \\ \text{S}=\text{C} \\ \quad\quad \backslash \\ \quad\quad \text{S}-\text{CH}_3 \end{array}$$

Heating the xanthate results in formation of the alkene.
The olefin *t*-butylethylene is prepared in this manner.

$$\begin{array}{c} \text{H} \quad \text{C(CH}_3)_3 \\ | \quad | \\ \text{H}-\text{C}-\text{C}-\text{H} \\ | \quad \backslash \\ \text{H} \quad \text{O} \\ \text{S}=\text{C} \\ \quad\quad \backslash \\ \quad\quad \text{SCH}_3 \end{array} \xrightarrow{\Delta} \begin{array}{c} \text{H} \quad\quad \text{C(CH}_3)_3 \\ \backslash \quad\quad / \\ \text{C}=\text{C} \\ / \quad\quad \backslash \\ \text{H} \quad\quad \text{H} \end{array} + \text{COS} + \text{CH}_3\text{SH}$$

This alkene could not have been prepared in good yield from the corresponding alcohol by a direct method. Dehydration of the alcohol leads to a mixture of products, and *t*-butylethylene is only a minor component of the mixture:

$$\begin{array}{c} \text{H} \quad \text{C(CH}_3)_3 \\ | \quad | \\ \text{H}-\text{C}-\text{C}-\text{H} \\ | \quad | \\ \text{H} \quad \text{OH} \end{array} \longrightarrow \begin{array}{c} \text{CH}_3 \quad\quad \text{CH}_3 \\ \backslash \quad\quad / \\ \text{C}=\text{C} \\ / \quad\quad \backslash \\ \text{CH}_3 \quad\quad \text{CH}_3 \end{array} + \begin{array}{c} \text{H} \quad\quad \begin{array}{c} \text{H} \\ | \\ \text{CH}_3-\text{C}-\text{CH}_3 \end{array} \\ \backslash \quad\quad / \\ \text{C}=\text{C} \\ / \quad\quad \backslash \\ \text{H} \quad\quad \text{CH}_3 \end{array}$$

$$+ \begin{array}{c} \text{H} \quad\quad \text{C(CH}_3)_3 \\ \backslash \quad\quad / \\ \text{C}=\text{C} \\ / \quad\quad \backslash \\ \text{H} \quad\quad \text{H} \end{array}$$

Thermal decomposition of **21** yields predominantly the *cis*-olefin, and this stereospecific decomposition is good evidence for the cyclic mechanism:

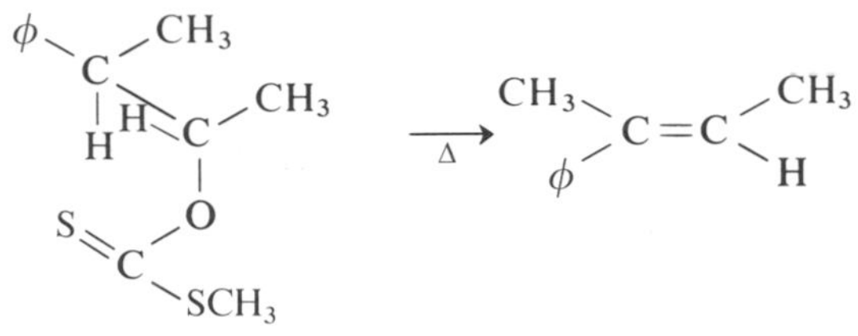

21

The transition state in the Chugaev reaction is,

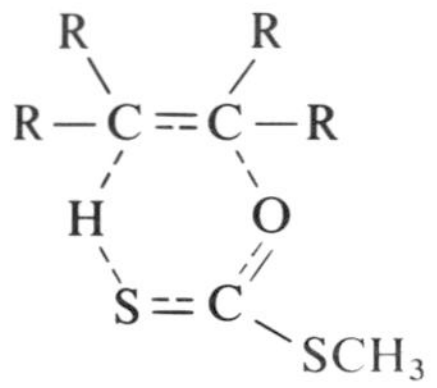

While the Chugaev reaction involves pyrolysis of the xanthate ester, thermal decompositions of other esters occur, and these reactions proceed in an analogous manner:

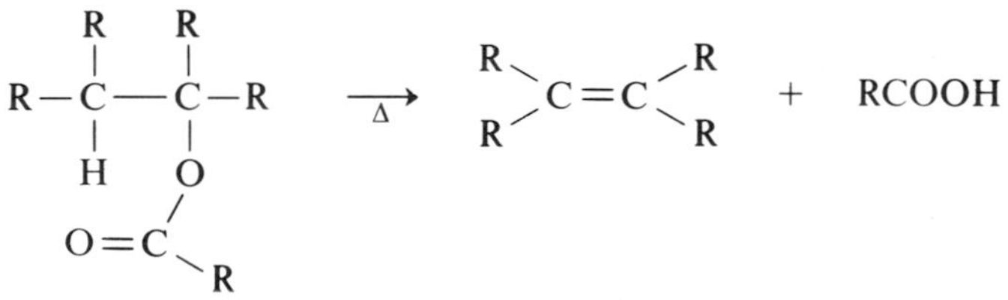

The transition state for this process is analogous to that in the Chugaev reaction.

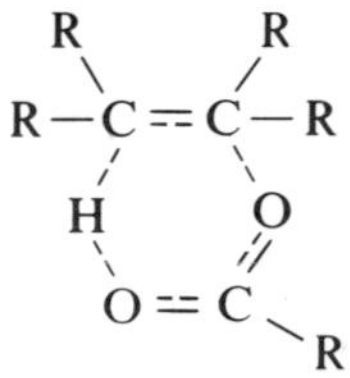

Thus, *t*-butylethylene, which can be prepared by heating the xanthate, is also formed by thermal decomposition of the acetate:

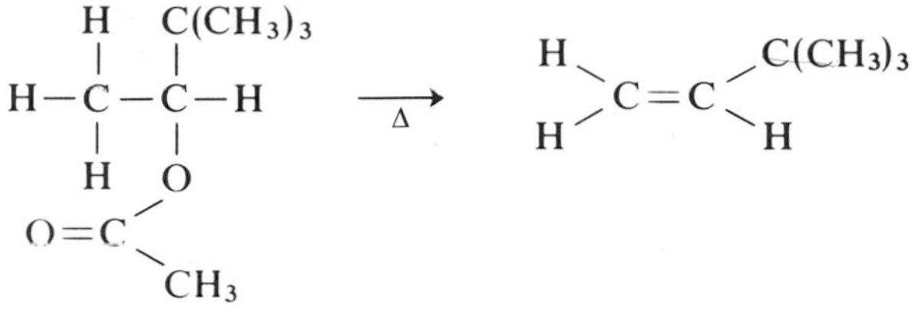

$$
\begin{array}{c}
\text{H} \quad \text{C(CH}_3)_3 \\
| \qquad | \\
\text{H}-\text{C}-\text{C}-\text{H} \\
| \qquad | \\
\text{H} \quad \text{O} \\
\quad \backslash \\
\text{O=C} \\
\qquad \backslash \\
\qquad \text{CH}_3
\end{array}
\xrightarrow{\Delta}
\begin{array}{c}
\text{H} \qquad\qquad \text{C(CH}_3)_3 \\
\quad \diagdown \qquad\quad \diagup \\
\qquad \text{C=C} \\
\quad \diagup \qquad\quad \diagdown \\
\text{H} \qquad\qquad \text{H}
\end{array}
$$

Acrylic acid is prepared by heating its ethyl ester,

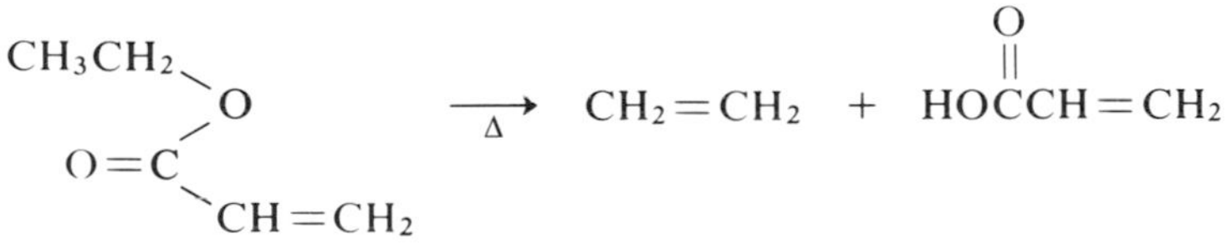

$$
\begin{array}{c}
\text{CH}_3\text{CH}_2 \\
\qquad\quad \diagdown \\
\qquad\qquad \text{O} \\
\qquad\quad \diagup \\
\text{O=C} \\
\qquad \backslash \\
\qquad\quad \text{CH=CH}_2
\end{array}
\xrightarrow{\Delta}
\text{CH}_2\text{=CH}_2 \;+\; \text{HOCCH=CH}_2 \quad (\overset{\text{O}}{\overset{||}{})}
$$

and heating the acetate **22** yields the corresponding alkene without rearrangement:

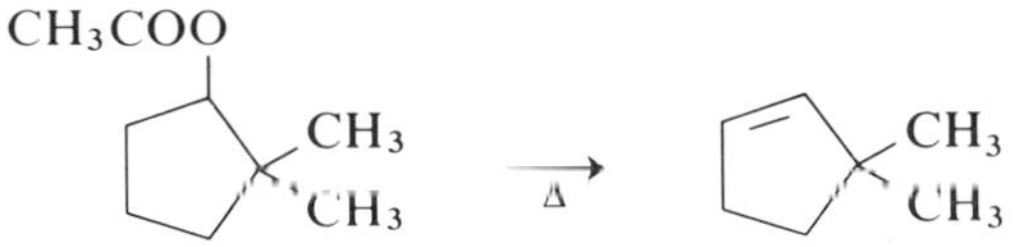

22

Pyrolysis of an ester yields an alkene and an acid, and the elimination proceeds by way of a cyclic transition state in which the groups —H and —OCOR are *cis*-oriented. A similar result is sometimes obtained in the thermal decomposition of alkyl halides; the products are olefins and halogen acids.

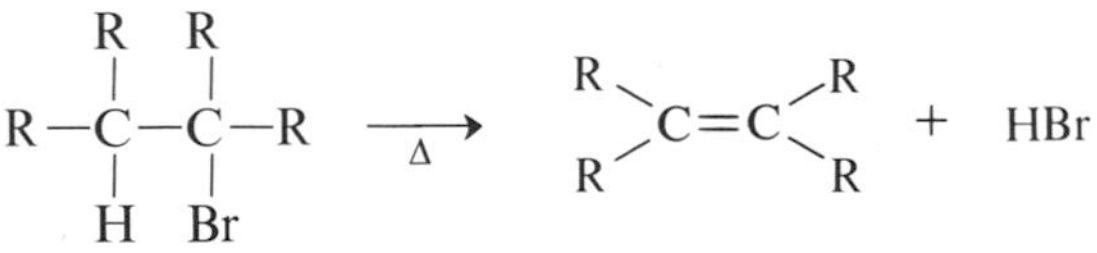

$$
\begin{array}{c}
\text{R} \quad \text{R} \\
| \quad\; | \\
\text{R}-\text{C}-\text{C}-\text{R} \\
| \quad\; | \\
\text{H} \quad \text{Br}
\end{array}
\xrightarrow{\Delta}
\begin{array}{c}
\text{R} \qquad\quad \text{R} \\
\quad \diagdown \qquad \diagup \\
\qquad \text{C=C} \\
\quad \diagup \qquad \diagdown \\
\text{R} \qquad\quad \text{R}
\end{array}
\;+\; \text{HBr}
$$

In some cases these thermal eliminations of hydrogen bromide proceed by way of free radical intermediates whereas in others a cyclic *cis*-elimination appears to be involved. In such *cis*-eliminations the bromide ion is partially negative and the organic fragment partially positive. The data in Table 12–4 show that replacement of hydrogen by methyl increases considerably the rate of elimination of hydrogen bromide, and this supports the idea of a transition state in which the organic fragment has considerable positive charge. In Table 12–4 we also present data for thermal decomposition of the corresponding acetates.

Table 12–4. Relative rates for Elimination of HX

Compound	$\dfrac{k_{RBr}}{k_{C_2H_5Br}}$	$\dfrac{k_{ROOCCH_3}}{k_{C_2H_5OOCCH_3}}$
CH_3CH_2X	1	1
$(CH_3)_2CHX$	170	25
$(CH_3)_3CX$	32 000	1660

The data support the following transition state where the carbon-bromine bond is to a large degree already broken:

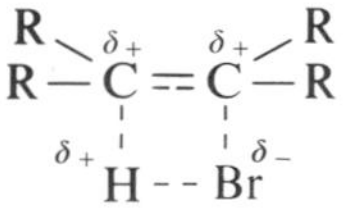

$$\begin{array}{c} R \diagdown{}_{\delta+} \quad {}_{\delta+}\diagup R \\ R - C = C - R \\ {}_{\delta+}\mid \quad \mid {}_{\delta-} \\ H - - Br \end{array}$$

This reaction (*cis*-elimination of HBr) yields an alkene and hydrogen bromide. Conversely, some alkenes undergo *cis*-addition of HBr. However, the additions are conducted under different conditions from the eliminations and different intermediates probably participate.

12.6 Carbenes

We mentioned previously that 1,1-eliminations also occur, that is, $CHCl_3$ loses HCl to form $:CCl_2$, and the mechanism for the transformation was presented as,

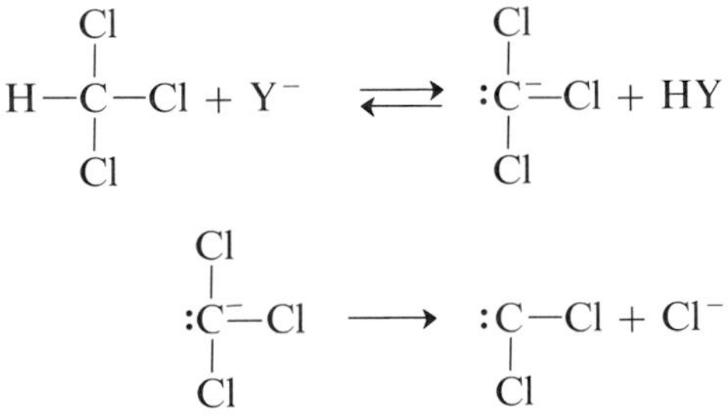

$$\begin{array}{ccc} \overset{\displaystyle Cl}{\underset{\displaystyle Cl}{H-C-Cl}} + Y^- & \rightleftharpoons & \overset{\displaystyle Cl}{\underset{\displaystyle Cl}{:C-Cl}} + HY \end{array}$$

$$\begin{array}{ccc} \overset{\displaystyle Cl}{\underset{\displaystyle Cl}{:C-Cl}} & \longrightarrow & \overset{\displaystyle}{\underset{\displaystyle Cl}{:C-Cl}} + Cl^- \end{array}$$

23

Now dichlorocarbene (or dichloromethylene) **23** is an unusual species. The carbon atom in $:CCl_3{}^-$ has eight valence electrons about it, and this intermediate bears a negative charge. This conjugate base ($:CCl_3{}^-$) then loses chloride ion which takes with it two electrons and the negative charge. What remains is a neutral material in which the carbon atom has only six valence electrons. (In **23** we have indicated the two unshared electrons as well as the four in the carbon-chlorine bonds). We have formed divalent carbon.

Furthermore, since this carbon atom has only six electrons rather than the customary eight, the carbon atom is electron deficient.

We have a material that is neither positively nor negatively charged yet in which the carbon atom is divalent and electron deficient.

Some carbene reactions involve complexed carbenes (carbenoids) rather than a free species; however, for simplicity we employ the simpler structure of a free carbene.

Of course, dichlorocarbene is extremely reactive. Since the carbon atom is an electron-pair acceptor, dichlorocarbene reacts with electron rich materials, Lewis bases and nucleophiles.

Typical reactions of dichlorocarbene include reaction with water and hydroxide ion,

$$:CCl_2 \xrightarrow[H_2O]{HO^-} HCOO^- + CO$$

reaction with other halogen anions,

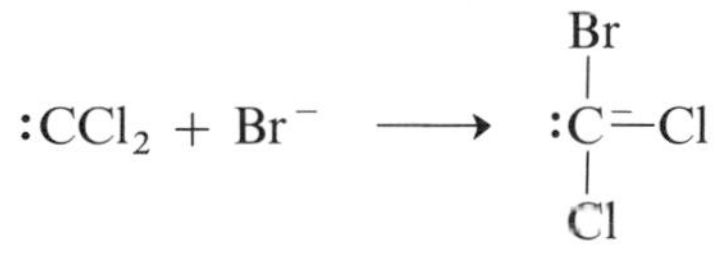

$$:CCl_2 + Br^- \longrightarrow \overset{\displaystyle Br}{\underset{\displaystyle Cl}{:C=Cl}}$$

reaction with cyclohexene (the π electrons of the double bond are available),

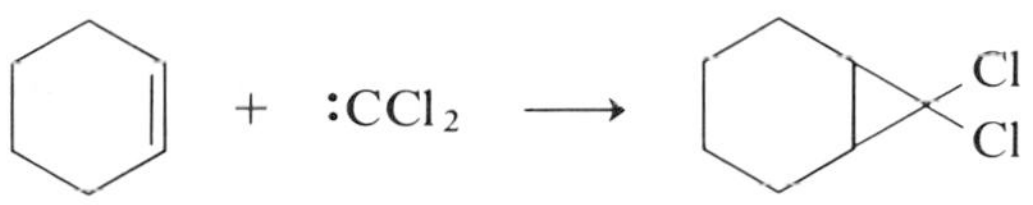

and reaction with other alkenes,

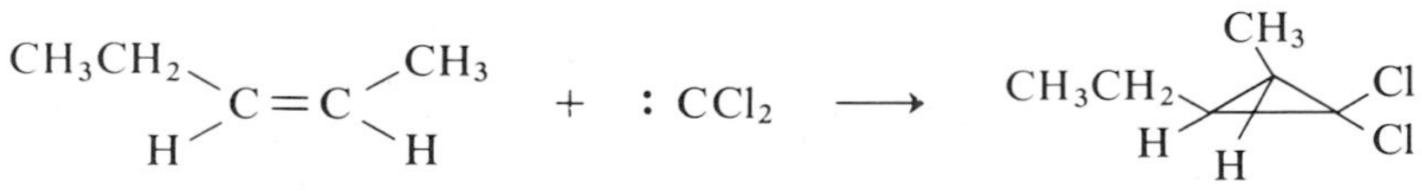

Dichlorocarbene is not the only known intermediate of this type. Other halocarbenes have also been reported. Treatment of bromoform with strong base affords dibromocarbene, and reaction of bromodifluoromethane under similar conditions yields difluorocarbene; the latter appears to be formed in a concerted one-step process:

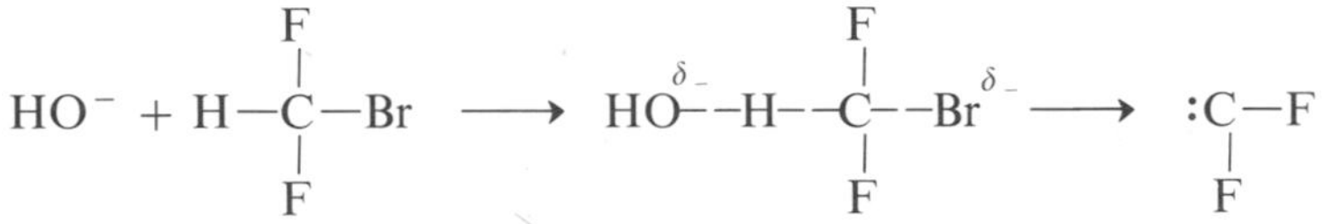

$$HO^- + H-\overset{\overset{\displaystyle F}{|}}{\underset{\underset{\displaystyle F}{|}}{C}}-Br \longrightarrow HO^{\delta-}-H--\overset{\overset{\displaystyle F}{|}}{\underset{\underset{\displaystyle F}{|}}{C}}--Br^{\delta-} \longrightarrow :\overset{}{\underset{\underset{\displaystyle F}{|}}{C}}-F$$

Irradiation of diazomethane, CH_2N_2, leads to carbene itself,

$$CH_2N_2 \xrightarrow{hv} :CH_2 + N_2$$

and this same intermediate is obtained upon irradiation of ketene.

$$CH_2{=}C{=}O \xrightarrow{hv} :CH_2 + CO$$

Photolysis of ethyl diazoacetate yields carboethoxycarbene,

$$N_2CH\overset{\overset{\displaystyle O}{||}}{C}OC_2H_5 \xrightarrow{hv} :CH\overset{\overset{\displaystyle O}{||}}{C}OC_2H_5 + N_2$$

and irradiation of phenyldiazomethane is reported to yield phenylcarbene:

$$\phi CHN_2 \xrightarrow{hv} :CH\phi + N_2$$

These are just a few examples. A wide variety of carbenes have been prepared using an assortment of techniques. The usual method of preparation of a carbene is to photolyze the corresponding diazo compound. Even dicarbenes have been reported. Carbon vapor contains a substance C_3 which is believed to be a dicarbene:

$$:C{=}C{=}C:$$

One possible method of preparing polycarbenes is from the corresponding diazo compounds.

Irradiation of,

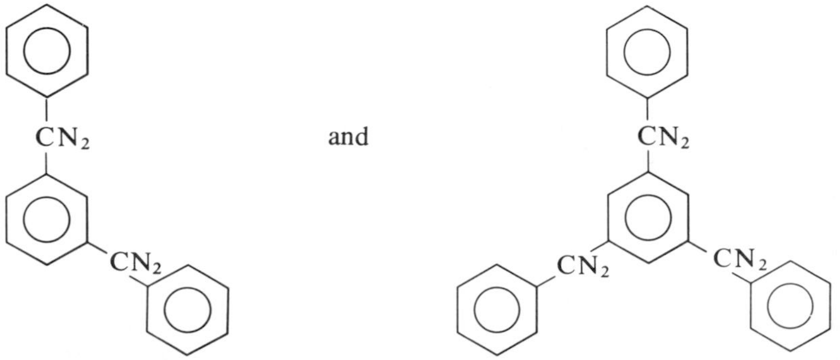

and

causes these materials to lose nitrogen and the initial products could be di- and tricarbenes.

A great deal of time has been spent investigating the structures of carbenes. A carbene contains two unshared valence electrons which could occupy a number of different orbitals. According to the Pauli exclusion principle, if the two electrons occupy the same orbital, they must have opposite spins, whereas if they occupy different orbitals, both parallel and antiparallel spins are allowed. Accordingly, the term singlet refers to carbenes having two electrons of opposite spin and the term triplet to carbenes with two electrons of parallel spin:

$$\uparrow\downarrow \qquad\qquad\qquad \uparrow\uparrow$$
$$\overset{}{C}H_2 \qquad\qquad\qquad \overset{}{C}H_2$$

singlet carbene   triplet carbene

Both singlet and triplet carbenes are known. In addition to the ground state, a number of excited states of carbene have been observed. Since the electrons can occupy a number of different orbitals of varying energy, a whole series of singlet and triplet states is possible. There are low energy singlets and low energy triplets, where the electrons occupy relatively stable orbitals, and high energy singlets and triplets where the electrons occupy less stable orbitals. The two electrons have parallel spin in each of the triplets and anti-parallel spin in the singlets. The high energy states are of interest to the spectroscopist; we shall consider only those of lower energy.

For carbene itself a triplet state is the ground state but there is also a singlet state which is slightly less stable. The difference in energy between these two states is small. Although a number of studies have been made, the structure of carbene in these two states is not yet certain. It appears that in the triplet the H—C—H bond angle is approximately but not exactly equal to 180°. In the second the two electrons both occupy the same orbital and the H—C—H angle is approximately 103°. In the ground state CH_2 is, to a good approximation, linear; it is bent in the singlet state:

$$H-\overset{.}{\underset{.}{C}}-H \qquad\qquad\qquad H\overset{\overset{..}{C}}{\underset{103°}{\curvearrowright}}H$$

A very simple picture of these two species in terms of hybridized orbitals would consider the carbon atom in the triplet state **24** to be sp hybridized and each of the electrons to occupy a different p orbital. The singlet state could be represented by an sp^3 hybridized carbon atom with the two electrons also in such an sp^3 orbital and an empty orbital (**25**). Alternatively, the singlet state could be represented by an sp^2 hybridized carbon atom with the electron pair in an *sp²* orbital and an empty *p* orbital **26**. The bond angle of 103° for the singlet favors the idea of *sp³* hybridization, but by analogy with carbonium ions which also contain six valence electrons and an empty *p* orbital, structure **26** is more satisfying:

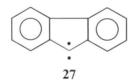

          24   **25**   **26**

For some carbenes, including CH_2 itself, the triplet state is the ground state while for other carbenes the singlet state is the state of lowest energy. Thus, fluorenylidene **27** is also a triplet in the ground state but difluorocarbene ($:CF_2$) is a singlet:

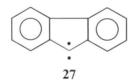

27

Structure **27**, although a ground state triplet, has a bond angle at the carbene carbon atom of only 140–150°. The carbene system is part of a five-membered ring, and this restricts the bond angle. The system may be discussed in terms of bent *τ*-like bonds:

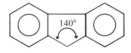

140°

Irradiation of diazomethane or ketene leads to carbene:

$$CH_2N_2 \xrightarrow{h\nu} :CH_2 + N_2$$
$$CH_2{=}C{=}O \xrightarrow{h\nu} :CH_2 + CO$$

The carbene that is formed initially in these reactions is apparently the singlet. This species can react directly, or it can lose energy by colliding with a chemically inert species such as nitrogen gas and thereby form triplet carbene. The product of a carbene reaction may result from direct reaction of the singlet or from reaction of triplet carbene that is formed subsequently. Furthermore, the energy of the initially formed singlet carbene varies with the energy of the light used in the irradiation. Photolysis of diazomethane and ketene leads to a higher energy carbene if the light used in the irradiation is of higher energy. (This extra energy is excess vibrational energy.)

As its reactions indicate, singlet carbene is an extremely high energy intermediate. This species is even able to insert itself into carbon-hydrogen bonds, and generating singlet carbene in the presence of methane leads to the formation of ethane. Triplet carbene does not appear to react by direct insertion:

$$
\begin{array}{ccc}
& \text{H} & \\
& | & \\
\text{H}-\text{C}-\text{H} + :\text{CH}_2 & \longrightarrow &
\end{array}
\qquad
\begin{array}{cc}
\text{H} & \text{H} \\
| & | \\
\text{H}-\text{C}-\text{C}-\text{H} \\
| & | \\
\text{H} & \text{H}
\end{array}
$$

Two mechanisms have been suggested for this reaction. One of these postulates direct insertion of a high energy carbene into the carbon-hydrogen bond, thereby forming vibrationally excited ethane. This high energy material then loses its excess energy through collisions with other molecules, or in the absence of such collisions it contains enough energy to dissociate into two methyl radicals:

$$CH_4 + :CH_2 \longrightarrow CH_3CH_3^*$$

$$CH_3CH_3^* \xrightarrow{\text{collisions}} CH_3CH_3$$

$$CH_3CH_3^* \longrightarrow CH_3\cdot + CH_3\cdot$$

The other mechanism postulates that direct insertion need not occur and that the ethane is formed by way of free radical reactions.

Evidence for direct insertion comes from the following experiment. Methylene was reacted with isobutylene in which carbon atom 1 had been labeled with C^{14}:

$$
\begin{array}{c}
\text{CH}_3 \\
\diagdown \\
\text{C}=\overset{14}{\text{C}} \\
\diagup \\
\text{CH}_3
\end{array}
\begin{array}{c}
\diagup\text{H} \\
\diagdown\text{H}
\end{array}
+ \quad :\text{CH}_2
$$

One of the products of this reaction is 2-methyl-1-butene **28** (the labeled atom is not indicated).

$$
\begin{array}{c}
\text{CH}_3 \\
\diagdown \\
\text{C}=\text{C} \\
\diagup \\
\text{CH}_3\text{CH}_2
\end{array}
\begin{array}{c}
\diagup\text{H} \\
\diagdown\text{H}
\end{array}
$$

28

If direct insertion of CH_2 occurs, all of the C^{14} in this product should remain at carbon atom 1; the product would be,

$$
\begin{array}{c}
\text{CH}_3 \\
\diagdown \\
\text{C}=\overset{14}{\text{C}} \\
\diagup \\
\text{CH}_3\text{CH}_2
\end{array}
\begin{array}{c}
\diagup\text{H} \\
\diagdown\text{H}
\end{array}
$$

* Vibrationally excited ethane.

Whereas if radical intermediates are involved, the following process ought to take place,

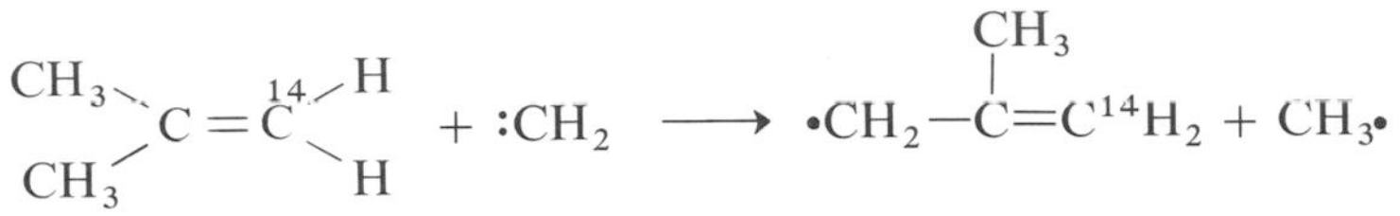

$$\underset{CH_3}{\overset{CH_3}{>}}C=\overset{14}{C}\overset{H}{\underset{H}{<}} \;+\; :CH_2 \;\longrightarrow\; \bullet CH_2-\overset{\overset{\displaystyle CH_3}{|}}{C}=C^{14}H_2 \;+\; CH_3\bullet$$

where

$$\underset{\bullet}{C}H_2-\overset{\overset{\displaystyle CH_3}{|}}{C}=C^{14}H_2 \;\longleftrightarrow\; CH_2=\overset{\overset{\displaystyle CH_3}{|}}{C}-\underset{\bullet}{C}^{14}H_2$$

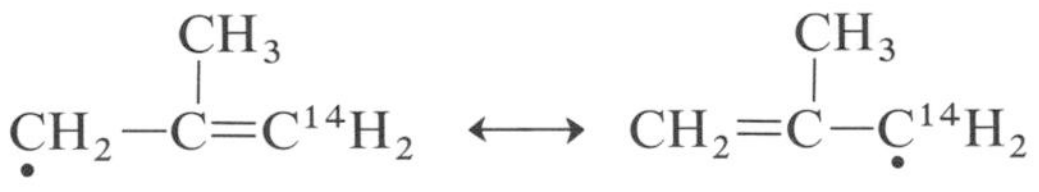

The free radical reaction involves an allylic radical, and the two carbon atoms become equivalent. If this intermediate is present, the resulting 2-methyl-1-butene would have the structures,

$$\underset{CH_3CH_2}{\overset{CH_3}{>}}C=\overset{14}{C}\overset{H}{\underset{H}{<}} \qquad\qquad \underset{CH_3C^{14}H_2}{\overset{CH_3}{>}}C=C\overset{H}{\underset{H}{<}}$$

The experiment was actually performed, and the C^{14} was found almost entirely at carbon atom 1, which is good evidence for direct insertion. The evidence is not conclusive because a possible radical mechanism for the reaction is,

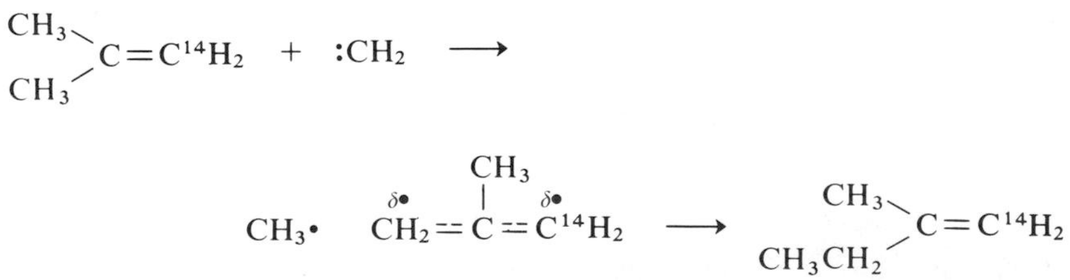

$$\underset{CH_3}{\overset{CH_3}{>}}C=C^{14}H_2 \;+\; :CH_2 \;\longrightarrow$$

$$CH_3\bullet \quad \overset{\delta\bullet}{CH_2}=\overset{\overset{\displaystyle CH_3}{|}}{C}\overset{\delta\bullet}{=}C^{14}H_2 \;\longrightarrow\; \underset{CH_3CH_2}{\overset{CH_3}{>}}C=C^{14}H_2$$

It is conceivable that the product is formed by the allylic radical reacting with that methyl radical which has just been generated. If the allylic radical reacts almost immediately after its formation, the methyl radical is closer to the carbon atom from which the hydrogen atom has just been abstracted and this leads to the observed product.

The C^{14} labeling experiment supports the idea of direct insertion. A free radical mechanism can also be employed to explain the results, but this requires that the methyl radical react more readily at one allylic position than at the other.

The 2-methyl-1-butene is just one of the products of this reaction; other products are formed:

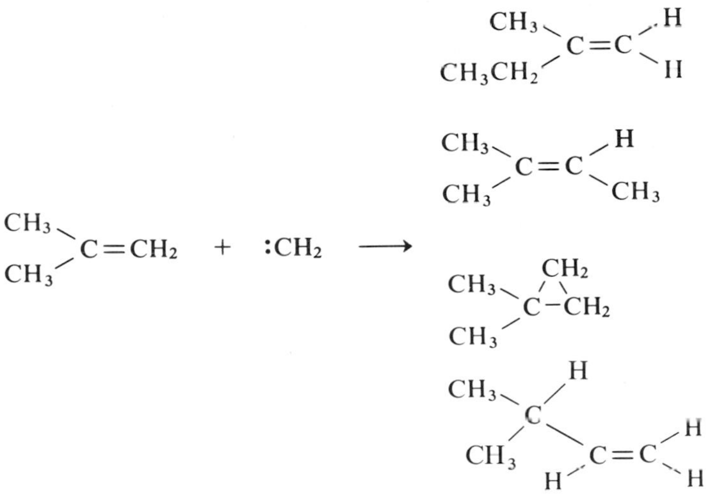

$$
\begin{array}{c}
CH_3 \\
\diagdown \\
CH_3 \diagup \\
\end{array}
C=CH_2 \quad + \quad :CH_2 \quad \longrightarrow
$$

$$
\begin{array}{c}
CH_3 \\
\diagdown \quad\quad\quad H \\
\quad\quad C=C \diagup \\
CH_3CH_2 \diagup \quad\quad \diagdown H
\end{array}
$$

$$
\begin{array}{c}
CH_3 \\
\diagdown \quad\quad\quad H \\
\quad\quad C=C \diagup \\
CH_3 \diagup \quad\quad \diagdown CH_3
\end{array}
$$

$$
\begin{array}{c}
\quad\quad\quad CH_2 \\
CH_3 \diagdown \diagup \diagdown \\
\quad\quad C-CH_2 \\
CH_3 \diagup
\end{array}
$$

$$
\begin{array}{c}
CH_3 \diagdown \quad H \\
\quad\quad C \diagup \\
CH_3 \diagup \diagdown \quad\quad H \\
\quad\quad\quad H \diagup C=C \diagdown \\
\quad\quad\quad\quad\quad\quad\quad H
\end{array}
$$

The isopropylethylene is formed by decomposition of vibrationally excited dimethylcyclopropane.

Singlet carbene reacts in a similar manner with other hydrocarbons:

$$
CH_3CH_2CH_3 + :CH_2 \longrightarrow CH_3CH_2CH_2CH_3 + CH_3\overset{\overset{\displaystyle CH_3}{|}}{C}HCH_3
$$

$$
CH_3CH_2CH_2CH_2CH_3 + :CH_2 \longrightarrow
\begin{array}{l}
CH_3CH_2CH_2CH_2CH_2CH_3 \\
CH_3CH_2CH_2\overset{\overset{\displaystyle CH_3}{|}}{C}HCH_3 \\
CH_3CH_2\overset{\underset{\displaystyle CH_3}{|}}{C}HCH_2CH_3
\end{array}
$$

and

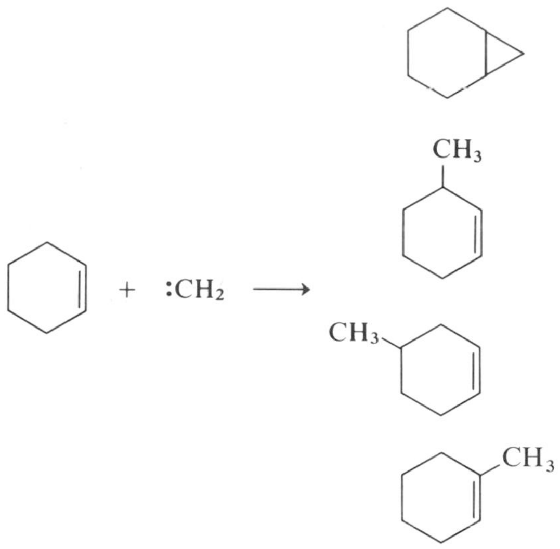

When carbene inserts itself into a molecule, the product that results contains excess vibrational energy. If this extra energy can be lost by way of collisions with other molecules, the product becomes stable; however, if few collisions occur, the product contains enough extra energy to allow bond breakage to take place and radicals are formed. Thus, in solution collisions with molecules of the solvent carry away this extra energy, whereas if the carbene reaction is carried out in the gas phase where molecular collisions are less frequent, bond breakage and radical reactions occur more readily.

Reaction of *cis-* and *trans-*2-butene with singlet carbene gives rise to cyclopropanes resulting from stereospecific addition of CH_2. Of course other products are also formed.

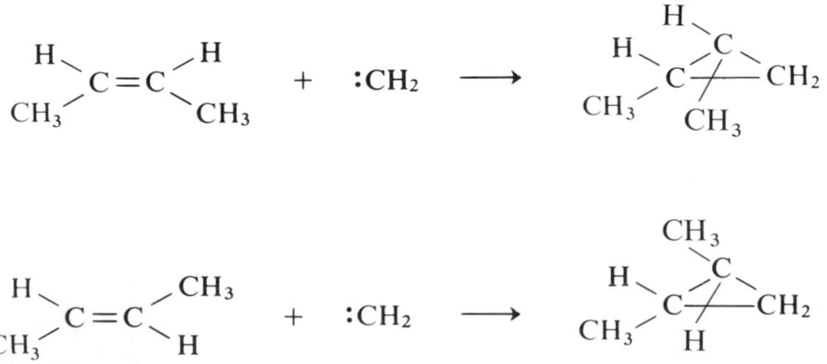

The fact that *cis*-2-butene yields *cis*-1,2-dimethylcyclopropane while *trans*-2-butene affords the *trans* isomer indicates that both new bonds may be formed simultaneously. Another possibility is that a diradical is the intermediate but that rotation cannot occur before ring closure and deactivation of the product to a lower energy vibrational state.

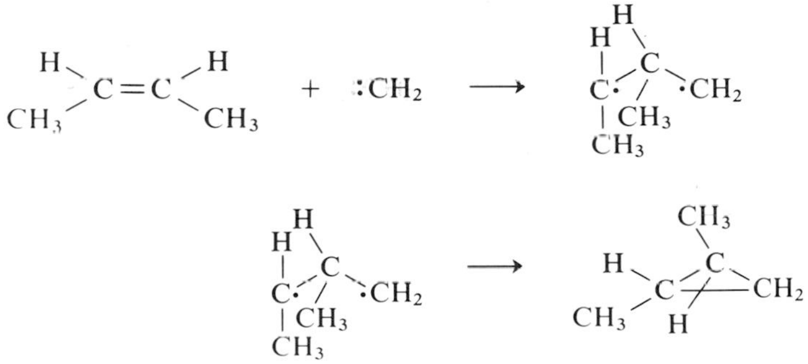

As was mentioned previously, triplet carbene does not readily undergo the direct insertion reaction into carbon-hydrogen bonds. It may, however, insert by way of a series of radical reactions, and it also adds to alkenes.

Reaction of what appears to be triplet carbene with *cis*-2-butene also affords cyclopropyl derivatives. However, in this reaction both *cis* and *trans* isomers are produced. A diradical is the postulated intermediate and rotation must occur about the carbon-carbon bond:

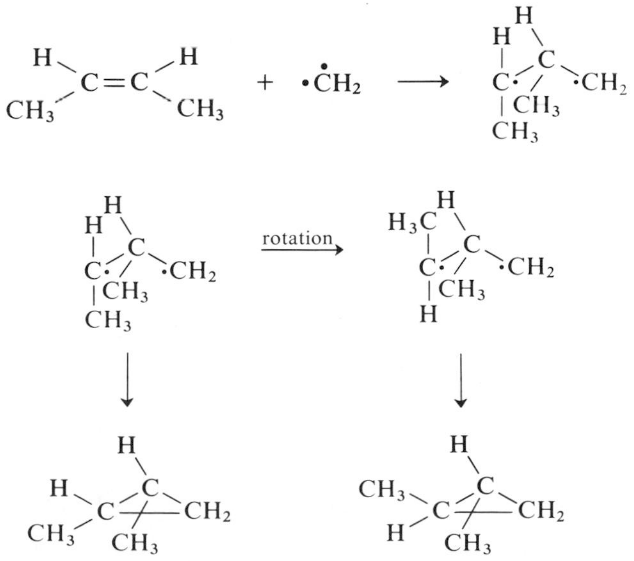

Reaction of *cis*-2-butene with triplet carbene yields a mixture of *cis*- and *trans*-1,2-dimethylcyclopropane. This can be explained by assuming a diradical intermediate. Rotation about the carbon-carbon bond in this diradical gives rise to a second diradical in which the two methyl groups are now *trans*.

Since the species $\cdot\ddot{C}H_2$ has two electrons of parallel spin, the initially formed diradicals also contain two electrons of parallel spin. The spin of one of these electrons must be reversed before bond formation can occur. For example, formation of *cis*-1,2-dimethylcyclopropane from the initial diradical requires the following sequence to take place. The first step is spin inversion:

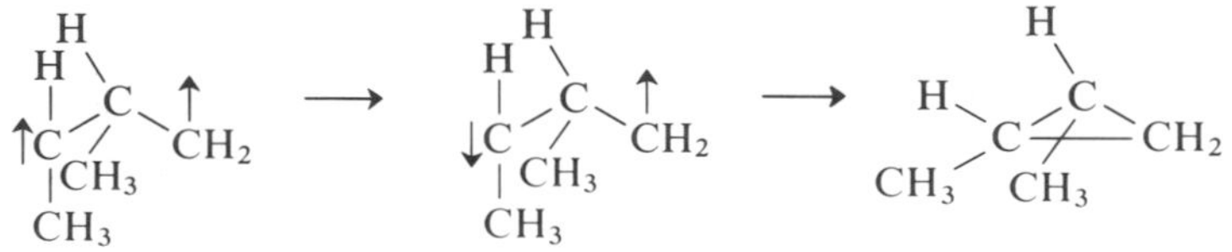

Reaction of triplet carbene with *trans*-2-butene does not afford the same mixture of isomers; only the *trans* product is formed (a trace of the *cis*-isomer can be detected):

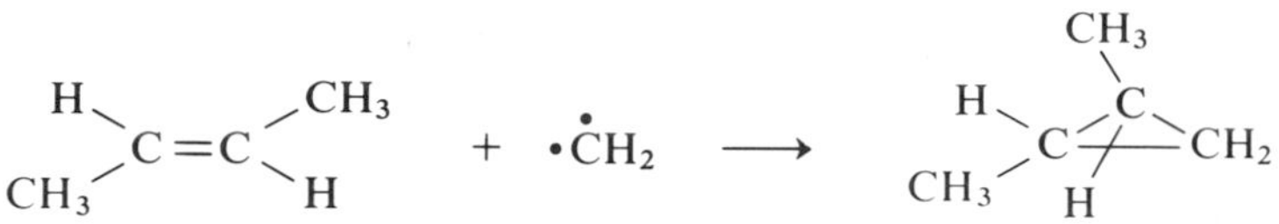

Singlet carbene inserts itself into carbon-hydrogen bonds and also adds to double bonds in a stereospecific fashion. Triplet carbene does not undergo the insertion process; it does add to the olefinic linkage, but the reaction is nonstereospecific. Dihalocarbenes, which are also singlets, do not generally undergo carbon-hydrogen insertion, although a few cases of insertion have been reported. They do, however, add to olefins stereospecifically:

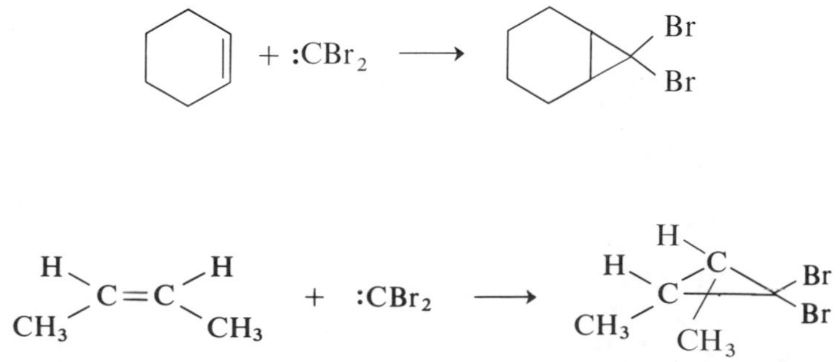

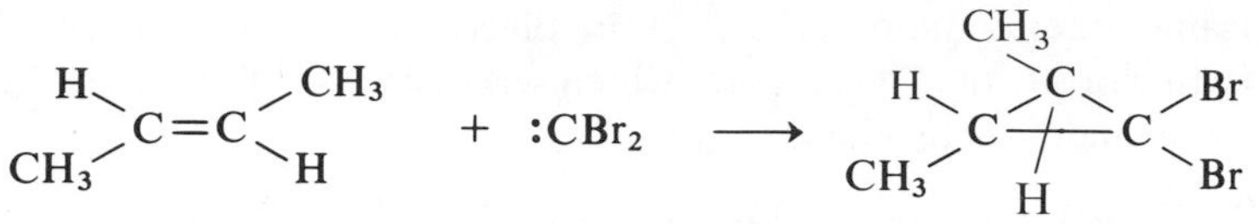

$$\underset{CH_3}{\overset{H}{\diagdown}}C=C\underset{H}{\overset{CH_3}{\diagup}} \quad + \quad :CBr_2 \quad \longrightarrow \quad$$

Dihalocarbenes are intermediates in many organic reactions. The reaction of phenols with chloroform in the presence of strong base yields derivatives of salicylaldehyde,

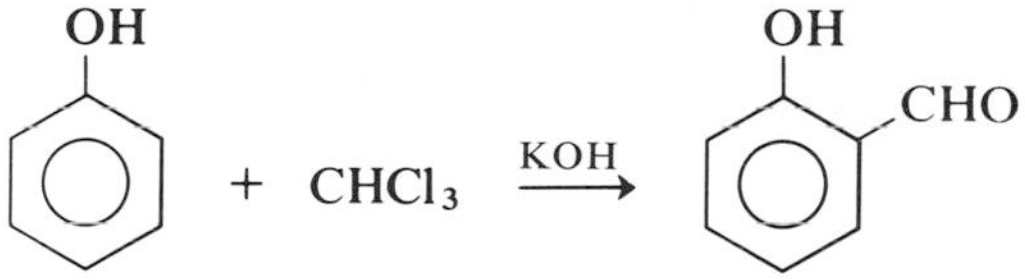

This reaction, which is called the Reimer-Tiemann reaction, involves dichlorocarbene reacting with the phenolate anion,

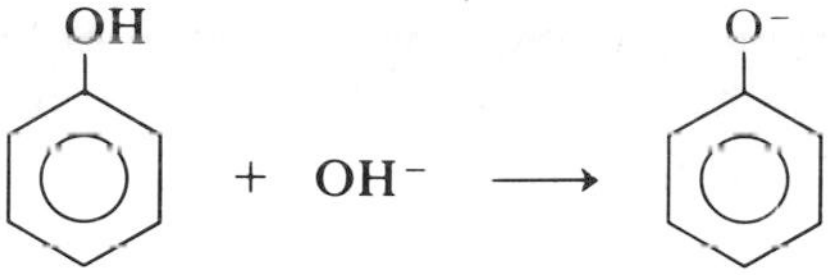

The electrons in the phenolate anion are delocalized,

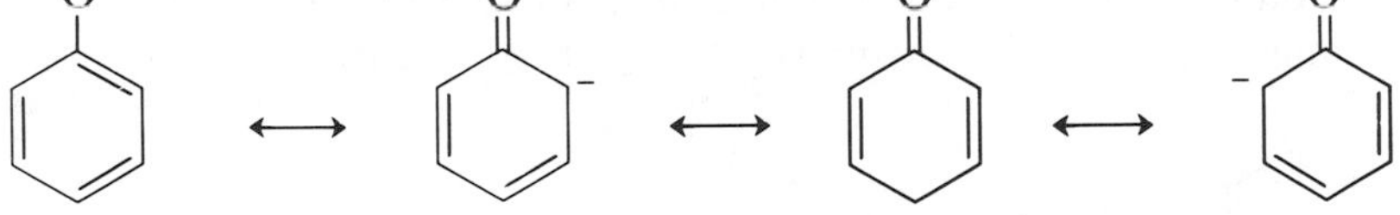

and this phenolate anion reacts with dichlorocarbene. The product of the first reaction reacts further with water and base and ultimately forms the anion of salicylaldehyde:

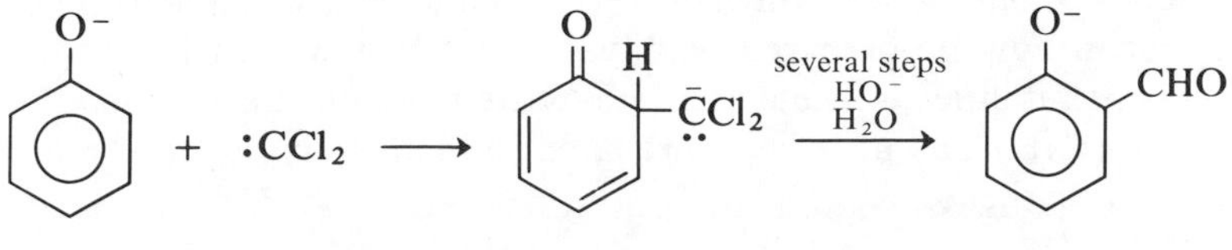

This same intermediate ($:CCl_2$) is involved in the reaction of primary amines with cloroform. The reaction which serves as a test for primary amines, affords isocyanides as products:

$$RNH_2 + CHCl_3 + 3NaOH \longrightarrow R-NC + 3NaCl + 3H_2O$$

Where,

$$R-NH_2 + :CCl_2 \longrightarrow R-\overset{\overset{\displaystyle H}{|}}{\underset{\underset{\displaystyle H}{|}}{N}}{}^{\!+}\!-\!\overset{..}{\underset{..}{\bar{C}}}Cl_2$$

$$R-\overset{\overset{\displaystyle H}{|}}{\underset{\underset{\displaystyle H}{|}}{N}}{}^{\!+}\!-\!\overset{..}{\underset{..}{\bar{C}}}Cl_2 \longrightarrow R-\overset{\overset{\displaystyle H}{|}}{N}-CHCl_2$$

$$R-\overset{\overset{\displaystyle H}{|}}{N}-CHCl_2 + 2NaOH \xrightarrow{\text{several steps}} R-NC + 2NaCl + 2H_2O$$

The reaction of secondary amines with chloroform and strong base gives rise to formamides as the major product. Again the process involves a dichlorocarbene intermediate:

$$R_2NH + CHCl_3 \xrightarrow[\text{H}_2\text{O}]{\text{base}} R_2NCHO$$

The material R_2NCHCl_2 is probably formed first in this reaction and subsequently hydrolyzes to the product.

The following conversion is typical of another carbene reaction, this one generating an intermediate capable of ring enlargement:

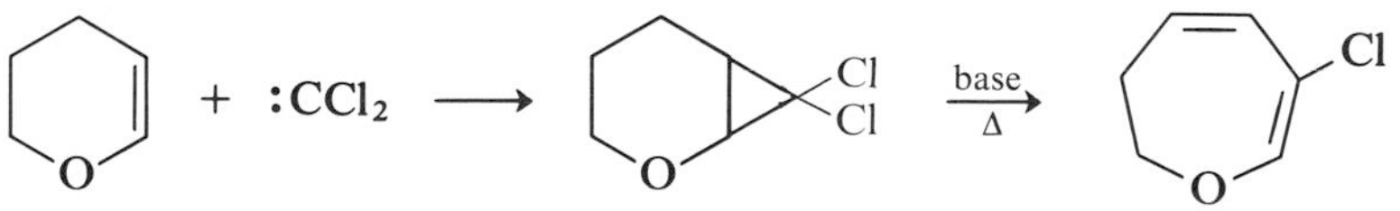

The reactions of carbenes are many and varied. Although postulated years ago, it was only recently that their existence was demonstrated conclusively. Use of these intermediates in organic chemistry opens the door to new synthetic possibilities. Compounds which were unattainable using older preparative methods can now be prepared readily. An entire new area has opened and countless possibilities for new and interesting reactions have arisen.

Nitrene ($:NH$) has also been prepared, and this species is similar in its behavior to carbene.

12.7 Benzyne

We have just discussed carbene whose existence although first postulated many years ago was only recently established. An equally interesting and unusual intermediate with a similar history is benzyne.

If we treat vinyl chlorides with sodamide, an elimination occurs yielding acetylenes as the products:

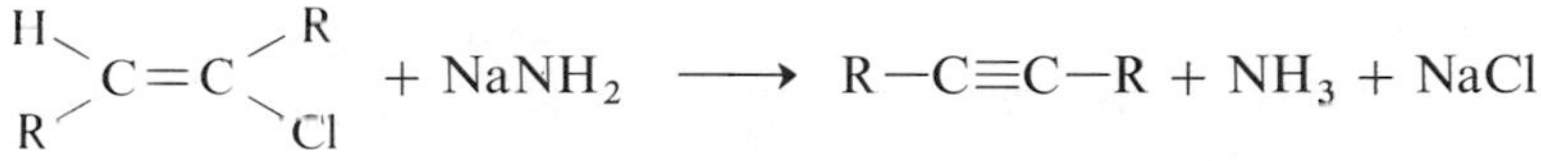

$$\underset{R}{\overset{H}{\diagdown}} C = C \underset{Cl}{\overset{R}{\diagup}} + NaNH_2 \longrightarrow R-C \equiv C-R + NH_3 + NaCl$$

In a similar fashion treatment of chlorobenzene with sodamide also yields NH_3, NaCl, and a material whose structure we write formally as,

This unusual species is benzyne.

Although we represent benzyne by a structure containing a triple bond, such a representation is for the sake of simplicity. A true triple bond is not possible in this system, for that requires the triply bonded carbon atoms to be *sp* hybridized with bond angles equal to 180°. A linear arrangement of the pertinent atoms cannot occur in a six-membered ring:

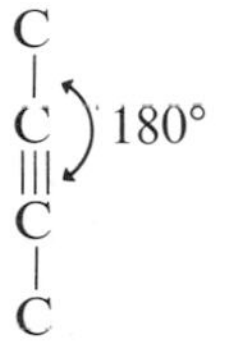

$$\begin{array}{c} C \\ | \\ C \\ ||| \\ C \\ | \\ C \end{array} \Big) \ 180°$$

The actual structure of benzyne is unknown although a number of speculations and theoretical calculations have been made. The simplest pictorial representation is one that considers the triply bonded carbon atoms to be sp^2 hybridized. It has been suggested that the hybridization of the carbon atoms in benzyne remains essentially the same as in benzene and that the third bond results from overlap of sp^2 orbitals (the *p* orbitals are not shown):

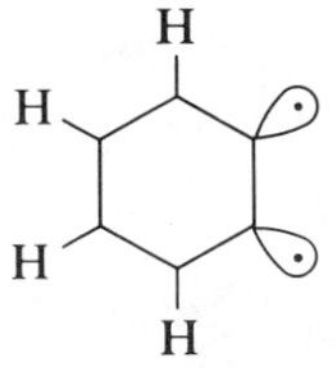

Other suggestions have been made, but in the absence of confirmatory evidence we shall simply continue to represent benzyne by the structure,

Benzyne is prepared in a variety of ways. An extremely reactive intermediate it combines readily with electron donors. This behavior is illustrated by the reaction of chlorobenzene with potassium amide to yield aniline (the solvent is liquid ammonia):

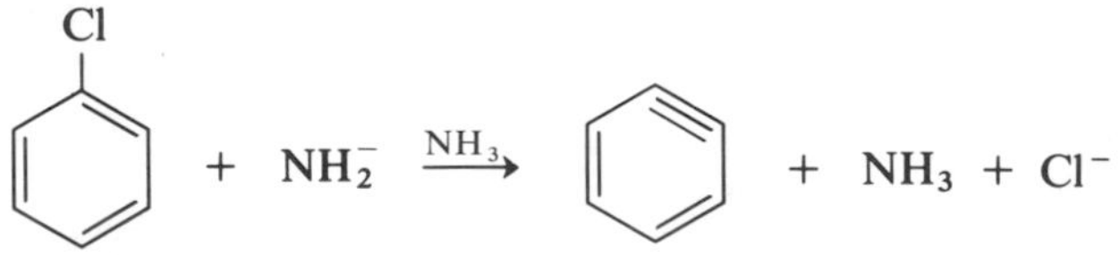

$$\text{Cl–C}_6\text{H}_5 \; + \; \text{NH}_2^- \; \xrightarrow{\text{NH}_3} \; \text{C}_6\text{H}_4 \; + \; \text{NH}_3 \; + \; \text{Cl}^-$$

The benzyne that is formed initially can react with either the solvent or amide ion, both of which are present, to yield intermediates capable of ultimate conversion to aniline:

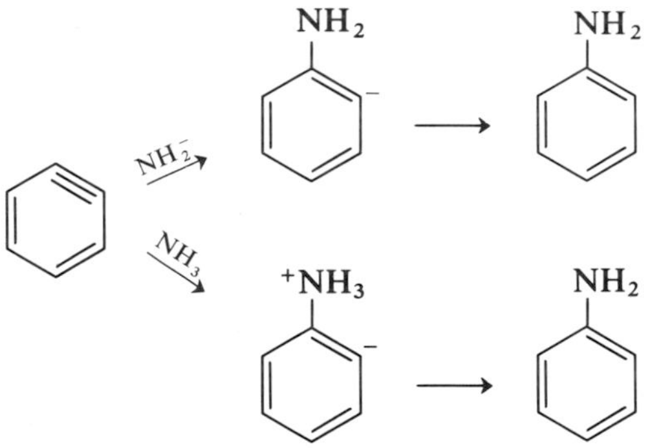

This particular reaction, the transformation of chlorobenzene to aniline, was employed to demonstrate the existence of a benzyne intermediate, for nucleophilic substitution of chloride by amide ion also accounts for the products. To eliminate one or the other of these possibilities, chlorobenzene was prepared in which carbon atom 1 was labeled with C^{14}:

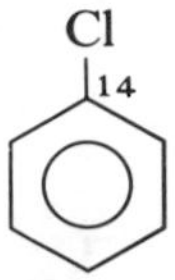

If aniline is formed by direct substitution of chloride by NH_2^-, all of the radioactive carbon should remain at atom 1. However if benzyne is the intermediate scrambling occurs; 50% of the radioactivity remains at carbon 1 and 50% is now at carbon 2. The experiment was conducted, and 48% of the radioactive carbon was found at position 1 while 52% occurred at position 2. This is excellent evidence for a symmetrical intermediate such as benzyne:

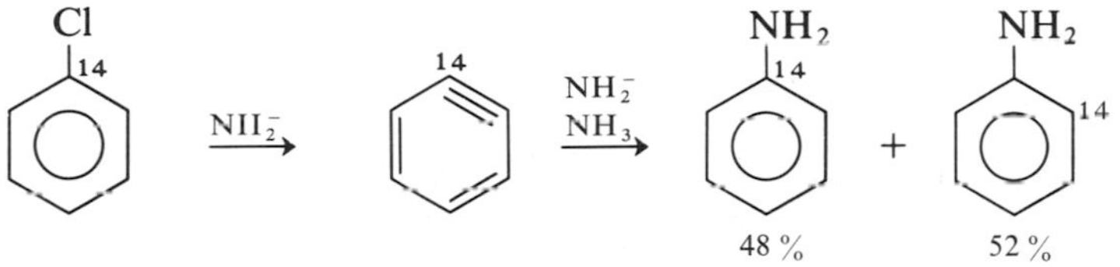

Of course, chlorobenzene is not the only aryl halide to react with potassium amide. The other halobenzenes suffer similar reactions:

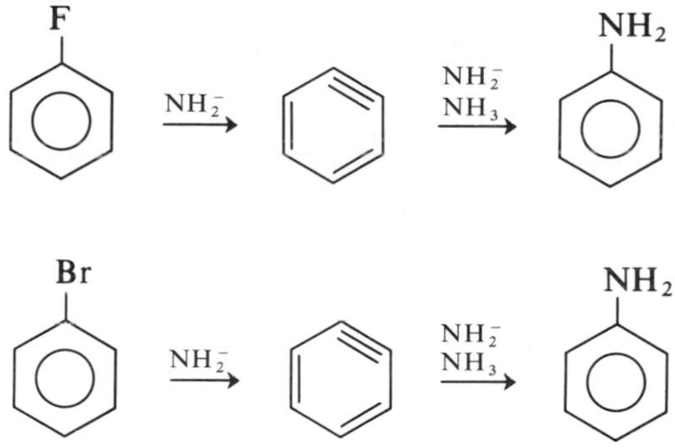

Both fluorobenzene and bromobenzene yield benzyne when treated with amide ion, and good evidence is available to indicate that the former reacts by way of a two-step mechanism. Fluorobenzene first forms its conjugate base and the reaction is of the $E1cB$ type:

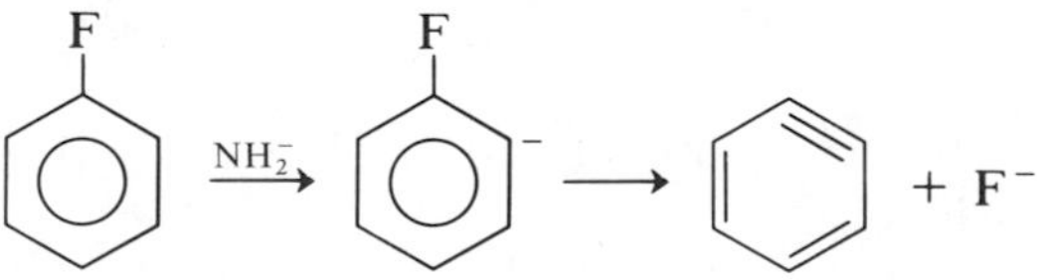

Evidence for this stepwise reaction of fluorobenzene comes from deuterium exchange experiments. Under the reaction conditions, 2-D-fluorobenzene undergoes deuterium exchange, and this process occurs much more rapidly than formation of aniline.

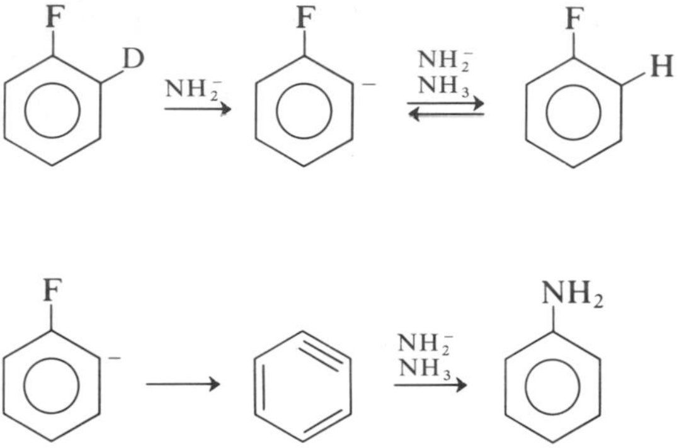

Bromobenzene behaves somewhat differently. In the reaction of bromobenzene the rate limiting step involves breakage of the carbon-hydrogen bond,
and two possible mechanisms are consistent with this fact. One of these is
a two-step mechanism analogous to that just presented. If the first step is
not reversible, that is, if the carbanion formed in the first step virtually always
loses bromide, the rate limiting step is this first step, and this is consistent
with the idea of carbon-hydrogen bond breakage in the rate limiting step.
Another possibility is a concerted single-step mechanism, and we cannot at
present distinguish between these two possibilities:

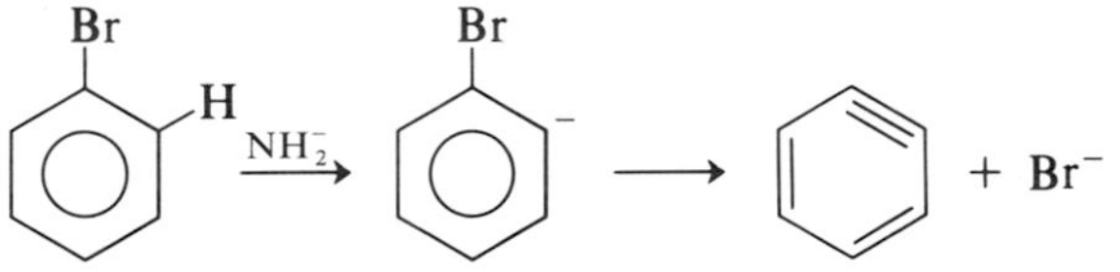

or,

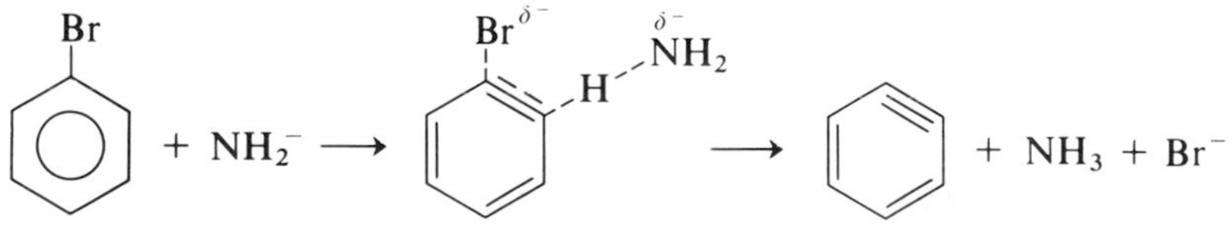

Reaction of halobenzenes with other strong bases may also proceed through
a benzyne intermediate:

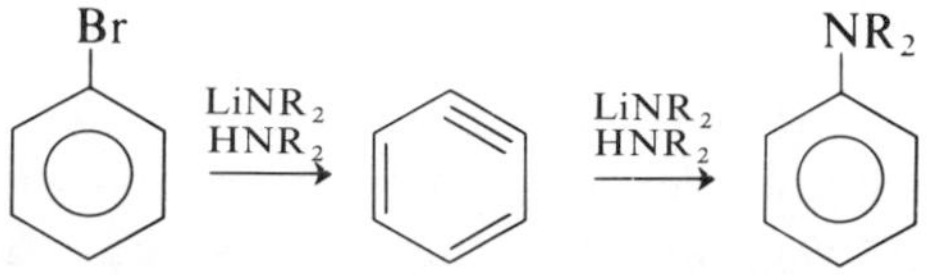

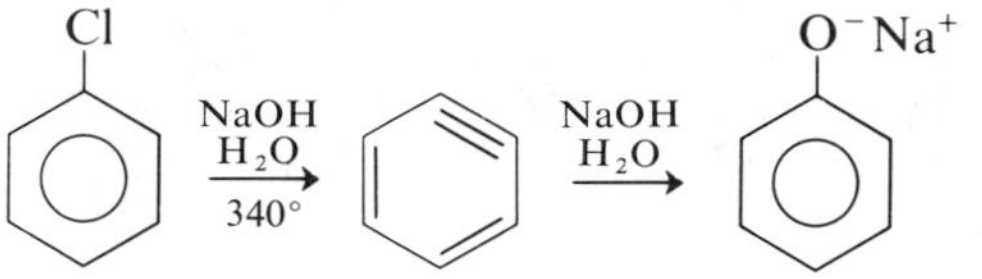

This last process is commercially important, for the Dow Chemical Company prepares phenol in this manner.

Benzyne is formed in a number of other ways. The reaction of o-dihalobenzenes with metals such as sodium, lithium, and magnesium yields benzyne:

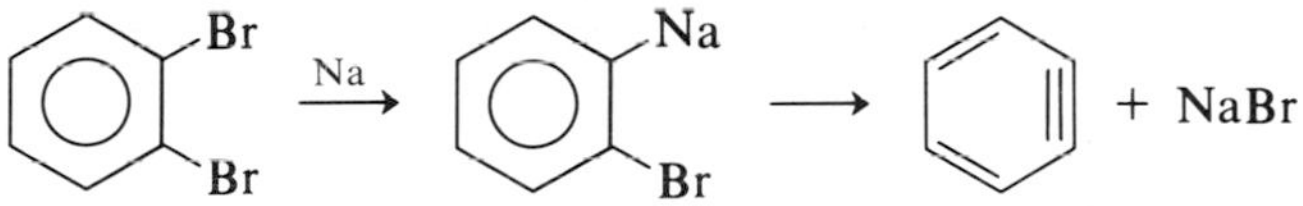

and

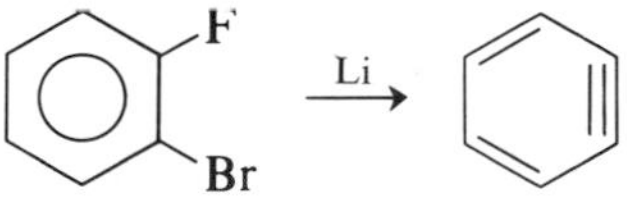

Photolysis of the mercuric salt presented below also affords benzyne,

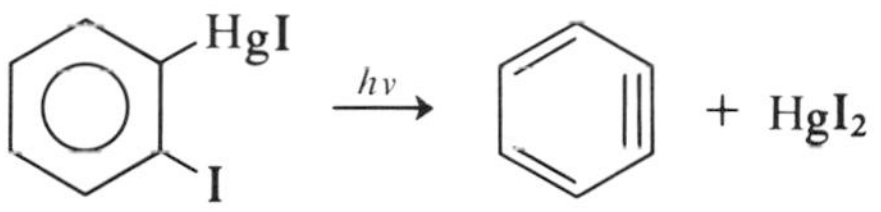

Besides reacting with bases, benzyne also serves as the dienophile in Diels-Alder reactions. This reaction with dienes leads to extremely interesting and unusual products. In addition, these reactions serve as additional evidence in favor of a benzyne intermediate:

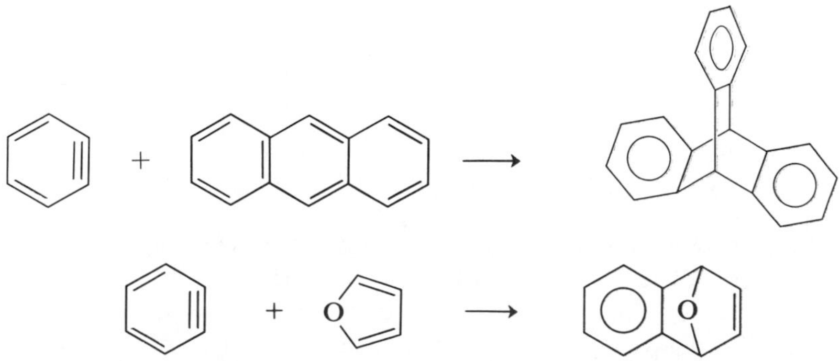

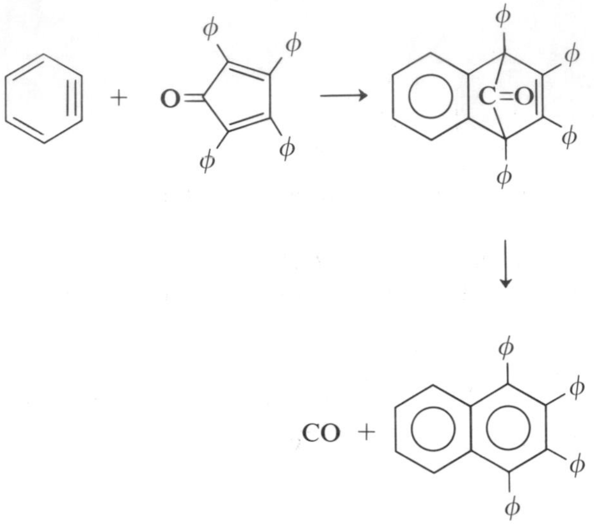

In the absence of another attacking reagent, benzyne dimerizes to form biphenylene:

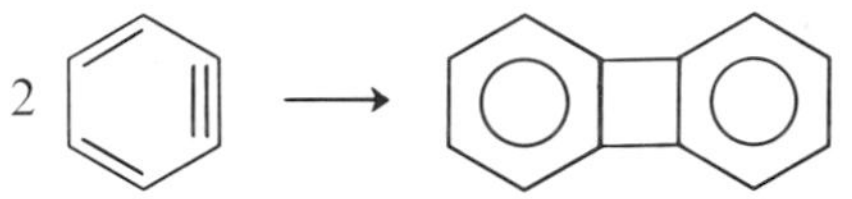

Further evidence for the existence of benzyne intermediates comes from the reactions of substituted halobenzenes with sodium and potassium amides. Materials of the type,

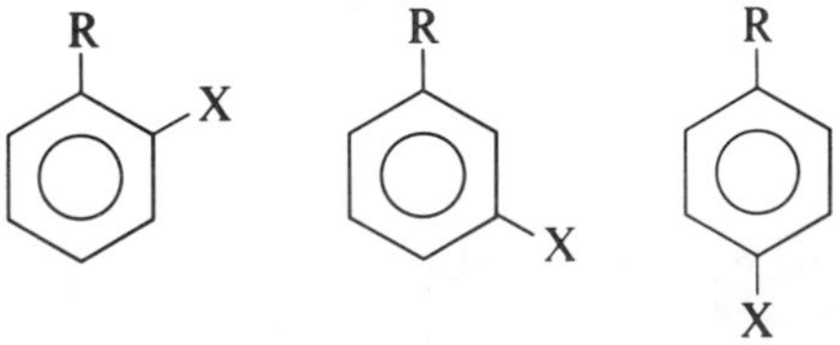

were reacted with amide ion. *Ortho* disubstituted benzenes form only a single benzyne intermediate, *meta* disubstituted benzenes are able to form two different benzynes, while *para* disubstituted materials again form only one. Thus, the following products are expected from the reaction of these materials with amide ion:

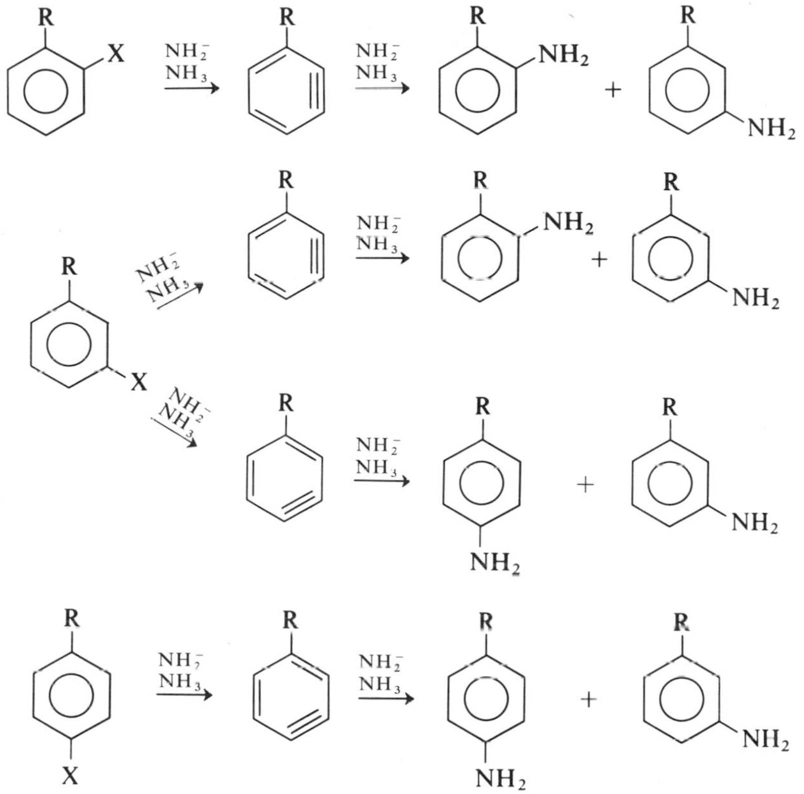

The *ortho* reactant yields a mixture of *ortho* and *meta* products; the *meta* reactant affords all three possible products; and the *para* gives rise to a mixture of *meta* and *para* disubstituted products.

The data in Table 12–5 give experimental confirmation of these ideas,

Table 12–5

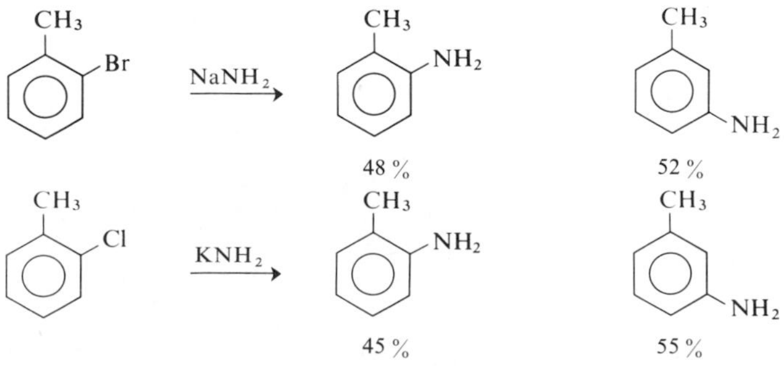

Table 12–5

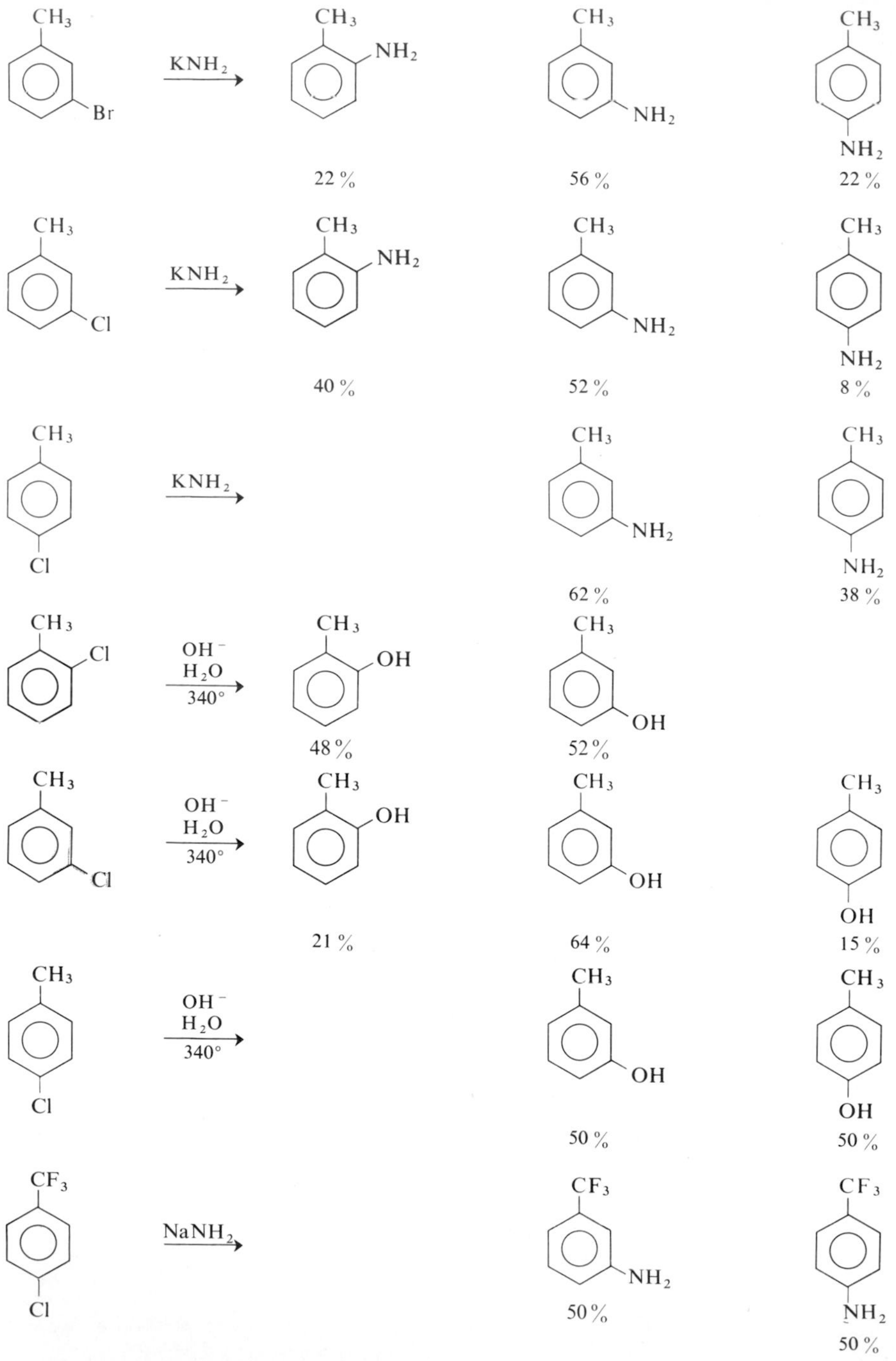

CH₃, Br (reactant)	→ KNH₂	CH₃, NH₂ (ortho) **22%**	CH₃, NH₂ (meta) **56%**	CH₃, NH₂ (para) **22%**

The page content consists of a large reaction table showing aromatic substitution/elimination products. Rendered as a structured table:

Reactant	Reagent	Product (ortho)	Product (meta)	Product (para)
3-bromotoluene (CH₃ / Br)	KNH₂	o-toluidine — 22%	m-toluidine — 56%	p-toluidine — 22%
3-chlorotoluene (CH₃ / Cl)	KNH₂	o-toluidine — 40%	m-toluidine — 52%	p-toluidine — 8%
4-chlorotoluene (CH₃ / Cl)	KNH₂	—	m-toluidine — 62%	p-toluidine — 38%
2-chlorotoluene (CH₃ / Cl)	OH⁻, H₂O, 340°	o-cresol (OH) — 48%	m-cresol (OH) — 52%	—
3-chlorotoluene (CH₃ / Cl)	OH⁻, H₂O, 340°	o-cresol (OH) — 21%	m-cresol (OH) — 64%	p-cresol (OH) — 15%
4-chlorotoluene (CH₃ / Cl)	OH⁻, H₂O, 340°	—	m-cresol (OH) — 50%	p-cresol (OH) — 50%
4-chlorobenzotrifluoride (CF₃ / Cl)	NaNH₂	—	CF₃, NH₂ (meta) — 50%	CF₃, NH₂ (para) — 50%

The data offer conclusive proof that benzyne and substituted benzynes are involved in organic reactions. Such intermediates are also involved in the following reactions,

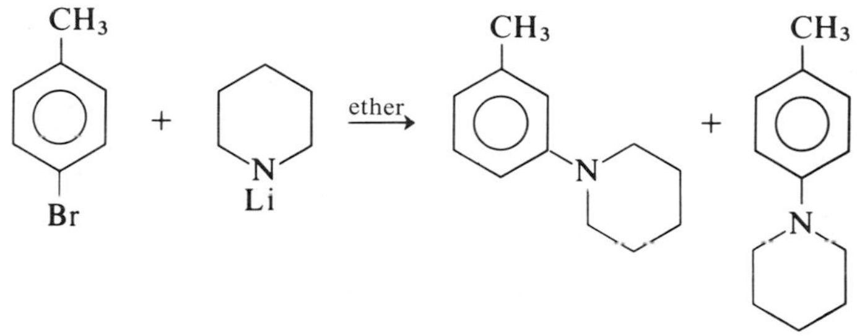

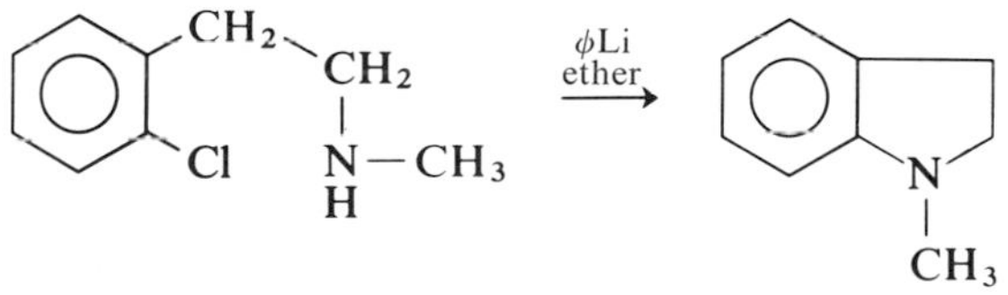

The *meta* compound yields the same product, and the six membered ring is formed under similar conditions:

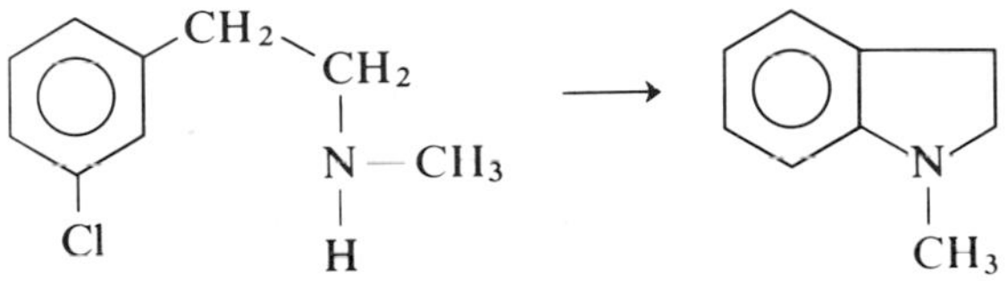

and

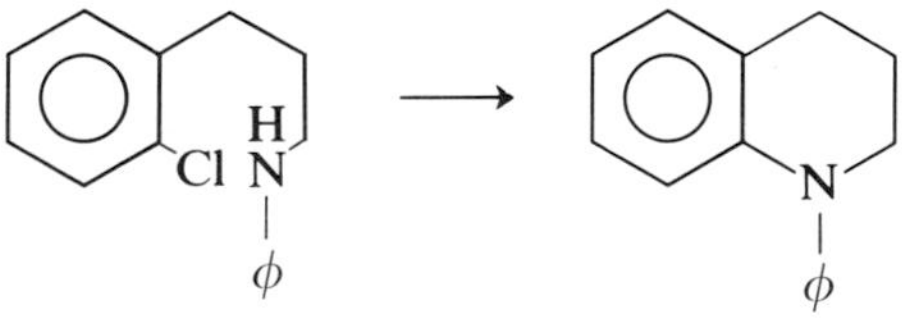

also

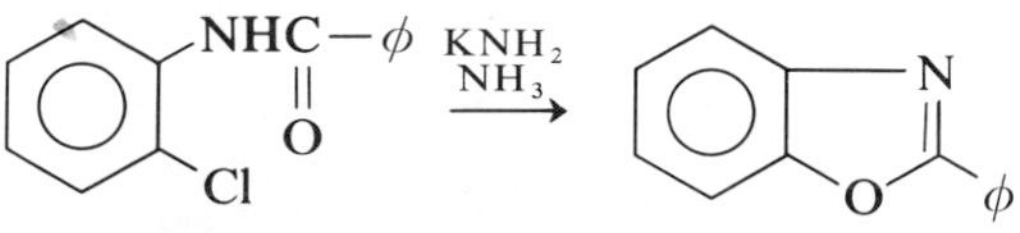

An intermediate analogous to benzyne has been postulated in the reaction of 3-bromopyridine with amide ion:

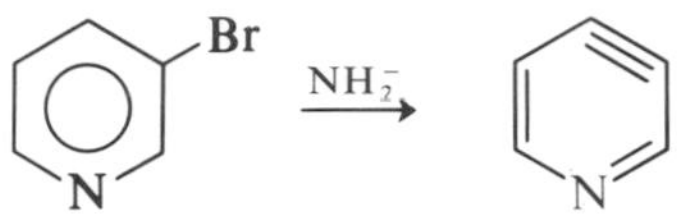

Naphthalynes have also been reported. Thus, the reactions of α-halo-naphthalenes with piperidine involve α-naphthalyne, while β-halonaphthalenes react to form both α- and β-naphthalyne,

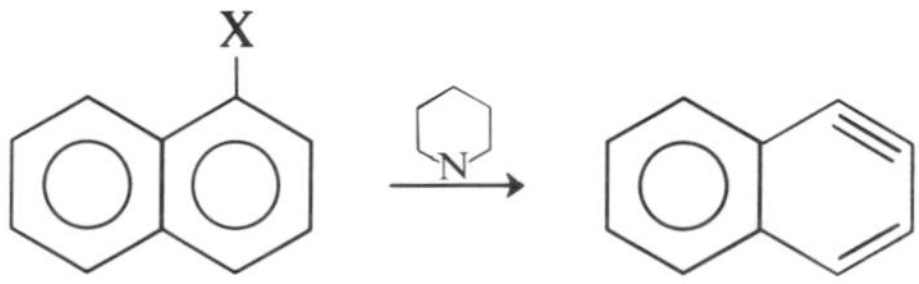

Additional and rather conclusive evidence for the existence of such intermediates comes from the trapping of α-naphthalyne with furan:

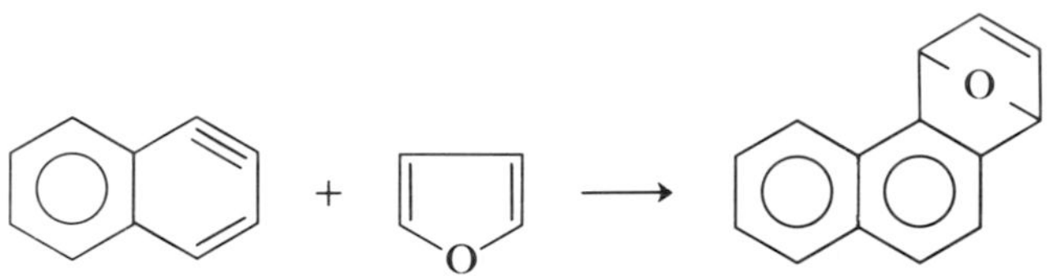

Intermediates of this type do not appear to be restricted to aromatic systems. Reaction of 1,2-dibromocyclopentene with magnesium gives rise to cyclopentyne whose presence was demonstrated by trapping it as a Diels-Alder adduct:

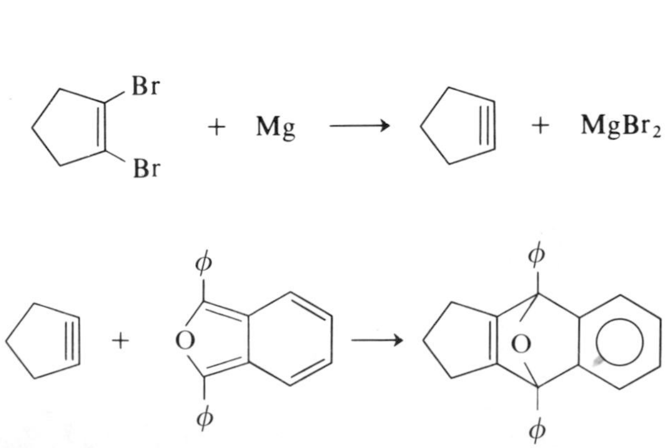

It has been suggested that the reaction of 1-chlorocyclohexene with phenyl-lithium involves cyclohexyne as an intermediate:

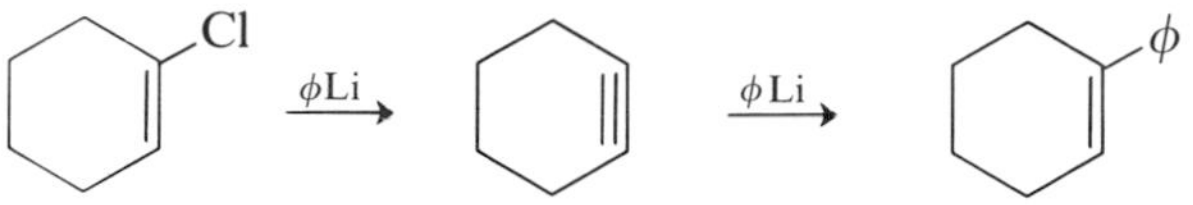

Like carbene, the reactions of benzyne and related intermediates are new. Different methods of preparing such intermediates will doubtless be found, and countless synthetic possibilities exist. No sooner do we progress in one area than a completely new field appears. These new and always changing prospects offer a continual challenge. Our knowledge of even the standard reactions such as S_N1, S_N2, $E1$ and $E2$ is far from complete and we have only begun to comprehend the behavior of carbenes and benzynes. In fact, even the separation of reactions into classes such as S_N1 and S_N2 is artificial. Molecules need not react by distinctly different mechanisms and borderline cases, where the reaction may not be distinctly of one type or another, certainly exist. Much more work is necessary and the job is neverending.

Supplementary Reading

1. Baker, J. W., *Electronic Theories of Organic Chemistry*. London, Oxford U.P., 1958.

2. Banthorpe, D. V., *Elimination Reactions*. London, Elsevier, 1963.

3. Bell, J. A., *Progress in Physical Organic Chemistry*, Vol. 2, (eds.) S. G. Cohen, A. Streitwieser, Jr., R. W. Taft. New York, Interscience, 1964.

4. Bunnett, J. F., *J. Chem. Ed.*, **38**, (1961) p. 278.

5. Fuson, R. C., *Reactions of Organic Compounds*. New York, Wiley, 1962.

6. Gould, E. S., *Mechanism and Structure in Organic Chemistry*. New York, Holt, 1959.

7. Heaney, H., *Chem. Revs.*, **62** No. 2, (1962) p. 81.

8. Hine, J., *Divalent Carbon*. New York, Ronald, 1964.

9. Hine, J., *Physical Organic Chemistry*. New York, McGraw-Hill, 1962.

10. Ingold, C. K., *Structure and Mechanism in Organic Chemistry*. Ithaca, New York, Cornell U.P., 1953.

11. Kirmse, W., *Carbene Chemistry*. New York, Academic, 1964.

Chapter 13

Addition Reactions

13.1 Introduction

The addition of a molecule AB to an alkene gives rise to a substituted alkane:

$$
\begin{array}{c}
\text{R} \quad\quad \text{R} \\
\diagdown \quad\quad \diagup \\
\text{C}=\text{C} \quad + \text{A}-\text{B} \longrightarrow \text{R}-\overset{\text{R}}{\underset{\text{A}}{\text{C}}}-\overset{\text{R}}{\underset{\text{B}}{\text{C}}}-\text{R} \\
\diagup \quad\quad \diagdown \\
\text{R} \quad\quad \text{R}
\end{array}
$$

The nature of the product depends upon which reactant AB is employed. Materials such as molecular chlorine, bromine, water, acids, and many others have been added successfully to the olefinic linkage. The mechanisms by which these additions to alkenes take place are varied and complex, and no single mechanism satisfactorily explains all the experimental results.

In certain cases the addition appears to be quite sensitive to changes in the environment, and under different conditions the mechanism for the reaction changes. In a number of cases the same reagent behaves differently with different alkenes. Thus, hydrogen chloride adds in a stereospecific manner to give a *trans*-addition product with 1,2-dimethylcyclopentene, yet it forms a *cis* adduct with indene:

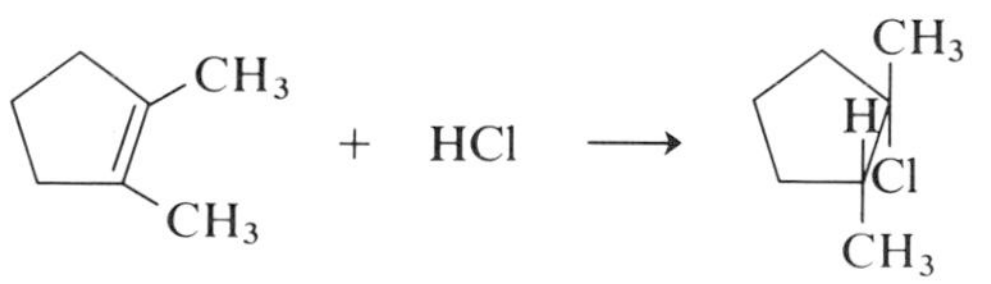

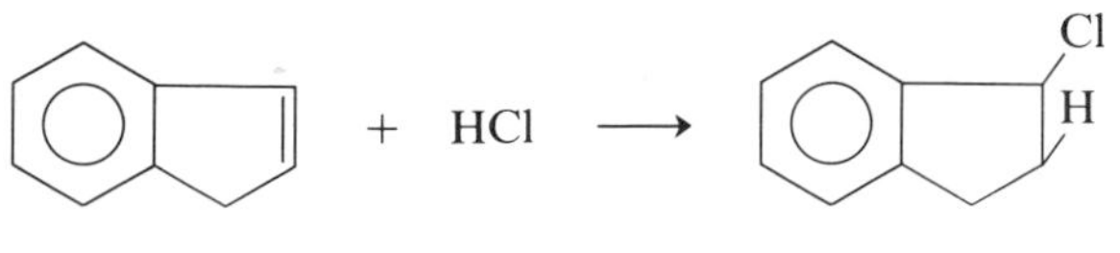

Explanations have been put forth, yet no general theory to account for all ionic additions is available. It appears that the olefinic linkage generally

368

behaves as a Lewis base, and the electrons in this linkage react with electron deficient materials; however, no detailed knowledge of all the intermediates involved is available.

Besides the ionic processes, free radical additions also take place, and many molecules can be added to alkenes under free radical conditions (hydrogen bromide is the classical example). Molecular hydrogen also adds to alkenes by a nonionic mechanism; the product is an alkane. Metallic catalysts such as nickel, platinum, or palladium (finely divided since a large surface area is necessary) are required in this reaction. Materials such as charcoal, barium sulfate, or silica gel serve as supports, and the active metal is on the surface of these supports. In hydrogenations, the alkene is adsorbed on the surface of the catalyst. Molecular hydrogen breaks up into atomic hydrogen on the surface of the catalyst, and hydrogen atoms are transferred in a stepwise process to the alkene:

$$
\underset{R}{\overset{R}{>}}C=C\underset{R}{\overset{R}{<}} \quad + \quad H_2 \quad \xrightarrow{\text{catalyst}} \quad R-\overset{\overset{\displaystyle R}{|}}{\underset{\underset{\displaystyle H}{|}}{C}}-\overset{\overset{\displaystyle R}{|}}{\underset{\underset{\displaystyle H}{|}}{C}}-R
$$

Both *cis-* and *trans-*isomers of a 1,2-disubstituted alkene react with hydrogen in the presence of a catalyst, yet the former usually react much more rapidly. Studies indicate that the transfer of two hydrogen atoms to the alkene does not occur simultaneously. Hydrogen molecules form hydrogen atoms on the surface of the catalyst, and two hydrogen atoms are transferred to the alkene separately.

Since the two hydrogen atoms generally add from the same side, frequently but not always, the product of a hydrogenation has the stereochemistry resulting from *cis-*addition of hydrogen. For example, the alkene 1,2-dimethylcyclohexene is catalytically reduced to *cis-*1,2-dimethylcyclohexane,

The reduction of alkynes with a single equivalent of hydrogen affords *cis-*alkenes.

$$
R-C\equiv C-R \quad + \quad H_2 \quad \xrightarrow{\text{catalyst}} \quad \underset{R}{\overset{H}{>}}C=C\underset{R}{\overset{H}{<}}
$$

Although addition of hydrogen frequently proceeds by *cis* attack to the less hindered side of an alkene, changing the reaction conditions alters the mechanism and leads to exceptions to this rule. Products in which the two hydrogen atoms are *trans*-oriented are also present and such products may predominate.

Addition of hydrogen to unsaturated compounds is probably the most general and most useful of the addition reactions. Other radical additions are discussed in Chapter 20.

13.2 Addition of Strong Acids

Most ionic additions follow moderately closely the same general mechanistic scheme, but the fine details vary considerably. An alkene behaves as a nucleophile with the electrons in the olefinic linkage being used to perform an S_N2 type reaction on some molecule AB. The initial intermediates are analogous to the π complexes discussed earlier in connection with the $E1$ reaction. In the case of unsymmetrical alkenes the π complexes are unsymmetrical, and the second intermediate below subsequently decomposes to products by various routes. The existence of the first π complex as an intermediate is assumed by analogy with arenes where such complexes are known to exist and have been studied:

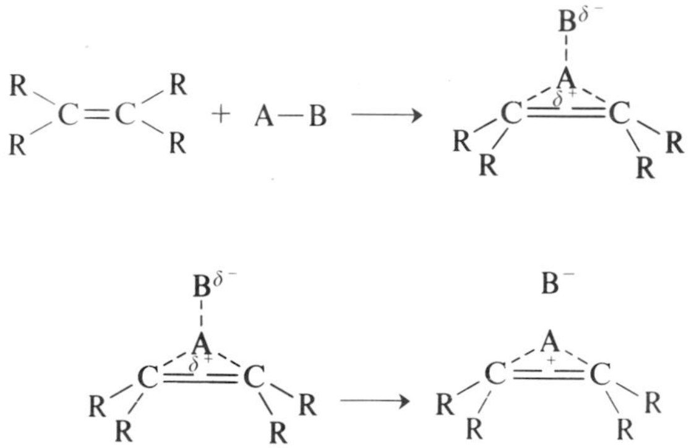

The addition to alkenes of strong acids such as hydrogen chloride, hydrogen bromide, and sulfuric acid must be studied in solvents where extensive dissociation does not occur. In solvents where appreciable ionization does take place, the conjugate acid of the solvent may be the major acidic component. For example, a dilute aqueous solution of any of these materials contains only the species H_3O^+.

The mechanism postulated for the addition of strong acids, which is along the lines just presented, is just the reverse of the $E1$ process. The intermediates are π complexes and carbonium ions, and the most stable carbonium ion is formed:

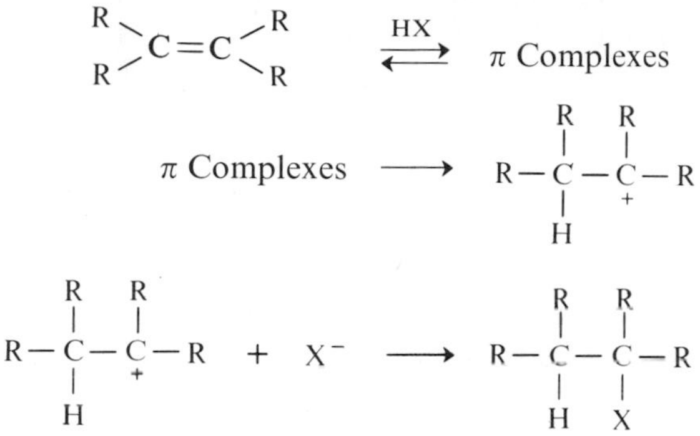

$$R \underset{R}{\overset{R}{>}}C=C\underset{R}{\overset{R}{<}} \quad \underset{HX}{\rightleftharpoons} \quad \pi \text{ Complexes}$$

$$\pi \text{ Complexes} \quad \longrightarrow \quad \begin{array}{cc} R & R \\ | & | \\ R-C-C-R \\ | & \overset{+}{} \\ H \end{array}$$

$$\begin{array}{cc} R & R \\ | & | \\ R-C-\overset{+}{C}-R \\ | \\ H \end{array} + \quad X^{-} \quad \longrightarrow \quad \begin{array}{cc} R & R \\ | & | \\ R-C-C-R \\ | & | \\ H & X \end{array}$$

The following reactions of propylene are additions of this type,

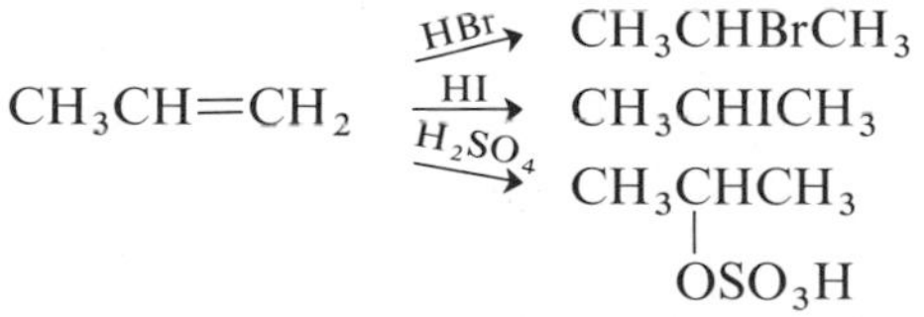

$$CH_3CH{=}CH_2 \quad \begin{array}{l} \xrightarrow{HBr} \; CH_3CHBrCH_3 \\ \xrightarrow[H_2SO_4]{HI} \; CH_3CHICH_3 \\ \longrightarrow \; CH_3\underset{OSO_3H}{\overset{|}{C}}HCH_3 \end{array}$$

Addition reactions can have rates proportional to h_0 (see Section 3.2), and this supports the idea of a transition state differing in composition from the reactant by a proton. It is generally assumed that the transition state in the rate limiting step is composed of the starting alkene plus a proton, and this prevents π complex formation from being rate limiting. No nucleophile enters into the transition state. The most plausible interpretation of the data is that formation of the carbonium ion from the π complex is the rate limiting

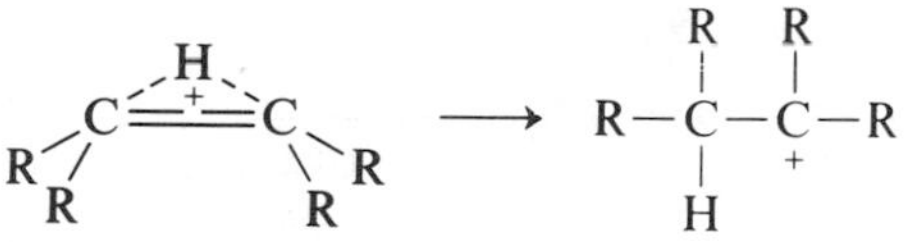

$$\underset{R}{\overset{R}{>}}C\overset{\overset{+}{H}}{\underset{\cdots}{=}}C\underset{R}{\overset{R}{<}} \quad \longrightarrow \quad \begin{array}{cc} R & R \\ | & | \\ R-C-\overset{+}{C}-R \\ | \\ H \end{array}$$

In those addition reactions where a strong acid is added to an unsymmetrical alkene, the most stable carbonium ion is produced.

Evidence for carbonium ion intermediates comes from the fact that in certain cases, addition of HX is accompanied by rearrangement. Such rearrangements are typical of carbonium ion reactions and cannot be explained easily in any other way:

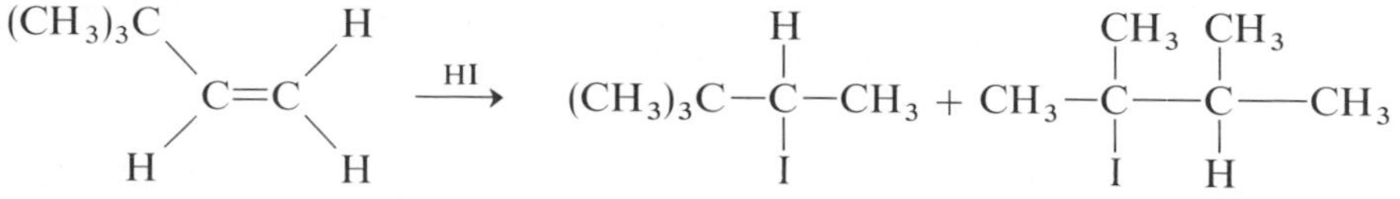

$$(CH_3)_3C \underset{H}{\overset{}{>}}C=C\underset{H}{\overset{H}{<}} \quad \xrightarrow{HI} \quad (CH_3)_3C-\underset{I}{\overset{H}{\overset{|}{C}}}-CH_3 + CH_3-\underset{I}{\overset{CH_3}{\overset{|}{C}}}-\underset{H}{\overset{CH_3}{\overset{|}{C}}}-CH_3$$

Rearrangements occur extensively in bicyclic systems, and the addition of hydrogen chloride to camphene **1** is typical. The reaction can yield both camphene hydrochloride **2**, and isobornyl chloride **3**:

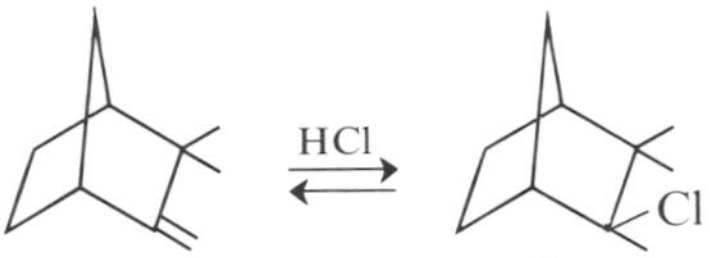

As its name indicates, camphene hydrochloride is prepared by addition of hydrogen chloride to camphene. The process is rapid, and in solution the two materials are in equilibrium. Camphene hydrochloride also isomerizes to isobornyl chloride **3**. This isomerization, which is less rapid than the previous equilibrium, is catalyzed by acids and depends upon the polarity of the solvent.

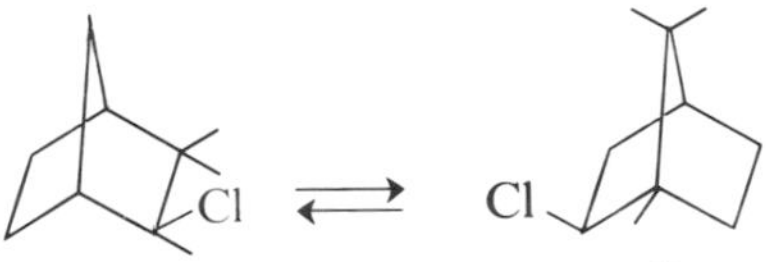

Isobornyl chloride itself isomerizes to bornyl chloride. This rearrangement is also acid catalyzed, and it is this last product, bornyl chloride, that is the most stable of the three, the thermodynamic product. This last reaction is, however, extremely slow:

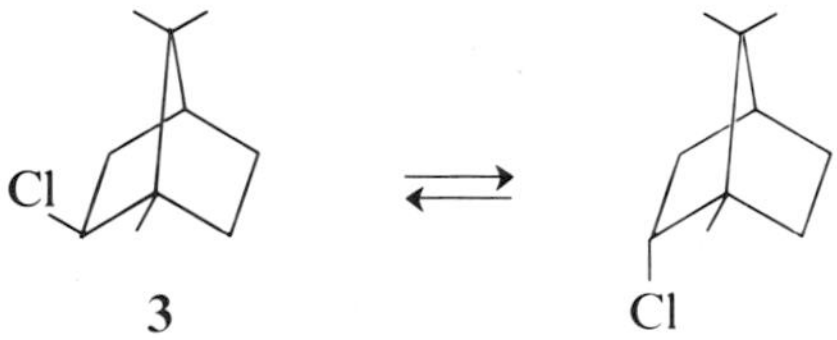

A kinetic study of the isomerization of **2** to **3** demonstrates that in the absence of added acid, product formation is governed by the rate law,

$$\frac{d[3]}{dt} = k[2]^{3/2}$$

This rate expression, although more complex than expected, is consistent with the mechanism,

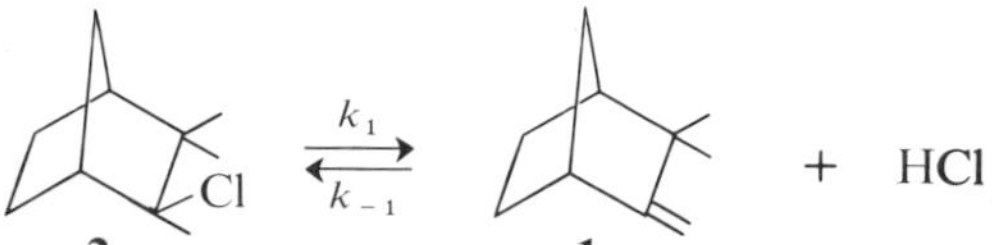

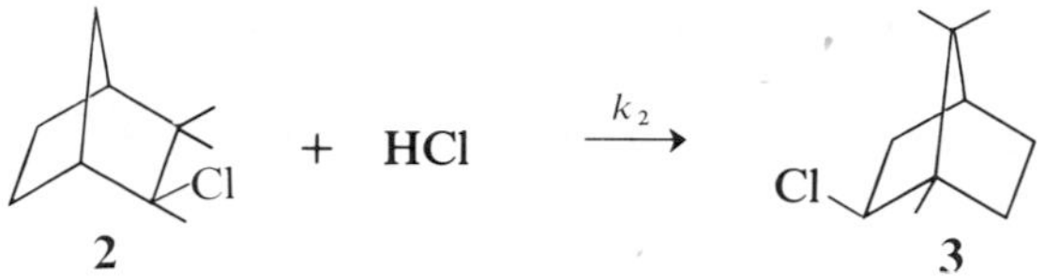

+ HCl $\xrightarrow{k_2}$

2   **3**

with hydrogen chloride catalyzing the second step which is rate limiting, and where the concentration of hydrogen chloride is given by,

$$[\mathbf{1}][HCl] = K[\mathbf{2}]$$

K is the equilibrium constant for the first step.

In the absence of added acid, the terms [**1**] and [HCl] are equal, and the expression in terms of the equilibrium constant for the first step becomes,

$$[HCl] = K^{1/2}[\mathbf{2}]^{1/2}$$

which leads a general rate expression consistent with the actual observation:

$$\frac{d[\mathbf{3}]}{dt} = k_2 K^{1/2}[\mathbf{2}]^{3/2}$$

Here the measured specific rate constant k equals the composite term,

$$k = k_2 K^{1/2}$$

The intermediates in this rearrangement of **2** to **3** are carbonium ions (as part of ion pairs), and these intermediates may be represented by classical or nonclassical structures:

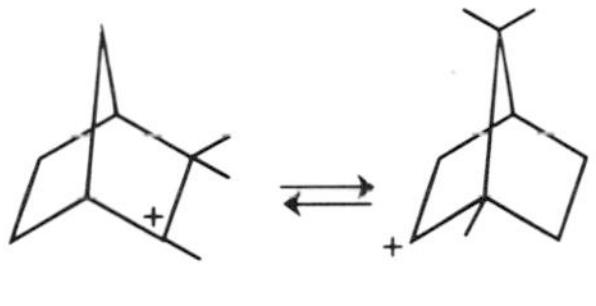

Nonclassically this becomes,

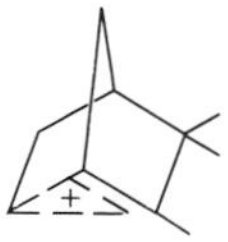

where

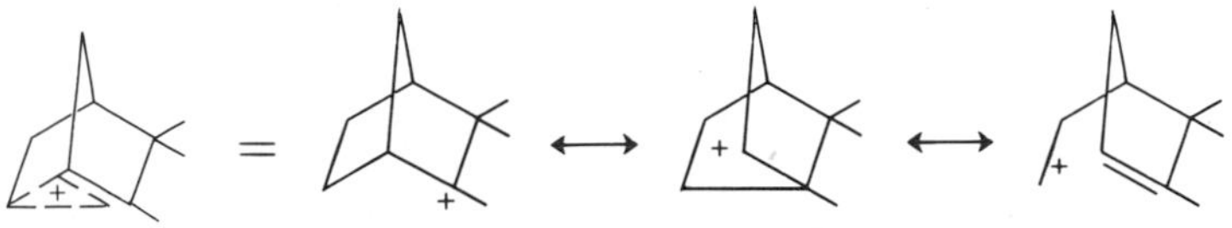

This problem of classical and nonclassical carbonium ions is discussed more fully in Chapter 18.

Since **1** and **2** are in rapid equilibrium and since **2** incorporates labeled chloride more rapidly than it isomerizes to **3**, the rate limiting step in the isomerization of **2** to **3** must be formation of **3** from the cationic intermediates. For the reverse reaction, ionization of **3** catalyzed by hydrogen chloride must be rate limiting.

Addition of a strong acid to an alkene gives rise to the more stable carbonium ion. Accordingly, the addition of hydrogen iodide to vinyl chloride,

$$CH_2{=}CHCl \xrightarrow{\text{HI}} CH_3\underset{\underset{I}{|}}{CHCl}$$

which gives rise to the 1,1-disubstituted product, has the following rate limiting step,

$$CH_2\overset{H}{\underset{+}{=}}CHCl \longrightarrow CH_3\overset{+}{CHCl}$$
4

This proceeds more rapidly than the alternative possibility,

$$CH_2\overset{H}{\underset{+}{=}}CHCl \longrightarrow \overset{+}{CH_2}CH_2Cl$$
5

The transition state leading to **4** is more stable than that leading to **5**, a general result. The transition state leading to the more stable carbonium ion is generally the more stable transition state.

Carbonium ion **4** is more stable than **5** because of charge delocalization onto the adjacent chlorine atom. This type of delocalization is not possible in **5**:

$$CH_3\overset{+}{CHCl} \longleftrightarrow CH_3CH{=}\overset{+}{Cl}$$
4

Such delocalization is also possible to a greater degree in the transition state leading to **4** than in that leading to **5** and causes this to be the more stable transition state.

Although **4** is formed more readily than **5**, addition of hydrogen iodide to vinyl chloride is slower than the rate of addition of hydrogen iodide to ethylene. The ethyl carbonium ion is formed faster than the 1-chloroethyl carbonium ion **4**:

$$CH_2\overset{H}{\underset{+}{=}}CH_2 \longrightarrow CH_3\overset{+}{CH_2}$$

$$CH_2\overset{H}{\underset{+}{=}}CHCl \longrightarrow CH_3\overset{+}{CHCl}$$
4

The fact that the ethyl cation is formed more readily is due to the electron withdrawing inductive effect of chlorine in **4**. Because of the inductive effect of chlorine, the formation of **4** is more difficult than the formation of the ethyl carbonium ion. The resonance effect of chlorine makes the transition state leading to **4** more stable than that leading to **5**, but this does not compensate completely for the influence of the inductive effect upon the free energy of these transition states. The problem is related to that of electrophilic aromatic substitution of halobenzenes. The halogens are deactivating yet *ortho-para* directing.

In all reactions involving charged species (such as carbonium ions) in solution, solvation of charges occurs. The addition of strong acids HX to alkenes must be conducted in solvents that are very weak bases otherwise HX is not present. Consequently, in reactions of this type, which are conducted either in solvents that do not promote ionization or in the absence of a solvent (except for the alkene or acid itself), solvation comes from other molecules of the acid HX. It has been found that the addition of hydrogen bromide to propylene involves approximately three molecules of the acid, and the most reasonable explanation of this observation is that two of these molecules solvate the charged transition state:

$$Br{-}H \quad \overset{\delta}{Br} \quad H{-}Br$$
$$CH_3CH{=}CH_2 + 3HBr \; \rightleftharpoons \; CH_3CH{\overset{\Vert}{=\!\!=}}CH_2$$
$$\mathbf{6}$$

$$Br{-}H \quad Br^{\delta-} \; H{-}Br \qquad\qquad\qquad Br{-}H \; Br^{-} \; H{-}Br$$
$$CH_3CH\overset{H}{\underset{\delta+}{=\!\!=}}CH_2 \quad \rightleftharpoons \quad CH_3CH\overset{H}{\underset{+}{=\!\!=}}CH_2$$
$$\qquad\qquad\qquad\qquad\qquad\qquad \mathbf{7}$$

$$Br{-}H \; Br^{-} \; H{-}Br$$
$$CH_3CH\overset{H}{\underset{+}{=\!\!=}}CH_2 \quad \longrightarrow$$

$$Br{-}H \; Br^{-} \; H{-}Br$$
$$CH_3\overset{+}{C}HCH_3$$
$$\mathbf{8}$$

$$Br{-}H \; Br^{-} \; H{-}Br$$
$$CH_3\overset{+}{C}HCH_3 \quad \longrightarrow \quad CH_3CHBrCH_3 + 2HBr$$

The carbonium ion **8** is part of an ion pair. If this ion pair is short-lived, that is, if the Br⁻ adds to the carbonium ion very quickly, it enters from the same side as did the proton and the addition of HBr is a *cis*-addition. If, on the other hand, *cis*-addition is unfavorable (due to steric factors or for some other reason), the Br⁻ then moves to the other side of the carbonium ion and enters *trans* to the proton.

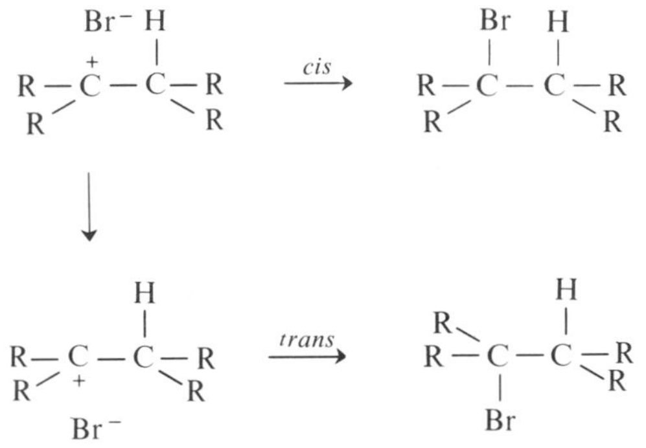

$$
\begin{array}{ccc}
\underset{R}{\overset{Br^- \; H}{R - \overset{+}{C} - \underset{R}{C} - R}} & \xrightarrow{\;cis\;} & \underset{R}{\overset{Br \; H}{R - C - \underset{R}{C} - R}}
\end{array}
$$

$$
\begin{array}{ccc}
\underset{Br^-}{\overset{H}{R - \underset{R}{\overset{+}{C}} - \underset{R}{C} - R}} & \xrightarrow{\;trans\;} & \overset{H}{\underset{Br}{\overset{R}{R - C - C \overset{R}{\underset{R}{}}}}}
\end{array}
$$

Naturally when rotation about the central carbon-carbon bond is possible, the stereochemistry of the adduct provides little information concerning the mode of collapse of the ion pair. However, when rotation is not possible (for example, with cyclic systems), the structure of the addition product does provide information concerning the nature of the addition of Br⁻, and this argument has been used to explain the *cis*-addition of hydrogen bromide to molecules such as indene. Addition of hydrogen bromide to 1-phenylpropylene follows a similar course:

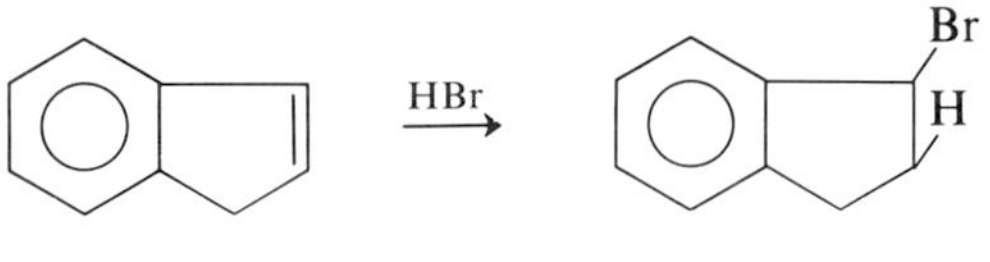

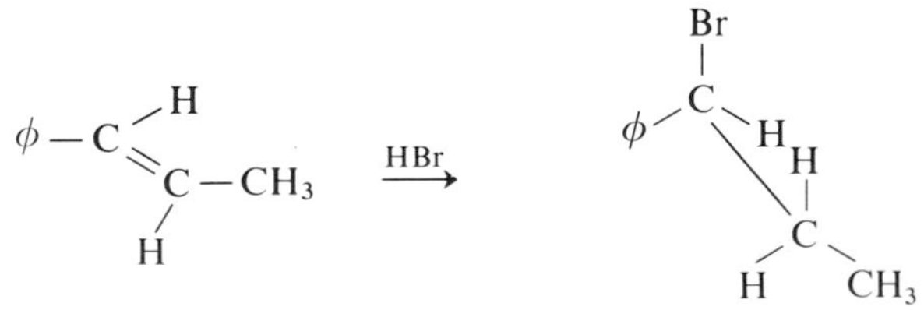

The actual experiments on indene and 1-phenylpropylene were conducted using deuterium bromide DBr and deuterium chloride DCl. It was found that in the cases studied, both *cis*- and *trans*-addition occurred but that the *cis*-adduct was the major product. It was further shown that the *trans*-product did not originate from an isomerization of the *cis*-material. Other alkenes

were also employed, with the results,

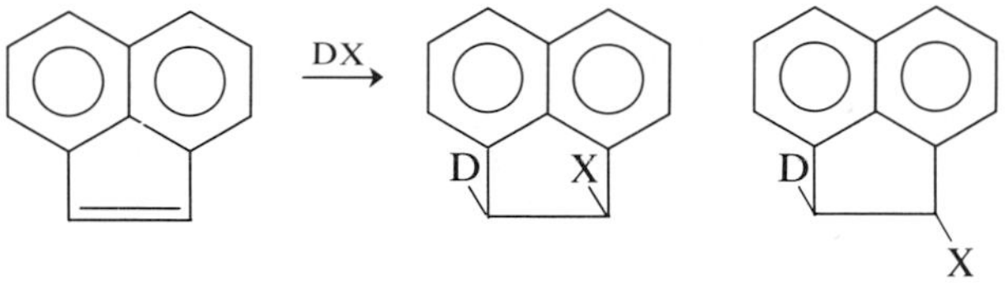

major product   minor product

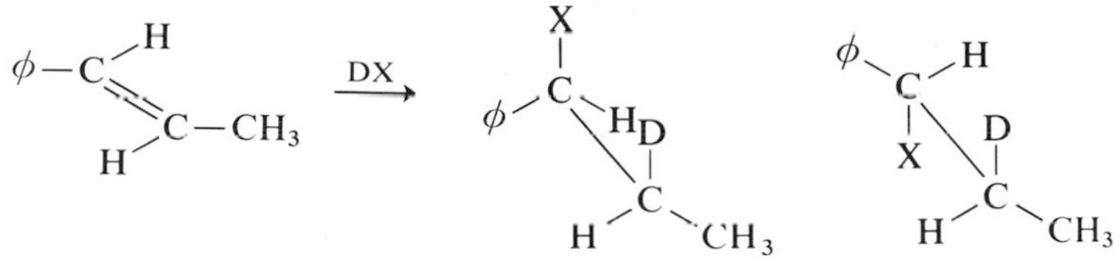

major product   minor product

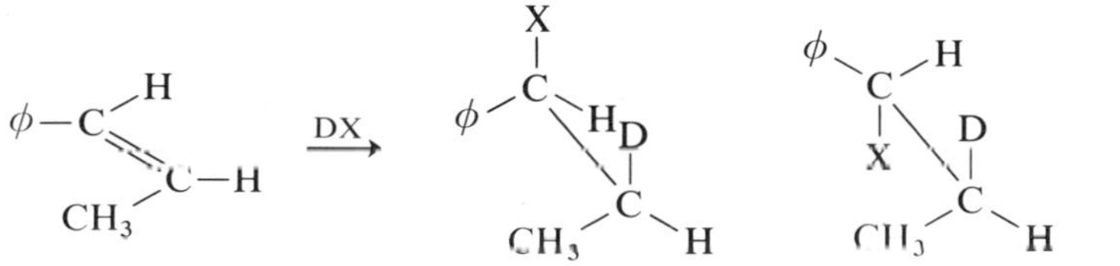

major product   minor product

In these reactions *cis*-addition predominates. In a number of other cases the *trans*-adduct is the major product. Both *cis*- and *trans*-additions of hydrogen halides occur, and the geometry of the major product depends upon the olefinic reactant. It is possible that in some additions of HX to alkenes, attack by X^- proceeds directly on the π complex,

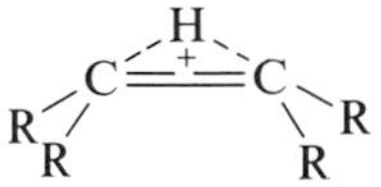

and that a carbonium ion is never formed:

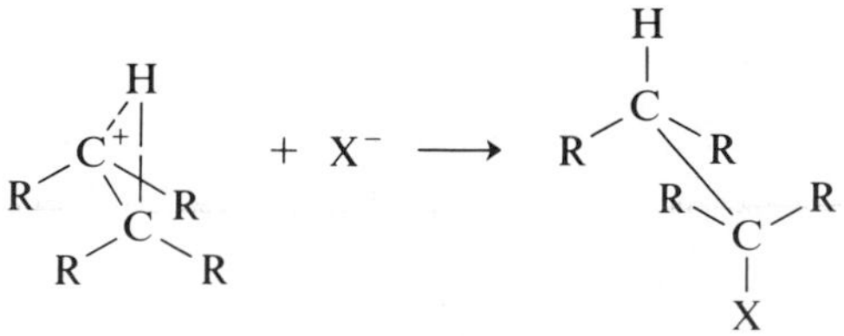

This explains most simply the observation that certain cyclohexyl systems yield *trans*-adducts.

If the formation of (stereochemistry not indicated)

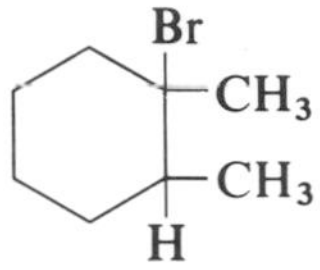

from the alkenes

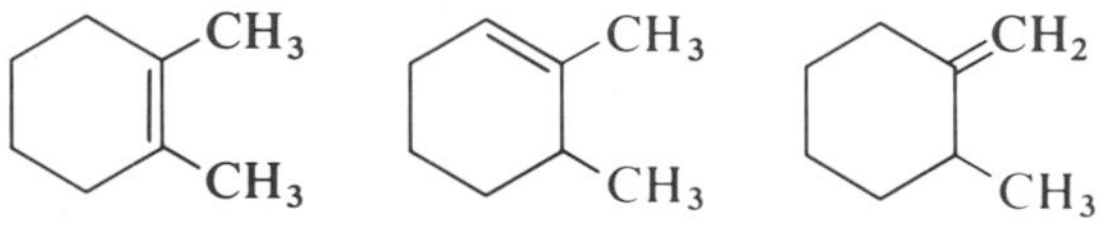

by treating them with hydrogen bromide proceeded through a common carbonium ion intermediate, the same *cis-trans* product ratio might be expected in all cases. Such a result is not observed. In all cases the major product is the *trans*-adduct, but the *cis-trans* ratio varies with the reactant. This is best explained by assuming that in these reactions the attack by Br⁻ occurs directly on the π complex.

The addition of hydrogen bromide was conducted using acetic acid as a solvent. The reaction was arrested before equilibrium was attained, and the three alkenes yielded different *cis-trans* ratios. Under these conditions it was found that 1,2-dimethylcyclohexene yielded no *cis*-adduct. Since this material which initially could form only the single ion pair,

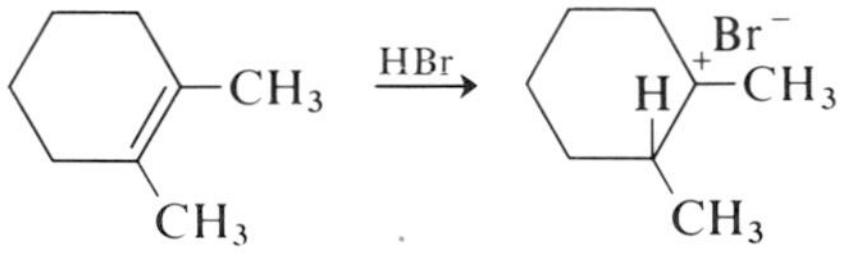

affords only *trans*-adduct, the result indicates that if open carbonium ions were involved, rearrangement must be faster than collapse to product:

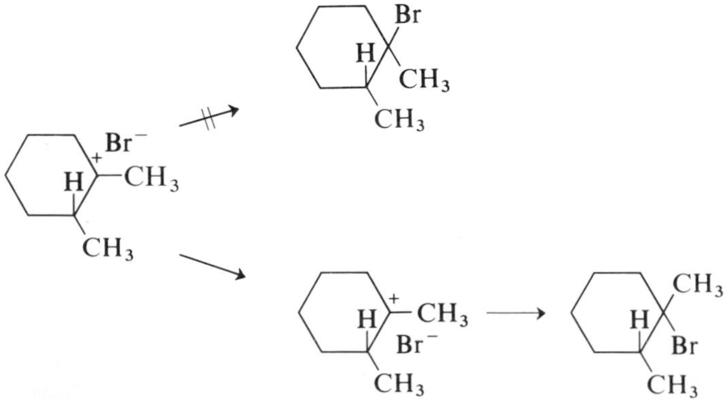

The other two alkenes can form both ion pairs initially.

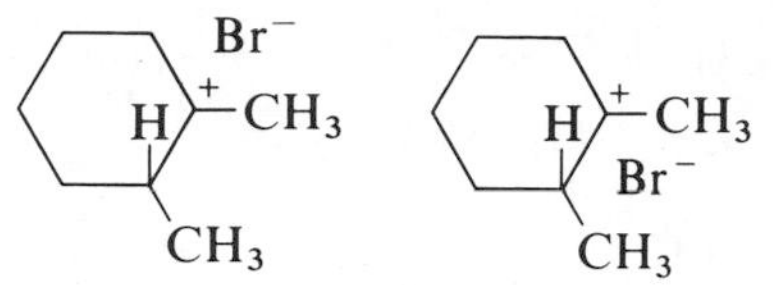

But again, the bromide must be able to migrate faster than the ion pair on the left collapses to product. Since 1,2-dimethylcyclohexene yields no *cis*-adduct, all three alkenes ought to behave in the same manner. All three ought to give the same product ratio (100% *trans*, if these ion pairs were involved). They do not, and this argues against the participation of open carbonium ions at least in this reaction.

When the addition of acids to alkenes is conducted in the presence of a nucleophilic solvent, then the solvent itself can add to the carbonium ion intermediate. Thus, if water is present in the solution alcohols are formed as products, and if alcohols are present ethers are formed:

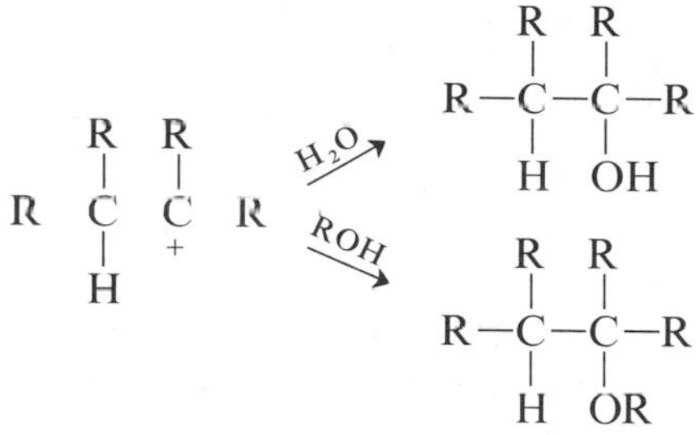

In the presence of any added nucleophile Y^-, the treatment of an alkene with HX affords the $Y-$ substituted product as well as the $X-$ substituted product, and the product ratio depends upon the concentration and reactivity of Y^-.

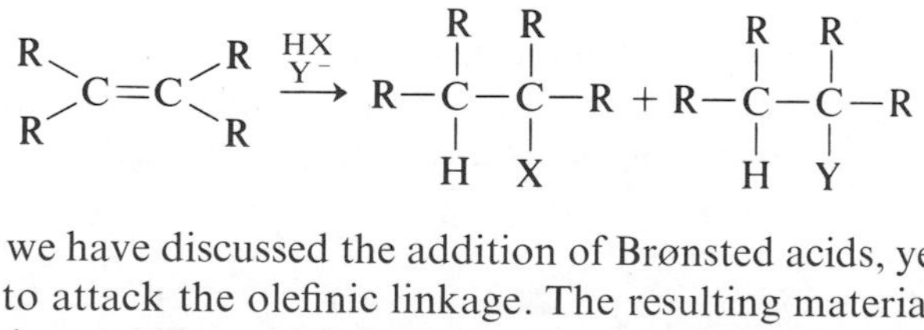

Up to now we have discussed the addition of Brønsted acids, yet Lewis acids are also able to attack the olefinic linkage. The resulting materials are π complexes of varying stability which in some cases break down to yield important synthetic products. For example, the reaction of diborane (B_2H_6) with alkenes, a process known as hydroboration, affords alkyl boron compounds capable of oxidation to the corresponding alcohols. The addition is largely anti-Markovnikov and provides a useful preparative method of alcohols not available by direct hydration of the alkene. Typical reactions are,

$$3CH_3CH_2CH_2CH=CH_2 \xrightarrow{B_2H_6} (CH_3CH_2CH_2CH_2CH_2)_3B \xrightarrow[H_2O_2]{NaOH} 3CH_3CH_2CH_2CH_2CH_2OH$$

$$3\phi CH=CH_2 \xrightarrow{B_2H_6} (\phi CH_2CH_2)_3B \xrightarrow[H_2O]{NaOH} 3\phi CH_2CH_2OH$$

The reaction is quite general and virtually all alkenes react with diborane. Diborane has the unusual structure,

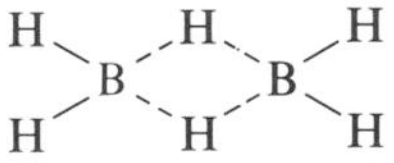

with the two electrons in a B—H—B bond delocalized over all three atoms; the idea is similar to delocalization in the allylic system. If the orbital used by boron is $sp^5{}_B$ and the orbital used by hydrogen is s_H, then the molecular orbital that describes the positions of the electrons in a B—H—B bond is composed of a linear combination of these orbitals:

$$\psi = a_1 sp^5{}_B + a_2 s_H + a_3 sp^5{}_B$$

There are two orbitals of this type. The τ bond description of ethylene is similar to this, except that in the present case two hydrogens have been inserted into the τ bonds.

Typical solvents for the reaction are diethylether, tetrahydrofuran, and diglyme, and in solution diborane is in equilibrium with its complexed monomer (BH_3). For example, with tetrahydrofuran,

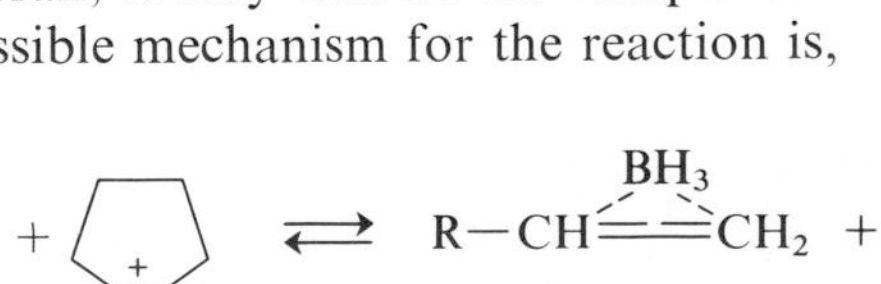

Since the reactions of diborane with alkenes are conducted in solvents such as tetrahydrofuran, it may well be the complexed monomer that is the active species. A possible mechanism for the reaction is,

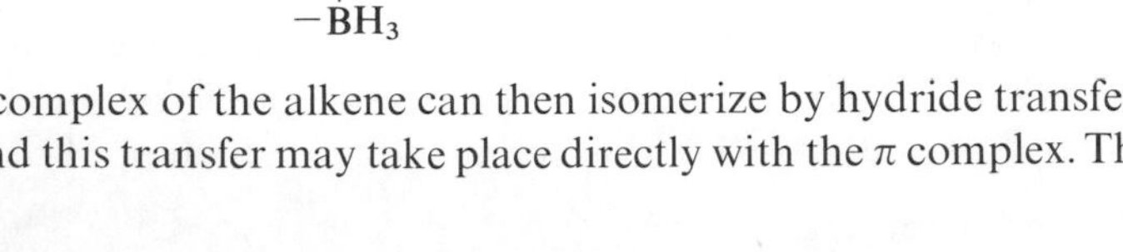

The π complex of the alkene can then isomerize by hydride transfer from the boron, and this transfer may take place directly with the π complex. The product

is an alkyl boron compound:

$$R-CH{=}{=}CH_2 \xrightarrow{BH_3} RCH_2CH_2BH_2$$

The boron atom in this initial alkyl boron compound, which has two more replaceable hydrogens, can react with additional molecules of the alkene to form the trialkyl boron intermediate. The mechanism is similar to that presented for incorporation of the first alkene molecule.

$$RCH_2CH_2-BH_2 + 2RCH{=}CH_2 \longrightarrow (RCH_2CH_2)_3B$$

The rate of incorporation of alkyl groups decreases; thus, it is easier to introduce the first alkyl group than the second, and the second is incorporated more readily than the third. This rate decrease has been attributed to steric factors. That steric factors do play some role is evidenced by the fact that alkenes such as $(CH_3CH_2)_2C{=}CHCH_3$ form only dialkylboranes:

$$\begin{array}{c}R \\ R\end{array}{>}C{=}C{<}\begin{array}{c}R \\ H\end{array} \xrightarrow{B_2H_6} \left(R-\underset{\underset{H}{|}}{\overset{\overset{R}{|}}{C}}-\underset{\underset{H}{|}}{\overset{\overset{R}{|}}{C}} \right)_2 BH$$

13.3 The Addition of Halogens

Halogenations, like the reactions with strong acids, can be carried out in both polar and nonpolar solvents, but the mechanism for addition of halogen can be ionic or free radical. The mechanism generally written for the ionic process involves intermediates similar to those presented for the addition of acids:

$$\begin{array}{c}R \\ R\end{array}{>}C{=}C{<}\begin{array}{c}R \\ R\end{array} + X_2 \longrightarrow \quad \underset{R{>}C{<}R}{\overset{R-C{<}R}{\overset{X^+}{}}} \quad \xrightarrow{X^-} \quad \underset{R{>}C{<}R}{\overset{R-C{<}R}{\overset{X}{}}}\underset{X}{}$$

The addition of halogens to the olefinic linkage can be accomplished under both free radical and ionic conditions, and caution must be exercised when studying one or the other of these routes to exclude the unwanted process. Of course, light, high temperatures, and free radical initiators favor one of these reactions while polar solvents, low temperatures, free radical inhibitors, and the absence of light favor the other. An additional complication is that polar reactions occur at glass surfaces and heterogeneous reactions of this type are not reproducible. This obstacle can be overcome by coating the glass reaction vessel with paraffin.

The reactions of molecular fluorine with alkenes are exothermic and bond rupture occurs. Consequently, these reactions are free radical processes, and degradation of the alkene is not unusual:

$$
\begin{array}{c}
R \\
\diagdown \\
R
\end{array}
C = C
\begin{array}{c}
R \\
\diagup \\
R
\end{array}
+ \; F_2 \; \longrightarrow \;
\begin{array}{c}
\quad R \quad R \\
\quad | \quad\; | \\
R - C - C - R \\
\quad | \quad\; | \\
\quad F \quad F
\end{array}
$$

The product of this addition is formed with sufficient excess vibrational energy to allow bond rupture and the generation of free radicals. This initiates free radical reactions.

The addition of iodine to alkenes is also generally unfavorable since the introduction of two large iodine atoms causes steric interactions in the product. The reaction is readily reversible. Some unsaturated materials do add iodine. Acetylene does, and the product is a mixture of *cis-* and *trans-*1,2-diiodoethylene:

$$
H - C \equiv C - H \; + \; I_2 \; \longrightarrow \;
\begin{array}{c}
H \\
\diagdown \\
I
\end{array}
C = C
\begin{array}{c}
I \\
\diagup \\
H
\end{array}
\; + \;
\begin{array}{c}
H \\
\diagdown \\
I
\end{array}
C = C
\begin{array}{c}
H \\
\diagup \\
I
\end{array}
$$

major product   minor product

As a result, most of the work on halogenation involves bromine and chlorine. Even here, side reactions are possible. Chlorine can give rise to substituted products as well as addition products. Bromine is also capable of such behavior but does so less readily:

$$
\begin{array}{c}
CH_3 \\
\diagdown \\
CH_3
\end{array}
C = C
\begin{array}{c}
H \\
\diagup \\
H
\end{array}
+ \; Cl_2 \; \longrightarrow \;
\begin{array}{c}
CH_3 \\
\diagdown \\
CH_2Cl
\end{array}
C = C
\begin{array}{c}
H \\
\diagup \\
H
\end{array}
$$

This substitution reaction appears to involve ionic intermediates, and the product is formed by expulsion of a proton.

Another difficulty is that not all alkenes react with halogens; tetraphenylethylene does not add bromine. It does add chlorine, yet even this reaction is characterized by an unfavorable equilibrium:

$$
\begin{array}{c}
\phi \\
\diagdown \\
\phi
\end{array}
C = C
\begin{array}{c}
\phi \\
\diagup \\
\phi
\end{array}
\quad
\begin{array}{c}
\xrightarrow{\;Br_2\;} \!\!\!\! / / \\[4pt]
\underset{Cl_2}{\overset{}{\rightleftharpoons}}
\end{array}
\quad
\begin{array}{c}
\quad \phi \quad \phi \\
\quad | \quad\; | \\
\phi - C - C - \phi \\
\quad | \quad\;\, | \\
\quad Br \quad Br \\[8pt]
\quad \phi \quad \phi \\
\quad | \quad\; | \\
\phi - C - C - \phi \\
\quad | \quad\; | \\
\quad Cl \quad Cl
\end{array}
$$

The behavior of tetraphenylethylene with bromine is due to an extremely unfavorable equilibrium and is attributed to steric crowding in the product and resonance stabilization of the olefinic reactant. Chlorine is smaller and carbon-chlorine bonds stronger.

Compounds such as cinnamic acid do add bromine, but formation of the adduct is slow:

$$\phi CH{=}CHCOOH + Br_2 \longrightarrow \phi CHBrCHBrCOOH$$

Although complications do arise, for most alkenes the addition of halogen is facile and leads to the expected products:

$$CH_2{=}CH_2 + Cl_2 \longrightarrow CH_2ClCH_2Cl$$

$$CH_3CH{=}CH_2 + Br_2 \longrightarrow CH_3CHBrCH_2Br$$

$$\phi CH{=}CH_2 + Br_2 \longrightarrow \phi CHBrCH_2Br$$

Mixed halogens such as iodine monochloride ICl and iodine monobromide IBr as well as materials such as nitrosyl chloride also add to alkenes,

$$CH_3CH{=}CH_2 + ICl \longrightarrow CH_3CHClCH_2I$$

$$\phi CH{=}CH_2 + ICl \longrightarrow \phi CHClCH_2I$$

$$(CH_3)_2C{=}CHCH_3 + NOCl \longrightarrow (CH_3)_2CClCHCH_3$$
$$\qquad\qquad\qquad\qquad\qquad\qquad\qquad\qquad\overset{|}{NO}$$

In polar solvents the addition of halogens to alkenes is a second order process, first order in olefin and first order in halogen. Thus with acetic acid as solvent, the kinetic form of the general rate law for chlorination (in terms of disappearance of chlorine) is,

$$-\frac{d[Cl_2]}{dt} = k[\text{alkene}][Cl_2]$$

It appears on the basis of this rate law that at least in polar solvents, a single molecule of the alkene reacts with a single molecule of the halogen and that the solvent solvates any charged species.

In polar solvents solvation is accomplished by the solvent which aids in separating opposite charges. In less polar solvents a second molecule of the halogen is required to perform this task.

A mechanism similar to that presented previously for the addition of strong acids also satisfies this kinetic picture:

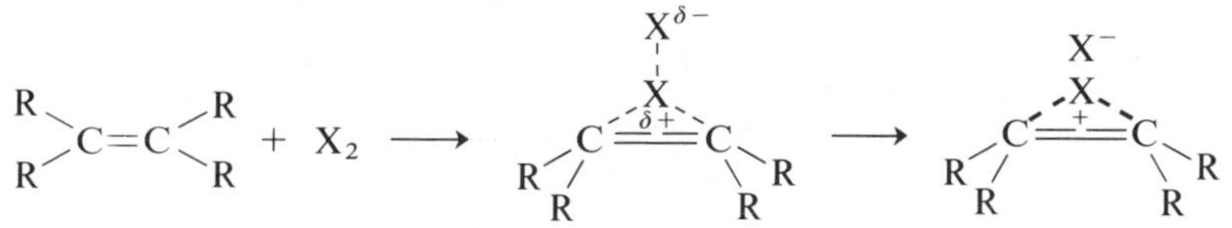

9   10

An example of the ion pair **10**, which in these reactions is not a π complex, is the familiar bromonium ion, usually written as,

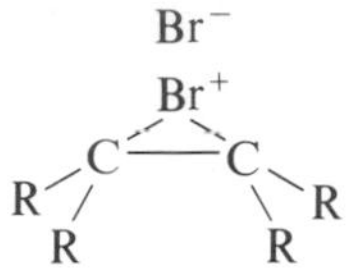

$$
\begin{array}{c}
Br^- \\
Br^+ \\
R{-}C{=\!\!=}C{-}R \\
R \qquad R
\end{array}
$$

If the alkene being brominated is an unsymmetrical olefin such as propylene, the bromonium ion is also unsymmetrical with more bonding to the primary position:

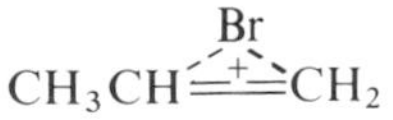

$$CH_3CH\overset{Br}{=\!\!=}CH_2$$

In any halogenation of an unsymmetrical alkene, the resulting bridged ion is also unsymmetrical.

The ion pair **10** can rearrange to another ion pair **11** in which the ion X^- is at the rear. Another possibility is that it opens up to the carbonium ions **12** and **13**:

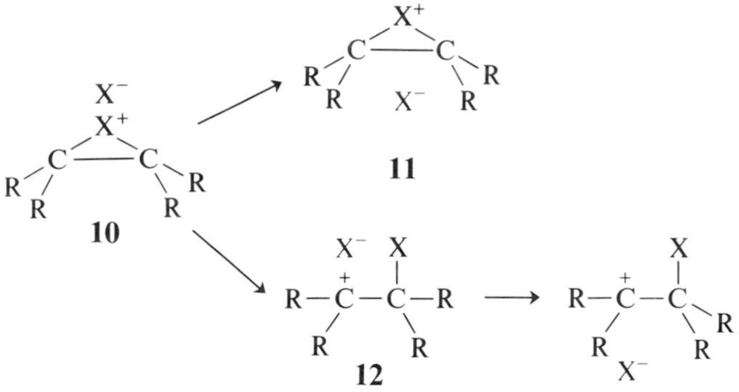

Some additions are explained best in terms of carbonium ion intermediates while other reactions appear not to involve a carbonium ion but to proceed directly on the bridged ion **10** or **11**. It is certainly possible that the choice of solvent and reactants influences the mechanism.

The following products are formed from **11**, **12** and **13**,

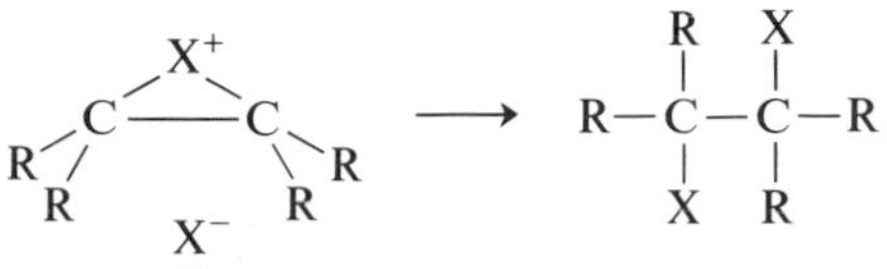

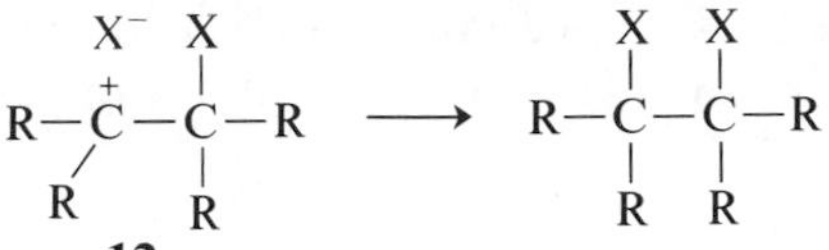

$$
\begin{array}{ccc}
\overset{X^-}{\underset{R}{\overset{+}{R-C}}}\overset{X}{\underset{R}{-C-R}} & \longrightarrow & \overset{X}{\underset{R}{R-C}}\overset{X}{\underset{R}{-C-R}} \\
\mathbf{12} & &
\end{array}
$$

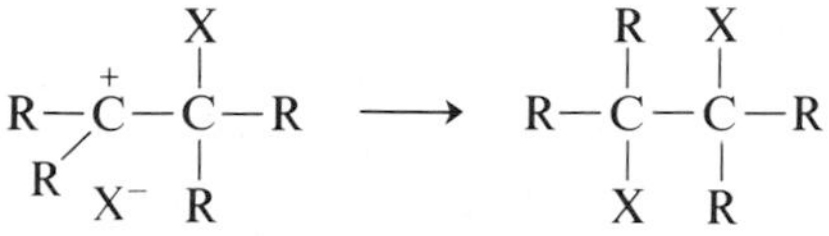

$$
\begin{array}{ccc}
\overset{X}{\underset{R\ \ X^-\ \ R}{\overset{+}{R-C}-C-R}} & \longrightarrow & \overset{R}{\underset{X\ \ \ R}{R-C}}\overset{X}{-C-R} \\
\mathbf{13} & &
\end{array}
$$

The intermediate **12** forms *cis*-products while both **11** and **13** give rise to *trans*-oriented products.

In the absence of complications due to steric factors, the ion pair **12** would be expected to collapse to *cis*-products; however, if steric factors prevent *cis*-attack, a rearrangement to **13** and subsequent *trans*-attack is conceivable.

Halogenations are predicted on the basis of this mechanism to form both *cis*- and *trans*-adducts. In agreement with this idea is the fact that chlorination of phenanthrene affords chiefly the *cis*-dichloride, while bromination of cyclohexene yields a *trans*-dibromide:

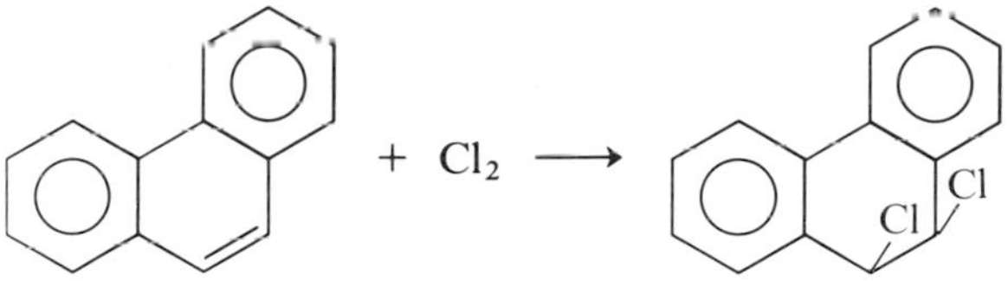

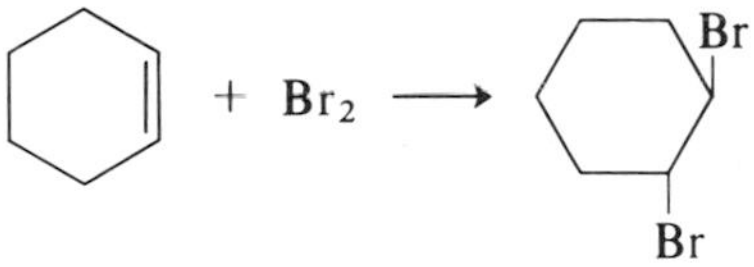

The *cis*-product obtained from the chlorination of phenanthrene almost certainly originates from an ion pair such as **12**:

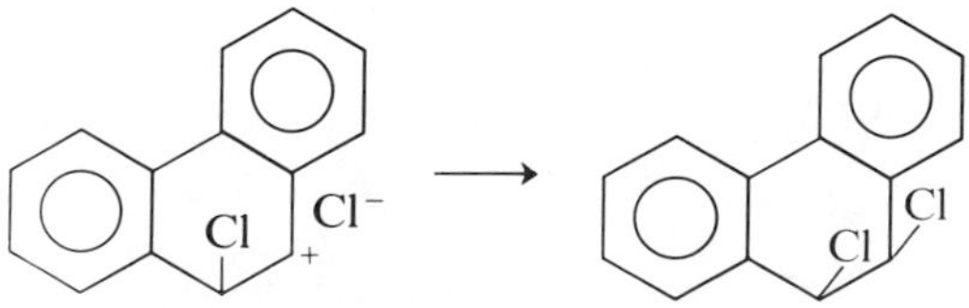

Whether the *trans*-1,2-dibromocyclohexane originates from an intermediate such as **11** (which we write here as the simple bromonium ion) or from a *trans*-ion pair such as **13** is not certain; however, the bromonium ion is the currently accepted intermediate in such *trans*-attacks:

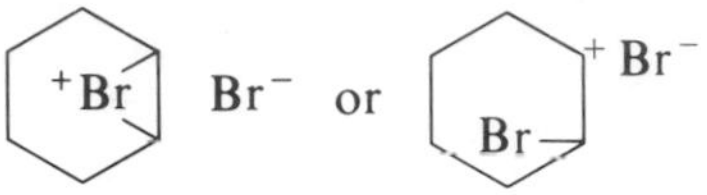

It has been argued by some investigators that intermediates such as **11** are never present in the reaction. Instead, only the carbonium ion pairs **12** and **13** are involved, and the *trans*-orientation that is observed in some halogenations comes from preferential attack by X^- from the *trans*-position.

The *trans*-addition of X_2 to an alkene yields the product,

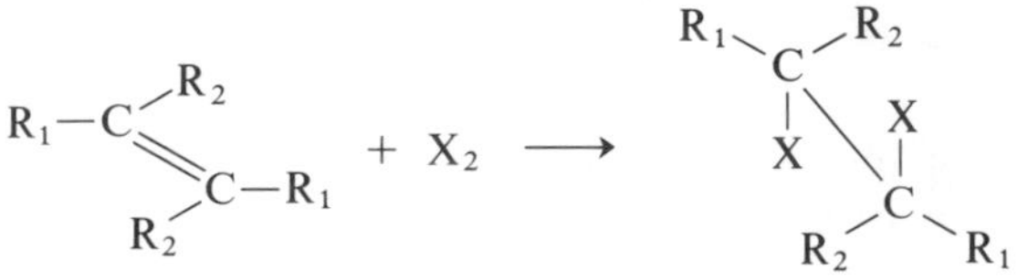

and this product is explained quite readily by assuming an intermediate such as,

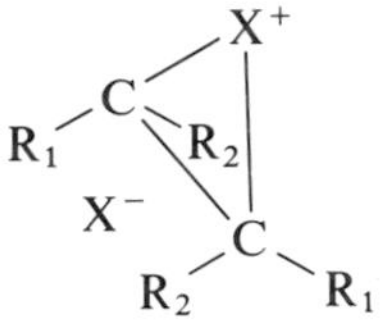

A carbonium ion intermediate also yields the desired product,

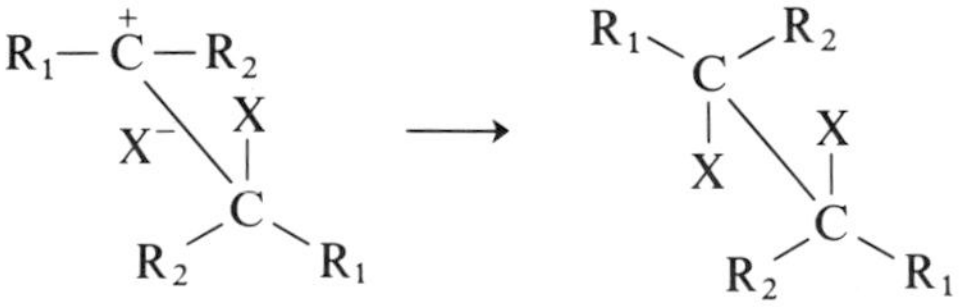

14

But if we allow rotation to occur,

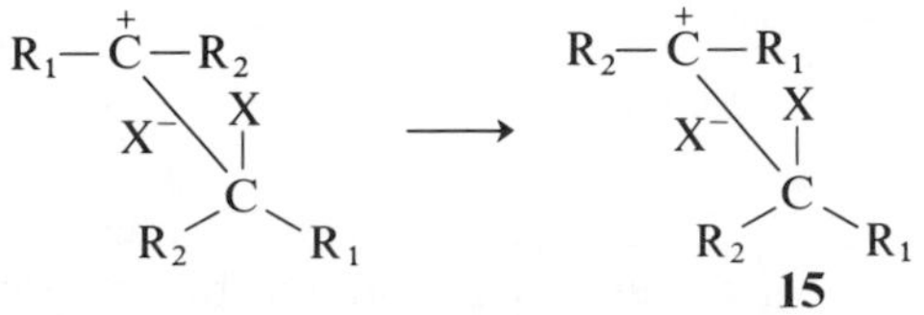

15

and now allow the carbonium ion to react, we form another product:

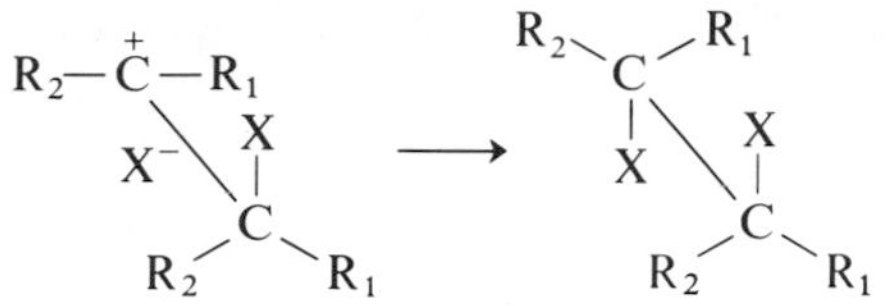

$$R_2-\overset{+}{\underset{\underset{\underset{R_2}{\overset{|}{\overset{C}{\diagdown}}}{\overset{|}{X}}}{\diagdown}}{C}}-R_1 \quad\quad X^- \quad\quad\quad\longrightarrow\quad\quad$$

A carbonium ion mechanism gives the correct product but also predicts the formation of considerable quantities of a second product. This is usually considered to be a weakness of the carbonium ion mechanism as a general explanation for *trans* addition.

We can overcome this shortcoming of the carbonium ion mechanism if we assume that steric factors influence the product geometry. We must assume that steric factors in **14** cause the X^- to attack from the side opposite the halogen atom already present (*trans* attack by X^- rather than *cis*). We must also assume that these interactions prevent rotation to form the cation **15**. In this way we are able to explain *trans*-addition of X_2 without the aid of a bridged intermediate. Unfortunately, there is no evidence that rotation should be seriously restricted in systems such as **14**, and we shall assume in the absence of evidence to the contrary that *trans*-addition to alkenes proceeds by way of the cyclic ion:

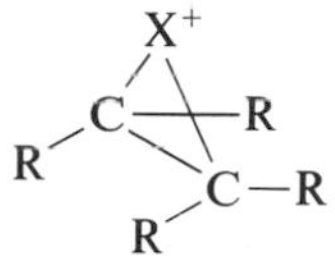

This type of an intermediate explains satisfactorily the bromination of *cis*- and *trans*-stilbene:

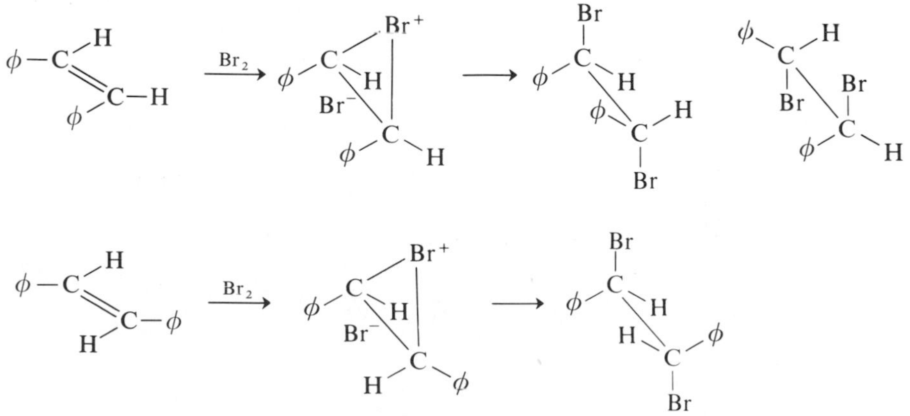

Bromination of *cis*-stilbene gives a racemic mixture of the D- and L-di-bromides, while bromination of *trans*-stilbene affords the *meso*-dibromide. Similar results can be obtained with maleic and fumaric acids (under the proper conditions):

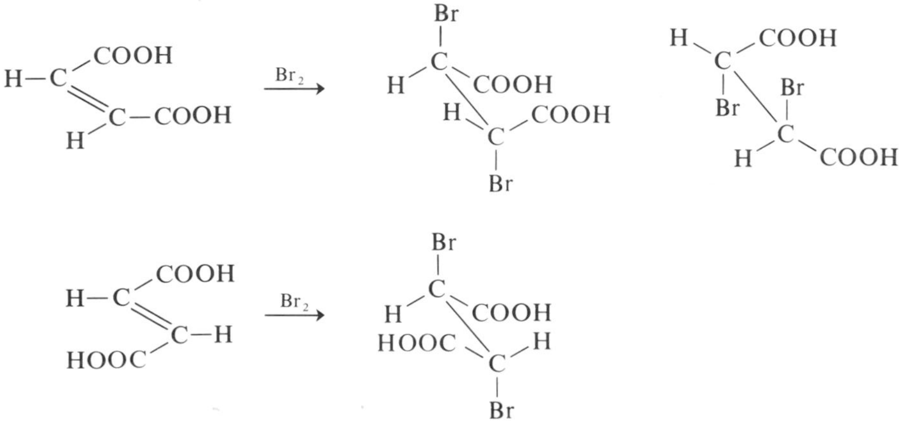

Although direct evidence for a bromonium ion is not available, the assumption of such an intermediate readily explains the observations.

If we carry out the halogenation of alkenes in the presence of nucleophilic solvents or add nucleophilic agents to the reaction, these materials can compete with halide ion. Thus, bromination of ethylene in the presence of added nucleophiles affords products containing these reagents:

$$CH_2=CH_2 + Br_2 \quad \begin{array}{l} \xrightarrow{NaCl} \quad CH_2ClCH_2Br \\ \xrightarrow{NaI} \quad CH_2ICH_2Br \\ \xrightarrow{H_2O} \quad CH_2OHCH_2Br \end{array}$$

The chlorination of ethylene in acetic acid also yields such mixed products,

$$CH_2=CH_2 + Cl_2 \xrightarrow{CH_3COOH} CH_3COOCH_2CH_2Cl$$

and other alkenes behave in a similar fashion:

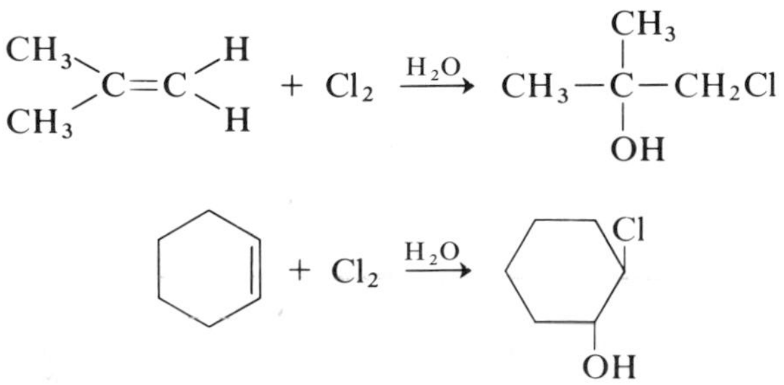

These last two reactions give rather interesting results. The one affords a product where attack has occurred at the most highly substituted carbon atom, and the other shows that *trans*-addition has occurred. Our mechanism must allow both *trans*-addition and $S_N 1$ type attack. These ideas are accommodated by an unsymmetrical chloronium ion **16** with more bonding to the primary carbon atom and an unsymmetrical transition state with similar characteristics, the free energy of activation being smaller for attack at the tertiary carbon atom:

$$
\underset{\textbf{16}}{
\begin{array}{c}
\text{Cl} \\
\text{CH}_3 / \overset{+}{C} = C \overset{H}{\underset{H}{\diagdown}} \\
\text{CH}_3
\end{array}
}
$$

Although a carbonium ion intermediate is possible, some evidence against it exists. The evidence against a carbonium ion intermediate in this type of reaction comes from the behavior of *t*-butylethylene which reacts with bromine in methanol to yield a methyl ether without rearrangement of the carbon skeleton.

Another problem in these halogenations is the nature of the halogenating agent. The reaction of alkenes with bromine in the presence of water yields bromohydrins and some dibromide:

$$
\underset{R}{\overset{R}{\diagdown}} C = C \underset{R}{\overset{R}{\diagup}} + Br_2 \xrightarrow{H_2O}
\underset{\textbf{17}}{
\begin{array}{c}
R \quad R \\
| \quad | \\
R - C - C - R \\
| \quad | \\
OH \quad Br
\end{array}
}
\qquad
\underset{\textbf{18}}{
\begin{array}{c}
R \quad R \\
| \quad | \\
R - C - C - R \\
| \quad | \\
Br \quad Br
\end{array}
}
$$

The bromohydrin could form by attack of water on the bromonium ion, yet an alternative route exists. It is possible that this product results from attack of hypobromous acid HOBr formed by the equilibrium,

$$
Br_2 + 2H_2O \; \rightleftharpoons \; HOBr + H_3O^+ + Br^-
$$

The HOBr might attack the alkene directly to form **17** while **18** would be formed by attack of Br_2. Now according to the equilibrium between bromine and hypobromous acid, the concentration of HOBr depends upon the acidity; adding extra acid decreases its concentration.

Adding extra acid shifts the equilibrium; the concentration of HOBr decreases and that of Br_2 increases. Therefore, if **17** is formed from HOBr and **18** from Br_2, we should find more dibromide and less bromohydrin under these conditions.

Such experiments have been conducted and the results indicate that the relative amounts of **17** and **18** are independent of the acidity. This implies that HOBr is not the active species.

A thorough investigation of this question was carried out on the system,

$$\phi CH=CH\phi + Br_2 \xrightarrow{CH_3OH} \underset{\underset{OCH_3}{|}}{\phi CHCHBr\phi} + \phi CHBrCHBr\phi$$

where the following equilibrium is possible,

$$Br_2 + 2CH_3OH \rightleftarrows CH_3OBr + CH_3\overset{\overset{H}{|}}{\underset{+}{OH}} + Br^-$$

It was found that both the rate of formation of the methyl ether and the fraction of methyl ether in the product were independent of the acidity.

Results such as these show that in the systems studied, it is a molecule of the halogen that is the active species. The halogen and the alkene react first, and the solvent attacks afterwards. The reaction proceeds by the pathway,

$$\underset{R}{\overset{R}{>}}C=C\underset{R}{\overset{R}{<}} + X_2 \longrightarrow R-\underset{R}{\overset{X^+}{\underset{|}{C——C}}}-R \xrightarrow{H_2O} R-\underset{\underset{OH}{|}}{\overset{\overset{R}{|}}{C}}-\underset{\underset{R}{|}}{\overset{\overset{X}{|}}{C}}-R$$

and not by the route,

$$X_2 + 2H_2O \rightleftarrows HOX + H_3O^+ + X^-$$

$$\underset{R}{\overset{R}{>}}C=C\underset{R}{\overset{R}{<}} \qquad HOX \longrightarrow R-\underset{\underset{OH}{|}}{\overset{\overset{R}{|}}{C}}-\underset{\underset{R}{|}}{\overset{\overset{X}{|}}{C}}-R$$

The mechanism that we have postulated for halogenation involves species such as,

$$\underset{R}{\overset{R}{/}}C\overset{\delta+}{=\!\!=\!\!=}C\underset{R}{\overset{\overset{Br^{\delta-}}{|}}{\underset{R}{\backslash}}} \quad and \quad \underset{R}{\overset{R}{/}}C\overset{Br^+}{=\!\!=\!\!=}C\underset{R}{\overset{Br^-}{\backslash}}$$

These are only slightly different from the intermediates presented for the addition of strong acids, and they are not really different from those postulated for the reaction of alkenes with peroxyacids. Peroxyacids react with alkenes to form epoxides and *trans*-diols (glycols); processes which are quite similar to those just presented:

$$\underset{R}{\overset{R}{>}}C=C\underset{R}{\overset{R}{<}} + R-\overset{\overset{O}{||}}{C}-O-O-H \longrightarrow R-\underset{R}{\overset{R}{\underset{|}{C}}}\overset{O}{——}\underset{R}{\overset{R}{\underset{|}{C}}}-R + R\overset{\overset{O}{||}}{C}OH$$

13.4 The Epoxidation of Alkenes

When treated with the appropriate reagents, alkenes are oxidized to a variety
of products. Epoxides, diols, dialdehydes, diketones, diacids, ketoacids, and
so forth can be prepared from olefinic materials. Oxidative reactions are also
useful for degradative purposes. An unknown alkene under oxidative conditions is degraded to simpler products. Elucidating the structure of these simpler
products allows one to determine the structure of the original material.

One of the milder oxidations results from treatment of the alkene with
peroxyacids. These peroxyacids have the structure,

$$R-\overset{\overset{\displaystyle O}{\|}}{C}-O-O-H$$

and treating an alkene with such an oxidizing agent can lead to the formation
of an epoxide:

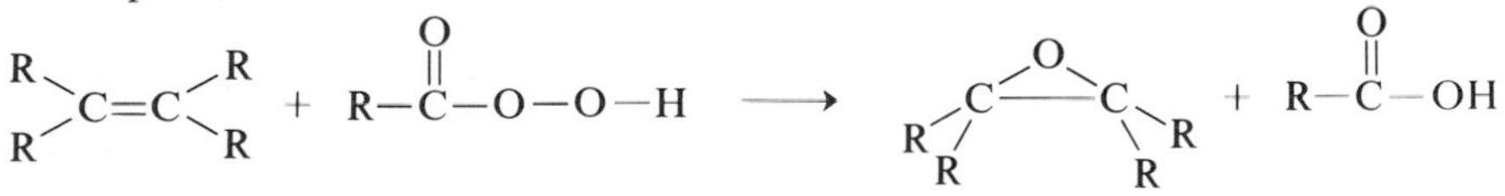

$$\underset{R}{\overset{R}{>}}C=C\underset{R}{\overset{R}{<}} \;+\; R-\overset{\overset{\displaystyle O}{\|}}{C}-O-O-H \;\longrightarrow\; \underset{R/\;\;\;R}{\overset{O}{C-C}} \;+\; R-\overset{\overset{\displaystyle O}{\|}}{C}-OH$$

The peroxyacids that are used in these reactions are easily prepared. Treatment of dibenzoylperoxide with sodium methoxide affords the sodium salt
of peroxybenzoic acid:

$$\phi-\overset{\overset{\displaystyle O}{\|}}{C}-O-O-\overset{\overset{\displaystyle O}{\|}}{C}-\phi + NaOCH_3 \;\longrightarrow\; \phi-\overset{\overset{\displaystyle O}{\|}}{C}-O-ONa + \phi-\overset{\overset{\displaystyle O}{\|}}{C}OCH_3$$

Careful neutralization of the sodium salt with sulfuric acid gives rise to the
acid, which is separated by extraction into chloroform.

A particularly useful acid for effecting epoxidations is peroxyphthalic acid:

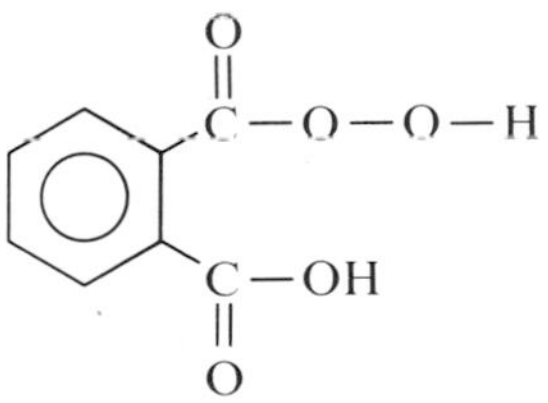

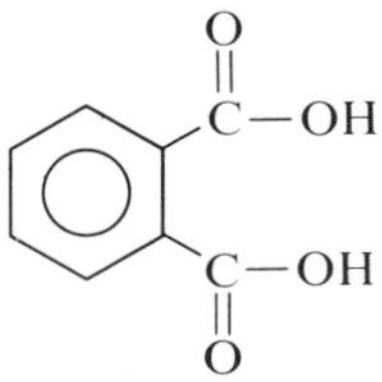

This reagent is soluble in ether; however, the phthalic acid, that results as a product of the reaction is insoluble in this solvent. Epoxides are sensitive to acid, yet if peroxyphthalic acid is used in ethereal solution, the resulting acid precipitates from the solution and is therefore unable to harm the epoxide.

This acid is prepared by mixing phthalic anhydride with sodium perborate and acidifying the resulting aqueous solution. The peroxy acid is then extracted into ether.

Peroxyacetic acid and peroxyformic acid are also commonly used peroxyacids. These are prepared directly in solution by treating the acid with hydrogen peroxide:

$$\underset{\substack{\| \\ O}}{CH_3C}-OH + H_2O_2 \; \rightleftarrows \; \underset{\substack{\| \\ O}}{CH_3C}-O-OH + H_2O$$

$$\underset{\substack{\| \\ O}}{H-C}-OH + H_2O_2 \; \rightleftarrows \; \underset{\substack{\| \\ O}}{H-C}-O-OH + H_2O$$

Other reagents of this type are peroxytrifluoroacetic acid and *p*-nitroperoxybenzoic acid, both of which are highly reactive:

$$\underset{\substack{\| \\ O}}{CF_3C}-O-OH \qquad O_2N-\underset{\substack{\| \\ O}}{\underset{\bigcirc}{}}C-O-OH$$

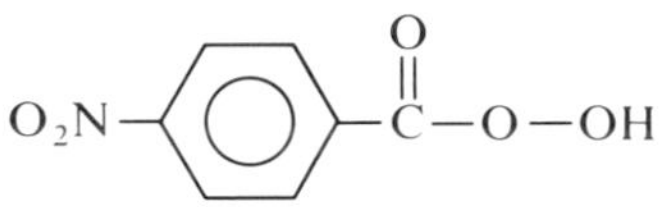

An alkene when treated with any of these reagents suffers oxidation. With the milder of these peroxyacids the product is usually an epoxide. The equation is,

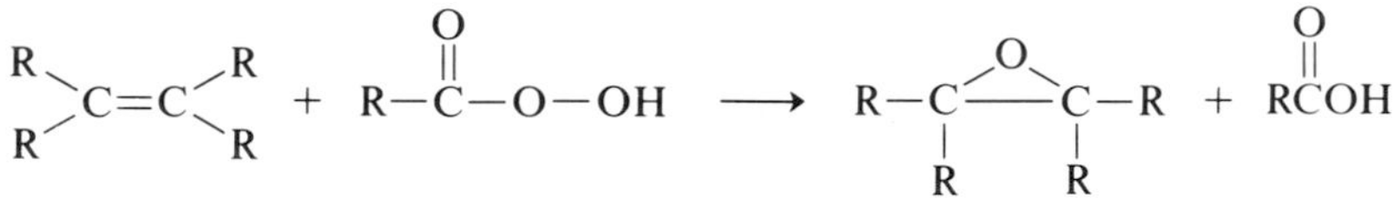

$$\underset{R}{\overset{R}{>}}C=C\underset{R}{\overset{R}{<}} + \underset{\substack{\| \\ O}}{R-C}-O-OH \longrightarrow R-\underset{R}{\overset{O}{\underset{|}{C}}}\overset{\diagdown}{\underset{R}{\underset{|}{C}}}-R + \underset{\substack{\| \\ O}}{RCOH}$$

Thus, when treated with peroxybenzoic acid, cyclopentene yields cyclopentene oxide, cyclohexene affords cyclohexene oxide, and styrene forms styrene oxide:

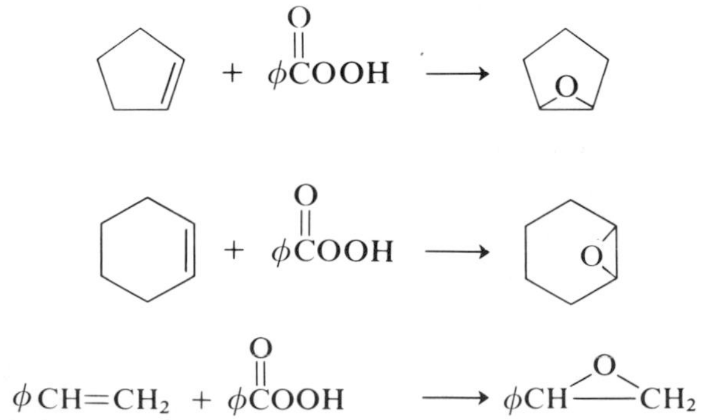

$$\phi CH=CH_2 + \underset{\substack{\| \\ O}}{\phi COOH} \longrightarrow \phi CH\overset{O}{\overline{\quad\diagup\diagdown\quad}}CH_2$$

   The mechanism usually given for this process is not much different from the previous mechanisms for addition to the double bond. The electrons in the olefinic linkage are available for bond formation. The alkene acts as a nucleophile and attacks the peroxyacid to yield the intermediate **19**. The group RCOO⁻ is a good leaving group.

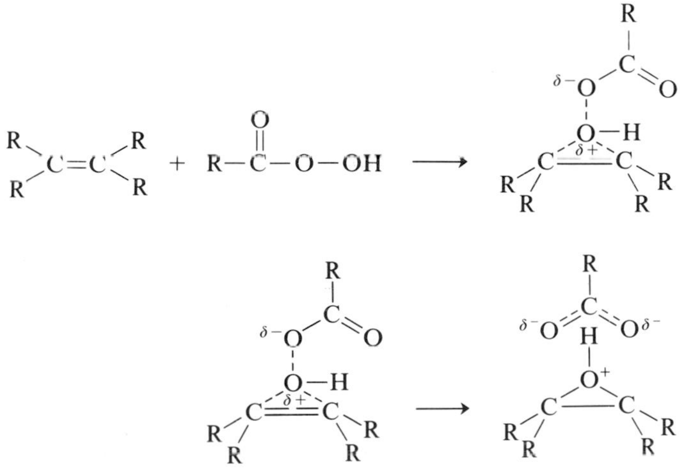

   This ion pair **19** decomposes by various routes. With the aromatic peroxyacids such as peroxybenzoic acid and peroxyphthalic acid a proton is abstracted by the anion RCOO⁻ and the product is an epoxide:

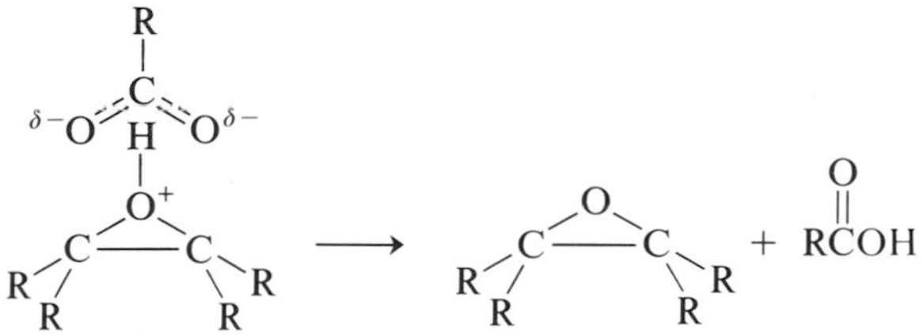

   In certain special cases it appears that the oxonium ion opens to a carbonium ion, and in these cases rearrangements and addition occur (both *cis-* and *trans-*additions are conceivable):

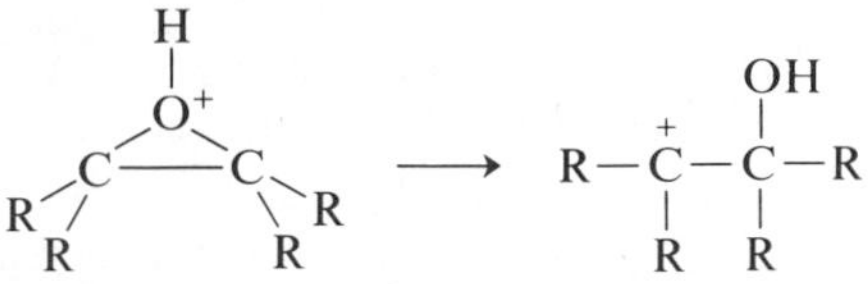

A third route is open for decomposition of the oxonium ion, and this is the route of preference when peroxyformic acid and peroxytrifluoroacetic acid are used. With these reagents the epoxide may be formed, but reversibly. The acids HCOOH and CF_3COOH are strong acids, and they are able to open up the epoxide ring. With these acids the concentration of protonated epoxide is high, and the conjugate bases of these acids ($HCOO^-$ and CF_3COO^-) carry out an S_N2 attack on the protonated epoxide:

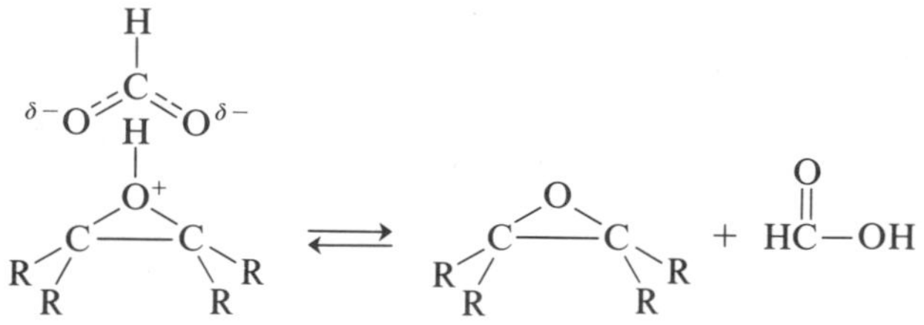

Then,

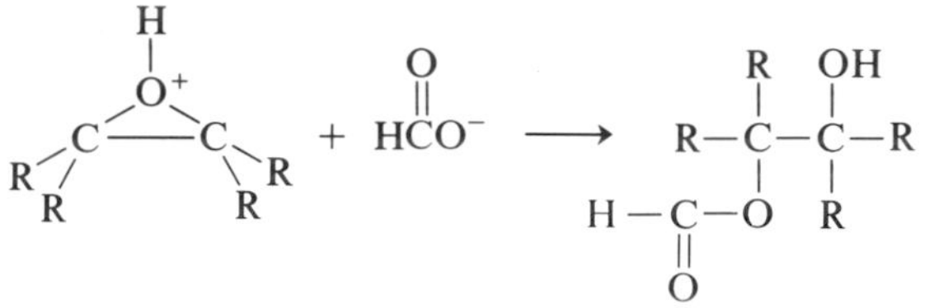

From peroxyformic acid the products are hydroxyformates, which when hydrolyzed with base, yield *trans*-diols,

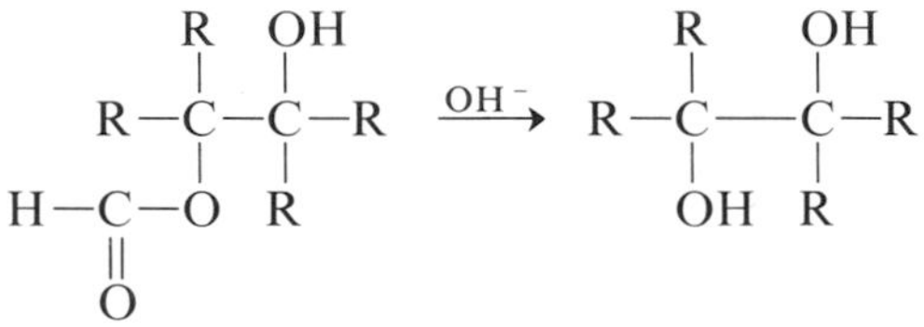

An alkene can be converted to an epoxide, which since it contains a three-membered ring, is quite reactive. Acids open the ring. We have already seen that formic acid is capable of doing so. The products in this case are formate esters. The epoxide ring behaves in a similar fashion towards other acids and is also opened by nucleophiles. An acid catalyst increases the rate but is not always required.

The mechanisms of these ring openings is a subject of much interest and at least two mechanisms can be written. One involves an S_N2 attack by a nucleophile at one of the carbon atoms of the epoxide, the nucleophile attacking from the side opposite the oxygen atom. A second mechanism is also an S_N2

displacement by a nucleophile but on the protonated epoxide. Thus ethylene oxide reacts with chloride ion and the mechanism for chlorohydrin formation is,

$$\overset{\displaystyle O}{CH_2\!\!-\!\!CH_2} + Cl^- \longrightarrow \underset{\underset{Cl}{|}}{CH_2CH_2O^-}$$

$$\underset{\underset{Cl}{|}}{CH_2\!-\!CH_2O^-} + H_2O \rightleftharpoons \underset{\underset{Cl}{|}}{CH_2CH_2OH} + OH^-$$

This reaction is reversible and the reverse process constitutes a general synthesis of epoxides. Thus, the treatment of ethylene chlorohydrin with hydroxide ion reaffords the epoxide:

$$\underset{\underset{Cl}{|}}{CH_2CH_2OH} + OH^- \rightleftharpoons \underset{\underset{Cl}{|}}{CH_2CH_2O^-} + H_2O$$

$$\underset{\underset{Cl}{|}}{CH_2CH_2O^-} \longrightarrow \overset{\displaystyle O}{CH_2\!-\!CH_2} + Cl^-$$

We are able to study the reaction in either direction and microscopic reversibility requires that the mechanism in one direction be the reverse of that for the other.

If these ideas are correct, the general rate expression for ethylene oxide formation in aqueous solution is expected to be,

$$\frac{d[\triangle]}{dt} = k[ClCH_2CH_2OH][OH^-]$$

while in the opposite direction,

$$-\frac{d[\triangle]}{dt} = k'[\triangle][Cl^-]$$

Furthermore, if the second step in epoxide formation is rate limiting, the first step in halohydrin formation must be rate limiting for the reaction in the opposite direction.

The reaction in either direction is expected to be a second order process, and such kinetic expressions have been observed in a number of cases. The reactions not only of ethylene chlorohydrin but of other chloro- and bromo-hydrins with sodium hydroxide are first order in hydroxide ion and first order in halohydrin; kinetic results that are consistent with the postulated mechanism. The epoxide cleavage is observed to be first order in chloride ion and first order in ethylene oxide, and this is also consistent with the mechanism presented. The kinetic results do not indicate the rate limiting step, but since proton transfers are generally rapid in reactions of this type, we assume that in either direction, the displacement process is rate limiting.

Another mechanism can be written for epoxide cleavage. This is an acid catalyzed process that proceeds as follows,

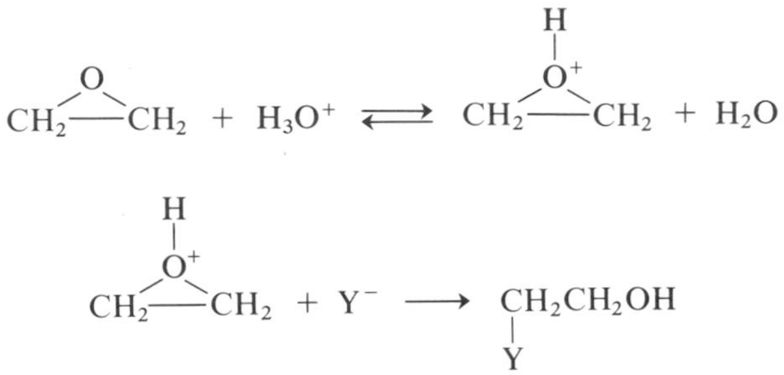

$$CH_2\overset{O}{-}CH_2 + H_3O^+ \rightleftharpoons CH_2\overset{\overset{H}{|}\overset{O^+}{}}{-}CH_2 + H_2O$$

$$CH_2\overset{\overset{H}{|}\overset{O^+}{}}{-}CH_2 + Y^- \longrightarrow CH_2CH_2OH \overset{|}{Y}$$

where the second step is an S_N2 displacement on the conjugate acid of the epoxide by a general nucleophile Y^-.

Both mechanisms are operative, and under the proper conditions the two processes can proceed to a measurable extent simultaneously. It has been shown that the reaction of ethylene oxide with dilute hydrochloric acid follows the rate law,

$$-\frac{d[\triangle]}{dt} = k_1[\triangle] + k_2[\triangle][H^+] + k_3[\triangle][Cl^-] + k_4[\triangle][H^+][Cl^-]$$

The first term is a reaction of the epoxide with the solvent to yield ethylene glycol (direct attack of the oxide by water). The second term is due to reaction of water with the conjugate acid of the epoxide. Analogous interpretations are given to the third and fourth terms, reaction of chloride ion with the oxide to yield chlorohydrin and reaction of chloride ion with its conjugate acid.

The constant k_4 is much larger than k_3 which indicates that the S_N2 process,

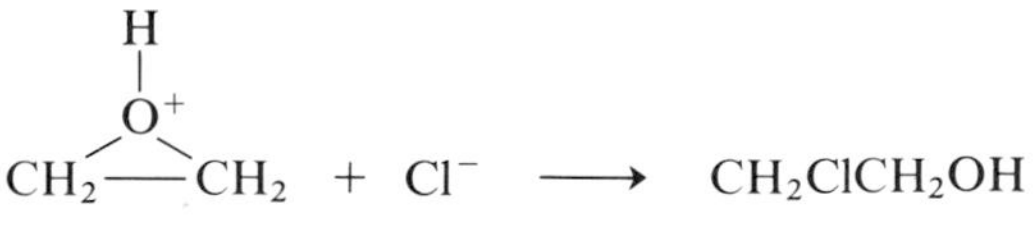

$$CH_2\overset{\overset{H}{|}\overset{O^+}{}}{-}CH_2 + Cl^- \longrightarrow CH_2ClCH_2OH$$

is more favorable than

$$CH_2\overset{O}{-}CH_2 + Cl^- \longrightarrow CH_2ClCH_2O^-$$

For the compound $CH_2OHCHCH_2$ reacting with bromide ion, the ratio k_4/k_3 has a value of several thousand at 20°C.

We mentioned that the reaction of ethylene oxide with chloride ion is reversible and that this reverse process is general and constitutes a synthesis of epoxides. The equilibrium has been studied in aqueous solution, and the equilibrium constant for the reaction,

$$CH_2ClCH_2OH + OH^- \rightleftharpoons \overset{O}{\overset{/\backslash}{CH_2CH_2}} + Cl^- + H_2O$$

has a value of 3.1×10^3. When equimolar concentrations of halohydrin and hydroxide ion are employed, this leads to the result that at equilibrium 98% of the material is in the form of the oxide,

$$3.1 \times 10^3 = \frac{\alpha^2}{(1 - \alpha)^2}$$

$$\alpha = 0.98$$

The terms $\Delta H°$ and $\Delta S°$ have also been evaluated, $\Delta H° = 4$ kcal while $\Delta S° = 30$ cal/deg. The positive $\Delta S°$ arises from an increase in the number of molecules upon passing to the products.

We have presented kinetic evidence. The general rate expression for reaction of ethylene oxide contains terms involving the nucleophile, and this is consistent with the proposed mechanisms, S_N2 attack on an oxide and S_N2 attack on its conjugate acid. Other evidence exists. When propylene and isobutylene oxides are reacted with water enriched in O^{18}, the following results are obtained,

$$\overset{O}{\overset{/\backslash}{CH_3CHCH_2}} \xrightarrow{HO^{18-}} \underset{82\%}{\overset{OH}{\underset{|}{CH_3CHCH_2O^{18}H}}} \quad \underset{18\%}{\overset{O^{18}H}{\underset{|}{CH_3CHCH_2OH}}}$$

$$\overset{O}{\overset{/\backslash}{\underset{\underset{CH_3}{|}}{CH_3C-CH_2}}} \xrightarrow{HO^{18-}} \underset{90\%}{\overset{OH}{\underset{\underset{CH_3}{|}}{CH_3CCH_2O^{18}H}}} \quad \underset{10\%}{\overset{O^{18}H}{\underset{\underset{CH_3}{|}}{CH_3CCH_2OH}}}$$

$$\overset{O}{\overset{/\backslash}{CH_3CHCH_2}} \xrightarrow{H_3O^{18+}} \underset{26\%}{\overset{OH}{\underset{|}{CH_3CHCH_2O^{18}H}}} \quad \underset{74\%}{\overset{O^{18}H}{\underset{|}{CH_3CHCH_2OH}}}$$

$$\overset{O}{\overset{/\backslash}{\underset{\underset{CH_3}{|}}{CH_3C-CH_2}}} \xrightarrow{H_3O^{18+}} \underset{100\%}{\overset{O^{18}H}{\underset{\underset{CH_3}{|}}{CH_3CCH_2OH}}}$$

The results of the base catalyzed reaction are clearly consistent with an S_N2 process. While the acid catalyzed reaction appears to be more consistent with a carbonium ion intermediate, remember that these epoxides are unsymmetrical and a preference for the transition state,

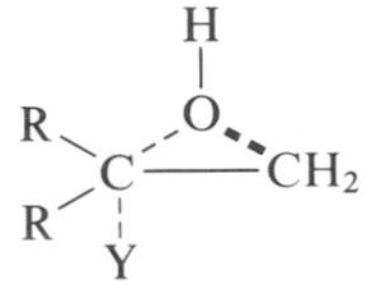

is not unreasonable.

A carbonium ion intermediate is not required to explain the acid catalyzed results. This mechanism for epoxide openings involving a cation is apparently ruled out by stereochemical results. Thus, cyclohexene oxide yields only the *trans*-diol when reacted with acid:

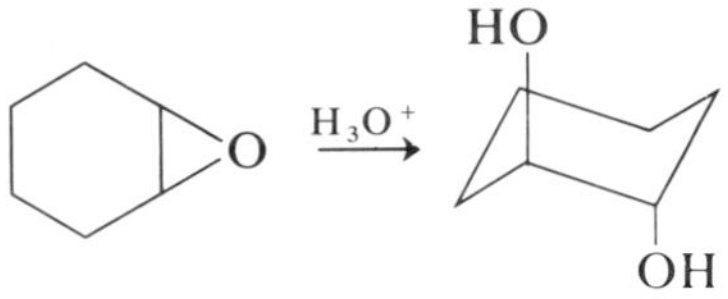

Addition of hydrogen chloride to cyclohexene oxide yields the *trans*-chlorohydrin:

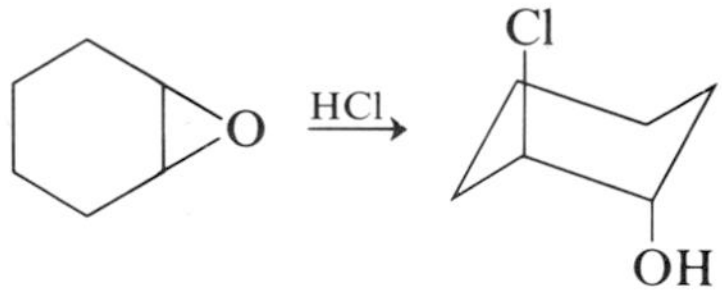

Although a diequatorial conformation is generally preferred, it is probably the diaxial conformation of the product that is formed first.

Cyclopentene oxide yields the *trans*-diol, and this same product originates from the reaction of cyclopentene with peroxyformic acid followed by hydrolysis of the formate ester:

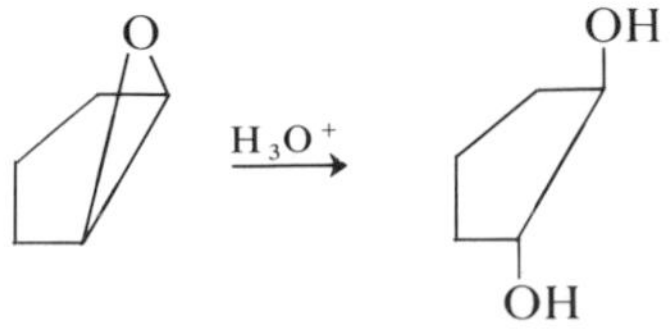

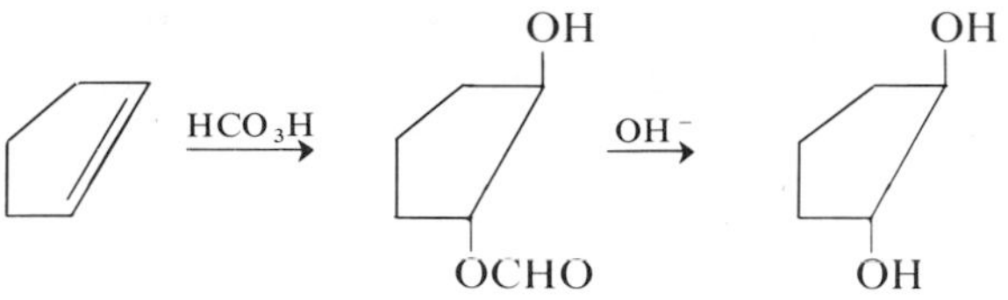

Thus peroxyformic acid also yields a *trans*-adduct.

The fact that cyclopentene and cyclohexene oxides are opened by acids to *trans*-products favors the idea of an S_N2 attack.

The epoxide, *trans*-butene oxide, reacts with ammonia to yield the *erythro* product, a reaction that provides additional evidence for the S_N2 opening:

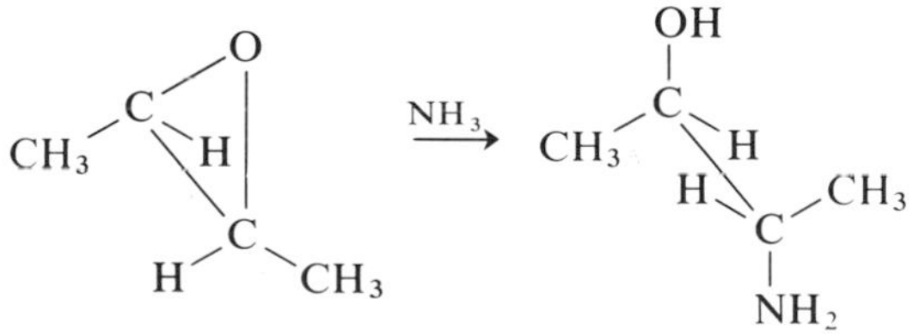

In the opposite direction, the reactions of the halohydrins with potassium hydroxide afford evidence for the S_N2 nature of the reaction. The *erythro* chlorohydrin **20** yields the *trans*-oxide while the *threo* chlorohydrin **21** affords the *cis*-isomer:

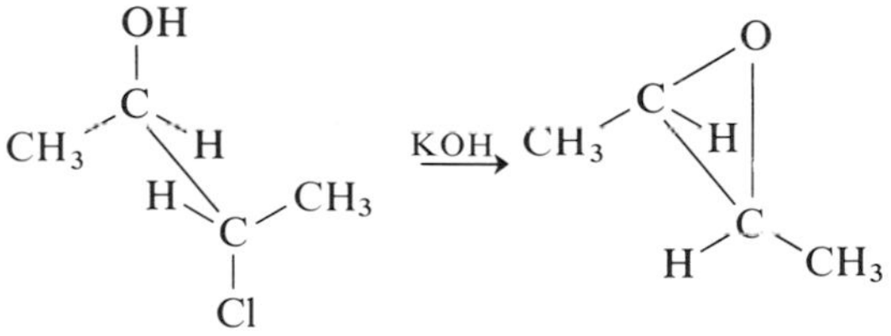

20

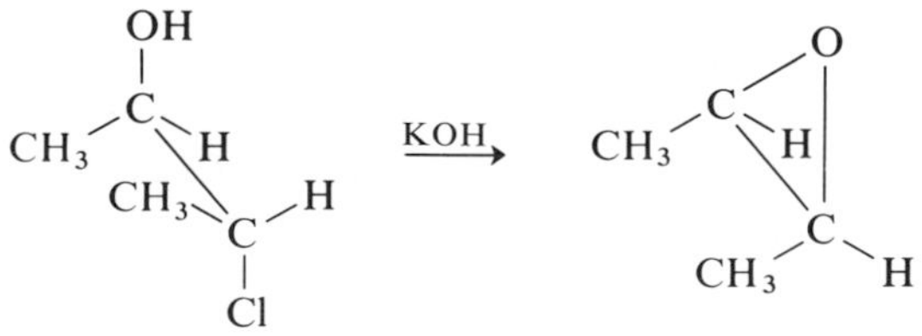

21

These results provide good evidence for transition states in which the pertinent atoms are *trans* and coplanar. The transition states are, for the *erythro* compound **20**,

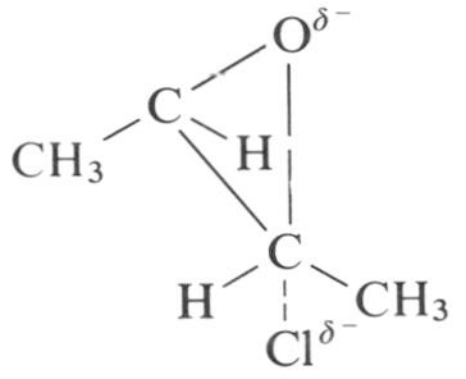

$$CH_3-C\overset{O^{\delta-}}{\underset{H}{\diagdown}}\cdots\overset{H}{\underset{Cl^{\delta-}}{C}}-CH_3$$

while for the *threo* material,

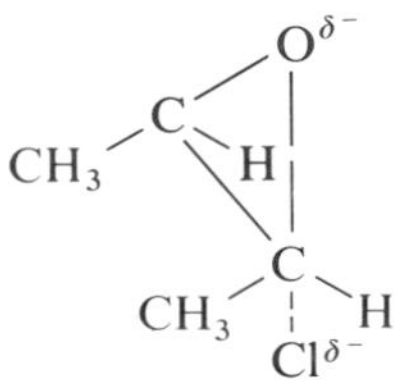

$$CH_3-C\overset{O^{\delta-}}{\underset{H}{\diagdown}}\cdots\overset{CH_3}{\underset{Cl^{\delta-}}{C}}-H$$

Since the two methyl groups are *cis*-oriented in the second transition state but *trans*-oriented in the first, we expect the *erythro* isomer to react more readily.

Assuming now that the reaction of the halohydrins with potassium hydroxide is definitely an S_N2 process, we can use these results to study the stereochemistry of the acid catalyzed openings of the *cis*- and *trans*-butene oxides.

When the *cis*- and *trans*-butene oxides are reacted with hydrogen chloride, hydrogen bromide, or hydrogen iodide, inversion of configuration occurs at one of the carbon atoms. The following results are obtained,

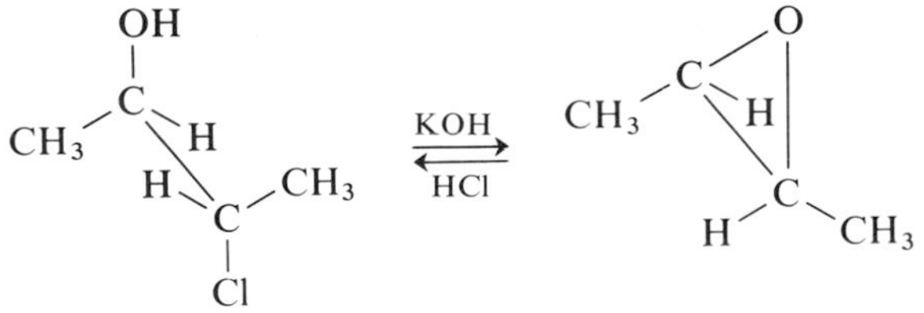

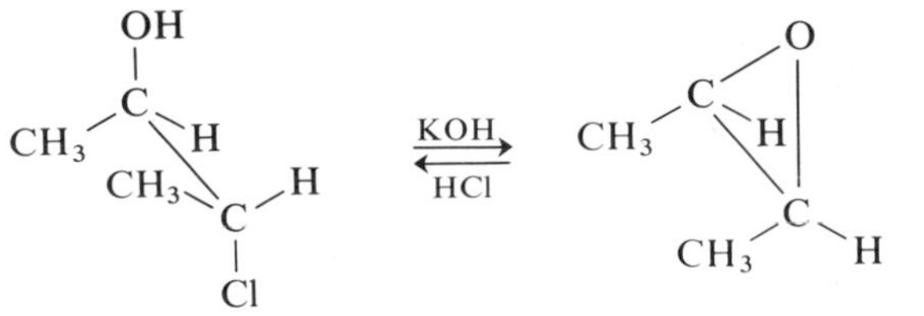

$$CH_3-\overset{OH}{\underset{H}{\overset{|}{C}}}\overset{H}{\underset{\underset{Cl}{|}}{C}}-CH_3 \quad\underset{HCl}{\overset{KOH}{\rightleftharpoons}}\quad CH_3-C\overset{O}{\diagdown}\overset{H}{\underset{H}{C}}-CH_3$$

$$CH_3-\overset{OH}{\underset{CH_3}{\overset{|}{C}}}\overset{H}{\underset{\underset{Cl}{|}}{C}}-H \quad\underset{HCl}{\overset{KOH}{\rightleftharpoons}}\quad CH_3-C\overset{O}{\diagdown}\overset{H}{\underset{CH_3}{C}}-H$$

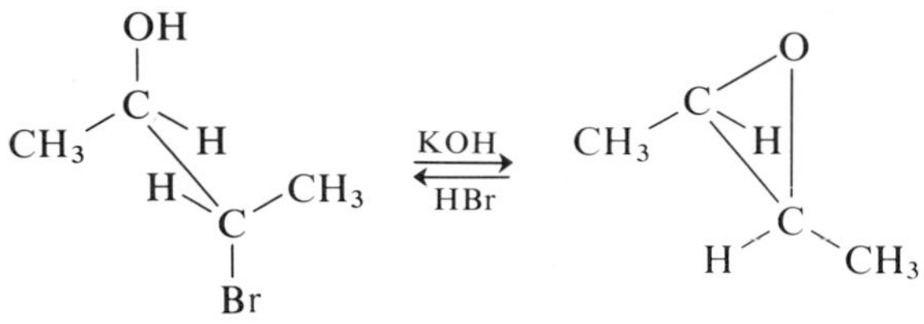

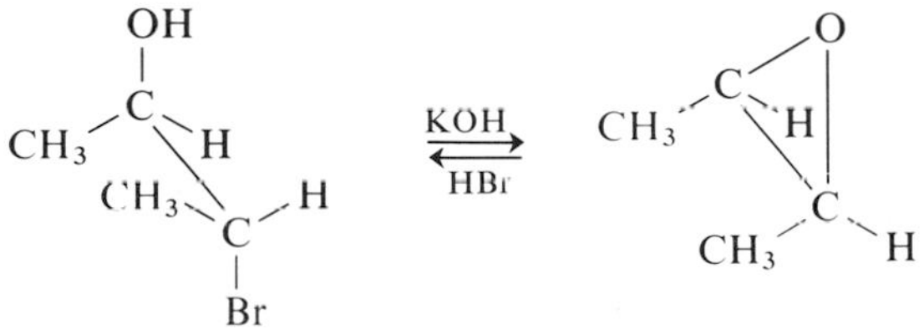

Since the reaction with KOH is certainly an S_N2 process, the epoxide opening with HX is best explained by a similar mechanism, and this eliminates a carbonium ion intermediate during the acid catalyzed opening.

The opening of the butene oxides occurs with inversion of configuration, and the cyclic oxides such as cyclohexene and cyclopentene oxide open to *trans*-products. Thus, a carbonium ion intermediate is probably not involved. Other mechanisms can be written that account for these stereochemical results (for example, open cations and restricted rotations), but a bimolecular displacement reaction is certainly the simplest.

The reactions of *meta* and *para* substituted styrene oxides with benzyl amine have been studied:

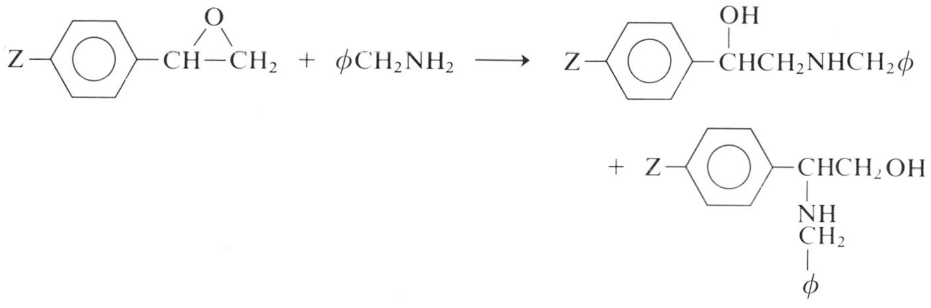

Reaction at the methylene position is characterized by a positive ρ (+0.87). Electron withdrawers increase the rate of this reaction. Attack at the benzyl position has a negative ρ (−1.15). These results can be explained in terms of the degree of bond making and bond breaking in the two transition states. For example, attack at the benzyl position leads to a transition state in which the benzyl carbon atom develops positive charge.

In some cases epoxide cleavage is governed by third order rate expressions containing terms for the epoxide, the nucleophile Y^-, and either the conjugate acid HY or a molecule of the solvent. The mechanism for these third order processes may be more complex than that presented; alternatively, the role of the third molecule may be to solvate the transition state.

Several epoxides have been observed to open with retention of configuration. For example, the following cyclic transformation has been conducted,

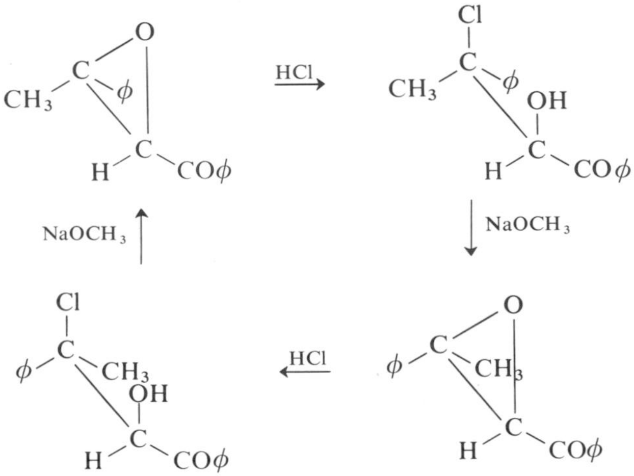

Since the closure with methoxide ion must proceed with inversion, addition of hydrogen chloride must be accompanied by retention of configuration at the halogen bearing carbon atom. The product geometries can be explained in no other way. Thus, this sequence of reactions affords proof that hydrogen chloride adds to these oxide systems with retention of configuration.

An explanation in terms of participation by the carbonyl oxygen atom has been advanced:

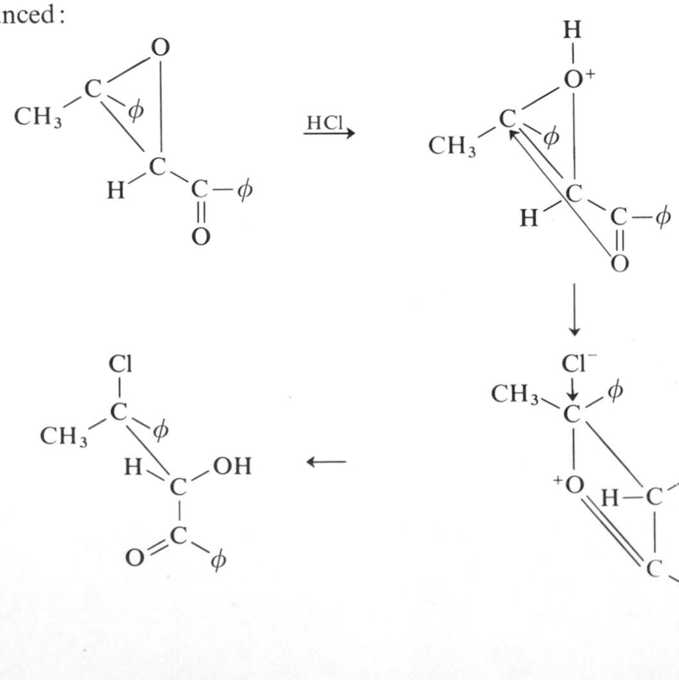

Amines open the epoxide ring:

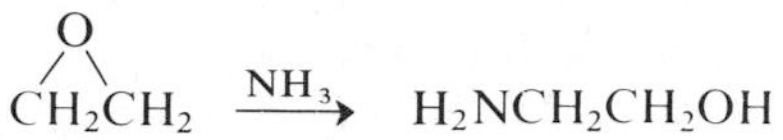

$$\overset{\displaystyle O}{\underset{\displaystyle CH_2CH_2}{\triangle}} \xrightarrow{NH_3} H_2NCH_2CH_2OH$$

If an excess of the epoxide is used, an amine can react with more than a single molecule:

$$RNH_2 + 2\overset{\displaystyle O}{\underset{\displaystyle CH_2CH_2}{\triangle}} \longrightarrow RN(CH_2CH_2OH)_2$$

Grignard reagents react with epoxides and this serves as a synthesis of alcohols,

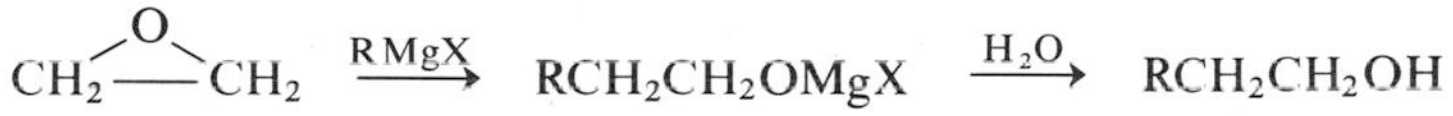

$$\overset{\displaystyle O}{\underset{\displaystyle CH_2\!-\!CH_2}{\triangle}} \xrightarrow{RMgX} RCH_2CH_2OMgX \xrightarrow{H_2O} RCH_2CH_2OH$$

As the following reaction illustrates, lithium aluminum hydride reduces epoxides to alcohols:

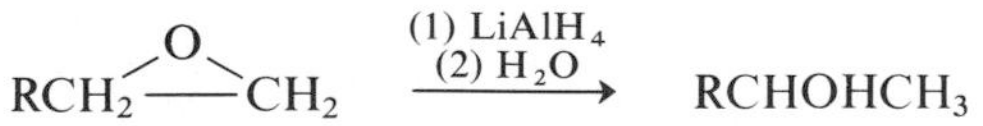

$$\overset{\displaystyle O}{\underset{\displaystyle RCH_2\!-\!CH_2}{\triangle}} \xrightarrow[(2)\ H_2O]{(1)\ LiAlH_4} RCHOHCH_3$$

An interesting reaction occurs in the carbohydrate series when the triacetate **22** reacts with aqueous hydroxide. The hydroxide ion hydrolyzes the esters to the alcohols and the conjugate base **23** effects a nucleophilic displacement at the epoxide carbon atom:

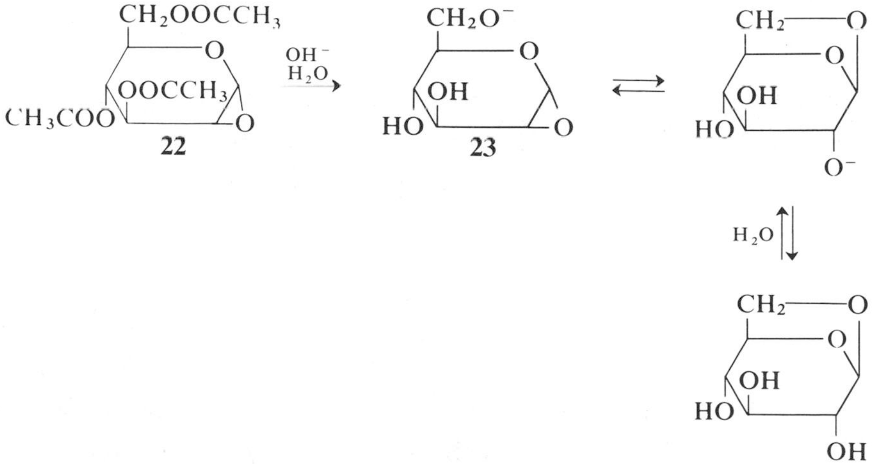

13.5 Other Oxidations

Diols are prepared by treating an alkene with peroxyformic acid and subsequently hydrolyzing the resulting ester or by opening an epoxide in the presence of water. An alternative method which also leads to these materials, one which involves a *cis*-addition to the olefinic linkage, is to treat the olefin with an alkaline solution of potassium permanganate. The products are diols; and the intermediate is an anion such as **24**:

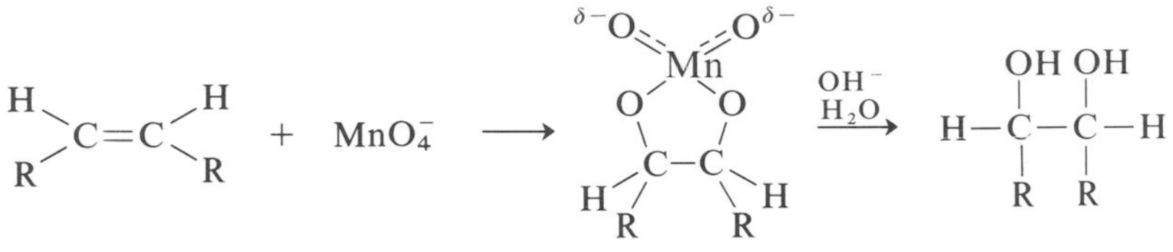

24

For compounds such as cyclopentene the diol that results from reaction with alkaline potassium permanganate is not the same as the product obtained by opening the epoxide. The former process gives rise to the *meso* compound **25** while the latter yields a racemic mixture of the *d* and *l* materials **26**:

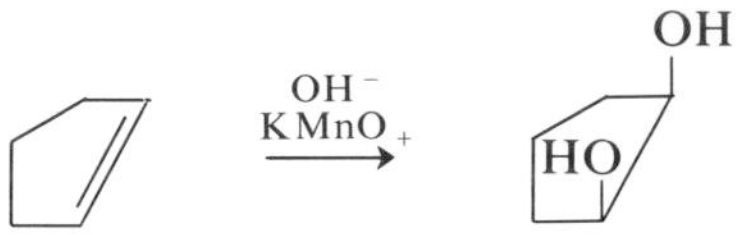

25

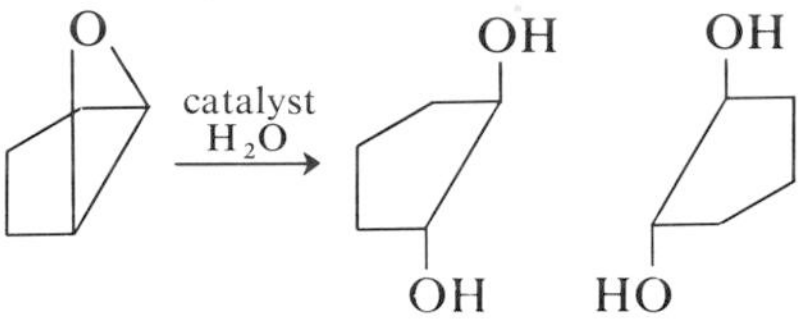

26

Of course, when the resulting diol does not contain the necessary asymmetric carbon atoms, the same product results from both processes:

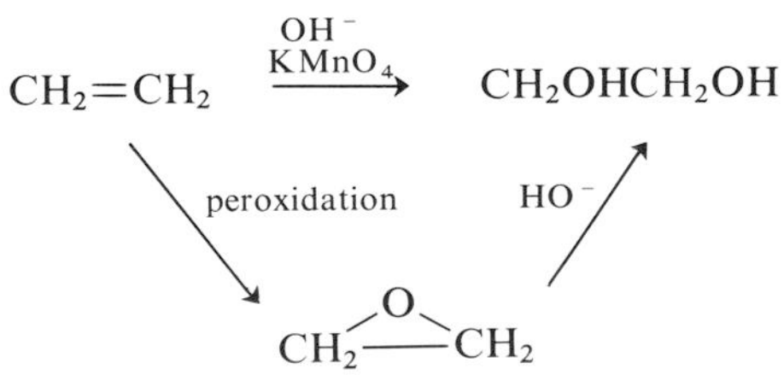

In the permanganate oxidation, all attempts to isolate intermediates such as **24** have been unsuccessful; however, it has been shown using permanganate labeled with O^{18} that both of the oxygen atoms in the diol come from the permanganate, and this fact is consistent with such an intermediate.

Osmium tetroxide OsO_4 also effects *cis*-hydroxylations. In this case an intermediate has been isolated, and this intermediate presumably has the cyclic structure **27**:

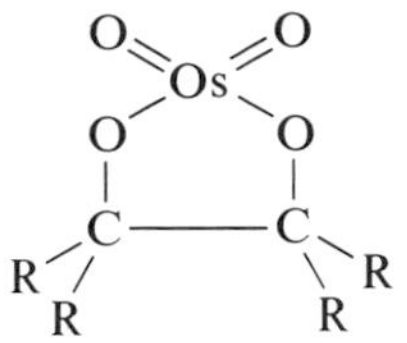

27

Since it is soluble in either, osmium tetroxide is extremely convenient. Most alkenes are also soluble in this solvent, and reaction proceeds readily. The cyclic osmate ester **27** is afterwards decomposed by heating it with a mixture of water and sodium sulfite. Alcohol serves as a convenient solvent for the decomposition. The product is the diol. Reactions have also been conducted using pyridine and dioxane as solvents instead of ether. These solvents are advantageous when the solubility of the alkene in ether is poor.

Examples of reactions with osmium tetroxide are numerous. Thus, 9,10-dimethylphenanthrene yields the *cis*-diol when treated with osmium tetroxide, and cyclohexene behaves similarly:

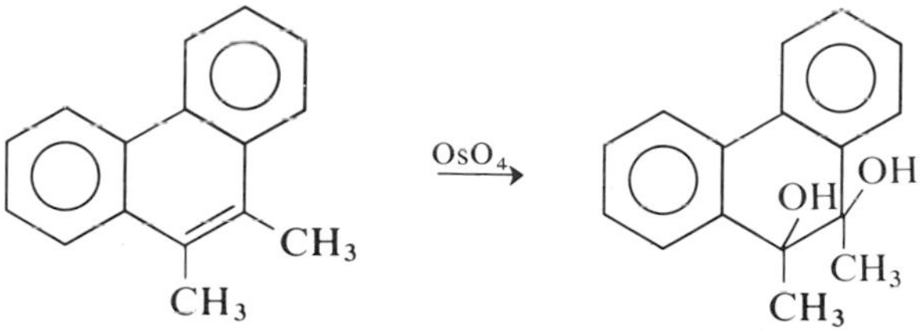

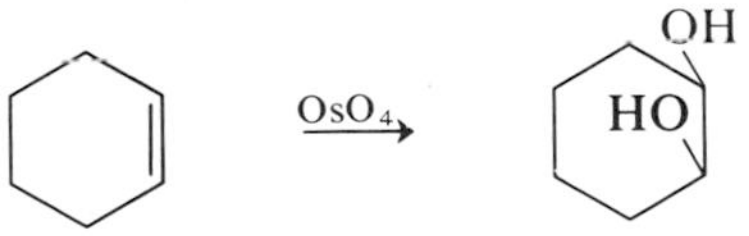

Potassium permanganate also converts cyclohexene to the *cis*-diol; however, this reagent is a powerful oxidizing agent which can also cleave the double bond. Thus, in addition to the *cis*-diol quantities of adipic acid (as the potassium salt) are present:

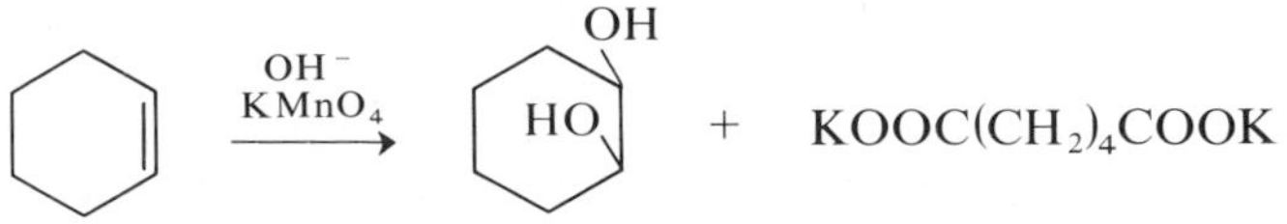

When an alkene is treated with permanganate at higher temperatures, cleavage products predominate. These reactions produce ketones and acids:

$$\underset{R}{\overset{H}{>}}C=C\underset{R}{\overset{H}{<}} \quad \xrightarrow{\text{KMnO}_4} \quad 2\,\text{RCOOK} \quad \xrightarrow{\text{HCl}} \quad 2\,\text{RCOOH}$$

$$\underset{R}{\overset{R}{>}}C=C\underset{R}{\overset{H}{<}} \quad \xrightarrow{\text{KMnO}_4} \quad \underset{R}{\overset{R}{>}}C=O \quad + \quad \text{RCOOK}$$

The reaction of an alkene with permanganate serves not only as a qualitative test for unsaturation (Baeyer's test), but the cleavage reaction has been used in structural elucidations. In simpler compounds the location of a double bond can be pinpointed by examining the cleavage products. For more complex alkenes this cleavage reaction breaks a complex olefin of unknown structure down to simpler molecules. These simpler systems can be identified more readily, and this ultimately leads to a knowledge of the structure of the original alkene.

Another reagent that is frequently used in this way is ozone. Treatment of an unknown alkene with ozone affords an ozonide **28**, and reduction of this ozonide gives rise to aldehydes and ketones. The latter with their simpler structures are easier to identify. Catalytic hydrogenation using a platinum catalyst or zinc and acetic acid serve to reduce the ozonide:

$$\underset{R}{\overset{R}{>}}C=C\underset{R}{\overset{R}{<}} \;+\; O_3 \;\longrightarrow\; \underset{R}{\overset{R}{>}}C\underset{O-O}{\overset{O}{<}}C\underset{R}{\overset{R}{>}} \;\xrightarrow{\text{Zn/CH}_3\text{COOH}}\; 2R_2C=O$$

28

The actual mechanism for ozonolysis is still not fully understood although suggestions have been made. What is known is that the alkene and ozone react to form an unstable ozonide whose probable structure is **29**. This re-arranges to the more stable ozonide **28**,

$$\underset{R}{\overset{R}{>}}C=C\underset{R}{\overset{R}{<}} \;+\; O_3 \;\longrightarrow\; R-\underset{R}{\overset{|}{C}}\underset{}{\overset{O-O}{\underset{|}{C}}}R \;\longrightarrow\; R-\underset{R}{\overset{O}{C}}\underset{O-O}{\overset{}{C}}R$$

29   **28**

The structure of the initial unstable material is not generally known, nor is the pathway for the isomerization certain. Evidence supporting **29** comes from the reaction of *trans*-di-*t*-butylethylene which reacts with ozone at −70° to form a crystalline product. This product yields the ozonide analogous to **28** at higher temperatures. This indicates that the original crystalline material contains three oxygen atoms and is unstable relative to the normal ozonide. Treatment with sodium in liquid ammonia reduces the material to the D,L-diol which was prepared independently. The reaction supposedly shows the positions and geometry of two of the oxygen atoms. An NMR study on this crystalline material also supports a structure such as **29**:

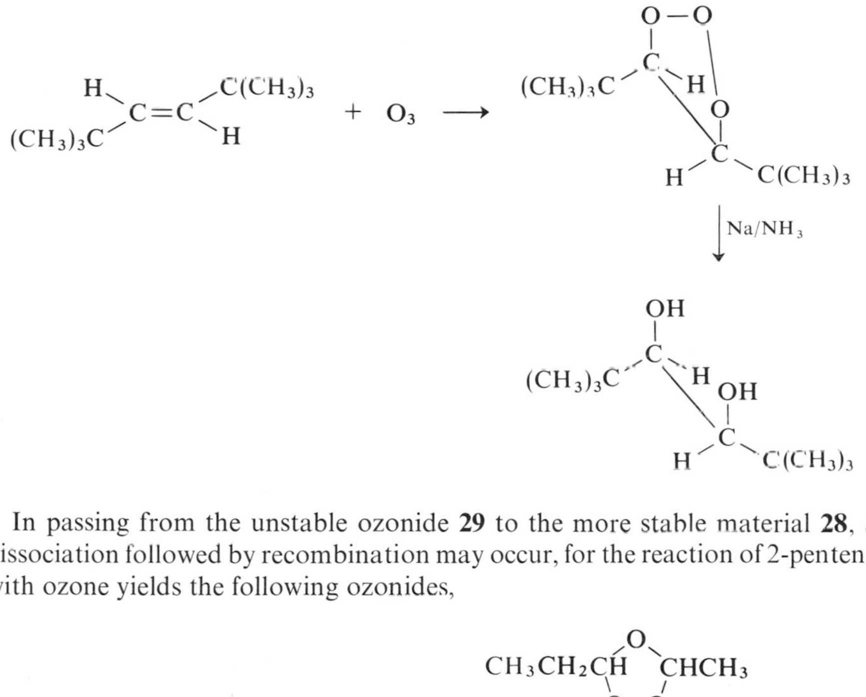

In passing from the unstable ozonide **29** to the more stable material **28**, a dissociation followed by recombination may occur, for the reaction of 2-pentene with ozone yields the following ozonides,

This mixture of products has been explained by assuming that the initial unstable ozonide, which is a trioxygenated material, decomposes by two routes. Each route gives rise to a dioxygenated material, **30** or **31**, and an

aldehyde,

$$CH_3CH_2CH-\overset{..}{C}HCH_3 \longrightarrow CH_3CH_2\overset{O-O^-}{\overset{/}{CH}}\quad \overset{O}{\overset{||}{HCCH_3}}$$

30

$$\longrightarrow CH_3CH_2\overset{O}{\overset{||}{CH}}\quad \overset{\bar{O}-O}{\overset{\backslash}{HCCH_3}}$$

31

These species then recombine to form the products:

$$CH_3CH_2\overset{O-O^-}{\overset{/}{CH}}\quad + \quad \overset{O}{\overset{||}{HCCH_2CH_3}} \longrightarrow CH_3CH_2\overset{O}{\overset{/}{CH}}\overset{}{\underset{O-O}{\backslash}}CHCH_2CH_3$$

$$CH_3CH_2\overset{O-O^-}{\overset{/}{CH}}\quad + \quad \overset{O}{\overset{||}{HCCH_3}} \longrightarrow CH_3CH_2\overset{O}{\overset{/}{CH}}\overset{}{\underset{O-O}{\backslash}}CHCH_3$$

$$CH_3\overset{O-O^-}{\overset{/}{CH}}\quad + \quad \overset{O}{\overset{||}{HCCH_2CH_3}} \longrightarrow CH_3\overset{O}{\overset{/}{CH}}\overset{}{\underset{O-O}{\backslash}}CHCH_2CH_3$$

$$CH_3\overset{O-O^-}{\overset{/}{CH}}\quad + \quad \overset{O}{\overset{||}{HCCH_3}} \longrightarrow CH_3\overset{O}{\overset{/}{CH}}\overset{}{\underset{O-O}{\backslash}}CHCH_3$$

There is no evidence that materials such as **30** and **31** are actually formed. Such materials are simply postulated because they explain the experimental results. Furthermore, if dioxygenated intermediates do participate in the isomerization of the less stable to the more stable ozonide, there is no guarantee that these intermediates actually have the structures assigned to them, structures like **30** and **31**.

Further evidence for this dissociation-recombination comes from the reactions of **32** and **33**. These two alkenes form the same ozonide:

$$\overset{CH_3}{\underset{CH_3}{>}}C=C\overset{CHO}{\underset{CH_3}{<}} \quad \overset{O_3}{\searrow}$$

32

$$\overset{CH_3}{\underset{CH_3}{>}}C\overset{O}{\underset{O-O}{<}}C\overset{H}{\underset{COCH_3}{<}}$$

$$\overset{CH_3}{\underset{CH_3}{>}}C=C\overset{H}{\underset{COCH_3}{<}} \quad \overset{O_3}{\nearrow}$$

33

The common intermediates in these reactions being,

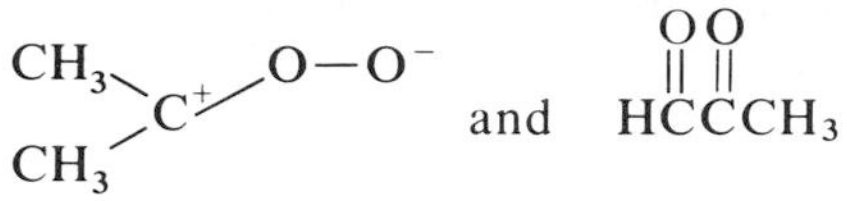

$$CH_3 \underset{CH_3}{\overset{CH_3}{>}}C^+ \diagdown O-O^- \quad \text{and} \quad \overset{O\,O}{\underset{||\,||}{HCCCH_3}}$$

and it is the more active aldehyde function that participates in the recombination.

Most, but not all, of the experimental results confirm the idea of dissociation-recombination. More work is necessary. This is not necessarily the only mechanism. An investigation of the ozonides formed from geometrical isomers and the dependence of ozonide *cis- trans*-ratios on olefinic geometry has recently been reported.

The step by step mechanism for ozonolysis must still be established. Nor is this reaction unique, while we have postulated mechanisms for addition to alkenes, these pathways have not been ascertained. The processes are complex; several intermediates are involved. The same reagent can be added to an alkene under different conditions, and the mechanism can change when the conditions do.

If our knowledge of addition to alkenes appears limited, the available information concerning additions to conjugated dienes is still more meager. Almost no modern mechanistic studies have been conducted. A mechanism which is analogous to that presented for simple alkenes can be written for these reactions, but confirmatory evidence is sparse. Furthermore, a complicating factor exists, for there occurs both 1,2- and 1,4-addition:

$$CH_2{=}CH{-}CH{=}CH_2 + A{-}B \longrightarrow ACH_2{-}CH{=}CH{-}CH_2B +$$
$$ACH_2{-}CHB{-}CH{=}CH_2$$

Both free radical and ionic additions give rise to such products, allylic carbonium ions and allylic radicals being the intermediates. Many examples of these 1,2- and 1,4-additions are known, and next we discuss this topic more fully.

13.6 Addition to Conjugated Dienes

The simplest conjugated diene is 1,3-butadiene which exists in both *s-cis* and *s-trans* forms, the *trans* being more stable:

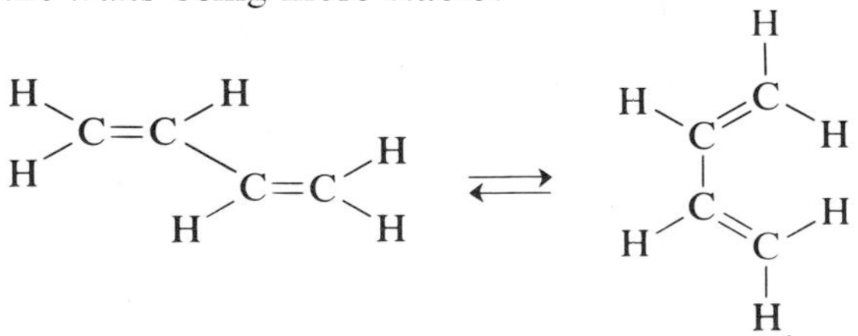

s-trans   *s-cis*

We assume that the electrons in this system can be separated into σ and π electrons and that the electrons in the π bond molecular orbitals are delocalized over the entire molecule:

$$\text{C} - \text{C} - \text{C} - \text{C}$$

$$\psi(\pi) = a_1 p_1 + a_2 p_2 + a_3 p_3 + a_4 p_4$$

In conjugated dienes such as this one the π bond covers four carbon atoms instead of two. Furthermore, the addition of an electron deficient material A^+ gives rise to an allylic carbonium ion, that is, two electrons remain in π bond orbitals, and these orbitals extend over three carbon atoms:

$$
\begin{array}{c}
\text{A} \\
| \\
\text{H} - \text{C} - \text{CH} - \text{CH} - \text{CH}_2 \\
| \\
\text{H}
\end{array}
$$

$$\psi = a_1 p_1 + a_2 p_2 + a_3 p_3$$

More pictorially this can be written as,

$$
\begin{array}{c}
\text{A} \\
| \\
\text{CH}_2 - \overset{\delta+}{\text{CH}} = \text{CH} = \overset{\delta+}{\text{CH}}_2
\end{array}
$$

According to the valence-bond point of view,

$$\text{CH}_2 = \text{CH} - \text{CH} = \text{CH}_2 + \text{A}^+ \longrightarrow$$

$$
\begin{array}{ccc}
\text{A} & & \text{A} \\
| & & | \\
\text{CH}_2 - \overset{+}{\text{CH}} - \text{CH} = \text{CH}_2 & \longleftrightarrow & \text{CH}_2 - \text{CH} = \text{CH} - \overset{+}{\text{CH}}_2
\end{array}
$$

The problem of addition becomes more complex when the alkene is a conjugated diene, for the original bond extends over four carbon atoms and the carbonium ion that is formed is allylic. Additions to conjugated dienes certainly proceed by way of π complexes; however, not much is known concerning their structure. The final products are usually a mixture of the 1,2- and 1,4-adducts. Thus, butadiene, when treated with chlorine affords the mixture of isomeric materials,

$$\text{CH}_2 = \text{CH} - \text{CH} = \text{CH}_2 + \text{Cl}_2 \longrightarrow$$

$$
\begin{array}{c}
\text{Cl} \quad\quad \text{Cl} \\
| \quad\quad\quad | \\
\text{CH}_2 - \text{CH} - \text{CH} = \text{CH}_2 \\
\\
\text{Cl} \quad\quad\quad\quad\quad \text{Cl} \\
| \quad\quad\quad\quad\quad\quad | \\
\text{CH}_2 - \text{CH} = \text{CH} - \text{CH}_2
\end{array}
$$

and other reagents and other systems behave in an analogous fashion:

$$CH_2=CH-CH=CH_2 + HBr \longrightarrow \begin{array}{l} CH_3-CHBr-CH=CH_2 \\ \\ CH_3-CH=CH-CH_2Br \end{array}$$

$$\underset{\displaystyle \overset{\displaystyle CH_3}{|}}{CH_2=C-CH=CH_2} + HCl \longrightarrow \begin{array}{l} \overset{\displaystyle CH_3}{\underset{\displaystyle Cl}{|}} \\ CH_3-\overset{|}{\underset{|}{C}}-CH=CH_2 \\ \\ \overset{\displaystyle CH_3}{|} \\ CH_3-C=CH-CH_2Cl \end{array}$$

Even peroxybenzoic acid behaves differently with conjugated dienes; the products are hydroxy esters:

$$R_2C=CH-CH=CR_2 + \overset{\displaystyle O}{\underset{\displaystyle ||}{\phi COOH}} \longrightarrow R_2\overset{\displaystyle HO}{\underset{\displaystyle |}{C}}-\overset{\displaystyle O-C-\phi}{\underset{\displaystyle |}{CH}}-CH=CR_2$$

Although a mixture of products is almost always obtained in these reactions, the product distribution varies with the reaction conditions. At lower temperatures, the reaction of butadiene with bromine leads to formation of the 1,2-product. Higher temperatures favor the 1,4-product. Furthermore, if the isomers are separated, at higher temperatures each isomer ultimately forms the same equilibrium mixture and the 1,4-product predominates. This is clearly a case of kinetic and thermodynamic control. The 1,2-adduct is less stable but is formed more rapidly, while the more slowly formed 1,4-adduct is the more stable.

At higher temperatures, the addition of bromine to 1,3-butadiene leads to an equilibrium mixture of products. However, some 1,4-product is also obtained under milder conditions where the interconversion of these materials is slow. Since some 1,4-product is obtained under conditions where it cannot originate by isomerization of the kinetic material, it must be a direct product of the reaction. Similar results are found in the chlorination of butadiene and in its reaction with hydrogen chloride. The 1,4-products are found under conditions where they cannot originate from the 1,2-isomers.

Further evidence that both the 1,2- and 1,4-isomers are direct products of the reaction comes from the chlorination of butadiene in methanol. The solvent acts as the nucleophile and methyl ethers are formed. The major product is the 1,2-isomer, yet the 1,4-product is also formed. Once bonded, methoxy groups do not migrate readily, and nucleophilic substitution on a previously formed dichloride is improbable. These are kinetic results,

$$
\begin{array}{c}
\underset{\displaystyle CH_2-CH-CH=CH_2}{\overset{\displaystyle Cl \quad\; OCH_3}{|\qquad\;\;|}} \\
70\%
\end{array}
$$

$$
CH_2{=}CH{-}CH{=}CH_2 + Cl_2 \xrightarrow{\ CH_3OH\ }
$$

$$
\begin{array}{c}
\underset{\displaystyle CH_2-CH=CH-CH_2}{\overset{\displaystyle Cl \qquad\qquad\quad OCH_3}{|\qquad\qquad\qquad\;\;|}} \\
30\%
\end{array}
$$

On the basis of the data, we postulate the following mechanism for addition to conjugated dienes (we use hydrogen bromide and 1,3-butadiene as an illustrative example):

$$CH_2{=}CH{-}CH{=}CH_2 \xrightarrow{\ HBr\ } \pi \text{ complexes}$$

$$\pi \text{ complexes} \longrightarrow \overset{\displaystyle Br^-}{CH_3\overset{\delta+}{C}H{=\!\!=}CH{=\!\!=}\overset{\delta+}{C}H_2}$$

34

$$CH_3{-}\overset{\delta+}{\underset{}{C}}H{=\!\!=}CH{=\!\!=}\overset{\delta+}{\underset{}{C}}H_2 \overset{Br^-}{} \longrightarrow CH_3CHBrCH{=}CH_2 + CH_3CH{=}CHCH_2Br$$

The intermediate **34** is an ion pair.

A similar mechanism involving the allylic carbonium ion as part of an ion pair is written for the interconversion of products:

$$CH_3CHBrCH{=}CH_2 \rightleftarrows \overset{\displaystyle Br^-}{CH_3\overset{\delta+}{C}H{=\!\!=}CH{=\!\!=}\overset{\delta+}{C}H_2} \rightleftarrows CH_3CH{=}CHCH_2Br$$

At higher temperatures where isomerization take place readily, the mechanism becomes,

$$CH_2{=}CH{-}CH{=}CH_2 \xrightarrow{\ HBr\ } \pi \text{ complexes} \longrightarrow \overset{\displaystyle Br^-}{CH_3\overset{\delta+}{C}H{=\!\!=}CH{=\!\!=}\overset{\delta+}{C}H_2}$$

34

$$
\overset{\displaystyle Br^-}{CH_3\overset{\delta+}{C}H{=\!\!=}CH{=\!\!=}\overset{\delta+}{C}H_2}
\;
\begin{array}{c}
\nearrow \quad CH_3CHBrCH{=}CH_2 \\[1em]
\\
\searrow \quad CH_3CH{=}CHCH_2Br
\end{array}
$$

34

The less stable 1,2-adduct rearranges to the more stable 1,4-isomer. The extra stability of the 1,4-adduct is derived from two factors; this is the more highly substituted alkene, and it contains a primary carbon-bromine bond. The less stable isomer has a weaker secondary carbon-bromine bond. The allylic rearrangement (1,2- to 1,4-product) is just an S_N1' reaction. A typical reaction profile is presented on page 309.

A more detailed mechanism would require more intimate knowledge of the π complexes and the ion pair **34**. More than a single ion pair is possible; these would vary in the position of the bromide ion relative to the allylic system. A knowledge of the geometry of the products is also necessary. Does the reaction of conjugated dienes with materials such as hydrogen bromide or bromine lead to *cis*-adducts or *trans*-adducts? Until such information is available for a large number of additions, a more detailed mechanism cannot be given.

With cyclic dienes it does become possible to study product geometry. For example, reacting 1,3-cyclopentadiene with a reagent such as deuterium chloride might provide a great deal of valuable data. In this case, if the *cis*-1,2-adduct were the kinetic product, the result would demonstrate the ability of the entering chloride ion to discriminate between allylic positions and indicate the presence of an intimate ion pair (or a concerted addition of deuterium chloride). Other products would allow the postulation of different mechanisms,

Unfortunately, it is not at all likely that cyclic dienes like cyclopentadiene are influenced by the same factors as open-chain dienes like butadiene. Thus, it is not necessary for cyclic dienes that the 1,4-products be the more stable. Some information concerning the mechanism and product geometry as well as the reactivity of the various adducts comes from the reaction of 1,3-cyclopentadiene with bromine.

Cyclopentadiene reacts at low temperatures ($-25°$ to $-35°$) with chloroform or petroleum ether as the solvent to yield the *cis*-dibromide **35**. It also yields the *trans*-dibromide **36**, but this could not be obtained in pure form:

Distillation of **35** under reduced pressure affords the *trans*-dibromide **37**:

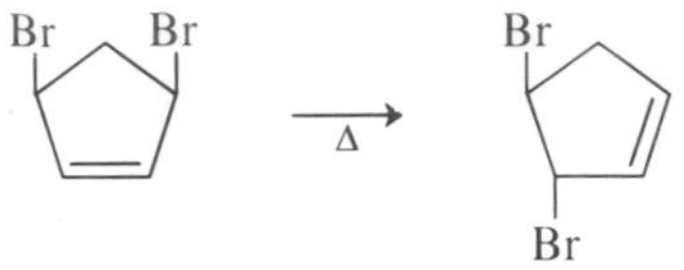

37

In an attempt to determine the reactivities of the various dibromides **35, 36, 37**, the initial rates of solvolysis were measured in 80% aqueous ethanol at $25°$. The results are presented in Table 13–1.

Table 13–1

Compound	$k \cdot 10^6 (\text{sec}^{-1})$
35	3.8
36 (impure)	3.1
37	1.2

The kinetic results show that differences in reactivity under these conditions are certainly not large. While more work is necessary, it does appear that the *cis*-1,4-adduct **35** is a direct product of the reaction, and a mechanism similar to that presented for butadiene can be written:

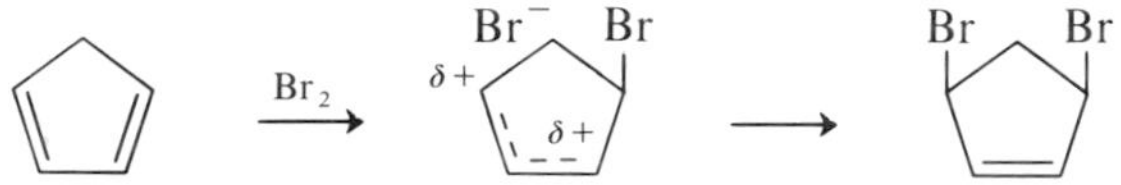

Cyclohexadiene also reacts with bromine (in hexane or chloroform at $-15°$). The products are a pair of dibromides of unknown geometry, one a solid, the other a liquid. The solid appears to be a 1,2-dibromide; the structure of the liquid was not determined. These two products both form the same 1,4-dibromide, also of undetermined geometry, upon heating:

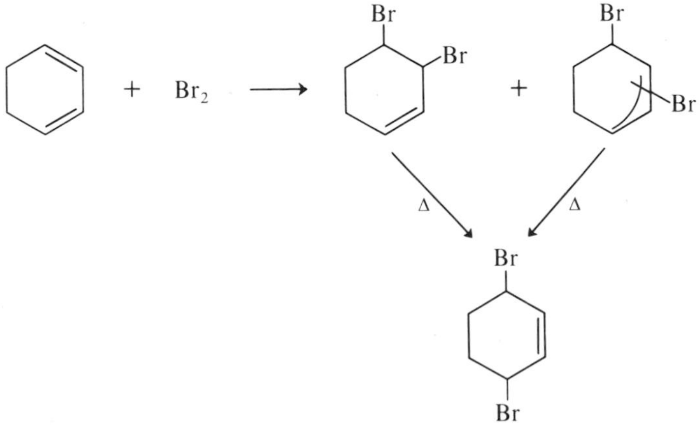

It appears that both *cis-* and *trans*-addition occurs with these conjugated dienes. However, much more work, including a detailed structural analysis of the products in a number of cases, is necessary before a definite mechanism can be written. In addition, kinetic measurements are required in order to determine kinetic and thermodynamic products in these reactions.

The reactions of conjugated dienes are of interest and other processes exist. Catalytic hydrogenation yields the expected products,

$$CH_2{=}CH{-}CH{=}CH_2 + H_2 \xrightarrow{\text{catalyst}}$$

$$CH_3CH{=}CHCH_3 + CH_3CH_2CH{-}CH_2$$

The expected results are also obtained upon ozonolysis:

$$
\underset{\underset{CH_2{=}CH{-}CH{=}CH_2}{\overset{|}{\underset{}{}}}{\overset{CH_3}{}}
\xrightarrow[\text{(2) Zn/H}_2\text{O}]{\text{(1) O}_3}
2CH_2O + CH_3COCHO
$$

$$CH_2{=}CH{-}CH{=}CH{-}CH{=}CH_2 \xrightarrow[\text{(2) Zn/H}_2\text{O}]{\text{(1) O}_3} 2CH_2O + 2HCOCHO$$

An interesting reaction occurs when isoprene is treated with liquid sulfur dioxide. The product, a sulfone, apparently results from 1,4-addition to the conjugated diene,

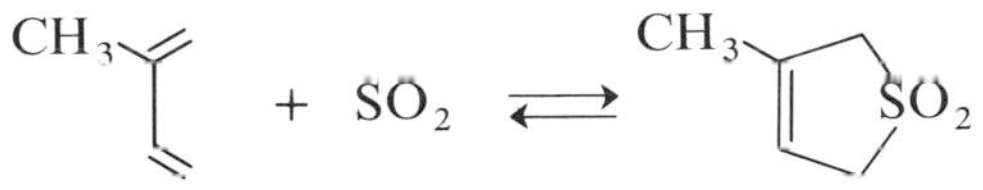

The reaction is reversible, and heating the sulfone regenerates the reactants.

Other reactions of this type are known. A very versatile yet common reaction that gives rise to substituted cyclohexenes is the Diels-Alder reaction.

13.7 The Diels-Alder Reaction

We have discussed alkenes and dienes; the Diels-Alder reaction can involve both. The diene reacts with a substituted alkene to form derivatives of cyclohexene,

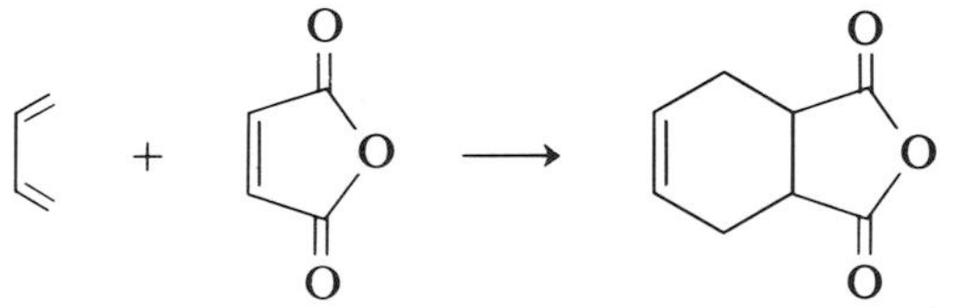

The transition state appears as follows:

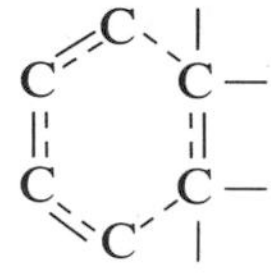

In perspective this becomes,

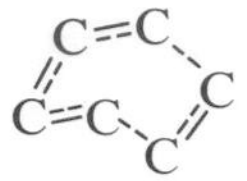

The reactions of butadiene with *p*-quinone and of cyclohexadiene with maleic anhydride are typical examples,

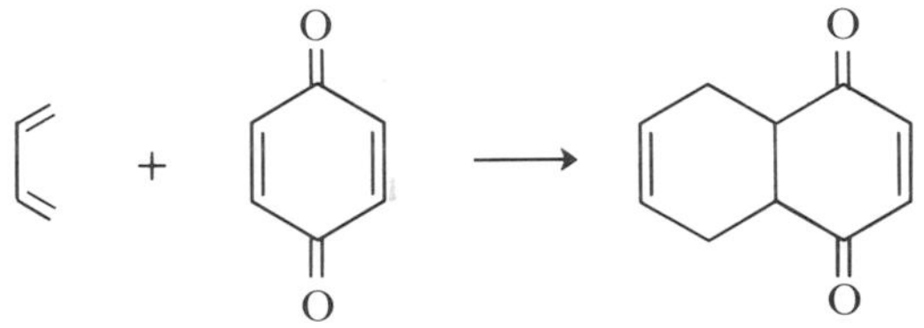

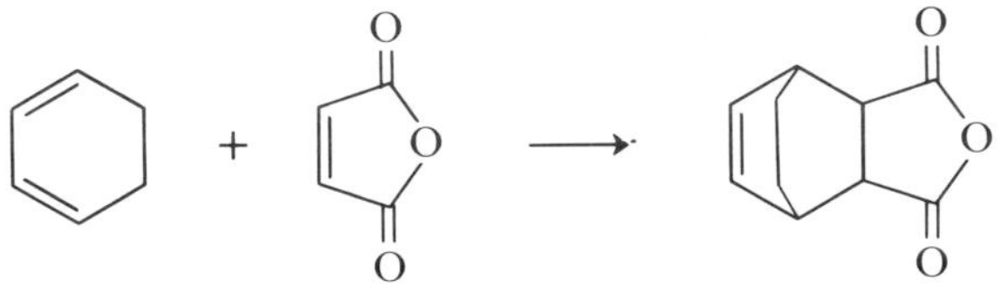

The reactions of dimethyl maleate and dimethyl fumarate take place stereospecifically, and this implies that both bonds to the dienophile are formed more or less simultaneously (rotation does not take place):

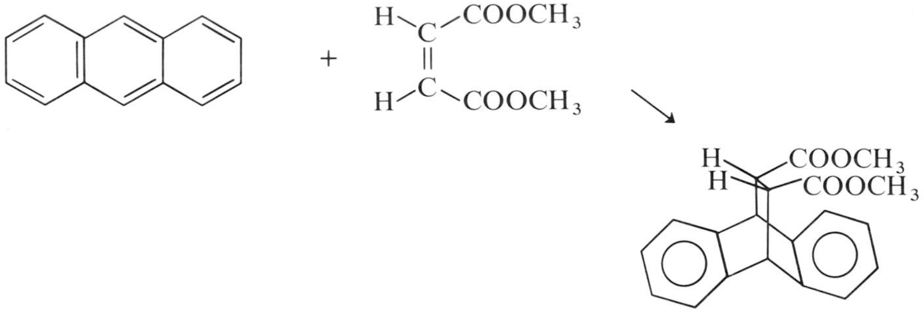

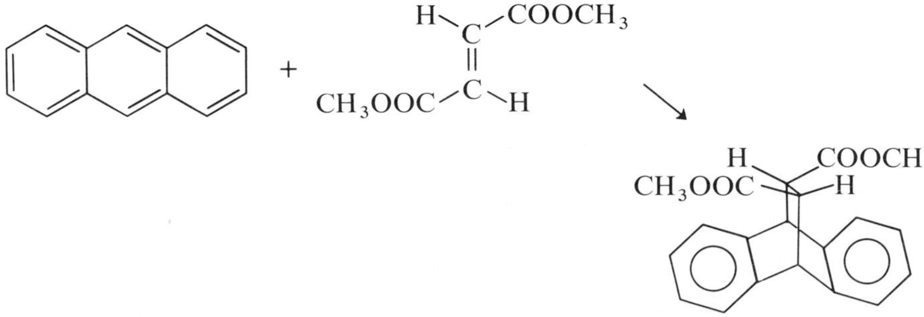

A Diels-Alder reaction on durene (tetramethylbenzene) affords the rather interesting substituted barrelane,

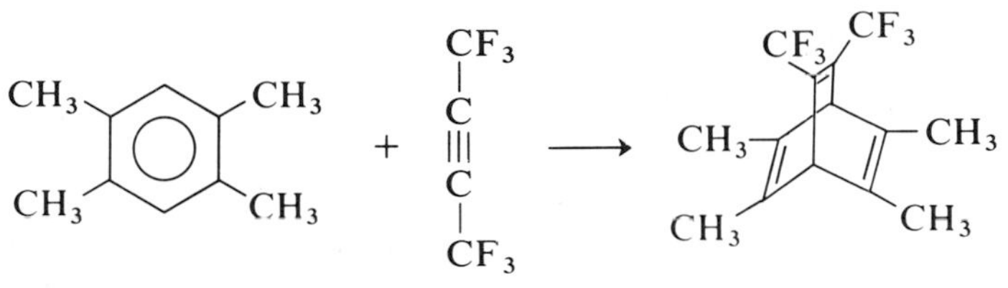

We also encounter the problem of kinetic versus thermodynamic control in Diels-Alder reactions. For example, if the reaction of cyclopentadiene with maleic anhydride is conducted at as low a temperature as possible for a short period of time, the product is the *endo* product **38**, whereas under more vigorous conditions the *exo* isomer **39** is the product. Careful heating of the *endo* material also affords the *exo*, which is the more stable, material,

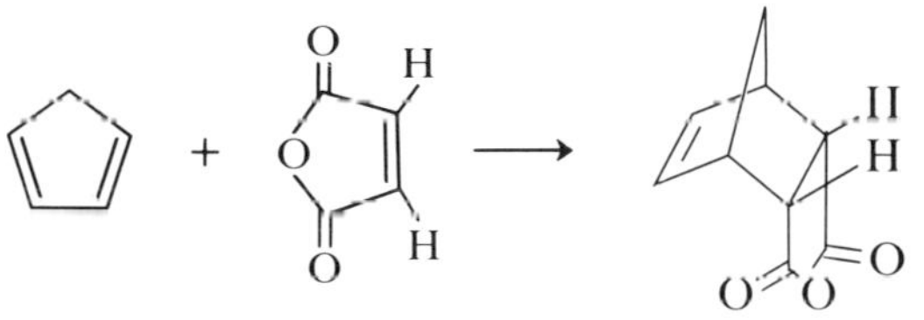

38

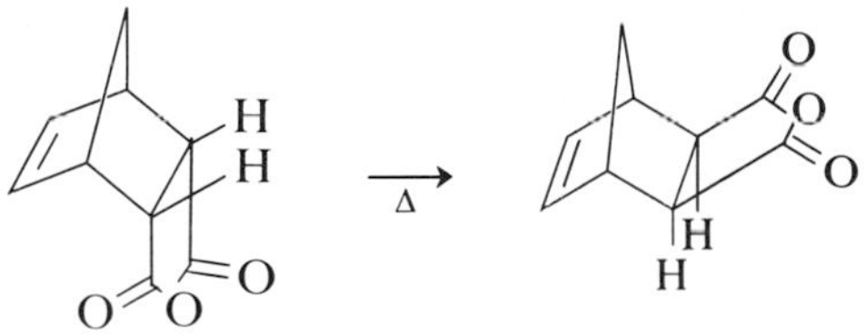

38   **39**

It is the *endo* isomer that is kinetically favored, yet the *exo* product is the more stable.

The Diels-Alder reaction is itself reversible, and heating an adduct regenerates the reactants:

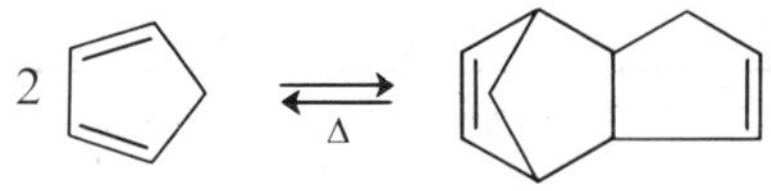

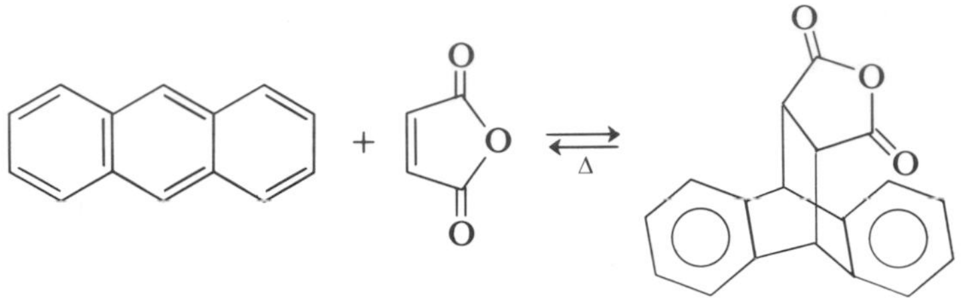

Occasionally this reversal can be put to good synthetic use. A Diels-Alder reaction is performed and the adduct heated. A "reverse Diels-Alder" occurs where the adduct does not revert to reactants. The following process illustrates this idea,

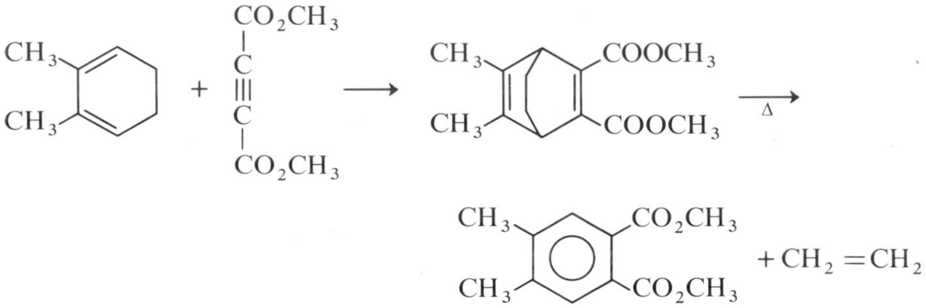

Systems such as cycloheptatriene, cyclooctatriene, and cyclooctatetraene undergo Diels-Alder reactions, and in these processes the reactant probably suffers a prior isomerization.

It has been demonstrated that at temperatures above 80°, cyclooctatriene is involved in a rapid equilibrium with the less stable bicyclic isomer **40**:

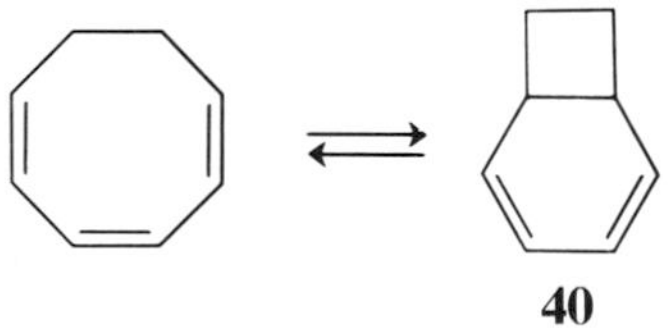

40

Under conditions where it cannot isomerize, cyclooctatriene does not react with malaic anhydride. However, the bicyclic material does, and the expected product is obtained:

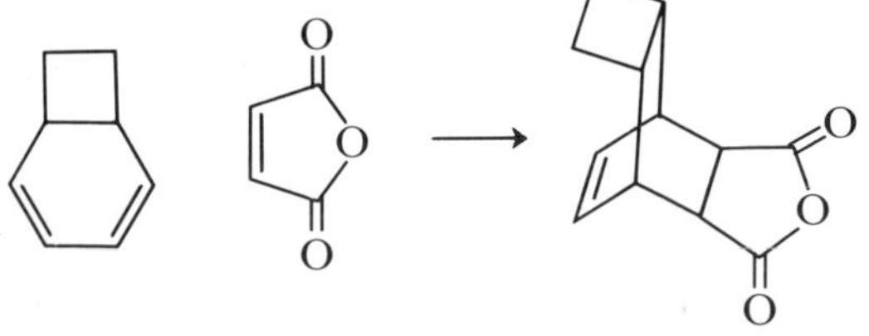

Under conditions where it can isomerize cyclooctatriene also affords this adduct, and it also reacts with other dienophiles in a manner that suggests the involvement of the bicyclic compound as an intermediate:

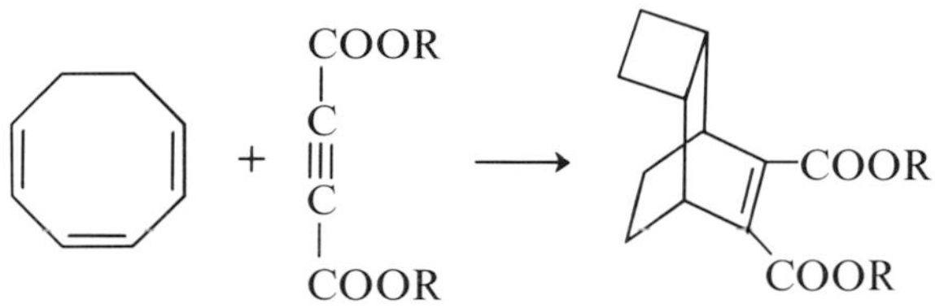

Cycloheptatriene and cyclooctatetraene also form adducts that can be explained by the intervention of bicyclic intermediates; however, these have not been isolated:

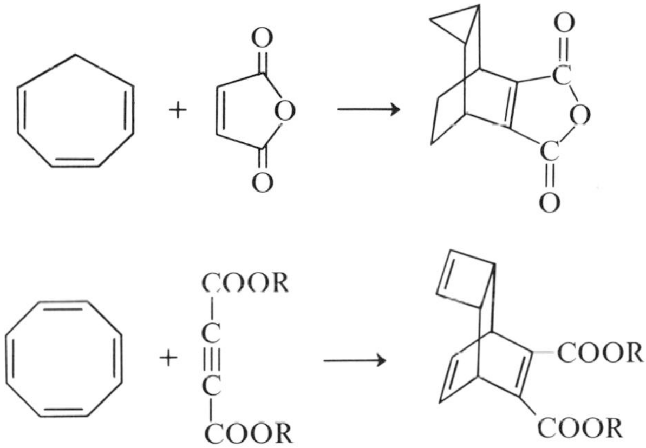

Another point that should be considered is that dienes must be in the *s-cis* form to undergo a Diels-Alder reaction, yet open-chain dienes such as butadiene exist largely in the more stable *s-trans* form. Cyclic dienes such as cyclopentadiene are fixed in the desired geometry, and these suffer Diels-Alder reactions much more readily. The reaction coordinates are shown in Figure 13–1.

We mentioned previously that in a Diels-Alder reaction, both bonds to the dienophile are formed more or less simultaneously, yet this does not require in a reaction such as

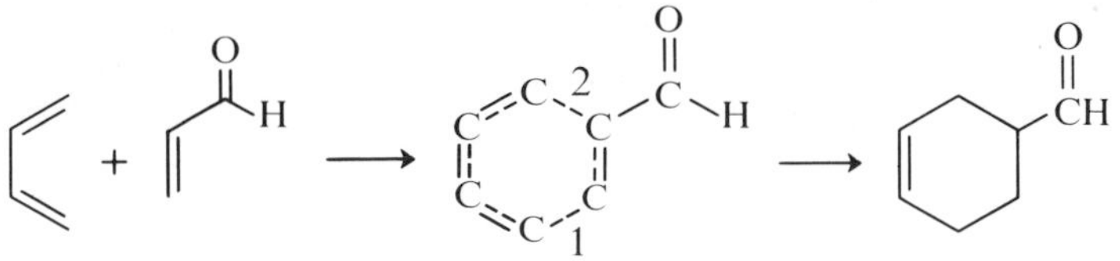

41

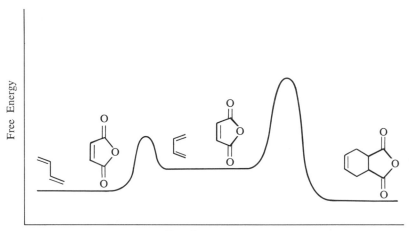

Reaction Coordinate

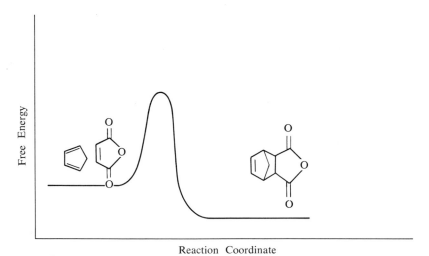

Reaction Coordinate

Figure 13–1

that both bonds 1 and 2 be formed to the same degree in the transition state.

Butadiene reacts with acrolein to form the adduct **41** and the two new carbon-carbon σ bonds (1 and 2) are both partially formed in the transition state. An ionic transition state with bond 1 formed to a greater degree than bond 2 appears as follows,

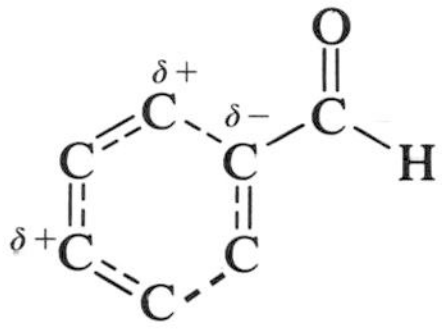

This transition state with some negative charge in conjugation with the carbonyl group is probably more favorable than other ionic possibilities such as,

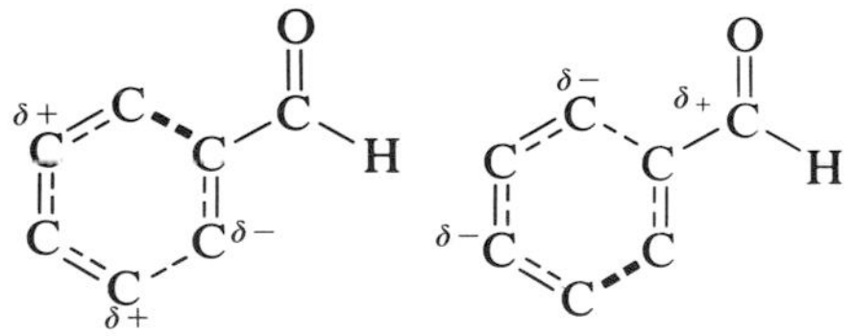

Of course, it is possible that the Diels-Alder reaction is a free radical process, but this leads to a similar conclusion; namely, that in the transition state the two new carbon-carbon σ bonds need not be formed to the same extent.

The mechanism of the Diels-Alder reaction is not known with certainty. Some of these additions may occur by free radical processes, and some may be ionic reactions. The ionic mechanism is currently favored. Certainly, those processes that are catalyzed by Lewis acids are ionic, but the mechanism for the catalyzed reaction is different from that of the uncatalyzed process.

Addition of maleic anhydride to 2,3-dimethylnaphthalene is effected both in the presence and absence of a catalyst. The same product is obtained, yet the reaction occurs much more readily when catalyzed:

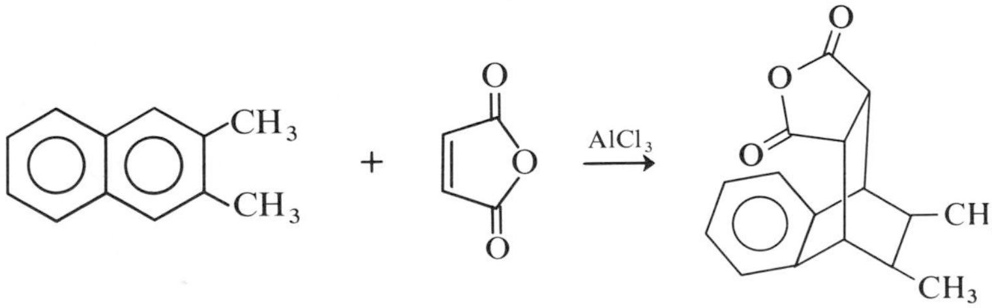

In the Diels-Alder reaction a cyclic system is generated from a conjugated diene. We discuss in Section 20.5 some related reactions.

Since the electrons in the olefinic linkage are available, alkenes and dienes usually behave as Lewis bases. Reactions take place with a variety of reagents (Lewis acids add more readily than Lewis bases do), and both *cis-* and *trans-* additions occur.

The behavior of the carbonyl group C=O is similar to that of the olefinic system, and additions to this linkage are common. Both Lewis acids and Lewis bases attack, the former enters the system at the oxygen atom and the latter at carbon. Aldehydes are more reactive than ketones, and the reactivity of either depends upon the type of groups attached to the carbonyl carbon atom.

Reagents add to the carbonyl group; they also add to the α, β-unsaturated system,

$$C{=}C{-}C{=}O$$

and just as with conjugated dienes both 1,2- and 1,4-addition can occur, but we discuss these topics more fully in Chapter 15.

Supplementary Reading

1. Cheronis, N. D. and Ma, T. S., *Organic Functional Group Analysis.* New York, Interscience, 1964.

2. Fieser, L. F. and Fieser, M., *Advanced Organic Chemistry.* New York, Reinhold, 1961.

3. Gould, E. S., *Mechanism and Structure in Organic Chemistry.* New York, Holt, 1959.

4. Hine, J., *Physical Organic Chemistry.* New York, McGraw-Hill, 1962.

5. Ingold, C. K., *Structure and Mechanism in Organic Chemistry.* Ithaca, New York, Cornell U.P., 1953.

6. Parker, R. E. and Isaacs, N. S., *Chem. Revs.,* 1959, p. 737.

7. Royals, E. E., *Advanced Organic Chemistry.* Englewood-Cliffs, New Jersey, Prentice-Hall, 1954.

8. Winstein, S. and Henderson, R. B., *Heterocyclic Compounds,* Vol. 1, (ed.) R. C. Elderfield. New York, Wiley, 1950.

Chapter 14

Aromatic Substitution

14.1 Introduction

In Section 6.11 we presented the idea of aromaticity in π electronic systems. According to molecular orbital theory those π systems are aromatic that possess closed-shell configurations, have all bonding and nonbonding orbitals complete, and possess a large resonance energy. The materials that satisfy these requirements need not be hydrocarbons, for heterocyclic systems can also be aromatic. Nor need the species be neutral; positively and negatively charged ions can be aromatic. An ion is aromatic when it is more stable than expected. It need not be, nor is it expected to be completely inert. The following systems represent a few of the numerous examples that satisfy these criteria and are aromatic:

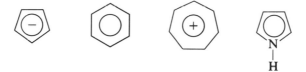

A neutral aromatic system such as benzene or pyrrole has the characteristic that if it is disturbed, it tends to reform, and this is the basis of electrophilic aromatic substitution. For example, the addition of nitronium ion to benzene disturbs the aromatic system. The tetrahedrally bonded carbon atom in the carbonium ion intermediate is sp^3 hybridized, and this cation is no longer aromatic. However, the aromatic system is regenerated by expulsion of a proton,

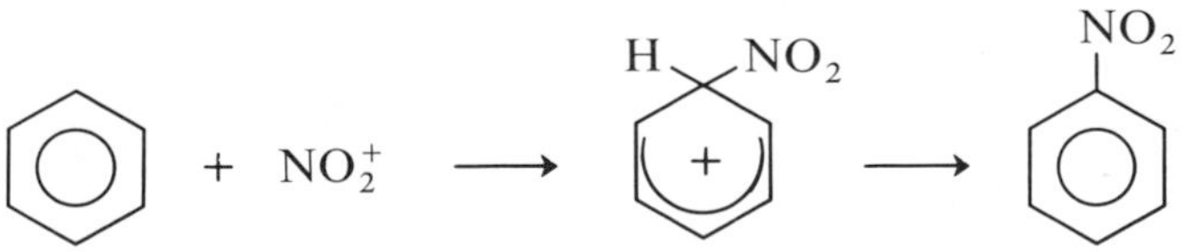

This sort of behavior by aromatic systems leads to products resulting from substitution (here NO_2 for H) rather than from addition. The latter (addition)

423

destroys the aromaticity of the system. In contrast, nonaromatic alkenes generally undergo addition rather than substitution.

Benzene usually suffers substitution rather than addition. However, the results are not always so clearcut. Anthracene serves as an excellent diene in the Diels-Alder reaction, and phenanthrene adds halogen:

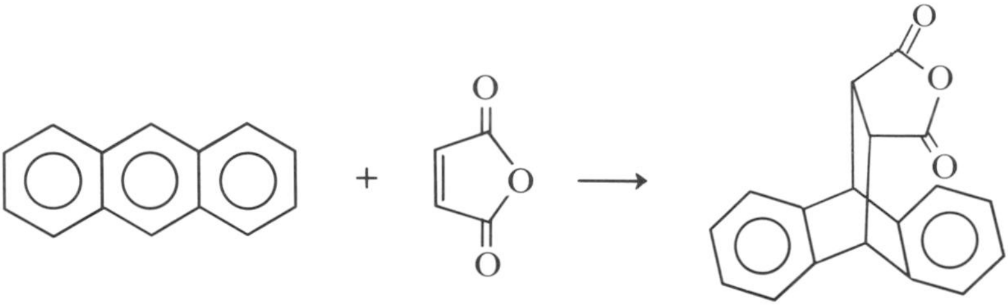

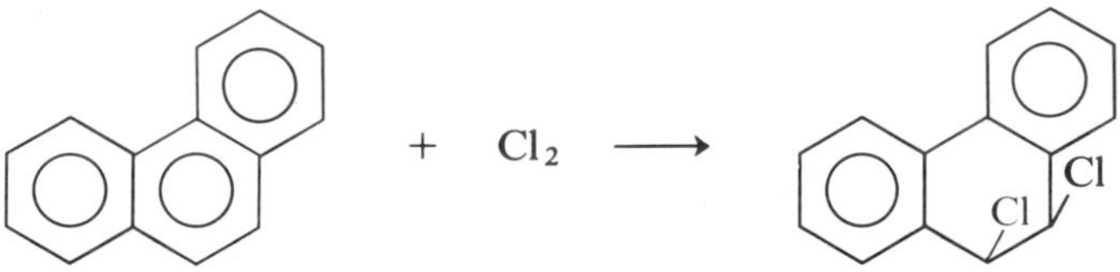

The aromatic systems, which are destroyed by such reactions can sometimes be regenerated. Heating compounds such as anthracene dibromide and phenanthrene dibromide causes them to eliminate hydrogen bromide and thereby form substituted anthracenic and phenanthrenic products. The Diels-Alder reaction is also reversible:

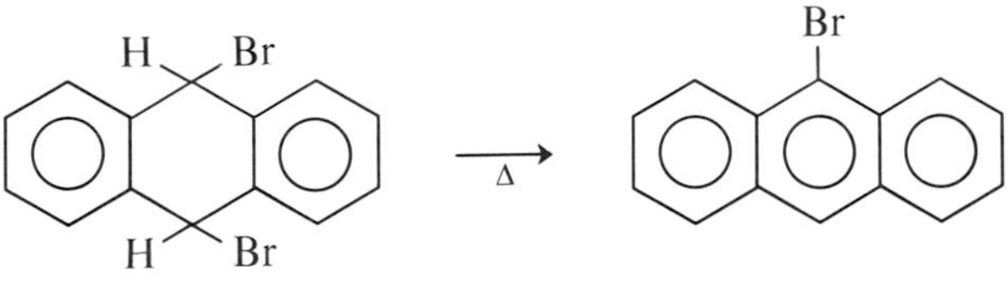

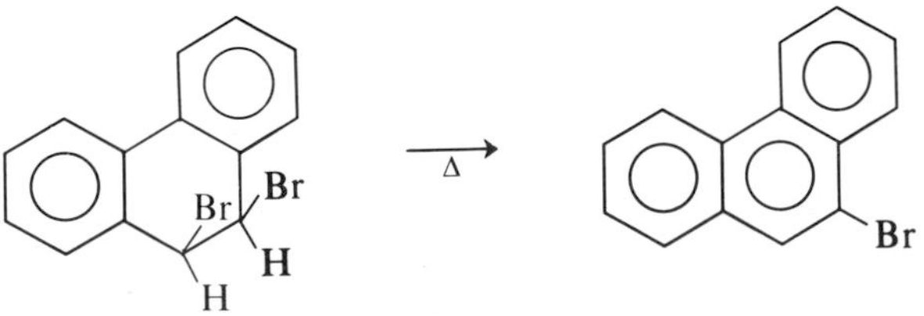

Even benzene undergoes addition, and furthermore the addition is exothermic. Thus, hydrogenation yields cyclohexane with a ΔH equal to -49.8

kcal/mole. This implies that the product is more stable than the reactants. The aromaticity of benzene is displayed by the fact that the measured ΔH is smaller than would be observed for nonaromatic systems adding three moles of hydrogen:

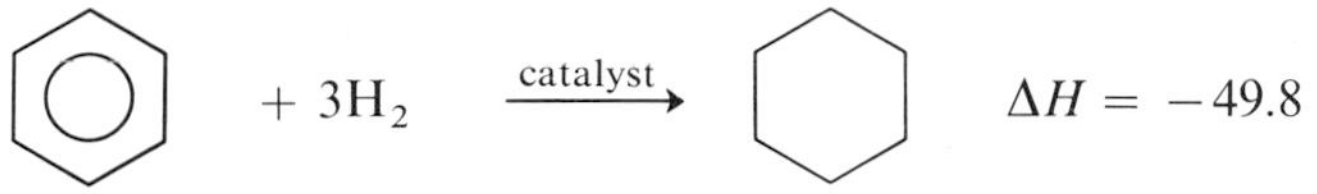

$$\text{(benzene)} + 3H_2 \xrightarrow{\text{catalyst}} \text{(cyclohexane)} \qquad \Delta H = -49.8$$

While alkenes are usually oxidized by potassium permanganate (Section 13.4), benzene derivatives can be inert when treated with this reagent. Ozone, on the other hand, converts benzene to a triozonide which yields glyoxal upon hydrolysis. Thus we see that the difference between the behavior of benzene and its derivatives and that of other alkenes is only one of degree:

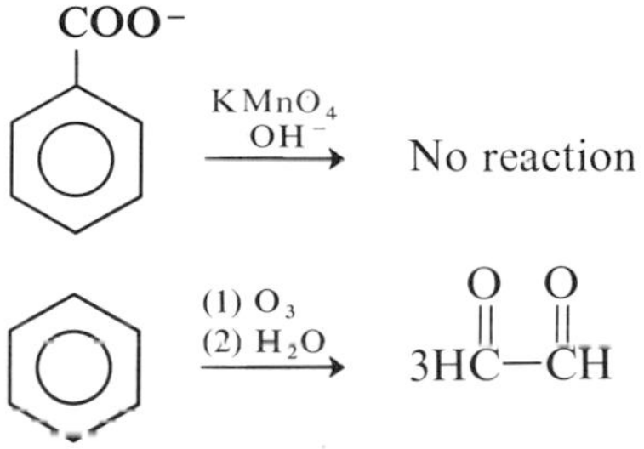

$$\text{(COO}^- \text{ benzene)} \xrightarrow[\text{OH}^-]{\text{KMnO}_4} \text{No reaction}$$

$$\text{(benzene)} \xrightarrow[\text{(2) H}_2\text{O}]{\text{(1) O}_3} \quad 3H\overset{O}{\overset{\|}{C}}-\overset{O}{\overset{\|}{C}}H$$

14.2 The Mechanism of Electrophilic Aromatic Substitution

The mechanism usually written for electrophilic aromatic substitution involves as intermediates both π complexes and σ complexes. The former are similar to the π complexes encountered in olefinic addition and the latter are just carbonium ions. The mechanism for formation of the carbonium ion 2 (the σ complex) is similar to the mechanism of olefinic addition (more than a single π complex is possible),

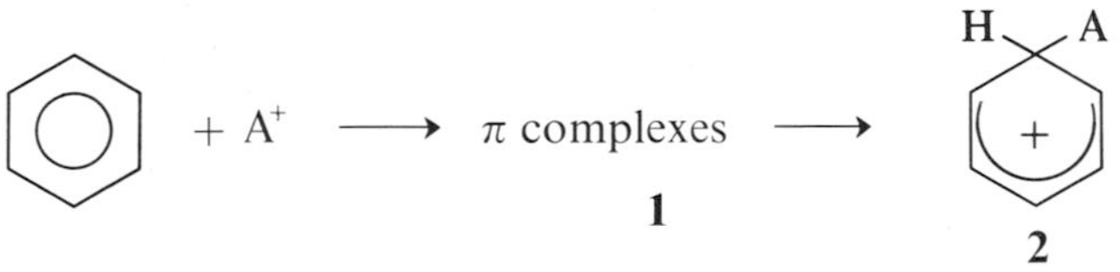

$$\text{(benzene)} + A^+ \longrightarrow \pi \text{ complexes} \longrightarrow \underset{2}{\text{(σ complex H A)}}$$

$$\underset{1}{}$$

The carbonium ion 2 can also be represented by the following valence-bond contributors,

$$\text{(H A +)} \longleftrightarrow \text{(H A +)} \longleftrightarrow \text{(H A +)}$$

This carbonium ion then loses a proton to some base, usually the solvent, to form the products. The mechanism for this proton loss can be similar to the $E1$ reaction, that is, it is just the reverse of the addition process. Again π complexes can be involved as intermediates. (We do not indicate the role of the solvent in this process):

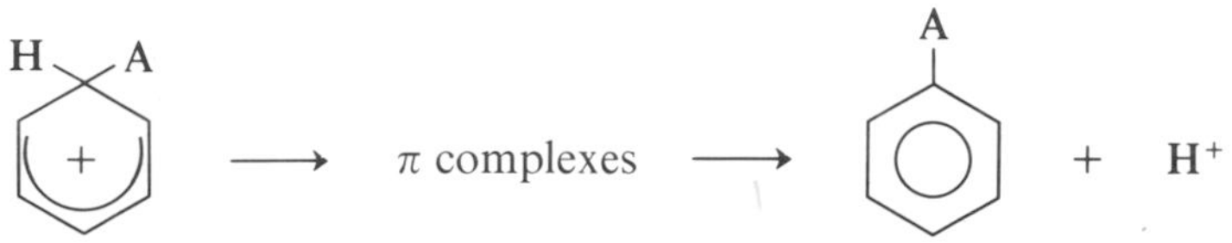

It is not necessary to assume that all electrophilic substitutions follow this mechanism exactly. The introduction of the electrophile need not proceed by way of a π complex, nor does the expulsion of the proton necessarily involve such a π complex. It is reasonable to assume, however, that some aromatic substitutions involve both π complexes while others may involve one or the other of them.

The rate limiting step in the reaction can be either the formation of **2** or the expulsion of the proton by **2**. If expulsion of the proton is rate limiting, catalysis by added bases becomes possible, and such catalysis has been observed for a number of substitution reactions. Furthermore, a primary kinetic isotope effect may be observed when proton loss is rate limiting. A bond to deuterium is more stable than a bond to hydrogen, and the rate of a reaction in which bond breakage to hydrogen occurs in the rate limiting step is decreased when the hydrogen atom is replaced by deuterium. This rate decrease is in fact expected in such cases and is known as a primary kinetic isotope effect. Such effects have been observed.

For the majority of aromatic substitutions it appears that decomposition of **1** into **2** is rate limiting. It is not always certain that π complexes are directly involved in aromatic substitution, and the problem of deciding whether or not a π complex is involved in a given reaction is a difficult one. For example, even if formation of **2** is known to be rate limiting, it is still not usually possible to say whether this carbonium ion is formed in a single-step process or by a two-step process that also involves a π complex. If decomposition of the carbonium ion intermediate constitutes the rate limiting portion of the reaction, a similar problem is encountered.

It is certain that π complexes are formed between aromatic compounds and electrophilic agents, but how important these complexes are in aromatic substitution is not always known. Their formation may sometimes be a side reaction. For very reactive reagents, π complex formation is sometimes rate limiting.

Accordingly, when formation of the carbonium ion (either directly or by way of the π complex) is the rate limiting step, the transition state is,

Whereas, if the decomposition of **2** into the final π complex or to products constitutes the rate limiting step, the transition state becomes,

If decomposition of the final π complex is rate limiting, we have for the transition state,

In the first of these transition states some aromatic character remains in the benzene ring; the σ bond to A^+ has not formed completely. In the second, aromatic character has partially returned to the system, but proton expulsion has not been completed. In the third transition state, the aromatic system is still π complexed to the proton, which is being removed.

In certain cases investigation of the structures of the π complexes formed between aromatic compounds and electrophilic reagents has been possible. Of course, the fact that such π complexes are formed does not require them to participate in aromatic substitution, and even assuming that π complexes do participate in some aromatic substitutions, there is no guarantee that those involved in aromatic substitution have the same structure or are in any way related to those actually studied. However, it is certainly reasonable to assume that if π complexes are formed, it is these complexes that eventually pass on to products. It is further reasonable to assume that a π complex has the same structure when studied independently and when involved in aromatic substitution.

Evidence for the existence of π complexes is overwhelming and stems from data on x-ray crystallography, refractive indexes, ultraviolet and infrared spectroscopy, dipole moments, and so forth. Thus, although neither benzene nor iodine have a dipole moment, a mixture of the two exhibits a dipole moment equal to 0.7 D. The existence of this dipole moment is explained by the formation of such a complex. The six π electrons of benzene are used to form a bond to iodine:

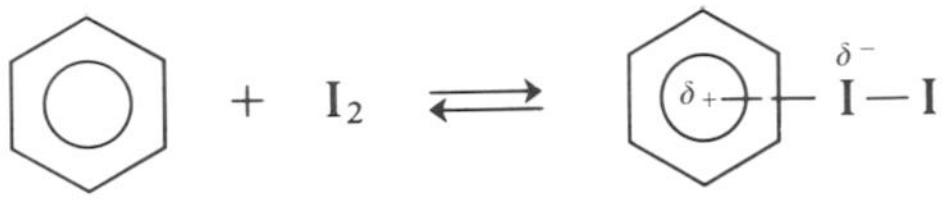

Infrared studies on this complex and on the benzene-bromine complex using deuterated and nondeuterated benzene show that the halogen molecule is perpendicular to the plane of the benzene ring and centrally located:

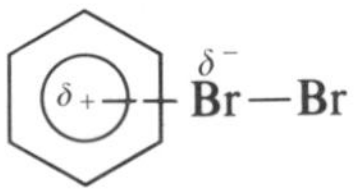

These ideas are extended by an x-ray study on the solid state which confirms these facts for a benzene-bromine complex and further discloses that a benzene-chlorine complex has the same geometry. This study indicates that the distance of a bromine atom from the benzene ring is 3.36 Å while the chlorine-benzene distance is 3.28 Å. It also discloses the fact that in these solid state complexes the halogen-halogen distance is essentially unaltered.

Infrared studies on complexes formed between aromatic compounds and halogens show that the more stable such complexes, the weaker the bond between the halogens. For example, bromine is not normally active in the infrared, but when bromine forms complexes with aromatic compounds, there appears in the infrared spectra of these complexes a band which can be assigned to the Br—Br stretching vibration. In a series of experiments involving solutions of bromine in benzene, chlorobenzene, and *o*-dichlorobenzene it was found that a decrease in the absorption frequency of the Br—Br band is accompanied by an increase in the absorption intensity. The result implies that the Br—Br bond weakens as the strength of the complex increases. In another series of x-ray experiments the length of the halogen-halogen bond in various complexes was determined, and it was found that this bond becomes longer as the complex becomes more stable.

While it appears that the halogen molecule in the benzene-halogen complexes is centrally located, this need not be true for all complexes. Certainly for benzene derivatives where one or more of the aromatic hydrogens have been replaced by other groups, a centrally located complexing agent is not expected. Silver ion is an excellent complexing agent, and the structure of the silver perchlorate-benzene complex has been elucidated by an x-ray diffraction study. In this complex the silver ion does not lie above the center of the ring.

Instead it lies above one of the carbon-carbon bonds, and this bond in the benzene ring is shortened to 1.35 Å. The two neighboring bonds are lengthened to 1.43 Å. Of course, changes in bond lengths are accompanied by changes in the bond angles.

The stability of these complexes depends upon the aromatic compound, the complexing agent, and the solvent. The presence of electron donors in the aromatic compound or electron withdrawers in the complexing agent increase its stability. Steric factors must also be considered, for these also affect the stability of the complex.

A variety of techniques have been developed for describing these complexes quantum mechanically. The distance between the two species involved in the complex is rather longer than the usual covalent bond distance. Consequently, a simple covalent description is not adequate. The complex **3** between some molecule B and some species A^+ can be considered as a resonance hybrid of the two structures **4** and **5**:

$$B + A^+ \quad \rightleftharpoons \quad \overset{\delta+}{B} \cdots \overset{\delta+}{A}$$

3

Where the complex **3** can be described by,

$$B \quad A^+ \quad \longleftrightarrow \quad \overset{+}{B}{-}A$$

4   **5**

In **4** the species are (figuratively speaking) held together by electrostatic attraction of the electrons in B for A^+. In **5** they are covalently bonded. Neither description is completely adequate and a better description is obtained by considering the actual complex **3** as a resonance hybrid of **4** and **5**. The problem is similar to the valence-bond description of hydrogen chloride (Section 7.4).

This resonance approach gives a good qualitative description, and a more quantitative description can also be obtained using these ideas. If the positions of the electrons in structure **4** are described by ψ_4, and the positions of the electrons in structure **5** by ψ_5, then the positions of the electrons in **3** are described by ψ_3, where ψ_3 is formed as a linear combination of ψ_4 and ψ_5:

$$\psi_3 = a_1\psi_4 + a_2\psi_5$$

The actual calculations required to determine the binding energy of the complex are much too difficult to be done except in a semiempirical way and use must be made of experimental evidence to evaluate the parameters.

All π complexes can be represented as resonance hybrids. Thus, in a similar way the complexes between benzene and bromine and between benzene and iodine can be represented as hybrids of nonbonded structure such as **6** and charge-separated covalently bonded structures like **7**:

$$\text{B} \ \text{X}_2 \longleftrightarrow \overset{+}{\text{B}} - \overset{-}{\text{X}}_2$$

6   **7**

In the benzene-halogen complexes the nonbonded structures are the major contributors to the ground states of the complexes while the charged structures are more representative of the excited states.

Hydrogen chloride and hydrogen bromide also form complexes with aromatic compounds. These complexes involve one molecule of the aromatic compound and a single molecule of the hydrogen halide. They do not conduct electricity which indicates that ions are not present. Experiments using deuterium chloride afford further evidence that these complexes are not carbonium ions of the type,

for when deuterium and tritium chloride are used to form the complexes, no exchange of isotopes occurs. The recovered aromatic hydrocarbon does not contain deuterium or tritium.

Aromatic hydrocarbons form complexes with hydrogen chloride and hydrogen bromide. These complexes do not conduct electricity nor do they give rise to isotopic exchange. However, in the presence of aluminum chloride or aluminum bromide, complexes are formed which are capable of conducting electricity and which, when DCl is used, do suffer deuterium exchange. It appears that a new complex is formed when aluminum salts are introduced and these new complexes are just carbonium ions:

When benzene is treated with a sufficient quantity of DCl and aluminum chloride, hexadeuterobenzene is produced, and this same product is formed upon treatment of benzene with D_2SO_4. These reactions are electrophilic aromatic substitutions,

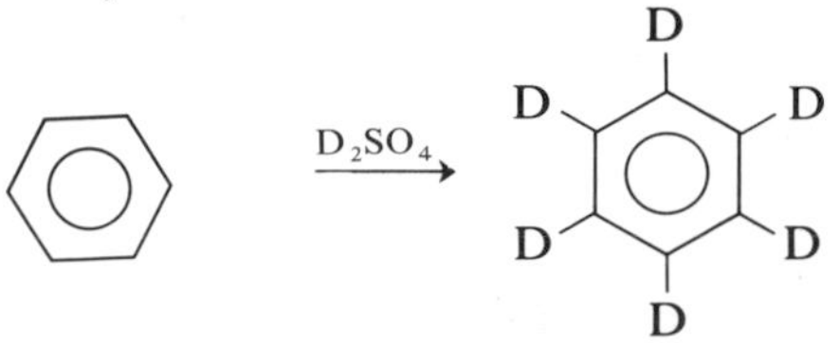

Another interesting characteristic associated with these carbonium ions is their color. The complexes formed between aromatic compounds and HX or between aromatic compounds and AlX_3 are colorless or pale yellow; however, when all three components are brought together, brightly colored products are produced.

In solution, these carbonium ions are highly solvated and even when isolated in crystalline form, additional molecules of the aromatic hydrocarbon still adhere to the carbonium ion salt.

Aromatic hydrocarbons also form complexes when dissolved in liquid hydrogen fluoride. Under these conditions some of the carbonium ion intermediate is produced. When anthracene is dissolved in hydrogen fluoride, the resulting solution conducts electricity. Solutions of certain other aromatic hydrocarbons do not conduct electricity as well; however, when boron trifluoride is added, solutions that do conduct electricity result. An aromatic hydrocarbon in liquid hydrogen fluoride, which is originally a poor conductor, becomes a better conductor of electricity when boron trifluoride is added to the solution. The conductivity continues to increase as more boron trifluoride is added and levels off when one equivalent has been introduced. Furthermore, when an aromatic hydrocarbon is reacted with DF and boron trifluoride, deuterium exchange occurs. The data support the idea that the intermediates in these reactions are also carbonium ions such as,

Hydrocarbons such as *ortho, meta* and *para* xylene are not very soluble in hydrogen fluoride, but their solubility increases tremendously when some boron trifluoride is also present. In addition, the carbonium ions formed by these aromatic hydrocarbons become more stable, that is, the equilibrium becomes more favorable as the number of methyl groups increases. The carbonium ion formed by hexamethylbenzene is more stable than that formed by mesitylene (1,3,5-trimethylbenzene). This in turn is more stable than those produced by the xylenes. Among the alkylbenzenes studied, toluene and benzene formed the least stable carbonium ions. The reaction is,

and in order of decreasing basicity,

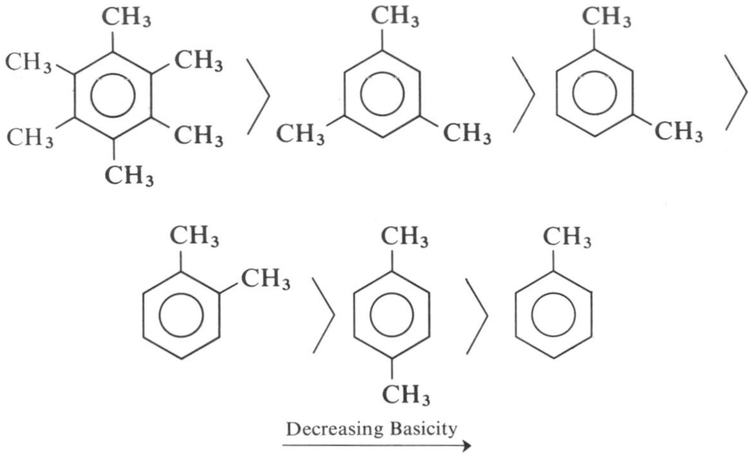

Decreasing Basicity

The observed order of basicity is due to stabilization by the methyl groups of the carbonium ion intermediate. We illustrate for mesitylene:

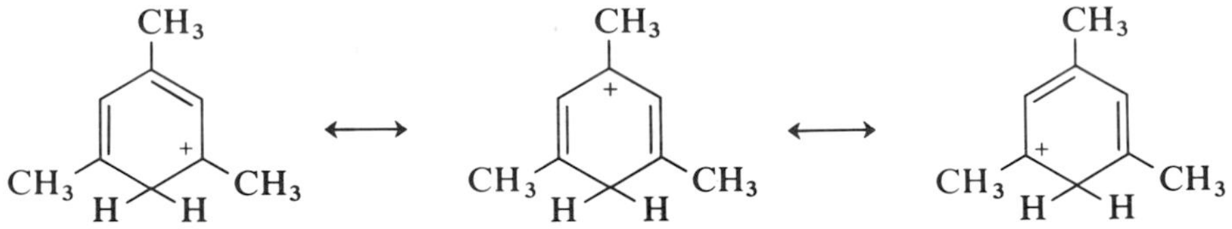

For the most part the properties and reactions of these carbonium ions have been studied in solution. However, they have also been prepared in crystalline form, their melting points have been determined, and their conductivities measured. Carbonium ion salts are prepared by mixing equimolar quantities of the aromatic hydrocarbon, anhydrous hydrogen fluoride, and boron trifluoride at low temperatures ($-25°$ to $-80°$). The complexes that result contain the materials in these proportions, and this is consistent with the structures presented previously.

An aromatic hydrocarbon is not very soluble in hydrogen fluoride, and when equimolar quantities of these two are mixed, a heterogeneous system results. The addition of boron trifluoride to this mixture causes the system to become brightly colored and when sufficient BF_3 has been added, to become homogeneous. The carbonium ion salt that is formed by this process reverts to the starting hydrocarbon at slightly higher temperatures. This decomposition is accompanied by evolution of BF_3, and the two phases are reformed. When

DF is used to form these salts, a mixture of deuterated and nondeuterated products is obtained after decomposition. The deuterated product predominates:

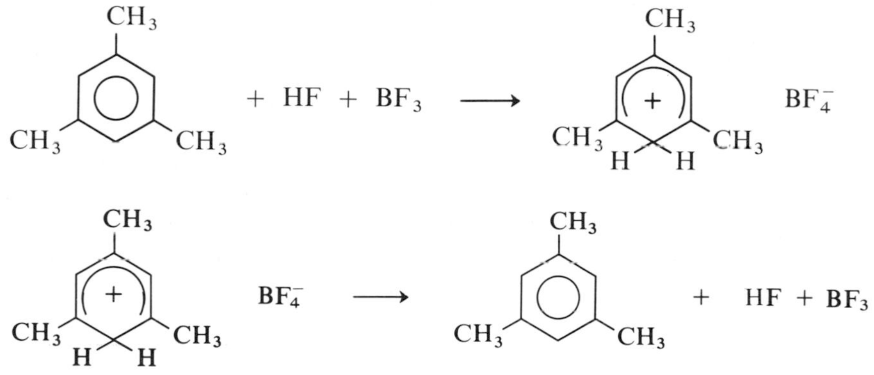

Using toluene as an example in the reaction with DF,

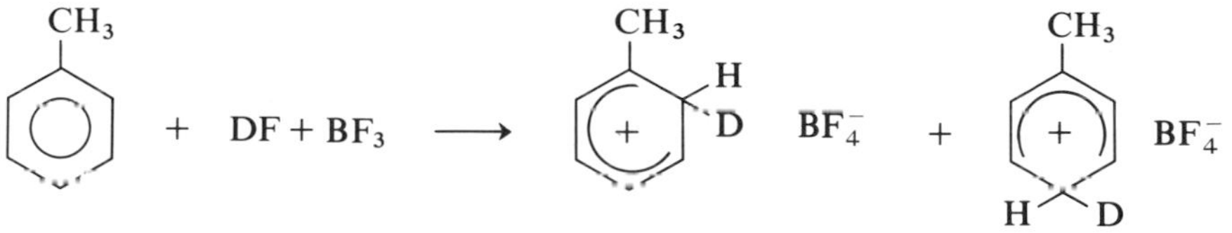

and

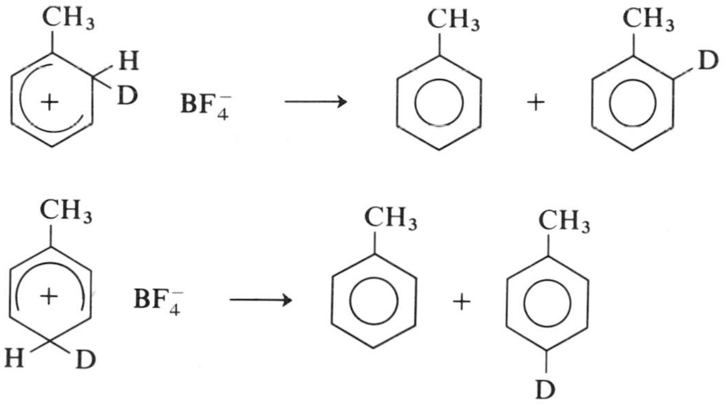

The colors and conductivities of these materials support the idea that carbonium ions are involved in the reactions. These processes are analogous to Friedel-Crafts reactions which involve the same type of carbonium ion intermediates, and in fact, similar experiments were conducted using alkyl fluorides and acid fluorides in place of hydrogen fluoride.

When an aromatic hydrocarbon is treated with equimolar amounts of an alkyl or acyl fluoride and boron trifluoride at low temperatures ($-20°$ to $-80°$), the initial products are colored and can conduct electricity. They decompose when heated above their melting points to form the usual Friedel-Crafts products, which supports the idea that carbonium ions are involved in aromatic substitution. Several different procedures were employed to obtain the Friedel-Crafts products, and it was shown that the same reaction occurred regardless of the procedure followed.

Alkyl fluorides are soluble in aromatic hydrocarbons, and when the two are mixed, a homogeneous solution is formed. Introduction of BF_3 at low temperatures causes a brightly colored ionic phase to separate immediately. This phase becomes larger as more BF_3 is added. When one equivalent of BF_3 has been added, the system again becomes homogeneous.

In one experiment ethyl fluoride and boron trifluoride were mixed. These formed a white nonionic complex. A bright yellow color appeared when an equimolar amount of toluene was introduced. Reactions were also carried out using acid fluorides, and the following reactions are typical,

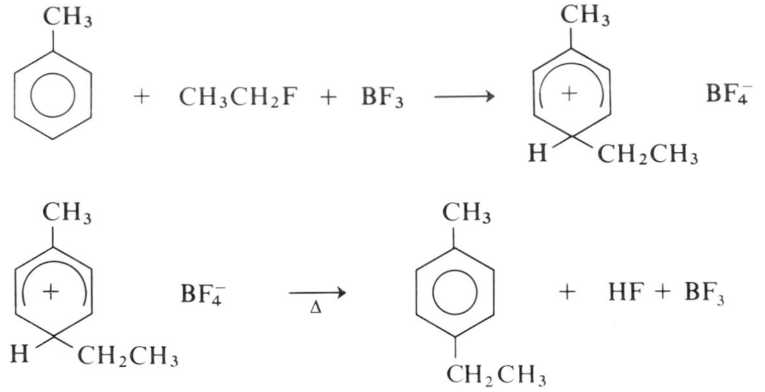

and

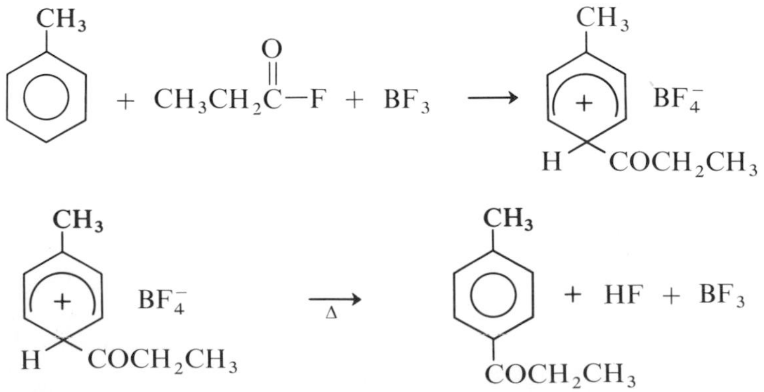

The evidence is conclusive that aromatic compounds can and do form both π complexes and carbonium ions. Although these intermediates have not been detected under the usual reaction conditions, it is reasonable to assume that the same intermediates are involved when electrophilic aromatic substitution is conducted under the more usual conditions.

The electrophile approaches an aromatic compound to form a π complex which then rearranges to the carbonium ion. In addition, if formation of the carbonium ion proceeds by way of a π complex, its decomposition probably does also. However, this is only a general scheme, and the actual mechanism must vary from reaction to reaction. Furthermore, the distinction between the two types of intermediates, the π complexes and the carbonium ions, need not be large. We have already indicated that in some π complexes the complexing agent is not centrally positioned but nearer to some of the carbon atoms than to others. The distinction between such localized π complexes and carbonium ions can be small, and in some cases they could become indistinguishable.

Kinetic investigations have been conducted for a large number of aromatic substitutions, but the data can give no information concerning the number of intermediates. Nor can the data give much information concerning their nature. In fact the rate limiting step for some processes remains ambiguous.

If we consider aromatic substitution as a two-step process involving only the carbonium ion,

2

we can say with certainty whether the rate limiting step is the formation of this ion from the reactants or its decomposition to the products. However, if we subdivide these steps and include the π complexes, we are not always able to say which of these subdivisions is rate limiting. There is evidence to indicate that formation of the carbonium ion **2** is more important than formation of the initial π complex **1** and that if π complexes are involved, it is generally their decomposition that is rate limiting.

In any reaction the transition state must resemble the product to some degree. We then assume that the more stable the product, the more stable the transition state leading to it. In a series of related reactions we may assume that those factors that stabilize the product also stabilize the transition state, the correlation being better the closer their resemblance. For example, two different hydrocarbons such as toluene and mesitylene both form π complexes, yet the π complexes formed by mesitylene are more stable than those formed by toluene. We assume that the methyl groups which stabilize the π complexes also stabilize the transition states leading to π complex formation.

The stability of various π complexes is indicated by the position of equilibria such as,

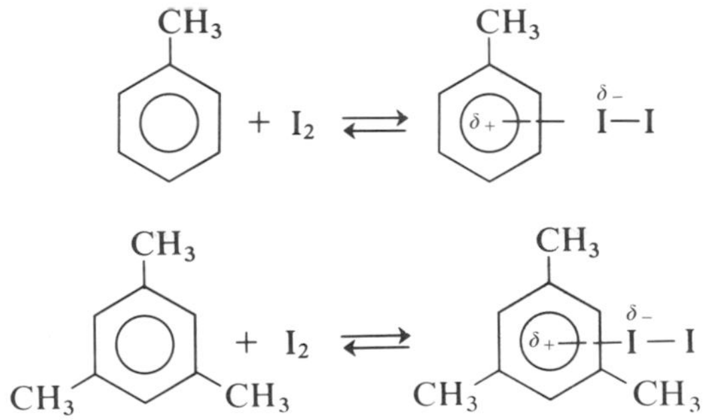

and is expressed in terms of the equilibrium constants K or in terms of the free energies of reaction $\Delta G°$.

The assumption that those factors that stabilize the product also help to stabilize the transition state leads to the conclusion that more stable materials are formed faster. The rate of a reaction, which depends upon $\Delta G^{\ddagger}$, is assumed to be related to the position of the equilibrium which depends upon $\Delta G°$.

We again consider the process,

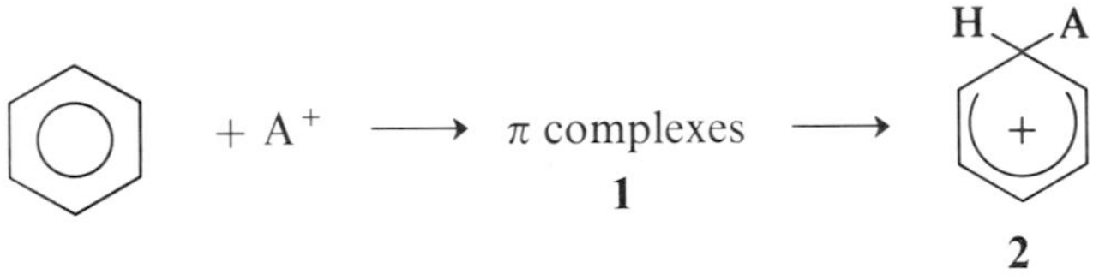

According to our assumption the rate of π complex formation ought to be related to the stability of the π complex. If π complex formation is the rate limiting step in aromatic substitution, then we should obtain a correlation between the stability of the π complexes formed by various aromatic hydrocarbons and their rates of aromatic substitution. Similarly, if formation of the carbonium ion is rate limiting, we expect a correlation between the stability of the carbonium ions formed by various hydrocarbons and their rates of aromatic substitution. We expect a correlation between the $\Delta G^{\ddagger}$ and the $\Delta G°$ of reaction.

Investigations have been conducted to determine whether $\Delta G°$ for carbonium ion formation or $\Delta G°$ for π complex formation correlates more successfully with $\Delta G^{\ddagger}$ for aromatic substitution. It was found that carbonium ion stability correlates very well with the rates of aromatic bromination, chlorination, and nitration. On the other hand, these determinations indicate that the stabilities of the π complexes do not correlate as well with the rates of these reactions. It appears that the transition state for aromatic substitution resembles the carbonium ion more closely than it resembles the π complex and that carbonium ion formation is the rate limiting step.

The extent of carbonium ion formation for a number of aromatic hydrocarbons was determined by experiments such as those described previously in liquid hydrogen fluoride:

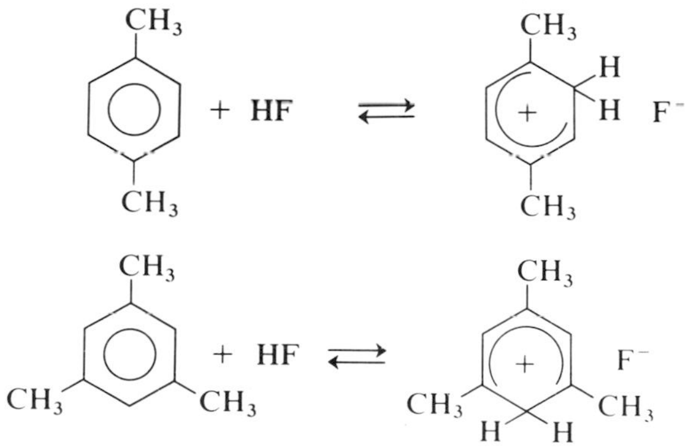

Although the equilibrium is more favorable with BF_3, the presence of BF_3 is not always required. The relative basicities of the hydrocarbons, as determined by such equilibria (BF_3 not present) were compared with their rates of aromatic substitution, and the correlation was good; the more favorable the equilibrium the faster the rate of aromatic substitution.

It appears that $\Delta G°$ for carbonium ion formation, as determined by these reactions, is proportional to $\Delta G^{\ddagger}$ for aromatic substitution. This proportionality implies a linear relationship and can be expressed as,

$$\Delta G^{\ddagger} = a\Delta G° + b$$

where a, the constant of proportionality, is the slope of the line and b is the intercept.

This equation compares the extent of carbonium ion formation with the rate of aromatic substitution, and the same equation ought to hold for a number of aromatic hydrocarbons. As a result, plots of $\Delta G^{\ddagger}$ against $\Delta G°$ or plots of $\log k$ against $\log K$, where k is the specific rate constant for some aromatic substitution and K the equilibrium constant as determined by the reactions in liquid hydrogen fluoride, ought to result in straight lines.

The assumption that for a series of related reactions a more stable product is also formed faster can be expressed as a linear free energy relationship between the free energy of activation and the free energy of reaction or between $\log k$ and $\log K$.

Since for two different hydrocarbons (1 and 2),

$$\Delta G^{\ddagger} = a\Delta G^{\circ} + b$$

plots of

$$\Delta G_2^{\ddagger} - \Delta G_1^{\ddagger} = a(\Delta G_2^{\circ} - \Delta G_1^{\circ})$$

ought to afford straight lines. Equivalently, plots of

$$\log k_2 - \log k_1 = c(\log K_2 - \log K_1)$$

or

$$\log \frac{k_2}{k_1} = c \log \frac{K_2}{K_1}$$

ought to be linear.

A straight line is obtained when, for a number of aromatic hydrocarbons, $\log k$ for aromatic bromination is plotted against $\log K$. Straight lines are also obtained (with different slopes) when $\log (k_2/k_1)$ for chlorination and $\log (k_2/k_1)$ for aromatic nitration are plotted against $\log (K_2/K_1)$.

The fact that such plots gave straight lines was one of the early pieces of evidence to indicate that carbonium ion formation was important in aromatic substitution. These linear relationships indicate that carbonium ion formation is more important in aromatic substitution than formation of the π complex and further indicate that in aromatic bromination (generally), chlorination, and nitration, carbonium ion formation is the rate limiting step.

These ideas can be extended into a general linear free energy relationship (the Brown equation), of the type,

$$\log \frac{f_p}{f_m} = \left(1 - \frac{\sigma_m^+}{\sigma_p^+}\right) \log f_p$$

where f_p, the partial rate factor for *para* substitution, compares the rate of *para* substitution for a substituted aromatic compound with the rate of aromatic substitution at a single position in benzene, and f_m, the partial rate factor for *meta* substitution, indicates the rate of aromatic substitution at a single *meta* position as compared to the rate at a single position in benzene. The terms σ_m^+ and σ_p^+ indicate the electron donating ability of the aromatic substituent.

The importance of carbonium ions in aromatic substitutions is also indicated by molecular orbital calculations. Changes in ΔS are not taken into account in these calculations, and linear plots are obtained when $\log k$ is plotted against what is essentially the calculated ΔH of reaction for carbonium ion formation.

This evidence indicates that carbonium ion formation rather than π complex formation is usually rate limiting. (Exceptions occur with very reactive reagents; here π complex formation can be rate limiting.) Although π complexes are involved in aromatic substitutions, their decomposition not their formation generally constitutes the rate limiting step. The transition state has the appearance:

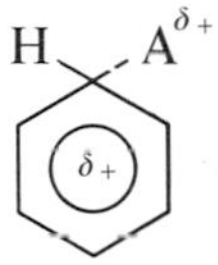

8

The transition state of importance is **8**. Since the free energy of activation does not depend upon the π complexes, it is not necessary to consider them explicitly in these reactions. When carbonium ion formation is rate limiting, we are able to discuss aromatic substitution as if it were a simple two-step process involving only the formation and decomposition of the carbonium ion intermediate:

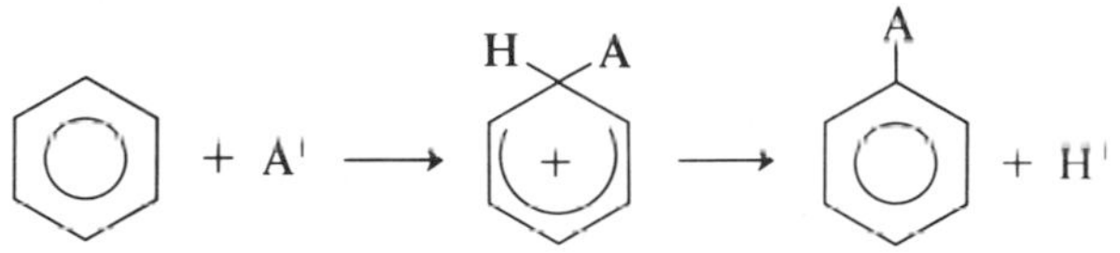

In benzene derivatives, where an orientational problem must also be considered, this two-step mechanism explains in a satisfactory manner the observed isomer distribution. The problem of orientation is discussed most simply by representing the carbonium ion intermediate as a hybrid of the following valence bond structures,

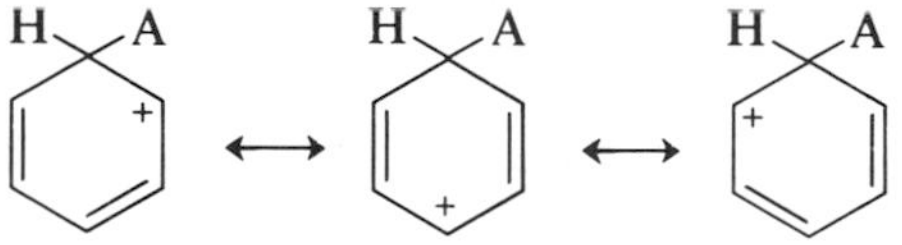

14.3 Orientation in Aromatic Substitution

When a benzene derivative undergoes electrophilic substitution, the problem arises of just where the electrophile will enter. A benzene derivative $Z-\phi$, where some group Z has replaced one of the aromatic hydrogens, gives rise to *ortho*, *meta*, and *para* products. Since five positions (two *ortho*, two *meta*, and a *para*) are available, on a purely statistical basis the expected isomer distribution is 40% *ortho*, 40% *meta*, and 20% *para*; however, this purely statistical result is never obtained. The isomer distribution varies with the group Z, the solvent, the temperature, the substituting agent, and so forth.

If we wish to compare the rate of electrophilic substitution at the *ortho* position of Z—ϕ with the rate of substitution of benzene, we must take into account the fact that there are only two *ortho* positions available in Z—ϕ yet six positions available for attack in benzene. Consequently, we must divide the rate constant for substitution in benzene by six and the rate constant for *ortho* substitution in Z—ϕ by two in order to make a fair comparison. We must compare $k_\ominus/6$ with $k_o/2$. A similar consideration must be made for *meta* substitution. For *para* substitution we must compare $k_\ominus/6$ with k_p. These are the partial rate factors f_o, f_m, f_p mentioned earlier.

Perhaps the most well-known effect of Z is its electronic influence upon the rate of substitution and upon the isomer distribution. We first discuss this electronic influence of Z in rather general terms and go into more detail later. We assume that the rate limiting step is formation of the carbonium ion intermediate and that the isomer distribution is kinetically controlled.

If the electrophile A^+ attacks at the *ortho* position, a carbonium ion intermediate is formed which decomposes to form the *ortho* product. Attack at the *meta* position leads to the *meta* product by way of a similar intermediate, and *para* attack leads to the *para* isomer. The mechanisms for these reactions are presented in Figure 14–1.

An electron deficient reagent attacks the aromatic ring, and the system develops a positive charge. Now, if Z is an electron donor, it is able to stabilize the transition states and thereby increase the rate of attack at all positions. Compared to the rate of attack at a position in benzene by A^+, the rate of attack of Z—ϕ increases at all positions (*ortho*, *meta* and *para*) when Z is an electron donor. However, Z stabilizes the transition states leading to *ortho-para* attack most effectively and these sites are attacked preferentially. Thus, the presence of electron donors in the aromatic system leads to *ortho-para* attack by A^+ and to the formation of *ortho* and *para* substituted products. It occasionally happens that Z is a powerful electron donor by resonance yet a powerful electron withdrawer by its inductive effect. In that case it may increase the attack of attack at the *ortho* and *para* positions, where the resonance effect comes into play, yet deactivate the *meta* positions. This alters the relative rates of attack at the various positions but still leads to *ortho-para* substitution.

If Z is an electron withdrawer, it deactivates the system at all positions. The rate of attack by A^+ at any position in the system is decreased as compared to the rate of attack of a position in benzene by A^+. However, attack at a *meta* position is least effected by the presence of an electron withdrawer. The rate decreases at all positions but least at the *meta* positions, and *meta* substituted products result when Z is an electron withdrawer.

If Z is a halogen, the problem becomes slightly more complex. The halogens are electron donors by resonance and electron withdrawers by their inductive

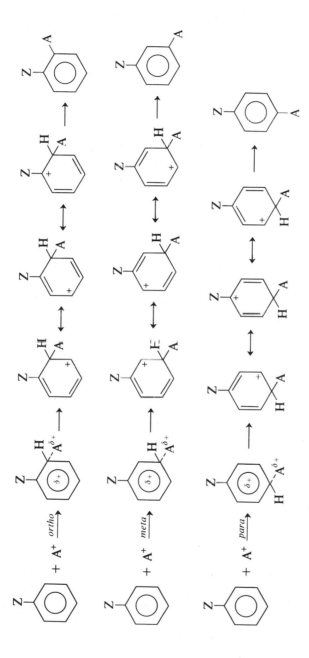

Figure 14-1

effect, and these two effects are comparable in magnitude. The inductive effect is more important, and consequently the rate of aromatic substitution of the halobenzenes is less than the rate of substitution of benzene itself. The resonance effect offers some compensation at the *ortho* and *para* positions; therefore, although the rate decreases at all positions, attack at the *meta* position decreases the most. Thus if Z is a halogen, *ortho-para* products predominate, yet the rate of aromatic substitution decreases at all positions.

We see that the importance of Z in the reaction varies with the position at which attack by the electrophile occurs. Its importance also depends upon whether the product is a kinetic or thermodynamic product and upon which step in the case of kinetic control is rate limiting. In aromatic nitration, chlorination, and bromination the rate limiting step is usually formation of the carbonium ion intermediate, while in aromatic sulfonation it can be the decomposition of this intermediate into the products. While the substitution reaction can be run under conditions where the products are kinetically favored, it can in a number of cases also be conducted under conditions leading to thermodynamic control, and the influence of Z upon the position of the equilibrium is not necessarily the same as its influence upon the rate. Furthermore, Z exerts both an inductive influence and a resonance effect upon the process, and these two effects need not be in the same direction. For groups such as CH_3, CN, NO_2 the two effects operate in the same direction. The methyl group is an electron donor both by resonance and by its inductive effect; the NO_2 and CN groups are electron withdrawers both because of resonance and due to their inductive effects. However, if Z represents the groups CH_3O or Cl, these groups are electron donors by resonance, yet inductively they are electron withdrawers, and when these two effects are in opposition, both the rate of aromatic substitution and the position of attack by the entering electrophile are influenced. The isomer distribution also depends upon the reaction conditions and upon the nature and reactivity of the entering electrophile. The more reactive the entering electrophile the less selective it is, and the isomer distribution somewhat approaches the statistical value with a more reactive reagent.

Toluene is sufficiently reactive that its halogenation can be accomplished without the aid of a catalyst. This halogenation involves the molecular halogen itself (Cl_2 or Br_2). Chlorine is more reactive than bromine and therefore less selective. In the chlorination of toluene by molecular chlorine about 0.5% of the *meta* compound is formed. Bromination yields 0.3% of the *meta* isomer. However, more significant than this, is the ratio of *para* to *meta* product, for this indicates the selectivity of the entering reagent (the *para* position being preferred). Toluene is chlorinated in the *para* position to form about 40% of the *para* isomer while bromination affords 67% of that isomer. We must also take into account the fact that there are two *meta* positions yet only a single *para* position:

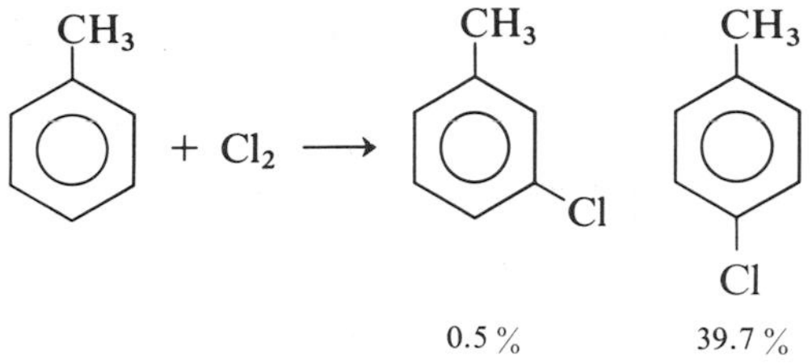

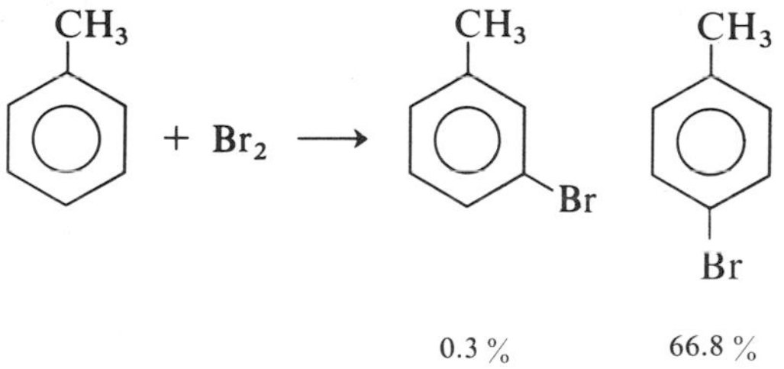

0.5 %   39.7 %

0.3 %   66.8 %

We find that the *para-meta* ratios for these reactions are,

$$\frac{para}{meta}\left(\text{bromination}\right) = 2\left(\frac{67}{0.3}\right) = 447$$

$$\frac{para}{meta}\left(\text{chlorination}\right) = 2\left(\frac{40}{0.5}\right) = 160$$

We see that for chlorination, attack of the *para* position occurs 160 times as often as attack at a *meta* position, while for bromination *para* attack takes place 447 times as often as *meta* attack and therefore, that bromine is more selective than chlorine.

When more reactive halogenating agents are employed, not only does the *para-meta* ratio become smaller, which indicates that the reagent is less discriminating, but the *para-meta* ratio for bromination approaches that for chlorination.

In the presence of a strong acid, a hypohalous acid HOX forms the species X^+ (we discuss the evidence for this later), which is an active halogenating agent. When toluene is halogenated by this species, the following *meta* to *para* percentages are obtained:

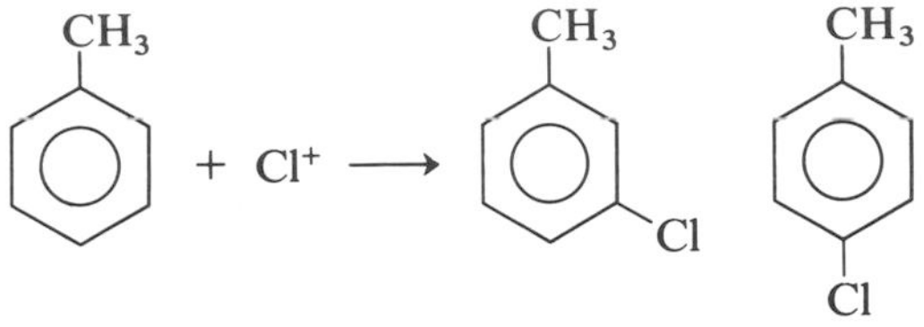

2.2 %   23.1 %

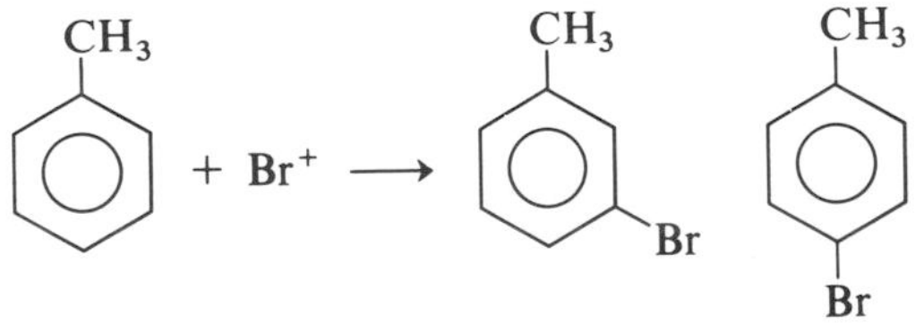

2.3 %   27.4 %

The *para-meta* ratios are:

$$\frac{para}{meta}\left(\text{bromination}\right) = 2\left(\frac{27.4}{2.3}\right) = 24$$

$$\frac{para}{meta}\left(\text{chlorination}\right) = 2\left(\frac{23.1}{2.2}\right) = 21$$

The isomer distribution varies and depends not only upon whether chlorine or bromine is being introduced but also upon the nature of the reagent effecting the introduction. Bromination by the more reactive Br^+ is less selective than chlorination by Cl_2. In addition, the overall rate of halogenation varies with the halogenating agent. Halogenation by X^+ is much more rapid than halogenation by X_2.

We have emphasized the changes in the *para-meta* ratios in these reactions; however, the most striking changes are in the *ortho-para* distributions. These changes indicate clearly that the isomer distribution depends upon the nature and reactivity of the entering electrophile. The data are presented in Table 14–1.

The idea that the isomer distribution varies with the reaction conditions is confirmed by numerous examples. The nitration of acetanilide has been conducted under a variety of conditions and it affords the various isomers in significantly different proportions; see Table 14–2.

Table 14–1

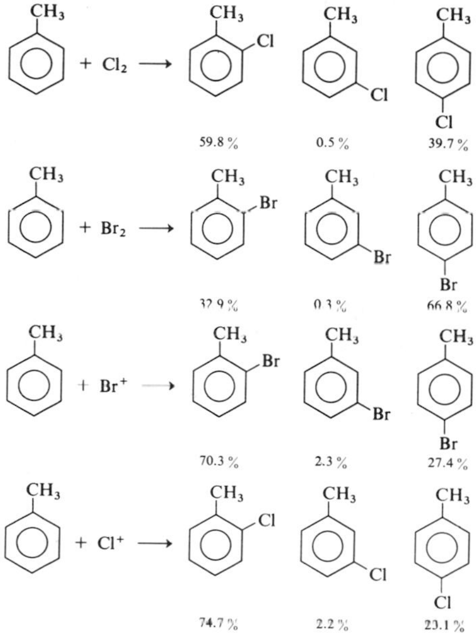
CH3
+ Cl2
Cl
59.8 %
0.5 %
39.7 %
+ Br2
Br
32.9 %
0.3 %
66.8 %
+ Br+
70.3 %
2.3 %
27.4 %
+ Cl+
74.7 %
2.2 %
23.1 %

Table 14–2

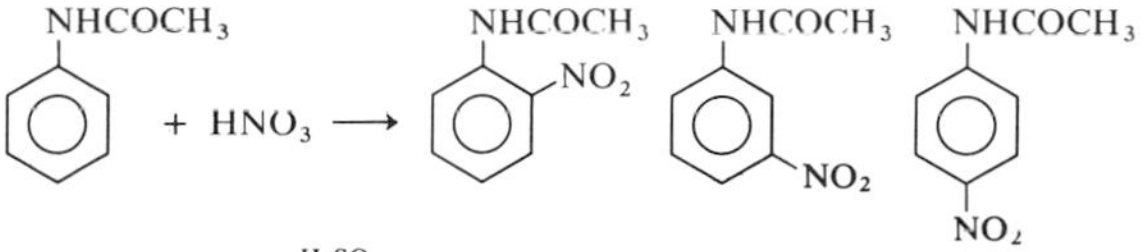
NHCOCH3
+ HNO3
NO2

$\xrightarrow{H_2SO_4}$	19%	2%	79%
$\xrightarrow{10\%\ H_2O}$	24%	—	76%
$\xrightarrow{20\%\ H_2O}$	41%	—	58%
$\xrightarrow{(CH_3CO)_2O}$	68%	2%	30%

Not only do the reaction conditions effect the isomer distribution, but the temperature at which the reaction is conducted also exerts an influence. In the nitration of toluene under the same experimental conditions the percentage of *meta* isomer increases as the temperature is raised. The *meta* isomer is only a minor product, and isotopic dilution experiments were employed to indicate the percentage of *meta* isomer that occurs at various temperatures:

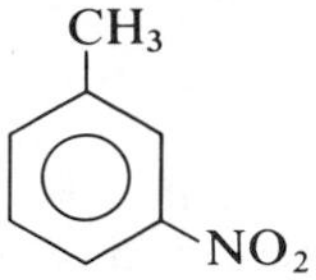
CH3
NO2

0°	30°	45°	60°
2.08%	3.44%	4.18%	4.70%

Such an increase is, of course, expected and indicates that the *meta* position becomes more susceptible to attack as the temperature is increased. The *ortho* and *para* positions also become more susceptible. However, the free energy of activation is larger for *meta* attack and the rate of substitution at this position is more sensitive to changes in temperature.

A change in temperature can have a much larger effect upon the isomeric distribution when both kinetic and thermodynamic products are possible, for the effect of a given substituent upon the position of the equilibrium may not be the same as its effect upon the rate.

The methyl group in toluene is considered to be an *ortho-para* director, and in accordance with this idea treatment of toluene with methyl chloride and aluminum chloride at 0° affords chiefly the *ortho* and *para* xylenes. However, when this same reaction is conducted at 80° or when the *ortho* and *para* xylenes are treated with aluminum chloride and hydrogen chloride at 80°, the *meta* isomer predominates. Here a change in temperature has an extremely large influence upon the isomeric distribution:

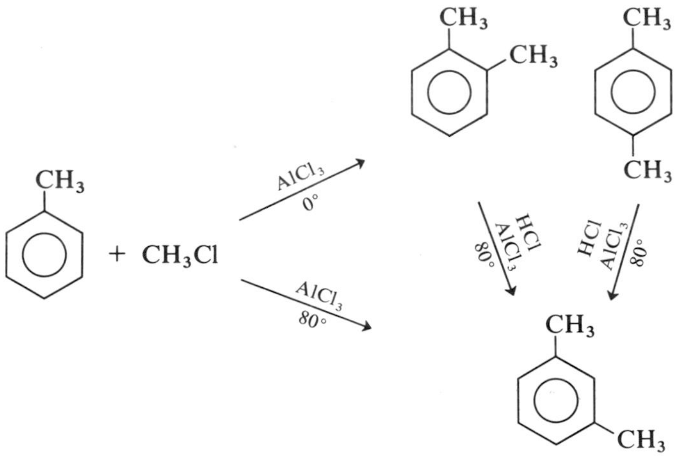

The isomerization of the xylenes does not appear to involve an intermolecular migration of the methyl group for neither toluene nor trimethylbenzenes have been found under these conditions. Furthermore, *ortho* and *para* xylene can be isomerized to the *meta* product without being directly interconverted. Thus, it appears that the isomerization is just a 1,2-shift by the methyl group.

Reaction of *ortho* or *para* xylene with hydrogen chloride and aluminum chloride affords the conjugate acids of these hydrocarbons. These conjugate acids can rearrange by a 1,2-migration of a methyl group to form the conjugate acids of *meta* xylene. Deprotonation affords the *meta* isomer. For example, when treated with hydrogen chloride and aluminum chloride, *para* xylene forms its conjugate acids **9** and **10**. Protonation and deprotonation of these materials as well as migration of hydrogen must occur but lead to no new product:

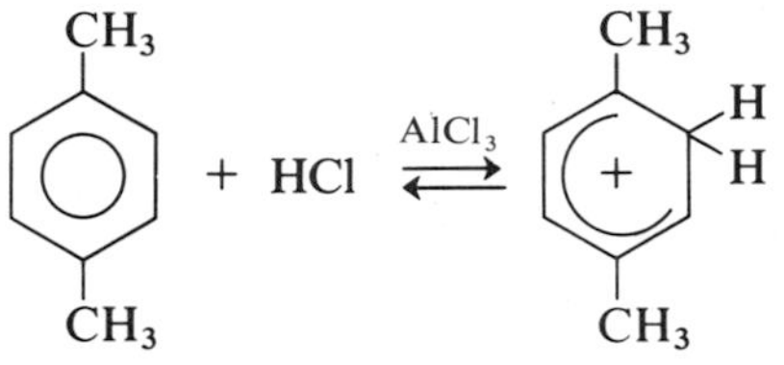

9

and

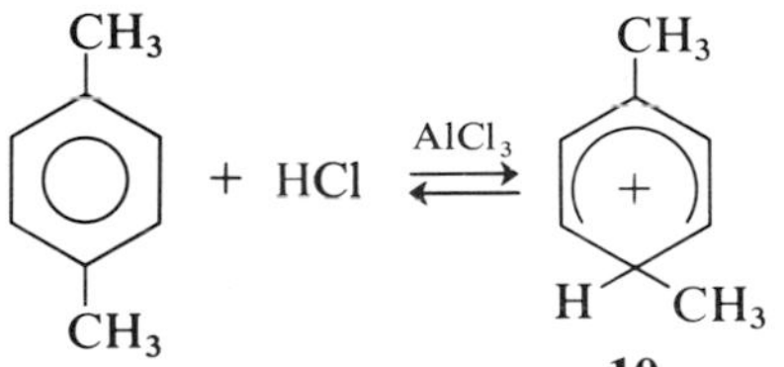

10

By migration of a methyl group **10** can rearrange to form a new carbonium ion **11**, and **11** is in equilibrium with much more stable carbonium ions such as **12** and **13**. All of the latter (**11**, **12**, **13** and **14**) are just conjugate acids of *meta* xylene and deprotonation affords this material:

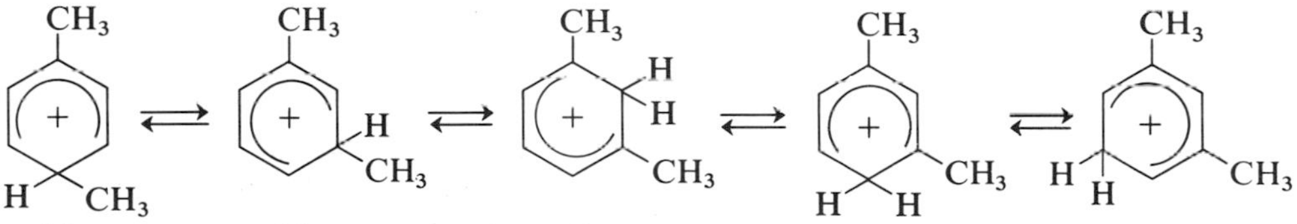

10   **11**   **12**   **13**   **14**

and,

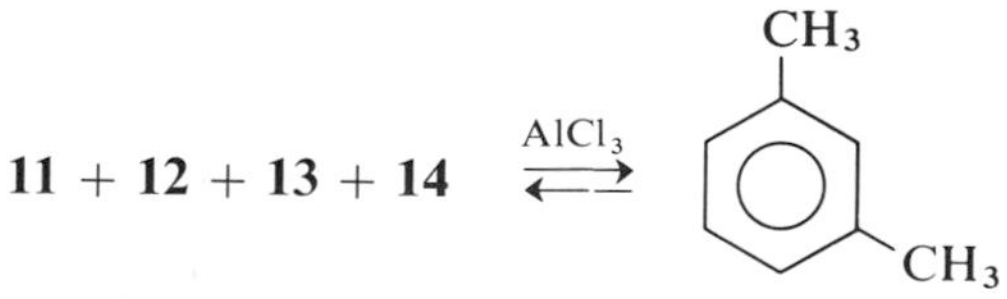

This equilibrium situation also occurs when *ortho* and *para* xylenes are treated with HF and BF_3. When only small amounts of BF_3 are used to perform the isomerization, the equilibrium is between the various xylenes, and the equilibrium mixture contains 60% *meta*, 22% *para*, and 18% *ortho* xylene.

However, when excess BF_3 is employed in the isomerization, the equilibrium is between the conjugate acids of the various xylenes. *Meta* xylene is the most basic of the xylenes, and under these conditions virtually only the *meta* isomer is obtained. Once again, we find that a change in the reaction conditions changes the isomeric distribution.

Kinetic and thermodynamic control cause the product distribution to vary in a number of other cases. When naphthalene is treated with concentrated sulfuric acid at 80° the product is the α-sulfonic acid. However, sulfonation is reversible, and at 165° it is the thermodynamically more stable β-isomer that forms the chief component of the equilibrium mixture (the rearrangement may be partially internal):

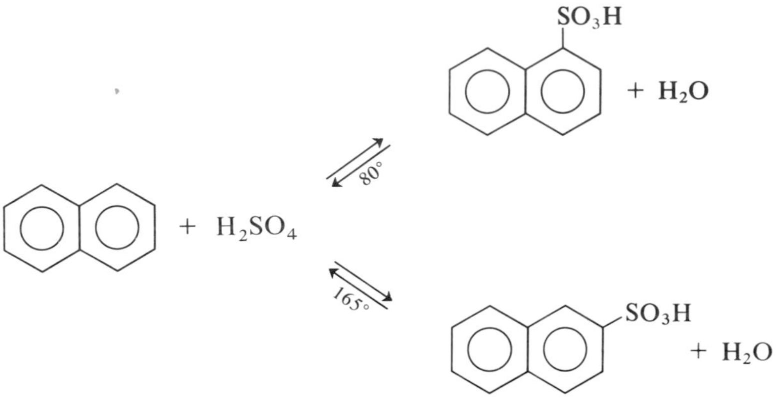

Similar behavior is observed with halobenzenes, and migrations also occur with alkyl groups other than methyl. These migrations may be intramolecular as in the xylene isomerization or intermolecular. When the migrations are accelerated by concentrated sulfuric acid, the reaction is called the Jacobsen reaction. Thus the following reaction which involves a rearrangement is known to occur:

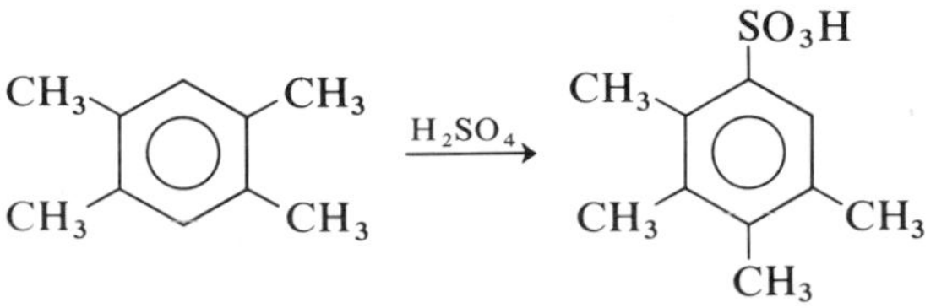

That this rearrangement is intermolecular is evidenced by the fact that products such as

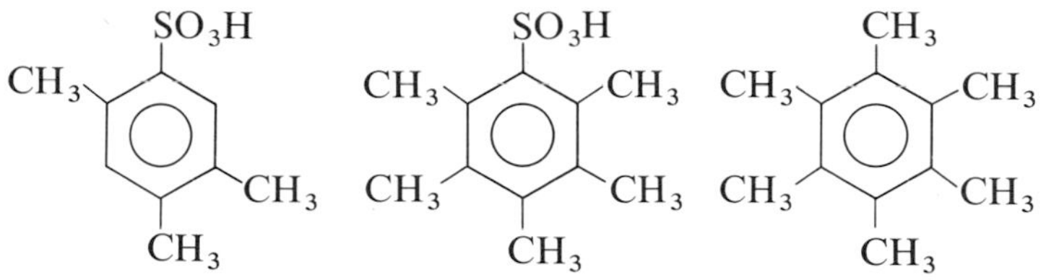

are also isolated.

Thus, we find that a number of factors affect the product distribution in electrophilic aromatic substitution, and the factors that are most important vary. We stated previously that electron donors were *ortho-para* directors while electron withdrawers were *meta* directing. We did not at that time distinguish between attack at the *ortho* positions and attack at the *para* position; however, just as certain generalizations can be made about *ortho-para* verses *meta* directors, generalizations are also possible to help predict whether attack at the *ortho* or attack at the *para* position is preferred.

14.4 The *Ortho-Para* Ratio

Since there are two *ortho* positions and only a single *para* position, on a purely statistical basis we expect twice as much *ortho* product as *para* isomer. Once again, this statistical expectation is never realized; however, the more reactive the electrophilic agent or the higher the temperature, the closer is the actual product ratio to this statistical value:

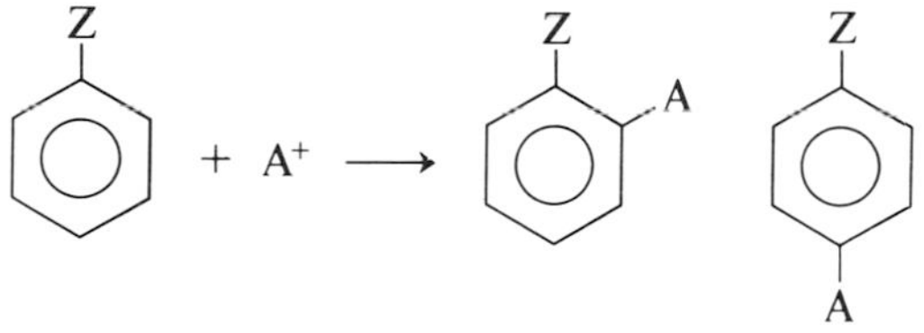

$$\frac{ortho}{para} \text{ (statistical expectation)} = 2$$

This statistical expectation does not depend upon whether Z is an electron donor or an electron withdrawer, for in either case the two to one possibility exists.

We expect *ortho* substitution to be preferred in those cases where the entering agent first complexes with Z before attacking the aromatic ring for coordination with Z leaves the entering reagent in good position for *ortho* attack but in poor position for *meta* and *para* attack.

Steric factors also affect the *ortho-para* ratio. When A$^+$ attacks Z—ϕ, the transition state leading to *ortho* substitution is,

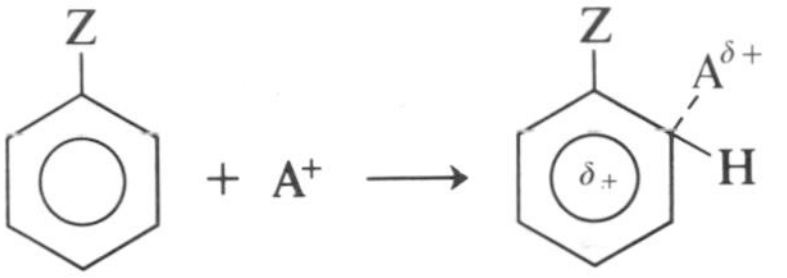

Steric interactions between A$^+$ and Z raise the free energy of this transition state. The transition states leading to *meta* and *para* substitution are not subject to these steric interactions. Consequently, as either A$^+$ or Z increases in size, *ortho* substitution becomes increasingly less favorable, and as a result we expect the portion of *meta* and *para* isomers in the product to increase.

A systematic increase in the size of either A$^+$ or Z is expected to decrease the percentage of *ortho* product and therefore to increase the percentages of *meta* and *para* products, and this expectation is substantiated. Nitration in the series R—ϕ affords an increasing percentage of *meta* and *para* isomers as R becomes larger; see Table 14–3. Similar results are observed in a series of reactions where Z is kept constant, and the size of the attacking electrophile is increased.

Table 14–3

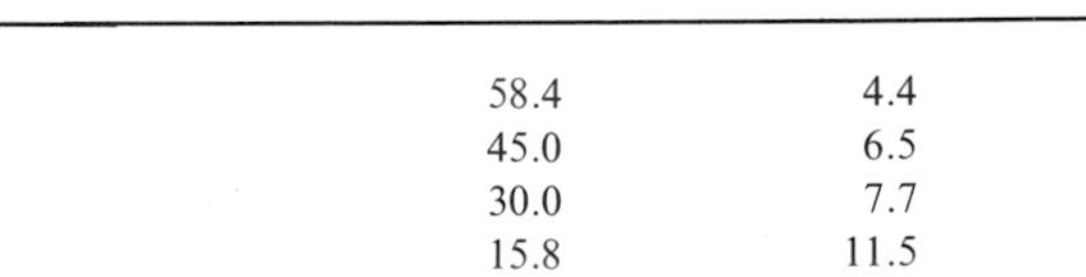

		Percentage	
R	*ortho*	*meta*	*para*
CH$_3$	58.4	4.4	37.2
CH$_3$CH$_2$	45.0	6.5	48.5
(CH$_3$)$_2$CH	30.0	7.7	62.3
(CH$_3$)$_3$C	15.8	11.5	72.7

Steric interactions influence to a considerable extent the *ortho-para* ratio. For toluene the value, *ortho*/*para* = 1.57, is not far from the statistical value. However, this ratio steadily decreases and for *t*-butylbenzene is not at all close (0.22).

Another factor that influences this ratio is the inductive effect of Z. Whereas the resonance effect operates equally on the *ortho* and *para* positions, the inductive effect decreases with increasing distance from Z. Since the *ortho* positions are closer than the *meta* which are closer than the *para* position, the inductive effect of Z is felt most strongly at the *ortho* positions and least strongly at the *para* position. Consequently, the presence of an electron donor by inductive effect favors *ortho* substitution while an electron withdrawer by inductive effect favors *para* substitution. Inductively the halogens are electron withdrawers, and the data for nitration listed in Table 14–4 agree with these ideas.

Table 14–4

		Percentage	
Z	*ortho*	*meta*	*para*
F	12.4	—	87.6
Cl	29.6	0.9	69.5
Br	36.5	1.2	62.4
I	38.3	1.8	59.7

The resonance effect causes *ortho-para* substitution to predominate in these reactions, but the inductive effect causes *para* substitution to be preferred. As the inductive effect of the halogen decreases, the percentage of *ortho* substitution increases.

Compared to aromatic substitution in benzene, the inductive effect of the halogens causes a decrease in the rate of substitution at all positions. This occurs most effectively at the *meta* positions, less effectively at the *ortho* positions where the resonance effect compensates, and least effectively at the *para* position where the inductive effect is weakest and the resonance effect also operates.

The factors that influence the product distribution are varied. While generalizations can be made easily, a more quantitative prediction is difficult. This is especially true since variations in the solvent and the temperature influence the results. The same reaction carried out at the same temperature in slightly different solvents leads to somewhat different results. This is seen readily in the nitration of acetanilide. When the solvent is 90% aqueous nitric acid, the *ortho-para* ratio is 0.32, yet in 80% aqueous nitric acid this ratio becomes 0.70. Such changes can be explained, and a more quantitative theory must take solvent effects into consideration. We mentioned previously that the product distribution also depends upon whether the reaction is kinetically or thermodynamically controlled. The rate limiting step in the process must also be considered. For most aromatic substitutions formation of the carbonium ion intermediate is rate limiting. However, the second step, decomposition of this intermediate, is rate limiting in some processes. For example, aromatic sulfonation and iodination can show kinetic isotope effects and basic catalysis. We discuss the actual mechanisms for aromatic substitution more fully in subsequent sections.

14.5 Aromatic Nitration

The electrophilic species in nitration is usually NO_2^+ which is formed either as a solvated ion or as part of an ion pair. In the more polar solvents a solvated ion is expected while in less polar media an ion pair or higher ionic aggregate containing NO_2^+ is probably responsible for effecting nitration.

Evidence for the existence of nitronium ion (NO_2^+) comes from cryoscopic measurements. These indicate that four ions are present when nitric acid is dissolved in concentrated sulfuric acid. The existence is confirmed by spectroscopic studies and by x-ray studies of nitronium salts:

$$HNO_3 + H_2SO_4 \rightleftharpoons NO_2^+ + H_3O^+ + 2HSO_4^-$$

The mechanism for the process is

$$HONO_2 + H_2SO_4 \rightleftharpoons H-\overset{\overset{\displaystyle H}{\displaystyle |}}{\underset{+}{O}}-NO_2 + HSO_4^-$$

$$H-\overset{\overset{\displaystyle H}{\displaystyle |}}{\underset{+}{O}}-NO_2 \rightleftharpoons NO_2^+ + H_2O$$

and

$$H_2O + H_2SO_4 \rightleftharpoons H_3O^+ + HSO_4^-$$

Aromatic nitrations can be accomplished by using mixtures of sulfuric acid and nitric acid or by using only nitric acid. In addition, the reaction can be conducted in the presence of organic solvents such as acetic acid, acetic anhydride, and nitromethane or in the absence of an organic solvent. When sulfuric acid is not present, the nitronium ion is formed in the following fashion,

$$HONO_2 + HNO_3 \rightleftharpoons H-\overset{\overset{\displaystyle H}{\displaystyle |}}{\underset{+}{O}}-NO_2 + NO_3^-$$

$$H-\overset{\overset{\displaystyle H}{\displaystyle |}}{\underset{+}{O}}-NO_2 \rightleftharpoons NO_2^+ + H_2O$$

The electron deficient nitronium ion then attacks an aromatic compound to form the substituted products, and the mechanism for product formation is,

We have indicated *para* attack; of course, *ortho* and *meta* substitution also occur.

The rate limiting step in the reaction varies. When Z is an electron withdrawer the rate limiting step is attack of the aromatic compound by NO_2^+. However, when Z is an electron donor, the rate limiting step depends upon the reaction conditions, and it can be the formation of nitronium ion from $H_2ONO_2^+$.

Nitronium ion can react with water to reform $H_2ONO_2^+$, or it can react with the aromatic compound to form substituted products. When the aromatic compound is sufficiently active, water is unable to compete with it successfully for the NO_2^+, the reversal to reform $H_2ONO_2^+$ virtually never occurs, and the rate limiting step becomes formation of the nitronium ion.

Kinetic evidence is available, and this indicates that a rate limiting formation of NO_2^+ does occur in certain nitrations. When compounds such as benzene and toluene are nitrated by nitric acid in nitromethane, or when more reactive aromatic compounds are nitrated using nitric acid and no added organic solvent, the rate of reaction is independent of the concentration of aromatic compound. The rate of the nitration reaction does not depend upon the concentration of the material being nitrated! Kinetics of this type, which are zeroth order in aromatic compound, can only be explained by a rate limiting step that does not involve the compound itself. The formation of NO_2^+ in the rate limiting step is entirely consistent with these results.

A rate limiting formation of NO_2^+ leads to kinetics that are zeroth order in aromatic compound and will be observed whenever the term $k\,[Z-\phi][NO_2^+]$ is much greater than the term $k'[H_2O][NO_2^+]$. Thus increasing the concentration of $Z-\phi$ favors a rate limiting formation of NO_2^+, while increasing the concentration of H_2O favors reversal of this step and a rate limiting attack by NO_2^+ on the aromatic compound.

When NO_2^+ reacts with water much more frequently than with the aromatic compound, the rate limiting step is reaction with $Z-\phi$. On the other hand, under certain conditions the nitronium ion reacts with the aromatic compound much more frequently than it reacts with water, and under these conditions formation of NO_2^+ becomes rate limiting. Naturally, it also happens that the two steps, reaction with water and reaction with $Z-\phi$, are comparable in rate.

The rate limiting step in nitration has never been observed to be the following decomposition of the carbonium ion intermediate into the product (perhaps by way of the π complex):

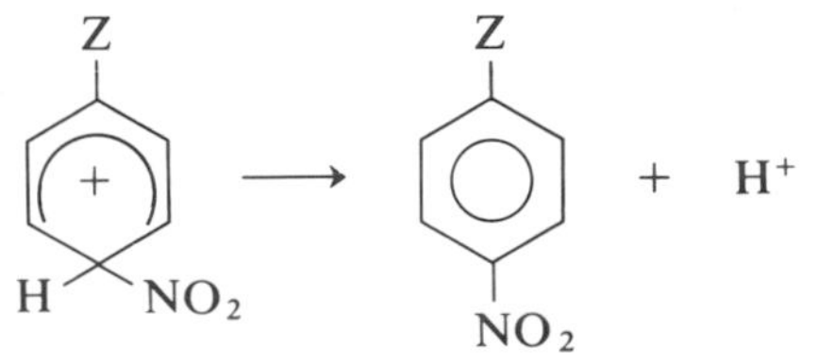

This process involves bond breakage to hydrogen, and when this breakage is rate limiting, the reaction becomes subject to a primary kinetic isotope effect. Such effects have not been found in aromatic nitrations. In all the cases studied, the deuterated aromatic compound reacted just as rapidly as the protonated analogue.

We have presented evidence for the existence of NO_2^+ and have assumed that this species is involved in aromatic nitration. The fact that it exists is not adequate evidence for its involvement in nitration. However, nitration does occur when nitronium ion is known to be present in the solution, and this is certainly a good indication. It is difficult to imagine that a species as potentially reactive as NO_2^+ could coexist with the aromatic compound yet not effect nitration. Further evidence in favor of NO_2^+ as the active species is kinetic in nature.

When Z is electron withdrawing, the general rate expression for the nitration of $Z-\phi$ in concentrated sulfuric acid (where the conversion of nitric acid to nitronium ion is virtually complete) follows moderately well the general rate law,

$$k[Z-\phi][HNO_3]\frac{f_{Z-\phi}f_{NO_2^+}}{f_{TS}^{\ddagger}}$$

or equivalently,

$$k[Z-\phi][NO_2^+]\frac{f_{Z-\phi}f_{NO_2^+}}{f_{TS}^{\ddagger}}$$

Since sulfuric acid is the solvent, this rate expression is in agreement with a rate limiting attack of the aromatic compound by nitronium ion.

All of the evidence presented thus far is in agreement with the idea that nitronium ion is the active species. The possibility that HNO_3 or $H_2ONO_2^+$ is the nitrating agent must be considered; however, these possibilities are eliminated by other experiments.

The nitration of $Z-\phi$ (with Z electron withdrawing) can also be conducted in concentrated nitric acid. The general rate expression is first order in the aromatic compound, and this is consistent with attack by NO_2^+ in the rate limiting step. The fact that addition of NO_3^- to the solution decreases the rate of aromatic substitution cannot be explained if nitric acid is the nitrating agent but this result is explained quite nicely by assuming the following equilibria,

$$HONO_2 + HNO_3 \underset{\longleftarrow}{\overset{K_1}{\longrightarrow}} \overset{\overset{\displaystyle H}{\displaystyle |}}{H-\underset{+}{O}-NO_2} + NO_3^-$$

$$\overset{\overset{\displaystyle H}{\displaystyle |}}{H-\underset{+}{O}-NO_2} \underset{\longleftarrow}{\overset{K_2}{\longrightarrow}} NO_2^+ + H_2O$$

The concentration of NO_2^+ is given by the expression,

$$[NO_2^+] = K_1 K_2 \frac{[HNO_3]^2}{[H_2O][NO_3^-]}$$

and its concentration is decreased when nitrate ion is added. The possibility of HNO_3 as the nitrating agent is eliminated by these experiments. The concentration of $H_2ONO_2^+$ is also decreased when NO_3^- is added, but the following experiment eliminates this possibility.

The nitration is conducted in nitromethane using reactive aromatic compounds. Consequently, the observed general rate expression is zeroth order in aromatic compound, and this means that the rate limiting step is formation of the nitrating agent ($H_2ONO_2^+$ or NO_2^+). If $H_2ONO_2^+$ is the active agent, the rate limiting step becomes,

$$HONO_2 + HNO_3 \longrightarrow \overset{\overset{\displaystyle H}{\displaystyle |}}{H-\underset{+}{O}-NO_2} + NO_3^-$$

and this step must be virtually irreversible. However, the rate of the nitration reaction is retarded when NO_3^- is added, yet the rate law remains zeroth order in aromatic compound even in the presence of added NO_3^-. These facts are not consistent with $H_2ONO_2^+$ as the active nitrating species, for NO_3^- can retard the rate only by reversing this first step.

The nitrating agent is formed in the rate limiting step, yet rate of reaction decreases when NO_3^- is added. The following process is consistent with these observations,

$$\text{HONO}_2 + \text{HNO}_3 \rightleftarrows \text{H}-\overset{\text{H}}{\underset{+}{\text{O}}}-\text{NO}_2 + \text{NO}_3^-$$

$$\text{H}-\overset{\text{H}}{\underset{+}{\text{O}}}-\text{NO}_2 \longrightarrow \text{NO}_2^+ + \text{H}_2\text{O}$$

This experiment proves that the nitrating agent is not H_2ONO_2^+. The reaction involves the formation of the nitrating agent in the rate limiting step, yet this agent is not H_2ONO_2^+. Furthermore, the rate of nitration is decreased by addition of nitrate ion to the solution. The only logical choice for such a nitrating agent is NO_2^+, for this species satisfies all requirements.

The species NO_2^+ does exist; it is known to be present in solution when the nitrations are conducted in concentrated sulfuric acid; it satisfies the kinetic requirements. The evidence is certainly excellent that NO_2^+ is the active species and that in most nitrations it is this agent that attacks the aromatic compound to form the substituted products. In fact, it remains to be demonstrated that the other species, nitric acid and its conjugate acid H_2ONO_2^+, actually can effect nitration. Although it certainly seems reasonable to assume that these materials (especially H_2ONO_2^+) could effect nitration, these reactions are much slower than nitration by nitronium ion and are not observed.

Other methods for introducing the NO_2 group into an aromatic compound do exist. One reaction that has been observed to occur with reactive aromatic compounds is nitration by way of nitrosation. Aqueous solutions of nitric acid also contain varying amounts of HNO_2 and N_2O_4. The nitrous acid does not effect nitrosation directly, but it is in equilibrium with N_2O_4 and with other reagents that can effect nitrosation.

Now in most aromatic nitrations the presence of HNO_2 and N_2O_4 influences indirectly the rate of reaction, yet under the usual conditions they do not exert a direct influence. Nitrosation is not observed. However, when the nitrous acid concentration is high or when the aromatic compound is sufficiently reactive, nitrosation does occur, and the nitroso compound formed in this way is then oxidized to the nitro compound by the nitric acid that is present. Nitrous acid is not consumed in the reaction, for it is regenerated in the second step of the sequence:

The second step, oxidation of the nitroso compound, occurs readily under the reaction conditions, and the rate of the first step determines whether or not this reaction takes place.

The two processes for nitration (by NO_2^+ and by way of the nitroso compound) proceed independently. In some reactions the first occurs exclusively, in others the second, and in certain cases both processes take place concurrently. The second process occurs with very reactive aromatic compounds such as phenol and anisole when the nitric acid concentration is low. At higher nitric acid concentrations and with less reactive compounds, nitration by NO_2^+ predominates. Only in certain special situations does nitrosation followed by oxidation afford the products. Generally nitronium ion effects the nitration.

14.6 Aromatic Halogenation

In contrast to nitration where the same species is almost always involved, the halogenation of aromatic compounds involves a number of different attacking agents. Both catalyzed and uncatalyzed reactions take place, and a variety of catalysts are known. The mechanism depends upon the solvent and the particular halogen being introduced. The rate limiting step varies with the reaction conditions and also depends upon the aromatic compound.

A compound Z—ϕ, where Z is an electron donor, reacts readily with molecular chlorine even in the absence of a catalyst to produce aromatic chloro compounds. This reaction proceeds most readily in polar solvents and involves a direct attack of the aromatic compound by the chlorine itself. A catalyst is not required in the reaction but is sometimes employed. On the other hand, compounds Z—ϕ, where Z is an electron withdrawer, do not react rapidly with Cl_2 unless a catalyst is present. Effective catalysts include Lewis acids such as $FeCl_3$, $AlCl_3$, $ZnCl_2$. The role of these Lewis acids is certainly to complex with the Cl_2 at some stage in the reaction, but whether this complexing occurs before or after attack of the aromatic compound by Cl_2 is not yet known. More work must be done on these Lewis acid catalyzed reactions to ascertain the role of the catalyst.

Molecular bromine is less reactive than molecular chlorine; however, when Z is an electron donor, these reactions still proceed at a moderately rapid rate. When Z is not an electron donor, catalysis is required.

Molecular iodine is the least reactive of the molecular halogens. Furthermore, the process is complicated by the fact that the reaction is reversible:

However, iodination can be effected. When Z is a sufficiently strong activator of the aromatic ring and when the hydroiodic acid is removed as it is formed (by reaction with base or by oxidation), the reaction does take place and yields iodo aromatics.

Other techniques exist. For example, iodination can also be accomplished by mixed halogens such as iodine chloride ICl; however, here too there are side reactions due to the equilibrium,

$$2ICl \rightleftharpoons I_2 + Cl_2$$

This equilibrium generates molecular chlorine which acts as a chlorinating agent.

Studies show that it is indeed the molecular halogen that is involved in certain reactions and not some other species formed from the halogen. Reactions such as,

$$Cl_2 + H^+ \rightleftharpoons Cl^+ + HCl$$

$$Cl_2 \rightleftharpoons Cl^+ + Cl^-$$

which lead to very reactive electrophiles are conceivable, but these as well as other possibilities have been eliminated. The reactions were run in the presence of added Cl^- and in the presence of added acids and bases. Except for a salt effect, there is no change in the rate of reaction. The salt effect causes a slight increase in the rate. The slight increase in rate with added salts is attributed to the fact that the transition state for chlorination is more polar than the reactants. As a result of such experiments it is safe to conclude that at least in certain cases the molecular halogens are themselves the halogenating agents.

While molecular halogens are involved in some reactions, they are not the only effective halogenating agents. In the presence of water the equilibrium,

$$X_2 + H_2O \rightleftharpoons HOX + H_3O^+ + X^-$$

takes place. It has been demonstrated that even when water is present, the molecular halogen can be the actual halogenating agent, for the hypohalous acids themselves are not very effective. However, in the presence of a strong acid and especially if the halide ion concentration is kept low, a species is formed in water that is a very powerful halogenating agent. This species has either the structure H_2OX^+ or X^+. It is not yet agreed upon which of these is involved.

Similarly, when reactions are conducted in acetic acid or in alcohol, species of the type

$$R-O-X \qquad R-\overset{\overset{\displaystyle H}{|}}{\underset{+}{O}}-X \qquad X^+$$

can be present as well as the species X_2.

For chlorine and bromine it is possible to distinguish between attack by molecular halogen and attack by the various other species. This is accomplished by determining the effect of added acids, bases, and halide ion upon the rate of reaction. Reaction rates and isomeric distributions also serve as a criterion of mechanism. The species H_2OX^+ or X^+ is much more powerful than X_2, and the specific rate constants for reactions by the former are manyfold larger than those encountered for reactions involving X_2 under similar conditions. The observed isomeric distribution is in accordance with this idea, for X_2 is a much more selective reagent.

Once it has been established that molecular halogen is not involved, the problem then becomes less straightforward. It is not always possible to distinguish between the species H_2OX^+ and X^+.

In principle, the problem of distinguishing between H_2OX^+ and X^+ is similar to that encountered previously with NO_2^+. However, with NO_2^+ spectroscopic evidence, x-ray crystallography, and melting point depressions in sulfuric acid all demonstrated the existence of this intermediate, and the problem was to prove that it was also involved in aromatic substitution. There is no similar evidence to prove the existence of Cl^+ or Br^+. If these species are formed, their concentrations are too small to be detected by the usual physical methods. Since their existence has not been demonstrated, they are less readily accepted as intermediates. The problem is further complicated by the fact that the molecular halogen is a halogenating agent, and this possibility must always be eliminated. Thus the problem of showing the involvement of X^+ is far more difficult.

The existence of I^+ has been demonstrated. Solutions of I_2 in H_2SO_4 containing varying amounts of SO_3 are colored and contain a positively charged species. When combined with aromatic compounds, iodination occurs; even deactivated aromatics are iodinated. However, while I^+ appears to be involved under these conditions, evidence for its participation in aromatic substitutions run under other conditions has not been obtained. Furthermore, Cl_2 and Br_2 do not form detectable quantities of Cl^+ and Br^+.

When an aromatic compound such as benzene is chlorinated by hypochlorous acid in the presence of a strong acid, the rate law at any given pH is,

$$-\frac{d[HOCl]}{dt} = k[\phi H][HOCl]$$

Since the rate also varies with the hydrogen ion concentration, a more complete expression is given by the rate law,

$$-\frac{d[HOCl]}{dt} = k'[\phi H][HOCl][H^+]$$

This rate law implies that the rate limiting step is attack of benzene by the halogenating agent. However, it does not further distinguish between possibilities such as,

$$HOCl + H^+ \rightleftharpoons H_2OCl^+$$

$$H_2OCl^+ \rightleftharpoons Cl^+ + H_2O$$

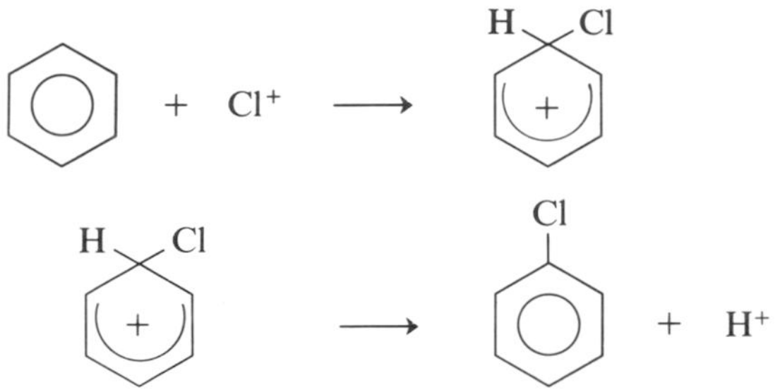

and

$$HOCl + H^+ \rightleftharpoons H_2OCl^+$$

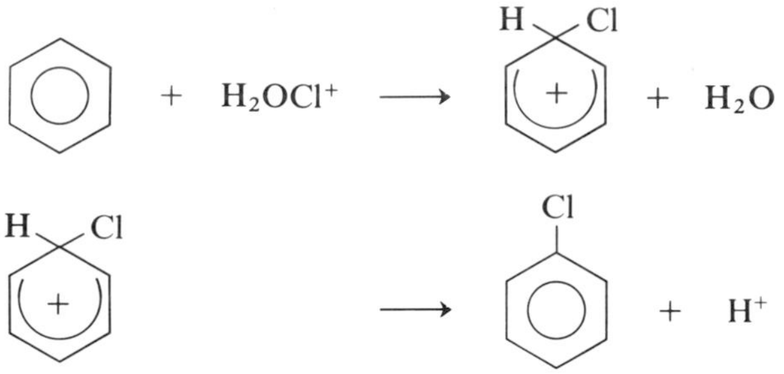

The general rate expression does not differentiate between attack by H_2OCl^+ and attack by Cl^+ in the rate limiting step.

For that matter, not only does this rate law fail to differentiate between these two possibilities, it does not eliminate other conceivable chlorinating agents formed from $HOCl + H^+$. The two presented here, H_2OCl^+ and Cl^+, are most probable, but other less likely chlorinating agents cannot be dismissed.

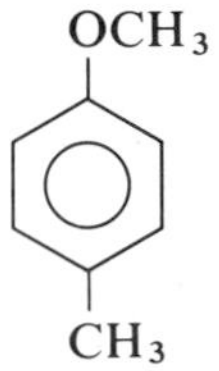

Under the proper conditions, when a more reactive compound such as methyl *para* tolyl ether is chlorinated, the rate law observed for chlorination is zeroth order in aromatic compound. The rate of reaction does not depend upon the concentration of the aromatic compound, and therefore, the rate limiting step does not involve the aromatic compound. Instead the active halogenating agent must be produced in the rate limiting step. Since the most logical halogenating agent is either H_2OCl^+ or Cl^+, one of these must be formed in the crucial step.

Evidence has been reported that eliminates a rate limiting formation of H_2OCl^+. Unlike the similar problem that occurs between $H_2ONO_2^+$ and NO_2^+, this evidence was not obtained by adding Cl^- to the reaction (this generates Cl_2). Instead the rate of chloronation of methyl *para* tolyl ether in the presence of D_2O and acid was compared with its rate in H_2O and acid. The reaction proceeded somewhat more rapidly in the deuterated solvent. Furthermore, the reaction was zeroth order in aromatic compound in both solvents. Deuterium transfer is slower than proton transfer, and this increase in rate is not consistent with the process

$$D_3O^+ + DOCl \longrightarrow D_2O + D_2OCl^+$$

being the rate limiting step. If this were the rate limiting step, the reaction rate should have decreased somewhat in D_2O. The possibility that H_2OCl^+ is formed in the rate limiting step is therefore eliminated.

The observed increase is consistent with a rate limiting transfer of Cl from D_2OCl^+ to the aromatic species, but this can also be eliminated because the aromatic compound is not involved in the rate limiting step. Finally, the rate increase is consistent with a unimolecular dissociation of D_2OCl^+ in the rate limiting step:

$$D_2OCl^+ \longrightarrow Cl^+ + D_2O$$

This unimolecular decomposition is the most reasonable explanation. It accounts for the fact that the rate is independent of the concentration of the aromatic compound and for the observed inverse secondary deuterium isotope effect. The kinetic evidence is good and completely in favor of a rate limiting formation of Cl^+ which then attacks the methyl *para* tolyl ether. For the still more reactive methyl *meta* tolyl ether, the complete general rate expression takes the form,

$$k[HOCl] + k'[HOCl][H^+] + k''[HOCl][H^+][ArH]$$

where ArH represents methyl *meta* tolyl ether.

The first term is explained by a rate limiting dissociation of hypochlorous acid into Cl^+ and OH^-. The second term implies a rate limiting dissociation of its conjugate acid into Cl^+ and H_2O. This compound is so reactive that it does not wait for these unimolecular dissociations but occasionally attacks the H_2OCl^+ before it dissociates, and this accounts for the third term.

It appears on the basis of the kinetic evidence that the mechanism for chlorination by hypochlorous acid at low pH's is usually,

$$HOCl + H^+ \rightleftharpoons H_2OCl^+$$

$$H_2OCl^+ \rightleftharpoons Cl^+ + H_2O$$

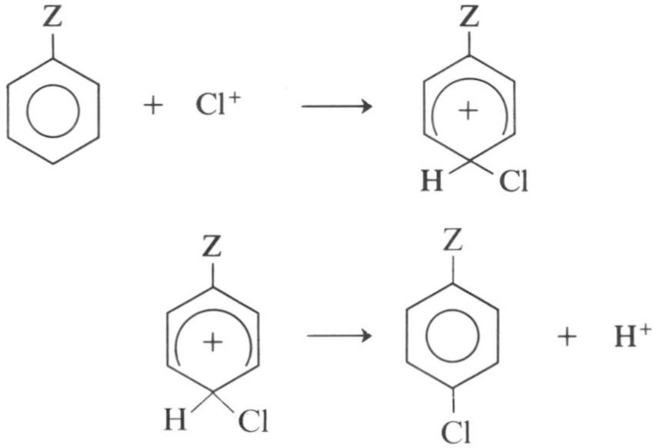

The rate limiting step in the process depends upon the reactivity of the aromatic compound. For the less reactive compounds it is attack of the aromatic compounds by Cl^+, while for the more reactive compounds it is the formation of Cl^+ that is rate limiting. These ideas are completely analogous to those presented for nitration by NO_2^+.

In addition to this process, which appears to hold for all aromatics, the unimolecular dissociation of HOCl and chlorination by the weaker chlorinating agent H_2OCl^+ also play a role in the chlorination of very reactive aromatic compounds.

The kinetic evidence is in favor of this interpretation. As we mentioned previously, any other chlorinating agent produced from HOCl or from $HOCl + H^+$ also satisfies these general rate expressions, but it is difficult to imagine another chlorinating agent (except Cl_2) that can be formed from these reactants.

Unfortunately, thermodynamic calculations are not in agreement with this interpretation. The concentrations of H_2OCl^+ and of Cl^+ in solution, according to the calculations, are much too small for them to play a role in chlorination. If these intermediates were involved, the rate of chlorination would be almost immeasurably slow.

These calculations have prevented a complete acceptance of the involvement of Cl^+ and even of H_2OCl^+ in chlorinations. The kinetics favor one interpretation; the thermodynamic calculations are opposed to this idea. The problem is not yet resolved. However, the calculations involve several assumptions which remain unconfirmed, and until the question is settled, we continue to assume that Cl^+ does participate in aromatic substitution.

Brominations can be effected under conditions that are similar to those employed for chlorination. When a solution containing HOBr is treated with a strong acid, an active brominating agent is produced. The general rate expression for bromination of an aromatic compound by this agent is,

$$k[\text{HOBr}][\text{H}^+][\text{ArH}]$$

This rate law is consistent with a rate limiting attack of the aromatic compound by either H_2OBr^+ or Br^+. Zero order brominations have not been observed, and the question of whether H_2OBr^+ or Br^+ is involved in the attack remains unsettled. However, by analogy with the mechanism presented for chlorination we postulate the following mechanism for bromination,

$$\text{HOBr} + \text{H}^+ \;\rightleftharpoons\; \text{H}_2\text{OBr}^+$$

$$\text{H}_2\text{OBr}^+ \;\rightleftharpoons\; \text{Br}^+ + \text{H}_2\text{O}$$

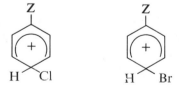

where the rate limiting step is attack of $Z-\phi$ by Br^+.

For chlorination by Cl^+ the rate limiting step can be either the formation of this species or its attack on the aromatic compound. For aromatic bromination the attack is rate limiting. Experiments on deuterated and tritiated aromatic compounds are in agreement with the idea that carbonium ion formation or some prior step is rate limiting. While these experiments throw no light on the active halogenating agent, they do indicate that the formation and not the decomposition of the carbonium ion intermediates:

is rate limiting. For example, hexadeuterobenzene is brominated at the same rate as benzene by Br^+.

When the aromatic hydrogens are replaced by deuterium, a decrease in the rate of reaction would indicate that bond breakage to hydrogen is involved in the rate limiting step. Such a decrease has not been found in chlorination and only occasionally has it been observed in bromination. Even in chlorinations by the less reactive Cl_2, the rate limiting step is still formation of the carbonium ion intermediate; however, bromination by Br_2 can be subject to isotope effects.

Isotope effects have not been observed in chlorinations and only occasionally in brominations; however, isotope effects are the rule in iodinations. For almost all of the systems studied the rate limiting step in iodination was found to be bond breakage to hydrogen. This was evidenced by isotope effects and confirmed by observed basic catalyses. Thus it appears that in aromatic iodination the carbonium ion intermediate gives up iodine and thereby reverts to reactants more frequently than it loses a proton and passes on to products.

The fact that carbonium ion formation is not rate limiting makes it difficult to distinguish between attack by H_2OI^+, I^+, or I_2. In certain investigations the isotope effect was observed to decrease with a decreasing concentration of I^-. This result, which indicates that the presence of I^- causes a reversal to reactants, can be interpreted as follows:

Apparently the aromatic compound is attacked by molecular iodine in these cases.

For aromatic chlorination and bromination it is usually possible to distinguish between attack by X_2 and attack by X^+. To distinguish between attack by H_2OX^+ and X^+ is more difficult. For aromatic iodination it is difficult to distinguish between any of these three possibilities. Attack by I_2 takes place in some reactions, and I^+ is involved in concentrated sulfuric acid. The conjugate acids H_2OBr^+ and H_2OI^+ are also possible halogenating agents, and it remains to be seen if these are involved in halogenation.

14.7 Aromatic Sulfonation

An aromatic compound can be converted into a sulfonic acid

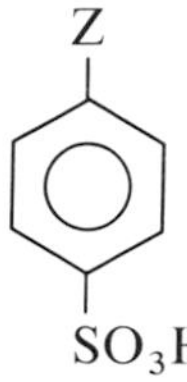

by a variety of techniques. One method consists of treatment with sulfur trioxide; a second employs oleum ($H_2SO_4 + SO_3$); while a third involves concentrated sulfuric acid. The reaction can be conducted as a heterogeneous or a homogeneous process and several solvents are available.

Sulfonation is reversible. Upon heating the sulfonic acid with water, desulfonation takes place and the original aromatic compound is reformed. Thus, when naphthalene is sulfonated at 80°, the α-sulfonic acid is produced. Heating this material with steam at 150° causes hydrolysis and regenerates the starting hydrocarbon:

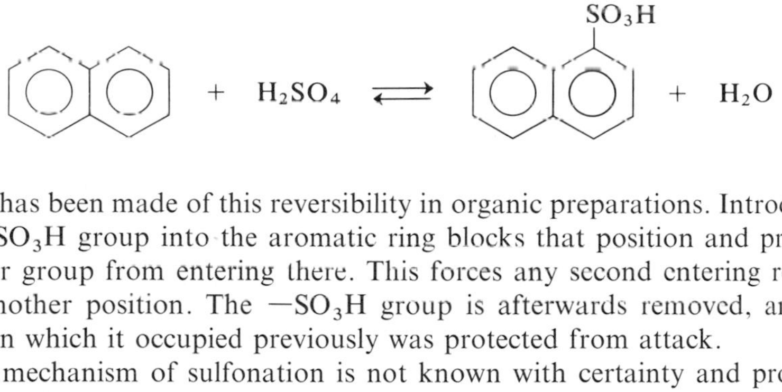

Use has been made of this reversibility in organic preparations. Introducing the $-SO_3H$ group into the aromatic ring blocks that position and prevents another group from entering there. This forces any second entering reagent into another position. The $-SO_3H$ group is afterwards removed, and the position which it occupied previously was protected from attack.

The mechanism of sulfonation is not known with certainty and probably changes with the reaction conditions. The reaction has been studied under a variety of conditions. Kinetic investigations have been undertaken, but in concentrated sulfuric acid and in oleum the results are not clearcut. It is difficult in such reactions to distinguish between attack by SO_3 and attack by its conjugate acid SO_3H^+. The evidence is in favor of the former being the active sulfonating agent, but the data are by no means conclusive. It is possible to distinguish between these two, in principle, but the actual reaction conditions are not very favorable for kinetic investigations.

Assuming that SO_3 is the active species in concentrated aqueous sulfuric acid, the rate of sulfonation is given by,

$$k[\text{ArH}][\text{SO}_3]$$

and in order to test this hypothesis it is necessary to ascertain the effect of changes in $[SO_3]$ upon the reaction rate. The concentration of SO_3 in aqueous sulfuric acid is not known, and it becomes necessary to express this concentration in terms of the known and measurable concentrations of other species. It is possible to relate the concentration of SO_3 to the concentrations of H_2O and H_2SO_4 by considering the equilibria,

$$SO_3 + H_2O \rightleftharpoons H_2SO_4$$

and,

$$H_2O + H_2SO_4 \rightleftharpoons H_3O^+ + HSO_4^-$$

By measuring the effect of added water upon the rate of sulfonation, it is possible to obtain some idea of the importance of SO_3 in the reaction. However, under these conditions the concentrations are not an adequate index of reactivity, and the activity coefficients of the various species must also be considered. The problem becomes difficult because the activity coefficients of H_2SO_4 and SO_3 must be introduced explicitly into the kinetic expression, and the values of these coefficients in aqueous sulfuric acid are not known. Consequently, it is not possible to determine accurately the effect of changes in $[SO_3]$ upon the reaction rate. Addition of water to the reaction mixture retards the rate of reaction because it decreases the SO_3 concentration. However, it causes a change in the activity coefficients of the various species, and the magnitude of these changes is not known. Approximations can be made, and the results of these approximations indicate that SO_3 is indeed the attacking species. The following mechanism is consistent with this idea:

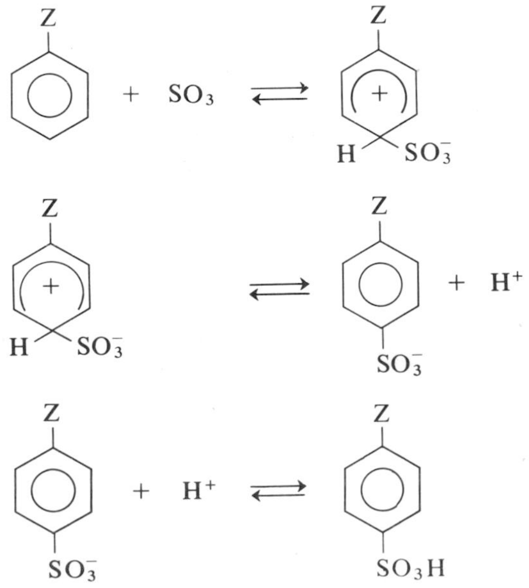

In oleum, a slightly different mechanism has been proposed. This mechanism stems from a study of deuterium isotope effects upon the rate of sulfonation. Here also, the evidence is good but not conclusive:

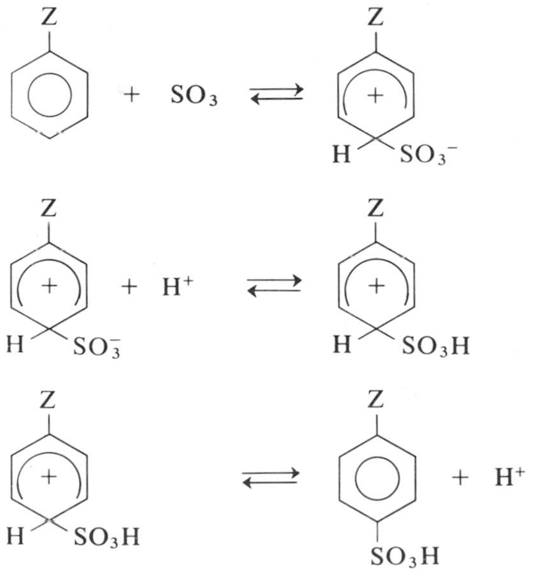

In oleum the attacking agent is probably SO_3, but the intermediate that results picks up a proton from the solvent before the aromatic proton is lost rather than afterwards.

Under both sets of conditions, aqueous sulfuric acid and oleum, the attacking species appears to be the sulfur trioxide itself rather than its conjugate acid, yet the mechanism postulated for the reaction differs in the order of the steps.

When the sulfonation is conducted with sulfur trioxide in an organic solvent still another mechanism is operative. Under these conditions the general rate law is first order in aromatic compound but second order in sulfur trioxide. Whether the attacking agent under these conditions is S_2O_6, or whether the second molecule of sulfur trioxide adds to the carbonium ion intermediate to form a second intermediate having the structure,

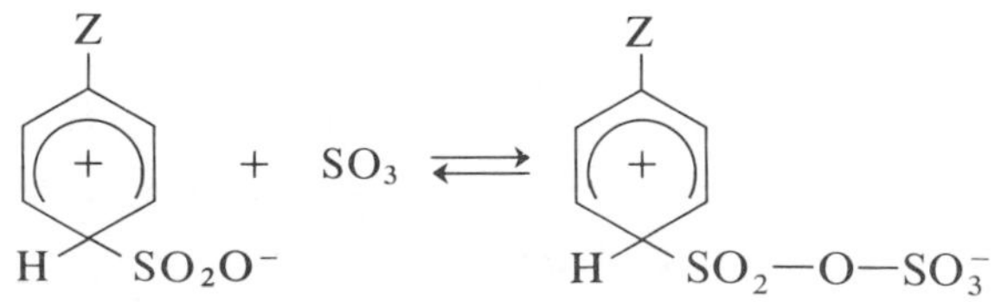

or whether the second molecule of sulfur trioxide is used simply to solvate the first intermediate is not known.

One more point should be mentioned in connection with aromatic sulfonation; namely, that the reaction in oleum is sometimes subject to a small kinetic isotope effect. This effect is a primary kinetic isotope effect and indicates that for some sulfonations the carbonium ion intermediate returns to the reactants at about the same rate that it loses a proton to the solvent.

Thus, we find that sulfonation like iodination is reversible and that in neither process is carbonium ion formation necessarily rate limiting. In iodination the equilibrium can be shifted by removing the hydroiodic acid as it forms, and in sulfonation removal of water shifts the equilibrium towards the products.

14.8 The Friedel-Crafts Reaction

When an aromatic compound is treated with an alkyl or acyl halide in the presence of a Lewis acid, electrophilic substitution occurs. This reaction, which is known as the Friedel-Crafts reaction, introduces an alkyl or acyl group into the aromatic ring:

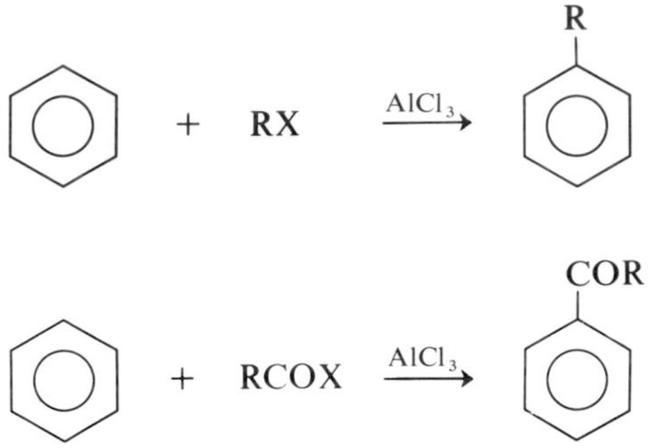

Alcohols and alkenes as well as acid anhydrides and esters serve as reactants. Even carboxylic acids, provided that the conditions are sufficiently vigorous, can be used,

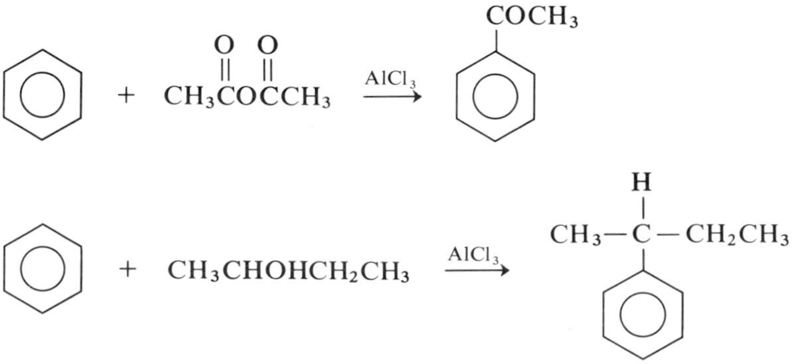

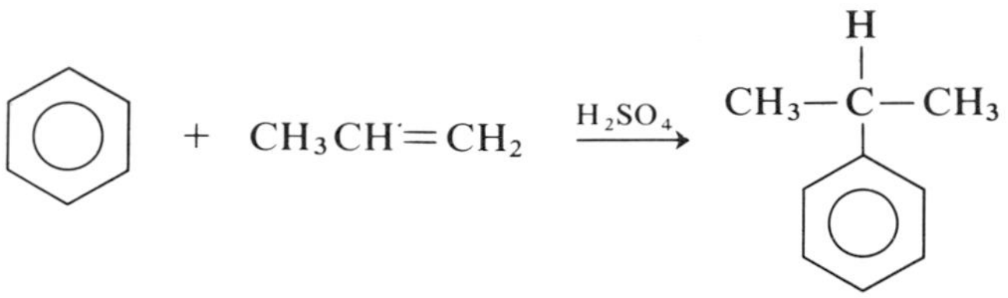

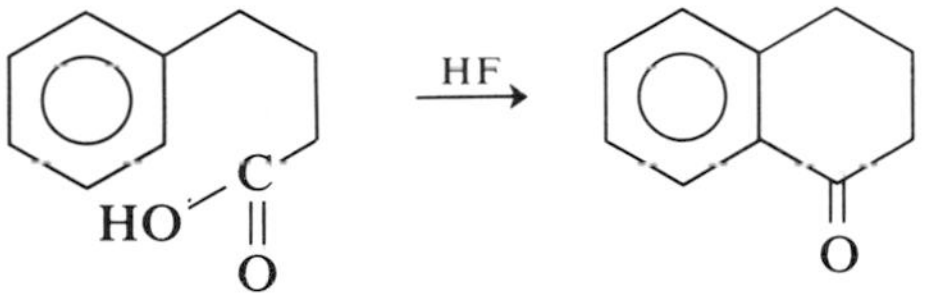

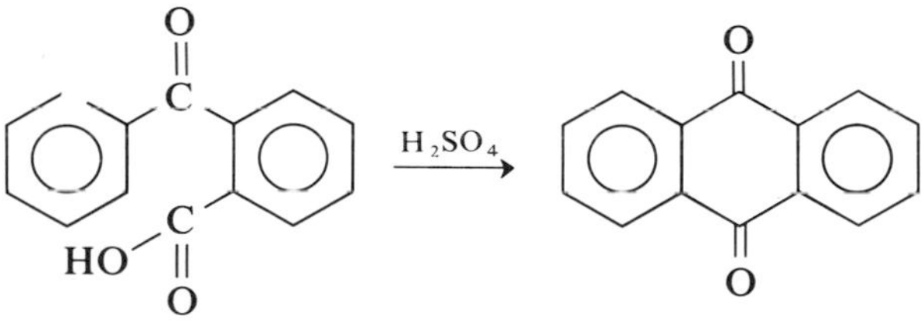

Under certain conditions the Friedel-Crafts reaction can be reversed. Thus hexamethylbenzene in the presence of aluminum chloride and hydrogen chloride at high temperatures affords a mixture of demethylated hydrocarbons and methyl chloride:

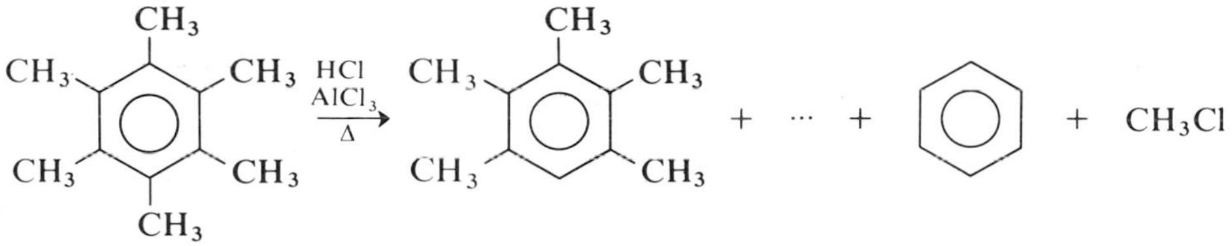

Friedel-Crafts alkylations appear in some cases to proceed by way of carbonium ions. However, it does not appear that the reactions of all alkyl halides proceed in this manner, and the following mechanism can be written for the Friedel-Crafts reaction.

$$RX + AlCl_3 \rightleftharpoons \overset{\delta+}{R}\text{-}\overset{\delta-}{X}AlCl_3$$

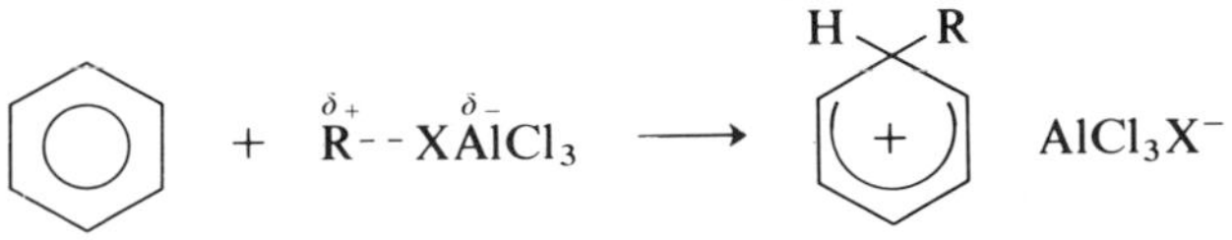

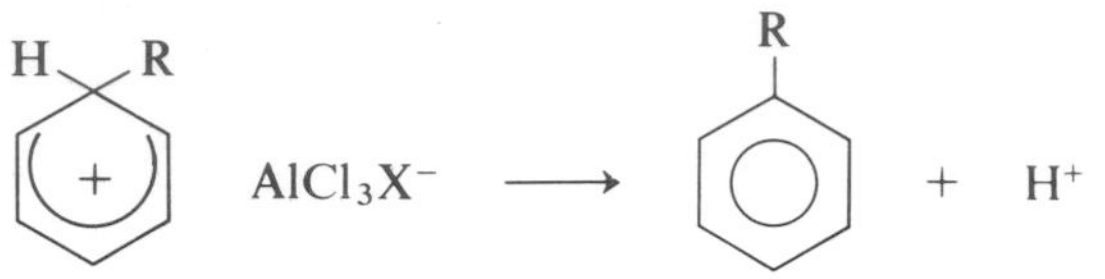

$$\text{H} \diagdown \text{R} \quad + \quad \text{AlCl}_3\text{X}^- \longrightarrow \quad \text{R} \quad + \quad \text{H}^+$$

Alkyl halides probably react in this manner with Lewis acids under milder conditions or when the carbonium ions R^+ would be unstable. When more stable carbonium ions are possible, a carbonium ion intermediate may well be involved. The mechanism becomes,

$$RCl + AlCl_3 \rightleftarrows R^+AlCl_4^-$$

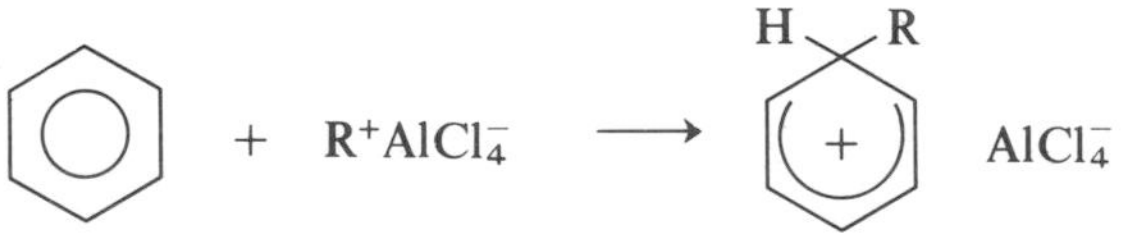

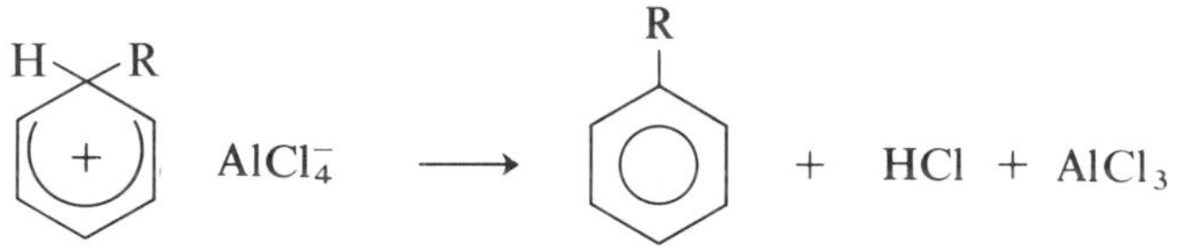

$$\bigcirc + R^+AlCl_4^- \longrightarrow \underset{H \diagdown R}{\bigoplus} AlCl_4^-$$

$$\underset{H \diagdown R}{\bigoplus} AlCl_4^- \longrightarrow \underset{R}{\bigcirc} + HCl + AlCl_3$$

Although alkyl halides RX may react with aluminum chloride to form carbonium ions R^+ in some cases, it is certainly not required that such intermediates be involved. In fact, good evidence exists to show that some Friedel-Crafts alkylations do not proceed by way of such an intermediate. The observance of straight-chain alkyl benzenes, when straight-chain alcohols or straight-chain alkyl halides are reacted with benzene and aluminum chloride at low temperatures, is not in agreement with a carbonium ion mechanism. Nor is the fact that neopentyl alcohol reacts with benzene in the presence of aluminum chloride to yield neopentylbenzene, consistent with a carbonium ion intermediate:

$$\bigcirc + CH_3 - \underset{\underset{CH_3}{|}}{\overset{\overset{CH_3}{|}}{C}} - CH_2OH \xrightarrow{AlCl_3} \underset{\bigcirc}{\overset{CH_3 - \underset{\underset{CH_2}{|}}{\overset{\overset{CH_3}{|}}{C}} - CH_3}{}}$$

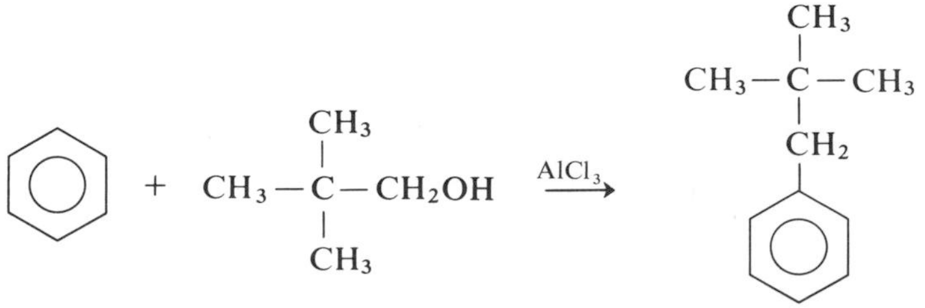

Toluene can be methylated to give a mixture of xylenes. Both methyl bromide and methyl iodide can be employed. However, the isomeric distribution is not the same in both cases. This implies that a true carbonium ion intermediate is not involved, for if a methyl carbonium ion were involved, exactly the same product ratios should be observed.

Isomerizations can occur in Friedel-Crafts alkylations. The alkylation of benzene using n-propyl chloride and aluminum chloride at higher temperatures affords isopropylbenzene. The employment of n-butyl chloride in this reaction can also lead to isomerization, and under the proper conditions sec-butyl-benzene is the major product:

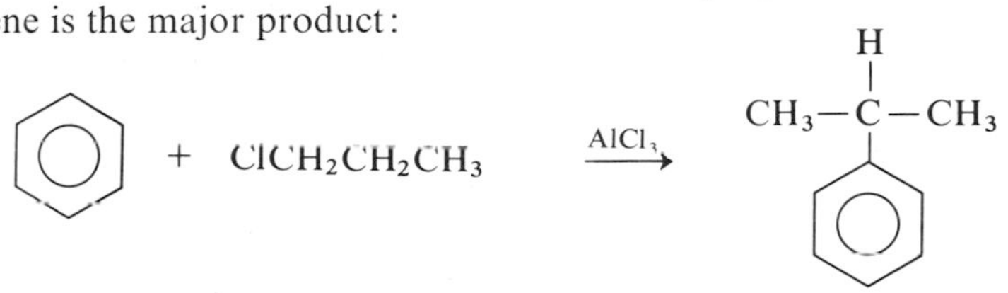

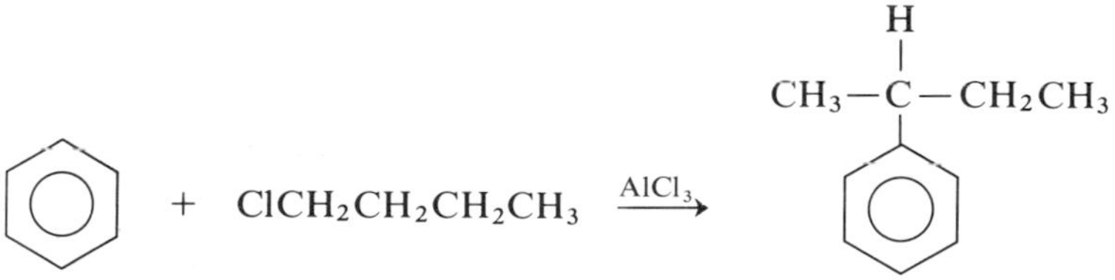

While these isomerizations are explained quite nicely by assuming that the alkyl halides react with aluminum chloride to form primary carbonium ions which then rearrange to the more stable secondary carbonium ions, other explanations are also possible. Furthermore, it is significant that n-propyl chloride reacts with benzene in the presence of aluminum chloride at low temperatures to form n-propylbenzene. The formation of unrearranged products at lower temperatures has been observed frequently.

In the presence of aluminum chloride, n-propyl chloride isomerizes to isopropyl chloride; n-butyl chloride forms sec-butyl chloride. Thus the original alkyl halide may isomerize. Furthermore, when treated with aluminum chloride or similar catalysts under more strenuous conditions, n-propylbenzene and n-butylbenzene isomerize to isopropylbenzene and sec-butylbenzene respectively. Thus isomerized products can sometimes occur because the initial unrearranged product isomerizes.

Evidence for product isomerization is conclusive. Not only does n-propyl-benzene isomerize to isopropylbenzene, but the latter isomer forms some n-propylbenzene. *Tertiary* amylbenzene isomerizes to 2-methyl-3-phenylbutane and ultimately to neopentylbenzene:

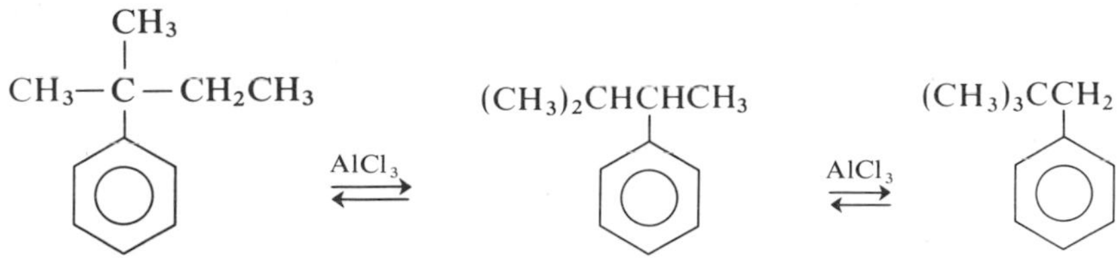

Although the Friedel-Crafts alkylations may not all proceed by way of a carbonium ion intermediate, the evidence is very good that the usual Friedel-Crafts acylations do. Thus, acid fluorides react with boron trifluoride to yield complexes that conduct electricity, and these complexes react with aromatic compounds to form acylated products:

$$RCOF + BF_3 \rightleftarrows RCO^+BF_4^-$$

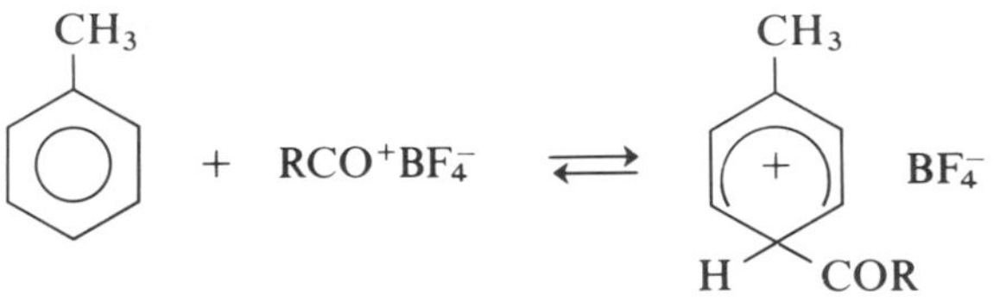

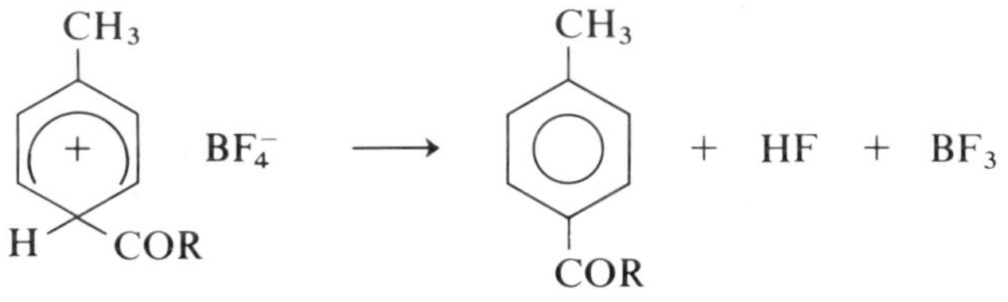

Friedel-Crafts alkylations require only catalytic quantities of the Lewis acid catalysts, yet Friedel-Crafts acylations require equivalent amounts of the catalyst. In the acylations the catalyst combines with the ketonic product; hydrolysis of this complex affords the ketone:

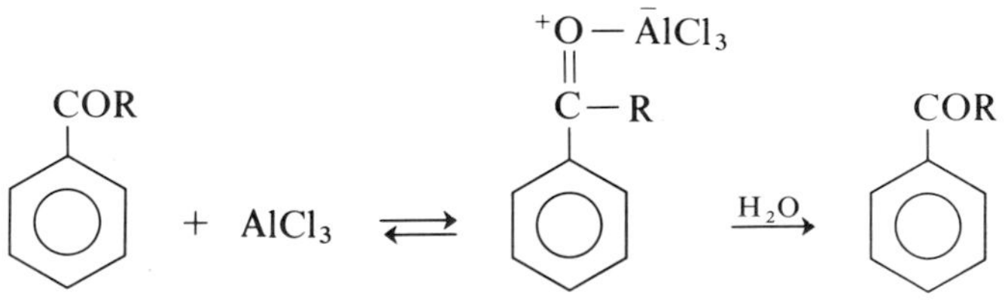

Studies have been made to ascertain whether deuterium isotope effects can be observed in Friedel-Crafts reactions, and it turns out that in a number of cases, although not in all of them, small kinetic isotope effects are found. The acylations are quite frequently subject to these effects, and their magnitude varies with the reaction conditions. Some of these are sufficiently large to be primary effects, and therefore, intermediates such as,

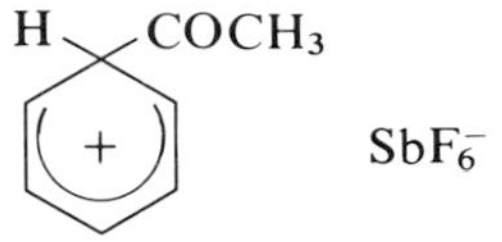

revert to reactants at a rate comparable to their conversion to products.

As we have just seen, in most reactions aromatic compounds behave as Lewis bases and react with electron deficient reagents. However, in those situations where electron withdrawers are present, nucleophilic reagents can also attack the aromatic system. We discuss these nucleophile aromatic substitutions more fully in the next section.

14.9 Nucleophilic Aromatic Substitution

Although aromatic systems do not usually react with electron rich materials, there exist certain special situations where such attack is possible. We have already discussed the reactions of benzyne (Section 12.7). Nucleophilic substitution is also possible. Electron withdrawers (these are usually nitro or cyano groups) on the benzene ring facilitate attack by a nucleophile Y^-.

For example, picryl chloride has the structure,

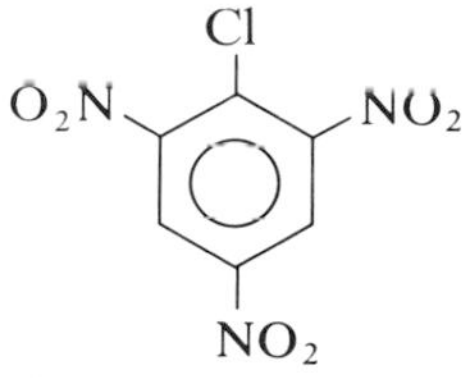

and the transition state for attack of picryl chloride by Y^- appears as follows,

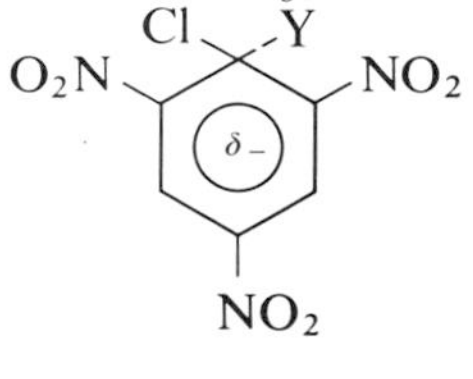

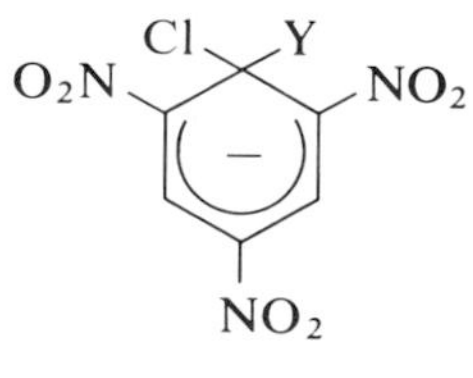

The incipient negative charge in the aromatic ring is stabilized by the nitro groups. The intermediate that results has the structure, where the charge is delocalized as follows:

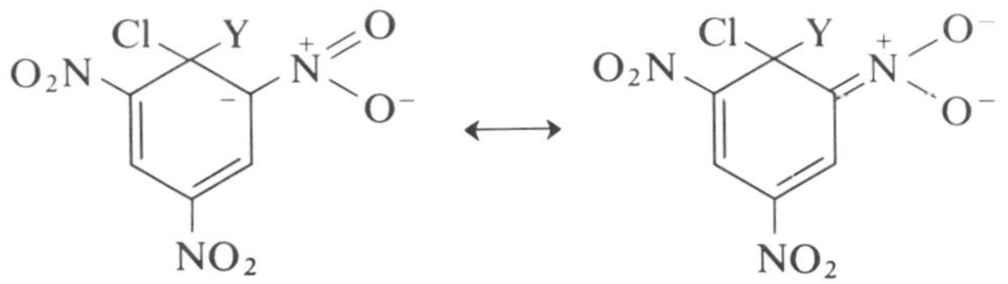

Other structures can be written involving the other nitro groups. This delocalization of charge stabilizes the intermediate, and such stabilization is also possible in the transition state.

The intermediate decomposes either by expelling Y^- and returning to reactants or by expulsion of Cl^- which converts it to the products.

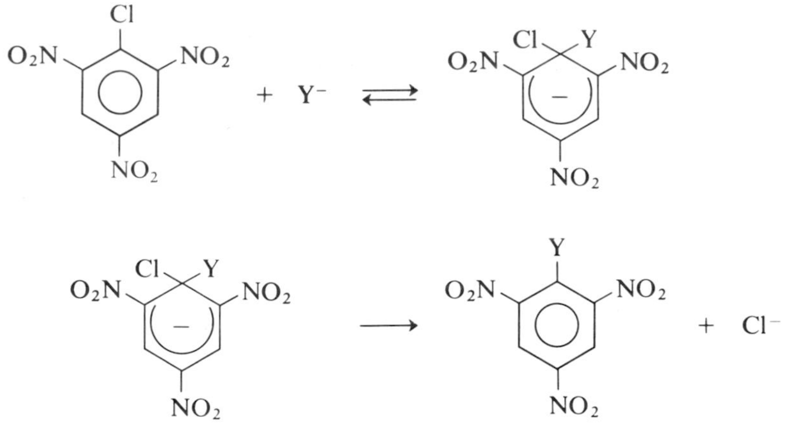

The transition state for expulsion of Cl^- is similar to the first.

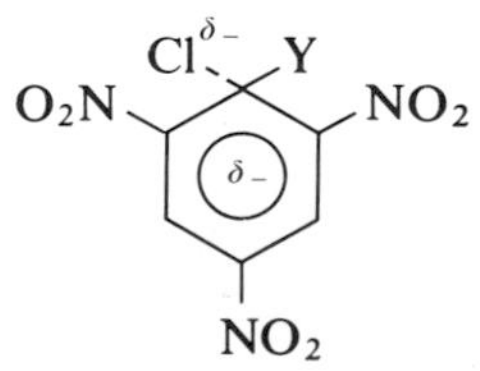

The evidence is very good that the reaction proceeds by this mechanism, for in certain cases the intermediate has actually been isolated. Thus when trinitroanisole **15** is treated with potassium ethoxide, a red salt **16** is obtained, and this same salt is formed when trinitrophenetole **17** is treated with potassium methoxide:

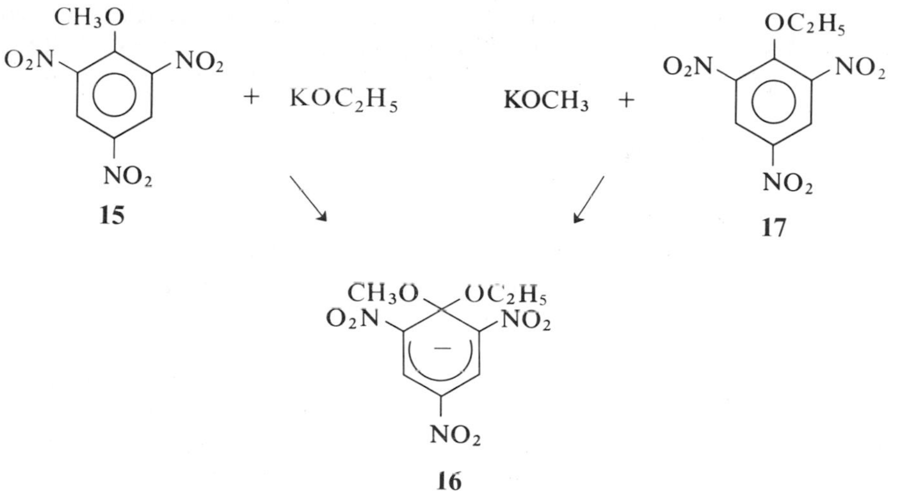

CH$_3$O
O$_2$N — [ring] — NO$_2$ +   KOC$_2$H$_5$ KOCH$_3$ +   OC$_2$H$_5$
                                                                  O$_2$N — [ring] — NO$_2$
NO$_2$ NO$_2$
15   ↘   ↙   **17**

CH$_3$O   OC$_2$H$_5$
O$_2$N — [ring (−)] — NO$_2$
              NO$_2$
              16

Decomposition of **16** with acid affords the same mixture of trinitroanisole and trinitrophenetole, regardless of the method used to prepare the salt. The infrared and visible spectra of the salt prepared from **15** are identical with those of the material resulting from **17** and are in accord with the proposed structure for the intermediate.

Picryl chloride reacts with sodium methoxide to form a similar intermediate **18**, and an elemental analysis of this intermediate is consistent with the structure presented:

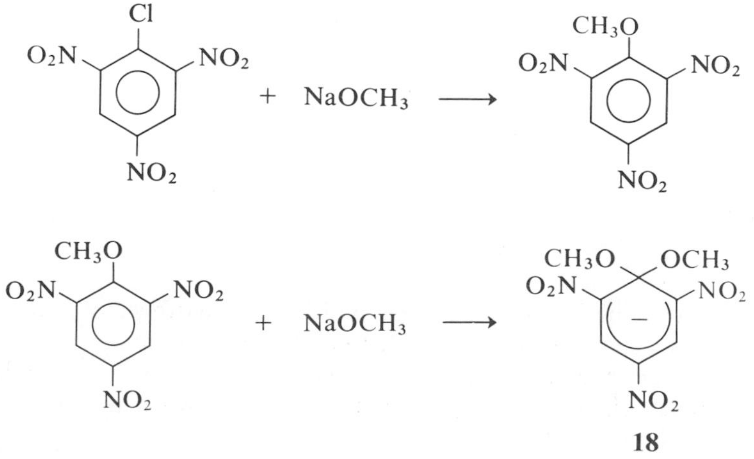

Cl
O$_2$N — [ring] — NO$_2$ +   NaOCH$_3$ ⟶   CH$_3$O
                                                O$_2$N — [ring] — NO$_2$
NO$_2$ NO$_2$

CH$_3$O
O$_2$N — [ring] — NO$_2$ +   NaOCH$_3$ ⟶   CH$_3$O   OCH$_3$
                                                O$_2$N — [ring (−)] — NO$_2$
NO$_2$ NO$_2$
                                                            18

Materials such as **19** and **20** react with methoxide, ethoxide, and other nucleophiles to produce colored solutions. Upon addition of water to the colored solution resulting from **19**, the color disappears, and the substituted product results. It is interesting, and somewhat unexpected, however, that the colors and spectra produced by solutions of **19** are quite different from those of **20** and that **21** does not form a colored solution:

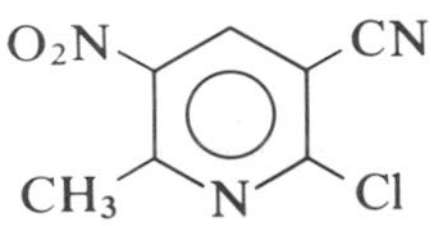

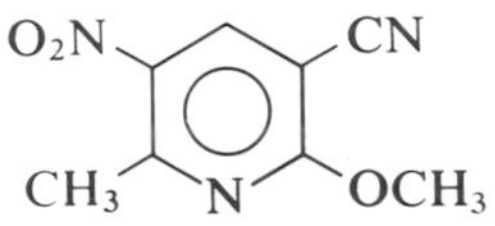

Kinetic analyses have not served as a criterion of mechanism, for the observed second order kinetics, first order in nucleophile and first order in aromatic compound, are consistent with several different proposals. The observed kinetics do not even indicate the rate limiting step in the reaction.

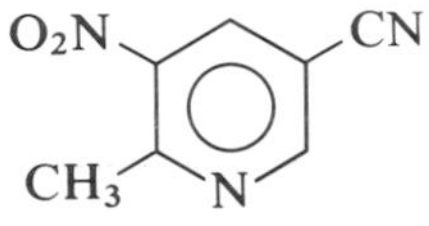

When the attacking nucleophile contains hydrogens, for example, when a primary or a secondary amine is used as the nucleophilic reagent, catalysis by added bases is observed. This basic catalysis implies that the nitrogen-hydrogen bond of the amine is ruptured prior to or in the rate limiting step. On the other hand, deuterium isotope effects have not been observed, and the absence of a large deuterium isotope effect implies that nitrogen-hydrogen bond breakage is not involved in the rate limiting step. It is difficult to present any mechanism that is consistent with both the observed basic catalysis and the absence of reasonably large isotope effects. The idea of a prior equilibrium is not satisfying, and more work is necessary to elucidate the mechanism when amines are the nucleophilic agents.

Another interesting point is that both **22** and **23** are subject to nucleophilic substitution:

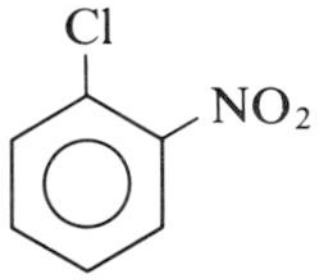

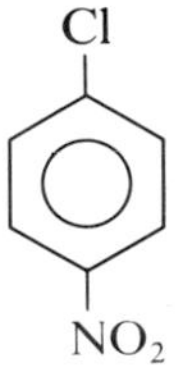

When the nucleophilic agent is neutral and bears a hydrogen atom, the *ortho* isomer reacts faster, yet when the nucleophilic agent does not bear a hydrogen, the *para* isomer reacts faster. Thus, the *ortho* isomer reacts more rapidly with primary and secondary amines while the *para* isomer reacts more rapidly with tertiary amines and alkoxides.

The intermediate resulting from attack of **22** by a primary amine is,

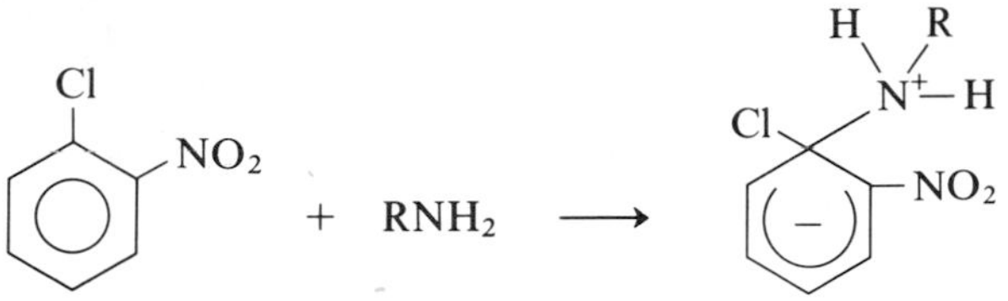

where the negative charge is delocalized onto the nitro group,

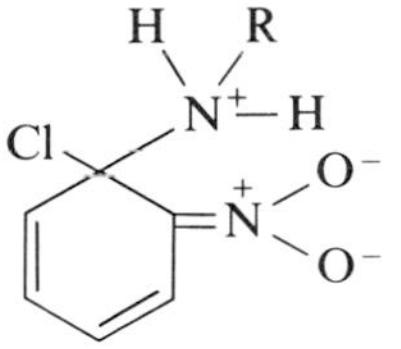

The partially positive hydrogen is hydrogen bonded to a partially negative oxygen atom of the nitro group. This hydrogen bond, which is largely electrostatic, stabilizes the *ortho* intermediate. The transition state as well as the intermediate are stabilized in this fashion. Since the transition state formed from the *para* isomer cannot be stabilized in this manner, the *para* isomer reacts more slowly. When the attacking agent is a tertiary amine or an alkoxide anion, hydrogen bonding is not present. Previously the electrostatic interactions were more important than the steric crowding that results from *ortho* attack. However, when hydrogen bonding is not present, steric crowding in the transition state now determines the reactivity, and the *para* isomer reacts more rapidly.

Many examples of nucleophilic substitution exist. Typical reactions are:

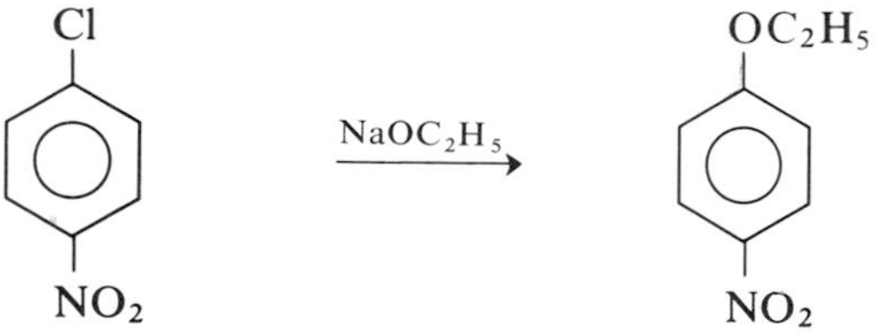

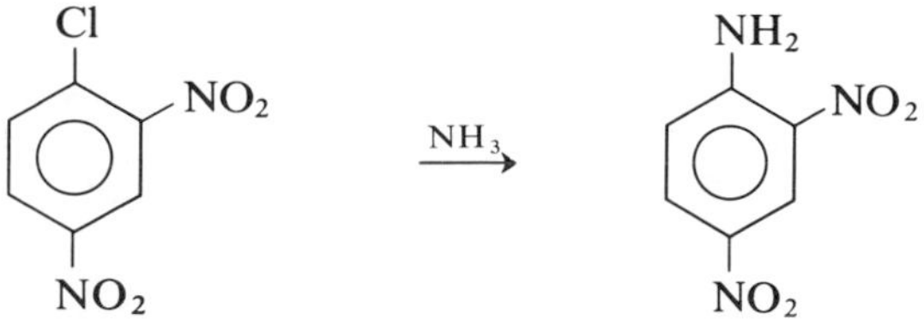

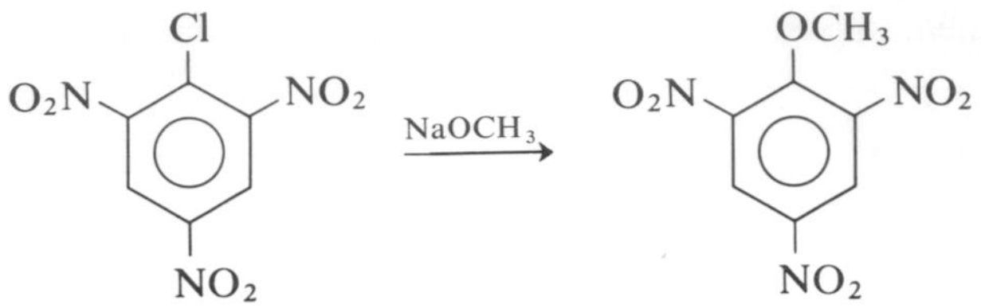

A rather interesting reaction takes place when a nitro aromatic is attacked by cyanide ion. The reaction, which is known as the von Richter rearrangement, affords the salts of carboxylic acids as the products:

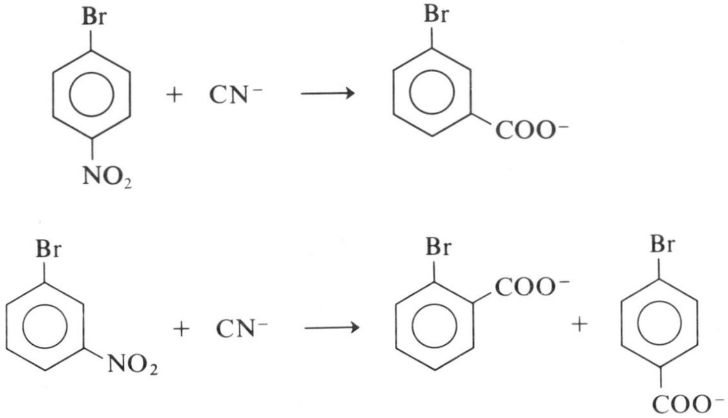

The exact mechanism of the von Richter reaction is not known although several proposals have been made. It is known that the cyano aromatic **23** and the corresponding amide **24** cannot be intermediates, for they do not hydrolyze to the carboxylic acid under the reaction conditions:

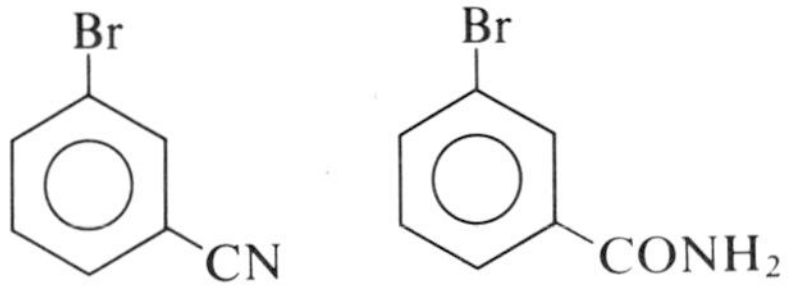

The mechanism most consistent with the known data is the following,

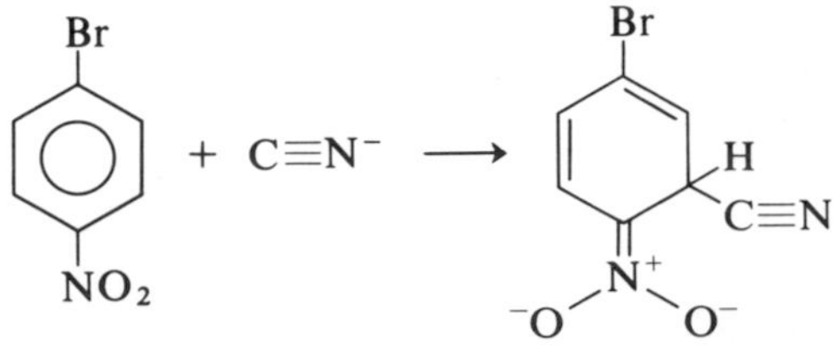

The aromatic system can be regenerated by loss of a proton:

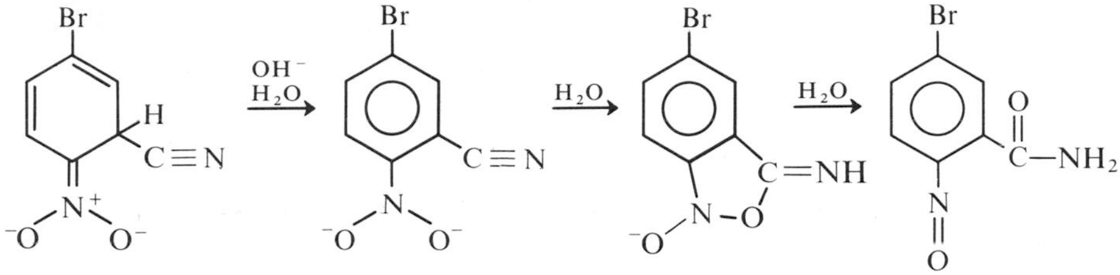

Nitrogen gas is liberated during the reaction, and attack of the nitroso nitrogen atom by the amide nitrogen, followed by loss of water yields **25**. This can react with water or hydroxide ion, lose nitrogen, and form the product:

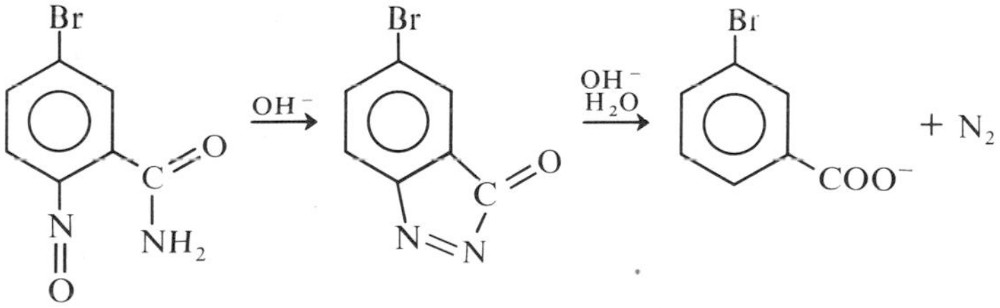

25

While this mechanism is not known to be correct, it does agree with all the observed facts.

Supplementary Reading

1. Berliner, E., *Progress in Physical Organic Chemistry*, Vol. 2, (eds.) S. G. Cohen, A. Streitwieser, Jr., R. W. Taft. New York, Interscience, 1964.

2. De La Mare, P. B. D. and Ridd, J. H., *Aromatic Substitution Nitration and Halogenation.* New York, Academic, 1959.

3. Ferguson, L. N., *The Modern Structural Theory of Organic Chemistry*. Englewood Cliffs, New Jersey, Prentice-Hall, 1963.

4. Gould, E. S., *Mechanism and Structure in Organic Chemistry*. New York, Holt, 1959.

5. Hine, J., *Physical Organic Chemistry*. New York, McGraw-Hill, 1962.

6. Nelson, K. L. and Brown, H. C., *The Chemistry of the Petroleum Hydrocarbons*, Vol. 3, (eds.) B. T. Brooks, S. S. Kurtz, Jr., C. E. Boord, and L. Schmerling. New York, Reinhold, 1955.

7. Olah, G. A., editor, *Friedel-Crafts and Related Reactions*. New York, Interscience, 1963.

8. Ross, S. D., *Progress in Physical Organic Chemistry*, Vol. 1, (eds.) S. G. Cohen, A. Streitwieser, Jr., R. W. Taft. New York, Interscience, 1963.

9. Stock, L. M. and Brown, H. C., *Advances in Physical Organic Chemistry*, Vol. 1, (ed.) V. Gould. New York, Academic, 1963.

10. Streitwieser, A., Jr., *Molecular Orbital Theory for Organic Chemists*. New York, Wiley, 1961.

Chapter 15

Addition to the Carbonyl Group

15.1 Structure and Reactivity

The carbonyl group consists of two atoms, carbon and oxygen, sharing four electrons. While the four electrons are shared more or less equally by the two carbon atoms in an alkene, the four electrons in the carbonyl system are more likely to be found near the oxygen atom; the electron density due to these four electrons is greater near the oxygen atom:

The electronic distribution of the carbonyl system can be described using either the concepts of molecular orbital theory or those of the valence bond theory. The usual description considers both atoms to be sp^2 hybridized and doubly bonded (by a σ bond and a π bond):

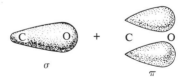

In terms of the usual valence bond pictures this becomes,

$$
\underset{R}{\overset{O}{\underset{}{\overset{\|}{C}}}}\underset{R}{} \longleftrightarrow \underset{R}{\overset{O^-}{\underset{}{\overset{|}{C^+}}}}\underset{R}{}
$$

In the ground state of the carbonyl group the electron density due to the four shared electrons is greater near oxygen than near carbon. In addition, oxygen has four nonbonded electrons occupying sp^2 orbitals.

In accordance with these ideas carbonyl systems display large dipole moments and relatively high boiling points. Formaldehyde has a dipole moment equal to 2.3D while that of acetone is 2.8D:

$$\mu = 2.3D \qquad\qquad\qquad \mu = 2.8D$$

The carbonyl system is subject to attack, and to determine which type of reagent attacks most readily at carbon and which at oxygen, we must compare the transition states for attack at oxygen and at carbon. Making such a comparison leads to the conclusion that electron-rich materials (Lewis bases, nucleophiles) attack at carbon while electron-deficient reagents (Lewis acids) enter preferentially at the oxygen atom. Reagents attacking at oxygen are σ bonded, that is, the bond involves one of the sp^2 orbitals of oxygen in the resulting intermediate, for in this way effective charge delocalization is possible. Structures of the type,

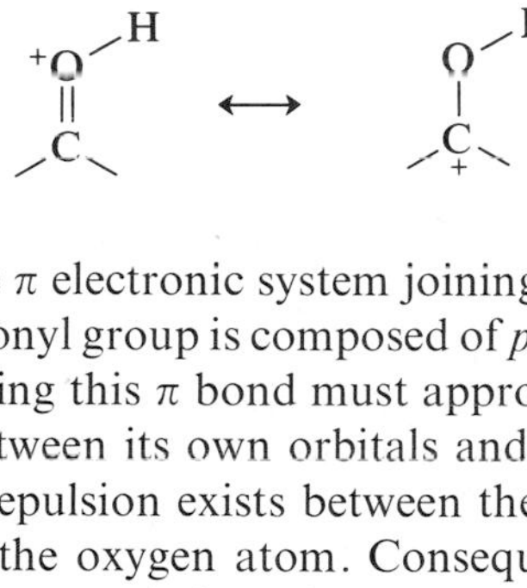

can be written only if the π electronic system joining the atoms is still present.

The π bond in the carbonyl group is composed of p orbitals, and it is assumed that a nucleophile attacking this π bond must approach carbon in such a way as to provide overlap between its own orbitals and that of the carbon atom. In addition, coulombic repulsion exists between the entering reagent and the high electron density at the oxygen atom. Consequently, an attacking agent probably enters from above or below the carbonyl group and from slightly to the rear of the carbon atom:

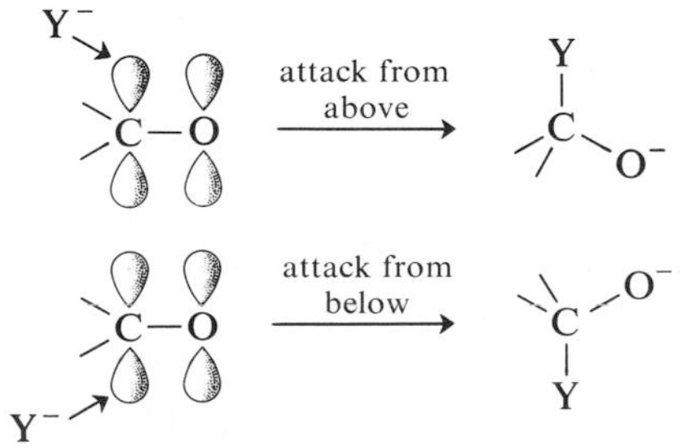

A number of substances add to the carbonyl group and lead to a variety of products. Water, alcohols, amines, hydrogen cyanide, Grignard reagents, and so forth all add. Stronger nucleophiles do not require catalysis although catalytic additions can be effected with them. The weaker nucleophiles are usually added in the presence of catalysts, and both acidic and basic catalyses take place. Many additions are reversible and equilibria are obtained. According to the principle of microscopic reversibility, under the same conditions the same intermediates must participate in both the forward and reverse processes. Application of this principle has helped to elucidate the mechanisms in a number of addition reactions.

The same reactant can enter into a favorable equilibrium with one carbonyl compound and an unfavorable equilibrium with another. The position of the equilibrium depends upon the nature of the carbonyl compound. Electron donors, either by inductive effect or by resonance, stabilize the carbonyl compound relative to the adduct. This results in a less favorable equilibrium. Thus acetone is not hydrated to an appreciable extent in aqueous solution, but acetaldehyde is about 73% hydrated at 0°,

$$
\underset{\substack{||\\ O}}{CH_3-C-CH_3} + H_2O \rightleftarrows CH_3-\underset{\substack{|\\ OH}}{\overset{\substack{OH\\ |}}{C}}-CH_3
$$

$$
\underset{\substack{||\\ O}}{CH_3-C-H} + H_2O \rightleftarrows CH_3-\underset{\substack{|\\ OH}}{\overset{\substack{OH\\ |}}{C}}-H
$$

With electron withdrawers the reverse is found; the adduct is favored. Chloral forms a stable hydrate,

$$
\underset{\substack{|\\ Cl}}{\overset{\substack{Cl\\ |}}{Cl-C}}-\underset{\substack{||\\ O}}{C}-H + H_2O \rightleftarrows \underset{\substack{|\\ Cl}}{\overset{\substack{Cl\\ |}}{Cl-C}}-\underset{\substack{|\\ OH}}{\overset{\substack{OH\\ |}}{C}}-H
$$

Addition to the carbonyl system is generally more favorable for aldehydes than for ketones.

Steric factors can also influence the position of the equilibrium, for the alkyl groups in a ketone are farther apart in the reactant than in the product. Steric interactions are more pronounced in the product, and with large alkyl groups this has an unfavorable influence upon the equilibrium:

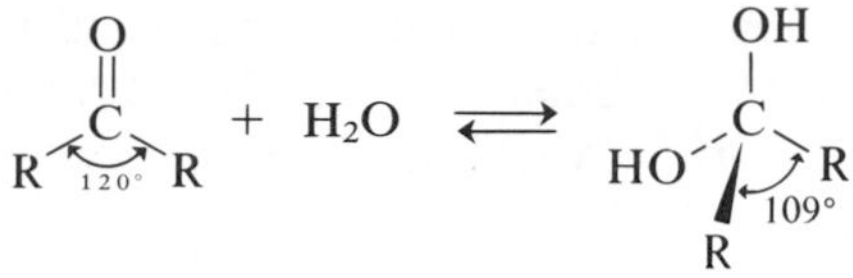

$$R \overset{O}{\underset{120°}{\underset{\parallel}{\overset{C}{\diagup\diagdown}}}} R \; + \; H_2O \; \rightleftharpoons \; HO \overset{OH}{\underset{R}{\overset{\mid}{\underset{109°}{\overset{C}{\diagup\diagdown}}}}} R$$

An interesting example of how strain affects a reaction occurs with cyclopropanone. Early attempts to prepare this system resulted in the hydrate. In this case strain is much more pronounced in the cyclic ketone and is alleviated in the hydrate:

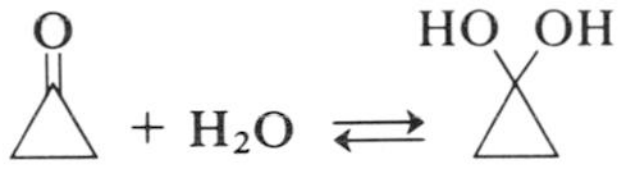

$$\triangle\!\!=\!\!O \; + \; H_2O \; \rightleftharpoons \; \overset{HO\;\;OH}{\triangle}$$

In those reactions where the rate limiting step of the addition is attack of a nucleophile upon the carbonyl group, the rate of nucleophilic addition is affected by the same factors as the equilibrium. For example, the rate limiting step in cyanohydrin formation **1** is attack of the carbonyl group by cyanide ion, and the effect of various alkyl and aryl groups upon the rate of reaction is straightforward. The rate of reaction is increased by electron withdrawers and decreased by electron donors. This reaction is influenced in the expected manner by various substituents in the starting material:

$$R\overset{O}{\underset{\parallel}{-C-}}R \; + \; HCN \; \longrightarrow \; R\overset{OH}{\underset{\underset{CN}{\mid}}{\overset{\mid}{-C-}}}R$$

1

Where

$$R\overset{O}{\underset{\parallel}{-C-}}R \; + \; CN^- \; \longrightarrow \; R\overset{O^-}{\underset{\underset{CN}{\mid}}{\overset{\mid}{-C-}}}R$$

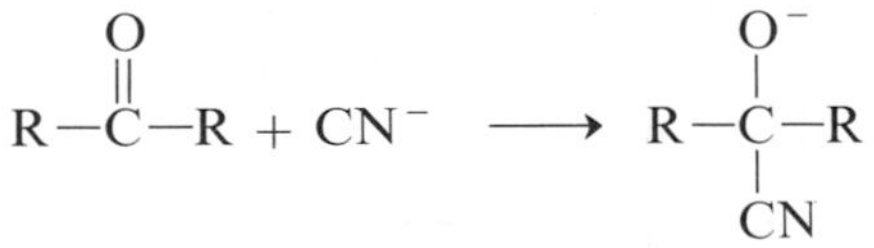

is rate limiting.

The situation here is clearcut; however, in a number of cases the problem is not so simple, the effect of various substituents less certain. If the addition to the carbonyl system is general acid catalyzed, as many additions are, the rate limiting step of the reaction must involve a molecule of the catalyzing acid (as HX or as H^+X^-) and a molecule of the carbonyl compound as well as the attacking nucleophile.[1] For the reaction,

$$
\begin{array}{c}
\quad\; O \qquad\qquad\qquad\qquad OH \\
\quad\; \| \qquad\qquad\qquad\qquad\; | \\
R-\!\!\overset{}{C}\!\!-R + H_2O \xrightarrow{\;HX\;} R-\!\!\overset{}{C}\!\!-R \\
\qquad\qquad\qquad\qquad\qquad\quad\; | \\
\qquad\qquad\qquad\qquad\qquad\;\; OH
\end{array}
$$

the transition state in the rate limiting step is,

$$
\begin{array}{c}
\overset{\delta-}{X} \\
\diagdown \\
H \\
O^{-}\diagup \\
\| \\
R-\overset{}{C}-R \\
| \\
\overset{}{O} \\
H^{\diagdown}\;{}_{\delta+}\;^{\diagup}H
\end{array}
$$

The proton and the water molecule are introduced in a concerted process, and as we might expect from a transition state of this type, the influence of electron donors and withdrawers is less significant than in the previous case and depends upon the extent of formation of the various bonds. In these cases, electron donors decrease the reactivity at the carbonyl carbon atom where the nucleophile enters but increase reactivity at the oxygen atom where the proton enters. Electron withdrawers have the opposite effect.

Addition of the weaker nucleophiles occurs readily in the presence of added acids and bases. If the reaction is general acid catalyzed, the rate depends upon the concentration of every acid present in the solution. This implies that a molecule of acid must participate in the rate limiting step; the transition state for the addition must contain a molecule of acid. For general base catalysis, a molecule of this substance must be included in the transition state. In specific acid catalysis, it is the protonated carbonyl compound, formed by a prior equilibrium, that undergoes addition. Specific base catalysis involves the conjugate base of the solvent or some other nucleophile in equilibrium with the conjugate base of the solvent.

15.2 Catalyzed and Uncatalyzed Additions

The mechanisms of acid and base catalyzed additions to the carbonyl group have been investigated. The stronger nucleophiles such as hydroxide ion,

[1] The problem of addition to carbonyl systems and to Schiff bases is discussed by W. P. Jencks, in *Progress in Physical Organic Chemistry*, Vol. 2, (eds.) S. G. Cohen, A. Streitwieser, Jr., R. W. Taft. New York, Interscience, 1964.

sulfite ion, hydroxylamine, and cyanide ion do not require catalysis (although in some cases catalytic additions can also be effected). The mechanism for addition is the same for all of these. The nucleophile attacks the carbonyl compound directly, and this attack constitutes the rate limiting step of the addition. For example, for addition of hydrogen cyanide,

$$
\underset{\substack{\|\\ \\}}{R-C-R} + HCN \longrightarrow R-\underset{\substack{|\\ CN}}{\overset{OH}{\underset{|}{C}}}-R
$$

the mechanism is,

$$
\underset{\substack{\|\\ O}}{R-C-R} + CN^- \longrightarrow R-\underset{\substack{|\\ CN}}{\overset{O^-}{\underset{|}{C}}}-R
$$

$$
R-\underset{\substack{|\\ CN}}{\overset{O^-}{\underset{|}{C}}}-R + H_2O \rightleftarrows R-\underset{\substack{|\\ CN}}{\overset{OH}{\underset{|}{C}}}-R + OH^-
$$

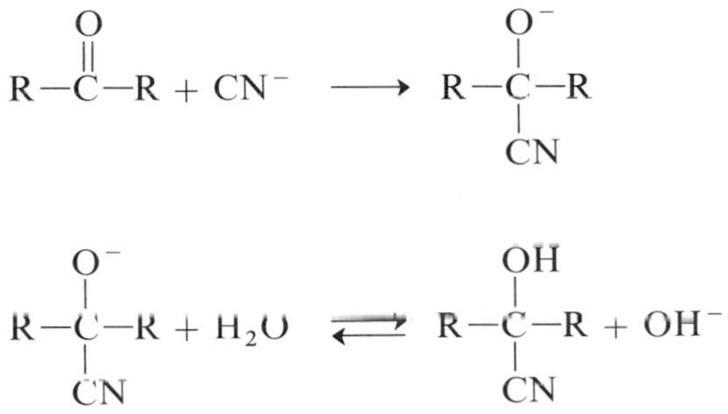

and,

$$
HCN + OH^- \rightleftarrows H_2O + CN^-
$$

The participating ions need not be free ions, but may exist in solution as ion pairs. This addition reaction is reversible, and the cyanohydrin can be hydrolyzed to regenerate the carbonyl system.

The addition of sodium bisulfite to carbonyl compounds is used to prepare solid derivatives of these materials. This reaction also serves as a means of purification of carbonyl compounds. The bisulfite adduct is prepared, purified, and then hydrolyzed to regenerate the pure carbonyl material:

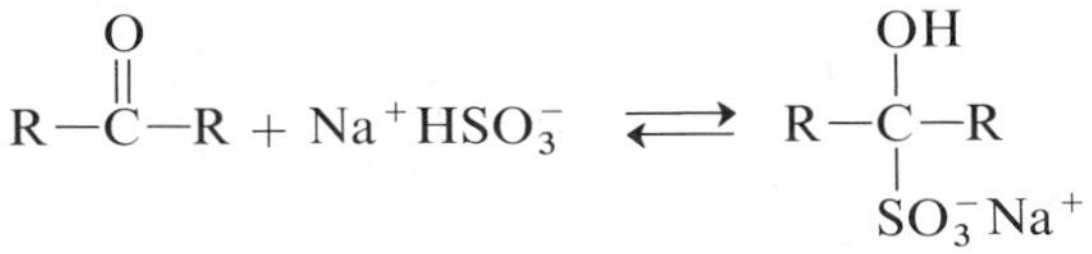

$$
\underset{\substack{\|\\ O}}{R-C-R} + Na^+HSO_3^- \rightleftarrows R-\underset{\substack{|\\ SO_3^- Na^+}}{\overset{OH}{\underset{|}{C}}}-R
$$

The mechanism for formation of the adduct involves attack by SO_3^{--},

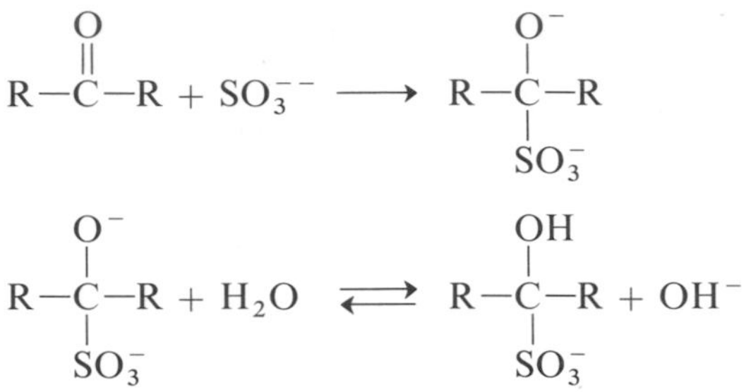

$$R-\overset{\overset{\textstyle O}{\|}}{C}-R + SO_3^{--} \longrightarrow R-\overset{\overset{\textstyle O^-}{|}}{\underset{\underset{\textstyle SO_3^-}{|}}{C}}-R$$

$$R-\overset{\overset{\textstyle O^-}{|}}{\underset{\underset{\textstyle SO_3^-}{|}}{C}}-R + H_2O \rightleftharpoons R-\overset{\overset{\textstyle OH}{|}}{\underset{\underset{\textstyle SO_3^-}{|}}{C}}-R + OH^-$$

and,

$$HSO_3^- + OH^- \rightleftharpoons SO_3^{--} + H_2O$$

These reactions represent uncatalyzed additions. The weaker nucleophiles such as water, alcohols, semicarbazide ($H_2NNHCONH_2$), aniline, and some other nitrogenous bases can be added by using acidic or basic catalysts. These catalyzed reactions frequently proceed either by general acid catalysis or general base catalysis or both. The mechanism for general acid catalysis involves a prior hydrogen bonding between the carbonyl compound and HX (the acid catalyst). The nucleophile then adds in a rate limiting step to the complexed carbonyl compound. The reaction is illustrated for the general acid catalyzed hydration of acetaldehyde:

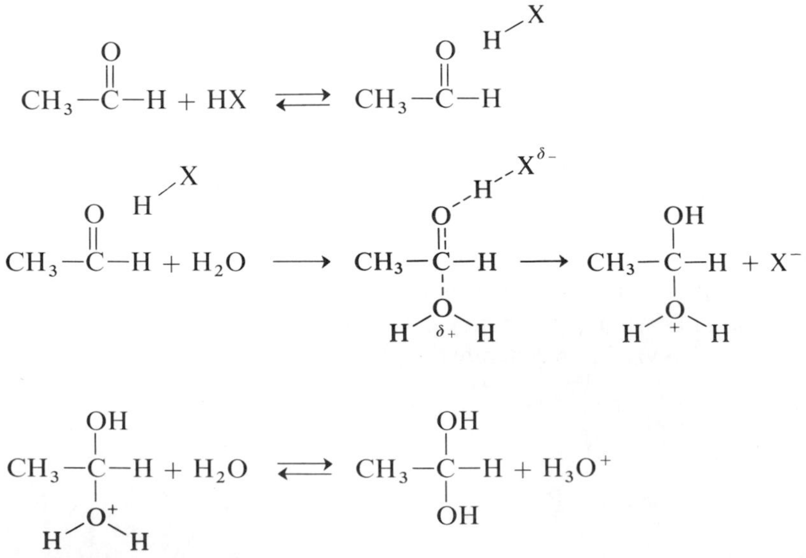

$$CH_3-\overset{\overset{\textstyle O}{\|}}{C}-H + HX \rightleftharpoons CH_3-\overset{\overset{\textstyle O}{\|}}{C}-H \cdots H-X$$

$$CH_3-\overset{\overset{\textstyle O}{\|}}{C}-H \cdots H-X + H_2O \longrightarrow CH_3-\overset{\overset{\textstyle O}{\|}}{\underset{\underset{\textstyle H \overset{\delta+}{\;} H}{|\;O}}{C}}-H \cdots H-X^{\delta-} \longrightarrow CH_3-\overset{\overset{\textstyle OH}{|}}{\underset{\underset{\textstyle H \overset{+}{\;} H}{|\;O}}{C}}-H + X^-$$

$$CH_3-\overset{\overset{\textstyle OH}{|}}{\underset{\underset{\textstyle H \overset{+}{\;} H}{|\;O^+}}{C}}-H + H_2O \rightleftharpoons CH_3-\overset{\overset{\textstyle OH}{|}}{\underset{\underset{\textstyle OH}{|}}{C}}-H + H_3O^+$$

and,

$$H_3O^+ + X^- \rightleftharpoons H_2O + HX$$

The transition state is the same as that presented previously. The proton is introduced by HX while the water attacks. Of course, H_3O^+ as well as any other added acid are also capable of catalyzing the reaction. The protonated hydrate loses a proton to the solvent (or to X^-) and forms the product.

This reaction is reversible, and according to the principle of microscopic reversibility the same intermediates and the same transition state are involved in the reverse process. In the reverse process the water and the proton are expelled simultaneously, and this expulsion constitutes the rate limiting step.

The addition of alcohols to the carbonyl group proceeds readily and reversibly. At moderate pH's this reaction is also general acid and general base catalyzed, and the acid catalyzed process occurs by a mechanism analogous to that just presented,

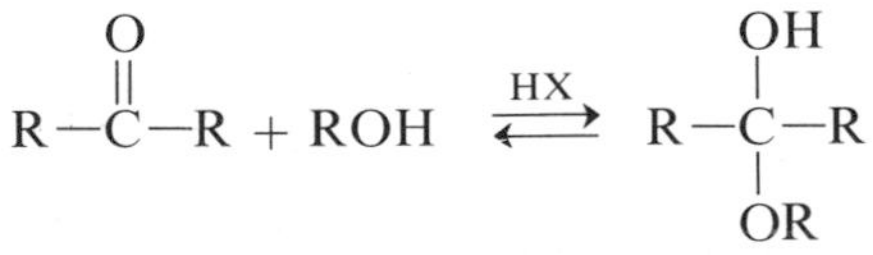

$$
\overset{\displaystyle O}{\underset{\displaystyle \|}{R-C-R}} + ROH \underset{}{\overset{HX}{\rightleftharpoons}} \quad R-\overset{\displaystyle OH}{\underset{\displaystyle OR}{\overset{\displaystyle |}{\underset{\displaystyle |}{C}}}}-R
$$

The general acid catalyzed addition of semicarbazide also proceeds by the same mechanism as the hydration of acetaldehyde. In fact, most general acid catalyzed additions to the carbonyl group follow this scheme (illustrated here for semicarbazide),

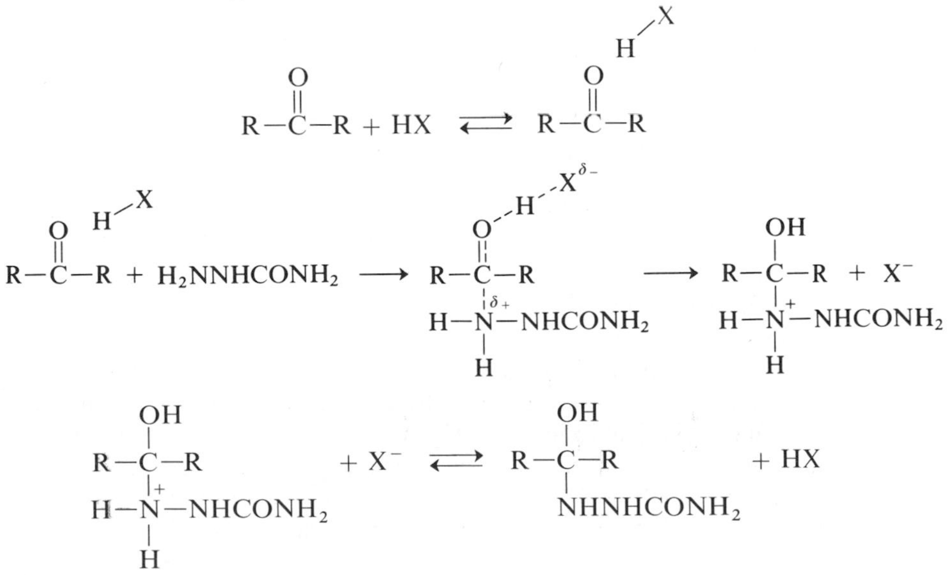

$$
\overset{\displaystyle O}{\underset{\displaystyle \|}{R-C-R}} + HX \rightleftharpoons \overset{\displaystyle H\diagup X}{\overset{\displaystyle O}{\underset{\displaystyle \|}{R-C-R}}}
$$

$$
\overset{O}{\underset{\|}{R-C-R}} + H_2NNHCONH_2 \longrightarrow \underset{\underset{\displaystyle H}{\overset{\displaystyle |}{H-N-NHCONH_2}}}{\overset{H\diagup X}{\overset{\displaystyle O}{\underset{\displaystyle \|\,\delta+}{R-C-R}}}} \longrightarrow \underset{\underset{\displaystyle H}{\overset{\displaystyle |}{H-N^+-NHCONH_2}}}{\overset{\displaystyle OH}{\overset{\displaystyle |}{R-C-R}}} + X^-
$$

$$
\underset{\underset{\displaystyle H}{\overset{\displaystyle |}{H-N^+-NHCONH_2}}}{\overset{\displaystyle OH}{\overset{\displaystyle |}{R-C-R}}} + X^- \rightleftharpoons \underset{\overset{\displaystyle |}{NHNHCONH_2}}{\overset{\displaystyle OH}{\overset{\displaystyle |}{R-C-R}}} + HX
$$

This product is dehydrated under the reaction conditions and yields the semicarbazone, a derivative of carbonyl compounds:

$$
\underset{\underset{\text{HNNHCONH}_2}{|}}{\overset{\overset{\text{OH}}{|}}{\text{R}-\text{C}-\text{R}}} \xrightarrow{\text{HX}} \underset{\underset{\text{NNHCONH}_2}{||}}{\text{R}-\text{C}-\text{R}} \quad + \text{H}_2\text{O}
$$

The mechanism for general base catalysis includes the base Y^- in the rate limiting step. The reaction is illustrated for the general base catalyzed hydration of acetaldehyde, and the first step is a hydrogen bonding of the base Y^-:

$$
\text{H}_2\text{O} + Y^- \rightleftharpoons \overset{\displaystyle \text{O}}{\underset{\displaystyle Y^-}{\text{H} \diagup \ \diagdown \text{H}}}
$$

$$
\text{CH}_3-\overset{\overset{\text{O}}{||}}{\text{C}}-\text{H} + \text{H} \diagup^{\text{O}}\diagdown_{\text{H}} \underset{Y^-}{} \longrightarrow \text{CH}_3-\overset{\overset{\text{O}^{\delta-}}{||}}{\underset{\underset{\text{H} \diagdown \text{H} \cdots Y^{\delta-}}{\text{O}}}{\text{C}}}-\text{H} \longrightarrow \text{CH}_3-\overset{\overset{\text{O}^-}{|}}{\underset{\underset{\text{OH}}{|}}{\text{C}}}-\text{H} + \text{HY}
$$

$$
\text{CH}_3-\overset{\overset{\text{O}^-}{|}}{\underset{\underset{\text{OH}}{|}}{\text{C}}}-\text{H} + \text{H}_2\text{O} \rightleftharpoons \text{CH}_3-\overset{\overset{\text{OH}}{|}}{\underset{\underset{\text{OH}}{|}}{\text{C}}}-\text{H} + \text{OH}^-
$$

and

$$
\text{HY} + \text{OH}^- \rightleftharpoons \text{H}_2\text{O} + Y^-
$$

General base catalyzed additions to the system C=O proceed by this mechanism. In other additions the molecule of water is replaced by the particular nucleophile adding to the system. The transition state involves simultaneous abstraction of a proton by the base and introduction of the nucleophile into the carbonyl system.

We see that introduction of the stronger nucleophiles is accomplished by their direct attack on the carbonyl group, whereas the weaker nucleophiles add most readily under catalytic conditions. The acid catalyzed reaction involves a prior hydrogen bonding of the carbonyl group while the base catalyzed addition is accompanied by simultaneous abstraction of a proton, and in the transition state this abstraction increases the nucleophilicity of the adding species.

15.3 Hydration of Aldehydes and Ketones

We have already presented the idea that in aqueous solutions aldehydes and ketones are hydrated, the degree of hydration depending upon the particular carbonyl compound. Hydration occurs primarily with aldehydes; most ketones are insignificantly hydrated:

$$
\underset{\substack{\| \\ \text{O}}}{\text{R}-\text{C}-\text{R}} + \text{H}_2\text{O} \; \rightleftharpoons \; \underset{\substack{| \\ \text{OH}}}{\overset{\substack{\text{OH} \\ |}}{\text{R}-\text{C}-\text{R}}}
$$

This hydration of the carbonyl system is present when a reaction is conducted in aqueous solution (especially if acids or bases which catalyze the process are also present). However, the equilibrium is rapid, and from a synthetic standpoint its occurrence does not effect subsequent irreversible reactions of the carbonyl compound. The formation of other products from carbonyl compounds proceeds as if the equilibrium were not present:

$$
\underset{\substack{\| \\ \text{O}}}{\text{R}-\text{C}-\text{R}} + \text{H}_2\text{O} \; \rightleftharpoons \; \underset{\substack{| \\ \text{OH}}}{\overset{\substack{\text{OH} \\ |}}{\text{R}-\text{C}-\text{R}}}
$$

and

$$
\underset{\substack{\| \\ \text{O}}}{\text{R}-\text{C}-\text{R}} \; \longrightarrow \; \text{products}
$$

Of course, if the product is in equilibrium with the carbonyl compound, the position of the equilibrium is affected when hydration is significant. Instead of the free carbonyl compound being in equilibrium with some product, the hydrate also enters into the equilibrium, and this alters the equilibrium position. We use the reversible addition of HCN as an example,

$$
\underset{\substack{\| \\ \text{O}}}{\text{R}-\text{C}-\text{H}} + \text{H}_2\text{O} \; \rightleftharpoons \; \underset{\substack{| \\ \text{OH}}}{\overset{\substack{\text{OH} \\ |}}{\text{R}-\text{C}-\text{H}}}
$$

$$
\underset{\substack{\| \\ \text{O}}}{\text{R}-\text{C}-\text{H}} + \text{HCN} \; \rightleftharpoons \; \underset{\substack{| \\ \text{CN}}}{\overset{\substack{\text{OH} \\ |}}{\text{R}-\text{C}-\text{H}}}
$$

The rate of a reaction (such as addition of HCN) may also be decreased when hydration is present, for the effective concentration of the carbonyl compound decreases.

The mechanism by which hydration occurs depends upon the pH of the solution. Hydration actually proceeds by way of a number of different mechanisms, and the pH determines which route is prevalent. At moderate pH's both general acid and some general base catalyzed hydration are observed for acetaldehyde. These hydrations involve attack by the weak nucleophile water. General acid catalysis also occurs with other carbonyl compounds, but general base catalysis is less common. At very high or very low pH's the major route for hydration changes. Thus, in alkaline solutions it is the strong nucleophile OH^- that adds directly to the carbonyl group, and the mechanism for hydration becomes,

$$
\underset{\substack{\| \\ O}}{R-C-R} + OH^- \longrightarrow \underset{\substack{| \\ OH}}{\overset{O^-}{R-C-R}}
$$

$$
\underset{\substack{| \\ OH}}{\overset{O^-}{R-C-R}} + H_2O \rightleftarrows \underset{\substack{| \\ OH}}{\overset{OH}{R-C-R}} + OH^-
$$

This reaction is specific base catalyzed, and carbonyl compounds are generally hydrated in this manner in basic solution. Even acetaldehyde is hydrated predominantly in this fashion.

Consistent with the idea that the acid catalysis is usually general while basic catalysis may be specific is the fact that acetone undergoes O^{18} exchange. The rate of exchange was measured, and the reaction was observed to be general acid but specific base catalyzed.

At high acidity, still another mechanism involving the conjugate acid of the carbonyl system $RCOHR^+$ is possible:

$$
\underset{\substack{\| \\ O}}{R-C-R} + HX \rightleftarrows \underset{\substack{\| \\ O}}{\overset{+OH}{R-C-R}} + X^-
$$

$$
\underset{\substack{\| \\ O}}{\overset{+OH}{R-C-R}} \xrightarrow{H_2O} \underset{\substack{| \\ \underset{H \overset{+}{} H}{O}}}{\overset{OH}{R-C-R}}
$$

$$\begin{array}{c} \text{OH} \\ | \\ \text{R}-\overset{|}{\underset{|}{\text{C}}}-\text{R} \\ \overset{\text{O}}{\underset{\text{H}\;\nearrow\;^{+}\;\nwarrow\;\text{H}}{}} \end{array} + \text{X}^{-} \;\rightleftharpoons\; \begin{array}{c} \text{OH} \\ | \\ \text{R}-\overset{|}{\underset{|}{\text{C}}}-\text{R} \\ \text{OH} \end{array} + \text{HX}$$

The positive charge in the conjugate acid is delocalized as follows,

$$\begin{array}{c} \text{H} \\ / \\ {}^{+}\text{O} \\ \| \\ \text{R}-\overset{}{\text{C}}-\text{R} \end{array} \;\longleftrightarrow\; \begin{array}{c} \text{H} \\ / \\ \text{O} \\ | \\ \text{R}-\underset{+}{\overset{}{\text{C}}}-\text{R} \end{array}$$

15.4 The Addition of Alcohols to the Carbonyl System

The addition of alcohols to the group C=O occurs readily. The products of these additions are either hemiacetals or hemiketals, or under some conditions, acetals or ketals. Hemiacetal and hemiketal formation like hydration is subject to acid and base catalysis, and the mechanisms for addition by these catalyzed processes are identical to those encountered in the hydration of acetaldehyde. This reaction is also reversible.

Under strongly basic conditions it is the alkoxide anion OR⁻, a strong nucleophile, that attacks directly:

$$\begin{array}{c} \text{O} \\ \| \\ \text{R}-\text{C}-\text{R} \end{array} + \text{ROH} \;\underset{}{\overset{\text{RO}^{-}}{\rightleftharpoons}}\; \begin{array}{c} \text{OH} \\ | \\ \text{R}-\overset{|}{\underset{|}{\text{C}}}-\text{R} \\ \text{OR} \end{array}$$

Hemiacetals and hemiketals are formed reversibly under mild conditions. The reaction can be carried a step further to yield acetals and ketals:

$$\begin{array}{c} \text{O} \\ \| \\ \text{R}-\text{C}-\text{R} \end{array} + \text{ROH} \;\rightleftharpoons\; \begin{array}{c} \text{OH} \\ | \\ \text{R}-\overset{|}{\underset{|}{\text{C}}}-\text{OR} \\ \text{OR} \end{array} + \text{ROH} \;\rightleftharpoons\; \begin{array}{c} \text{OR} \\ | \\ \text{R}-\overset{|}{\underset{|}{\text{C}}}-\text{R} \\ \text{OR} \end{array} + \text{H}_2\text{O}$$

This reaction is also reversible; however, under anhydrous conditions (if necessary by removal of one of the products as it is formed) the equilibrium is shifted and the acetal (or ketal) produced.

The conversion of a carbonyl compound to an acetal or ketal is carried out under acidic conditions, and carbonium ion intermediates are involved in their formation:

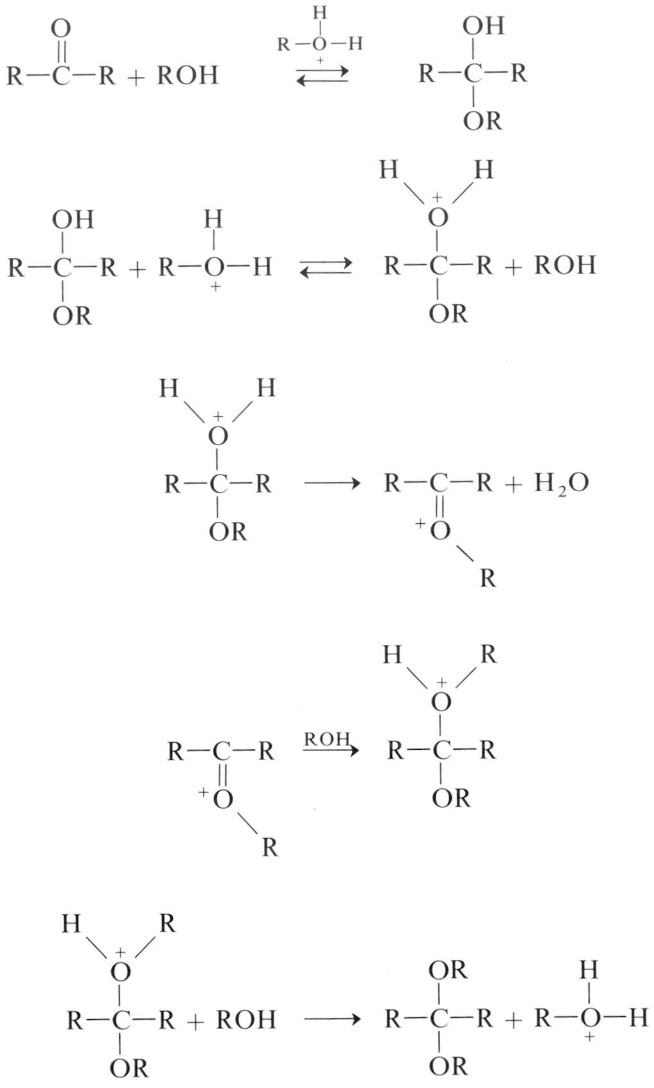

$$
\underset{\overset{\|}{\underset{R-C-R}{}}+ROH}{O} \quad \xrightarrow[\text{R}-\overset{H}{\underset{+}{O}}-H]{} \quad R-\overset{OH}{\underset{OR}{\underset{|}{C}}}-R
$$

$$
R-\overset{OH}{\underset{OR}{\underset{|}{C}}}-R + R-\overset{}{\underset{+}{O}}-H \;\rightleftharpoons\; R-\overset{\overset{H}{\underset{+}{O}}\overset{}{H}}{\underset{OR}{\underset{|}{C}}}-R + ROH
$$

$$
R-\overset{\overset{H}{\underset{+}{O}}\overset{}{H}}{\underset{OR}{\underset{|}{C}}}-R \;\longrightarrow\; R-\overset{}{\underset{\underset{R}{\overset{+}{O}}}{\underset{\|}{C}}}-R + H_2O
$$

$$
R-\overset{}{\underset{\underset{R}{\overset{+}{O}}}{\underset{\|}{C}}}-R \;\xrightarrow{ROH}\; R-\overset{\overset{H}{\underset{+}{O}}\overset{}{R}}{\underset{OR}{\underset{|}{C}}}-R
$$

$$
R-\overset{\overset{H}{\underset{+}{O}}\overset{}{R}}{\underset{OR}{\underset{|}{C}}}-R + ROH \;\longrightarrow\; R-\overset{OR}{\underset{OR}{\underset{|}{C}}}-R + R-\overset{H}{\underset{+}{O}}-H
$$

Acetals and ketals are stable to alkali, but treatment with dilute acid regenerates the carbonyl compound or its hydrate. Thus, acetal is hydrolyzed to acetaldehyde upon treatment with dilute acid. The process is specific acid catalyzed, and the mechanism is the reverse of that just presented. The observation of specific acid catalysis supports the mechanism written for the process,

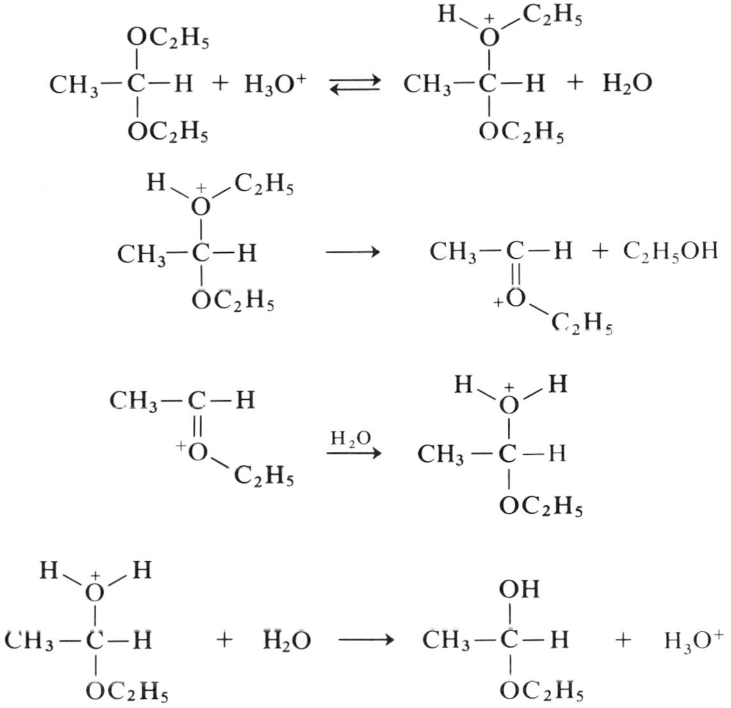

$$CH_3-\underset{\underset{OC_2H_5}{|}}{\overset{\overset{OC_2H_5}{|}}{C}}-H + H_3O^+ \;\rightleftharpoons\; CH_3-\underset{\underset{OC_2H_5}{|}}{\overset{\overset{\overset{+}{O}\diagdown{}^{C_2H_5}}{H}}{C}}-H + H_2O$$

$$CH_3-\underset{\underset{OC_2H_5}{|}}{\overset{\overset{\overset{+}{O}\diagdown{}^{C_2H_5}}{H}}{C}}-H \;\longrightarrow\; CH_3-\underset{\overset{+O}{\diagdown{}_{C_2H_5}}}{\overset{\|}{C}}-H + C_2H_5OH$$

$$CH_3-\underset{\overset{+O}{\diagdown{}_{C_2H_5}}}{\overset{\|}{C}}-H \;\xrightarrow{H_2O}\; CH_3-\underset{\underset{OC_2H_5}{|}}{\overset{\overset{\overset{+}{O}\diagdown{}^{H}}{H}}{C}}-H$$

$$CH_3-\underset{\underset{OC_2H_5}{|}}{\overset{\overset{\overset{+}{O}\diagdown{}^{H}}{H}}{C}}-H + H_2O \;\longrightarrow\; CH_3-\underset{\underset{OC_2H_5}{|}}{\overset{\overset{OH}{|}}{C}}-H + H_3O^+$$

The hemiacetal is quickly converted into a mixture of the free aldehyde and its hydrate,

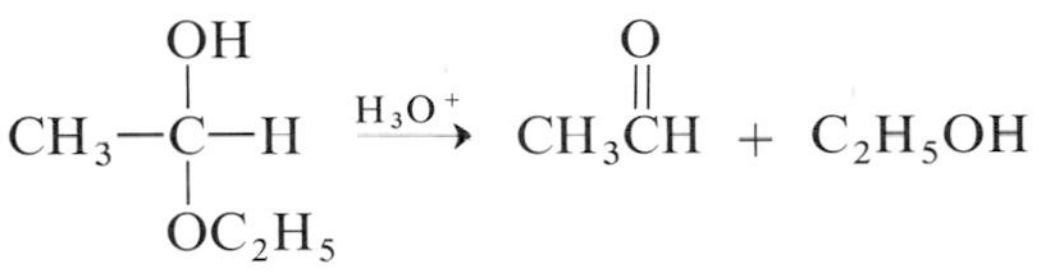

$$CH_3-\underset{\underset{OC_2H_5}{|}}{\overset{\overset{OH}{|}}{C}}-H \;\xrightarrow{H_3O^+}\; CH_3CH + C_2H_5OH$$

and

$$CH_3-\overset{\overset{O}{\|}}{C}-H + H_2O \;\underset{}{\overset{H_3O^+}{\rightleftharpoons}}\; CH_3-\underset{\underset{OH}{|}}{\overset{\overset{OH}{|}}{C}}-H$$

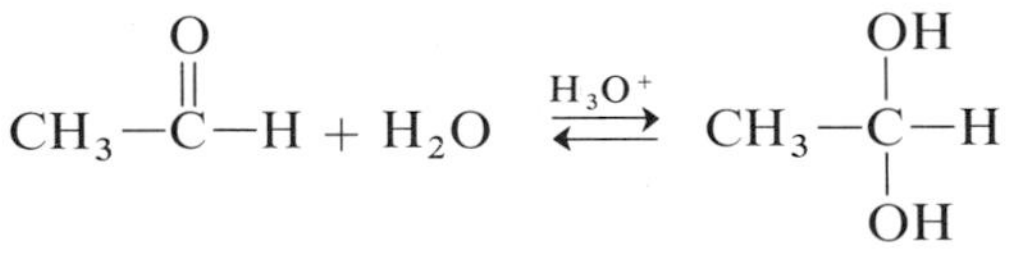

It is formation of the hemiacetal from acetal that is rate limiting in the hydrolysis. The principle of microscopic reversibility affords the mechanism in the other direction, and the same mechanism applies for nearly all preparations and hydrolyses of acetals and ketals.

15.5 Addition of Nitrogenous Bases

Nitrogenous bases such as ammonia, aniline, hydroxylamine, hydrazine, 2,4-dinitrophenylhydrazine, semicarbazide, and many others add to the carbonyl group. These additions all involve the same sort of intermediate:

$$
\begin{array}{c}
OH \\
| \\
R-C-R \\
| \\
NHR
\end{array}
$$

Thus, ammonia reacts with carbonyl compounds in the following manner,

$$
\underset{\displaystyle R-\overset{\displaystyle O}{\overset{\|}{C}}-R}{} + NH_3 \longrightarrow
\begin{array}{c}
OH \\
| \\
R-C-R \\
| \\
NH_2
\end{array}
\longrightarrow
\underset{}{R-\overset{\displaystyle NH}{\overset{\|}{C}}-R} + H_2O
$$

Some of these products revert readily to the carbonyl compounds or react further. Thus, reversal takes place,

$$
R-\overset{O}{\overset{\|}{C}}-R + NH_3 \rightleftharpoons
\begin{array}{c}
OH \\
| \\
R-C-R \\
| \\
NH_2
\end{array}
\rightleftharpoons
R-\overset{NH}{\overset{\|}{C}}-R + H_2O
$$

while the reaction of ammonia with formaldehyde can lead on to hexamethylenetetramine:

$$
6CH_2O + 4NH_3 \longrightarrow
$$

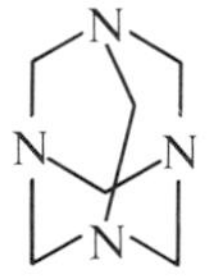

In other cases the final products actually serve as solid derivatives for aldehydes and ketones, yet these materials can also be hydrolyzed back to the carbonyl compounds:

$$
R-\overset{O}{\overset{\|}{C}}-R + H_2NOH \rightleftharpoons
\begin{array}{c}
OH \\
| \\
R-C-R \\
| \\
NHOH
\end{array}
\rightleftharpoons
R-\overset{NOH}{\overset{\|}{C}}-R + H_2O
$$

$$
R-\overset{O}{\overset{\|}{C}}-R + H_2NNHCONH_2 \rightleftharpoons
\begin{array}{c}
OH \\
| \\
R-C-R \\
| \\
HNNHCONH_2
\end{array}
\rightleftharpoons
\begin{array}{c}
NNHCONH_2 \\
\| \\
R-C-R
\end{array} + H_2O
$$

Secondary amines also react with carbonyl compounds. The products of these reactions are enamines, for in these cases the dehydration cannot take place in the usual way,

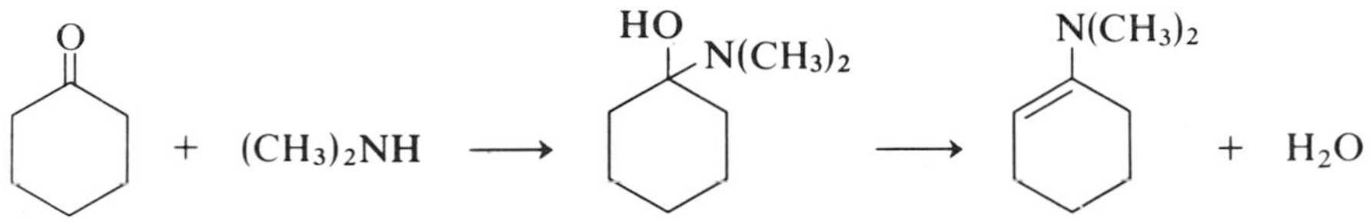

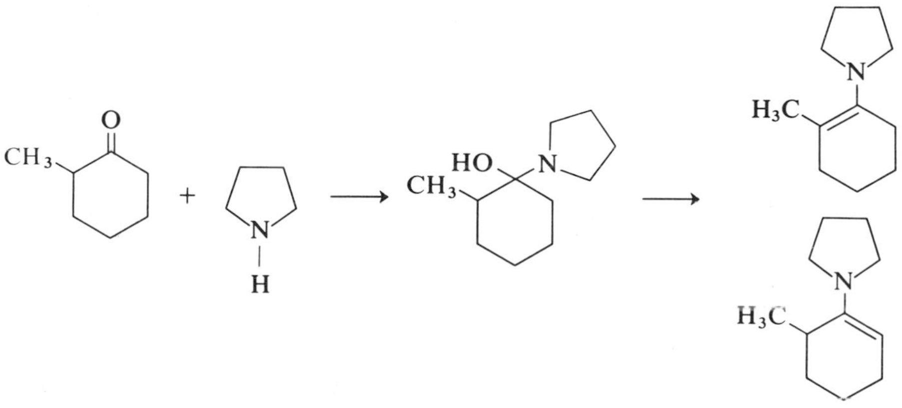

In cases where the enamine is much more stable than the imine, this type of a product is also obtained from simple amines such as ammonia and primary amines,

$$CH_3\overset{O}{\overset{\|}{C}}CH_2\overset{O}{\overset{\|}{C}}OC_2H_5 + NH_3 \longrightarrow CH_3-\overset{OH}{\underset{NH_2}{\overset{|}{C}}}-CH_2\overset{O}{\overset{\|}{C}}OC_2H_5$$

$$CH_3-\overset{OH}{\underset{NH_2}{\overset{|}{C}}}-CH_2\overset{O}{\overset{\|}{C}}OC_2H_5 \longrightarrow CH_3-\overset{NH_2}{\overset{|}{C}}=CH\overset{O}{\overset{\|}{C}}OC_2H_5 + H_2O$$

In this last example, the enamine is stabilized by resonance and by hydrogen bonding. Therefore, although the enamine and the imine are in equilibrium with each other, the former is present to a far greater degree.

$$CH_3-\overset{NH_2}{\overset{|}{C}}=CH-\overset{O}{\overset{\|}{C}}OC_2H_5 \rightleftarrows CH_3-\overset{NH}{\overset{\|}{C}}-CH_2\overset{O}{\overset{\|}{C}}OC_2H_5$$

In all of these reactions an intermediate such as

$$
\begin{array}{c}
\text{OH} \\
| \\
\text{R}-\text{C}-\text{R} \\
| \\
\text{HNR}
\end{array}
$$

2

is postulated, and this intermediate suffers dehydration to the product:

$$
\begin{array}{c}
\text{OH} \\
| \\
\text{R}-\text{C}-\text{R} \\
| \\
\text{HNR}
\end{array}
\longrightarrow
\begin{array}{c}
\text{NR} \\
|| \\
\text{R}-\text{C}-\text{R} + \text{H}_2\text{O} \\
\\
\end{array}
$$

2   **3**

There is excellent evidence for the existence of such intermediates. Under mild conditions, concentrated solutions of hydroxylamine, hydrazine, or semicarbazide react with carbonyl compounds. The carbonyl absorption disappears in the ultraviolet and infrared, but the characteristic peak due to the final dehydrated product **3** appears slowly. Some intermediate, which is formed rapidly, slowly decomposes to form the dehydrated product **3**. The logical structure for this intermediate is that presented, and in certain cases intermediates of this type have actually been isolated.

A nitrogenous base RNH_2 reacts with an aldehyde or a ketone, and the reaction proceeds by way of **2**.

The mechanism by which this species is formed depends upon the nature of the nucleophile RNH_2. Strong nucleophiles such as ammonia and hydroxylamine do not require a catalyst. Addition of the weaker nucleophiles such as semicarbazide and aniline is effected most readily in the presence of an acid catalyst (uncatalyzed additions do occur). The addition is general acid catalyzed and proceeds by the same mechanism as that already presented for such additions.

Since the entire reaction is reversible, this same intermediate **2** is also generated by addition of water to the Schiff base **3**:

$$
\begin{array}{c}
\text{N}-\text{R} \\
|| \\
\text{R}-\text{C}-\text{R} + \text{H}_2\text{O} \\
\\
\end{array}
\rightleftharpoons
\begin{array}{c}
\text{HNR} \\
| \\
\text{R}-\text{C}-\text{R} \\
| \\
\text{OH}
\end{array}
\rightleftharpoons
\begin{array}{c}
\text{O} \\
|| \\
\text{R}-\text{C}-\text{R} + \text{RNH}_2 \\
\\
\end{array}
$$

3   **2**

The Schiff bases serve as derivatives for aldehydes and ketones, yet the reaction can be reversed and the carbonyl compound regenerated. The intermediate **2** can lose water to form **3**, or it loses a molecule of the nitrogenous base and forms the carbonyl compound.

The addition of water to the Schiff base **3** can occur by uncatalyzed and by catalyzed processes. This is also possible with the group $C=O$; however, the mechanisms for these processes differ from those presented previously.

The overall reaction is a two-step process, and we have already discussed the mechanism by which **2** is transformed into the carbonyl compound. According to the principle of microscopic reversibility, the formation of the carbonyl system must be just the reverse of the route by which **2** is prepared from a ketone or aldehyde. We next discuss the other step in the process; namely, the formation of **2** from **3**. We need only discuss this step in one direction. Microscopic reversibility again dictates the mechanism for the reverse process.

Several mechanisms are observed for hydration. At high pH's the addition can involve a direct attack of the Schiff base by hydroxide ion. This mode of addition is specific base catalyzed and occurs most readily when the incipient negative charge on the nitrogen atom in the transition state is stabilized by R (R contains electron withdrawers):

$$
\underset{\underset{R-C-R}{||}}{N-R} + OH^- \longrightarrow \underset{\underset{\underset{OH^{\delta-}}{|}}{R-C-R}}{\overset{\delta-}{N}-R} \longrightarrow \underset{\underset{OH}{|}}{\overset{-}{N}R} \atop R-C-R
$$

$$
\underset{\underset{OH}{|}}{\overset{-}{N}R} \atop R-C-R + H_2O \rightleftharpoons \underset{\underset{OH}{|}}{HNR} \atop R-C-R + HO^-
$$

A second addition that occurs even in somewhat basic solutions involves the protonated Schiff base. Protonation of nitrogen takes place more readily than protonation of oxygen; consequently, even at moderate pH's, it is the conjugate acid of the Schiff base that takes part in some of these hydrations.

$$
\underset{\underset{R-C-R}{||}}{H-\overset{+}{N}-R}
$$

This pathway may be observed when the positive charge on the nitrogen atom is stabilized sufficiently (electron donors present),

$$
\begin{array}{ccc}
\overset{\displaystyle N-R}{\underset{\displaystyle \|}{R-C-R}} + H_2O & \rightleftarrows & \overset{\displaystyle H-\overset{+}{N}-R}{\underset{\displaystyle \|}{R-C-R}} + HO^-
\end{array}
$$

$$
\begin{array}{ccc}
\overset{\displaystyle H-\overset{+}{N}-R}{\underset{\displaystyle \|}{R-C-R}} + OH^- & \longrightarrow & \overset{\displaystyle HNR}{\underset{\displaystyle |}{R-\underset{\displaystyle |}{\underset{\displaystyle OH}{C}}-R}}
\end{array}
$$

At still lower pH's, where the hydroxide ion concentration is low, a molecule of water can attack the protonated Schiff base. This reaction is specific acid catalyzed and for some compounds proceeds by the following mechanism,

$$
\begin{array}{ccc}
\overset{\displaystyle N-R}{\underset{\displaystyle \|}{R-C-R}} + H_3O^+ & \rightleftarrows & \overset{\displaystyle H-\overset{+}{N}-R}{\underset{\displaystyle \|}{R-C-R}} + H_2O
\end{array}
$$

$$
\begin{array}{ccc}
\overset{\displaystyle H-\overset{+}{N}-R}{\underset{\displaystyle \|}{R-C-R}} & \overset{H_2O}{\longrightarrow} & \overset{\displaystyle H-N-R}{\underset{\displaystyle |}{R-\underset{\displaystyle |}{\underset{\displaystyle \overset{+}{O}}{C}}-R}} \\
& & \qquad \swarrow\; \searrow \\
& & H \qquad H
\end{array}
$$

$$
\begin{array}{ccc}
\overset{\displaystyle H-N-R}{\underset{\displaystyle |}{R-\underset{\displaystyle |}{\underset{\displaystyle O}{C}}-R}} + H_2O & \rightleftarrows & \overset{\displaystyle H-N-R}{\underset{\displaystyle |}{R-\underset{\displaystyle |}{\underset{\displaystyle OH}{C}}-R}} + H_3O^+ \\
\quad \swarrow\overset{+}{\;}\searrow \\
H \qquad H
\end{array}
$$

Hydration of some Schiff bases involves general acid catalysis, which requires a molecule of HX (in this case as H^+X^-) to enter into the transition state. The mechanism for the general acid catalyzed process is almost the same as that just presented; however, the conjugate base X^- abstracts a proton as the water molecule attacks the protonated Schiff base:

$$
\begin{array}{ccc}
\overset{\displaystyle N-R}{\underset{\displaystyle \|}{R-C-R}} + HX & \rightleftarrows & \overset{\displaystyle H-\overset{+}{N}-R}{\underset{\displaystyle \|}{R-C-R}} + X^-
\end{array}
$$

$$
\begin{array}{ccccc}
\overset{\displaystyle H-\overset{+}{N}-R}{\underset{\displaystyle \|}{R-C-R}} + H_2O + X^- & \longrightarrow & \overset{\displaystyle \overset{\delta+}{HNR}}{\underset{\displaystyle \|}{R-C-R}} & \longrightarrow & \overset{\displaystyle HNR}{\underset{\displaystyle |}{R-\underset{\displaystyle |}{\underset{\displaystyle OH}{C}}-R}} + HX \\
& & \underset{\displaystyle H}{\overset{\displaystyle \diagup}{O}}\cdots H \\
& & \qquad\qquad \diagdown_{\delta-}X
\end{array}
$$

Hydration may take place to a measurable extent by more than one of these routes. The differences in the free energy of activation for the various routes can be small, and the processes then occur simultaneously. Naturally, the mechanism by which hydration of a Schiff base occurs also depends upon the pH of the solution.

All of the additions are reversible, and the mechanisms observed for the dehydration are the reverse of those just discussed.

The preparation of carbonyl derivatives involves the formation and decomposition of the hydrated intermediate **2**. Under some conditions the rate of formation of this intermediate is the rate limiting portion of the reaction; under others its decomposition is rate limiting,

$$
\underset{\substack{\|\\ \text{R—C—R}}}{\overset{O}{}} + RNH_2 \underset{k_{-1}}{\overset{k_1}{\rightleftarrows}} \underset{\substack{|\\ \text{R—C—R}\\|\\ \text{HNR}}}{\overset{OH}{}} \xrightarrow{k_2} \underset{\substack{\|\\ \text{R—C—R}}}{\overset{NR}{}} + H_2O
$$

The rate of this reaction of carbonyl compounds with nitrogenous bases is pH dependent, and the experimental observations are interesting. As the pH is lowered from slightly alkaline to slightly acidic, the rate of Schiff base formation from the carbonyl compound increases. A further decrease in the pH then causes a decrease in the rate of reaction.

This behavior can be ascribed to a change in rate limiting portion of the reaction. At alkaline pH's, it is the dehydration of the intermediate that constitutes the rate limiting step ($k_{obs} = K_1 k_2$), while at low pH's it is attack of the carbonyl compound by the nucleophile RNH_2 that is rate limiting ($k_{obs} = k_1$).

The dehydration is subject to acid catalysis. Lowering the pH, increases the rate of this step, and as long as this dehydration is rate limiting, the reaction proceeds more rapidly. Continued lowering of the pH causes attack of the carbonyl group by RNH_2 to become the rate limiting portion of the reaction. The rate of dehydration no longer influences the rate of the overall reaction. Furthermore, the rate of attack of the carbonyl system by RNH_2 depends upon the concentration of this nucleophile, and as the pH is lowered, its concentration decreases; it is converted to its conjugate acid RNH_3^+. Consequently, when attack by RNH_2 becomes the rate limiting portion of the reaction, decreasing the pH further decreases the rate of reaction.

15.6 Addition of Organometallic Reagents

The reaction of an alkyl or aryl halide with magnesium gives rise to the Grignard reagent. The structure of this material appears to vary with the solvent in which it is prepared. In some solvents it is largely monomeric whereas in others it exists as a dimer $(RMgX)_2$. Furthermore, the magnesium behaves as a Lewis acid and forms bonds with ethers. The structure of phenylmagnesium bromide dietherate has been determined by x-ray analysis, and the material has a tetrahedral structure:

$$
\begin{array}{c}
Br \\
| \\
(C_2H_5)_2O^{+}{\diagdown}{}^{Mg^{--}}{\diagup}\phi \\
(C_2H_5)_2O
\end{array}
$$

Thus, the structure and behavior of a Gignard reagent is more complex than the simple structure RMgX usually written for it. Few kinetic studies have been conducted on reactions involving Grignard reagents, for these reactions usually proceed too rapidly to be investigated by conventional techniques. The reaction of *n*-butylmagnesium bromide with phenyl cyanide proceeds more slowly, and the kinetics of this reaction have been studied. The reaction shows second order kinetics. A single molecule of C_4H_9MgBr and a single molecule of ϕCN are involved in the transition state (together with solvent). The mechanism suggested for this reaction assumes prior complexing of the magnesium in the Grignard reagent with the nitrogen atom in the nitrile, and there is good evidence that, at least in some cases, such prior complexing occurs.

The reaction of benzophenone $\phi_2 CO$ with phenylmagnesium bromide gives rise to a precipitate. Hydrolyzing this precipitate regenerates the ketone. Treatment of this precipitate with excess phenylmagnesium bromide and then with water affords triphenylcarbinol $\phi_3 COH$:

$$
\begin{array}{ccc}
O & & O-MgBr \\
\| & & \| \\
\phi-C-\phi + \phi MgBr & \longrightarrow & \phi-C-\phi \\
 & & \overset{\displaystyle\phi}{|}
\end{array}
$$

$$
\begin{array}{ccc}
\overset{\displaystyle\phi}{|} & & \\
O-MgBr & & O \\
\| & & \| \\
\phi-C-\phi + H_2O & \longrightarrow & \phi-C-\phi + \phi H + MgBrOH
\end{array}
$$

and

$$
\begin{array}{ccc}
\overset{\displaystyle\phi}{|} & & OH \\
O-MgBr & \xrightarrow[\text{(2) } H_2O]{\text{(1) } \phi MgBr} & | \\
\| & & \phi-C-\phi \\
\phi-C-\phi & & | \\
 & & \phi
\end{array}
$$

Molecules of the solvent are also involved, but their role has not been indicated in our mechanism.

We see that the behavior of Grignard reagents is not so straightforward as we might like. We shall continue to indicate this reactant by the formula RMgX but must bear in mind that this oversimplifies the situation.

Ketones react with RMgX to yield magnesium salts of alcohols, and the actual alcohols are produced by hydrolyzing these magnesium salts,

$$
R-\underset{\displaystyle \overset{\displaystyle O}{\|}}{C}-R \xrightarrow{RMgX} R-\underset{\displaystyle \underset{R}{|}}{\overset{\displaystyle O-MgX}{\underset{|}{C}}}-R \xrightarrow{H_2O} R-\underset{\displaystyle \underset{R}{|}}{\overset{\displaystyle OH}{\underset{|}{C}}}-R
$$

This reaction can be utilized to prepare alcohols of all classes. Reaction of Grignard reagents with formaldehyde and hydrolysis of the resulting magnesium salts affords primary alcohols. Treatment of RMgX with any other aldehyde gives rise to secondary alcohols, while using a ketone generates tertiary alcohols:

$$
RMgX + HCOH \longrightarrow RCH_2OMgX \xrightarrow{H_2O} RCH_2OH
$$

$$
RMgX + RCHO \longrightarrow R_2CHOMgX \xrightarrow{H_2O} R_2CHOH
$$

$$
RMgX + R_2CO \longrightarrow R_3COMgX \xrightarrow{H_2O} R_3COH
$$

Other organometallic compounds can be used in this type of reaction. The Reformatsky reaction for the preparation of β-hydroxy esters employs zinc salts made from the corresponding halo ester:

$$
\underset{\displaystyle Br-CHCOOC_2H_5}{\overset{\displaystyle CH_3}{\underset{|}{}}} + Zn \longrightarrow BrZn\underset{\displaystyle CHCOOC_2H_5}{\overset{\displaystyle CH_3}{\underset{|}{}}}
$$

$$
\phi COCH_3 + BrZn\underset{\displaystyle CHCOOC_2H_5}{\overset{\displaystyle CH_3}{\underset{|}{}}} \longrightarrow \phi-\underset{\displaystyle \underset{OZnBr}{|}}{C}-\underset{\displaystyle CHCOOC_2H_5}{\overset{\displaystyle CH_3}{\underset{|}{}}}
$$

$$
\phi-\underset{\displaystyle \underset{OZnBr}{|}}{C}-\underset{\displaystyle CHCOOC_2H_5}{\overset{\displaystyle CH_3}{\underset{|}{}}} \xrightarrow{H_3O^+} \phi-\underset{\displaystyle \underset{OH}{|}}{C}-\underset{\displaystyle CHCOOC_2H_5}{\overset{\displaystyle CH_3}{\underset{|}{}}}
$$

This hydroxy ester is easily dehydrated to the α,β-unsaturated ester, and the Reformatsky reaction is commonly used for the preparation of such materials. Organosodium compounds react with carbonyl compounds as do organo-lithiums, and these materials can also be prepared by treating the halo compound with the metal:

$$RX + 2Na \longrightarrow RNa + NaX$$

$$RX + 2Li \longrightarrow RLi + LiX$$

Some organometallic compounds are made more readily by treating the hydrocarbon itself with the metal. This works particularly well when the hydrogen atom in the original compound is acidic,

Compounds of the type $RC{\equiv}CMgX$ cannot be prepared easily in a direct manner; however, the acid-base reaction of an alkyne with methylmagnesium iodide affords these compounds in good yield:

$$RC{\equiv}C-H + CH_3MgI \longrightarrow RC{\equiv}C-MgI + CH_4$$

The structure of organometallic compounds is of interest. If the halogen bearing carbon atom is sp^3 hybridized, then this atom should retain its tetrahedral bonding when the halogen is replaced by a metal and whenever the carbon-metal bond is covalent:

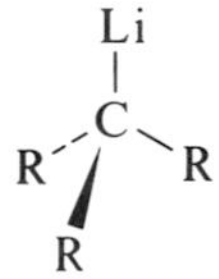

A tetrahedral shape is expected when the carbon-metal bond is covalent. The use of sp^3 orbitals is also expected when the bond is ionic. In these ionic situations the electronic configuration at the carbon atom is similar to that in ammonia, and ammonia uses sp^3 orbitals:

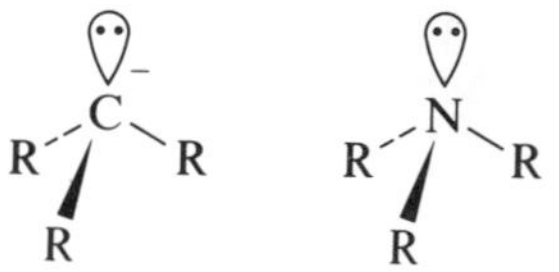

However, ammonia has the peculiar property of inverting its configuration, and we expect analogous behavior from carbanions $(R_3C:^-)$. Organometallic materials in which the carbon atom is asymmetric should, when the bond is ionic, racemize, and it appears from the available data that such racemization does occur with organometallic compounds. It is promoted by higher temperatures and more polar solvents,

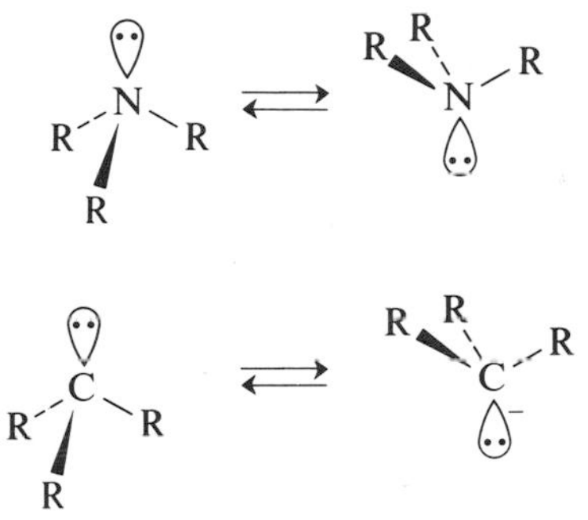

At low temperatures or in nonpolar solvents, optically active 2-octyllithium racemizes slowly. At higher temperature in more polar solvents it racemizes rapidly. The data imply an ionization of a covalently bonded organolithium compound:

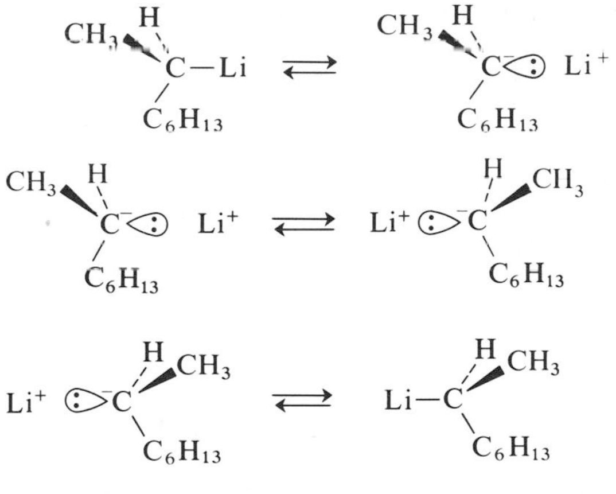

Naturally, when the charge in a carbanion can be delocalized such as in the allyl and benzyl anions, we expect the use of sp^2 hybridization by the carbon atom, with the two electrons becoming part of the π system. This change in hybridization from sp^3 to sp^2 requires energy but is more than compensated for, by the stabilization gained by charge delocalization. The sp^2 hybridization is better suited for delocalization. For example, in Figure 15–1 in the benzyl carbanion, an sp^3 orbital is poorly overlapped with the π system of the benzene ring, while the use of sp^2 hybridization by the benzyl carbon atom leads to more effective charge delocalization.

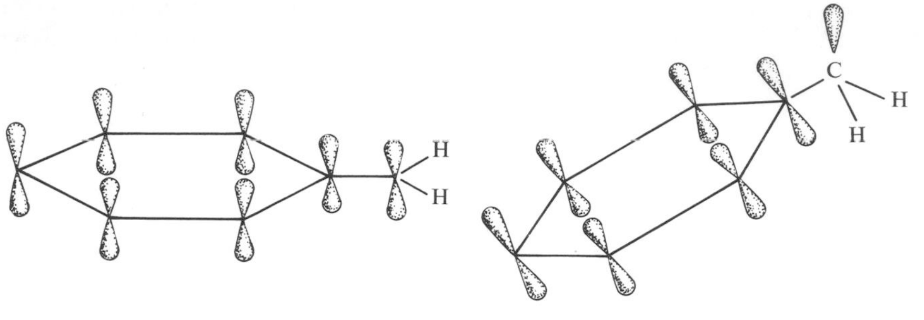

Good Overlap   Poor Overlap

Figure 15-1

Another point is that we expect a greater degree of ionic character in the carbon-metal bond when metals such as sodium or potassium are used to prepare organometallics than when lithium or magnesium are employed. Also, the behavior of the former pair while apparently similar to that of the latter differs in its finer aspects. Thus, both benzylsodium and *n*-butyllithium react with optically active 2-bromobutane to yield substituted products; however, the reaction of the sodium salt is accompanied by inversion of configuration at the optically active center while the organolithium compound produces a nearly racemic product:

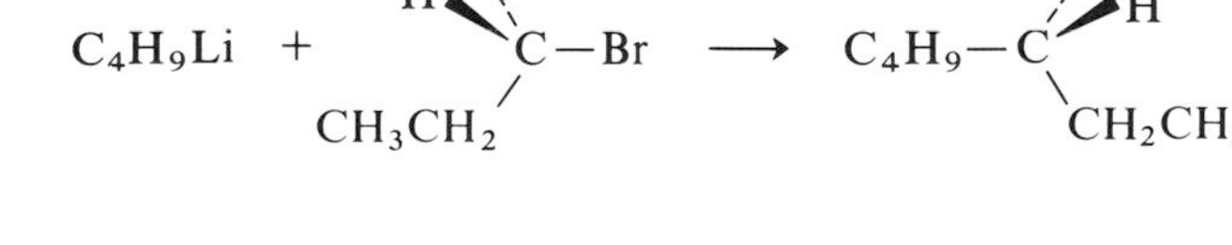

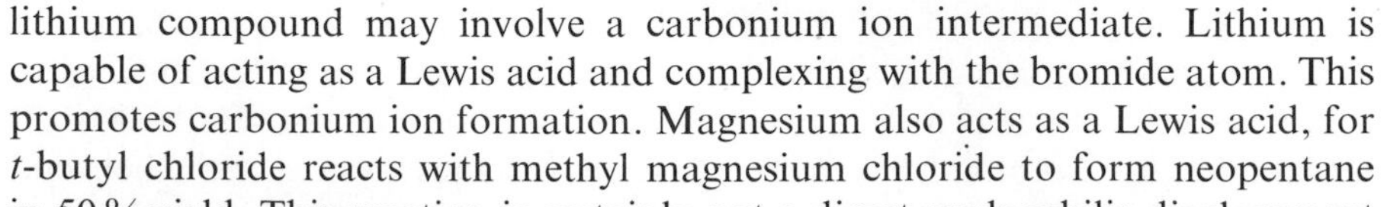

The sodium salt reacts chiefly by an S_N2 mechanism, yet reaction of the lithium compound may involve a carbonium ion intermediate. Lithium is capable of acting as a Lewis acid and complexing with the bromide atom. This promotes carbonium ion formation. Magnesium also acts as a Lewis acid, for *t*-butyl chloride reacts with methyl magnesium chloride to form neopentane in 50% yield. This reaction is certainly not a direct nucleophilic displacement by $CH_3:^-$ on the alkyl chloride. A carbonium ion intermediate or a complex in which the tertiary carbon atom has considerable carbonium ion character is probably involved:

$$\begin{array}{ccc} & \text{CH}_3 & \text{CH}_3 \\ & | & | \\ \text{CH}_3\text{MgCl} + \text{CH}_3-\text{C}-\text{CH}_3 & \longrightarrow & \text{CH}_3-\text{C}-\text{CH}_3 \\ & | & | \\ & \text{Cl} & \text{CH}_3 \\ & & 50\% \end{array}$$

Organometallic reagents react readily with most carbonyl compounds. The behavior of lithium derivatives is similar to that of Grignard reagents, yet the former offer a distinct advantage in reactions with sterically hindered ketones. Diisopropyl ketone reacts with isopropyllithium to yield, after hydrolysis, triisopropylcarbinol. The reaction of isopropylmagnesium bromide with this same ketone affords no addition product. Other products are observed, and this inability of Grignard reagents to add to sterically hindered ketones is typical of these materials. The transition state for addition to the carbonyl group is much more crowded when Grignard reagents are used, and this raises the free energy of activation for the addition:

$$(\text{CH}_3)_2\text{CH}-\overset{\overset{\text{O}}{\|}}{\text{C}}-\text{CH}(\text{CH}_3)_2 \quad \xrightarrow[\text{2) H}_2\text{O}]{\text{1) (CH}_3)_2\text{CHLi}} \quad (\text{CH}_3)_2\text{CHC}\overset{\overset{\text{OH}}{|}}{\underset{\overset{|}{\text{CH}(\text{CH}_3)_2}}{}}\text{CH}(\text{CH}_3)_2$$

$$(\text{CH}_3)_2\text{CH}-\overset{\overset{\text{O}}{\|}}{\text{C}}-\text{CH}(\text{CH}_3)_2 \quad \xrightarrow{(\text{CH}_3)_2\text{CHMgBr}} \quad \begin{array}{l} (\text{CH}_3)_2\text{CH}-\overset{\overset{\text{OMgBr}}{|}}{\underset{\overset{|}{\text{H}}}{\text{C}}}-\text{CH}(\text{CH}_3)_2 + \text{CH}_3\text{CH}=\text{CH}_2 \\ \\ \qquad\qquad\qquad\qquad \mathbf{4} \\ \\ \begin{array}{c} \text{CH}_3 \\ \diagdown \\ \qquad \text{C}=\overset{\overset{\text{OMgBr}}{|}}{\text{C}}-\text{CH}(\text{CH}_3)_2 + \text{CH}_3\text{CH}_2\text{CH}_3 \\ \diagup \\ \text{CH}_3 \qquad\qquad \mathbf{5} \end{array} \end{array}$$

Instead of the expected addition products a reduced product **4**, obtained by hydride transfer from the Grignard reagent, and an enolic product **5**, obtained by proton abstraction by the Grignard reagent, are observed. The proton abstraction is just an acid-base reaction, and in fact, Grignard addition reactions are frequently accompanied by side reactions such as aldol condensations, which may originate from initially formed enolic products such as **5**.

A reasonable mechanism for formation of the reduced product **4**, assumes rapid and reversible complex formation followed by a rate limiting hydride transfer. A cyclic transition state is involved:

$$R-\overset{\overset{\displaystyle O}{\|}}{C}-R \ + \ CH_3-\overset{\overset{\displaystyle MgBr}{|}}{\underset{\underset{\displaystyle H}{|}}{C}}-CH_3 \ \rightleftarrows \ R_2C \begin{matrix} O^{\cdots MgBr} \\ \| \end{matrix} \begin{matrix} CH_3 \\ C-H \\ | \\ CH_2 \\ H \end{matrix}$$

$$R_2C \begin{matrix} MgBr \\ O \end{matrix} \begin{matrix} CH_3 \\ C-H \\ | \\ CH_2 \\ H \end{matrix} \longrightarrow R_2CH \overset{\overset{\displaystyle OMgBr}{|}}{} + \begin{matrix} H \\ C \\ \| \\ C \\ H \end{matrix} \begin{matrix} CH_3 \\ \\ H \end{matrix}$$

The transition state is,

$$R_2C \begin{matrix} MgBr \\ O \\ \| \\ H \end{matrix} \begin{matrix} CH_3 \\ C \\ \| \\ CH_2 \\ H \end{matrix}$$

The product **4** of the hydride transfer reaction is the magnesium salt of diisopropylcarbinol, and hydrolysis of the reaction mixture affords this alcohol. The reduction as a matter of fact, while an undesirable side reaction during Grignard additions, can be put to good use, for it serves as a convenient technique for preparing alcohols from the corresponding ketones. Other organometallic salts occasionally perform this hydride transfer reaction, and this reaction predominates when aluminum isopropoxide **6** is used as the hydride source:

$$Al \left(O-CH \begin{matrix} CH_3 \\ \\ CH_3 \end{matrix} \right)_3$$

6

The reaction, which was frequently used for the reduction of ketones under mild conditions, is known as the Meerwein-Ponndorf-Verley reduction.

15.7 The Meerwein-Ponndorf-Verley-Oppenauer Reaction

The reduction of a ketone by aluminum isopropoxide is called the Meerwein-Ponndorf-Verley reduction. The process is reversible, an alcohol can be converted to the corresponding ketone by this same material, and the oxidation is called the Oppenauer oxidation. Since one of these two reactions is just the forward part of an equilibrium while the other is the reverse portion, we discuss them together.

The reduction of a carbonyl group is usually carried out using aluminum isopropoxide in the presence of isopropyl alcohol. However, the reaction can also be conducted in the absence of isopropyl alcohol.

Aluminum isopropoxide, which serves as a source of hydride, transfers this to the carbonyl group. The mechanism is the same as that presented for reduction by Grignard reagents:

$$R-\overset{\overset{\textstyle O}{\|}}{C}-R \; + \; \underset{H}{\overset{\overset{\textstyle \overset{\displaystyle \diagdown Al \diagup}{O}}{|}}{C}} \diagup\!\!\!\diagdown\!\!\!\overset{CH_3}{\underset{CH_3}{}} \;\rightleftharpoons\; R_2\overset{\overset{\textstyle O}{\|}}{C} \quad \underset{H}{\overset{\overset{\textstyle \overset{\diagdown Al \diagup}{O}}{|}}{C}}\!\!\overset{CH_3}{\underset{CH_3}{}}$$

$$R_2\overset{\overset{\textstyle O}{\|}}{C}\quad\underset{H}{\overset{\overset{\textstyle \overset{\diagdown Al \diagdown}{O}}{|}}{C}}\overset{CH_3}{\underset{CH_3}{}} \;\rightleftharpoons\; R_2\overset{O}{C}\ldots\underset{H}{\ldots}\overset{O}{C}\overset{CH_3}{\underset{CH_3}{}} \;\rightleftharpoons\; R_2CH \;+\; CH_3\overset{\overset{\textstyle O}{\|}}{C}CH_3$$

The transition state for this reaction is,

$$\underset{R}{\overset{R}{\diagdown}}C\underset{H}{\overset{\overset{\textstyle \overset{\diagdown Al \diagdown}{O}}{\|}}{\ldots}}\,C\overset{CH_3}{\underset{CH_3}{}}$$

The products are the aluminum salt of the alcohol and acetone. The reaction is reversible. However, if conducted in an inert solvent at moderate temperatures, the acetone distills out as it is formed, and the equilibrium is shifted towards the products. The free alcohol is then obtained by hydrolyzing the aluminum salt with acid. Alternatively, the reaction can be conducted in isopropyl alcohol, and this procedure generates the free alcohol directly.

When isopropyl alcohol is present, the isopropyl alcohol enters into an equilibrium with the aluminum salt **7** of the desired alcohol. The free alcohol is generated, and the aluminum salt of isopropyl alcohol is formed instead:

$$\underset{\underset{R}{|}}{\overset{\overset{R}{|}}{H-C}}-OAl\left(OCH\diagup\!\!\!\diagdown^{CH_3}_{CH_3}\right)_2 \;+\; \underset{\underset{CH_3}{|}}{\overset{\overset{CH_3}{|}}{H-C}}-OH \;\rightleftharpoons\; \underset{\underset{R}{|}}{\overset{\overset{R}{|}}{H-C}}-OH \;+$$

(7)

$$\underset{\underset{CH_3}{|}}{\overset{\overset{CH_3}{|}}{H-C}}-O-Al\left(OCH\diagup\!\!\!\diagdown^{CH_3}_{CH_3}\right)_2$$

Since an excess of isopropyl alcohol is present, this equilibrium is also shifted towards the products. The aluminum salt of isopropyl alcohol is just the starting reagent, aluminum isopropoxide, which has been regenerated.

Of course, **7** also contains two isopropoxide groups that can react with isopropyl alcohol, but in this case no new products arc formed.

The overall reaction becomes,

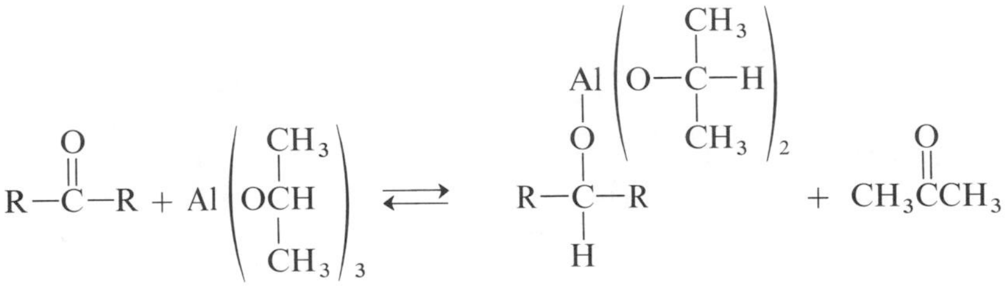

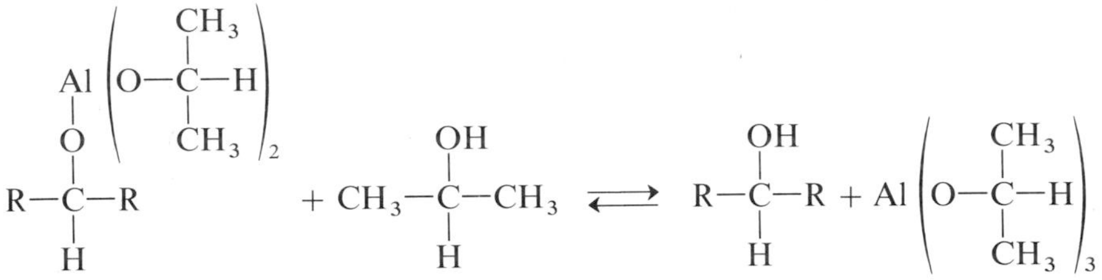

$$R-\underset{\substack{\|\\O}}{C}-R + Al\left(O\underset{\substack{|\\CH_3}}{\overset{\substack{CH_3\\|}}{C}}H\right)_3 \rightleftharpoons R-\underset{\substack{|\\H}}{\overset{\substack{Al\left(O-\underset{\substack{|\\CH_3}}{\overset{\substack{CH_3\\|}}{C}}-H\right)_2\\|\\O|}}{C}}-R + CH_3\underset{\substack{\|\\O}}{C}CH_3$$

$$R-\underset{\substack{|\\H}}{\overset{\substack{Al\left(O-\underset{\substack{|\\CH_3}}{\overset{\substack{CH_3\\|}}{C}}-H\right)_2\\|\\O|}}{C}}-R + CH_3-\underset{\substack{|\\H}}{\overset{\substack{OH\\|}}{C}}-CH_3 \rightleftharpoons R-\underset{\substack{|\\H}}{\overset{\substack{OH\\|}}{C}}-R + Al\left(O-\underset{\substack{|\\CH_3}}{\overset{\substack{CH_3\\|}}{C}}-H\right)_3$$

which we write simply as,

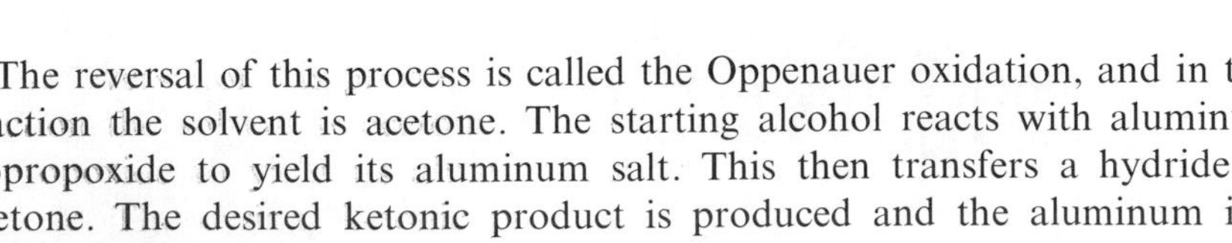

$$R-\underset{\substack{\|\\O}}{C}-R + CH_3-\underset{\substack{|\\H}}{\overset{\substack{OH\\|}}{C}}-CH_3 \underset{\longleftarrow}{\overset{Al\left(O\underset{\substack{|\\CH_3}}{\overset{\substack{CH_3\\|}}{C}}-H\right)_3}{\longrightarrow}} R-\underset{\substack{|\\H}}{\overset{\substack{OH\\|}}{C}}-R + CH_3\underset{\substack{\|\\O}}{C}CH_3$$

The reversal of this process is called the Oppenauer oxidation, and in this reaction the solvent is acetone. The starting alcohol reacts with aluminum isopropoxide to yield its aluminum salt. This then transfers a hydride to acetone. The desired ketonic product is produced and the aluminum iso-propoxide regenerated.

Naturally, an isopropoxide group in the aluminum salt is also capable of transferring hydride to acetone, but no new products result from this reaction:

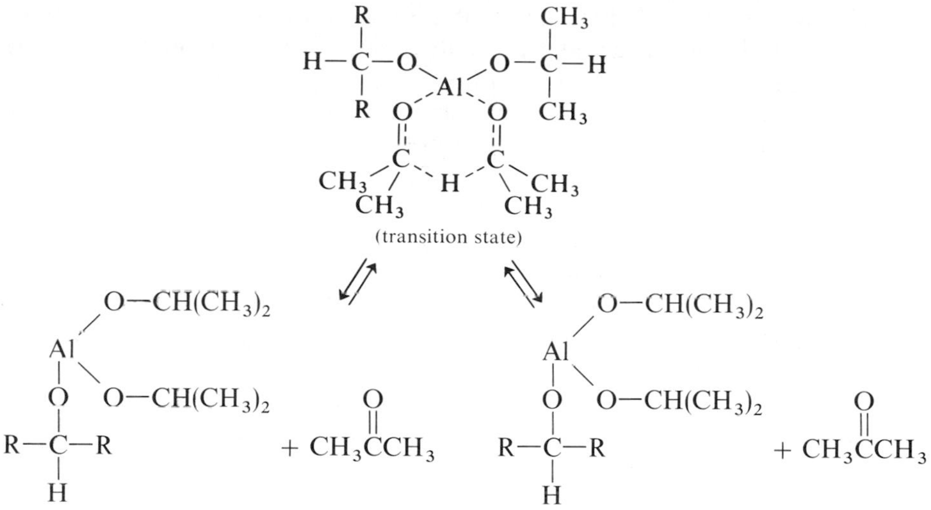

$$
\begin{array}{c}
\text{R} \qquad\qquad\qquad \text{CH}_3 \\
| \qquad\qquad\qquad\quad | \\
\text{H}-\text{C}-\text{O}\diagdown\qquad\diagup\text{O}-\text{C}-\text{H} \\
| \qquad\quad\text{Al}\qquad\quad | \\
\text{R}\quad\text{O}\diagdown\quad\diagup\text{O}\quad\text{CH}_3 \\
\quad\text{C}\quad\quad\text{C} \\
\text{CH}_3\diagup\diagup\ \diagdown\ \text{H}\ \diagup\ \diagdown\text{CH}_3 \\
\text{CH}_3 \qquad\qquad \text{CH}_3
\end{array}
$$

(transition state)

At one time, the Meerwein-Ponndorf-Verley reduction was the most convenient available method for the preparation of alcohols from the corresponding ketones. It still finds occasional use; however, for the most part, the use of aluminum isopropoxide as a hydride source has been superseded by another reagent, lithium aluminum hydride $LiAlH_4$. This reagent, discovered in 1947, is not only convenient to use, it is extremely reactive and converts all types of carbonyl compounds to alcohols. The yields are excellent, and it is this reagent or sodium borohydride $NaBH_4$ that is now employed for reductions of the carbonyl system.

The Meerwein-Ponndorf-Verley reaction worked best for ketones and could give rise to other products when aldehydes were the potential hydride acceptors. These side reactions do not occur with lithium aluminum hydride or sodium borohydride.

15.8 Lithium Aluminum Hydride and Sodium Borohydride

Lithium aluminum hydride appears to exist in solution as solvated ion pairs and larger ionic aggregates of $Li^+AlH_4^-$. In ethereal solution the structure of the anionic portion of the salt is apparently,

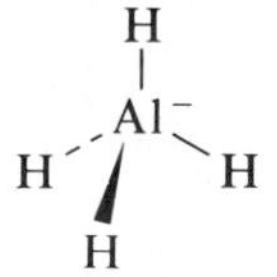

$$
\begin{array}{c}
\text{H} \\
| \\
\ .\text{Al}^- \\
\text{H}\diagup\ |\ \diagdown\text{H} \\
\text{H}
\end{array}
$$

where the species AlH_4^- has a tetrahedral geometry.

The complexity of the ionic aggregates is a function of the concentration of the lithium aluminum hydride. In dilute solutions, the predominant species is $(LiAlH_4)_2$, while in more concentrated solutions, it is $(LiAlH_4)_3$.

The mode of addition of lithium aluminum hydride to the carbonyl group involves a prior complexing or perhaps simply an electrostatic attraction between the oxygen atom of the carbonyl group and the lithium cation. Since the aluminum atom in AlH_4^- has its octet of electrons and a negative charge, it is unlikely that this species enters into prior complex formation with the oxygen atom. A hydride is then transferred by the AlH_4^- to the carbon atom of the carbonyl group. A single mole of lithium aluminum hydride is able to reduce four moles of the carbonyl compound.

Sodium borohydride $Na^+BH_4^-$ behaves similarly and is also a capable reducing agent for the carbonyl system. This reagent can be employed in aqueous solutions, which sometimes offers an advantage. Potassium borohydride and lithium borohydride are also used for effecting reductions, and all of these materials react with aldehydes and ketones to generate alcohols in good yield.

Carbon-carbon double bonds in conjugation with the carbonyl system are sometimes reduced but isolated double bonds are not usually affected by these hydride transfer reagents. Typical reactions of lithium aluminum hydride are,

$$CH_3COCH_3 \xrightarrow[\text{(2) } H_3O^+]{\text{(1) LiAlH}_4} CH_3CHOHCH_3$$

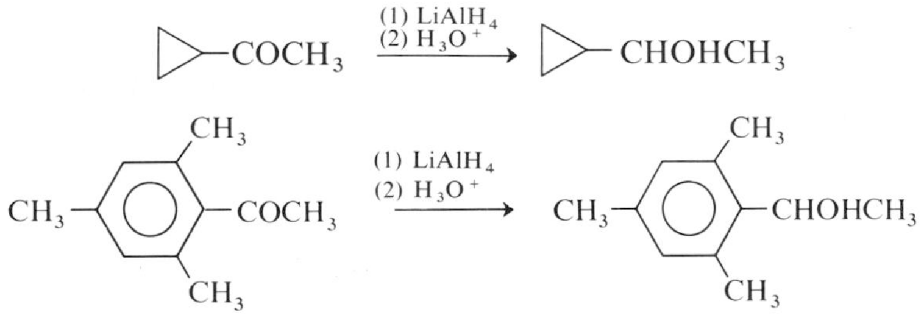

while sodium and lithium borohydride reductions include,

$$CH_3CH=CHCHO \xrightarrow{\text{NaBH}_4} CH_3CH=CHCH_2OH$$

$$CH_3COCH_2COCH_3 \xrightarrow{\text{NaBH}_4} CH_3CHOHCH_2CHOHCH_3$$

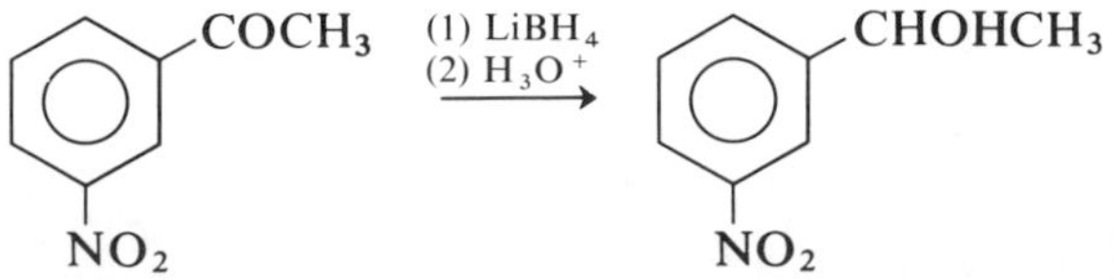

The following mechanism can be written for hydride transfer by lithium aluminum hydride (we do not consider explicity the role of the lithium).

$$
\begin{array}{ccc}
\overset{\overset{\displaystyle O}{\|}}{R-C-R} \; H-\overset{\overset{\displaystyle H}{|}}{\underset{\underset{\displaystyle H}{|}}{Al}}=H & \longrightarrow & \overset{\overset{\displaystyle O^-}{|}}{\underset{\underset{\displaystyle H}{|}}{R-C-R}} + AlH_3
\end{array}
$$

$$
\overset{\overset{\displaystyle O^-}{|}}{\underset{\underset{\displaystyle H}{|}}{R-C-R}} + AlH_3 \longrightarrow \overset{\overset{\displaystyle O-Al\overline{H}_3}{|}}{\underset{\underset{\displaystyle H}{|}}{R-C-R}}
$$

8

All four hydrogens in lithium aluminum hydride are available, and the product **8** reacts further. The exact route by which **8** reacts is not certain, but it is known that with $LiAlH_4$ as the starting material, the first transfer of hydride occurs most rapidly and each succeeding transfer is slower than the previous one. Thus, reducing agents such as **9** and **10**, which are more selective than lithium aluminum hydride, can be prepared by allowing the reaction to go only part way:

$$LiAlH_2(OR)_2 \qquad LiAlH(OR)_3$$

9   **10**

In **9** and **10**, several of the hydrogen atoms have been replaced by alkoxide, and these materials are less reactive and more selective sources of hydride.

This order of reactivity is not observed for borohydrides.

There are interesting stereochemical implications that arise in connection with hydride transfer reactions. In the absence of strong polar (electrostatic) effects, it is assumed that the product resulting from the least crowded transition state is formed most readily and is the major component of the mixture. While more crowded transition states are also formed, the free energies of activation are greater in these cases, and the products resulting from these higher energy processes represent only minor components of the final mixture.

Grignard additions as well as Meerwein-Ponndorf-Verley-Oppenauer reactions are also susceptible to steric control of product formation. Thus, a hydride source with dissimilar R groups

$$
\begin{array}{c}
\qquad \quad >Al \overset{\textstyle R}{\underset{\textstyle O}{\diagdown}} \\[4pt]
H-C \overset{\diagup}{\underset{\textstyle R}{\diagdown}}
\end{array}
$$

transfers hydride to a carbonyl compound with dissimilar R groups,

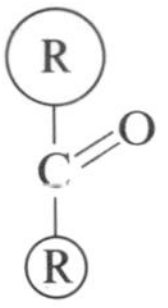

in such a way that the larger groups are *trans*-oriented in the transition state:

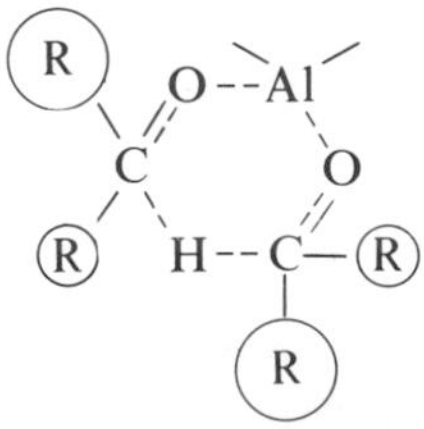

A still more subtle steric influence, which is also involved in determining product geometry, has been expressed as Cram's rule. This rule is also based upon the assumption that addition to the carbonyl group is controlled by steric interactions; that the addition occurs preferably by way of the least crowded transition state. Exceptions can be observed when strong electrostatic interactions due to polar substituents are present. In these cases, the electrostatic interactions can be more important in determining the geometry of the transition state than steric factors.

Neighboring group participation influences product geometry. Accordingly, given a carbonyl system such as,

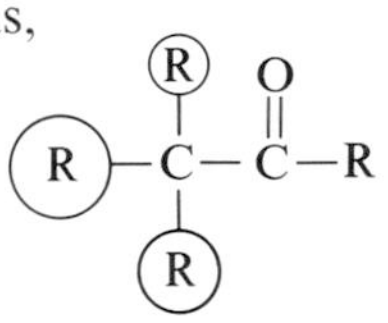

with three dissimilar groups attached to one of the α carbon atoms, we are able to predict the major product when an optically active form of this ketone is used, by assuming a transition state in which the largest group lies *trans* (or nearly *trans*) to the carbonyl oxygen atom, and the entering group Y^- enters from the less hindered side (from the same side as small R):

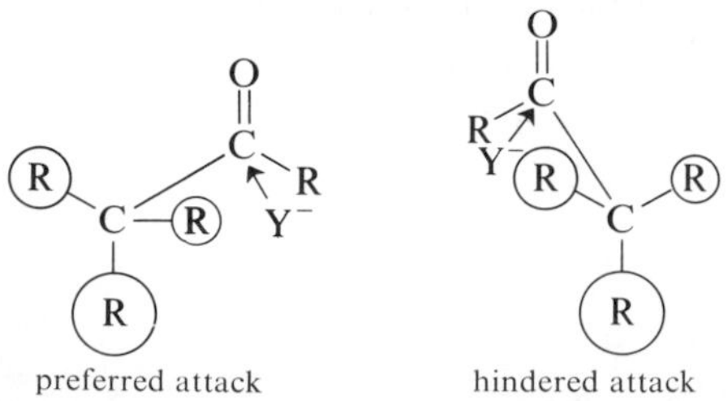

preferred attack   hindered attack

This rule works in many cases, yet exceptions have been reported. Meerwein-Ponndorf-Verley reductions do not behave as predicted. Benzoins such as,

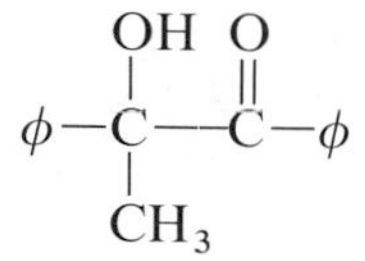

$$\phi-\underset{\underset{CH_3}{|}}{\overset{\overset{OH}{|}}{C}}-\overset{\overset{O}{||}}{C}-\phi$$

definitely show the effects of neighboring group participation but not in the expected manner. Here the acidic hydroxyl hydrogen is first abstracted by Y^- acting as a strong base. For example, methyl lithium behaves in this manner, and the resulting lithium salt forms a complex that influences the product geometry.

With α-chloroaldehydes and α-chloroketones, the geometry of the transition state is not determined by steric factors alone but also by dipole-dipole and nonbonded interactions between halogen and oxygen. Thus for **11**, the transition state of minimum free energy is that in which the oxygen atom is *trans* to the chlorine atom; the entering group Y^- adds preferably from the less hindered side:

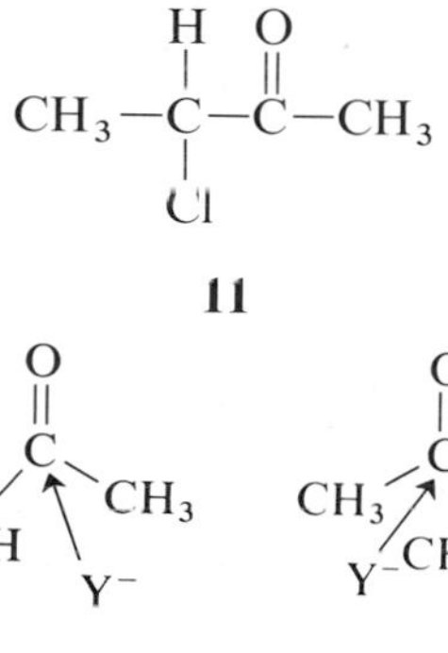

$$CH_3-\underset{\underset{Cl}{|}}{\overset{\overset{H}{|}}{C}}-\overset{\overset{O}{||}}{C}-CH_3$$

11

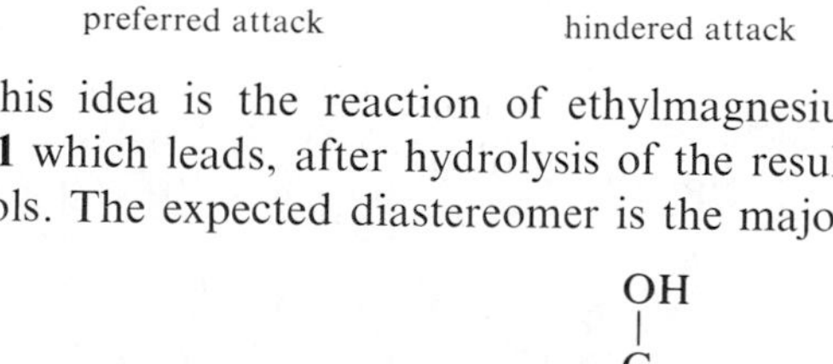

preferred attack   hindered attack

Exemplifying this idea is the reaction of ethylmagnesium bromide with optically active **11** which leads, after hydrolysis of the resulting adduct, to a mixture of alcohols. The expected diastereomer is the major product:

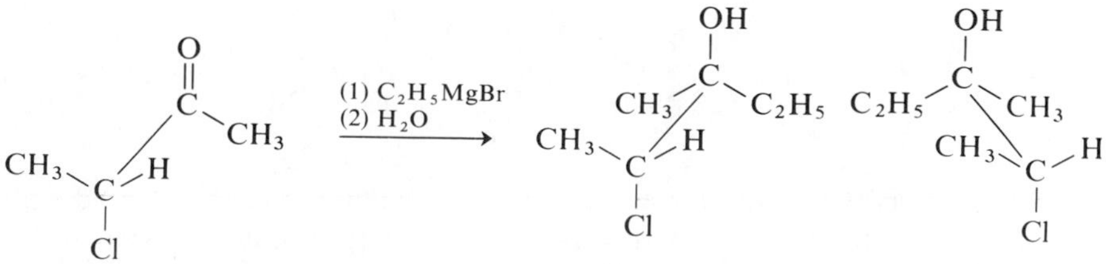

major product   minor product

The more favorable transition state in this reaction is that in which the ethyl group enters from the side occupied by the hydrogen atom. In the less favorable transition state, attack occurs from the side occupied by methyl.

The product geometry can depend entirely upon steric factors, or upon complex formation, or upon dipole-dipole interactions. Furthermore, not only do substituents on adjacent carbon atoms influence attack at the carbonyl system, but substituents several atoms removed may also affect the geometry of the product.

Additions to the carbonyl system are many and varied. Some like the Grignard reagent, which was discovered at the turn of the century, are old; others are comparatively new. Even more recently discovered additions than those just discussed, are known, and one of these more recent reactions, the Wittig reaction, enables us to convert aldehydes and ketones to olefins.

15.9 The Wittig Reaction

The Wittig reaction, reported in 1954, consists of treating a carbonyl compound with a substance such as,

$$\phi_3P{=}C\diagdown{\begin{array}{c}R\\R\end{array}}$$

The products are alkenes,

$$\begin{array}{c}R\\R\end{array}\!\!\diagup\!\!C{=}O + \phi_3P{=}C\diagdown{\begin{array}{c}R\\R\end{array}} \longrightarrow \begin{array}{c}R\\R\end{array}\!\!\diagup\!\!C{=}C\diagdown{\begin{array}{c}R\\R\end{array}} + \phi_3P{=}O$$

The substance $\phi_3P{=}CR_2$ is usually referred to as an ylid because a major valence bond contributor is the charge-separated structure,

$$\phi_3\overset{+}{P}{-}\overset{-}{C}\diagdown{\begin{array}{c}R\\R\end{array}}$$

Valence bond structures with the positive charged delocalized onto the phenyl groups are also important. There are nine structures of this last type:

$$\phi_3P{=}C\diagdown{\begin{array}{c}R\\R\end{array}} \longleftrightarrow \phi_3\overset{+}{P}{-}\overset{-}{C}\diagdown{\begin{array}{c}R\\R\end{array}} \longleftrightarrow \left\langle{+}\!\!\!\bigcirc\!\!\!\right\rangle{=}\overset{\overset{\displaystyle\phi}{|}}{\underset{\underset{\displaystyle\phi}{|}}{P}}{-}\overset{-}{C}\diagdown{\begin{array}{c}R\\R\end{array}} \longleftrightarrow \text{ and so forth}$$

It is usually assumed that the carbon atom in the ylid is sp^2 hybridized and that the second bond between this atom and the phosphorus results from overlap of the remaining $2p$ orbital of carbon with an orbital of phosphorus.

The ylid is generally prepared in two steps. Triphenylphosphine, $\phi_3P:$, is first reacted with an alkyl halide. The phosphine is a good nucleophile and the reaction is an S_N2 process:

$$\phi_3P: + H-\underset{\underset{R}{|}}{\overset{\overset{R}{|}}{C}}-X \longrightarrow \phi_3\overset{+}{P}-\underset{\underset{R}{|}}{\overset{\overset{R}{|}}{C}}-H \ X^-$$

In the presence of a strong base, the resulting phosphonium halide is converted to the ylid, and bases such as phenyllithium, butyllithium, lithium ethoxide, sodium hydride, and sodamide are capable of abstracting the proton:

$$\phi_3\overset{+}{P}-\underset{\underset{R}{|}}{\overset{\overset{R}{|}}{C}}-H \ X^- + Y^- \longrightarrow \phi_3\overset{+}{P}-\overset{-}{C}{\overset{R}{\underset{R}{\diagdown}}} + HY + X^-$$

The presence of the positively charged triphenylphosphonium group aids proton abstraction. If the R groups are able to delocalize negative charges, the process becomes still more favorable.

The ylid formed by this two-step reaction then reacts with carbonyl compounds to form alkenes. The triphenylphosphene oxide $\phi_3P=O$ that results is also stabilized; valence bond contributors are,

$$\phi_3P=O \longleftrightarrow \phi_3\overset{+}{P}-O^- \longleftrightarrow \text{and so forth}$$

Typical reactions of the ylid are,

$$\underset{\phi}{\overset{\phi}{\diagdown}}C=O + \phi_3P=CH_2 \longrightarrow \underset{\phi}{\overset{\phi}{\diagdown}}C=C{\overset{H}{\underset{H}{\diagdown}}} + \phi_3PO$$

$$\text{cyclohexanone} + \phi_3P=CH_2 \longrightarrow \text{methylenecyclohexane} + \phi_3PO$$

$$\phi CHO + \phi_3P=CH-CH=CH\phi \longrightarrow \phi CH=CH-CH=CH\phi + \phi_3PO$$

$$\phi CHO + \phi_3P=CHCOOC_2H_5 \longrightarrow \phi CH=CHCOOC_2H_5 + \phi_3PO$$

$$CH_3CH_2CHO + \phi_3P=CH\phi \longrightarrow CH_3CH_2CH=CH\phi + \phi_3PO$$

The mechanism for this reaction involves attack by the ylid at the carbon atom of a carbonyl system. The intermediate **12**, that results, decomposes to form the products. The decomposition of **12** to products may occur directly, or the reaction may proceed, as appears to be the case in some processes, by way of the four-membered cyclic intermediate:

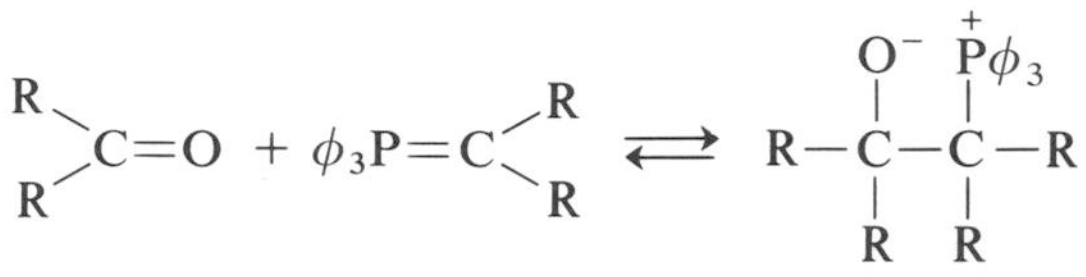

$$
\begin{array}{c}
\underset{R}{\overset{R}{>}}C=O \ + \ \phi_3P=C\underset{R}{\overset{R}{<}} \ \rightleftarrows \ \underset{\substack{| \\ R}}{\overset{O^- \ \overset{+}{P}\phi_3}{R-C-C-R}}
\end{array}
$$
$$
\mathbf{12}
$$

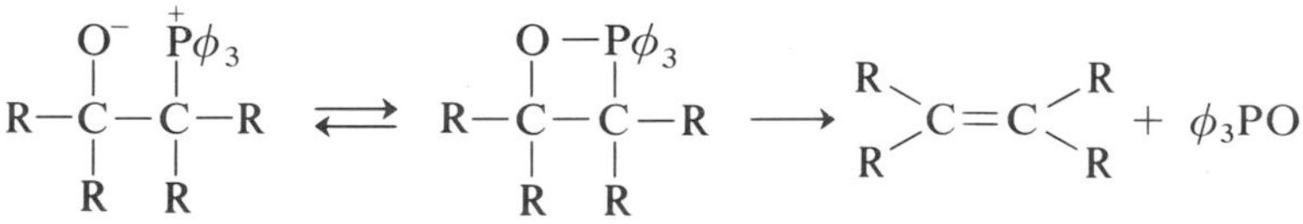

$$
\underset{\substack{| \\ R \quad R}}{\overset{O^- \ \overset{+}{P}\phi_3}{R-C-C-R}} \ \rightleftarrows \ \underset{\substack{| \\ R \quad R}}{\overset{O-P\phi_3}{R-C-C-R}} \ \longrightarrow \ \underset{R}{\overset{R}{>}}C=C\underset{R}{\overset{R}{<}} \ + \ \phi_3PO
$$
$$
\mathbf{12}
$$

The transition state for the decomposition is

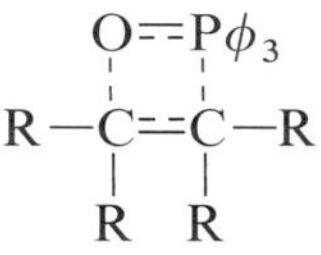

$$
\underset{\substack{| \\ R \quad R}}{\overset{O=P\phi_3}{R-C=C-R}}
$$

The first step, attack of the carbonyl system, is facilitated by electron withdrawing substituents in the carbonyl compound. Formation of **12** is frequently reversible, and the decomposition step is then rate limiting.

Ylids are reactive materials, and their preparation and reactions are generally conducted in inert solvents under an atmosphere of nitrogen. It has been shown that environmental conditions are important not only for the reaction to proceed, but that these conditions also affect the geometry of the products. The preparation of 1-phenyl-1-butene gives a mixture of *cis*- and *trans*-products, and the predominant isomer varies. Under the usual reaction conditions the *trans*-product is the major product:

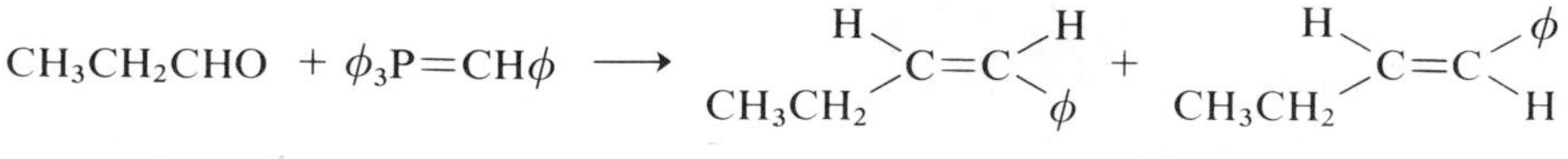

$$
CH_3CH_2CHO \ + \ \phi_3P=CH\phi \ \longrightarrow \ \underset{CH_3CH_2}{\overset{H}{>}}C=C\underset{\phi}{\overset{H}{<}} \ + \ \underset{CH_3CH_2}{\overset{H}{>}}C=C\underset{H}{\overset{\phi}{<}}
$$

Since the decomposition of the four-membered cyclic intermediate to the alkene is a *cis*-elimination, the geometry of a product is determined by the geometry of the intermediate from which it is formed. Thus *trans*-1-phenyl-1-butene must originate from **13** and *cis*-1-phenyl-1-butene from **14**:

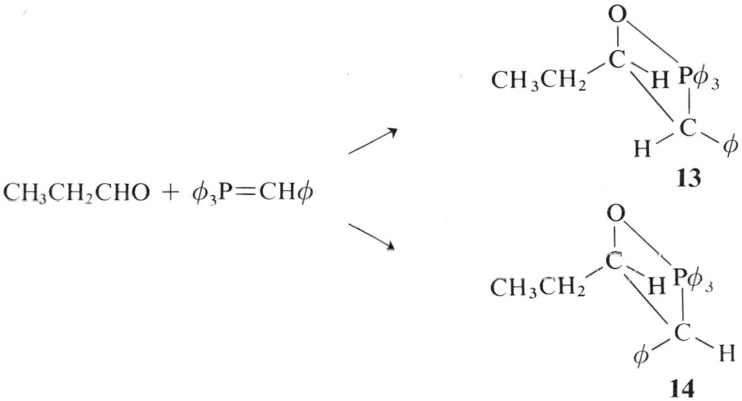

The *trans*-alkene stems from **13** and the *cis*-isomer from **14**:

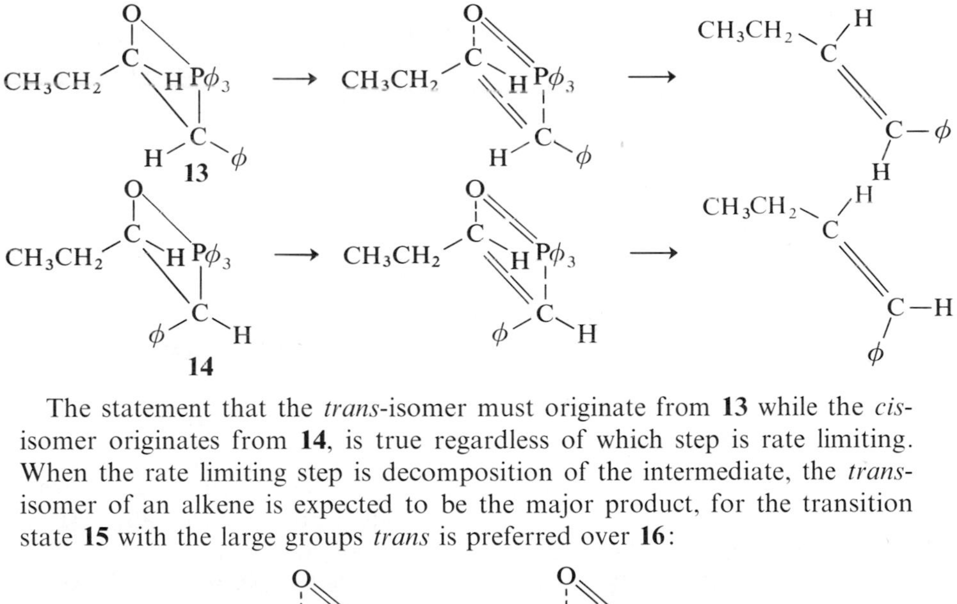

The statement that the *trans*-isomer must originate from **13** while the *cis*-isomer originates from **14**, is true regardless of which step is rate limiting. When the rate limiting step is decomposition of the intermediate, the *trans*-isomer of an alkene is expected to be the major product, for the transition state **15** with the large groups *trans* is preferred over **16**:

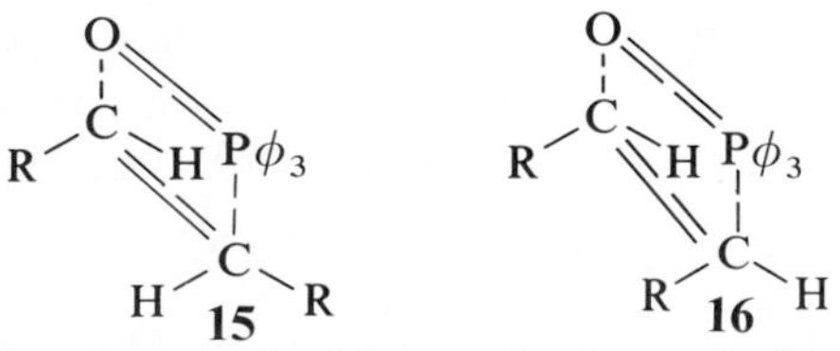

The Wittig reaction is a valuable synthetic tool. Since its discovery, a number of important applications have followed. For example, stereospecific preparations of certain natural products employ the ylid reagent. The reaction is new, the reductions with metal hydrides are not much older, and many new uses of these materials will certainly be forthcoming.

All addition reactions are important. Addition of nitrogenous bases gives rise to products that serve as carbonyl derivatives. These aid in characterizing the original compound. The bisulfite adduct serves not only as a derivative, it can be used for purification of a carbonyl compound. The addition of hydrogen cyanide has been employed in the carbohydrate series, where the reaction is used to increase by one the length of the carbon chain. This process, known as the Kiliani synthesis, was instrumental in determining the relative spacial geometries of the carbohydrates, at one time a very important problem:

$$
\underset{\substack{|| \\ \mathrm{O}}}{\mathrm{R}-\mathrm{C}-\mathrm{H}} + \mathrm{HCN} \longrightarrow \underset{\substack{| \\ \mathrm{H}}}{\overset{\mathrm{OH}}{\underset{|}{\mathrm{R}-\mathrm{C}-\mathrm{CN}}}} \longrightarrow \underset{\substack{| \\ \mathrm{H}}}{\overset{\mathrm{OH}}{\underset{|}{\mathrm{R}-\mathrm{C}-\mathrm{CHO}}}}
$$

Two diastereomeric cyanohydrins result. These are separated, and the cyano groups subsequently converted to aldehydes. Thus, two new sugars are produced.

Because R in the sugar series is asymmetric, the cyanide ion does not add equally readily to both sides of the aldehydic system. Consequently, the two cyanohydrins are not present to the same extent:

$$
\underset{\mathrm{R}}{\overset{\mathrm{O}}{\underset{\mathrm{H}}{\parallel}}}\mathrm{C} + \mathrm{HCN} \xrightarrow{\mathrm{CN}^-} \underset{\mathrm{R}}{\overset{\mathrm{OH}}{\underset{\mathrm{H}}{\mathrm{C}}}}\mathrm{CN} \quad \mathrm{NC}\underset{\mathrm{R}}{\overset{\mathrm{OH}}{\underset{\mathrm{H}}{\mathrm{C}}}}
$$

15.10 Additions to α, β-Unsaturated Systems

Of course, all of the additions that we have just discussed can be equally well employed with the more complex α,β-unsaturated carbonyl compounds. Here products resulting from both 1,2- and 1,4-addition are formed.

The α,β-unsaturated system is in equilibrium with the β,γ-unsaturated system. Therefore, additions to what is apparently the former may occasionally result in γ-substituted products. The isomerization is catalyzed by strong bases:

$$
\underset{\mathrm{CH_3CH_2}}{\overset{\mathrm{CH_3CH_2}}{>}}\mathrm{C}{=}\mathrm{C}\underset{\mathrm{H}}{\overset{\mathrm{CCH_3}}{<}} \underset{\mathrm{C_2H_5OH}}{\overset{\mathrm{C_2H_5O^-}}{\rightleftharpoons}} \underset{\mathrm{H}}{\overset{\mathrm{CH_3}}{>}}\mathrm{C}{=}\mathrm{C}\underset{\mathrm{CH_2CH_3}}{\overset{\mathrm{CH_2CCH_3}}{<}}
$$

The introduction of γ-substituents favors the β,γ-isomers. Thus at equilibrium **17** exists entirely as an α,β-unsaturated substance while **18** forms an isomeric mixture:

$$CH_3 \\ CH_3 \\ \diagdown C=C \diagup \ COO^- \atop H \qquad 17 \qquad\qquad CH_3CH_2 \\ CH_3CH_2 \diagdown C=C \diagup \ COO^- \atop H \qquad 18$$

where

$$CH_3CH_2 \\ CH_3CH_2 \diagdown C=C \diagup COO^- \atop H \qquad \underset{21\%}{} \quad \overset{OH^-}{\underset{H_2O}{\rightleftharpoons}} \quad CH_3 \\ H \diagdown C=C \diagup CH_2COO^- \atop CH_2CH_3 \qquad \underset{79\%}{}$$

Such equilibria can influence product formation, and their occurrence should always be considered in the reactions of α,β-unsaturated systems.

The α,β-unsaturated carbonyl compounds react with the same reagents as the simpler carbonyl compounds, yet here both 1,2- and 1,4-adducts are possible. The 1,4-products are enols that rearrange under the usual reaction conditions to the keto form (when these are more stable). Thus an α,β-unsaturated system can react with a reagent HX to form the enol **19** and a 1,2-adduct **20**. The 1,2-adduct may be formed reversibly, and the enol **19** is in equilibrium with the keto form **21**:

$$R \\ R \diagdown C=CH-\overset{O}{\underset{\|}{C}}-R \ + \ HX \ \underset{}{\rightleftharpoons} \ R \\ R \diagdown C=CH-\overset{OH}{\underset{\underset{X}{|}}{\underset{|}{C}}}-R \quad \mathbf{20}$$

$$R-\overset{R}{\underset{\underset{X}{|}}{\underset{|}{C}}}-CH=\overset{OH}{\underset{|}{C}}-R \ \rightleftharpoons \ R-\overset{R}{\underset{\underset{X}{|}}{\underset{|}{C}}}-CH_2-\overset{O}{\underset{\|}{C}}-R$$
$$\mathbf{19} \qquad\qquad\qquad \mathbf{21}$$

The weak nucleophiles such as water and alcohols as well as the hydrogen halides behave in the manner illustrated. They add to the unsaturated carbonyl system to form products resulting from 1,4-addition, that is, the only isolable products are those in which the entering nucleophile is attached to the β-carbon atom. The 1,2-adducts, which can also be formed, revert in these cases to the reactants. For example,

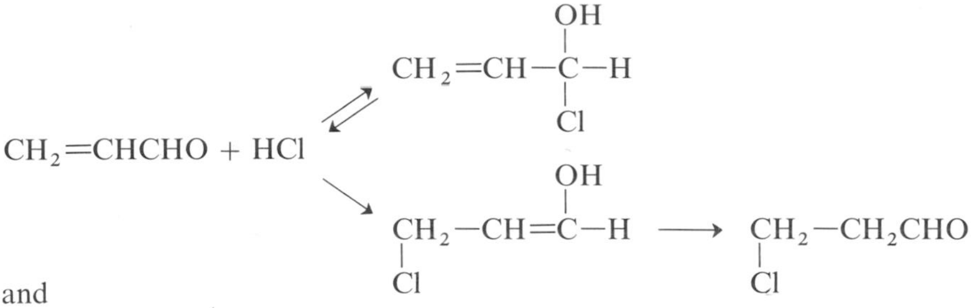

$$CH_2{=}CHCHO + HCl
\begin{cases}
\nearrow & \underset{\underset{Cl}{|}}{CH_2{=}CH{-}\underset{\underset{|}{OH}}{C}{-}H} \\
\searrow & \underset{\underset{Cl}{|}}{CH_2{-}CH{=}\underset{\underset{|}{OH}}{C}{-}H} \longrightarrow \underset{\underset{Cl}{|}}{CH_2{-}CH_2CHO}
\end{cases}$$

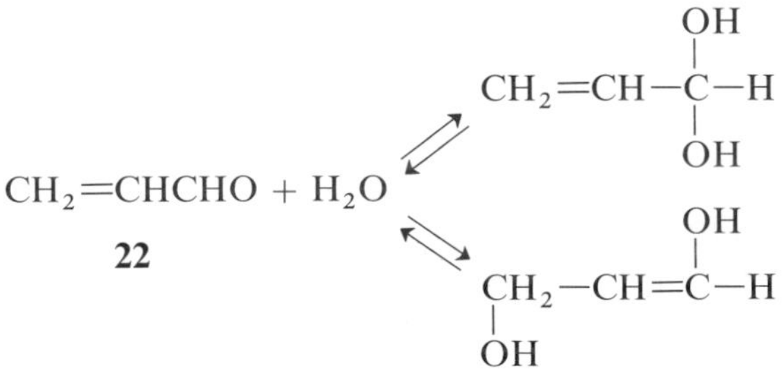

and

$$\underset{\textbf{22}}{CH_2{=}CHCHO} + H_2O
\begin{cases}
\nearrow & \underset{\underset{OH}{|}}{CH_2{=}CH{-}\underset{\underset{|}{OH}}{C}{-}H} \\
\searrow & \underset{\underset{OH}{|}}{CH_2{-}CH{=}\underset{\underset{|}{OH}}{C}{-}H}
\end{cases}$$

$$\underset{\underset{OH}{|}}{CH_2{-}CH{=}\overset{\overset{OH}{|}}{C}{-}H} \rightleftarrows \underset{\underset{OH}{|}}{CH_2CH_2\overset{\overset{O}{\|}}{CH}} \overset{H_2O}{\rightleftarrows} \underset{\underset{OH}{|}}{CH_2CH_2{-}\overset{\overset{OH}{|}}{C}\underset{\underset{OH}{|}}{{-}H}}$$

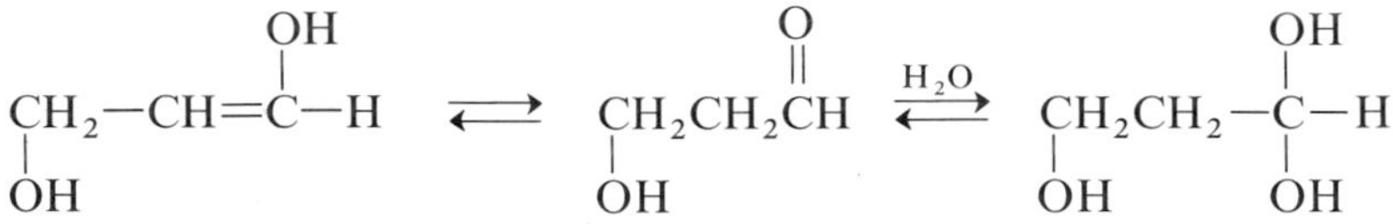

23

The reaction of acrolein **22** with water yields the product **23**. The process is catalyzed by acids and is readily reversible. Both the kinetic and equilibrium processes have been investigated. The reactions were studied in aqueous solution, and under these conditions it was found that the rate of formation of the hydroxy aldehyde **23** from acrolein was proportional to the concentration of acrolein itself and hydronium ion. The reverse reaction is first order in **23** and hydronium ion. The general rate expression for the forward reaction takes the form,

$$k[CH_2{=}CHCHO][H_3O^+]$$

while that for the reverse process is,

$$k'[CH_2OHCH_2CHO][H_3O^+]$$

We postulate the following mechanism for the forward reaction,

$$CH_2{=}CH{-}CHO + H_3O^+ \rightleftarrows CH_2{=}CH{-}\overset{\overset{+O-H}{\|}}{C}{-}H$$

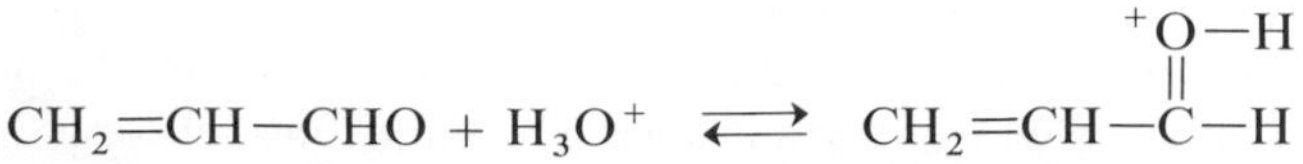

where the positive charge in the conjugate acid is delocalized,

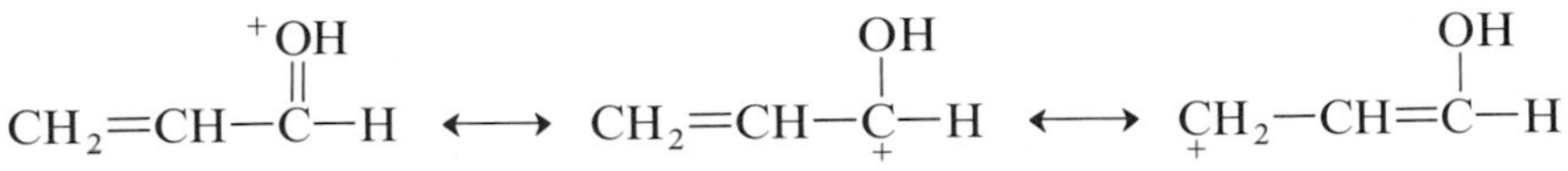

$$CH_2=CH-\overset{\overset{+}{O}H}{\underset{||}{C}}-H \longleftrightarrow CH_2=CH-\overset{OH}{\underset{|}{\underset{+}{C}}}-H \longleftrightarrow \overset{}{\underset{+}{CH_2}}-CH=\overset{OH}{\underset{|}{C}}-H$$

and this species adds water to form the enol,

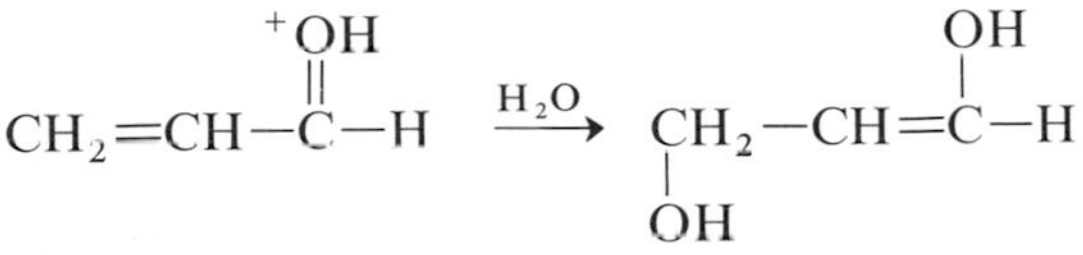

$$CH_2=CH-\overset{\overset{+}{O}H}{\underset{||}{C}}-H \xrightarrow{H_2O} CH_2-CH=\overset{OH}{\underset{|}{\underset{OH}{C}}}-H$$

This step is rate limiting, and the enolic product then rearranges to the more stable aldehydic material:

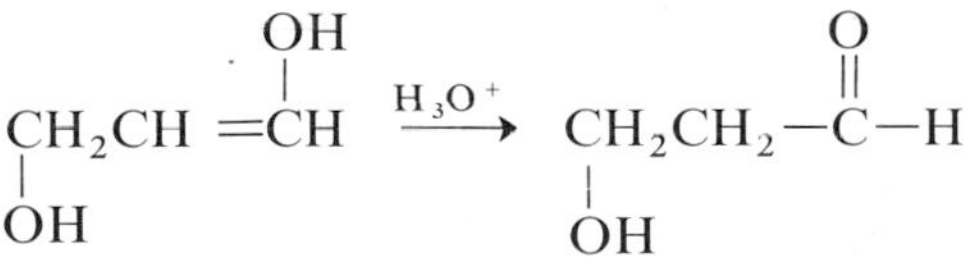

$$\overset{}{\underset{OH}{CH_2CH}}=\overset{OH}{\underset{|}{CH}} \xrightarrow{H_3O^+} \overset{}{\underset{OH}{CH_2CH_2}}-\overset{O}{\underset{||}{C}}-H$$

The reverse reaction involves the conversion of the hydroxy aldehyde back to acrolein:

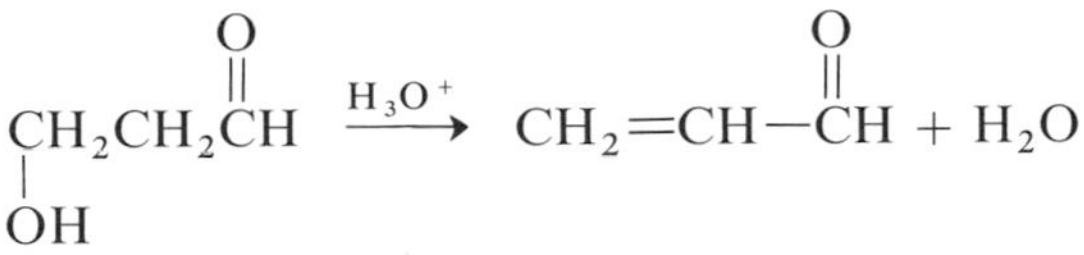

$$\overset{}{\underset{OH}{CH_2CH_2CH}}\overset{O}{\overset{||}{}} \xrightarrow{H_3O^+} CH_2=CH-\overset{O}{\underset{||}{CH}} + H_2O$$

The mechanism for the dehydration must be just the reverse of that for the forward process (principle of microscopic reversibility). Consequently, the acid catalyzed dehydration must proceed by way of the enol,

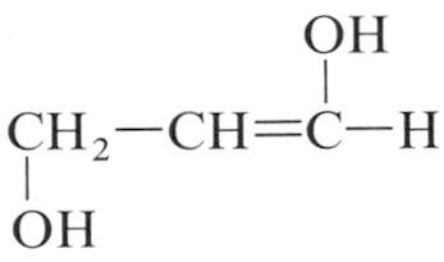

$$\overset{}{\underset{OH}{CH_2}}-CH=\overset{OH}{\underset{|}{C}}-H$$

which reacts with acid, loses water, and ultimately forms the conjugate acid of acrolein. Deprotonation of the resulting conjugate acid by the solvent yields acrolein.

The addition of a weak nucleophile can be acid or base catalyzed and proceeds by way of the enol. The products are those in which the entering nucleophile has become attached to the β-carbon atom. Although strong nucleophiles add directly to an α,β-unsaturated system, here again, the products generally result from attack at the β-position. Ammonia, cyanide ion, and methoxide ion are examples,

$$\begin{array}{c} CH_3 \\ \diagdown \\ \diagup \\ CH_3 \end{array} C{=}CHCOCH_3 \;+\; NH_3 \;\longrightarrow\; CH_3{-}\underset{\underset{NH_2}{|}}{\overset{\overset{CH_3}{|}}{C}}{-}CH_2COCH_3$$

$$\begin{array}{c} H \\ \diagdown \\ \diagup \\ \phi \end{array} C{=}C \begin{array}{c} CO\phi \\ \diagup \\ \diagdown \\ H \end{array} \;+\; CN^- \;\xrightarrow{H_2O}\; \phi{-}\underset{\underset{CN}{|}}{\overset{\overset{H}{|}}{C}}{-}CH_2CO\phi$$

$$\begin{array}{c} H \\ \diagdown \\ \diagup \\ \phi \end{array} C{=}C \begin{array}{c} COOCH_3 \\ \diagup \\ \diagdown \\ COOCH_3 \end{array} \;+\; \bar{O}CH_3 \;\xrightarrow{CH_3OH}\; \phi{-}\underset{\underset{OCH_3}{|}}{\overset{\overset{H}{|}}{C}}{-}CH \begin{array}{c} COOCH_3 \\ \diagup \\ \diagdown \\ COOCH_3 \end{array}$$

These additions undoubtedly proceed by direct nucleophilic attack to form the relatively stable anion **24** in which the negative charge is delocalized:

$$\begin{array}{c} H \\ \diagdown \\ \diagup \\ \phi \end{array} C{=}C \begin{array}{c} CO\phi \\ \diagup \\ \diagdown \\ H \end{array} \;+\; CN^- \;\longrightarrow\; \phi{-}\underset{\underset{CN}{|}}{\overset{\overset{H}{|}}{C}}{-}\overset{\delta-}{C}H{=}\overset{\overset{O^{\delta-}}{\|}}{C}{-}\phi \quad \textbf{24}$$

In terms of valence bond structures this enolate anion is represented as,

$$\phi{-}\underset{\underset{CN}{|}}{\overset{\overset{H}{|}}{C}}{-}CH{=}\overset{\overset{O^-}{|}}{C}{-}\phi \;\longleftrightarrow\; \phi{-}\underset{\underset{CN}{|}}{\overset{\overset{H}{|}}{C}}{-}\bar{C}H{-}\overset{\overset{O}{\|}}{C}{-}\phi$$

The anion then abstracts a proton from the solvent to form the product. There are two positions at which the proton may enter, and both reactions occur:

$$\phi{-}\underset{\underset{CN}{|}}{\overset{\overset{H}{|}}{C}}{-}\overset{\delta-}{C}{=}\overset{\overset{O^{\delta-}}{\|}}{C}{-}\phi \;+\; H_2O$$

$$\phi{-}\underset{\underset{CN}{|}}{\overset{\overset{H}{|}}{C}}{-}\underset{\underset{H}{|}}{C}{=}\overset{\overset{OH}{|}}{C}{-}\phi \;+\; OH^-$$

$$\phi{-}\underset{\underset{CN}{|}}{\overset{\overset{H}{|}}{C}}{-}CH_2{-}\overset{\overset{O}{\|}}{C}{-}\phi \;+\; OH^-$$

Under the usual reaction conditions, the final products in reactions of this type are the ketonic tautomers, for these are generally the more stable materials. However, while these are the thermodynamic products, they are not the kinetic products, and careful work up of the reaction mixture can lead to the isolation of enolic materials. Furthermore, in certain special cases the enol is the more stable tautomer.

Reaction of **25** with phenylmagnesium bromide and hydrolysis of the adduct gives rise to an isolable enol **26**, which is only slowly converted to the ketone,

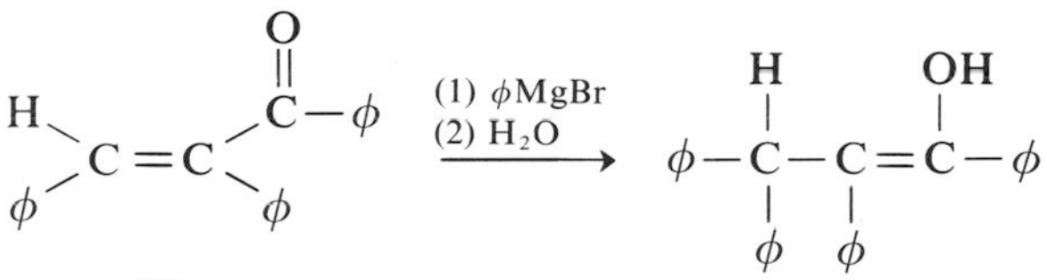

Grignard additions to α,β-unsaturated ketonic systems may give rise to a mixture of 1,2- and 1,4-adducts, and steric factors are influential in determining the major product:

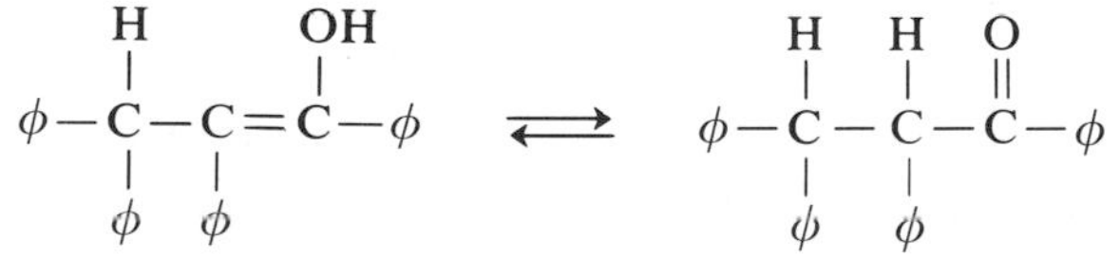

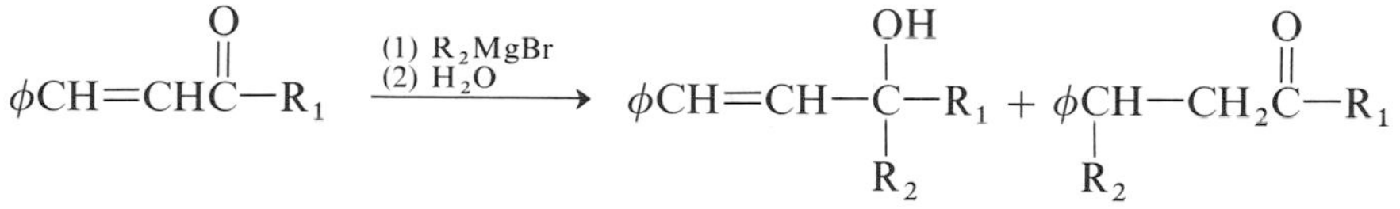

R_1	R_2		
CH_3-	C_2H_5-	40%	60%
CH_3-	$\phi-$	88%	12%
$(CH_3)_2CH-$	C_2H_5-	0%	100%
$(CH_3)_2CH-$	$\phi-$	12%	88%

Most additions give rise to products resulting from attack by the entering nucleophile at the terminal position of the α,β-unsaturated system. Grignards appear to be exceptions, for with these reagents, large amounts of 1,2-products are obtained. This result is probably due to prior complexing of the magnesium portion of the Grignard reagent with the oxygen atom of the carbonyl system, and in confirmation of this idea, the addition of Lewis acids to a Grignard reaction mixture favors 1,4-addition.

Under the proper conditions, some nucleophilic additions are reversible, and once again bearing in mind the principle of microscopic reversibility, these eliminations must proceed by the *E1cB* mechanism:

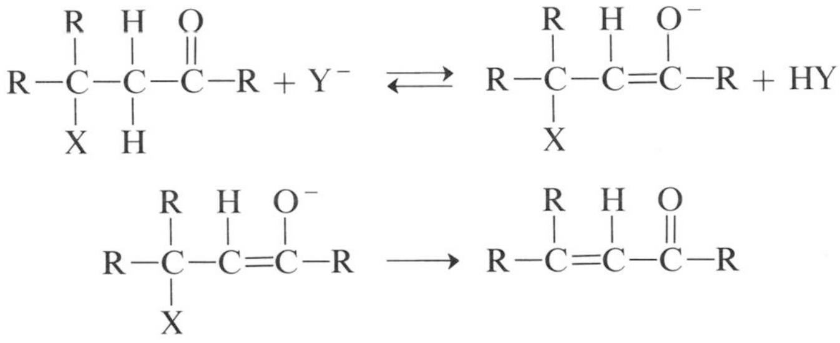

$$
\begin{array}{c}
\text{R} \quad \text{H} \quad \text{O} \\
| \quad\quad | \quad\quad \| \\
\text{R}-\overset{|}{\underset{|}{\text{C}}}-\overset{|}{\underset{|}{\text{C}}}-\overset{}{\text{C}}-\text{R} + \text{Y}^- \\
\text{X} \quad \text{H}
\end{array}
\;\rightleftharpoons\;
\begin{array}{c}
\text{R} \quad \text{H} \quad \text{O}^- \\
| \quad\quad | \quad\quad | \\
\text{R}-\overset{|}{\underset{|}{\text{C}}}-\text{C}=\text{C}-\text{R} + \text{HY} \\
\text{X}
\end{array}
$$

$$
\begin{array}{c}
\text{R} \quad \text{H} \quad \text{O}^- \\
| \quad\quad | \quad\quad | \\
\text{R}-\overset{|}{\underset{|}{\text{C}}}-\text{C}=\text{C}-\text{R} \\
\text{X}
\end{array}
\;\longrightarrow\;
\begin{array}{c}
\text{R} \quad \text{H} \quad \text{O} \\
| \quad\quad | \quad\quad \| \\
\text{R}-\text{C}=\text{C}-\text{C}-\text{R}
\end{array}
$$

Supplementary Reading

1. Gaylord, N. G., *Reduction with Complex Metal Hydrides.* New York, Wiley, 1956.

2. Gould, E. S., *Mechanism and Structure in Organic Chemistry.* New York, Holt, 1959.

3. Hine, J., *Physical Organic Chemistry.* New York, McGraw-Hill, 1962.

4. House, H. O., *Modern Synthetic Reactions.* New York, Benjamin, 1965.

5. Jencks, W. P., *Progress in Physical Organic Chemistry*, Vol. 2, (eds.) S. G. Cohen, A. Streitwieser, Jr., R. W. Taft. New York, Interscience, 1964.

Chapter 16

Condensations at the Carbonyl Group

16.1 Keto-Enol Tautomerism

It is only proper to begin a discussion of condensations involving the carbonyl group with some data on keto-enol tautomerism since the first step in many condensations is formation of the enol or enolate anion:

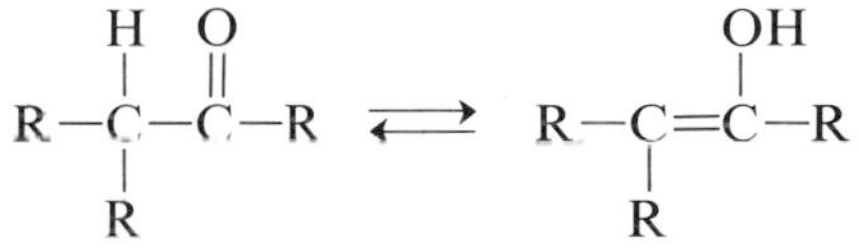

$$\underset{R}{\overset{H\ \ O}{R-C-C-R}} \rightleftharpoons \underset{R}{\overset{OH}{R-C=C-R}}$$

These two species, the ketone and the enol, are in equilibrium, and on the basis of bond energies alone, the keto form is calculated to be more stable by about 15–18 kcal/mole. Thus for most systems the equilibrium lies well to the side of the carbonyl compound. However, such calculations do not include steric effects, resonance effects, or solvent effects, all of which tend to change the value of the equilibrium constant and in some cases cause the enolic form to become the more stable.

The percentage of enolic tautomer present in pure liquid acetone is extremely small. Cyclohexanone exists to a greater extent as an enol. For some compounds the enolic form is the more stable, and a few materials exist entirely (at least as far as the measurements indicate) in the enolic form:

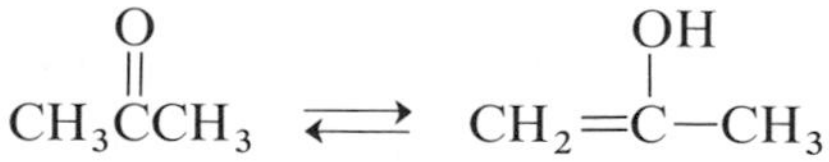

$$\underset{}{\overset{O}{CH_3CCH_3}} \rightleftharpoons \underset{0.00025\,\%}{\overset{OH}{CH_2=C-CH_3}}$$

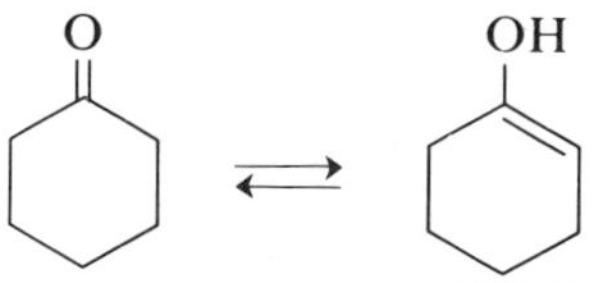

$$\rightleftharpoons \qquad \underset{0.020\,\%}{}$$

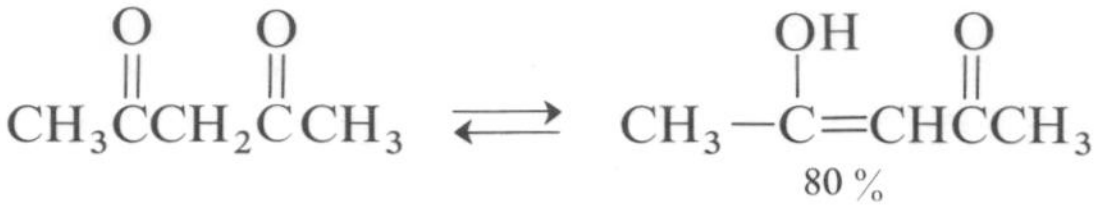

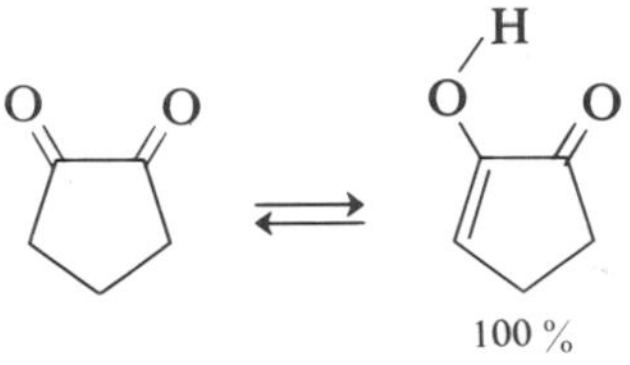

$$CH_3\overset{O}{\overset{\|}{C}}CH_2\overset{O}{\overset{\|}{C}}CH_3 \rightleftharpoons CH_3-\overset{OH}{\overset{|}{C}}=CH\overset{O}{\overset{\|}{C}}CH_3$$

80 %

100 %

The high degree of enolization of acetylacetone $CH_3COCH_2COCH_3$ can be attributed to increased resonance stabilization and hydrogen bonding in the enolic material,

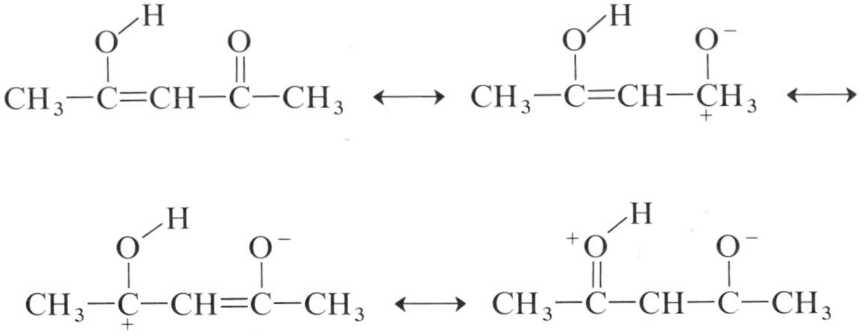

$$CH_3-\overset{O^{H}}{\overset{|}{C}}=CH-\overset{O}{\overset{\|}{C}}-CH_3 \longleftrightarrow CH_3-\overset{O^{H}}{\overset{|}{C}}=CH-\overset{O^-}{\overset{|}{\underset{+}{C}H_3}} \longleftrightarrow$$

$$CH_3-\overset{O^{H}}{\underset{+}{\overset{|}{C}}}-CH=\overset{O^-}{\overset{|}{C}}-CH_3 \longleftrightarrow CH_3-\overset{{}^+O^{H}}{\overset{\|}{C}}-CH-\overset{O^-}{\overset{|}{C}}-CH_3$$

and

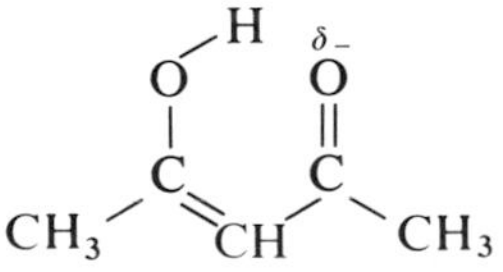

Of course, while many β-diketones exist to a large degree in the enolic form, a high degree of enolization is not expected for the following bicyclo compound (remember Bredt's rule):

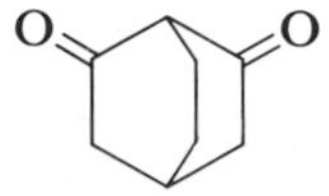

The α-diketone, 1,2-cyclopentanedione, is enolic because of resonance stabilization and hydrogen bonding in the enol and largely because of dipole-dipole and nonbonded interactions in the diketone which destabilize this material:

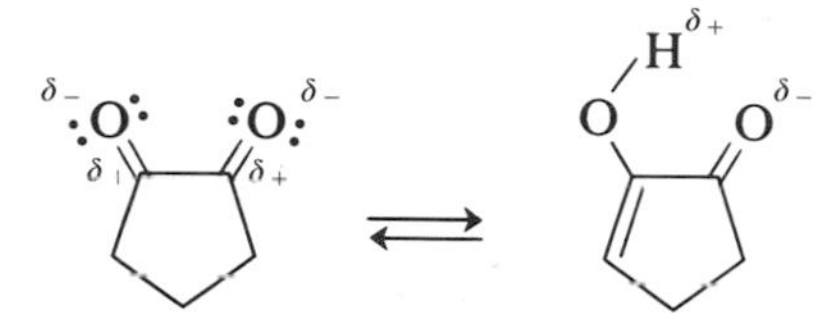

Such interactions are less pronounced in noncyclic α diketones, for these materials can exist with the carbonyl groups *trans*-oriented. As a result, the percentage of enolic tautomer decreases, for example:

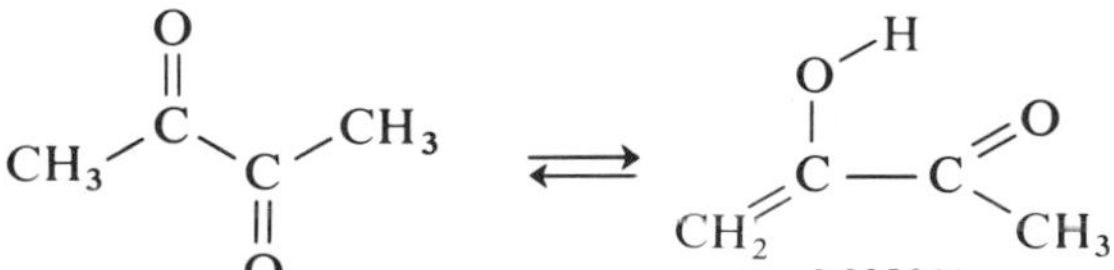

For most simple ketones (for example, 2-butanone and 3-hexanone), where more than a single enol is possible, both are present. Thus, while the exact position of the equilibrium mixture is not known, we expect for compounds such as 2-butanone and 3-hexanone that both enols are present (though not necessarily in equal amounts):

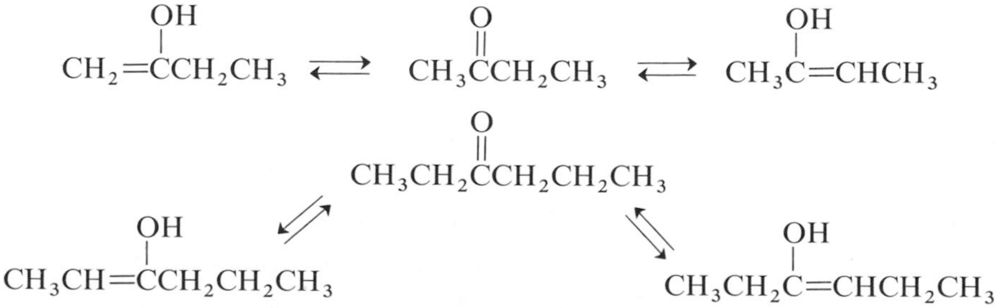

The polarity of the solvent exerts a tremendous influence upon the extent of enolization, and as the data in Table 16–1 for acetylacetone illustrate, the enol is present to a greater degree in less polar solvents.

Table 16–1

$$CH_3\overset{O}{\overset{||}{C}}CH_2\overset{O}{\overset{||}{C}}CH_3 \rightleftharpoons CH_3\overset{OH}{\overset{|}{C}}=CH\overset{O}{\overset{||}{C}}CH_3$$

Solvent	Per cent enol
Water	15
Acetonitrile	58
Pure liquid	80
Hexane	92
Pure gas	92

In fact, such data led to an early type of linear free energy relationship which was developed in terms of the equilibrium constant for keto-enol tautomerism:

$$\Delta G° = -RT \ln K = -RT \ln \frac{[\text{enol}]}{[\text{ketone}]}$$

Here one should make a distinction between solvents that are capable of hydrogen bonding and solvents that cannot behave in this way. It is assumed that the difference in the free energy of some keto-enol pair is a fixed value, dependent on the keto-enol pair but independent of the solvent. The only contribution made by the solvent to the free energy of reaction (as measured by the equilibrium constant) is due to solvation. The solvent does not react chemically. Furthermore, the contribution made by a given solvent is the same for all keto-enol equilibria. Of course, factors such as the temperature must be kept constant.

These ideas lead to the conclusion that the total free energy of reaction for the keto-enol equilibrium in solution can be assumed to be equal to the free energy of reaction in the gas phase (or in a reference solvent) and a solvation term. Thus, for a given solvent 1,

$$\Delta G_1° = [G°(\text{enol}) - G°(\text{ketone})]_1 +$$

$$[G(\text{solvation of enol}) - G(\text{solvation of ketone})]_1$$

Where the first term is always the same for a given keto-enol pair, and the second term is always the same for a given solvent.

Then for solvent 2,

$$\Delta G_2° = [G°(\text{enol}) - G°(\text{ketone})]_2 +$$

$$[G(\text{solvation of enol}) - G(\text{solvation of ketone})]_2$$

For a given keto-enol equilibrium, the only effect of a change in solvent upon the free energy of reaction is due to the second term:

$$\Delta G_2° - \Delta G_1° = [G(\text{solvation of enol}) - G(\text{solvation of ketone})]_2$$

$$- [G(\text{solvation of enol}) - G(\text{solvation of ketone})]_1$$

For,

$$[G°(\text{enol}) - G°(\text{ketone})]_2 = [G°(\text{enol}) - G°(\text{ketone})]_1$$

Therefore,

$$\Delta G_2° - \Delta G_1° = \Delta G(\text{solvation of enol}) - \Delta G(\text{solvation of ketone})$$

The original work was not done in terms of free energy changes. Instead, expressions were developed in terms of equilibrium constants. Since the free energy of a reaction is related to the equilibrium constant, these ideas are equivalent.

One is able to measure the position of a keto-enol equilibrium in one solvent, and knowing the solvation terms, predict the equilibrium position in other solvents. These solvation terms can conceivably be employed in connection with other reactions.

The position of the keto-enol equilibrium varies with the solvent and with the nature of the carbonyl compound. The rate of enolization depends upon these factors and also varies with the reaction conditions. Enolization occurs by an uncatalyzed reaction (solvent catalyzed) as well as by acid and base catalyzed processes, and at moderate pH's, all of these processes proceed simultaneously. At high pH's, the enol is formed primarily by the base catalyzed reaction. At low pH's, the acid catalyzed process predominates. The reaction is general acid and base catalyzed, and we assume an aqueous solution.

The enolate anion that is the intermediate in base catalyzed isomerizations can be represented by the structures,

$$\overset{\overset{\displaystyle -O}{|}}{R-C}\overset{\overset{\displaystyle R}{|}}{=C}-R \quad \longleftrightarrow \quad \overset{\overset{\displaystyle O}{\|}}{R-C}-\overset{\overset{\displaystyle R}{|}}{\underset{\displaystyle \cdot\cdot}{C}}{=}R$$

or simply as,

$$\overset{\overset{\displaystyle O^{\delta -}}{|}}{R-C}\overset{\overset{\displaystyle R}{|}}{=\!=\underset{\delta-}{C}}-R$$

In the following mechanism Y^- represents any general added base, and the base catalyzed process is,

$$\overset{\overset{\displaystyle O}{\|}}{R-C}-\overset{\overset{\displaystyle R}{|}}{\underset{\underset{\displaystyle H}{|}}{C}}-R + Y^- \quad \longrightarrow \quad \overset{\overset{\displaystyle -O}{|}}{R-C}\overset{\overset{\displaystyle R}{|}}{=C}-R + HY$$

$$\overset{\overset{\displaystyle -O}{|}}{R-C}\overset{\overset{\displaystyle R}{|}}{=C}-R + H_2O \quad \rightleftarrows \quad \overset{\overset{\displaystyle HO}{|}}{R-C}\overset{\overset{\displaystyle R}{|}}{=C}-R + OH^-$$

and

$$HY + OH^- \rightleftharpoons H_2O + Y^-$$

Naturally, hydroxide ion also abstracts protons.

The first step is rate limiting, and if more than a single proton is available for abstraction, either can be removed by the base. However, the rate of formation of the two enols, for example from 2-butanone and 3-hexanone, is not the same:

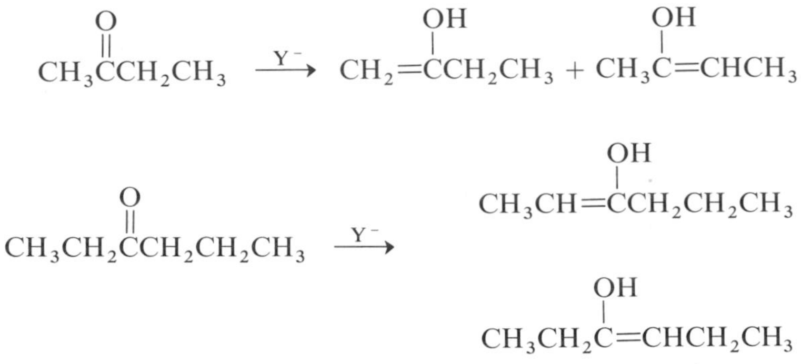

$$\underset{\text{O}}{\overset{\text{O}}{\underset{\|}{CH_3CCH_2CH_3}}} \xrightarrow{Y^-} \underset{\text{OH}}{\overset{\text{OH}}{CH_2=CCH_2CH_3}} + \underset{\text{OH}}{\overset{\text{OH}}{CH_3C=CHCH_3}}$$

$$\underset{\text{O}}{\overset{\text{O}}{\underset{\|}{CH_3CH_2CCH_2CH_2CH_3}}} \xrightarrow{Y^-} \begin{array}{c} \overset{\text{OH}}{CH_3CH=CCH_2CH_2CH_3} \\[2ex] \overset{\text{OH}}{CH_3CH_2C=CHCH_2CH_3} \end{array}$$

The acid catalyzed enolization is subject to general acid catalysis, and the intermediate is the conjugate acid of the carbonyl compound. Here HX is the general acid, and since proton transfer is not the rate limiting step, the nature of the proton source is immaterial. However, general acid catalysis requires that a molecule of HX be involved in the rate limiting step, in this case as H^+X^-:

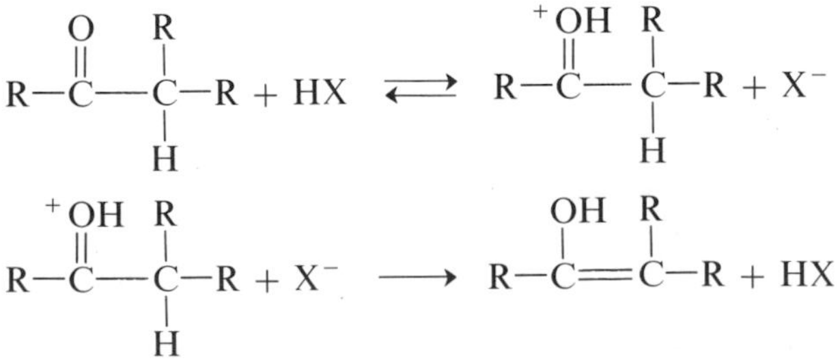

$$\underset{\text{H}}{\overset{\overset{\text{O}}{\|}\,\overset{\text{R}}{|}}{R-C-C-R}} + HX \rightleftharpoons \underset{\text{H}}{\overset{\overset{+\text{OH}}{\|}\,\overset{\text{R}}{|}}{R-C-C-R}} + X^-$$

$$\underset{\text{H}}{\overset{\overset{+\text{OH}}{\|}\,\overset{\text{R}}{|}}{R-C-C-R}} + X^- \longrightarrow \underset{}{\overset{\overset{\text{OH}}{|}\,\overset{\text{R}}{|}}{R-C=C-R}} + HX$$

In this reaction any acid present in solution (H_3O^+ or HX) can deliver the proton, and any base (H_2O, X^-) can abstract a proton in the second step.

A minor degree of enolization can also occur by a second mechanism in which proton transfer is the rate limiting step. The first step is a hydrogen bonding between the carbonyl compound and the general acid HX:

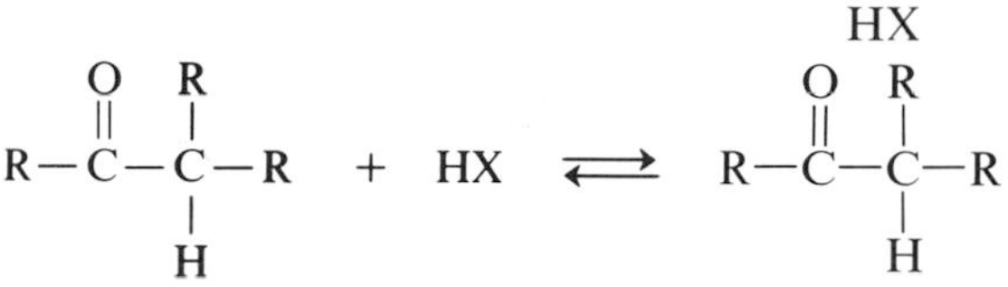

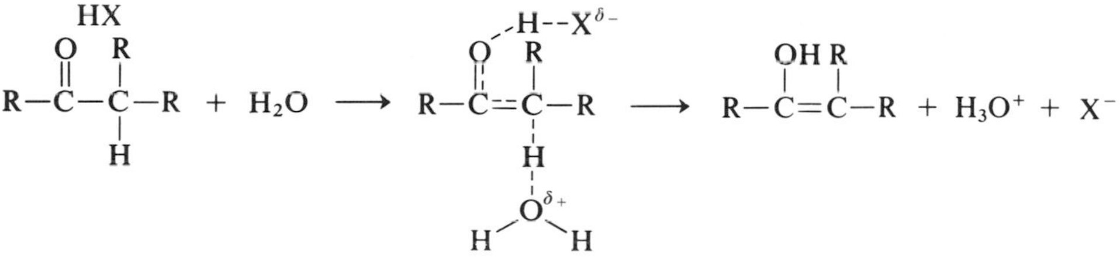

$$\underset{H}{\overset{\overset{\displaystyle O}{\|}\,\overset{\displaystyle R}{|}}{R-C-C-R}} \;+\; HX \;\rightleftharpoons\; \underset{H}{\overset{\overset{\displaystyle HX}{}\;\;\overset{\displaystyle O}{\|}\,\overset{\displaystyle R}{|}}{R-C-C-R}}$$

$$\underset{H}{\overset{\overset{\displaystyle HX}{}\;\;\overset{\displaystyle O}{\|}\,\overset{\displaystyle R}{|}}{R-C-C-R}} + H_2O \longrightarrow \; R-\overset{\displaystyle O}{\overset{\|}{C}}=\overset{\displaystyle R}{\underset{\displaystyle H}{\overset{|}{C}}}-R \longrightarrow \; \underset{}{\overset{\overset{\displaystyle OH}{|}\,\overset{\displaystyle R}{|}}{R-C=C-R}} + H_3O^+ + X^-$$

and

$$H_3O^+ + X^- \;\rightleftharpoons\; H_2O + HX$$

Enolization proceeds by several mechanisms, and this resulting intermediate, or the enolate anion in basic solutions, is the reactive species in several reactions. For example, at moderate pH's both the bromination and iodination of a ketone occur at the same rate, and the rate is independent of the halogen concentration. Furthermore, the ketone **1**, which has an asymmetric carbon atom, can be prepared in optically active form. This optically active ketone under the same conditions of temperature, solvent, and acid catalysts undergoes racemization and iodination at the same rate. When conducted under acidic conditions, the common intermediate in all of these reactions is the enol which is formed in the rate limiting step,

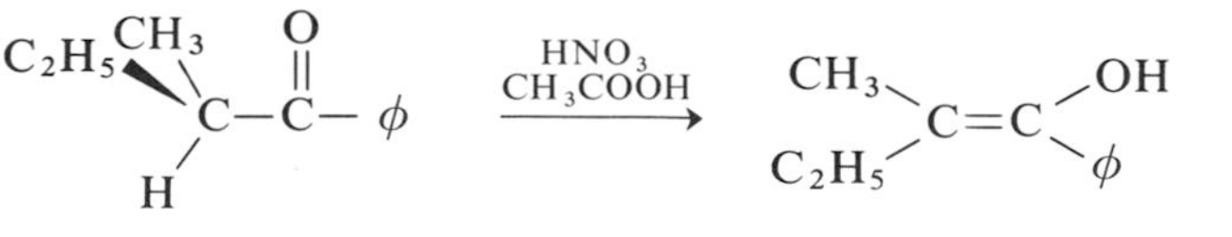

1

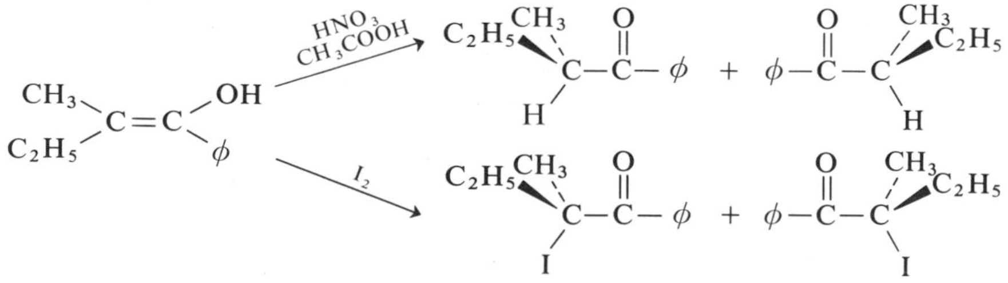

All of these reactions that seem to occur at the same rate have a common rate limiting step, and any reaction that takes place after this step is not directly measurable. Since the rate limiting step in these reactions determines the rate of the overall process ($k_{obs} = k_1$), the rate of halogenation or racemization of a ketone can be employed to measure the rate of enolization of that ketone.

Base catalyzed reactions involve the enolate anion, and the observations are similar. Ketone **1** undergoes bromination and racemization at the same rate and under the proper conditions also suffers deuterium exchange and racemization at equal rates. In these reactions the enolate anion can be the common intermediate,

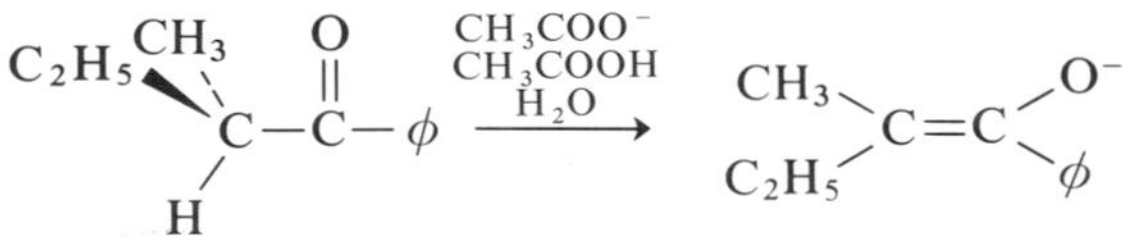

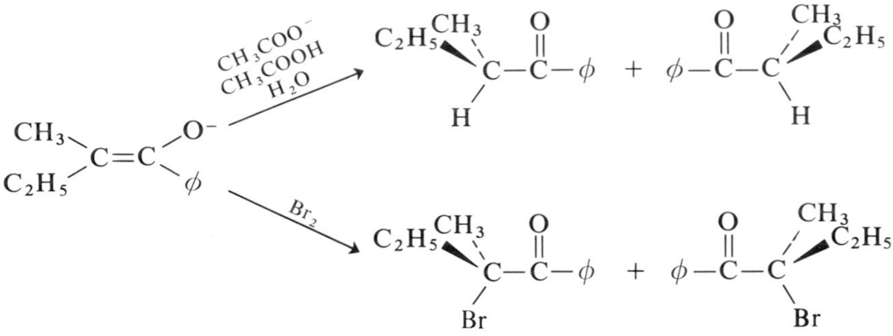

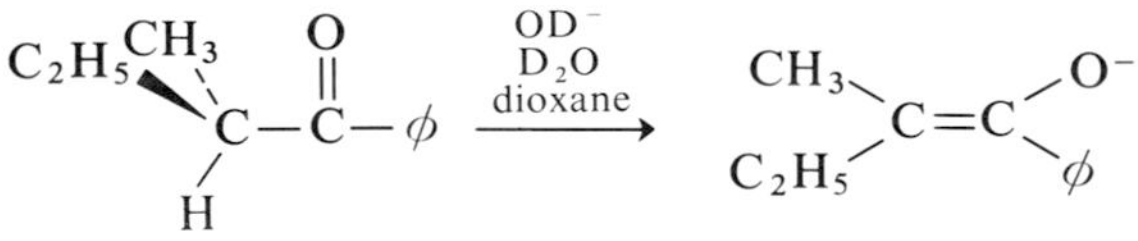

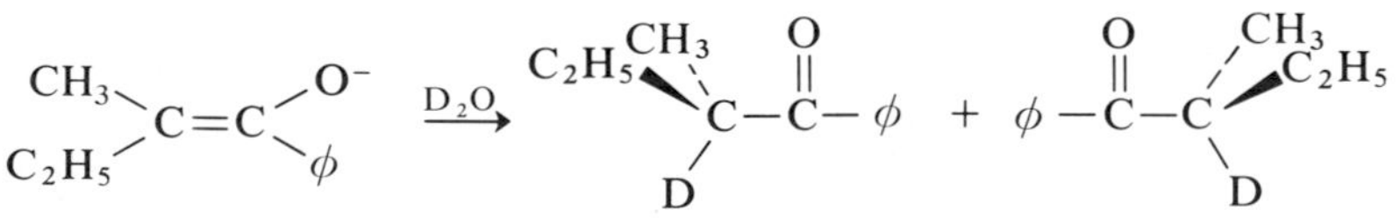

The rate limiting step in these base catalyzed reactions is formation of the enolate anion, and all subsequent processes are kinetically indistinguishable. The enol is also formed in these base catalyzed reactions, but this equilibrium

occurs after the rate limiting step and is not kinetically observable. The entire process for base catalyzed reactions becomes (we use deuterium exchange as an example),

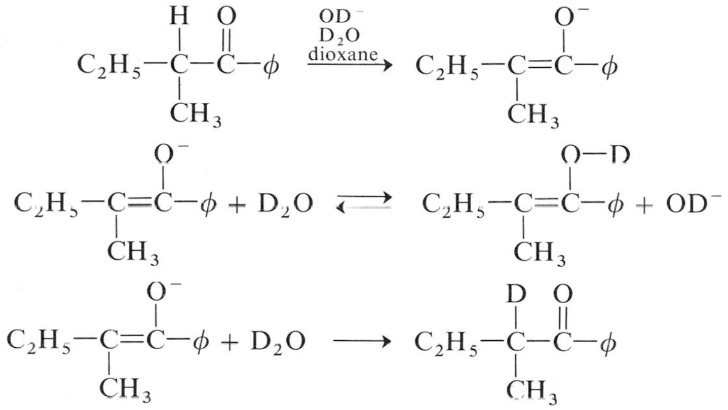

$$C_2H_5-\underset{\underset{CH_3}{|}}{\overset{\overset{H}{|}}{C}}-\overset{O}{\overset{||}{C}}-\phi \xrightarrow[\text{dioxane}]{\overset{OD^-}{D_2O}} C_2H_5-\underset{\underset{CH_3}{|}}{C}=\overset{\overset{O^-}{|}}{C}-\phi$$

$$C_2H_5-\underset{\underset{CH_3}{|}}{C}=\overset{\overset{O^-}{|}}{C}-\phi + D_2O \;\rightleftharpoons\; C_2H_5-\underset{\underset{CH_3}{|}}{C}=\overset{\overset{O-D}{|}}{C}-\phi + OD^-$$

$$C_2H_5-\underset{\underset{CH_3}{|}}{C}=\overset{\overset{O^-}{|}}{C}-\phi + D_2O \;\longrightarrow\; C_2H_5-\underset{\underset{CH_3}{|}}{\overset{\overset{D}{|}}{C}}-\overset{O}{\overset{||}{C}}-\phi$$

Under acidic conditions, when two different enols are possible, these are formed at different rates. Similarly, in basic solution two different enolate anions are formed at different rates. Thus, 2-butanone reacts with sodium hydroxide and iodine (the iodoform reaction) to yield products resulting from substitution at the 1-position:

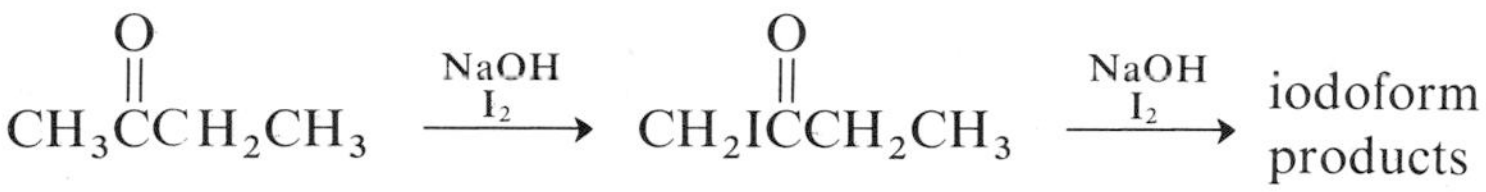

$$CH_3\overset{O}{\overset{||}{C}}CH_2CH_3 \xrightarrow[I_2]{NaOH} CH_2I\overset{O}{\overset{||}{C}}CH_2CH_3 \xrightarrow[I_2]{NaOH} \begin{array}{l}\text{iodoform}\\\text{products}\end{array}$$

This reaction proceeds by way of the enolate anion,

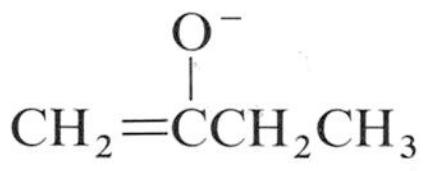

$$CH_2=\overset{\overset{O^-}{|}}{C}CH_2CH_3$$

which is formed more readily than the alternative,

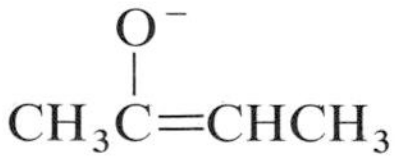

$$CH_3\overset{\overset{O^-}{|}}{C}=CHCH_3$$

On the other hand, this same ketone behaves differently under acidic conditions. It has been shown that under these conditions the reaction can proceed chiefly by way of the enol,

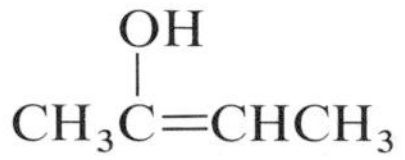

$$CH_3\overset{\overset{OH}{|}}{C}=CHCH_3$$

rather than by way of,

$$\underset{\underset{\displaystyle CH_2=CCH_2CH_3}{|}}{OH}$$

and the acid catalyzed bromination of 2-butanone leads predominantly to,

$$\underset{\underset{\displaystyle CH_3CCHBrCH_3}{\|}}{O}$$

The overall reaction for the acid catalyzed bromination becomes,

$$\underset{\underset{\displaystyle CH_3CCH_2CH_3}{\|}}{O} \quad \overset{k_1}{\underset{k_2}{\Large\diagup}}\quad \begin{array}{l} \underset{\underset{\displaystyle CH_3C=CHCH_3}{|}}{OH} \\[1em] \underset{\underset{\displaystyle CH_2=CCH_2CH_3}{|}}{OH} \end{array}$$

$$\underset{\underset{\displaystyle CH_3C=CHCH_3}{|}}{OH} + Br_2 \longrightarrow \underset{\underset{\displaystyle CH_3CCHBrCH_3}{\|}}{O}$$

$$\underset{\underset{\displaystyle CH_2=CCH_2CH_3}{|}}{OH} + Br_2 \longrightarrow \underset{\underset{\displaystyle CH_2BrCCH_2CH_3}{\|}}{O}$$

The major product is $CH_3COCHBrCH_3$, and this implies that the enol leading to this product is formed more rapidly ($k_1 > k_2$).

Several condensations at the carbonyl group involve enolization or enolate anion formation as the first step. The aldol condensation, for example, is both acid and base catalyzed and involves in basic solution an attack upon an aldehyde or ketone by the enolate anion of a second molecule of an aldehyde or ketone:

$$\underset{\underset{\displaystyle R-C=CHR}{|}}{O^-} + \underset{\underset{\displaystyle R-C-R}{\|}}{O} \quad \xrightarrow{H_2O} \quad \underset{\underset{\displaystyle R\ \ \ R}{\underset{\displaystyle |\ \ \ \ |}{}}}{\underset{\displaystyle R-C-C-C-R}{\overset{O\ \ H\ OH}{\overset{\|\ \ |\ \ |}{}}}}$$

In acidic solutions, the conjugate acid of a carbonyl compound attacks the enol of an aldehyde or ketone:

$$\underset{\underset{\displaystyle R-C=CHR}{|}}{OH} + \underset{\underset{\displaystyle R-C-R}{\|}}{^+O-H} \quad \xrightarrow{H_2O} \quad \underset{\underset{\displaystyle R\ \ \ R}{\underset{\displaystyle |\ \ \ \ |}{}}}{\underset{\displaystyle R-C-C-C-R}{\overset{O\ \ H\ OH}{\overset{\|\ \ |\ \ |}{}}}}$$

These reactions may proceed further, and the final products are then the dehydrated materials:

$$R-\overset{\overset{\displaystyle O}{\|}}{C}-\overset{\overset{\displaystyle H}{|}}{\underset{\underset{\displaystyle R}{|}}{C}}-\overset{\overset{\displaystyle OH}{|}}{\underset{\underset{\displaystyle R}{|}}{C}}-R \longrightarrow R-\overset{\overset{\displaystyle O}{\|}}{C}-\underset{\underset{\displaystyle R}{|}}{C}=\underset{\underset{\displaystyle R}{|}}{C}-R + H_2O$$

16.2 The Aldol Condensation

In the presence of an acid or a base, an aldehyde or a ketone condenses with itself, and this condensation is known as the aldol condensation. Thus,

$$2CH_3CHO \xrightarrow{\text{OH}^-} CH_3\overset{\overset{\displaystyle OH}{|}}{\underset{\underset{\displaystyle H}{|}}{C}}-CH_2CHO$$

and

$$2CH_3COCH_3 \xrightarrow{\text{OH}^-} CH_3-\overset{\overset{\displaystyle OH}{|}}{\underset{\underset{\displaystyle CH_3}{|}}{C}}-CH_2COCH_3$$

These hydroxy aldehydes (aldols) and hydroxy ketones (ketols) are easily dehydrated, and in some cases only the dehydrated products are isolated. Acetophenone condenses with itself and the product is the α,β-unsaturated carbonyl compound,

$$2\phi COCH_3 \xrightarrow{\bar{O}C_2H_5} \underset{\underset{\displaystyle CH_3}{|}}{\phi C}=CHCO\phi$$

The intermediate in the reaction is the ketol,

$$\phi-\overset{\overset{\displaystyle OH}{|}}{\underset{\underset{\displaystyle CH_3}{|}}{C}}-CH_2CO\phi$$

If an aldehyde or a ketone possessing α-hydrogens is reacted with an aldehyde that does not possess such α-hydrogens, crossed aldols take place (Claisen-Schmidt reaction). The products are generally α,β-unsaturated aldehydes and ketones,

$$\phi CHO + CH_3COC(CH_3)_3 \xrightarrow{\text{OH}^-} \phi CH=CHCOC(CH_3)_3$$

and

$$\phi CHO + CH_3CO\phi \xrightarrow{\bar{O}C_2H_5} \phi CH=CHCO\phi$$

If care is exercised, it is sometimes possible to conduct the crossed aldol reaction of a ketone with an aldehyde that does possess α-hydrogens. In these reactions the aldehyde is added to a mixture of the ketone and the basic catalyst. At lower temperatures the ketol is the major product, while at higher temperatures the α,β-unsaturated ketone resulting from its dehydration is the principal material:

$$CH_3CHO + CH_3COCH_3 \xrightarrow{\text{OH}^-} CH_3CHOHCH_2COCH_3$$

Condensations may also involve more than two molecules of the aldehyde or ketone. Thus, when pure acetone is saturated with hydrogen chloride and allowed to stand for several days, a mixture of products is obtained. Among these are the dimeric and trimeric condensation products,

$$2CH_3COCH_3 \xrightarrow{\text{HCl}} (CH_3)_2C{=}CHCOCH_3$$

$$3CH_3COCH_3 \xrightarrow{\text{HCl}} (CH_3)_2C{=}CHCOCH{=}C(CH_3)_2$$

It is generally the dimer that is the desired product in aldol condensations, and any tendency to polymerize therefore constitutes an unwanted side reaction.

All of the condensations that we have considered are reversible, and the products hydrolyze back to starting materials under the proper conditions.

The entire condensation can be discussed most conveniently by separating it into two steps, the formation of the aldol or ketol condensation product and its subsequent dehydration when this occurs.

$$2RCOCH_3 \xrightarrow[\text{OH}^-]{\text{H}^+ \text{ or}} R\underset{\underset{CH_3}{|}}{\overset{\overset{OH}{|}}{C}}{-}CH_2COR$$

$$R\underset{\underset{CH_3}{|}}{\overset{\overset{OH}{|}}{C}}{-}CH_2COR \xrightarrow[\text{OH}^-]{\text{H}^+ \text{ or}} R\underset{\underset{CH_3}{|}}{C}{=}CCOR + H_2O$$

The aldol condensation (the first step), as it is usually conducted, is an equilibrium process. As a result aldol or ketol formation depends not upon the rate of any step in the reaction but upon the free energy of all the materials present at equilibrium. All of the materials (reactants, products, hydrates of these, and all intermediates) are present in their equilibrium concentrations, and the equilibrium concentration of the aldol or ketol is related to the equilibrium concentration of reactant by the free energy of reaction for the process,

$$2R\overset{\overset{O}{\|}}{C}CH_3 \underset{\text{OH}^-}{\rightleftharpoons} R\underset{\underset{CH_3}{|}}{\overset{\overset{OH}{|}}{C}}{-}CH_2\overset{\overset{O}{\|}}{C}{-}R$$

and

$$\Delta G° = -RT \ln K$$

$$\Delta G° = -RT \ln \frac{\left[\begin{array}{c} \text{OH} \\ | \\ \text{RC-CH}_2\text{COR} \\ | \\ \text{CH}_3 \end{array}\right]}{[\text{RCOCH}_3]^2}$$

In an equilibrium process the extent of product formation depends upon the free energy of all the species present, and the more stable materials are present in the higher concentrations. When the starting material is a ketone, the only materials present in reasonably high concentration are the starting ketone and the ketol condensation product. The equilibrium concentration of ketol depends directly upon the free energy of reaction for the condensation process, but unfortunately, the free energy for ketol formation is unfavorable. Acetone condenses with itself, but the equilibrium is so unfavorable that virtually no product is obtained. However, shifting the equilibrium by removing the product as it forms, does allow it to accumulate.

This shifting of the equilibrium is accomplished by placing the basic catalyst (barium hydroxide) in the thimble of a Soxhlet extractor and refluxing acetone over the thimble. The ketol is formed in the thimble and drops to the flask below. The ketol, which is higher boiling, then builds up in the flask out of contact with the catalyst:

$$2\text{CH}_3\text{COCH}_3 \xrightarrow{\text{Ba(OH)}_2} \begin{array}{c} \text{OH} \quad \text{O} \\ | \qquad || \\ \text{CH}_3-\text{C}-\text{CH}_2\text{CCH}_3 \\ | \\ \text{CH}_3 \end{array}$$

The equilibrium constant has been determined for the condensation of acetone. The results are presented in Table 16–2 for various aqueous acetone mixtures at 25°C. It was found that the concentration of basic catalyst (potassium hydroxide) had no pronounced effect upon the equilibrium position.

Table 16–2

Water (Weight per cent)	K (liters/mole)
4	0.024
20	0.029
39.5	0.032
60	0.035
80	0.037

From the data, $\Delta G°$ can be calculated. The value is approximately 2 kcal. The terms $\Delta H°$ and $\Delta S°$ have also been evaluated. These can be very dependent on solvent composition. For a 60% acetone-water solution the values are $\Delta H° = -7.8$ kcal, $\Delta S° = -32$ cal/deg. Thus, the $\Delta H°$ term for condensation is favorable but is not sufficient to offset the unfavorable change in entropy. The negative entropy change is due to loss of translational freedom in proceeding from two moles of acetone to the ketol. In passing from acetone to the product, changes in solvation are probably small.

When the reactants are aldehydes, the aldol condensation is accompanied by a favorable free energy of reaction, and the products are formed in good yields. Low temperatures also favor product formation. Lowering the temperature is expected to have a favorable effect, for it is the $T\Delta S°$ term that is unfavorable, and this becomes less important at lower temperatures.

If the aldol condensation is conducted in a nonhydroxylic solvent, the only materials present in high equilibrium concentrations are the starting aldehyde and the aldol produced from it, and in such cases the degree of product formation depends only upon the free energy of reaction (neglecting the possibility of polycondensation).

If the starting aldehyde (for example, acetaldehyde) is condensed in a hydroxylic solvent (such as H_2O), then not only are the starting material and product present in high concentrations, but their hydrates are also present,

$$2CH_3\overset{\overset{\displaystyle OH}{|}}{\underset{\underset{\displaystyle OH}{|}}{C}}-H \underset{H_2O}{\overset{OH^-}{\rightleftarrows}} 2CH_3\overset{\overset{\displaystyle O}{||}}{C}-H$$

$$2CH_3\overset{\overset{\displaystyle O}{||}}{C}-H \underset{H_2O}{\overset{OH^-}{\rightleftarrows}} CH_3\overset{\overset{\displaystyle OH}{|}}{\underset{\underset{\displaystyle H}{|}}{C}}-CH_2CHO \underset{H_2O}{\overset{OH^-}{\rightleftarrows}} CH_3\overset{\overset{\displaystyle OH}{|}}{\underset{\underset{\displaystyle H}{|}}{C}}-CH_2-\overset{\overset{\displaystyle OH}{|}}{\underset{\underset{\displaystyle OH}{|}}{C}}-H$$

The equilibrium concentration of aldol is still related to the equilibrium concentration of acetaldehyde by the free energy of reaction, yet the formation of hydrates alters the concentration of each present in the equilibrium mixture. Presumably a greater fraction of the acetaldehyde is hydrated, yet despite this, the free energy of reaction is sufficiently favorable to allow a large amount of product to form. In fact, the equilibrium lies too far towards the aldol to allow an accurate determination of the equilibrium constant.

Cyanide ion serves as a basic catalyst, and the condensation of acetaldehyde has been conducted using this catalyst:

$$2CH_3CHO \underset{\text{low temperatures}}{\overset{CN^-}{\rightleftarrows}} \underset{\text{45\% isolated}}{CH_3CHOHCH_2CHO}$$

We find that aldol formation is reasonably favorable whereas ketol formation is unfavorable, and the yield depends largely upon the equilibrium constant for the reaction.

An unfavorable equilibrium is shifted away from the reactants by dehydration of the initially formed aldol or ketol products. In this case the reaction becomes.

$$2RCOCH_3 \underset{\overset{H^+ \text{ or}}{OH^-}}{\rightleftharpoons} R-\underset{\underset{CH_3}{|}}{C}=CHCOCH_3 + H_2O$$

and if the reaction is run under equilibrium conditions, the yield of α,β-unsaturated product depends upon the free energy of reaction for this process.

Many reactions for which aldol or ketol formation is unfavorable proceed quite readily to form the α,β-unsaturated carbonyl compounds. This is particularly true when phenyl groups are present, for these stabilize the α,β-unsaturated material. Of course, the entropy change is also more favorable, for a mole of water is produced along with the condensation product. Thus the condensation of acetophenone, a reaction that is not expected to yield the ketol, takes place quite easily to yield the α,β-unsaturated ketone, dypnone:

$$2\phi COCH_3 \rightleftharpoons \phi-\underset{\underset{CH_3}{|}}{\overset{\overset{OH}{|}}{C}}-CH_2CO\phi \rightleftharpoons \phi-\underset{\underset{CH_3}{|}}{C}=CHCO\phi + H_2O$$

The partial reaction coordinate for this process must look qualitatively as indicated in Figure 16–1.

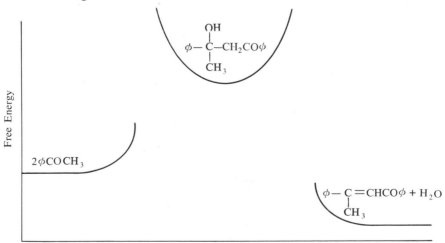

Reaction Coordinate

Figure 16–1

Of course, removal of a product as it forms, shifts the equilibrium and increases the yield.

Both steps of the reaction, the formation of aldols and ketols and their subsequent dehydration, are acid and base catalyzed. The mechanism for the base catalyzed reaction is (we illustrate for acetophenone),

$$\phi-\overset{\overset{\text{O}}{\|}}{\text{C}}-CH_3 + C_2H_5O^- \rightleftharpoons \phi-\overset{\overset{\text{O}^{\delta-}}{\|}}{\text{C}}\overset{\delta-}{=\!=}CH_2 + C_2H_5OH$$

This enolate anion, which is stabilized by charge delocalization, reacts as follows,

$$\phi-\overset{\overset{\text{O}}{\|}}{\text{C}}-CH_3 + \overset{\delta-}{CH_2}\overset{\overset{\overset{\delta-}{\text{O}}}{\|}}{=\!\!=C}-\phi \rightleftharpoons \phi-\overset{\overset{\text{O}^-}{|}}{\underset{\underset{\text{CH}_3}{|}}{\text{C}}}-CH_2-\overset{\overset{\text{O}}{\|}}{\text{C}}-\phi$$

$$\phi-\overset{\overset{\text{O}^-}{|}}{\underset{\underset{\text{CH}_3}{|}}{\text{C}}}-CH_2-\overset{\overset{\text{O}}{\|}}{\text{C}}-\phi + C_2H_5OH \rightleftharpoons \phi-\overset{\overset{\text{OH}}{|}}{\underset{\underset{\text{CH}_3}{|}}{\text{C}}}-CH_2\overset{\overset{\text{O}}{\|}}{\text{C}}-\phi + C_2H_5O^-$$

This is the portion of the reaction that is characterized by an unfavorable equilibrium. The mechanism for the second portion, dehydration to yield an α,β-unsaturated ketone, has been discussed previously. The process is just the reverse of addition of hydroxide ion to an α,β-unsaturated carbonyl system, and according to the principle of microscopic reversibility, this reversal must proceed by way of the conjugate base and an *E1cB* mechanism,

$$\phi-\overset{\overset{\text{OH}}{|}}{\underset{\underset{\text{CH}_3}{|}}{\text{C}}}-CH_2\overset{\overset{\text{O}}{\|}}{\text{C}}-\phi + C_2H_5O^- \rightleftharpoons \phi-\overset{\overset{\text{OH}}{|}}{\underset{\underset{\text{CH}_3}{|}}{\text{C}}}\overset{\delta-}{-\!\!-}CH\overset{\overset{\overset{\delta-}{\text{O}}}{\|}}{=\!\!=C}-\phi + C_2H_5OH$$

$$\phi-\overset{\overset{\text{OH}}{|}}{\underset{\underset{\text{CH}_3}{|}}{\text{C}}}-\overset{\delta-}{CH}\overset{\overset{\overset{\text{O}^{\delta-}}{\|}}{}}{=\!\!=C}-\phi \rightleftharpoons \phi-\overset{\overset{\text{O}}{\|}}{\text{C}}=CH-\overset{\overset{\text{O}}{\|}}{\text{C}}-\phi + OH^-$$

The enol,

$$\phi-\overset{\overset{\text{OH}}{|}}{\underset{\underset{\text{CH}_3}{|}}{\text{C}}}-CH=\overset{\overset{\text{OH}}{|}}{\text{C}}-\phi$$

is certainly produced in these reactions, but this material is formed reversibly.

The condensation and dehydration can also be conducted using acidic catalysis, and under such conditions the conjugate acid of acetophenone is formed first. This cation then attacks the enol of a second molecule of the ketone:

$$\phi-\overset{\displaystyle O}{\overset{\|}{C}}-CH_3 + HX \rightleftarrows \phi-\overset{\displaystyle \overset{+}{O}\diagup H}{\overset{\|}{C}}-CH_3 + X^-$$

$$\phi-\overset{\displaystyle \overset{+}{O}\diagup H}{\overset{\|}{C}}-CH_3 + X^- \rightleftarrows \phi-\overset{\displaystyle OH}{\overset{|}{C}}=CH_2 + HX$$

This enol is attacked by the conjugate acid of a second molecule of acetophenone:

$$\phi-\overset{\displaystyle \overset{+}{O}\diagup H}{\overset{\|}{C}}-CH_3 + CH_2=\overset{\displaystyle OH}{\overset{|}{C}}-\phi \rightleftarrows \phi-\overset{\displaystyle OH}{\underset{\displaystyle CH_3}{\overset{|}{C}}}-CH_2-\overset{\displaystyle \overset{+}{O}\diagup H}{\overset{\|}{C}}-\phi$$

and,

$$\phi-\overset{\displaystyle OH}{\underset{\displaystyle CH_3}{\overset{|}{C}}}-CH_2-\overset{\displaystyle \overset{+}{O}\diagup H}{\overset{\|}{C}}-\phi + X^- \rightleftarrows \phi-\overset{\displaystyle OH}{\underset{\displaystyle CH_3}{\overset{|}{C}}}-CH_2-\overset{\displaystyle O}{\overset{\|}{C}}-\phi + HX$$

The dehydration proceeds by way of the enol which loses a molecule of water to form the conjugate acid of the product,

$$\phi-\overset{\displaystyle OH}{\underset{\displaystyle CH_3}{\overset{|}{C}}}-CH_2-\overset{\displaystyle O}{\overset{\|}{C}}-\phi \overset{HX}{\rightleftarrows} \phi-\overset{\displaystyle OH}{\underset{\displaystyle CH_3}{\overset{|}{C}}}-CH=\overset{\displaystyle OH}{\overset{|}{C}}-\phi$$

$$\phi-\overset{\displaystyle OH}{\underset{\displaystyle CH_3}{\overset{|}{C}}}-CH=\overset{\displaystyle OH}{\overset{|}{C}}-\phi + HX \rightleftarrows \phi-\overset{\displaystyle OH}{\underset{\displaystyle CH_3}{\overset{|}{C}}}=CH-\overset{\displaystyle \overset{+}{O}\diagup H}{\overset{\|}{C}}-\phi + H_2O + X^-$$

This conjugate acid ultimately loses a proton to yield the dehydrated product.

$$\phi-\underset{\underset{CH_3}{|}}{C}=CH-\overset{\overset{+O}{\overset{\diagup H}{}}}{\underset{\|}{C}}-\phi + X^- \; \rightleftarrows \; \phi-\underset{\underset{CH_3}{|}}{C}=CH-\overset{\overset{O}{\|}}{C}-\phi + HX$$

Although formation of the α,β-unsaturated carbonyl compound can be an equilibrium process, it is still of interest to determine which part of the reaction, the formation of the aldol condensation product or its dehydration, is rate limiting. This can be accomplished quite simply by subjecting some of the aldol or ketol to the reaction conditions. If it dehydrates faster than it reverts to the starting aldehyde or ketone, then its formation is the rate limiting portion of the reaction. If it reverts to aldehyde or ketone, dehydration is rate limiting.

As we might have expected, in some cases the two processes occur at about the same rate; in some cases aldol formation is rate limiting, and in others the dehydration is rate limiting. The rate of the various processes depends upon the particular carbonyl compound and the catalyst. We can, however, make some generalizations to which exceptions do occur.

It is found that although the nature of the carbonyl compound is important, the rate limiting portion of the reaction depends to a large degree upon the catalyst. With basic catalysts, dehydration is usually rate limiting, whereas, in acidic solution the condensation of the conjugate acid with the enol is considered to be rate limiting. Therefore, in the reaction of the ketol **2** with base, this material forms benzaldehyde and acetophenone more readily than it dehydrates:

$$\phi CHO + CH_3 CO\phi \; \overset{OH^-}{\rightleftarrows} \; \phi\overset{\overset{OH}{|}}{C}HCH_2 CO\phi \; \overset{OH^-}{\longrightarrow} \; \phi CH=CHCO\phi + H_2O$$

2

The ketol **3** does dehydrate in basic solution to form the α,β-unsaturated system, but some benzaldehyde is also formed in the solution,

$$\phi CHO + CH_3 COCH_2 CH_3 \; \overset{OH^-}{\rightleftarrows} \; \phi\overset{\overset{OH}{|}}{C}HCH_2 COCH_2 CH_3$$

3

$$\phi\overset{\overset{OH}{|}}{C}HCH_2 COCH_2 CH_3 \; \longrightarrow \; \phi CH=CHCOCH_2 CH_3$$

3

The ketol **4** not only fails to yield detectable amounts of the normal dehydrated product, it eventually leads to the same unsaturated product as **3**.

$$\phi-\overset{\displaystyle OH}{\underset{\displaystyle CH_3}{\underset{|}{CH}}}\overset{}{\underset{}{CHCOCH_3}} \quad\xrightarrow{\hspace{0.3cm}/\!\!\!\!\longrightarrow}\quad \begin{array}{l} \phi CH=\overset{\displaystyle |}{\underset{\displaystyle CH_3}{C}}-COCH_3 \\[1.2em] \phi CH=CHCOCH_2CH_3 \end{array}$$

4

$$\phi-\overset{\displaystyle OH}{\underset{\displaystyle CH_3}{\underset{|}{CH}}}\overset{}{\underset{|}{CHCOCH_3}} \quad\overset{OH^-}{\rightleftharpoons}\quad \phi CHO + CH_3COCH_2CH_3$$

4

$$\phi CHO + CH_3COCH_2CH_3 \quad\xrightarrow{OH^-}\quad \phi CH=CHCOCH_2CH_3$$

Although the rates of the two processes (dehydration to product and cleavage to the original carbonyl compounds) are in some cases nearly the same, the data indicate that dehydration is generally rate limiting when a basic catalyst is employed.

In certain reactions more than a single aldol condensation product is possible. Thus, the condensation of benzaldehyde with 2-butanone in basic solution leads exclusively to the straight chain isomer. However, under acidic conditions, the other isomer is produced:

$$\phi CHO + CH_3COCH_2CH_3 \quad\overset{OH^-}{\underset{H^+}{\rightrightarrows}}\quad \begin{array}{l} \phi CH=CHCOCH_2CH_3 \\[1.2em] \phi CH=\overset{}{\underset{\displaystyle CH_3}{\underset{|}{C}}}-COCH_3 \end{array}$$

A similar result has been observed in other cases where more than a single product is possible. The following condensation leads to a mixture of products:

$$(CH_3)_2CHCHO + CH_3COCH_2CH_3 \quad\longrightarrow\quad \begin{array}{l} (CH_3)_2CHCH=CHCOCH_2CH_3 \\[1.2em] (CH_3)_2CHCH=\overset{}{\underset{\displaystyle CH_3}{\underset{|}{C}}}-COCH_3 \end{array}$$

In basic solution the product resulting from condensation at the methyl group of 2-butanone predominates, while acidic catalysts lead to the other isomer as the principal product.

We mentioned previously that product formation in the aldol condensation and in the dehydration following it was generally thermodynamically controlled. However, in the examples just presented, basic catalysis leads to a preference for one isomer while acidic catalysis leads to the other. It is unlikely that the reaction leads to the thermodynamic product under both sets of conditions. Although the environment does influence the value of the equilibrium constant for the process:

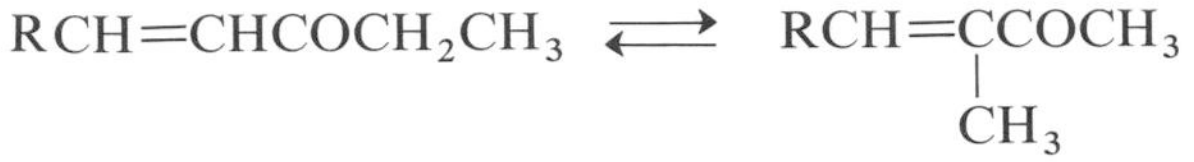

$$RCH=CHCOCH_2CH_3 \rightleftharpoons RCH=\underset{\underset{CH_3}{|}}{C}COCH_3$$

simply changing the catalyst ought not to have a profound effect, and it is more reasonable to assume that kinetic products are sometimes formed.

This idea of kinetic control of product formation would, in certain cases, explain why a change in the catalyst influences to a considerable extent the composition of the product mixture. Thus when dehydration is rate limiting, the various ketols are in equilibrium, and the relative rates in the dehydration step determine the product distribution,

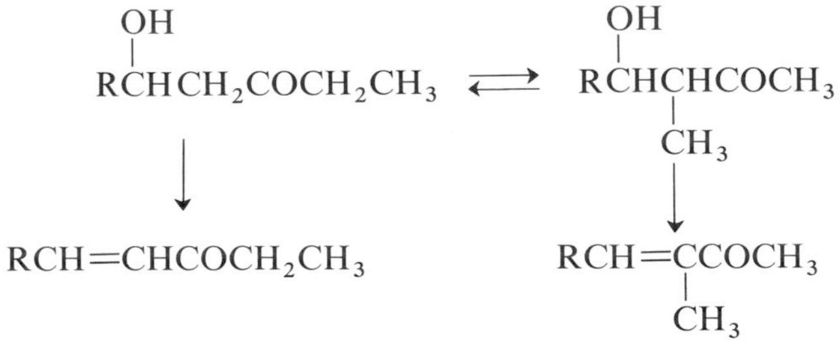

$$\underset{\underset{RCHCH_2COCH_2CH_3}{|}}{OH} \rightleftharpoons \underset{\underset{RCHCHCOCH_3}{|}\atop{\underset{CH_3}{|}}}{OH}$$

$$\downarrow \qquad\qquad\qquad \downarrow$$

$$RCH=CHCOCH_2CH_3 \qquad RCH=\underset{\underset{CH_3}{|}}{C}COCH_3$$

It appears that the straight-chain product predominates in these cases.

If in certain reactions the condensation is rate limiting, the free energy of the transition state in the condensation step is the important consideration. (If product formation is kinetically controlled.)

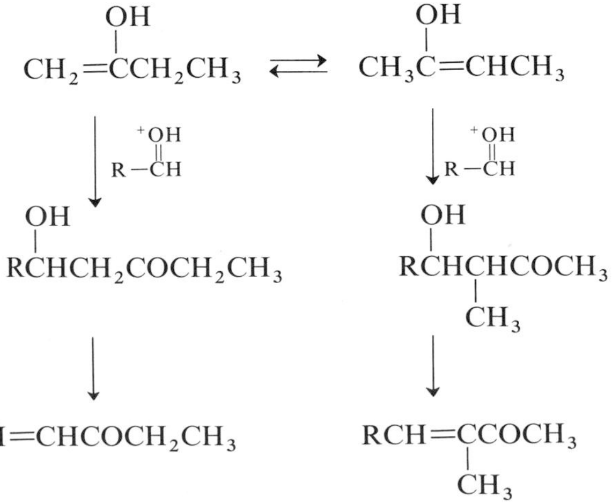

$$\underset{\underset{CH_2=CCH_2CH_3}{|}}{OH} \rightleftharpoons \underset{\underset{CH_3C=CHCH_3}{|}}{OH}$$

$$\downarrow{\overset{{}^+OH}{\underset{R-CH}{\|}}} \qquad\qquad \downarrow{\overset{{}^+OH}{\underset{R-CH}{\|}}}$$

$$\underset{\underset{RCHCH_2COCH_2CH_3}{|}}{OH} \qquad \underset{\underset{RCHCHCOCH_3}{|}\atop{\underset{CH_3}{|}}}{OH}$$

$$\downarrow \qquad\qquad\qquad \downarrow$$

$$RCH=CHCOCH_2CH_3 \qquad RCH=\underset{\underset{CH_3}{|}}{C}COCH_3$$

16.3 Reactions Related to the Aldol Condensation

Many reactions related to the aldol condensation exist. Thus the Mannich reaction is a condensation involving two carbonyl compounds in the presence of an amine hydrochloride. The mechanism postulated is analogous to that presented for the acid catalyzed aldol condensation. However, the first step is an attack on the more reactive carbonyl compound by the amine:

$$
\underset{\substack{\|\\ \text{O}}}{\text{H}-\text{C}-\text{H}} + \text{HNR}_2 \; \rightleftharpoons \; \underset{\substack{\|\\ \overset{+}{\text{N}}\text{R}_2}}{\text{II}-\text{C}-\text{H}}
$$

This intermediate is electronically analogous to the conjugate acid of a carbonyl compound and condenses with an enol. The reaction is,

$$
\underset{\substack{\|\\ \text{O}}}{\text{H}-\text{C}-\text{H}} + \text{HNR}_2 \; \underset{}{\overset{\text{H}^+}{\rightleftharpoons}} \; \underset{\substack{\|\\ {}^+\text{NR}_2}}{\text{H}-\text{C}-\text{H}}
$$

$$
\underset{\substack{|\\ \text{OH}}}{\text{CH}_3-\text{C}=\text{CH}_2} + \underset{\substack{\|\\ {}^+\text{NR}_2}}{\text{H}-\text{C}-\text{H}} \; \longrightarrow \; \text{CH}_3\text{COCH}_2\text{CH}_2\text{NR}_2
$$

The products in the Mannich reaction are actually amine hydrochlorides, for the material formed in the last step is a base, and in the presence of hydrogen chloride it exists as the hydrochloride. Treatment with aqueous hydroxide generates the free base.

This particular Mannich base formed from acetone, formaldehyde, and diethylamine finds use in the Robinson synthesis of cyclic ketones. The Mannich base is first reacted with methyl iodide and yields the quaternary ammonium iodide **5**:

$$
\text{CH}_3\text{COCH}_2\text{CH}_2\text{N}(\text{C}_2\text{H}_5)_2 + \text{CH}_3\text{I} \; \longrightarrow \; \text{CH}_3\text{COCH}_2\text{CH}_2\underset{\substack{+\\ \text{I}^-}}{\overset{\substack{\text{CH}_3\\ |}}{\text{N}}}(\text{C}_2\text{H}_5)_2
$$

5

A solution of **5** yields methyl vinyl ketone **6** when treated with a strong base, and **6** in the presence of the base and another carbonyl compound undergoes a cyclic condensation:

$$
\text{CH}_3\text{COCH}_2\text{CH}_2\underset{\substack{+\\ \text{I}^-}}{\overset{\substack{\text{CH}_3\\ |}}{\text{N}}}(\text{C}_2\text{H}_5)_2 \; \overset{\substack{\text{strong}\\ \text{base}}}{\longrightarrow} \; \underset{\substack{\|\\ \text{O}}}{\text{CH}_3\text{CCH}}=\text{CH}_2 + \text{CH}_3\text{N}(\text{C}_2\text{H}_5)_2
$$

        5   **6**

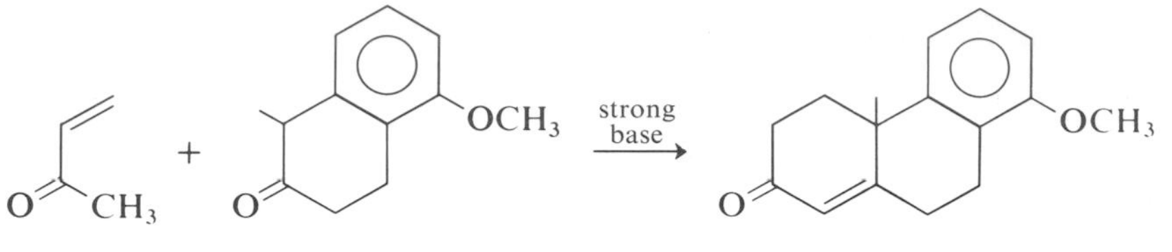

6   7   8

With the ketone **7**, the product has the structure **8**, another six membered ring having been introduced into the system. This application of the reactions of methyl vinyl ketone is particularly useful in the synthesis of steroids.

The strong bases employed in the Robinson synthesis are materials such as sodium ethoxide, potassium *t*-butoxide, sodium hydroxide, sodamide, potassium amide, and so forth. The methyl vinyl ketone need not be isolated, for a better yield of product is obtained if it is formed and reacted in the same solution. Simply combining **5** and **7** in the presence of the base affords the product.

The Mannich reaction is just one of a number of reactions that are related to the aldol condensation. Another is Michael addition to α,β-unsaturated carbonyl systems. In the previous condensation, one of the steps in the cyclization to **8** was an attack on the terminal position of the α,β-unsaturated carbonyl system **6** by the enolate anion of the ketone **7**, and this attack is one example of Michael addition.

Many examples of Michael attack exist. The mechanism for the process is analogous to the aldol condensation in that an enolate anion attacks a carbonyl system; however, instead of a direct attack, it is at the terminal atom of an α,β-unsaturated carbonyl compound that the nucleophile enters.

The previous reaction of methyl vinyl ketone was typical, and the enolate anion **9** behaves similarly:

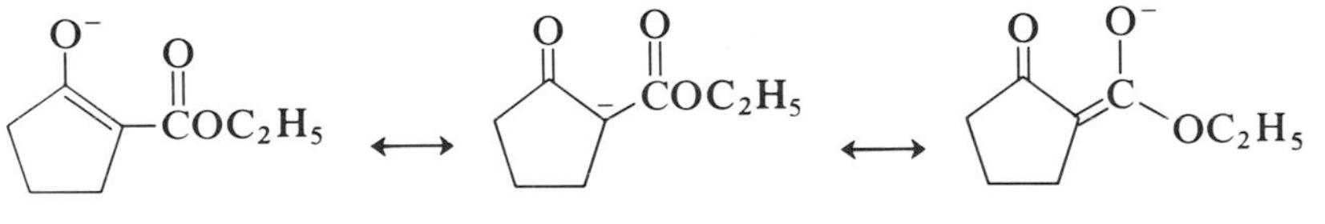

9

The product resulting from attack of methyl vinyl ketone by **9** is,

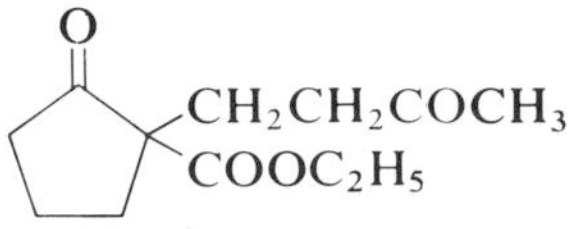

Diethylmalonate **10** is frequently the nucleophile (as the sodium salt **11**), and, in fact, it was with **10** that Michael did his original work,

$$\begin{array}{c} \text{COOC}_2\text{H}_5 \\ / \\ \text{CH}_2 \qquad + \text{C}_2\text{H}_5\text{O}^- \rightleftharpoons \\ \backslash \\ \text{COOC}_2\text{H}_5 \\ \mathbf{10} \end{array} \qquad \begin{array}{c} \text{COOC}_2\text{H}_5 \\ / \\ \bar{\text{C}}\text{H} \qquad + \text{C}_2\text{H}_5\text{OH} \\ \backslash \\ \text{COOC}_2\text{H}_5 \\ \mathbf{11} \end{array}$$

$$\phi\text{CH}=\text{CHCOOC}_2\text{H}_5 + \bar{\text{C}}\text{H}(\text{COOC}_2\text{H}_5)_2 \rightleftharpoons \phi-\text{CH}-\ddot{\bar{\text{C}}}\text{HCOOC}_2\text{H}_5$$
$$\begin{array}{c} | \\ \text{CH} \\ / \backslash \\ \text{C}_2\text{H}_5\text{OOC} \quad \text{COOC}_2\text{H}_5 \end{array}$$

$$\begin{array}{c} \phi-\text{CHC}\ddot{\bar{\text{H}}}\text{COOC}_2\text{H}_5 + \text{C}_2\text{H}_5\text{OH} \rightleftharpoons \phi-\text{CHCH}_2\text{COOC}_2\text{H}_5 + \text{C}_2\text{H}_5\text{O}^- \\ | \qquad\qquad\qquad\qquad\qquad\qquad\qquad\qquad\quad | \\ \text{CH} \qquad\qquad\qquad\qquad\qquad\qquad\qquad\qquad\quad \text{CH} \\ / \backslash \qquad\qquad\qquad\qquad\qquad\qquad\qquad\quad / \backslash \\ \text{C}_2\text{H}_5\text{OOC} \quad \text{COOC}_2\text{H}_5 \qquad\qquad\quad \text{C}_2\text{H}_5\text{OOC} \quad \text{COOC}_2\text{H}_5 \\ \qquad\qquad\qquad\qquad\qquad\qquad\qquad\qquad\qquad\qquad \mathbf{12} \end{array}$$

$$\begin{array}{c} \phi \quad \text{CHCH}_2\text{COOC}_2\text{H}_5 + \text{C}_2\text{H}_5\text{O}^- \rightleftharpoons \phi \quad \text{CHCH}_2\text{COOC}_2\text{H}_5 + \text{C}_2\text{H}_5\text{O}^- \\ | \qquad\qquad\qquad\qquad\qquad\qquad\qquad\qquad\quad | \\ \text{CH} \qquad\qquad\qquad\qquad\qquad\qquad\qquad\qquad\quad \bar{\text{C}}: \\ / \backslash \qquad\qquad\qquad\qquad\qquad\qquad\qquad\quad / \backslash \\ \text{C}_2\text{H}_5\text{OOC} \quad \text{COOC}_2\text{H}_5 \qquad\qquad\quad \text{C}_2\text{H}_5\text{OOC} \quad \text{COOC}_2\text{H}_5 \\ \qquad\qquad\qquad\qquad\qquad\qquad\qquad\qquad\qquad\qquad \mathbf{13} \end{array}$$

The reaction is an equilibrium process with better yields being obtained at lower temperatures, thus implying that a favorable $\Delta H°$ accompanies the addition. Furthermore, the reaction can be run using either molar equivalents of sodium ethoxide or only catalytic quantities. The original work was done using equivalent amounts of base. In that case the equilibrium was probably between the anion **13** and the sodium salt of diethylmalonate **11**. Better yields are obtained if only catalytic amounts of sodium ethoxide are employed, and under these conditions it is the esters themselves **10** and **12** that enter into the equilibrium. Only small amounts of the anions are present.

Michael addition is quite general and a number of other nucleophiles add to α,β-unsaturated systems. Nitromethane when treated with methoxide ion forms its conjugate base which adds to the ketone **14**,

$$\text{CH}_3\text{NO}_2 + \bar{\text{O}}\text{CH}_3 \rightleftharpoons {}^{-}\!\text{:CH}_2\text{NO}_2 + \text{CH}_3\text{OH}$$

The charges in this anion are delocalized as follows,

$$\bar{\text{C}}\text{H}_2-\overset{+}{\text{N}}\overset{\displaystyle\text{O}^-}{\underset{\displaystyle\text{O}}{\diagdown}} \quad\longleftrightarrow\quad \bar{\text{C}}\text{H}_2-\overset{+}{\text{N}}\overset{\displaystyle\text{O}}{\underset{\displaystyle\text{O}^-}{\diagdown}} \quad\longleftrightarrow\quad \text{CH}_2=\overset{+}{\text{N}}\overset{\displaystyle\text{O}^-}{\underset{\displaystyle\text{O}^-}{\diagdown}}$$

It is this conjugate base that adds to **14** (generated from the Mannich base) to form, after hydrolysis, the product **15**:

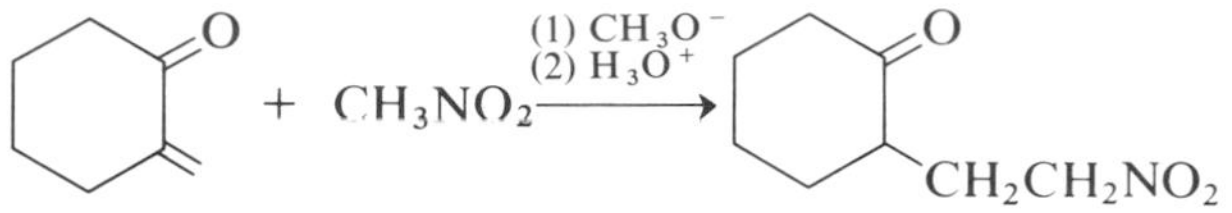

Amines are also effective catalysts in Michael additions,

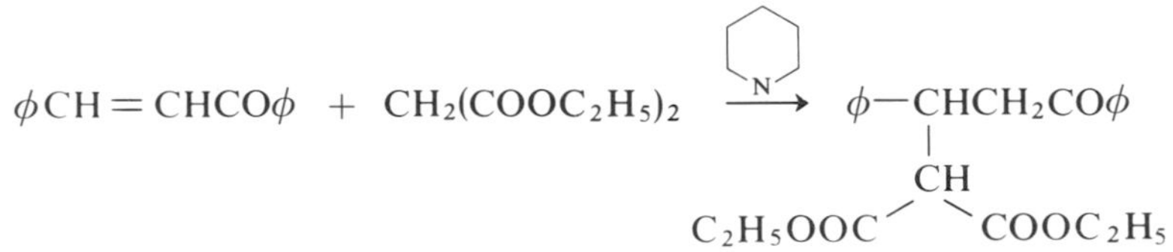

This innovation was introduced by Knoevenagel who also extended the reaction to simple carbonyl systems. Accordingly, the reaction of a carbonyl compound with an active hydrogen compound in the presence of an amine is called the Knoevenagel reaction. Notice the similarity between this reaction, the aldol condensation, and the Claisen-Schmidt reaction:

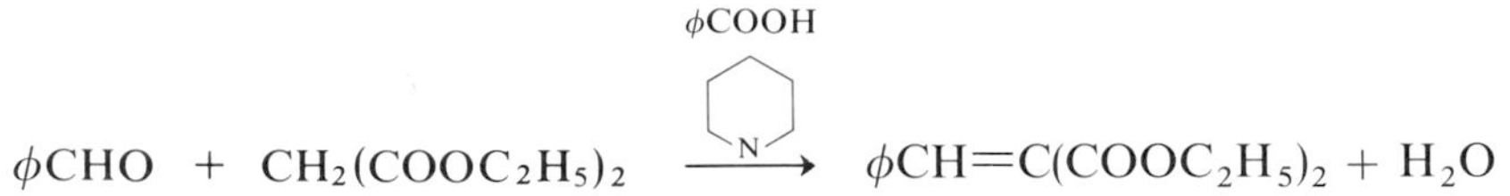

The Knoevenagel, as do most of these processes, involves a series of equilibria, and in the example just presented the equilibrium is shifted by removing the water as it forms.

Malonic acid can itself be employed in these condensations; furthermore, amines are not the only effective catalysts. As the following reaction illustrates, other strong bases can be utilized:

Still other condensations such as the Perkin reaction and the Stobbe condensation also involve attack of a carbonyl compound by an enolate anion. All of these reactions are similar to the aldol condensation.

Not only do aldehydes and ketones condense in the presence of a strongly basic catalyst, but esters also undergo condensation. This reaction, known as the Claisen condensation, is illustrated for ethyl acetate.

Ethyl acetate condenses in the presence of sodium ethoxide according to the equation,

$$2CH_3COOC_2H_5 \xrightarrow{C_2H_5O^-} CH_3COCH_2COOC_2H_5 + C_2H_5OH$$

where the mechanism is,

$$CH_3COOC_2H_5 + C_2H_5O^- \rightleftarrows CH_2\!\!=\!\!\overset{\displaystyle O^-}{\overset{|}{C}}OC_2H_5 + C_2H_5OH$$

$$CH_3COOC_2H_5 + CH_2\!\!=\!\!\overset{\displaystyle O^-}{\overset{|}{C}}OC_2H_5 \rightleftarrows CH_3\!-\!\overset{\displaystyle O^-}{\underset{\displaystyle OC_2H_5}{\overset{|}{\underset{|}{C}}}}\!-\!CH_2COOC_2H_5$$

$$CH_3\!-\!\overset{\displaystyle O^-}{\underset{\displaystyle OC_2H_5}{\overset{|}{\underset{|}{C}}}}\!-\!CH_2COOC_2H_5 \rightleftarrows CH_3COCH_2COOC_2H_5 + C_2H_5O^-$$

$$CH_3COCH_2COOC_2H_5 + C_2H_5O^- \rightleftarrows CH_3CO\overset{..}{\overset{-}{C}}HCOOC_2H_5 + C_2H_5OH$$

16

Again, the reaction is an equilibrium which is shifted towards the products by the last step, the charge in the resulting anion being delocalized over several atoms. The desired product is obtained upon workup of the reaction mixture with aqueous acetic acid.

The charge in anion **16** is delocalized as follows,

$$CH_3\overset{\displaystyle O^-}{\overset{|}{C}}\!\!=\!\!CH\overset{\displaystyle O}{\overset{\|}{C}}OC_2H_5 \longleftrightarrow CH_3\overset{\displaystyle O}{\overset{\|}{C}}\overset{..}{\overset{-}{C}}H\overset{\displaystyle O}{\overset{\|}{C}}OC_2H_5 \longleftrightarrow CH_3\overset{\displaystyle O}{\overset{\|}{C}}CH\!\!=\!\!\overset{\displaystyle O^-}{\overset{|}{C}}OC_2H_5$$

Since the last step requires abstraction of a proton by the base, esters such as ethyl isobutyrate **17** do not form isolable condensation products in the presence of sodium ethoxide. The product **18** does not contain the very labile hydrogen required, and the equilibrium lies far to the left. However, treatment of this ester with the stronger base triphenylmethylsodium **19** converts the reactant almost completely to its conjugate base and this can be employed for effecting condensations:

$$2CH_3-\underset{\underset{H}{|}}{\overset{\overset{CH_3}{|}}{C}}-\overset{\overset{O}{||}}{C}OC_2H_5 \underset{}{\overset{C_2H_5O^-}{\rightleftharpoons}} CH_3-\underset{\underset{H}{|}}{\overset{\overset{CH_3}{|}}{C}}-\overset{\overset{O}{||}}{C}-\underset{\underset{CH_3}{|}}{\overset{\overset{CH_3}{|}}{C}}-\overset{\overset{O}{||}}{C}OC_2H_5 + C_2H_5OH$$

17   **18**

However,

$$CH_3-\underset{\underset{H}{|}}{\overset{\overset{CH_3}{|}}{C}}-\overset{\overset{O}{||}}{C}OC_2H_5 + \phi_3C^-Na^+ \longrightarrow CH_3-\underset{}{\overset{\overset{CH_3}{|}}{C}}=\underset{}{\overset{\overset{O^-Na^+}{|}}{C}}OC_2H_5 + \phi_3CH$$

17   **19**

and

$$\phi\overset{\overset{O}{||}}{C}Cl + CH_3-\underset{}{\overset{\overset{CH_3}{|}}{C}}=\underset{}{\overset{\overset{O^-Na^+}{|}}{C}}OC_2H_5 \longrightarrow \phi\overset{\overset{O}{||}}{C}-\underset{\underset{CH_3}{|}}{\overset{\overset{CH_3}{|}}{C}}-\overset{\overset{O}{||}}{C}OC_2H_5 + NaCl$$

This reagent **19** also converts ethyl isobutyrate to the product **18**:

$$2CH_3-\underset{\underset{H}{|}}{\overset{\overset{CH_3}{|}}{C}}-\overset{\overset{O}{||}}{C}OC_2H_5 \overset{\phi_3CNa}{\longrightarrow} CH_3-\underset{\underset{H}{|}}{\overset{\overset{CH_3}{|}}{C}}-\overset{\overset{O}{||}}{C}-\underset{\underset{CH_3}{|}}{\overset{\overset{CH_3}{|}}{C}}-\overset{\overset{O}{||}}{C}OC_2H_5$$

17   **18**

Another reaction related to these processes is the Dieckmann reaction which is essentially an intramolecular Claisen condensation,

$$\underset{CH_2}{\overset{CH_2}{\underset{|}{\overset{|}{\underset{CH_2}{\overset{}{}}}}}}\begin{matrix}CH_2 \\ COOC_2H_5 \\ \\ COOC_2H_5\end{matrix} \overset{C_2H_5ONa}{\longrightarrow} \text{(cyclopentanone)}-COOC_2H_5$$

Thusfar we have discussed the reactions of carbonyl compounds possessing α-hydrogens. These α-hydrogens are sufficiently acidic that the carbonyl compound is converted to some degree to its conjugate base, and the latter is capable of attacking another carbonyl system.

Carbonyl compounds such as benzaldehyde and formaldehyde that do not possess α-hydrogens cannot form conjugate bases, they are, however, subject to attack by other nucleophiles. For example, we have already described the reaction of benzaldehyde with cyanide ion to form the cyanohydrin in Section 15.2.

Another reaction of benzaldehyde that involves cyanide is the benzoin condensation.

16.4 The Benzoin Condensation

The benzoin condensation is a dimerization of benzaldehyde to yield the ketone benzoin, and cyanide ion appears to be the only effective catalyst in this reaction,

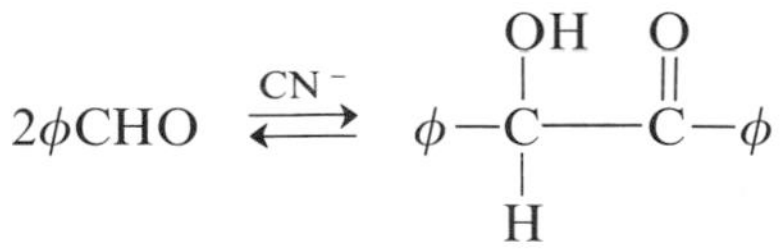

$$2\phi CHO \overset{CN^-}{\rightleftharpoons} \phi-\overset{\overset{\displaystyle OH}{|}}{\underset{\underset{\displaystyle H}{|}}{C}}-\overset{\overset{\displaystyle O}{\|}}{C}-\phi$$

Mixed benzoins can be effected if the reactants are properly chosen. Thus,

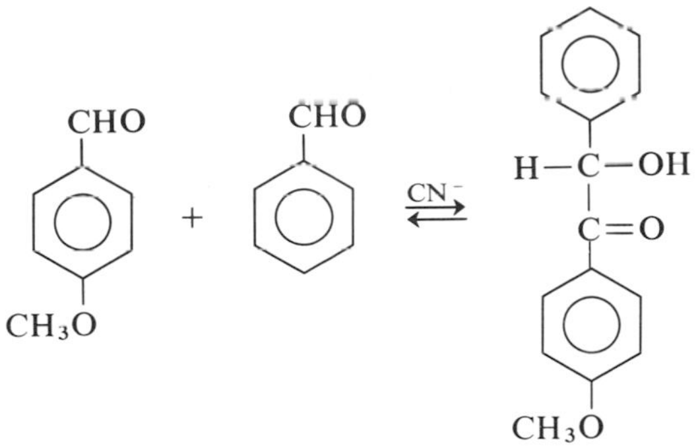

The reversibility of the reaction is demonstrated by the reaction of benzoin with potassium cyanide in the presence of anisaldehyde. The equilibrium lies to the right,

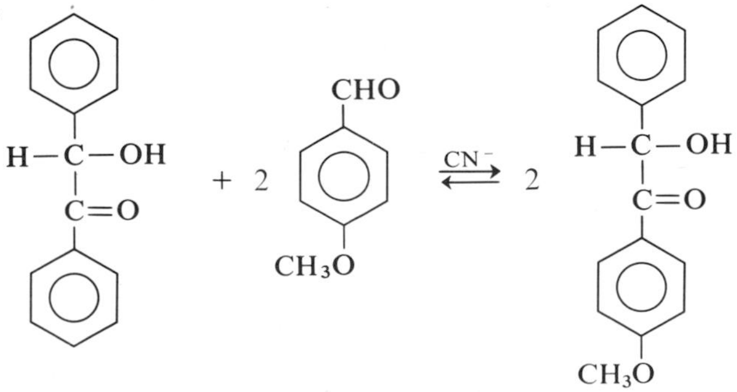

In this experiment the benzoin reverts to benzaldehyde which then condenses with anisaldehyde:

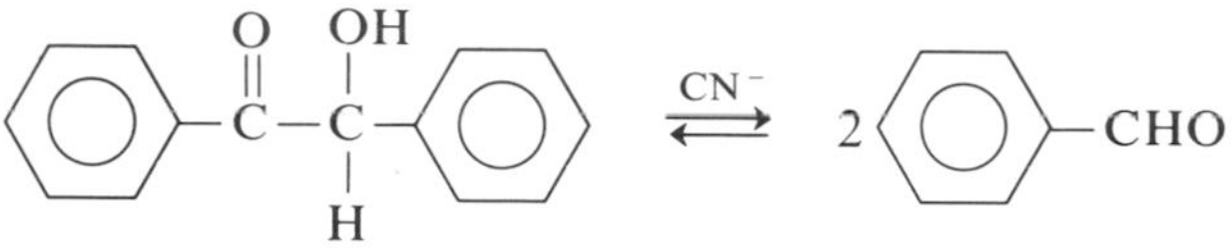

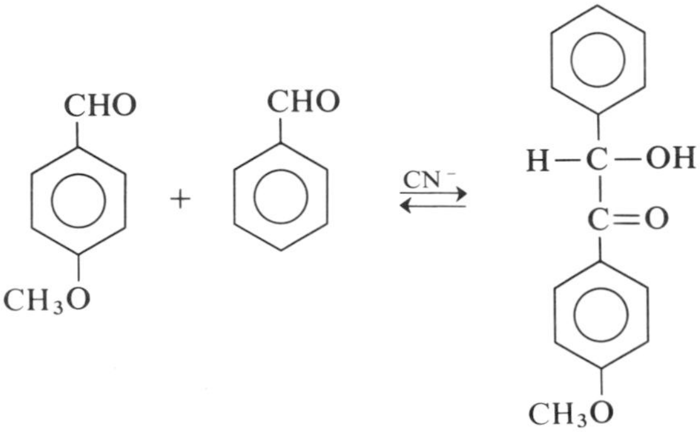

The kinetics of the benzoin condensation have been investigated, and the general rate expression is third order, second order in benzaldehyde and first order in cyanide ion. Consequently the rate limiting step involves two molecules of benzaldehyde and one cyanide ion:

$$-\frac{d[\phi CHO]}{dt} = k[\phi CHO]^2[CN^-]$$

The following mechanism with the condensation step rate limiting is consistent with this evidence:

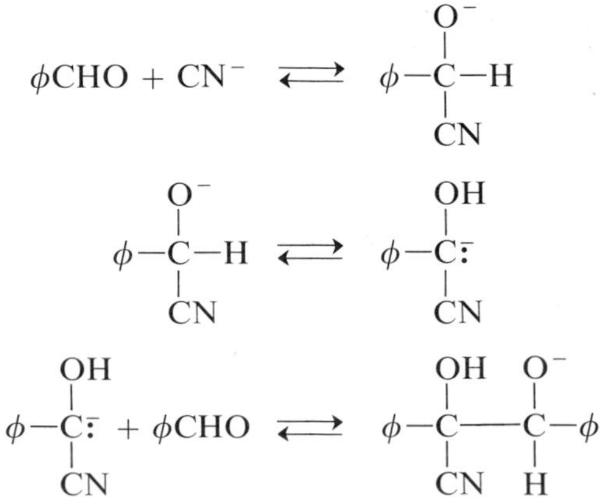

$$\phi-\overset{\displaystyle OH}{\underset{\displaystyle CN}{\overset{|}{\underset{|}{C}}}}-\overset{\displaystyle O^-}{\underset{\displaystyle H}{\overset{|}{\underset{|}{C}}}}-\phi \quad \rightleftharpoons \quad \phi-\overset{\displaystyle O^-}{\underset{\displaystyle CN}{\overset{|}{\underset{|}{C}}}}-\overset{\displaystyle OH}{\underset{\displaystyle H}{\overset{|}{\underset{|}{C}}}}-\phi$$

$$\phi-\overset{\displaystyle O^-}{\underset{\displaystyle CN}{\overset{|}{\underset{|}{C}}}}-\overset{\displaystyle OH}{\underset{\displaystyle H}{\overset{|}{\underset{|}{C}}}}-\phi \quad \rightleftharpoons \quad \phi-\overset{\displaystyle O}{\underset{}{\overset{||}{C}}}-\overset{\displaystyle OH}{\underset{\displaystyle H}{\overset{|}{\underset{|}{C}}}}-\phi + CN^-$$

The first step is attack of the carbonyl group by cyanide ion, and this is the same as the first step in cyanohydrin formation. This anion is then converted to the resonance stabilized tautomer which condenses, in what is most probably the rate limiting step, with another molecule of benzaldehyde. The product of this step next rearranges to the tautomeric material which expels cyanide ion. This last step is the same as that involved in the decomposition of cyanohydrins.

The reason why cyanide ion is apparently the only effective catalyst is that it is the only material (that has been tried so far) that can both attack the carbonyl group and effectively stabilize the anion intermediate,

$$\phi-\overset{\displaystyle OH}{\underset{\displaystyle \underset{||}{\underset{N}{C}}}{\overset{|}{C}\colon^{\overline{}}}} \quad \longleftrightarrow \quad \phi-\overset{\displaystyle OH}{\underset{\displaystyle \underset{||}{\underset{N^-}{C}}}{\overset{|}{C}}}$$

One reaction that benzaldehyde undergoes is the benzoin condensation. Another reaction more typical of carbonyl systems not possessing α-hydrogens is the Cannizzaro reaction.

16.5 The Cannizzaro Reaction

Carbonyl compounds possessing α-hydrogens undergo the aldol condensation when treated with base. Compounds not possessing such hydrogens cannot behave in this way; they do, however, under somewhat more strenuous conditions react. This reaction, which is common for these compounds, is an oxidation-reduction process known as the Cannizzaro reaction. One molecule of the aldehyde is reduced to the alcohol while a second is oxidized to the conjugate base of a carboxylic acid:

$$2\phi CHO + OH^- \longrightarrow \phi CH_2OH + \phi COO^-$$

The reaction appears to proceed by a number of mechanisms, and these vary with the carbonyl compound and the reaction conditions. If the reaction is conducted under ionic conditions and where all of the materials are soluble in the solvent, the process proceeds by two distinct mechanisms. The general rate expression for the reaction of formaldehyde appears to have the form,

$$k_1[\text{HCHO}]^2[\text{OH}^-] + k_2[\text{HCHO}]^2[\text{OH}^-]^2$$

where the fourth order term is expected to become more important at higher hydroxide ion concentrations.

Both terms in the rate law are second order in formaldehyde. Two molecules of formaldehyde are involved in the rate limiting step, and it is logical to assume that one of these molecules transfers hydride to the other. The donor becomes oxidized, and the hydride acceptor becomes reduced.

In agreement with this is the observation that the reaction of formaldehyde in D_2O leads to products having no deuterium attached to the carbon atoms; thus, the reduction does not involve the solvent.

A logical first step is the attack of formaldehyde by hydroxide ion, and under the reaction conditions this process is expected to be rapid and reversible:

$$
\underset{\begin{array}{c}\text{H}-\overset{\displaystyle \text{O}}{\overset{\|}{\text{C}}}-\text{H} + \text{OH}^-\end{array}}{} \quad \rightleftharpoons \quad \underset{\begin{array}{c}\text{H}-\overset{\displaystyle \text{O}^-}{\overset{|}{\underset{|}{\text{C}}}}-\text{H}\\[-2pt]\text{OH}\end{array}}{}
$$

The rate limiting step is a transfer of hydride from this species to a second molecule of formaldehyde:

$$
\text{H}-\overset{\text{O}^-}{\underset{\text{OH}}{\overset{|}{\underset{|}{\text{C}}}}}-\text{H} + \overset{\text{H}}{\underset{\text{H}}{\overset{|}{\underset{|}{\text{C}}}}}=\text{O} \longrightarrow \text{H}-\overset{\text{O}}{\overset{\|}{\text{C}}}-\text{OH} \quad \text{H}-\overset{\text{H}}{\underset{\text{H}}{\overset{|}{\underset{|}{\text{C}}}}}-\text{O}^-
$$

where the transition state is,

$$
\underset{\text{HO}}{\text{H}-\overset{\text{O}^{\delta-}}{\overset{\|}{\text{C}}}} \underset{\text{H}}{\diagdown} \quad \overset{}{\underset{\text{H}}{\diagup}} \underset{\text{H}}{\overset{\text{O}^{\delta-}}{\overset{\|}{\text{C}}}-\text{H}}
$$

These two intermediates undergo a rapid acid-base reaction to yield the products:

$$
\text{H}-\overset{\text{O}}{\overset{\|}{\text{C}}}-\text{OH} \quad \text{CH}_3\text{O}^- \longrightarrow \text{HCOO}^- + \text{CH}_3\text{OH}
$$

This is the third order reaction. The fourth order reaction also involves the species,

$$
\text{H}-\overset{\text{O}^-}{\underset{\text{OH}}{\overset{|}{\underset{|}{\text{C}}}}}-\text{H}
$$

Consider the equilibria,

$$
\underset{\substack{\text{O}\\ \|}}{\text{H}-\text{C}-\text{H}} + \text{OH}^- \; \rightleftarrows \; \underset{\substack{\text{O}^-\\ |}}{\text{H}-\underset{\substack{|\\ \text{OH}}}{\text{C}}-\text{H}}
$$

$$
\underset{\substack{\text{O}^-\\ |}}{\text{H}-\underset{\substack{|\\ \text{OH}}}{\text{C}}-\text{H}} + \text{OH}^- \; \rightleftarrows \; \underset{\substack{\text{O}^-\\ |}}{\text{H}-\underset{\substack{|\\ \text{O}^-}}{\text{C}}-\text{H}} + \text{H}_2\text{O}
$$

20

where **20**, although present in very low concentration, is expected to be highly reactive.

The equilibrium concentration of **20** depends upon the concentration of formaldehyde to the first power and the square of the hydroxide ion concentration. A rate limiting hydride transfer from this species to a molecule of formaldehyde satisfies the fourth order term in the rate law:

$$
\underset{\substack{\text{O}^-\\ |}}{\text{H}-\underset{\substack{|\\ \text{O}^-}}{\text{C}}-\text{H}} + \underset{\substack{\text{H}\\ |}}{\underset{\substack{|\\ \text{H}}}{\text{C}}=\text{O}} \longrightarrow \underset{\substack{\text{O}\\ \|}}{\text{H}-\text{C}-\text{O}^-} + \underset{\substack{\text{H}\\ |}}{\text{H}-\underset{\substack{|\\ \text{H}}}{\text{C}}-\text{O}^-}
$$

and

$$
\text{CH}_3\text{O}^- + \text{H}_2\text{O} \; \rightleftarrows \; \text{CH}_3\text{OH} + \text{OH}^-
$$

Formaldehyde reacts by both of these processes, so does furfural, but changing the solvent and the hydroxide ion concentration causes one or the other of these processes to predominate.

When the reaction is carried out using aqueous alkali and organic aldehydes that are only sparingly soluble, still another mechanism is in evidence. In the aqueous portion of the reaction mixture, the aldehyde reacts by one or both of the mechanisms just presented. In the organic portion of the reaction mixture another process occurs.

Thus benzaldehyde when treated with aqueous alkali affords benzyl alcohol and sodium benzoate, and in the aqueous phase the reaction ordinarily proceeds by the third order process just discussed,

$$
2\phi\text{CHO} + \text{OH}^- \longrightarrow \phi\text{CH}_2\text{OH} + \phi\text{COO}^-
$$

In the organic phase it appears that some of the conjugate base of benzyl alcohol, formed in the aqueous phase, attacks the carbonyl carbon atom:

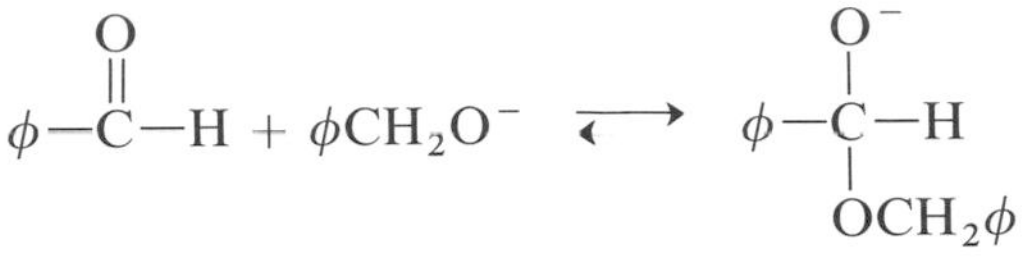

$$\phi-\overset{\overset{\textstyle O}{\|}}{C}-H + \phi CH_2O^- \; \rightleftharpoons \; \phi-\overset{\overset{\textstyle O^-}{|}}{\underset{\underset{\textstyle OCH_2\phi}{|}}{C}}-H$$

This intermediate is an effective hydride transfer agent and delivers hydride to a molecule of benzaldehyde:

$$\phi-\overset{\overset{\textstyle O^-}{|}}{\underset{\underset{\textstyle OCH_2\phi}{|}}{C}}-H \;\; + \overset{\overset{\textstyle H}{|}}{\underset{\underset{\textstyle \phi}{|}}{C}}=O \;\; \longrightarrow \;\; \phi-\overset{\overset{\textstyle O}{\|}}{C}-OCH_2\phi + \phi CH_2O^-$$

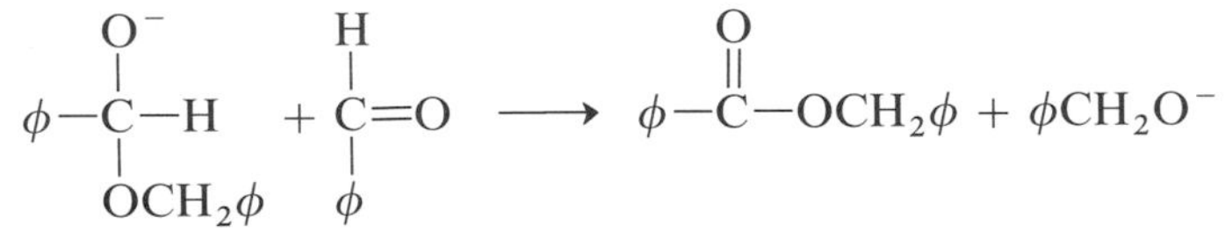

The products are benzyl benzoate, which is subsequently hydrolyzed by the alkali to benzoate anion and benzyl alcohol, and the alkoxide anion ϕCH_2O^-. This can either attack another molecule of benzaldehyde and thereby continue the process or react with water to form benzyl alcohol. Evidence for this reaction comes from the isolation of benzyl benzoate as the actual reaction product when the reaction is conducted under mild conditions, and from the fact that ϕCH_2O^- is known to convert benzaldehyde to benzyl benzoate.

Just as crossed aldols were possible, crossed Cannizzaros can also be carried out. In these reactions formaldehyde is the second aldehyde, and this generally acts as the hydride donor. Aldehydes are reduced to alcohols in this manner,

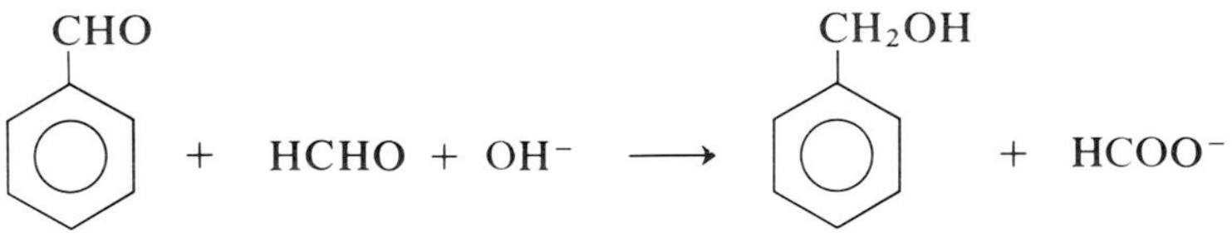

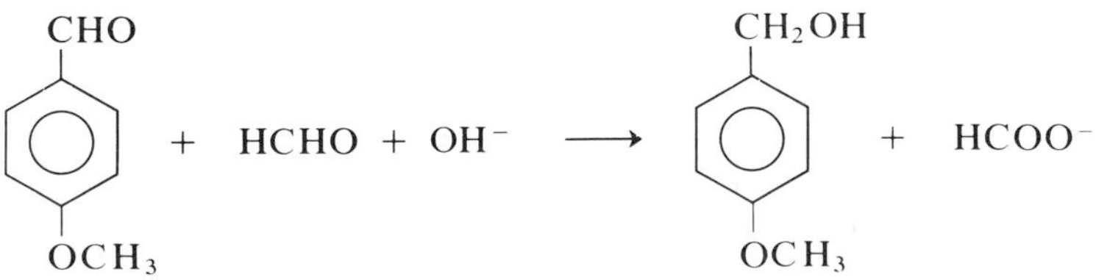

The synthesis of pentaerythritol **21** is an industrial preparation using acetaldehyde and formaldehyde. The reaction involves three aldol condensations followed by a crossed Cannizzaro.

The three α-hydrogens are available, and three aldol condensations occur. This product is not isolated, but under the reaction conditions it reacts with a fourth molecule of formaldehyde, the aldehyde being reduced to a primary alcohol:

$$
CH_3CHO + 3HCHO \xrightarrow{\ OH^-\ } HOCH_2-\overset{\displaystyle CH_2OH}{\underset{\displaystyle CH_2OH}{C}}-CHO
$$

$$
HOCH_2-\overset{\displaystyle CH_2OH}{\underset{\displaystyle CH_2OH}{C}}-CHO + HCHO + OH^- \longrightarrow C(CH_2OH)_4 + HCOO^-
$$

21

Intramolecular reactions are also possible. Thus glyoxal when treated with sodium hydroxide affords the anion of glycolic acid,

$$
\underset{\displaystyle}{H-\overset{\displaystyle O}{\overset{\displaystyle \|}{C}}-\overset{\displaystyle O}{\overset{\displaystyle \|}{C}}-H} + OH^- \longrightarrow H-\overset{\displaystyle OH}{\underset{\displaystyle H}{\overset{\displaystyle |}{\underset{\displaystyle |}{C}}}}-\overset{\displaystyle O}{\overset{\displaystyle \|}{C}}-O^-
$$

Phenylglyoxal behaves similarly.

$$
\phi-\overset{\displaystyle O}{\overset{\displaystyle \|}{C}}-\overset{\displaystyle O}{\overset{\displaystyle \|}{C}}-H + OH^- \longrightarrow \phi-\overset{\displaystyle OH}{\underset{\displaystyle H}{\overset{\displaystyle |}{\underset{\displaystyle |}{C}}}}-\overset{\displaystyle O}{\overset{\displaystyle \|}{C}}-O^-
$$

In this reaction it is possible that a hydride shifts (Cannizzaro reaction) or that a phenyl group migrates (benzilic acid rearrangement). Studies involving deuterium and radioactive carbon indicate that it is the hydrogen that actually migrates.

When hydrogens are not present, phenyl groups do migrate. The reaction of benzil with concentrated alkali affords the conjugate base of benzilic acid. The reaction is appropriately named the benzilic acid rearrangement.

$$
\phi-\overset{\displaystyle O}{\overset{\displaystyle \|}{C}}-\overset{\displaystyle O}{\overset{\displaystyle \|}{C}}-\phi + OH^- \longrightarrow \phi-\overset{\displaystyle OH}{\underset{\displaystyle \phi}{\overset{\displaystyle |}{\underset{\displaystyle |}{C}}}}-\overset{\displaystyle O}{\overset{\displaystyle \|}{C}}-O^-
$$

The mechanism that one is tempted to write for this process, and which is substantiated by the experimental evidence, involves a rapid and reversible attack of the carbonyl function by hydroxide ion followed by a rate limiting phenyl migration:

$$\phi-\overset{\overset{\displaystyle O}{\|}}{C}-\overset{\overset{\displaystyle O}{\|}}{C}-\phi + OH^- \;\rightleftharpoons\; \phi-\overset{\overset{\displaystyle O}{\|}}{C}-\underset{\underset{\displaystyle OH}{|}}{\overset{\overset{\displaystyle O^-}{|}}{C}}-\phi$$

$$\phi-\overset{\overset{\displaystyle O}{\|}}{C}-\underset{\underset{\displaystyle \phi}{|}}{\overset{\overset{\displaystyle O^-}{|}}{C}}-OH \;\longrightarrow\; \phi-\underset{\underset{\displaystyle \phi}{|}}{\overset{\overset{\displaystyle {}^-O}{|}}{C}}-\overset{\overset{\displaystyle O}{\|}}{C}-OH$$

$$\phi-\underset{\underset{\displaystyle \phi}{|}}{\overset{\overset{\displaystyle {}^-O}{|}}{C}}-\overset{\overset{\displaystyle O}{\|}}{C}-OH \;\longrightarrow\; \phi-\underset{\underset{\displaystyle \phi}{|}}{\overset{\overset{\displaystyle OH}{|}}{C}}-\overset{\overset{\displaystyle O}{\|}}{C}-O^-$$

The general rate law predicted by this mechanism concurs with the experimental findings,

$$k[\phi COCO\phi][OH^-]$$

where the measured rate constant k is a composite specific rate constant.

The reaction is accelerated by hydroxide ion, and except for a salt effect does not depend upon the concentration of other bases.

Furthermore, addition to the carbonyl carbon atom is known to be much more rapid than the benzilic acid rearrangement itself. This is illustrated by the isolation of an adduct from the reaction between benzil and potassium hydroxide. This adduct presumably has the structure,

$$\phi-\overset{\overset{\displaystyle O}{\|}}{C}-\underset{\underset{\displaystyle OH}{|}}{\overset{\overset{\displaystyle O^-K^+}{|}}{C}}-\phi$$

and is formed rapidly (2-3 minutes) while the benzilic acid rearrangement proceeds much more slowly.

Additional evidence comes from O^{18} exchange. In the presence of H_2O^{18} and $O^{18}H^-$, benzil exchanges its oxygen atoms more rapidly than it undergoes rearrangement,

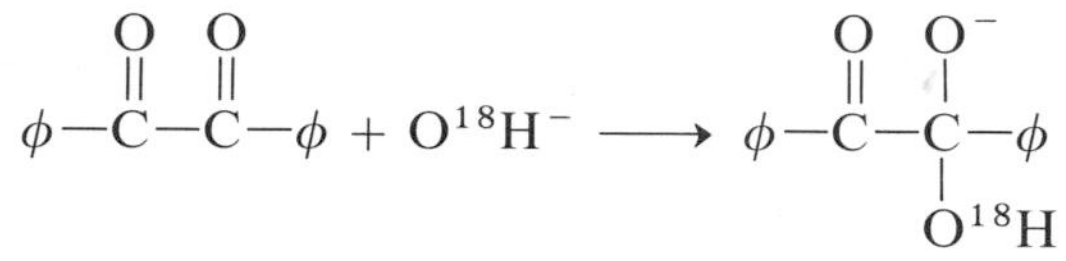

$$\phi-\overset{O}{\overset{||}{C}}-\overset{O}{\overset{||}{C}}-\phi + O^{18}H^- \longrightarrow \phi-\overset{O}{\overset{||}{C}}-\overset{O^-}{\underset{\underset{O^{18}H}{|}}{\overset{|}{C}}}-\phi$$

22

The intermediate **22** either by an intramolecular proton transfer or by way of the hydrate forms the equivalent material **23** which, when it eliminates hydroxide ion, forms benzil containing O^{18},

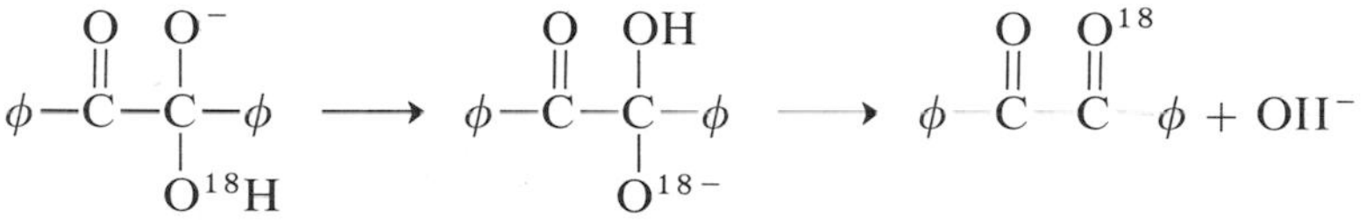

$$\phi-\overset{O}{\overset{||}{C}}-\underset{\underset{O^{18}H}{|}}{\overset{O^-}{\overset{|}{C}}}-\phi \longrightarrow \phi-\overset{O}{\overset{||}{C}}-\underset{\underset{O^{18-}}{|}}{\overset{OH}{\overset{|}{C}}}-\phi \longrightarrow \phi-\overset{O}{\overset{||}{C}}-\overset{O^{18}}{\overset{||}{C}}-\phi + OH^-$$

22   **23**

Still other evidence confirming this mechanism exists. Benzil reacts with sodium methoxide to form the methyl ester of benzilic acid, and this indicates that the hydrogen atom of hydroxide is not required in the rate limiting step. Reaction in D_2O confirms this fact,

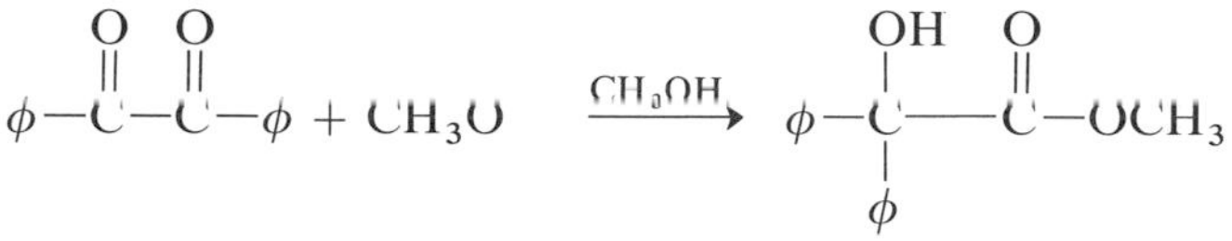

$$\phi-\overset{O}{\overset{||}{C}}-\overset{O}{\overset{||}{C}}-\phi + CH_3O \xrightarrow{CH_3OH} \phi-\underset{\underset{\phi}{|}}{\overset{OH}{\overset{|}{C}}}-\overset{O}{\overset{||}{C}}-OCH_3$$

There are other α-diketones which, when treated with strong base, behave similarly. Phenanthrenequinone suffers a benzilic acid rearrangement, and other aromatic ketones do also,

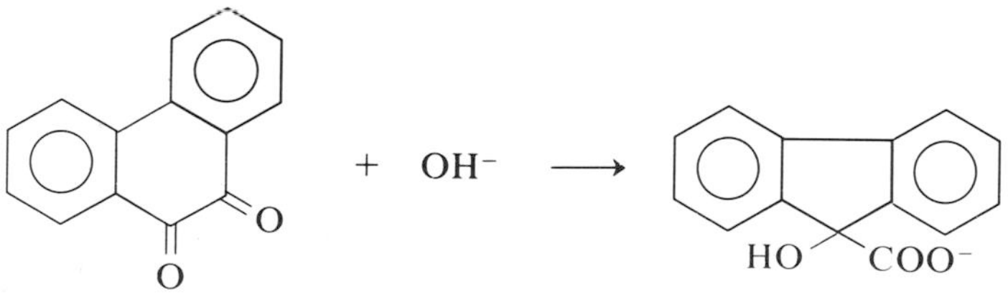

Most aliphatic diketones such as diacetyl $CH_3COCOCH_3$ react by way of aldol condensations. There are, however, some aliphatic exceptions.

We find that possible routes of reaction for carbonyl compounds are the aldol condensation (and related processes), the Cannizzaro reaction, and the benzilic acid rearrangement. The reaction that occurs depends upon the particular carbonyl compound and the reaction conditions. The Cannizzaro reaction proceeds by a number of different mechanisms all leading to the same products, an alcohol and a carboxylate anion, and as a matter of fact, the three mechanisms we have presented here for this reaction are not the only ones. Other pathways leading to these products exist.

Supplementary Reading

1. Fuson, R. C., *Reactions of Organic Compounds*. New York, Wiley, 1962.

2. Gould, E. S., *Mechanism and Structure in Organic Chemistry*. New York, Holt, 1959.

3. Hammett, L. P., *Physical Organic Chemistry*. New York, McGraw-Hill, 1940.

4. Hine, J., *Physical Organic Chemistry*. New York, McGraw-Hill, 1962.

5. House, H. O., *Modern Synthetic Reactions*. New York, Benjamin, 1965.

6. Ingold, C. K., *Structure and Mechanism in Organic Chemistry*. Ithaca, New York, Cornell U.P., 1953.

7. Royals, E. E., *Advanced Organic Chemistry*. Englewood Cliffs, New Jersey, Prentice-Hall, 1954.

Chapter 17

Esters and Related Compounds

17.1 General Discussion

We present in this chapter some of the reactions of amides, esters, acid anhydrides, and acid chlorides. These materials are all stabilized in the following fashion,

$$\underset{\substack{\| \\ R-C-X}}{O} \longleftrightarrow \underset{\substack{| \\ R-C=\overset{+}{X}}}{O^-}$$

and all behave similarly. However, acid chlorides and acid anhydrides are less stabilized by electronic delocalization (resonance) of this type than esters, and these less stabilized than amides. Consequently, in any reaction where this electronic delocalization is partially or completely destroyed in the transition state, the reactivity of these reagents decreases as stabilization increases, for the free energy of activation increases as the reactant becomes more stable.

This electronic delocalization, which puts double bond character into the C—X bond, accounts for, in esters and amides, the restricted rotation about this bond:

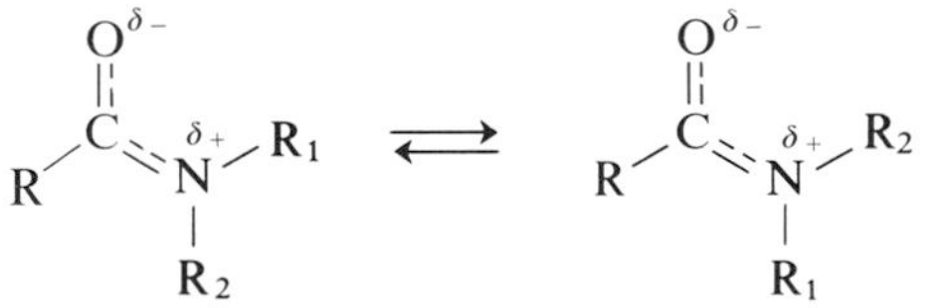

$$\underset{\substack{| \\ R_2}}{\overset{O^{\delta-}}{\underset{R}{\overset{\|}{C}}\underset{N}{\overset{\delta+}{\diagdown}}R_1}} \rightleftharpoons \underset{\substack{| \\ R_1}}{\overset{O^{\delta-}}{\underset{R}{\overset{\|}{C}}\underset{N}{\overset{\delta+}{\diagdown}}R_2}}$$

The NMR spectrum of dimethylacetamide in Figure 17–1 shows two N—CH$_3$ peaks at −24°C, indicating that at this temperature the two groups are not equivalent. At 63° only the single average peak is observed. (The C—CH$_3$ peak is not shown.) The energy barrier to rotation is 12 kcal/mole.

Of course, in amides containing N—H bonds, intramolecular hydrogen bonding is important and also provides a barrier to rotation.

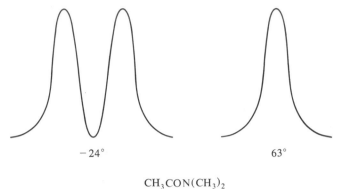

$$-24°\qquad\qquad\qquad 63°$$

$$CH_3CON(CH_3)_2$$

Figure 17–1

Esters also exhibit restricted rotation and the small dipole moment (~ 1.9 D) favors the structure,

The alternative,

would have a much larger moment (~ 4 D).

The reactions that we shall discuss involve nucleophilic attack by some reagent Y^- on the system RCOX. The equation for the transformation can be written simply as

$$R-\overset{\displaystyle O}{\overset{\|}{C}}-X + Y^- \longrightarrow R-\overset{\displaystyle O}{\overset{\|}{C}}-Y + X^-$$

and this process is generally considered to be a two-step reaction where either step can be rate limiting. The mechanism becomes,

$$R-\overset{\overset{\displaystyle O}{\|}}{C}-X + Y^- \ \rightleftharpoons\ R-\overset{\overset{\displaystyle O^-}{|}}{\underset{\underset{\displaystyle Y}{|}}{C}}-X$$

1

$$R-\overset{\overset{\displaystyle O^-}{|}}{\underset{\underset{\displaystyle Y}{|}}{C}}-X \ \longrightarrow\ R-\overset{\overset{\displaystyle O}{\|}}{C}-Y + X^-$$

The rate limiting step depends upon which group X^- or Y^- is lost more readily by the intermediate **1**. If Y^- is lost much more easily than X^-, then **1** reverts to reactants much more frequently than it passes on to products, and the second step becomes rate limiting. If X^- is lost more readily, the intermediate passes on to products and virtually never returns to reactants. In such cases the first step is rate limiting. The transition states are,

$$R-\overset{\overset{\displaystyle \overset{..}{O}^{\delta-}}{\|}}{\underset{\underset{\displaystyle Y^{\delta-}}{|}}{C}}-X \qquad R-\overset{\overset{\displaystyle \overset{..}{O}^{\delta-}}{\|}}{\underset{\underset{\displaystyle Y}{|}}{C}}--X^{\delta-}$$

where the first is the transition state for the first step and the other that in the second step. It is also possible for neither step to be truly rate limiting. This occurs when **1** returns to reactants and passes on to products at about the same rate.

The strengths of the $C-X$ and $C-Y$ bonds as well as the ability of X and Y to accommodate a negative charge must be considered. Steric factors can also play a role. For the series–amide, ester, acid anhydride, acid chloride–the reactivity is in the expected order. The NR_2 and OR groups are poorer leaving groups than the $OCOR$ and Cl groups.

There is one reaction which certain amides can undergo that the other reagents in this group cannot undergo. If the nitrogen in an amide bears hydrogen atoms, that amide can react with Y^- to form its charge delocalized conjugate base,

$$R-\overset{\overset{\displaystyle O}{\|}}{C}-NH_2 + Y^- \ \rightleftharpoons\ R-\overset{\overset{\displaystyle O^{\delta-}}{\|}}{C}{=}\overset{\delta-}{N}H + HY$$

Since the conjugate base is similar to a carboxylate anion RCOO⁻, the amide hydrogens are relatively labile. In fact if the base is sufficiently strong and the reaction conditions vigorous, both hydrogens in an amide of the type $RCONH_2$ can be lost. For example, these substances liberate a single equivalent of methane when treated with methyl magnesium iodide at room temperature and two equivalents upon heating:

$$R-\overset{\overset{\displaystyle O}{\|}}{C}-NH_2 + 2CH_3MgI \xrightarrow{\Delta} RCON(MgI)_2 + 2CH_4$$

We have just discussed the idea that when treated with Grignard reagents certain amides behave as acids. Such behavior is not possible for esters, acid anhydrides and acid chlorides, and these can be converted easily to ketones or alcohols:

$$R-\overset{\overset{\displaystyle O}{\|}}{C}-X \xrightarrow{RMgX} R-\overset{\overset{\displaystyle OMgX}{|}}{\underset{\underset{\displaystyle R}{|}}{C}}-X \longrightarrow R-\overset{\overset{\displaystyle O}{\|}}{C}-R$$

$$R-\overset{\overset{\displaystyle O}{\|}}{C}-R \xrightarrow{RMgX} R-\overset{\overset{\displaystyle OMgX}{|}}{\underset{\underset{\displaystyle R}{|}}{C}}-R \xrightarrow{H_2O} R-\overset{\overset{\displaystyle OH}{|}}{\underset{\underset{\displaystyle R}{|}}{C}}-R$$

The ketone can be obtained as the major product if inverse addition is employed, that is, if the Grignard reagent is added to excess reactant. This arrests the reaction at the first stage.

These same three classes of reagents–esters, acid anhydrides, and acid chlorides–also behave similarly with lithium aluminum hydride. All are converted to primary alcohols by this reagent and the mechanism is the same for each:

$$R-\overset{\overset{\displaystyle O}{\|}}{C}-X \xrightarrow{LiAlH_4} RCH_2OH$$

The mechanism involves transfers of hydride from AlH_4^- to the carbonyl carbon atom:

$$R-\overset{\overset{\displaystyle O}{\|}}{C}-X \xrightarrow{LiAlH_4} R-\overset{\overset{\displaystyle O^-}{|}}{\underset{\underset{\displaystyle H}{|}}{C}}-X \longrightarrow R-\overset{\overset{\displaystyle O}{\|}}{C}-H$$

$$R-\overset{\overset{\displaystyle O}{\|}}{C}-H \xrightarrow{LiAlH_4} R-\overset{\overset{\displaystyle O-Al}{|}}{\underset{\underset{\displaystyle H}{|}}{C}}-H \xrightarrow{H_2O} RCH_2OH$$

N,N-disubstituted amides behave differently, for these materials afford
amines and, under special conditions, aldehydes when reacted with lithium
aluminum hydride,

$$\begin{matrix} O \\ \| \\ R-C-NR_2 \end{matrix} \xrightarrow{\text{LiAlH}_4} RCH_2NR_2$$

The intermediate **2** is involved, but the electrons on the nitrogen are used to
displace the group OAl and the resulting species is reduced further:

$$\begin{matrix} O \\ \| \\ R-CNR_2 \end{matrix} \xrightarrow{\text{LiAlH}_4} \begin{matrix} OAl \\ | \\ R-C-NR_2 \\ | \\ H \end{matrix} \longrightarrow \begin{matrix} \\ R-C=\overset{+}{N}R_2 \\ | \\ H \end{matrix} \xrightarrow{\text{LiAlH}_4} RCH_2NR_2$$

2

A reaction common to all of these materials is their hydrolysis to carboxylic
acids; a reaction accelerated by bases and catalyzed by acids. Most of the
research in this area has been in connection with the behavior of esters under
hydrolysis conditions. We discuss their behavior first.

17.2 The Base Accelerated Hydrolyses of Esters

When hydrolyzed, esters form carboxylic acids and alcohols, and like many of
the reactions in which the carbonyl function participates, this can be an
equilibrium process. One way of shifting the equilibrium and carrying the
hydrolysis to completion is to employ a large excess of water:

$$\begin{matrix} O \\ \| \\ R-C-OR \end{matrix} + H_2O \rightleftharpoons \begin{matrix} O \\ \| \\ R-C-OH \end{matrix} + ROH$$

By the same token, the equilibrium can be shifted in the other direction
(esterification) by removing the water as it forms or by employing an excess
of the acid or alcohol.

Another way to shift the equilibrium is to conduct the hydrolysis under
basic conditions. The anion of the carboxylic acid is then the product, and this
does not revert to ester,

$$\begin{matrix} O \\ \| \\ R-C-OR \end{matrix} + HO^- \longrightarrow R-COO^- + ROH$$

This base accelerated hydrolysis is an irreversible process and proceeds by either of two mechanisms. The first is a direct S_N2 displacement by hydroxide ion on the alkyl carbon atom; the second an addition of hydroxide ion to the carbonyl carbon atom:

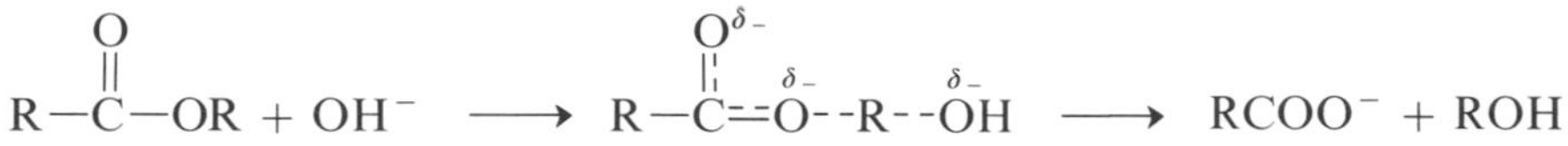

$$R-\overset{\overset{\text{O}}{\|}}{C}-OR + OH^- \longrightarrow R-\overset{\overset{\text{O}^{\delta-}}{\|}}{C}\!=\!\overset{\delta-}{O}\text{-}\text{-}R\text{-}\text{-}\overset{\delta-}{OH} \longrightarrow RCOO^- + ROH \tag{17--1}$$

$$R-\overset{\overset{\text{O}}{\|}}{C}-OR + OH^- \longrightarrow R-\underset{\underset{\text{OH}}{|}}{\overset{\overset{\text{O}^-}{|}}{C}}-OR \longrightarrow R-COO^- + ROH \tag{17--2}$$

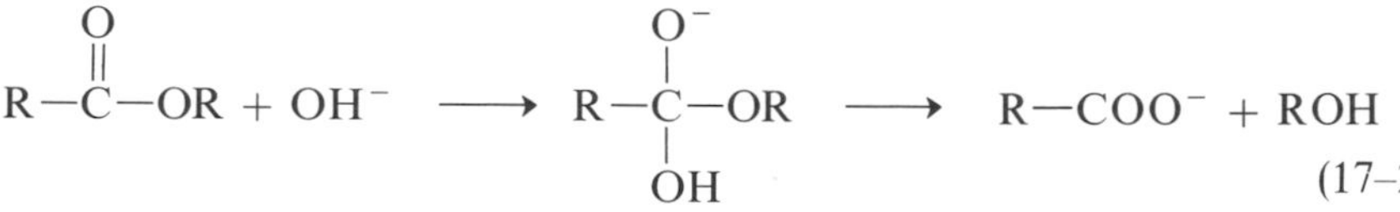

3

With the esters of carboxylic acids, the first process is much slower than the second and is not usually observed. However, the related reaction of methyl benzoate with sodium methoxide does yield dimethyl ether:

$$\phi-\overset{\overset{\text{O}}{\|}}{C}-OCH_3 + OCH_3^- \longrightarrow \phi COO^- + CH_3OCH_3$$

The other reaction, attack at the carbonyl carbon, also takes place but effects no change in the system,

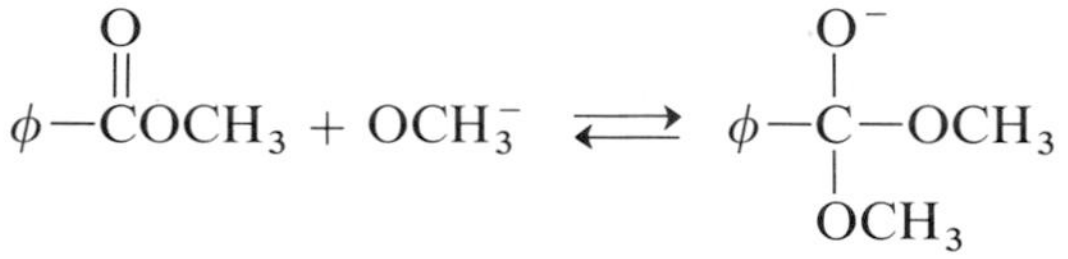

$$\phi-\overset{\overset{\text{O}}{\|}}{C}OCH_3 + OCH_3^- \rightleftharpoons \phi-\underset{\underset{\text{OCH}_3}{|}}{\overset{\overset{\text{O}^-}{|}}{C}}-OCH_3$$

Certain special systems such as β-lactones **4** are hydrolyzed by the S_N2 process at neutral or near neutral pH's. The evidence is that compounds such as **4** can be prepared in optically active form and undergo hydrolysis at neutral or near neutral pH's with inversion of configuration at the optically active center:

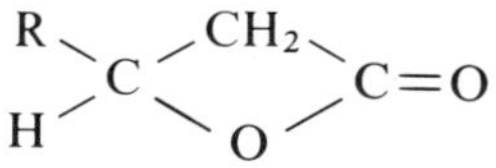

R CH₂
 C C=O
H O

4

At very high or very low pH's, the mechanism changes and the β-lactone is hydrolyzed with retention, indicating that the bond between the asymmetric carbon and oxygen remains intact.

The treatment of β-propiolatone **5** with methanol affords an ether, and this supports the idea of an S_N2 mechanism:

$$\begin{array}{c} H \\ \diagdown \\ \diagup \\ H \end{array} C \begin{array}{c} CH_2 \\ \diagdown \\ O \end{array} C = O \ + \ CH_3OH \ \longrightarrow \ CH_3OCH_2CH_2\overset{\overset{\displaystyle O}{\parallel}}{C}OH$$

5

In the presence of water enriched in O^{18}, compounds such as **4** yield hydroxy acids and the alcohol function contains excess O^{18}:

$$\begin{array}{c} R \\ \diagdown \\ \diagup \\ H \end{array} C \begin{array}{c} CH_2 \\ \diagdown \\ O \end{array} C = O \ + \ H_2O^{18} \ \longrightarrow \ R-\underset{\underset{\displaystyle O^{18}H}{|}}{C}HCH_2COOH$$

However, these reactions are the special cases, and the normal route for hydrolysis is by addition to the carbonyl function. The kinetics for the alkaline hydrolysis of a number of esters have been investigated, and the reaction is a second order process, first order in ester and first order in hydroxide ion,

$$k[RCOOR][OH^-]$$

While both mechanisms Eqs. (17–1) and (17–2) are consistent with this general rate law, other evidence indicates that Eq. (17–2) is operative.

The ester *n*-amyl acetate was treated with hydroxide ion labeled with O^{18}. Possibilities are,

$$CH_3\overset{\overset{\displaystyle O}{\parallel}}{C}OR \ | \ HO^{18-} \ \xrightarrow{S_N2} \ CH_3COO^- + RO^{18}H$$

or

$$CH_3\overset{\overset{\displaystyle O}{\parallel}}{C}OR + HO^{18-} \ \longrightarrow \ CH_3-\underset{\underset{\displaystyle O^{18}H}{|}}{\overset{\overset{\displaystyle O^-}{|}}{C}}-OR \ \longrightarrow \ CH_3COO^{18-} + ROH$$

The *n*-amyl alcohol that resulted was analyzed yet did not contain excess O^{18}, and this is excellent evidence that hydrolysis proceeds by the second mechanism.

A variant of this second mechanism has been proposed. It has been suggested that the second mechanism Eq. (17–2) may not actually involve the intermediate **3** but may proceed as a concerted process involving the transition state **6**.

While this other mechanism Eq. (17–3) agrees with the kinetic data and the O^{18} labeling experiment, there exists strong evidence against this proposal,

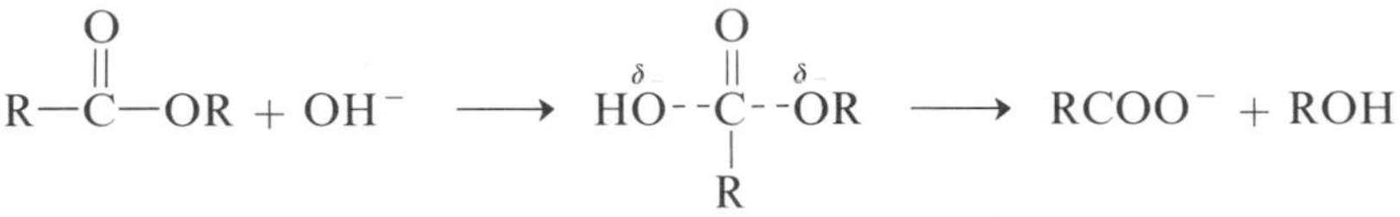

$$
\underset{\substack{\| \\ O}}{R-\overset{O}{\overset{\|}{C}}-OR} + OH^- \longrightarrow \overset{\overset{O}{\|}}{HO\overset{\delta}{-}-\overset{\|}{C}\overset{\delta}{-}-OR} \longrightarrow RCOO^- + ROH \quad (17\text{–}3)
$$

$$
R
$$

6

The evidence against Eq. (17–3) also involves O^{18} labeling but this time in the acyl oxygen atom,

$$
\overset{O^{18}}{\overset{\|}{R-COR}}
$$

Esters of this type were hydrolyzed in the presence of H_2O and hydroxide ion. Portions of the starting ester were recovered and analyzed for O^{18} at intervals during the hydrolysis, and it was found that the percentage of O^{18} in the ester decreased as the reaction proceeded:

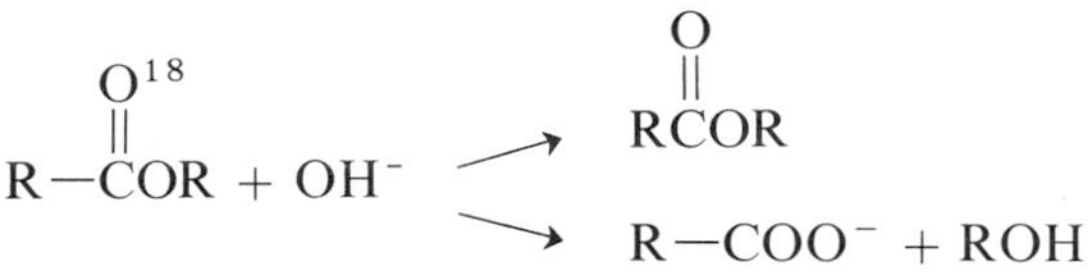

$$
\overset{O^{18}}{\overset{\|}{R-COR}} + OH^- \overset{\displaystyle \nearrow \overset{O}{\overset{\|}{RCOR}}}{\searrow R-COO^- + ROH}
$$

It was found that exchange of O^{18} occurred in the starting ester, and Eq. (17–3) cannot account for this fact. Equation (17–2), on the other hand, leads to the expectation that some exchange will occur when the intermediate reverts to the starting ester. The mechanism for the reaction becomes,

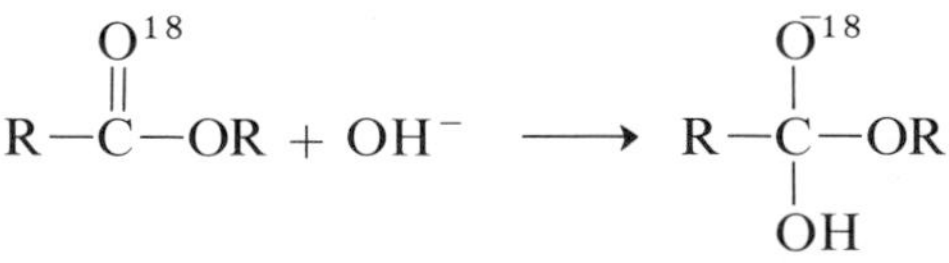

$$
\overset{O^{18}}{\overset{\|}{R-C-OR}} + OH^- \longrightarrow \overset{\overset{-}{O}{}^{18}}{\underset{\underset{OH}{|}}{\overset{|}{R-C-OR}}}
$$

This intermediate has three modes of decomposition open to it. It can expel hydroxide ion and revert to reactant. It can expel alkoxide ion and generate the products. Finally, this intermediate can pick up a proton from the solvent to form first the hydrate and then **7** or undergo an intramolecular proton transfer to form **7** directly:

$$
\begin{array}{c}
\overset{\displaystyle O^{18-}}{\underset{\displaystyle OH}{\underset{|}{\overset{|}{R-C-OR}}}}
\end{array}
\quad
\begin{array}{c}
\nearrow \\
\longrightarrow \\
\searrow
\end{array}
\quad
\begin{array}{c}
\overset{\displaystyle O^{18}}{\underset{}{\overset{\|}{R-C-OR}}} + OH^- \\[2mm]
\overset{\displaystyle O^{18}}{\underset{}{\overset{\|}{R-C-O^-}}} + ROH \\[2mm]
\overset{\displaystyle O^{18}H}{\underset{\displaystyle O^-}{\underset{|}{\overset{|}{R-C-OR}}}} \\[2mm]
\mathbf{7}
\end{array}
$$

Thus, Eq. (17–2) accounts for the observed O^{18} exchange, for it accommodates the formation of **7**, which when it reverts to reactant loses $O^{18}H$,

$$
\overset{\displaystyle O^{18}H}{\underset{\displaystyle O^-}{\underset{|}{\overset{|}{R-C-OR}}}} \longrightarrow \overset{\displaystyle O}{\overset{\|}{R-COR}} + O^{18}H^-
$$

Mechanism (17–2) satisfies all the experimental observations; hence it is reasonable to assume that the hydrolysis of esters occurs by this route. Mechanism (17–3) cannot account for the exchange of O^{18}, and it is unlikely that the exchange is due to a side reaction.

In these O^{18} exchange experiments, the O^{18} containing ester is converted to the normal ester and both of these hydrolyze to products. The kinetic scheme is:

$$
\overset{\displaystyle O^{18}}{\underset{\mathbf{8}}{\overset{\|}{R-C-OR}}} \xrightarrow[HO^-]{k_1} \overset{\displaystyle O}{\underset{\mathbf{9}}{\overset{\|}{R-C-OR}}}
$$

$$
\searrow{\scriptstyle k_2 \atop OH^-} \qquad \swarrow{\scriptstyle k_2 \atop OH^-}
$$

$$
RCOO^- + ROH
$$

As the reaction proceeds, the concentration of **8** and the total ester concentration [**8** + **9**] both decrease. The decrease in total ester concentration is due entirely to hydrolysis of these materials and is proportional to the concentration of the two esters:

$$
-\frac{d[OH^-]}{dt} = -\frac{d[\mathbf{8}+\mathbf{9}]}{dt} = k_2[\mathbf{8}+\mathbf{9}][OH^-]
$$

The O^{18} containing ester also decreases in concentration. There exist two pathways for its decomposition,

$$-\frac{d[\mathbf{8}]}{dt} = k_1[\mathbf{8}][OH^-] + k_2[\mathbf{8}][OH^-]$$

There result two equations in two unknowns (k_1 and k_2). The total ester concentration can be measured either directly or indirectly (in terms of the hydroxide ion concentration) at various intervals, and the concentration of O^{18} containing ester can also be determined. From the data, the rate constants k_1 and k_2 can be compared. Alternatively, k_2 can be evaluated simply by hydrolyzing **9** under the reaction conditions.

Experiments of this type were conducted for a number of esters, and it was found that while k_2 was always greater than k_1, some exchange did occur (see Table 17–1). This result is incompatible with a mechanism such as Eq. (17–3).

Table 17–1

Ester	Solvent	T	k_2/k_1
$\phi\overset{\overset{O^{18}}{\|\|}}{C}OC_2H_5$	H_2O	25.1	4.8
	33% Dioxane—H_2O	25.1	10.6
$\phi\overset{\overset{O^{18}}{\|\|}}{C}OCH(CH_3)_2$	H_2O	25.1	2.7
	33% Dioxane—H_2O	62.5	3.7
$\phi\overset{\overset{O^{18}}{\|\|}}{C}OC(CH_3)_3$	33% Dioxane—H_2O	62.5	7.6

Further evidence supporting Eq. (17–2) stems from the detection of an adduct when ethyl trifluoroaceate is treated with sodium ethoxide. This adduct probably has the structure **10**:

$$CF_3\overset{\overset{O}{\|\|}}{C}OC_2H_5 + C_2H_5O^- \rightleftarrows CF_3\overset{\overset{O^-}{\|}}{\underset{\underset{OC_2H_5}{\|}}{C}}-OC_2H_5$$

$$\mathbf{10}$$

Three mechanisms have been postulated for the base accelerated hydrolyses of esters. These are Eqs. (17–1), (17–2), and (17–3). Apparently, Eq. (17–1) operates only in special cases. The usual mechanism, which is consistent with all of the experimental data, is Eq. (17–2). There is no positive evidence that hydrolysis ever proceeds by way of Eq. (17–3), and while this last possibility is consistent with some of the evidence, it does not concur with all of it.

Mechanism (17–2) is a two-step process and either step could be rate limiting,

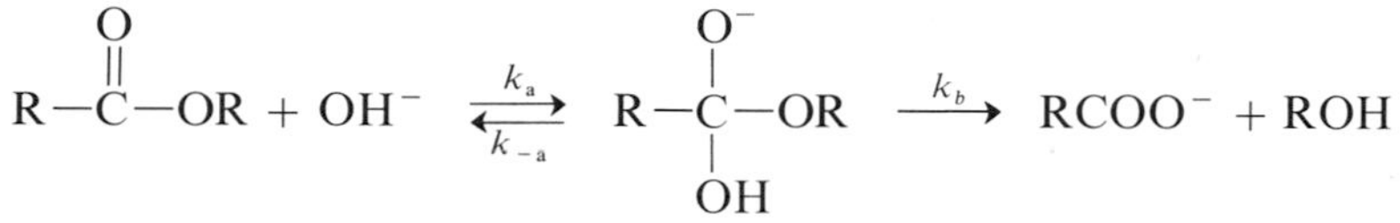

$$
\underset{\overset{\displaystyle \|}{O}}{R-C-OR} + OH^- \;\underset{k_{-a}}{\overset{k_a}{\rightleftarrows}}\; \underset{\overset{\displaystyle |}{OH}}{\overset{\overset{\displaystyle O^-}{|}}{R-C-OR}} \;\xrightarrow{k_b}\; RCOO^- + ROH
$$

The evidence indicates that the intermediate does pass on to products more readily than it returns to reactants. While the difference in these rate constants is not often large, the reaction is generally discussed in terms of a rate limiting first step with k_a being most influential. A more exact discussion must consider the composite rate constant,

$$
k_{obs} = \frac{k_a k_b}{k_{-a} + k_b}
$$

The reaction is subject to steric and electronic effects, and introducing electron withdrawers into either of the R groups is expected to affect the rate of reaction. Increasing the steric requirements of the R groups decreases the rate of reaction. Experimental evidence supports these ideas.

The specific rate constants have been evaluated for the basic hydrolyses of *meta* and *para* substituted ethyl benzoates. These materials have the general structure presented below, and the specific rate constant is smaller when Z is an electron donor, larger when Z is an electron withdrawer. The reaction is characterized by a large positive ρ ($\rho = 2.5$),

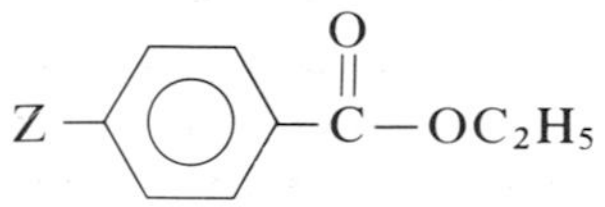

$$
Z-\underset{}{\underline{\bigcirc}}-\overset{\overset{\displaystyle O}{\|}}{C}-OC_2H_5
$$

The effect is most pronounced when direct interactions are possible. For example,

Table 17–2

Z	k_Z/k_H
para-OCH_3	0.209
para-NO_2	110.

The ethyl ester of *para* methoxybenzoic acid hydrolyzes more slowly than ethylbenzoate while the ethyl ester of *para* nitrobenzoic acid hydrolyzes more rapidly. The methoxy ester is stabilized by the methoxy group in the following fashion:

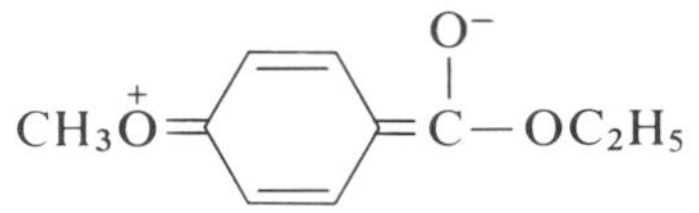

The nitro ester is destabilized by the presence of the nitro group.

The expected steric retardations are indicated by the specific rate constants for basic hydrolysis of the esters,

$$CH_3COOC_2H_5 \qquad CH_3CH_2COOC_2H_5 \qquad (CH_3)_2CHCOOC_2H_5$$

where the ratios of specific rate constants are presented in Table 17–3. Care must be exercized here, for when changing alkyl groups, both steric and electronic factors change. However, some of the rate decrease is due to steric interactions.

Table 17–3

R	k_R/k_{CH_3}
CH_3	1.00
CH_3CH_2	0.47
$(CH_3)_2CH$	0.10

We discussed previously certain special cases such as β-lactones where the ester hydrolyzes by an S_N2 mechanism. There also exist esters that hydrolyze readily by the S_N1 mechanism. Most notable for this type of behavior are the brosylates and tosylates which are esters of sulfonic acids. At moderate pH's these ionize to form carbonium ion intermediates and ultimately alcohols,

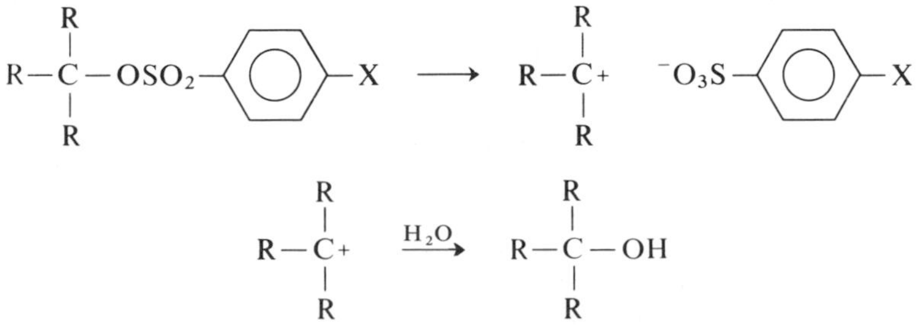

The carboxylate esters of tertiary alcohols also ionize in this manner. The reaction can be acid catalyzed, but over a certain pH range the acid catalyzed reaction is not prominent,

$$
\begin{array}{ccc}
\underset{\substack{| \\ R}}{\overset{\substack{R \\ |}}{R-C-\underset{}{O}\overset{\overset{O}{||}}{C}CH_3}} & \longrightarrow & \underset{\substack{| \\ R}}{\overset{\substack{R \\ |}}{R-C^+}} \quad \overset{-}{O}OCCH_3
\end{array}
$$

$$
\underset{\substack{| \\ R}}{\overset{\substack{R \\ |}}{R-C^+}} \xrightarrow{\ H_2O\ } \underset{\substack{| \\ R}}{\overset{\substack{R \\ |}}{R-C-OH}}
$$

Whenever the reaction leads to a stable carbonium ion, an ester can hydrolyze by the S_N1 mechanism. Since, except for a salt effect, the S_N1 process is not accelerated by added base, reaction by this pathway is expected to be most important when the hydroxide ion concentration is low. When the base is present in high concentration, other reactions such as hydrolysis by mechanism (17–2) are more likely. The reactions of **11** support these ideas. The ester **11** contains an asymmetric carbon atom, and when an optically active form of this material is hydrolyzed by strong alkali, the alcohol that results is also optically active. This indicates that hydrolysis has taken place by attack of the carbonyl function by base. However, when **11** is hydrolyzed under milder conditions, racemic mixtures of the alcoholic products are produced. The reaction has proceeded by way of a carbonium ion intermediate, in this case an allylic carbonium ion,

$$
\phi CH=CH-\underset{\substack{| \\ H}}{\overset{\substack{CH_3 \\ |}}{C}}-O-\overset{\overset{O}{||}}{C}\underset{\underset{O}{\overset{||}{HOC}}}{\bigcirc}
$$

11

Related to this is the hydrolysis of the allylic isomer **12**. Treatment of **12** with concentrated alkali in methanol yields only the expected unrearranged alcohol. However, in aqueous methanol using smaller amounts of base, a mixture of products is obtained. The allylically rearranged alcohol **13** is the major product and its formation is an S_N1' process:

$$\underset{\textbf{12}}{CH_3CH=CH-\overset{\displaystyle \phi}{\underset{\displaystyle H}{C}}-O-\overset{\displaystyle O}{\underset{\displaystyle }{C}}\text{—}\bigcirc\text{—}\underset{\displaystyle O}{\overset{\displaystyle }{HOC}}} \xrightarrow[\underset{CH_3OH}{H_2O}]{Base} \underset{\textbf{13}}{CH_3CH-CH=CH-\phi \atop \underset{\displaystyle OH}{}}$$

These reactions are consistent with a reaction mechanism involving carbonium ion intermediates. Additional evidence comes from the reactions of **14** and **15**, which in alcoholic solutions form ethers,

$$\underset{\textbf{14}}{\phi_3C-\overset{\displaystyle O}{\overset{\|}{O}}CCH_3} \longrightarrow \phi_3C^+ \ \bar{O}OCCH_3$$

$$\phi_3C^+ \xrightarrow{CH_3OH} \phi_3COCH_3$$

The products of this reaction are acetic acid and an ether. The benzoate **15** behaves in an analogous fashion:

$$\underset{\textbf{15}}{\phi_3C-\overset{\displaystyle O}{\overset{\|}{O}}C\phi} \longrightarrow \phi_3C^+ \ \bar{O}OC\phi$$

$$\phi_3C^+ \xrightarrow{C_2H_5OH} \phi_3COC_2H_5$$

These last reactions display first order kinetics, and except for a salt effect, they are unaccelerated by base (up to the point where the mechanism changes).

The dissociations just discussed involve the ester itself. Unimolecular hydrolyses also occur with the conjugate acid. Such reactions are acid catalyzed and we present them in the next section.

17.3 The Acid Catalyzed Hydrolyses of Esters

The acid catalyzed hydrolysis of an ester is a reversible process, and the equilibrium is shifted either by removal of a product as it forms or by employing a large excess of water,

$$R-\overset{\displaystyle O}{\overset{\|}{C}}-OR + H_2O \underset{}{\overset{H^+}{\rightleftarrows}} R-\overset{\displaystyle O}{\overset{\|}{C}}-OH + ROH$$

At least three different mechanisms have been observed for ester hydrolysis. Two infrequent processes are unimolecular second order reactions involving the conjugate acid of the ester in the rate limiting step. In the third, the rate limiting step of the reaction involves water and the catalyzing acid as well as the ester. The last reaction, which is a third order process, shows pseudo second order kinetics when water is present in high concentration and the third order nature of the reaction is observed only when the reaction is conducted under conditions involving a limited concentration of water. This third order process is the most common route for ester hydrolysis, and reactions conducted in acetone and in concentrated acid solutions demonstrate the participation of water in the rate limiting step.

We discuss these mechanisms for hydrolysis, and according to the principle of microscopic reversibility, the mechanism for esterification must be just the reverse.

One of the less frequent pathways is an S_N1 dissociation of the conjugate acid of the starting ester. Since the rate limiting step is the dissociation, the reaction is expected to be specific acid catalyzed. The mechanism becomes,

$$
\underset{\underset{R}{|}}{\overset{\overset{R}{|}}{R-C}}-O-\overset{\overset{O}{||}}{C}-R + HX \;\rightleftharpoons\; \underset{\underset{R}{|}}{\overset{\overset{R}{|}}{R-C}}-O-\overset{\overset{\overset{+}{O}\diagup^{H}}{||}}{C}-R + X^-
$$

$$
\underset{\underset{R}{|}}{\overset{\overset{R}{|}}{R-C}}-O-\overset{\overset{\overset{+}{O}\diagup^{H}}{||}}{C}-R \;\longrightarrow\; \underset{\underset{R}{|}}{\overset{\overset{R}{|}}{R-C^+}} + R-\overset{\overset{O}{||}}{C}-OH
$$

$$
\underset{\underset{R}{|}}{\overset{\overset{R}{|}}{R-C^+}} \;\xrightarrow{H_2O}\; \underset{\underset{R}{|}}{\overset{\overset{R}{|}}{R-C}}-OH
$$

Where we have chosen to involve the carbonium ion **16** rather than **17** because of more effective charge delocalization in the former,

$$
\underset{\underset{R}{|}}{\overset{\overset{R}{|}}{R-C}}-O-\overset{\overset{\overset{+}{O}\diagup^{H}}{||}}{C}-R \;\longleftrightarrow\; \underset{\underset{R}{|}}{\overset{\overset{R}{|}}{R-C}}-O-\underset{+}{\overset{\overset{O\diagup^{H}}{|}}{C}}-R \;\longleftrightarrow\; \underset{\underset{R}{|}}{\overset{\overset{R}{|}}{R-C}}-O=\underset{+}{\overset{\overset{O\diagup^{H}}{|}}{C}}-R
$$

16

$$
\underset{\underset{R}{|}}{\overset{\overset{R}{|}}{R-C}}-\underset{+}{\overset{\overset{H}{|}}{O}}-\overset{\overset{O}{||}}{C}-R
$$

17

The two cations **16** and **17** are in equilibrium, but **16** is probably present in greater concentration. Evidence exists to support this idea, and there is no reason why it should not also be the kinetically active intermediate.

The sensitivity of the protonation reaction of substituted benzoic acids to substituent effects indicates that the positive charge is delocalized into the aromatic ring:

$$Z-\bigcirc-\overset{\overset{\displaystyle O}{\|}}{C}-OH + H^+ \rightleftarrows Z-\bigcirc-\overset{\overset{\displaystyle +OH}{\|}}{C}-OH$$

Further evidence favoring protonation at the carbonyl oxygen stems from the NMR spectrum of dimethylformamide in concentrated acid solution. The conjugate acid of the amide is formed under these conditions and its NMR spectrum retains the N-methyl doublet (two different methyl groups). This indicates that the carbon-nitrogen bond still has double bond character:

$$H-\overset{\overset{\displaystyle O}{\|}}{C}-N\overset{\diagup CH_3}{\diagdown CH_3} + H^+ \rightleftarrows H-\overset{\overset{\displaystyle OH}{|}}{C}=\overset{+}{N}\overset{\diagup CH_3}{\diagdown CH_3}$$

Cations of structure **16** are formed in preference to **17** and there is no reason why these cations should not then go on to products. The transition state resulting from **16** should be more stable than that from **17** and $\Delta G^{\ddagger}$ from ester to transition state less.

Methyl acetate is hydrolyzed by aqueous acid, yet *t*-butyl acetate, under the same conditions, is hydrolyzed somewhat more rapidly. Since the large *t*-butyl group is expected to retard the rate, the unexpected increase must be due to a change in mechanism. The *t*-butyl ester must hydrolyze to a large extent by the mechanism just presented. This idea is confirmed, for hydrolysis of the ester in water containing excess O^{18} leads to labeled oxygen in the *t*-butyl alcohol:

$$(CH_3)_3CO\overset{\overset{\displaystyle O}{\|}}{C}CH_3 \overset{H^+}{\rightleftarrows} (CH_3)_3CO-\overset{\overset{\displaystyle +O}{\|}}{C}CH_3$$

$$(CH_3)_3CO\overset{\overset{\displaystyle +O}{\|}}{C}CH_3 \longrightarrow (CH_3)_3C^+ + CH_3COOH$$

$$(CH_3)_3C^+ \overset{H_2O^{18}}{\longrightarrow} (CH_3)_3CO^{18}H$$

In methanolic solution, *t*-butyl benzoate behaves in an analogous fashion. Reaction of *t*-butyl benzoate affords methyl *t*-butyl ether, benzoic acid, and methyl benzoate, the last material being produced by subsequent esterification of the benzoic acid:

$$(CH_3)_3CO\overset{\overset{\displaystyle O}{\|}}{C}\phi \xrightarrow{CH_3OH} (CH_3)_3COCH_3 + \phi COOH$$

and

$$\phi COOH + CH_3OH \rightleftarrows \phi COOCH_3 + H_2O$$

The mechanism for this reaction must be similar to that presented for *t*-butyl acetate. It must also involve the *t*-butyl carbonium ion. Direct attack on the carbonyl function of the starting ester is expected to yield *t*-butyl alcohol, yet none was isolated.

This mechanism, involving carbonium ions as intermediates, is expected to operate only when moderately stable carbonium ions are possible, and it becomes increasingly important when attack of the carbonyl group by water is simultaneously restricted. The acid catalyzed hydrolyses of esters of tertiary alcohols proceed chiefly by this mechanism while the esters of primary and secondary alcohols generally undergo hydrolysis by another pathway. This second mechanism involves the hydrate **18** which is formed from the starting ester, water, and the catalyzing acid. This hydrate can lose a molecule of water and revert to the reactant, or (and this second process generally takes place more readily) it can lose a molecule of alcohol and form the products:

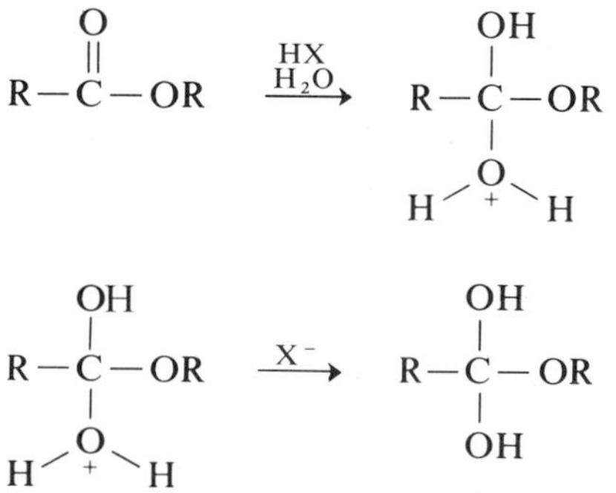

$$R-\overset{\overset{\displaystyle O}{\|}}{C}-OR \xrightarrow[H_2O]{HX} R-\overset{\overset{\displaystyle OH}{|}}{\underset{\underset{H \nearrow \overset{+}{O} \nwarrow H}{|}}{C}}-OR$$

$$R-\overset{\overset{\displaystyle OH}{|}}{\underset{\underset{H \nearrow \overset{+}{O} \nwarrow H}{|}}{C}}-OR \xrightarrow{X^-} R-\overset{\overset{\displaystyle OH}{|}}{\underset{\underset{OH}{|}}{C}}-OR$$

18

$$R-\underset{\underset{\displaystyle OH}{|}}{\overset{\overset{\displaystyle OH}{|}}{C}}-OR \quad \xrightarrow{HX} \quad R-\underset{\underset{\displaystyle OH}{|}}{\overset{\overset{\displaystyle OH\ H}{|\ \ |}}{C}}-\overset{+}{O}-R$$

$$R-\underset{\underset{\displaystyle OH}{|}}{\overset{\overset{\displaystyle OH\ H}{|\ \ |}}{C}}-\overset{+}{O}-R \quad \xrightarrow{X^-} \quad RCOOH \ + \ ROH$$

The characteristics of this mechanism are that the hydrate **18** is an intermediate, that at least a single molecule of water must participate in the rate limiting step (regardless of whether formation of **18** or its decomposition is rate limiting), and that the alkyl bearing oxygen atom becomes the alcoholic oxygen atom. The oxygen atom that in the original ester is bound to the alkyl group, remains with this group throughout the process and eventually becomes the alcoholic oxygen atom. Implicit in this last statement is the idea that the alkyl group in the original ester is converted to the alcohol without opportunity to alter its configuration. Therefore the reaction should proceed with retention of configuration in this group. Investigations have been conducted to check all of these characteristics, and we next present the results of these studies.

Evidence for the existence of **18** stems from the same type of O^{18} exchange experiment described previously:

$$\phi-\overset{\overset{\displaystyle O^{18}}{\|}}{C}OC_2H_5 \quad \xrightarrow{k_1} \quad \phi\overset{\overset{\displaystyle O}{\|}}{C}OC_2H_5$$

$$\searrow^{k_2} \qquad\qquad \swarrow_{k_2}$$

$$\phi COOH \ + \ C_2H_5OH$$

Ethyl benzoate containing O^{18} in the carbonyl function was hydrolyzed under acid catalyzed conditions, and O^{18} exchange occurred with the solvent. Once again, k_2 was found to be larger than k_1. It was found that k_2/k_1 was 5.2, and the observed exchange is explained most reasonably by an intermediate such as **19** in which the two oxygen atoms are equivalent:

$$\phi-\underset{\underset{\displaystyle OH}{|}}{\overset{\overset{\displaystyle O^{18}H}{|}}{C}}-OC_2H_5$$

19

It is not required that **19** be an intermediate; another possibility is a direct intramolecular proton transfer,

$$\phi-\underset{\underset{\overset{\displaystyle O}{\underset{H^{\,+}\,H}{\diagdown\,\diagup}}}{\overset{\displaystyle O^{18}H}{|}}}{C}-OC_2H_5 \quad\longrightarrow\quad \phi-\underset{\underset{\overset{\displaystyle O}{\diagdown}}{\overset{\displaystyle O^{18}}{|}}}{\underset{}{C}}-OC_2H_5$$

The involvement of **19** is certainly reasonable however, and we continue to assume that it participates.

Assuming **19** to be an intermediate leads to the kinetic scheme,

$$\phi-\overset{\overset{\displaystyle O^{18}}{\|}}{C}OC_2H_5 \underset{1}{\rightleftarrows} \phi-\underset{\underset{\displaystyle OH}{|}}{\overset{\overset{\displaystyle O^{18}H}{|}}{C}}-OC_2H_5 \xrightarrow{\ 1\ } \phi\overset{\overset{\displaystyle O}{\|}}{C}-OC_2H_5$$

$$5.2 \Big\downarrow \quad \mathbf{19}$$

$$\phi COOH + C_2H_5OH$$

where **19** is partitioned in three ways. It hydrolyzes to products 5.2 times as readily as it suffers O^{18} exchange. Furthermore, the return of **19** to reactant must occur at the same rate as its decomposition to unlabeled ester.

In the absence of the label the two steps, return to reactant and loss of the label, become equivalent; the kinetic scheme becomes,

$$\phi-\overset{\overset{\displaystyle O}{\|}}{C}OC_2H_5 \underset{2}{\rightleftarrows} \phi-\underset{\underset{\displaystyle OH}{|}}{\overset{\overset{\displaystyle OH}{|}}{C}}OC_2H_5 \xrightarrow{\ 5.2\ } \phi COOH + C_2H_5OH$$

and we see that the hydrate forms products 5.2/2 times as readily as it returns to reactants ($k_b/k_{-a} = 2.6$). The hydrate does lose water and revert to reactant, but more frequently it loses alcohol to form the products.

Evidence for the formation of the hydrate comes from this O^{18} labeling experiment. Evidence for the second characteristic, the inclusion of a molecule of water in the transition state, stems from the acid catalyzed hydrolysis of methyl acetate in acetone. Employing acetone as solvent and in the presence of only small quantities of water, it was found that the rate of hydrolysis depended upon the concentration of this material. Confirmation (for the inclusion of water in the rate limiting step) comes from reactions conducted in concentrated acid. Under these conditions, if a molecule of water is not involved, the rate is proportional to h_0, whereas if water does participate, the rate depends upon both the hydrogen ion concentration and water. This shows up kinetically as a dependence upon $[H_3O^+]$. The reactions were run and dependence upon $[H_3O^+]$ observed. Although the h_0 criterion is not always reliable, the data indicate that water participates in the rate limiting step.

The third point, that the oxygen atom remains bound to the alkyl group, has been observed both for hydrolysis and for esterification. The hydrolysis of methyl succinate in water enriched in O^{18} gave methyl alcohol containing no excess O^{18}. In the opposite direction, esterification of acetic acid using optically active 2-octanol affords the acetate with retention of configuration in the alcohol. Finally, the esterification of benzoic acid with methanol enriched in O^{18} yields enriched methyl benzoate. All of these facts point out that the oxygen atom remains with the alkyl group during the reaction:

$$\underset{\text{HOCCH}_2\text{CH}_2\text{COCH}_3}{\overset{\text{O}\qquad\ \text{O}}{\overset{\|\qquad\ \|}{}}} \xrightarrow[\text{H}_2\text{O}^{18}]{\text{H}^+} \text{CH}_3\text{OH}$$

$$\underset{\text{CH}_3\text{COH}}{\overset{\text{O}}{\overset{\|}{}}} + \text{HO}-\underset{\text{H}}{\overset{\diagup\text{C}_6\text{H}_{13}}{\underset{\diagdown\text{CH}_3}{\text{C}}}} \xrightarrow{\text{H}^+} \underset{\ }{\overset{\text{O}}{\overset{\|}{}}}\text{CH}_3\text{C}-\text{O}-\underset{\text{H}}{\overset{\diagup\text{C}_6\text{H}_{13}}{\underset{\diagdown\text{CH}_3}{\text{C}}}}$$

$$\phi\text{COOH} + \text{HO}^{18}\text{CH}_3 \xrightarrow{\text{H}^+} \overset{\text{O}}{\overset{\|}{\phi\text{CO}^{18}\text{CH}_3}} + \text{H}_2\text{O}$$

The reaction kinetics have been investigated for the preparation of methyl acetate from acetic acid in methanol. The esterification is general acid catalyzed and therefore depends upon the concentration of every acid present in the solution. In methanolic solution, the rate law governing the process is,

$$k + k_1[\text{CH}_3\text{COOH}][\text{CH}_3\text{OH}_2^+] + k_2[\text{CH}_3\text{COOH}]^2$$

where the second term can be interpreted as catalysis by the acid CH_3OH_2^+ while the third term represents catalysis by the acid CH_3COOH. Presumably the concentration of methanol also influences the rate, but this was the solvent and dependence upon its concentration is not apparent. Furthermore, since acetic acid ionizes according to the equation,

$$\text{CH}_3\text{COOH} + \text{CH}_3\text{OH} \rightleftharpoons \text{CH}_3\text{COO}^- + \text{CH}_3\text{OH}_2^+$$

kinetically equivalent expressions must also be considered.

A number of investigations have probed into electronic and steric effects upon the rate and the position of the equilibrium. Both the rate and the position of the equilibrium are influenced. Electronic effects are usually small. The acid catalyzed hydrolysis of *meta* and *para* substituted ethyl benzoates has a ρ of only 0.1. For the base accelerated process, ρ was 2.5. We find, for example, the following results for the system,

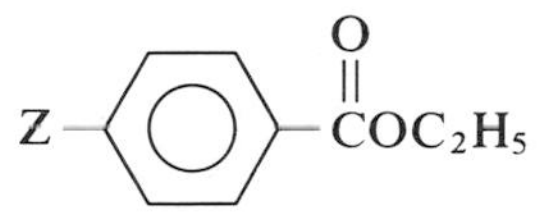

$$Z-\underset{}{\bigcirc}-\overset{\overset{\text{O}}{\|}}{\text{C}}\text{OC}_2\text{H}_5$$

Z	k_Z/k_H
para-OCH$_3$	0.92
para-NO$_2$	1.03

Compare these with the data on basic hydrolysis (Table 17–2).

Electronic effects in the acid fragment of the ester are small; furthermore, when the alcohol is a phenol, electronic effects in this portion of the ester can also be studied conveniently and lead to a small (but negative) value for ρ.

Steric factors also exert an influence, and in esters RCOOR increasing the steric requirements of either R group decreases the rate of hydrolysis. In Table 17–4 we compare the specific rate constants for hydrolysis of methyl, ethyl, and isopropyl acetates in water at 25° under both acidic and basic conditions.

Table 17–4

CH_3COOR

R	k_R/k_{CH_3} (acidic hydrolysis)	k_R/k_{CH_3} (basic hydrolysis)
CH$_3$	1.00	1.00
CH$_3$CH$_2$	0.97	0.60
(CH$_3$)$_2$CH	0.53	0.15

Steric interactions decrease the rate under both sets of conditions. The conclusion to be drawn from the data is not that basic hydrolysis is necessarily more susceptible to steric interactions. Remember that different alkyl groups also have different electron donating abilities, and basic hydrolysis is more susceptible to electronic effects. It is, in fact, difficult to decide how much this difference,

$$\left(\frac{k_{\mathrm{R}}}{k_{\mathrm{CH_3}}}\right)_B - \left(\frac{k_{\mathrm{R}}}{k_{\mathrm{CH_3}}}\right)_A$$

depends upon steric effects and how much it depends upon a greater sensitivity of basic hydrolysis to electronic effects.

It is clear that increased steric interactions decrease the rate under both sets of conditions and increasing the size of either R group in RCOOR decreases the rate of reaction. The Taft equation (Section 4.11) assumes that steric effects are pretty much the same under both acidic and basic conditions and attributes differences in

$$\log\left(\frac{k_{\mathrm{R}}}{k_{\mathrm{CH_3}}}\right)_B - \log\left(\frac{k_{\mathrm{R}}}{k_{\mathrm{CH_3}}}\right)_A$$

to the greater importance of the inductive effect of R in basic hydrolysis.

Steric interactions decrease the rate of reaction because these interactions are more pronounced and more important in the transition state than they are in the reactants. The groups are closer in the transition state. Consequently, increased steric requirements for R raise the free energy of the transition state more than they raise the free energy of the reactants. The free energy of activation for the process increases and the rate goes down. Furthermore, such factors influence not only the rate, they also influence the position of the equilibrium,

$$\underset{\mathrm{R-COR}}{\overset{\mathrm{O}}{\parallel}} + \mathrm{H_2O} \underset{}{\overset{\mathrm{H^+}}{\rightleftharpoons}} \underset{\mathrm{R-COH}}{\overset{\mathrm{O}}{\parallel}} + \mathrm{ROH}$$

We have discussed two pathways by which ester hydrolysis proceeds. One of these involves an alkyl carbonium ion, the other a molecule of water and a catalyzing acid. Hydrolysis occurs by at least one other mechanism which has been observed in a small number of cases. It involves the acylium ion,

$$\mathrm{R-C}{\equiv}\overset{+}{\mathrm{O}} \longleftrightarrow \mathrm{R-C}{=}\overset{+}{\mathrm{O}}$$

One case where this intermediate has been observed is in the esterification and hydrolysis of 2,4,6-trimethylbenzoic acid (mesitoic acid) and its derivatives.

When dissolved in concentrated sulfuric acid, benzoic acid displays a freezing point depression which indicates that two ions are formed. These two ions are the bisulfate ion and protonated benzoic acid,

A cryoscopic measurement using 2,4,6-trimethylbenzoic acid indicates that four ions are present:

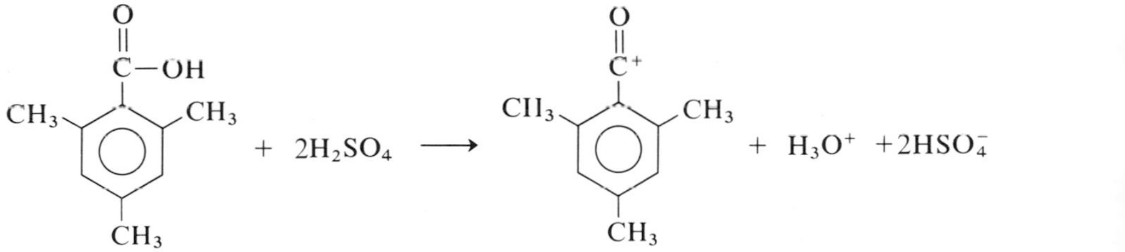

In this case, the adjacent methyl groups interfere sterically with the usual type of stabilization (steric inhibition of resonance). Steric interactions increase the free energy of **21**, and **20** with its smaller steric requirements is formed instead. The latter (**20**) is also stabilized by charge delocalization, and both factors, steric interactions in **21** and stabilization of **20** by delocalization of charge into the ring and onto the methyl groups, contribute to its formation:

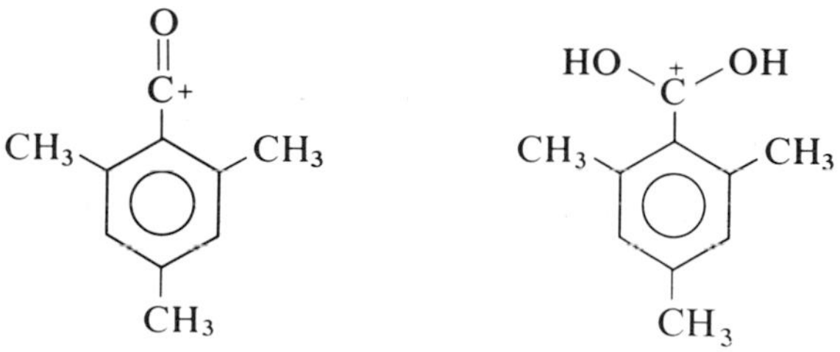

When solutions of mesitoic acid in concentrated sulfuric acid (these contain **20**) are added to methanol, the methyl ester is produced in good yield. Esterification under the usual conditions is most difficult,

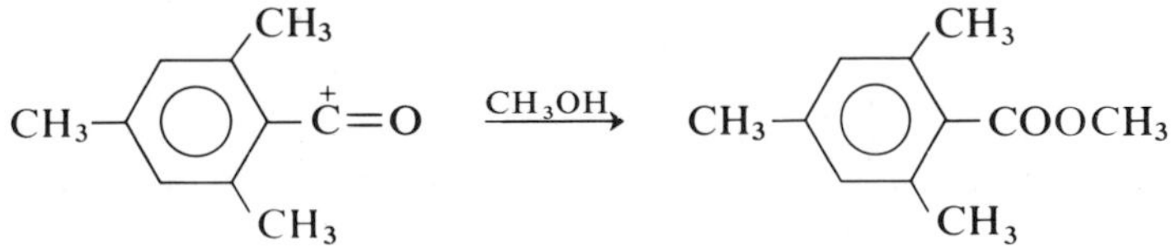

Since esterification of mesitoic acid proceeds by way of **20**, it should not be surprising that hydrolysis does also. Esters of mesitoic acid are resistant to

hydrolysis under the usual conditions. However, when dissolved in concentrated sulfuric acid, these esters form **20**, and when the solution is added to water, mesitoic acid is produced.

A solution of the ester in concentrated sulfuric acid displays a freezing point depression that indicates the presence of five materials,

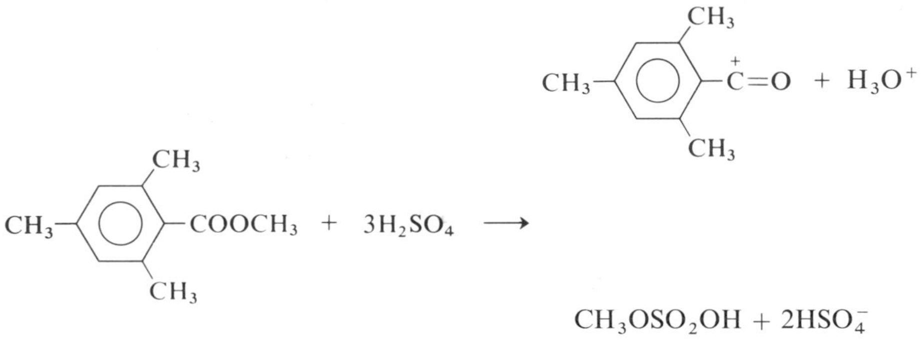

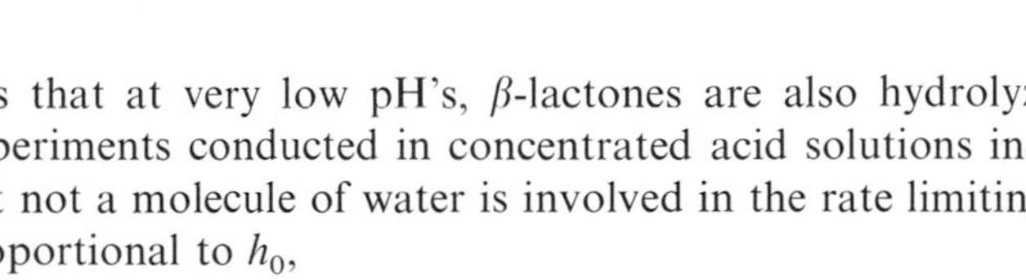

It appears that at very low pH's, β-lactones are also hydrolyzed in this manner. Experiments conducted in concentrated acid solutions indicate that a proton but not a molecule of water is involved in the rate limiting step; the rates are proportional to h_0,

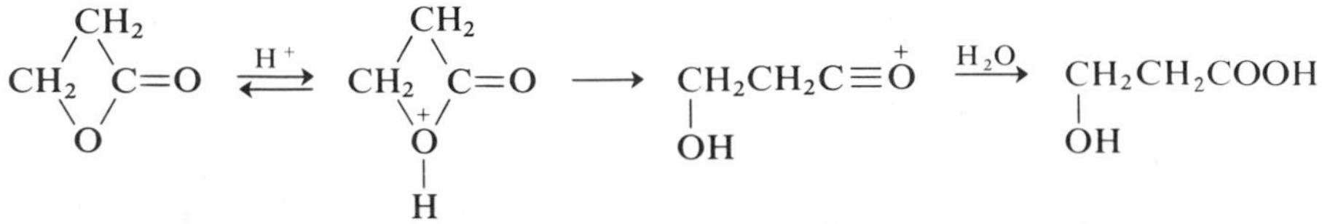

This reaction proceeds by way of an acylium cation, and under special conditions (employing concentrated sulfuric acid), other esters can react in this manner. However, under the usual reaction conditions with water present in high concentration, this process is not observed for most esters. In fact, as we have mentioned, even β-lactones do not hydrolyze in this fashion at neutral or near neutral pH's. The $S_N 2$ mechanism takes place instead.

Esters hydrolyze by a number of different mechanisms. The type of ester and the reaction conditions determine the mechanism. For most esters, a single process predominates under a given set of conditions and the other pathways are insignificant. However, it is certainly possible that conditions can be found where an ester hydrolyzes to a measurable extent by more than a single route.

17.4 Reactions of Acid Anhydrides, Acid Chlorides, and Amides

Since the reactions of acid anhydrides, acid chlorides, and amides are analogous to those of esters, these materials are also hydrolyzed to carboxylic acids,

$$RCOX + H_2O \longrightarrow RCOOH$$

When treated with water (a catalyst is sometimes required) these substances are hydrolyzed; when treated with alcohols, esters are produced. Even amides sometimes form esters; the reaction is reversible with high temperatures favoring the ester,

$$RCOX + ROH \longrightarrow RCOOR$$

Since the reaction of an acid chloride or acid anhydride with an alcohol or alkoxide ion is irreversible, this process serves as a convenient route to esters. The other possibility, esterification by refluxing the acid itself with the alcohol, is characterized by a less favorable equilibrium and may result in lower yields. A number of other nucleophiles react with these materials—Grignard reagents, metal hydrides, enolate anions as in the Claisen condensation. Amides are formed when an amine is employed.

$$RCOX + RNH_2 \longrightarrow RCONHR$$

These amides can be hydrolyzed to carboxylic acids, and the mechanism is by and large the same as that observed for esters. The base accelerated reaction involves nucleophilic attack at the carbonyl carbon atom while hydrolysis in the presence of added acids involves attack at the carbonyl oxygen atom and hydrates such as **22**. The mechanisms become, in the presence of acid,

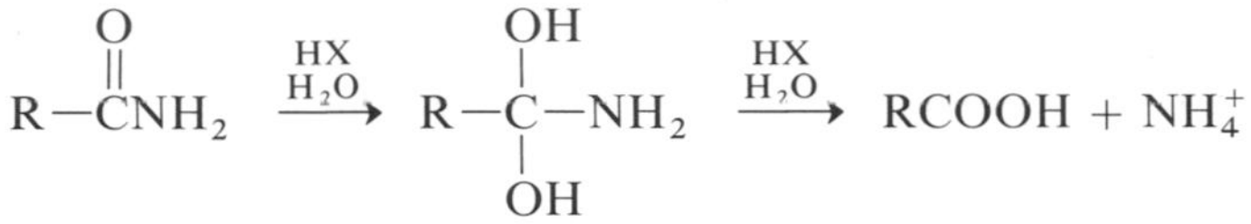

$$
\underset{\substack{\| \\ R-CNH_2}}{O} \xrightarrow[\text{H}_2\text{O}]{\text{HX}} \underset{\substack{| \\ \underset{22}{\text{OH}}}}{\overset{\text{OH}}{R-C-NH_2}} \xrightarrow[\text{H}_2\text{O}]{\text{HX}} RCOOH + NH_4^+
$$

and for the base accelerated reaction,

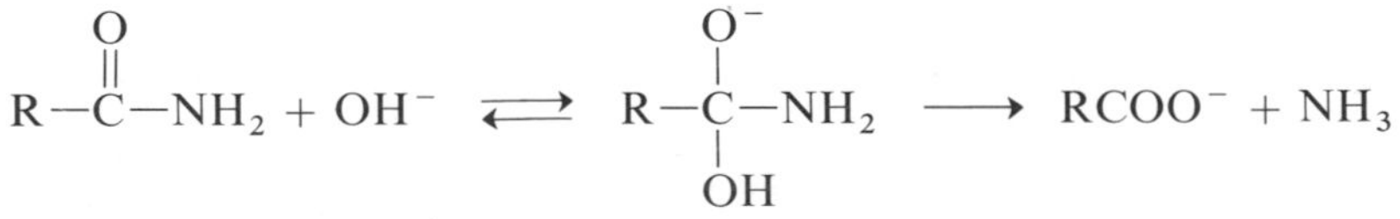

$$
\underset{\substack{\| \\ R-C-NH_2}}{O} + OH^- \rightleftarrows \underset{\substack{| \\ \underset{23}{\text{OH}}}}{\overset{O^-}{R-C-NH_2}} \longrightarrow RCOO^- + NH_3
$$

Intermediate **22** is also present in the base accelerated process but is not the active intermediate:

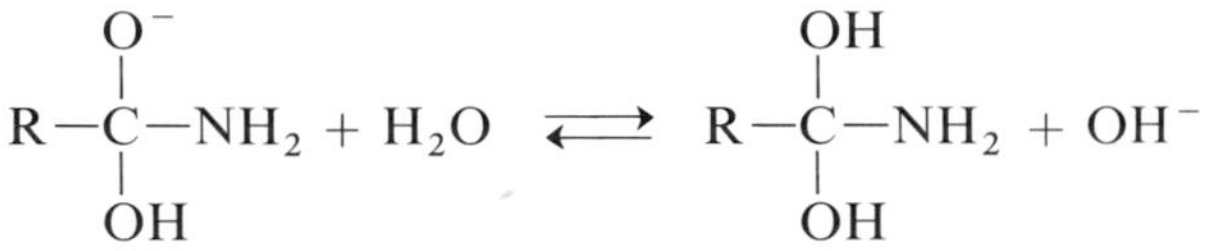

$$
\underset{\substack{| \\ \underset{23}{\text{OH}}}}{\overset{O^-}{R-C-NH_2}} + H_2O \rightleftarrows \underset{\substack{| \\ \underset{22}{\text{OH}}}}{\overset{\text{OH}}{R-C-NH_2}} + OH^-
$$

Evidence supporting the presence of **22** and **23** during basic hydrolysis comes from O^{18} exchange experiments. There is evidence from other kinetic studies that an intermediate such as **24** may sometimes be involved,

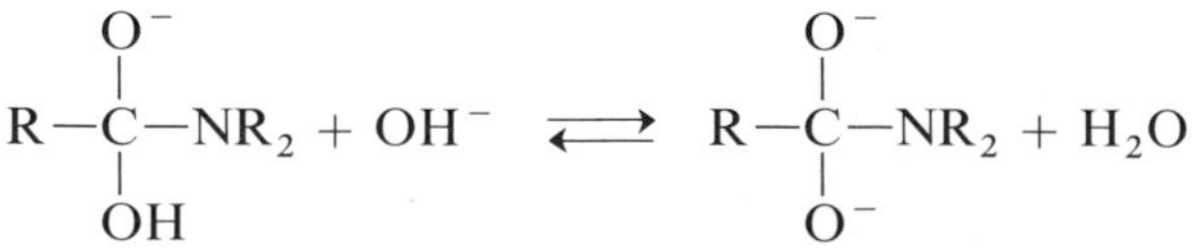

$$
\underset{\substack{| \\ \underset{23}{\text{OH}}}}{\overset{O^-}{R-C-NR_2}} + OH^- \rightleftarrows \underset{\substack{| \\ \underset{24}{O^-}}}{\overset{O^-}{R-C-NR_2}} + H_2O
$$

$$
\underset{\substack{| \\ O^-}}{\overset{O^-}{R-C-NR_2}} \longrightarrow RCOO^-
$$

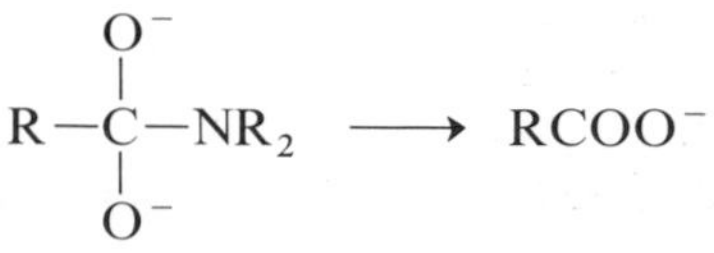

The intermediate **24** is analogous to that postulated for the Cannizzaro reaction. The general rate expression for the basic hydrolysis of some amides contains a term first order in $[OH^-]$ and a second order term $[OH^-]^2$. The first order term is explained by **23** passing on to products, the term $[OH^-]^2$ by a rate limiting loss of NR_2 from **24**. This term in $[OH^-]^2$ is not always observed and for most amides, it is **23** that forms the product.

The hydrolysis of an amide involves intermediates that are not much different from those encountered in the hydrolysis of an ester. The kinetics of the reaction have been investigated, and the results are in agreement with the mechanisms just presented. For example, the base accelerated process is usually a second order reaction, first order in amide and first order in hydroxide ion.

In addition the formation of amides from esters, acid anhydrides, and acid chlorides takes place by mechanisms that are not much different. The amide can be formed by attack of HNR_2 or NR_2^- on the carbonyl carbon atom. Although some of these amide-forming processes can be catalyzed, added catalysts are not required. The reactions of acid anhydrides and acid chlorides are not significantly different from those just discussed. Acid chlorides react with optically active alcohols to yield esters with retention of configuration at the optically active carbon atom. This is also true of sulfonyl chlorides,

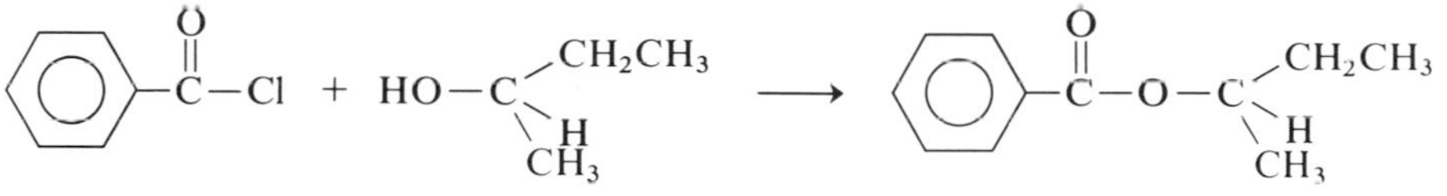

and

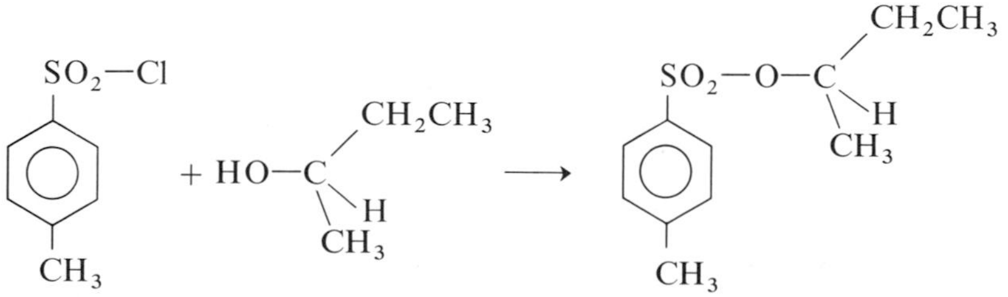

There is, however, one distinction that should be made at this time. Since the groups RCOO and Cl are good leaving groups, unimolecular dissociations as well as bimolecular additions become possible for acid chlorides and acid anhydrides:

$$
\begin{array}{ccc}
\underset{\displaystyle R-\overset{\displaystyle O}{\overset{\|}{C}}-Cl}{} & \longrightarrow & \underset{\displaystyle R-\overset{\displaystyle O^+}{\overset{\||\,|}{C}}}{} + Cl^-
\end{array}
$$

25

$$
R-\overset{O^+}{\overset{\||\,|}{C}} + Y^- \longrightarrow R-\overset{O}{\overset{\|}{C}}-Y
$$

This type of a process is expected to occur most readily when the intermediate **25** is resonance stabilized and when the normal addition to the carbonyl carbon atom is unfavorable. The fact that mesitoyl chloride behaves in this fashion should come as no surprise,

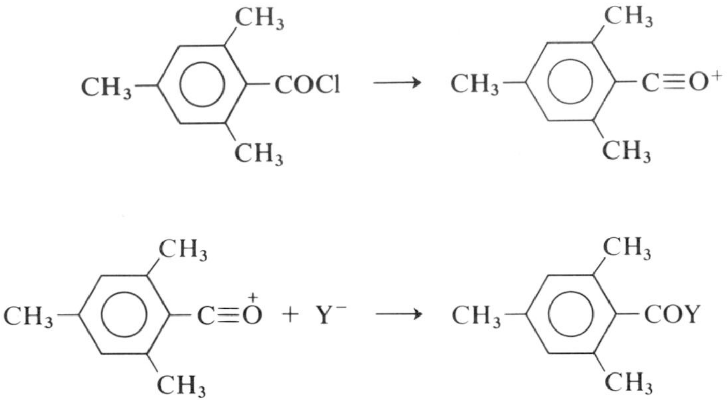

This unimolecular ionization is not the usual mode of reaction, and despite such behavior in some cases, acid chlorides and acid anhydrides generally undergo nucleophilic addition. In all cases where the rate limiting step involves nucleophilic attack at the carbonyl carbon atom, electronic factors and steric factors are similar to those for ester hydrolysis.

We have not yet mentioned nitriles RCN which are also considered to be derivatives of acids; they behave similarly to the other derivatives. They react with lithium aluminum hydride to yield, after hydrolysis of the salts, primary amines; they react with Grignard reagents; and they can be hydrolyzed to carboxylic acids. The rate of this last process increases when strong acids or bases are present. All carboxylic acid derivatives behave in a similar fashion. They react with metal hydrides and organometallic reagents. Enolate anions attack them. They are to some degree interconvertible, and all can be hydrolyzed to carboxylic acids. Furthermore, the mechanism for reaction is pretty much the same for all.

Supplementary Reading

1. Bender, M. L., *Chem. Revs.*, 1960, p. 53.

2. Gould, E. S., *Mechanism and Structure in Organic Chemistry*. New York, Holt, 1959.

3. Hammett, L. P., *Physical Organic Chemistry*. New York, McGraw-Hill, 1940.

4. Hine, J., *Physical Organic Chemistry*. New York, McGraw-Hill, 1962.

5. Ingold, C. K., *Structure and Mechanism in Organic Chemistry*. Ithaca, New York, Cornell U.P., 1953.

6. Royals, E. E., *Advanced Organic Chemistry*. Englewood Cliffs, New Jersey, Prentice-Hall, 1954.

Chapter 18

Neighboring Group Participation and Molecular Rearrangements

18.1 Introduction

It frequently occurs, especially in cyclic systems where the loss in ΔS and $\Delta S^{\ddagger}$ is not great, that a group initially at some distance along the carbon chain from the reaction site actually influences the course of a reaction. Such participation can be due to steric interactions or electronic effects.

Interactions such as changes in hybridization caused by large groups and restricted vibrations and restricted rotations arising from nonbonded interactions are classified here as steric interactions. A group far along the carbon chain may be spacially close to the reaction site, and such a group can influence the outcome of reactions by exerting a steric influence. A large group on one side of the molecule can hinder the approach of an attacking agent, thereby favoring attack from the less hindered side. Numerous examples of this type of behavior are known, and the idea serves as a basis for Cram's rule as illustrated in Figure 18–1.

Neighboring group participation influences the geometry of the product. In this example the influence is steric. Electronic participation by neighboring

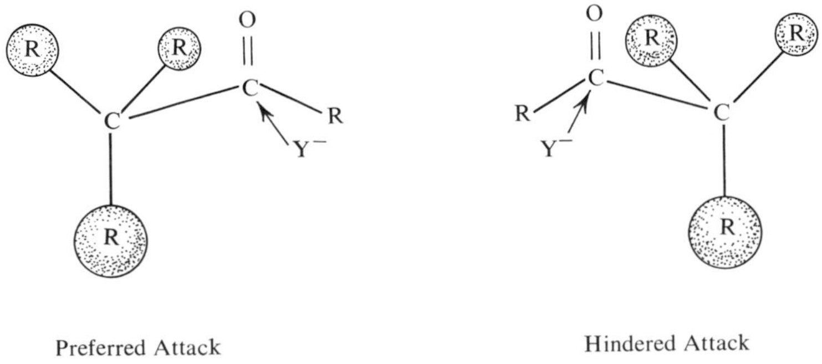

Preferred Attack   Hindered Attack

Figure 18–1

590

groups is also found, and there is, in principle, little difference between electronic participation by a neighboring group and a molecular rearrangement.

In molecular rearrangements a group initially occupying one position in a molecule ends up occupying another. The group migrates from its original position to another, and at some time during the migration it must be at least partially bonded to both positions. When a neighboring group participates electronically, the same situation exists. The group is at least partially bonded to two different positions in the molecule. For example, in the solvolysis of the material R_2CYCR_2X, where X is the leaving group and Y is the participating group, Y assists the departure of X by donating a pair of electrons, and in the intermediate **2**, Y is bonded to two positions,

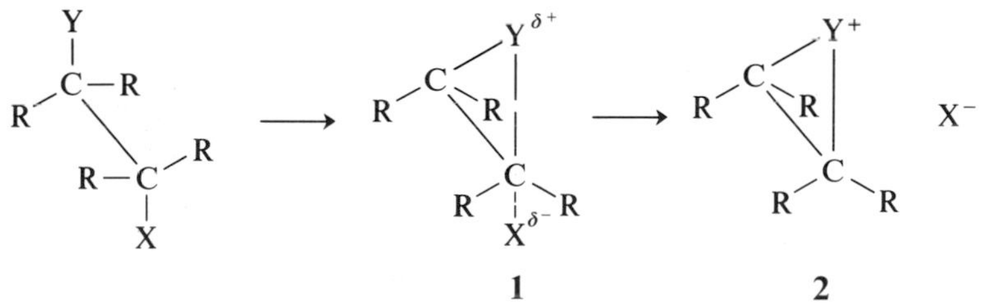

1   **2**

When the solvent HS enters, Y either returns to its original position as in **3**, or it becomes bonded to the new position **4**. In a strict sense the formation of **3** proceeds with the aid of Y as a neighboring group, but this process is not a molecular rearrangement. The formation of **4** is ! The only difference between **3** and **4** is that in **3**, Y has returned to its original position while in **4** it has become bonded to a new position, yet this distinction is sufficient. The difference between a molecular rearrangement and neighboring group participation depends upon whether the group occupies its original position in the product, and this difference, as we see, can be subtle,

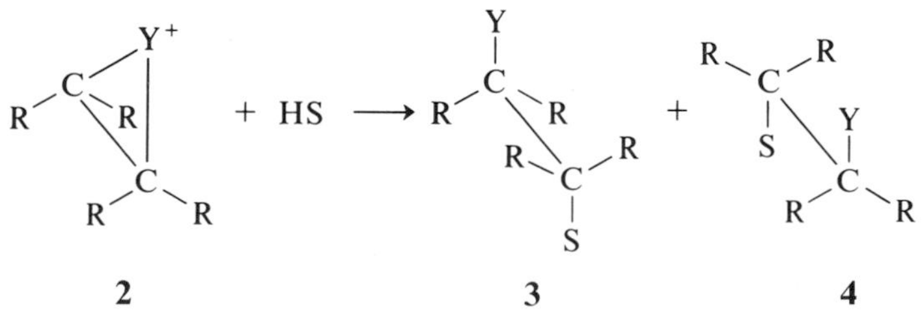

2   **3**   **4**

We postulated the cation **2** rather than the cation **5** as the intermediate in the solvolysis. The donation of electrons by Y leads to bond formation as well as delocalizing the positive charge. This stabilizes **2**,

$$
\begin{array}{c}
Y \\
| \\
R \diagdown C \diagup R \\
\diagdown \\
R-\overset{+}{C}-R \\
\mathbf{5}
\end{array}
$$

It is not necessary for a neighboring group to assist in a reaction. Many processes are known where extensive participation by neighboring groups is not involved. Consequently, when Y does assist in a reaction, this assistance must stabilize the system. If an increase in stability did not accompany the participation, it would not take place, and the usual carbonium ion **5** would be formed. Furthermore, since participation by Y stabilizes the cation **2**, such participation must also stabilize the transition state **1**. We expect Y to participate as soon as excess positive charge begins to accumulate at the reaction site, and it seems intuitively unlikely that assistance by Y, which stabilizes **2**, should not have a similar effect upon the free energy of **1**. Thus, participations are expected to be concerted rather than stepwise processes, and rate enhancement should accompany the reaction (the free energy of the transition state is lower). When the groups are bulky, steric interactions, which can be more pronounced in **1** than in **2**, may occasionally cause exceptions.

Assistance by Y is essentially an intramolecular nucleophilic substitution. Participation takes place most readily when the assisting group attacks the reaction site from the rear while the leaving group departs from the front.

An interesting reaction involving benzoate participation is the Prévost reaction for the preparation of *trans* diols. Treatment of cyclohexene with two equivalents of silver benzoate and an equimolar quantity of iodine affords first the intermediate **7**, probably by way of the iodonium ion **6**, and after heating the mixture, the dibenzoate **8**. Decomposition of **8** affords the *trans* diol **9**. As expected for a reaction following the mechanism presented, the product is a racemic mixture and optically inactive,

The carbonium ion intermediate is stabilized by charge delocalization not only into the aromatic ring but also onto the oxygen atoms:

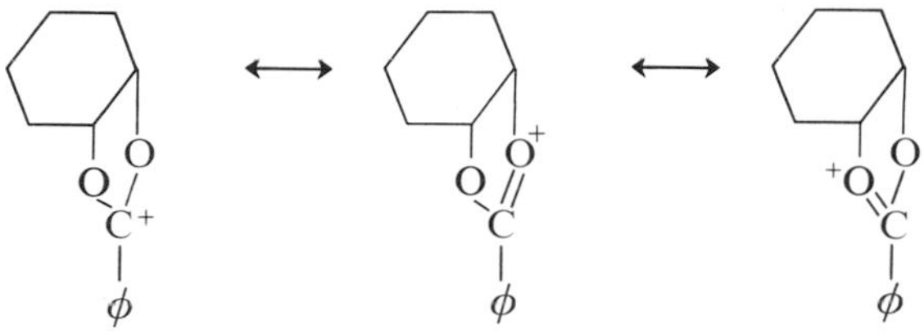

In the examples just presented the neighboring group was attached to the carbon atom adjacent to the site of reaction; however, this need not be the case. Groups several carbon atoms away can influence a reaction. Examples of this type of participation are found most frequently in cyclic systems where the groups are held in a fixed geometry and are spacially close to the reaction site. Thus, the treatment of **10** with potassium *t*-butoxide affords the cyclic ether **11**:

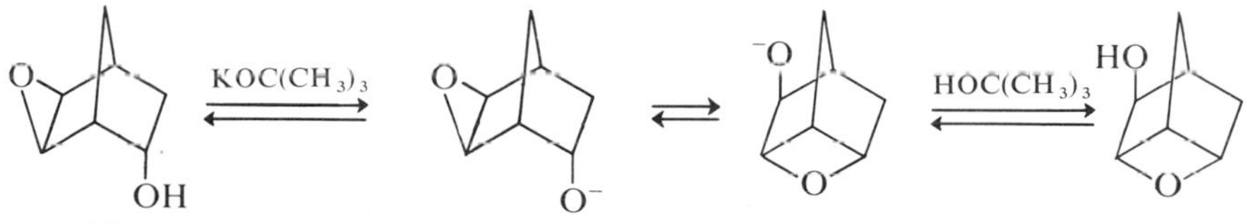

Similar to this process is the hydrolysis of the triacetate **12**. Hydrolysis of **12** affords **15** presumably by way of the intermediates **13** and **14**:

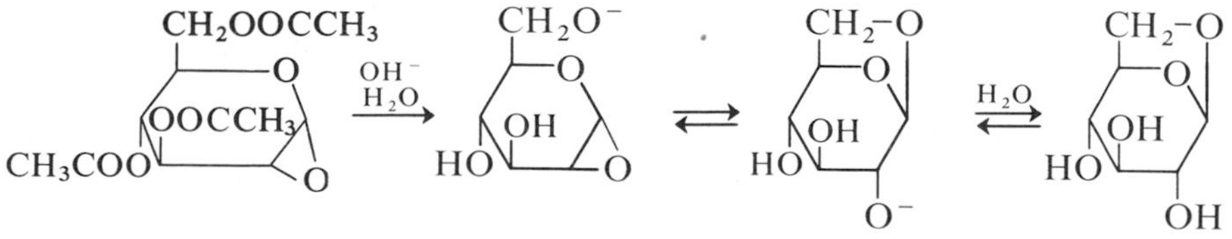

We have mentioned that the assisting group should be *trans* to the leaving group and that neighboring group participations are probably concerted rather than stepwise processes. The same holds true for some migrations. This is illustrated quite convincingly by the following isomerization,

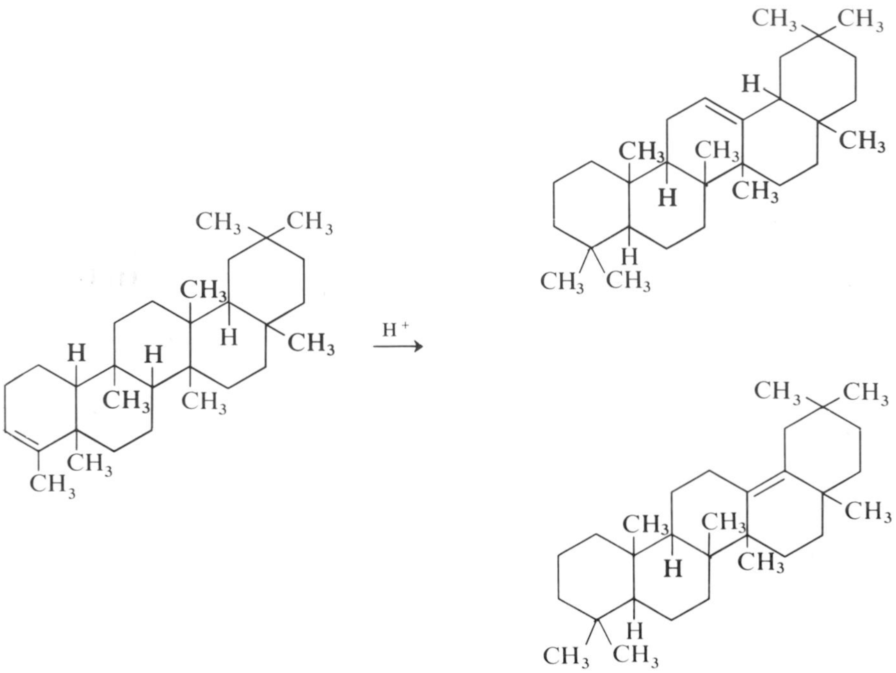

Conformationally, the picture for the transformation is shown in Figure 18.2.

The isomerization is best explained by assuming a concerted process; all groups migrate simultaneously. In each case the migrating group is *trans* to the leaving group, and each migration is accompanied by inversion of configuration.

It appears that some migrations, like participations, are best explained on the basis of a concerted mechanism such as this one. Other migrations are best explained by assuming stepwise mechanisms, that is, formation of a carbonium ion and subsequent migration rather than simultaneous processes.

We see how reactive groups at one position in the molecule influence reactions taking place at another. The reactions may be ionic or free radical; they may be uncatalyzed or effected with the aid of acids, bases, light, heat, or free radical catalysts. Many examples are known, and we present just a few of them.

18.2 Anionic Rearrangements

Anionic rearrangements are those involving anions as intermediates. Some of these have already been presented. For example, in Section 16.5 the benzilic acid rearrangement, which involves the conversion of benzil to the conjugate

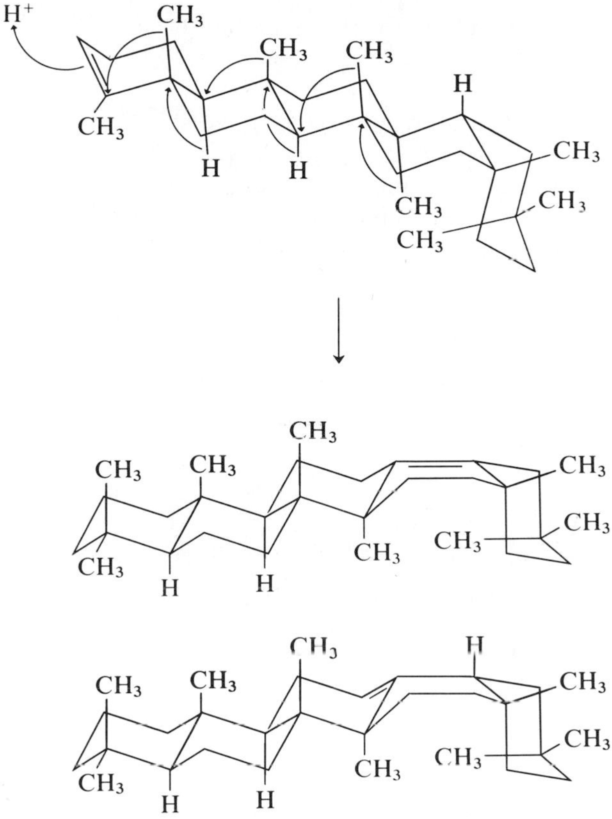

Figure 18–2

base of benzilic acid under the influence of alkali, was discussed in detail. The mechanism involves attack of the carbonyl function by hydroxide ion and a rate limiting migration of phenyl. After completion of the reaction, acidification affords benzilic acid:

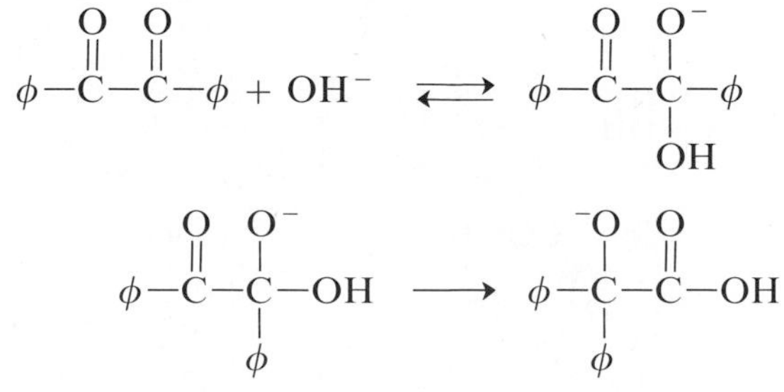

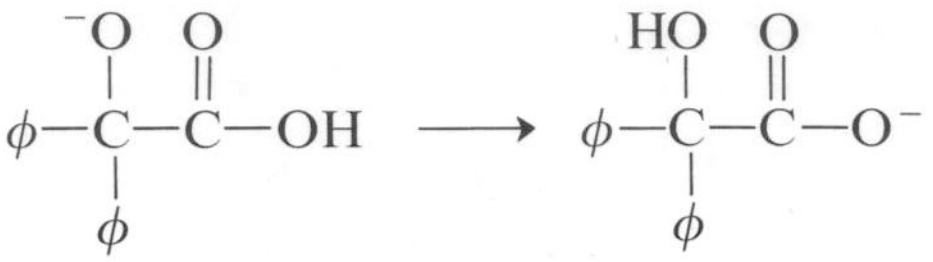

$$\phi-\overset{\overset{\displaystyle -O}{|}}{\underset{\underset{\displaystyle \phi}{|}}{C}}-\overset{\overset{\displaystyle O}{\|}}{C}-OH \longrightarrow \phi-\overset{\overset{\displaystyle HO}{|}}{\underset{\underset{\displaystyle \phi}{|}}{C}}-\overset{\overset{\displaystyle O}{\|}}{C}-O^-$$

Another anionic rearrangement is the Favorskii rearrangement. This process, whereby an α-halo ketone is converted to the conjugate base of a carboxylic acid, is generally assumed to proceed by way of a cyclopropanone intermediate. Thus 2-chlorocyclohexanone is transformed by alkali into the conjugate base of cyclopentanecarboxylic acid,

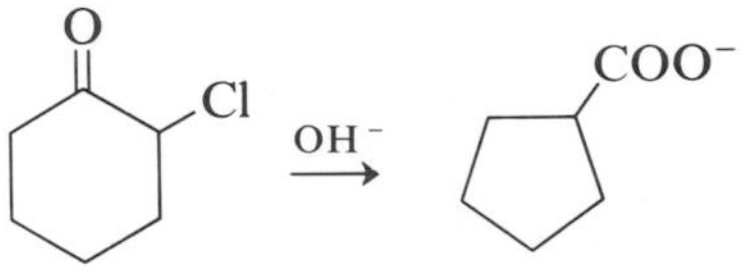

The following mechanism is postulated,

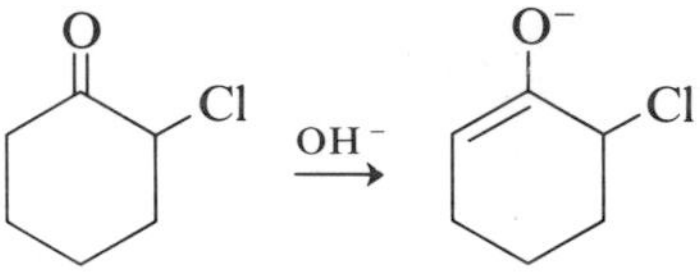

The enolate anion is stabilized in the usual way,

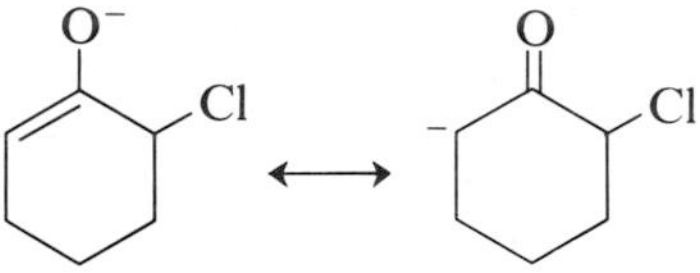

and an intramolecular displacement of chloride ion affords the cyclopropanone intermediate:

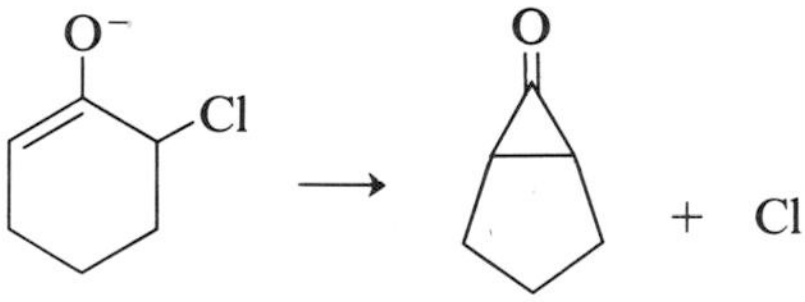

Then,

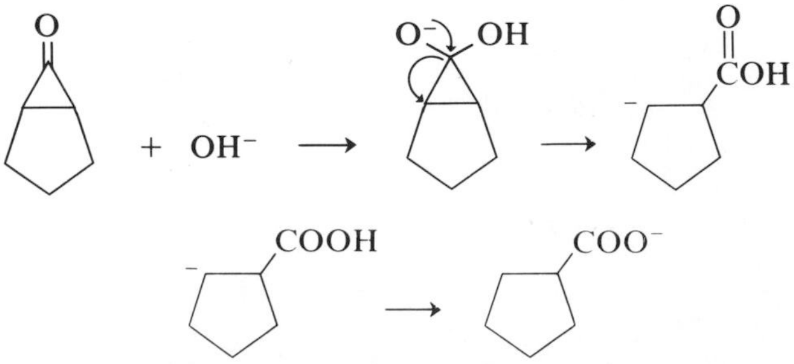

When alkoxides are used in place of hydroxide, esters are produced,

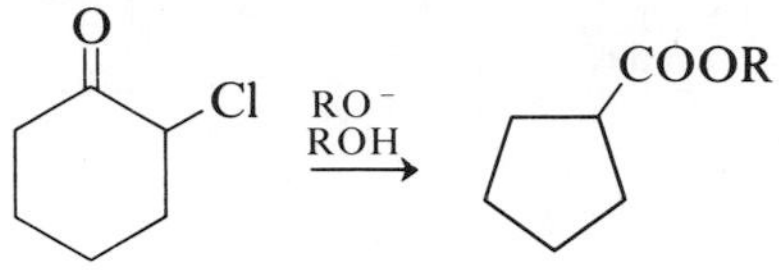

There is strong evidence in favor of this mechanism and some arguments against it. When the carbon atom bearing the chlorine is labeled with C^{14}, the experimental results are:

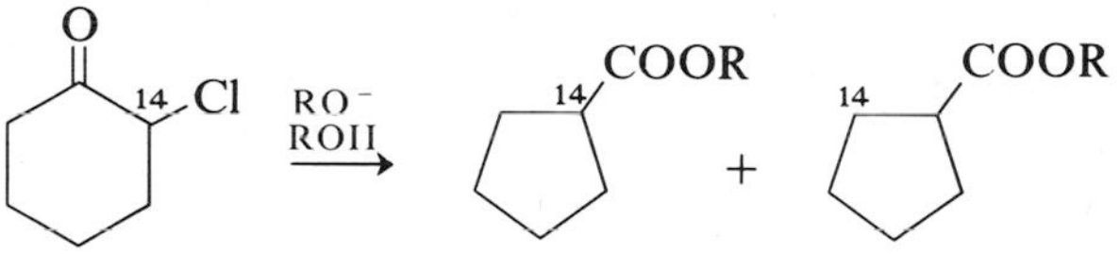

These results are in agreement with the postulated mechanism. The cyclopropanone intermediate, when attacked by the nucleophilic agent, affords the adduct,

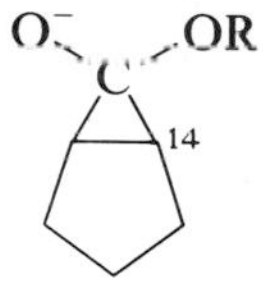

which can decompose by two equivalent routes into,

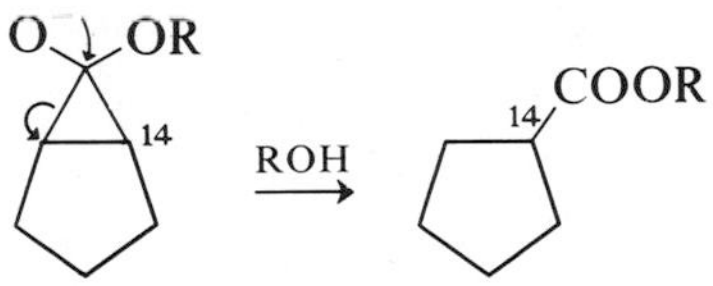

and

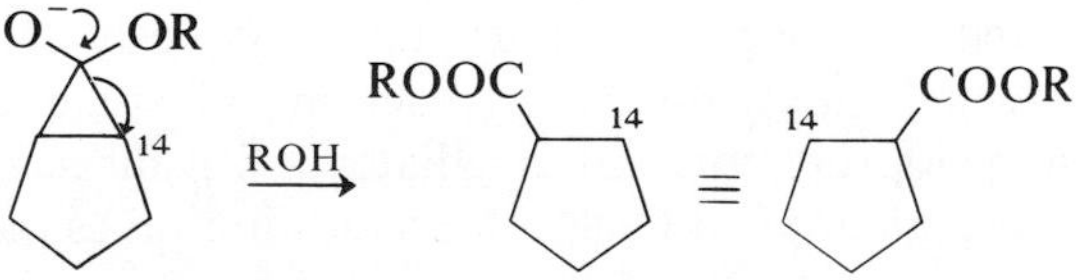

The results of the C^{14} labeling experiment concur with the proposed mechanism. Also in agreement is the fact that **16** undergoes the Favorskii rearrangement in ether with inversion of configuration at the chlorine bearing carbon atom:

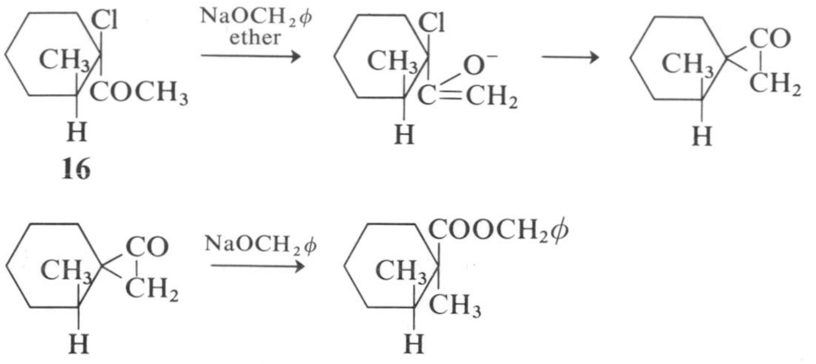

It has been argued that in a conjugate base such as the one resulting from 2-chlorocyclohexanone **17**, the electrons occupy orbitals that are not in a favorable position for effecting an S_N2 rearward attack and that to do so would destroy resonance or cause considerable strain in the ring. This is true, and if the reaction does proceed by way of the cyclopropanone intermediate, extensive sidewise overlap of the pertinent orbitals must be involved during the displacement process,

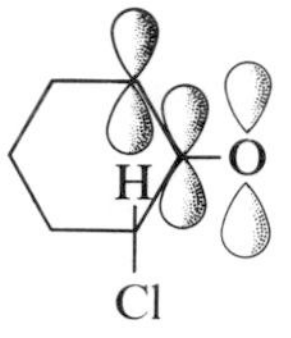

It has, in fact, been suggested that under some conditions the normal structure for a cyclopropanone may be one in which the α-carbon atoms are joined by a bond having much more π character than the usual carbon-carbon single bond:

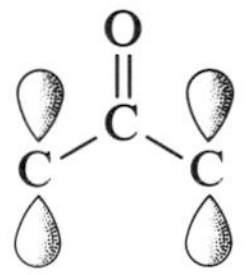

There exists some evidence to support this hypothesis. When α-chlorodibenzyl ketone is treated with strong bases, reactions take place that indicate the involvement of a cyclopropanone intermediate, and if furan is present in the solution, a process analogous to Diels-Alder addition takes place:

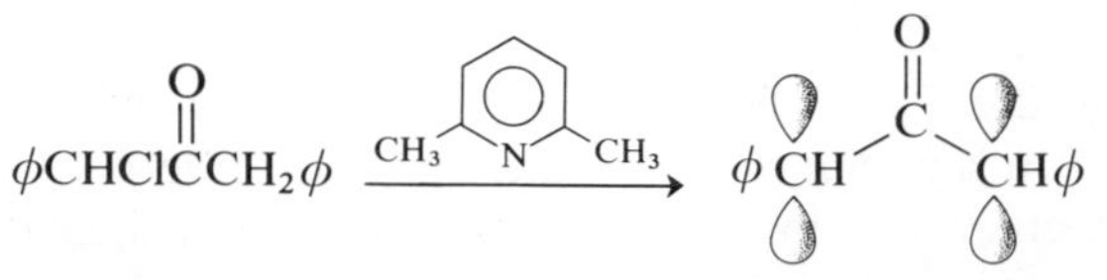

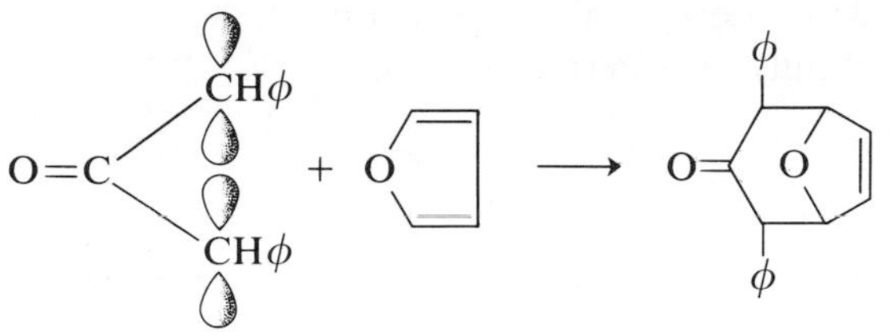

Further support for this unusual structure comes from the reactions of **16** with alkoxide in alcohol. Using sodium benzoate in ether, the process proceeds with inversion of configuration; however, in alcohols, inversion is not observed and a structure such as

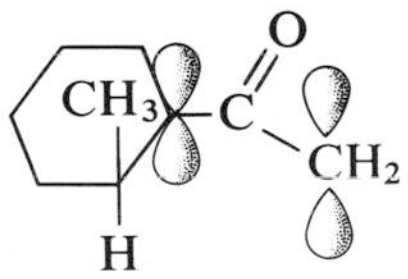

has been suggested.

Cyclopropanones have recently been prepared. For example, *trans-di-t-* butylcyclopropanone is synthesized by treating the α-bromo ketone with a sterically hindered base. The material is reasonably stable,

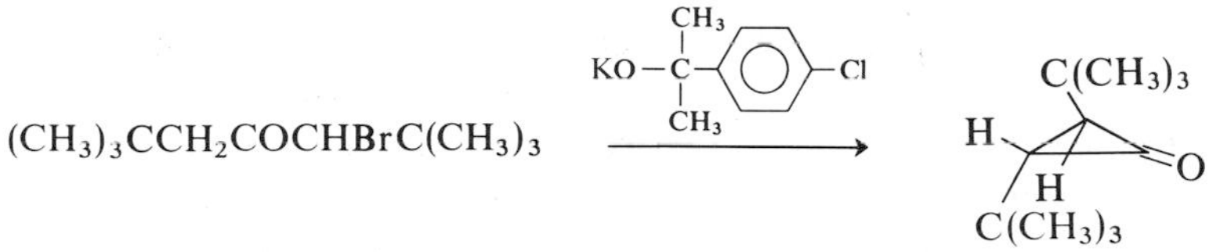

Other cyclopropanones including cyclopropanone itself have been reported. Extensive studies of these systems under Favorskii conditions have not been disclosed, but the information that is available indicates that these materials behave as expected, that is, they do rearrange to carboxylic acids and their esters.

When two α-halogens are present, the products are hydroxy acids, unsaturated acids, or cyclopropenones. Thus, treatment of **18** with aqueous potassium hydroxide affords **19**:

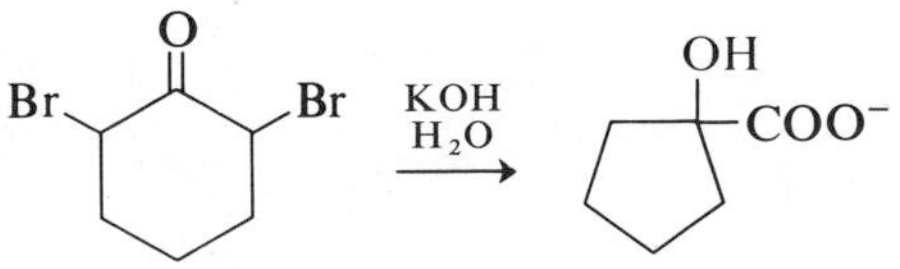

18   **19**

Treating **20** with triethylamine yields diphenylcyclopropenone. A cyclopropanone is certainly the intermediate,

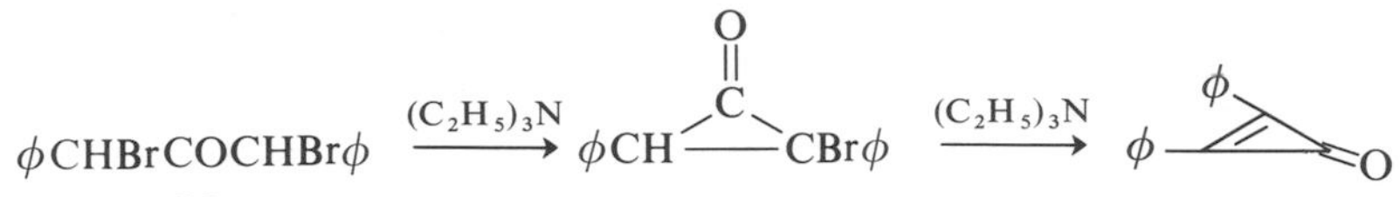

$$\phi CHBrCOCHBr\phi \quad \xrightarrow{(C_2H_5)_3N} \quad \phi CH \underset{\underset{O}{\parallel}}{\overset{\overset{O}{\parallel}}{\underset{}{\overset{}{C}}}} CBr\phi \quad \xrightarrow{(C_2H_5)_3N} \quad \phi \underset{}{\overset{\phi}{\triangle}} O$$
$$\mathbf{20}$$

The transformation of **21** into **22** involves a Favorskii rearrangement; a cyclopropanone is the postulated intermediate:

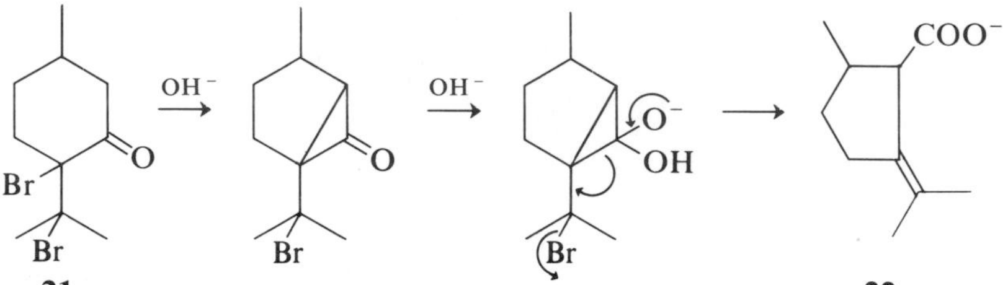

The Favorskii rearrangement must occasionally proceed by a mechanism not involving a cyclopropanone, for ketones such as **23** not having the necessary α-hydrogens also undergo the reaction. In these cases, where the cyclopropanone is not possible, the process must proceed by a mechanism similar to the benzilic acid rearrangement,

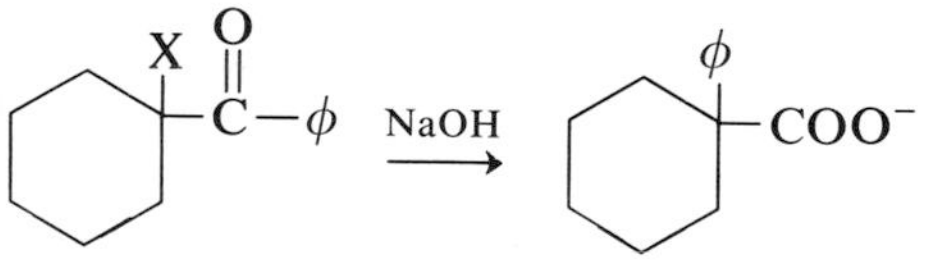

Reaction of the ester **24** with the strong base triphenylmethylsodium transforms it to the bicyclic compound **25**:

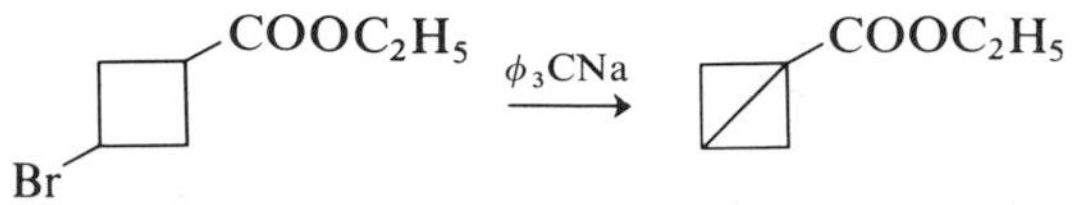

More complex transformations are known. Treatment of carvone hydrobromide with base yields the anion **26**, and this rearranges to encarvone **27**:

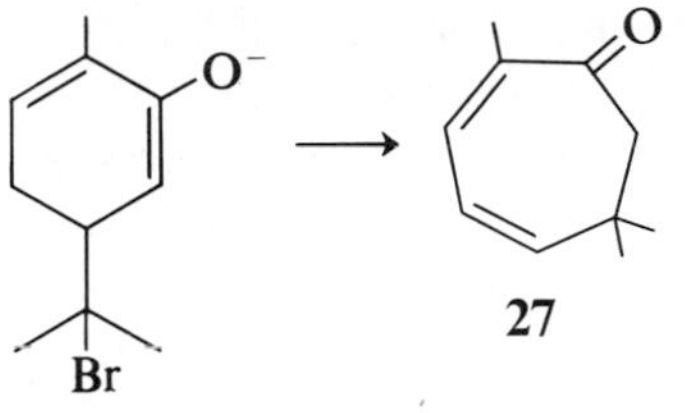

27

26

The conversion is assumed to involve **28** as an intermediate. This compound, which has been isolated under mild conditions, does isomerize to the product.

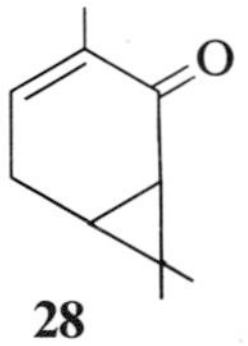

28

A possible route for the isomerization is,

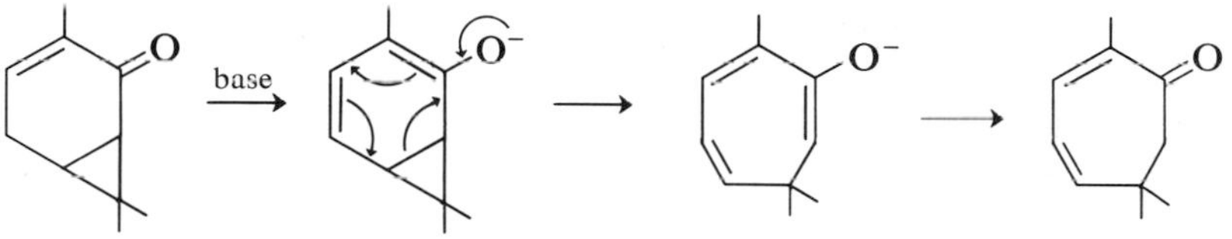

Analogous to this reaction is the conversion of the tosylate **29** to cycloheptadienone **30**:

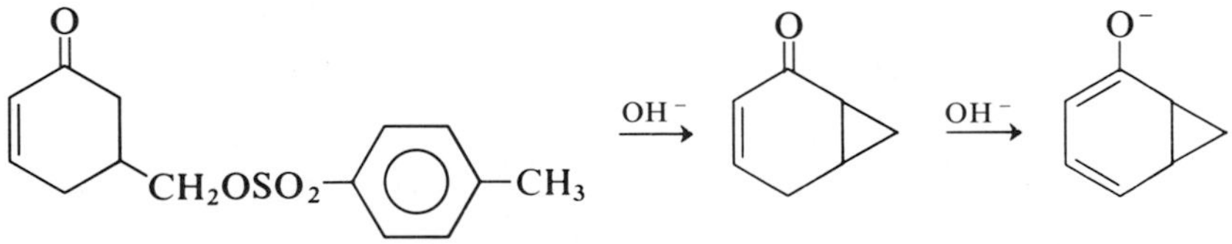

29

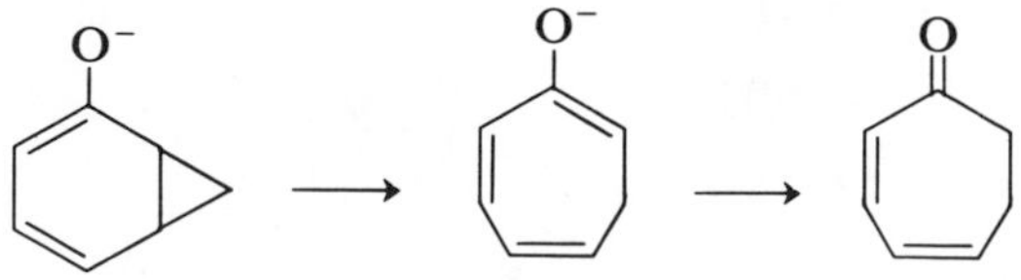

30

18.3 The Pinacol-Pinacolone Rearrangement

Treating pinacol **31** with acid transforms it into pinacolone **32**. The reaction is reversible. Under somewhat different conditions, either of these compounds can be converted into 2,3-dimethyl-1,3-butadiene. Thus, it appears that all three compounds can take part in the equilibrium process with the major product depending upon the reaction conditions. Since formation of the olefin is simply a dehydration of the alcohol, we do not consider this further,

$$
CH_3{-}\underset{\underset{CH_3}{|}}{\overset{\overset{CH_3}{|}}{C}}{-}\overset{\overset{O}{\|}}{C}{-}CH_3 + H_2O
$$

32

$$
CH_3{-}\underset{\underset{OH}{|}}{\overset{\overset{CH_3}{|}}{C}}{-}\underset{\underset{OH}{|}}{\overset{\overset{CH_3}{|}}{C}}{-}CH_3
$$

31

$$
2H_2O + CH_2{=}\underset{}{\overset{\overset{CH_3}{|}}{C}}{-}\underset{}{\overset{\overset{CH_3}{|}}{C}}{=}CH_2
$$

The mechanism usually written for the rearrangement is,

$$
CH_3{-}\underset{\underset{OH}{|}}{\overset{\overset{CH_3}{|}}{C}}{-}\underset{\underset{OH}{|}}{\overset{\overset{CH_3}{|}}{C}}{-}CH_3 + H^+ \rightleftharpoons CH_3{-}\underset{\underset{\underset{H \quad H}{\diagup \overset{+}{} \diagdown}}{O}}{\overset{\overset{CH_3}{|}}{C}}{-}\underset{\underset{OH}{|}}{\overset{\overset{CH_3}{|}}{C}}{-}CH_3
$$

$$
CH_3{-}\underset{\underset{\underset{H \quad H}{\diagup \overset{+}{} \diagdown}}{O}}{\overset{\overset{CH_3}{|}}{C}}{-}\underset{\underset{OH}{|}}{\overset{\overset{CH_3}{|}}{C}}{-}CH_3 \rightleftharpoons CH_3{-}\underset{+}{\overset{\overset{CH_3}{|}}{C}}{-}\underset{\underset{OH}{|}}{\overset{\overset{CH_3}{|}}{C}}{-}CH_3 + H_2O
$$

33

$$
CH_3{-}\overset{\overset{CH_3}{|}}{\underset{+}{C}}{\overset{\frown}{}}\underset{\underset{OH}{|}}{\overset{\overset{CH_3}{|}}{C}}{-}CH_3 \rightleftharpoons CH_3{-}\underset{\underset{CH_3}{|}}{\overset{\overset{CH_3}{|}}{C}}{-}\overset{\overset{+O\diagup^{H}}{\|}}{C}{-}CH_3
$$

33   OH

$$
CH_3{-}\underset{\underset{CH_3}{|}}{\overset{\overset{CH_3}{|}}{C}}{-}\overset{\overset{+O\diagup^{H}}{\|}}{C}{-}CH_3 \rightleftharpoons CH_3{-}\underset{\underset{CH_3}{|}}{\overset{\overset{CH_3}{|}}{C}}{-}\overset{\overset{O}{\|}}{C}{-}CH_3 + H^+
$$

The reaction proceeds by way of the tertiary carbonium ion **33**, followed by migration of the methyl group. This migration leads to the conjugate acid of pinacolone which is stabilized in the following way,

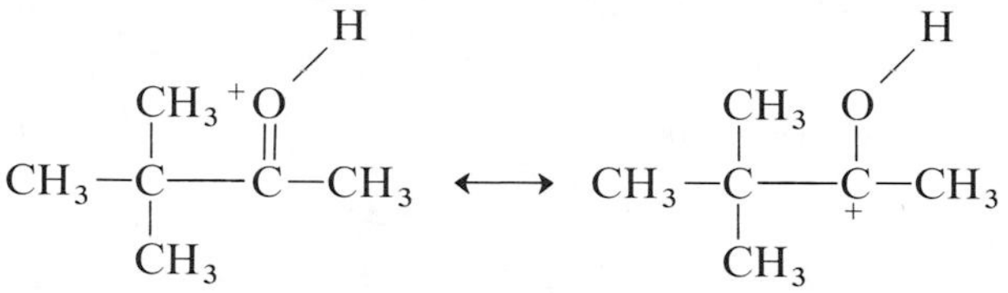

$$
\begin{array}{ccc}
& \overset{\text{H}}{\underset{\text{O}}{\diagup}} & \\
\text{CH}_3\,\overset{+}{\text{O}} \;\overset{\|}{} & & \text{CH}_3 \;\; \text{O} \\
\text{CH}_3-\underset{|}{\overset{|}{\text{C}}}\text{---}\text{C}-\text{CH}_3 & \longleftrightarrow & \text{CH}_3-\underset{|}{\overset{|}{\text{C}}}\text{---}\underset{+}{\text{C}}-\text{CH}_3 \\
\overset{|}{\text{CH}_3} & & \overset{|}{\text{CH}_3}
\end{array}
$$

A measurement of the rate of oxygen exchange for pinacol indicates that the exchange occurs about three times as rapidly as the rearrangement, and this provides good evidence for the carbonium ion intermediate **33**. The carbonium ion reacts with water and reverts to reactant nearly three times as rapidly as it passes on to product.

The reaction takes place with other glycols. When the following cyclic compound is treated with acid, ring expansion takes place:

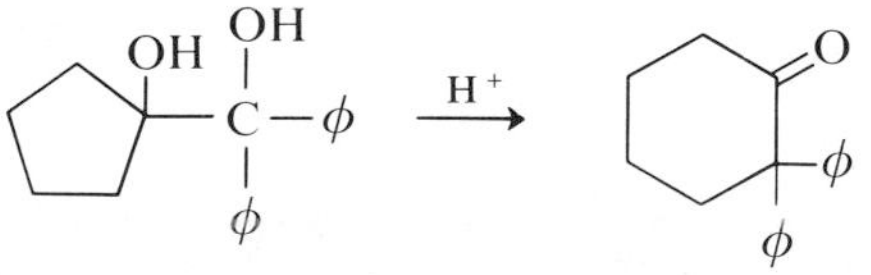

Aromatic compounds behave in the same manner:

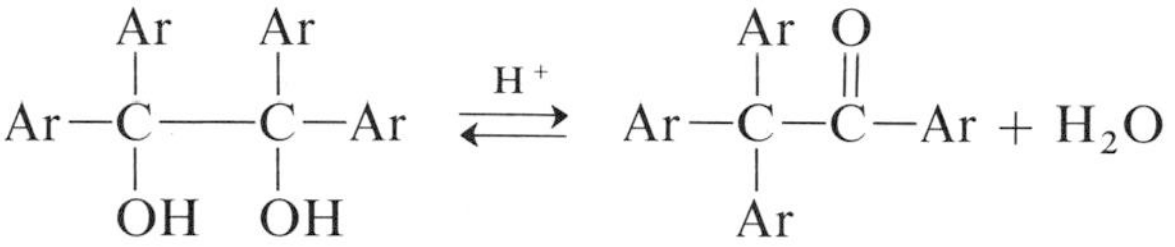

$$
\begin{array}{ccc}
\text{Ar}\quad\text{Ar} & & \text{Ar}\;\;\text{O} \\
\underset{|}{\overset{|}{}}\quad\underset{|}{\overset{|}{}} & \overset{\text{H}^+}{\rightleftharpoons} & \underset{|}{\overset{|}{}}\;\;\overset{\|}{} \\
\text{Ar}-\text{C}\text{---}\text{C}-\text{Ar} & & \text{Ar}-\text{C}-\text{C}-\text{Ar} + \text{H}_2\text{O} \\
\overset{|}{\text{OH}}\;\;\overset{|}{\text{OH}} & & \overset{|}{\text{Ar}}
\end{array}
$$

Here complications may arise; for example, tetraphenylethylene glycol **34** affords tetraphenylethylene oxide. Under somewhat different conditions **34** does undergo the pinacol rearrangement, yet this last reaction also involves the epoxide:

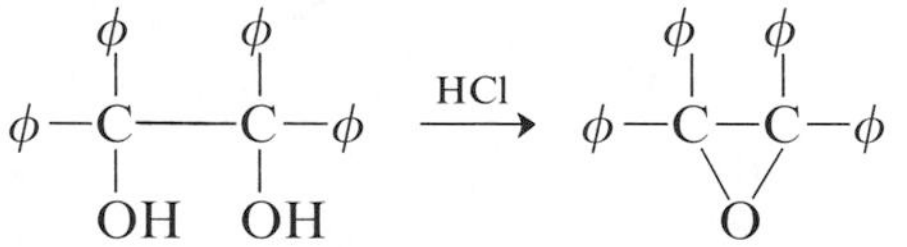

34

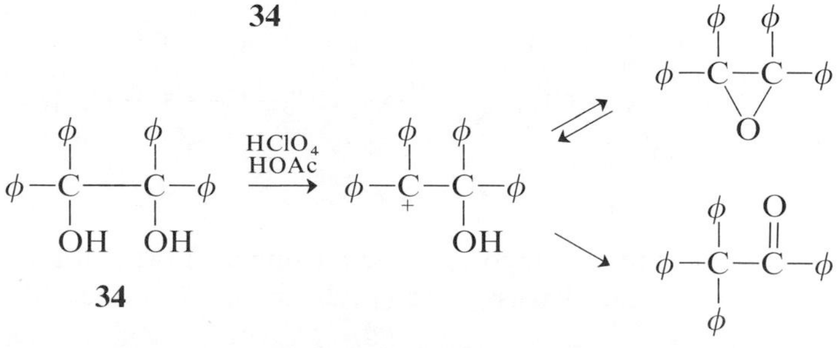

34

35

Kinetic studies show that at a fixed pH the disappearance of **34** follows the pseudo first order rate law,

$$-\frac{d[34]}{dt} = k[34]$$

However, the increase in the concentration of **35** is not equal to this decrease,

$$-\frac{d[34]}{dt} \neq \frac{d[35]}{dt}$$

These results indicate storage of some compound. Kinetic studies indicate the formation of a relatively stable material. This material was isolated from a solution of the incompletely rearranged pinacol and identified as tetra-phenylethylene oxide. It was further shown that most of the reactant molecules first formed the epoxide.

Reactions related to the pinacol rearrangement are known. These may also involve **33** as an intermediate. This carbonium ion, which is formed from different reactants, is in all cases converted into a mixture of pinacol and pinacolone,

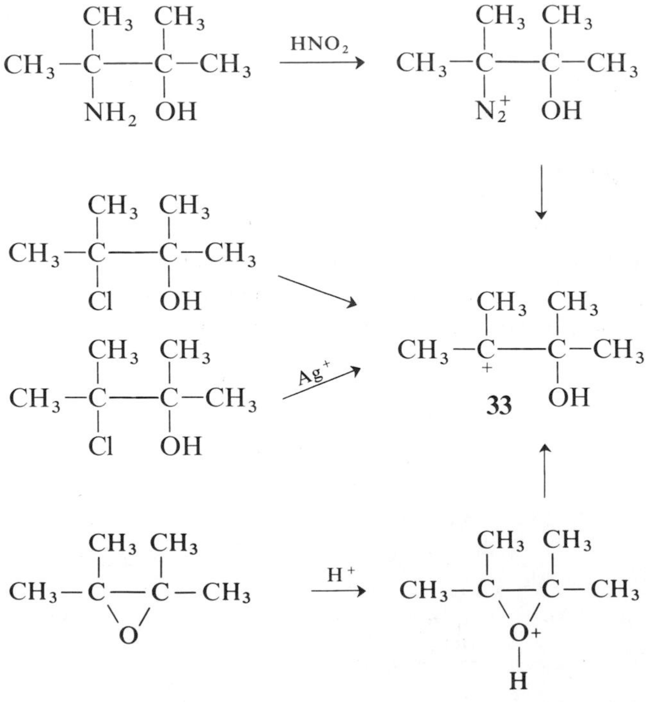

An interesting reaction analogous to the retropinacol is the transformation of **36**. The carbonium ion that is formed after migration of the phenyl group

carries out an electrophilic substitution:

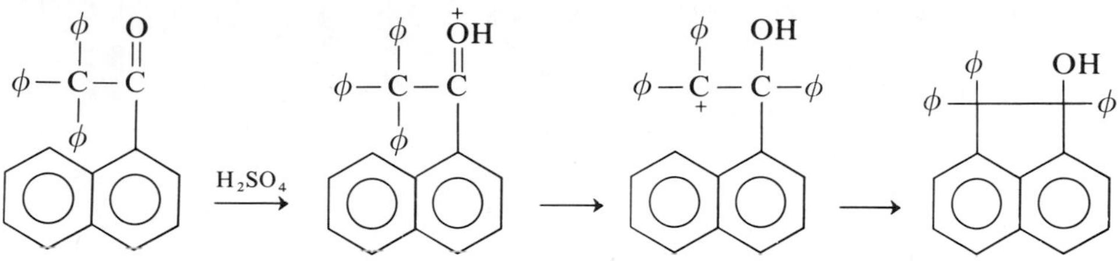

36

In the pinacol reaction of glycols such as

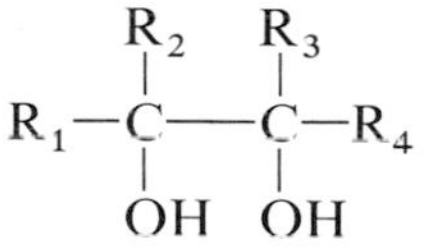

$$R_1-\underset{\underset{OH}{|}}{\overset{\overset{R_2}{|}}{C}}---\underset{\underset{OH}{|}}{\overset{\overset{R_3}{|}}{C}}-R_4$$

the question comes up concerning which group (R_1, R_2, R_3, or R_4) will migrate. Much research has been done on this phase of the reaction. In some cases the results are clearcut; in others it appears that more work is necessary.

In the aliphatic series, glycols of the type

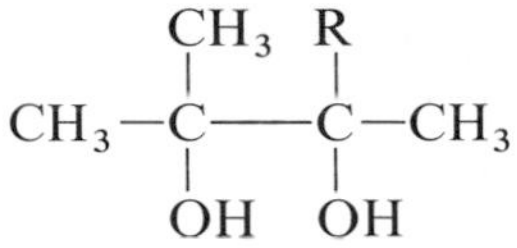

$$CH_3-\underset{\underset{OH}{|}}{\overset{\overset{CH_3}{|}}{C}}---\underset{\underset{OH}{|}}{\overset{\overset{R}{|}}{C}}-CH_3$$

were investigated. Here R was either methyl, ethyl, or *t*-butyl. The migratory tendencies were expressed in terms of partial rates, and it was found that the migratory aptitudes were,

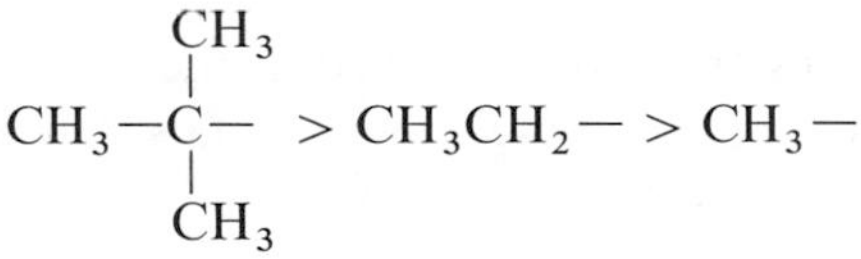

$$CH_3-\underset{\underset{CH_3}{|}}{\overset{\overset{CH_3}{|}}{C}}- \; > \; CH_3CH_2- \; > \; CH_3-$$

The difficulty comes in interpreting the data. Replacing one alkyl group by another alters both the electronic factors and the steric interactions. One cannot say whether *t*-butyl migrates most readily merely because it best stabilizes the positive charge, or whether the different steric requirements and restricted rotations must also be considered. It is quite certain that *t*-butyl is best able to stabilize the positive charge, but it is uncertain just how much of the rate enhancement to attribute to steric factors and restricted rotations.

In the aromatic series the problem appears to be even more complex, and further work will be necessary before a proper understanding of the rearrangement is achieved.

The following carbonium ion is generated from the symmetrical diol (the epoxide may be the precursor):

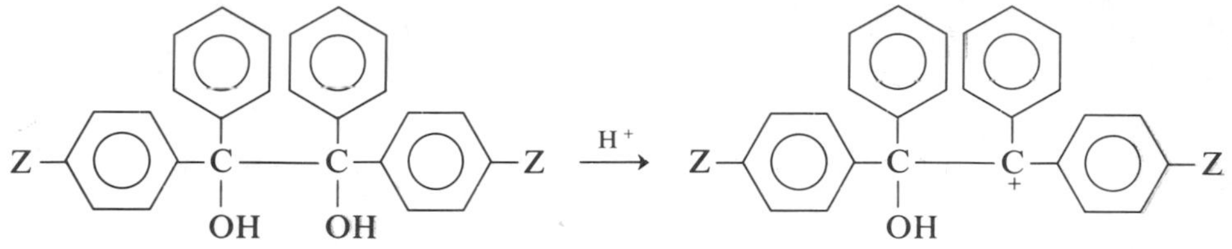

This rearranges to the following two products:

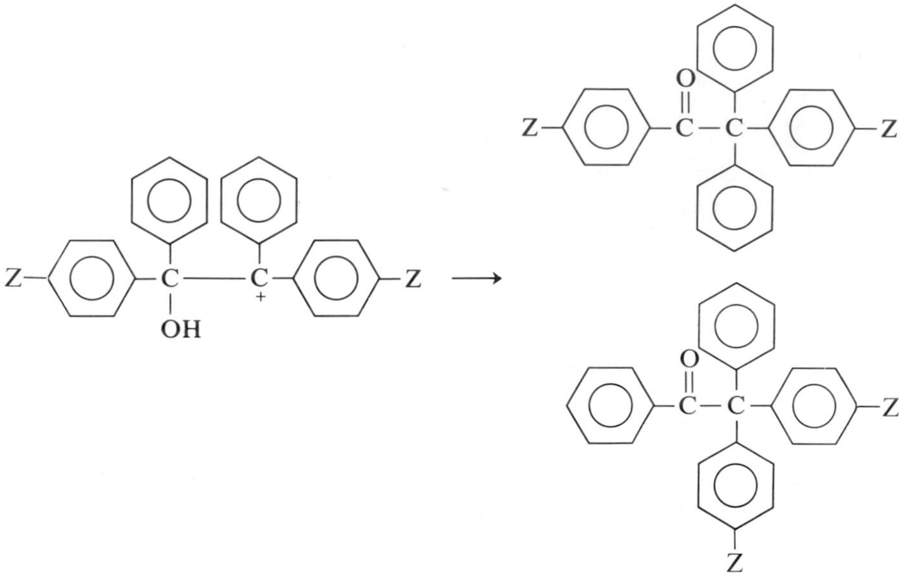

In order for the transformation to proceed, the migrating group must be properly oriented. This requires that its own orbitals be in a position to overlap with the empty orbital of the carbonium ion,

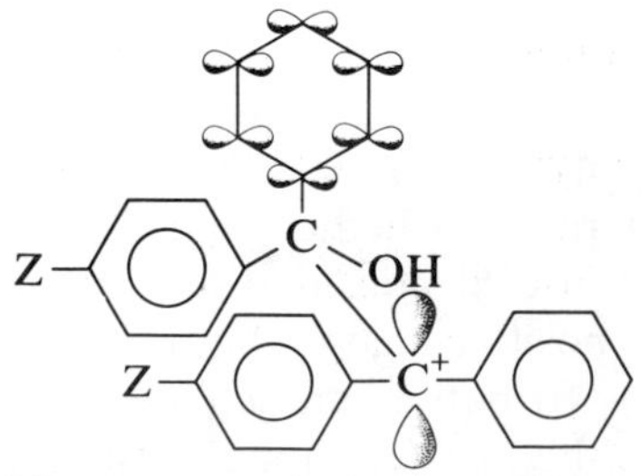

Two suitable conformations and the rearrangement scheme are presented in Figure 18–3.

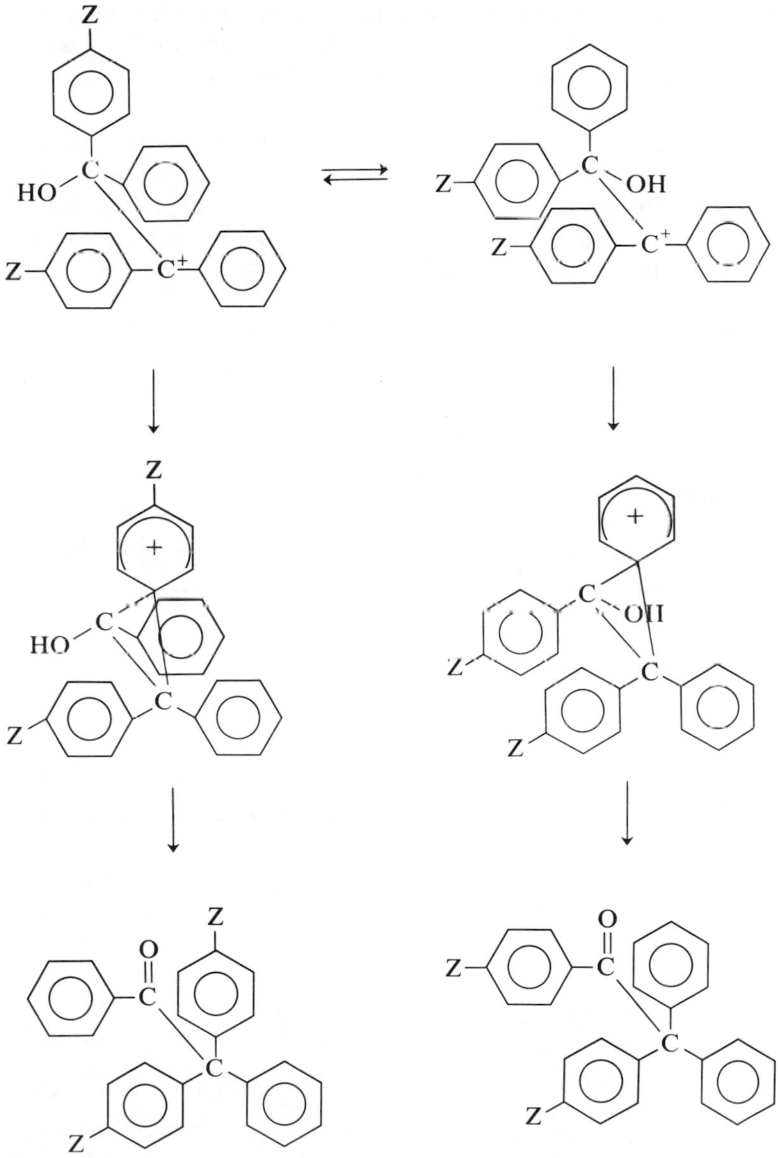

Figure 18-3

If the free energy required for rotation from one conformation to the other is assumed to be much less than the free energy of activation for rearrangement, then the rate of rotation will be faster than the rate of rearrangement, and the various rotational conformations will be in equilibrium. In that case, either of the groups can be placed in the proper position, and the group that best stabilizes the positive charge migrates.

The migrating group donates two electrons, and the situation is the same, as far as the migrating group is concerned, as an aromatic substitution. Naturally, we expect the same order of reactivity. Using symmetrical glycols such as these, the migratory aptitudes of various aromatic groups have been determined. The results confirm our predictions,

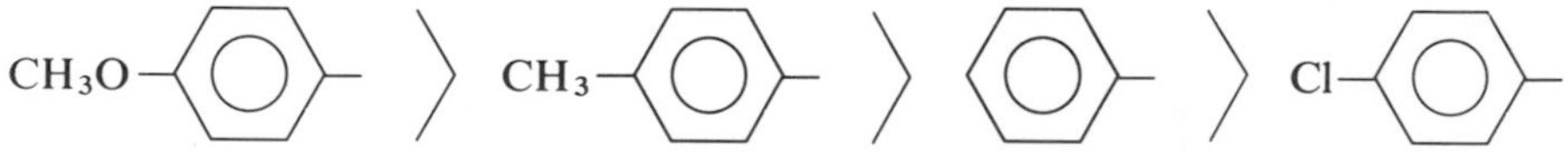

$$CH_3O-\langle\bigcirc\rangle- \ \rangle \ CH_3-\langle\bigcirc\rangle- \ \rangle \ \langle\bigcirc\rangle- \ \rangle \ Cl-\langle\bigcirc\rangle-$$

These results seem to be straightforward. However, difficulties arise when one considers cases such as,

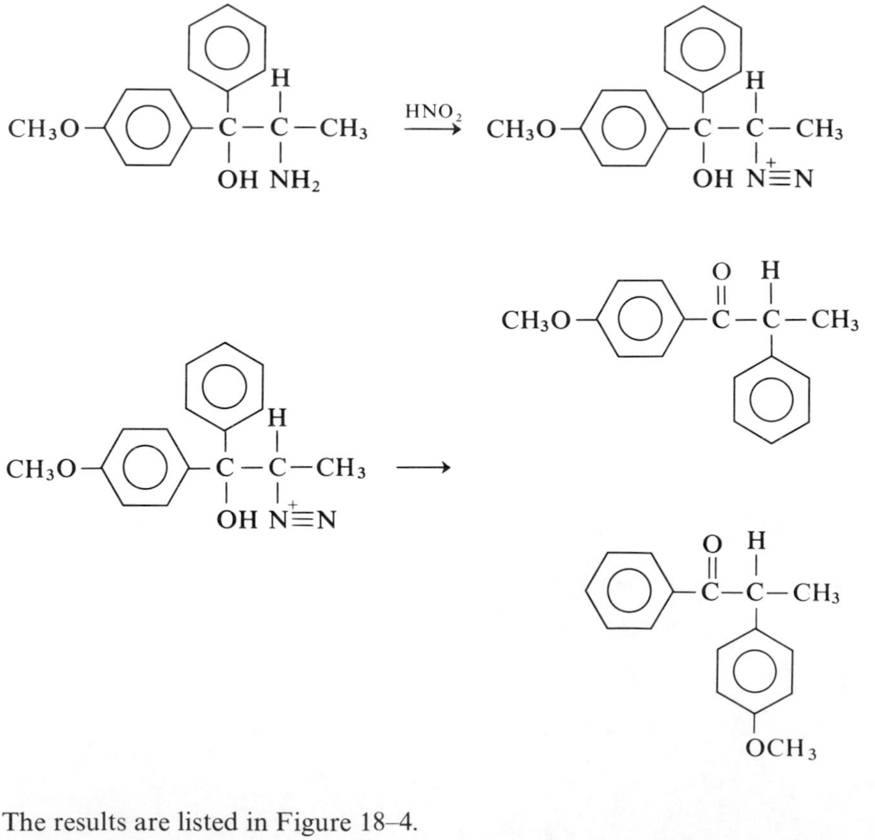

The results are listed in Figure 18–4.

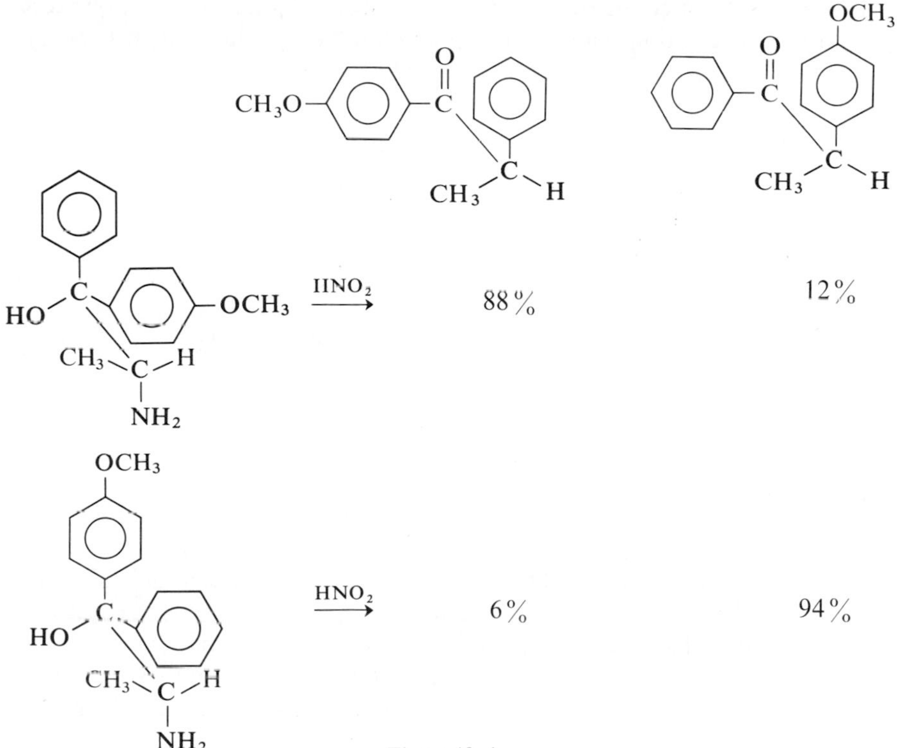

Figure 18–4

These results cannot be explained by assuming free rotation and migration by the most favorable group. They can be justified by assuming a concerted mechanism with participation by the migrating group. If one postulates that the reaction proceeds most readily by a concerted process and by way of the less crowded transition state, the results are explained adequately. The data can be explained on the basis of neighboring group participation; however, the following experiment demonstrates clearly that such participation does not occur.

Optically active **37** was prepared with one of the phenyl groups labeled with C^{14}. This material upon deamination yielded the two products **38** and **39**,

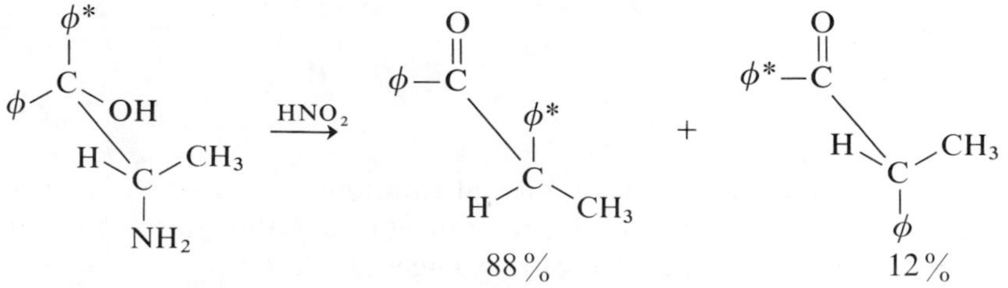

Now inversion of configuration must accompany the participation process. Therefore, participation leads to the prediction that **38** and **40** will be the products,

$$\phi - \overset{\overset{\displaystyle O}{\|}}{C} \diagdown \overset{\displaystyle \phi^*}{\underset{\displaystyle \underset{H}{\diagup} \overset{\displaystyle C}{\diagdown} CH_3}{|}}$$

38

$$\phi^* - \overset{\overset{\displaystyle O}{\|}}{C} \diagdown \overset{\displaystyle \phi}{\underset{\displaystyle \underset{H}{\diagup} \overset{\displaystyle C}{\diagdown} CH_3}{|}}$$

40

Compounds **39** and **40** are enantiomers. Therefore, the assumption of neighboring group participation leads to the wrong conclusion. It predicts the formation of a compound **40** that is not present, and it cannot explain the formation of **39** which is actually produced.

An explanation has been advanced that satisfies both the previous data and the present results. The theory assumes that the free carbonium ion **41** is involved, that this carbonium ion is formed preferentially in the conformation presented (determined by the least crowded transition state for formation), and that it reacts from this conformation before it has a chance to rotate. The idea is put forth that in these cases the rate of rotation is not much more rapid than the rate of rearrangement, that it is in fact slower than the rearrangement process, and that restricted rotations can account for the observed products.

$$\phi - \overset{\displaystyle \phi^*}{\underset{\displaystyle C}{|}} \diagdown \overset{\displaystyle OH}{\underset{\displaystyle H \diagdown \underset{NH_2}{\overset{\displaystyle C}{|}} \diagup CH_3}{}} \quad \xrightarrow{HNO_2} \quad \phi - \overset{\displaystyle \phi^*}{\underset{\displaystyle C}{|}} \diagdown \overset{\displaystyle OH}{\underset{\displaystyle H - \overset{+}{C} - CH_3}{}}$$

41

The free energy required for the internal rotation is assumed to be greater than the free energy of activation for rearrangement. Although some rotation to **42** is possible, it is assumed that **41** rearranges at a faster rate.

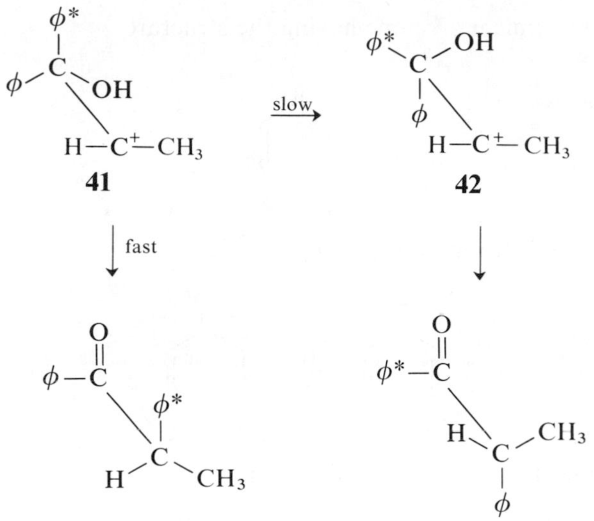

This theory explains the observed product geometry in a satisfactory manner. It must also be assumed that the free energy required for rotation into conformations such as

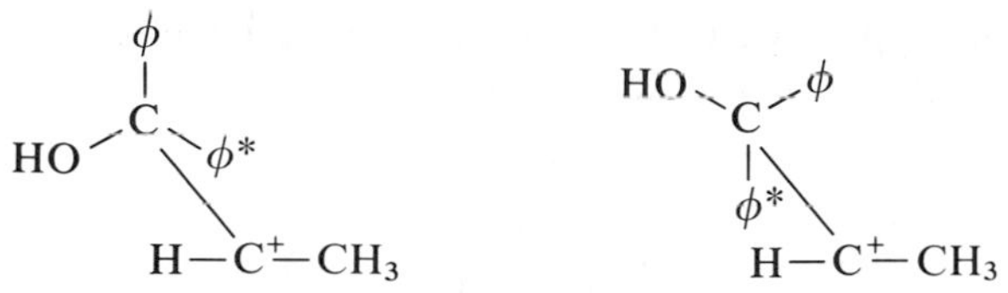

is still greater (phenyl must eclipse methyl during the process), and therefore that such conformations are not formed in significant quantities.

Other processes related to the pinacol and retropinacol reactions are known. The retropinacol reaction involves the transformation

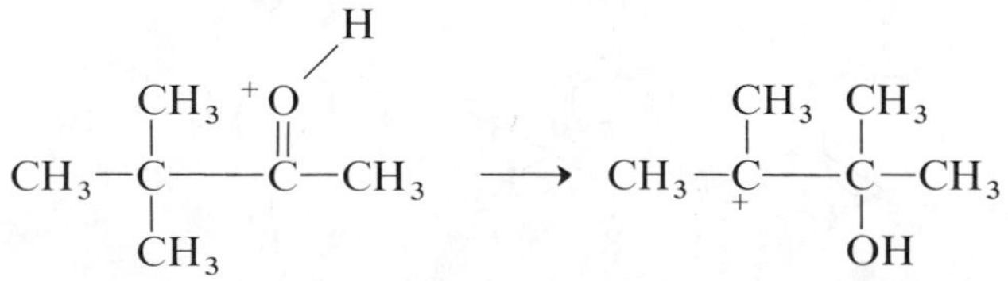

whereby the conjugate acid of a carbonyl compound is converted by migration of an alkyl group into a carbonium ion. Related to this process is the dienone-phenol rearrangement.

In this rearrangement a ketone having the structure

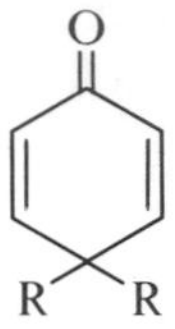

is treated with acid. It forms the conjugate acid,

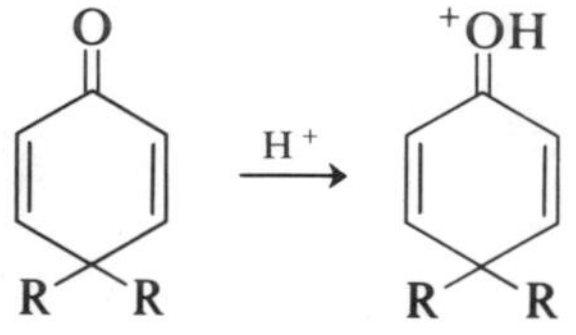

which is stabilized by charge delocalization:

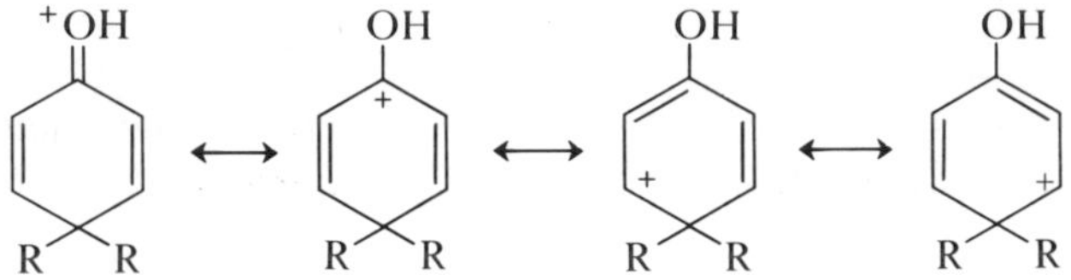

This is the same type of carbonium ion encountered in electrophilic aromatic substitution, and it can be represented as,

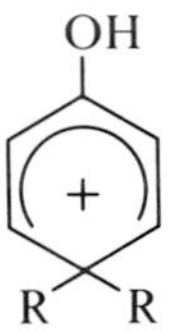

Migration of an alkyl group leads to the carbonium ion **43**, which can lose a proton to form the substituted phenol,

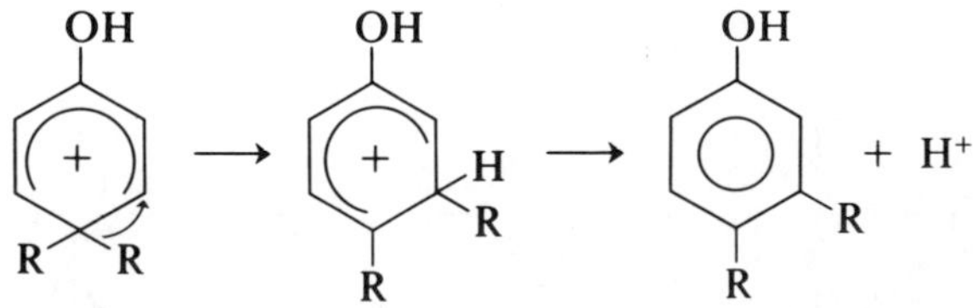

43

This process involves a rearrangement of the conjugate acid of a ketone into a carbonium ion by migration of an alkyl group, and it is similar, therefore, to the retropinacol reaction.

Examples are the following conversions:

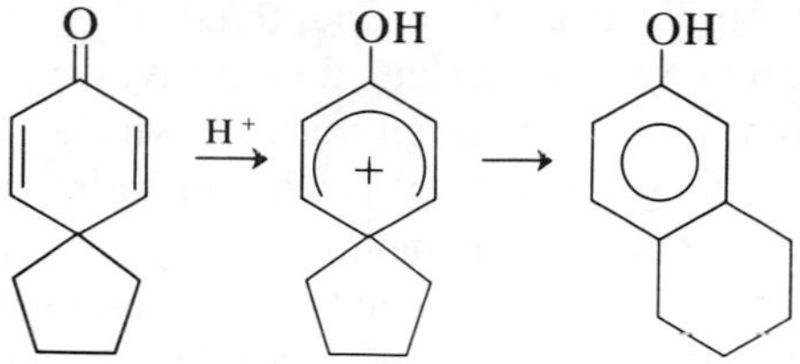

and

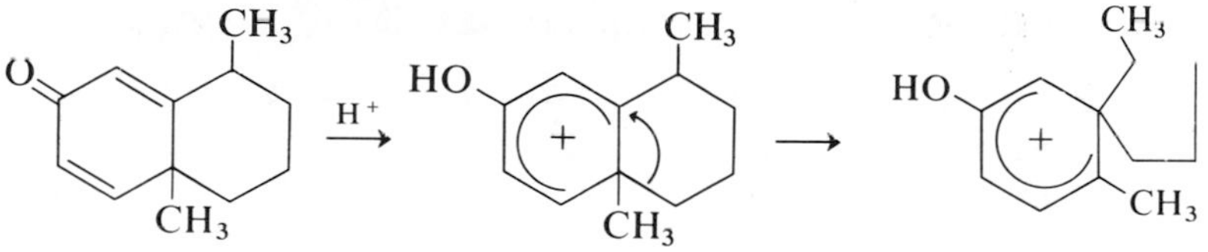

(this new carbonium ion must undergo a second such rearrangement),

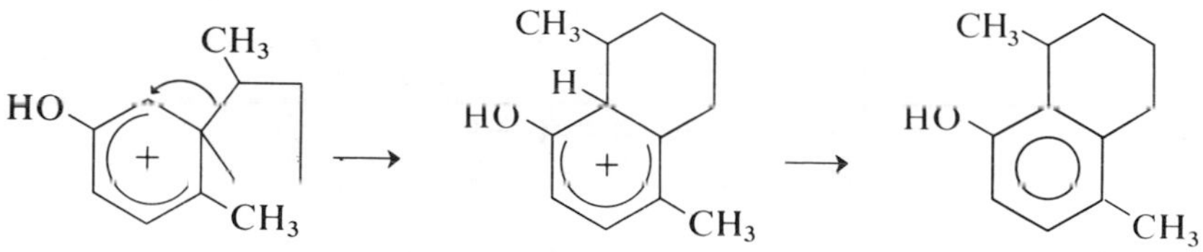

In the second example we see again the greater migratory aptitude of the larger alkyl group. In this instance it is reasonably certain that the migration takes place as indicated because the larger alkyl group is better able to stabilize the positive charge and not because of steric interactions.

This second example also demonstrates that the reaction does take place by way of the spiro compound and not by the direct route,

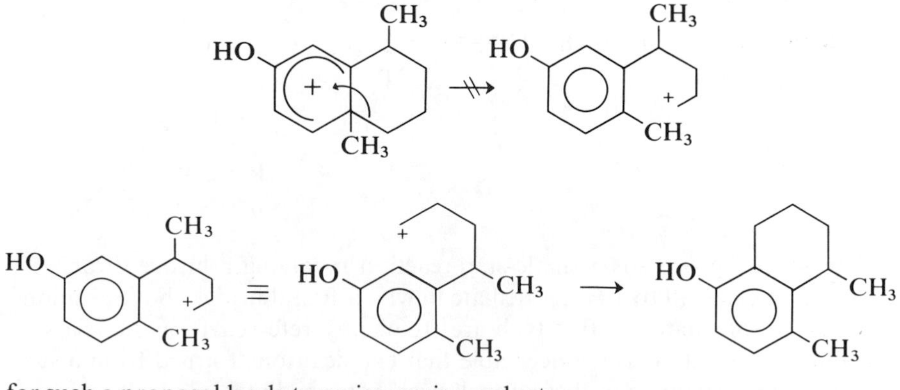

for such a proposal leads to an isomeric product.

18.4 Carbonium Ion Rearrangements

Carbonium ion rearrangements are encountered in many different areas of organic chemistry. These rearrangements do not involve a free carbonium ion. Instead the carbonium ion is part of an ion pair which is formed either prior to or during the rearrangement step. Such ion pairs have been discussed previously, and we do not consider them explicitly at this time.

Some rearrangements can be formulated as stepwise reactions; a nonbridged carbonium ion is formed first, and some group subsequently migrates. Many carbonium ion reactions proceed in this way,

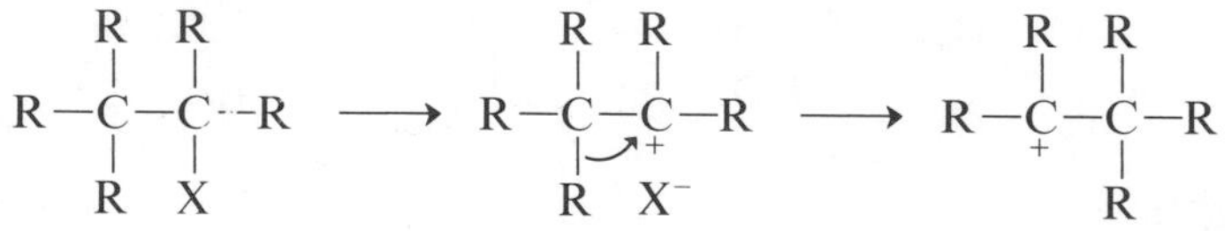

In the transition state for the second step the migrating group is partially bonded to both positions and this transition has the following appearance,

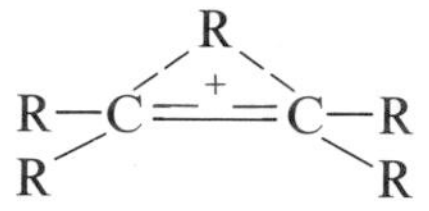

An alternative process also takes place; it is the concerted migration, whereby R assists the departure of X^-:

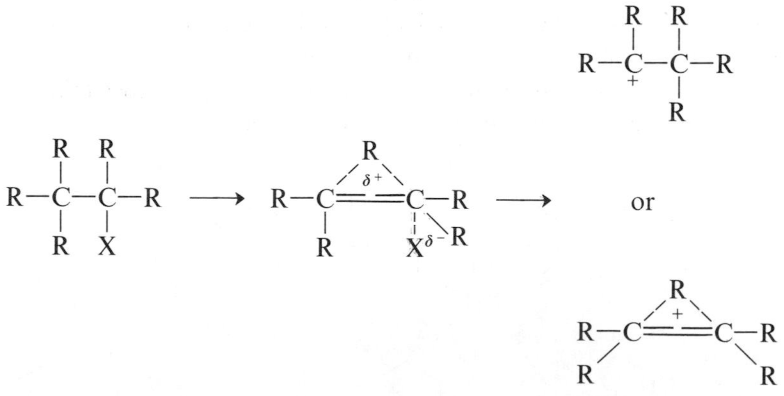

This second process is a single-step reaction involving a bridged transition state, and it can lead to an intermediate in which R still bridges both positions. Bridged intermediates of this type are frequently referred to as nonclassical carbonium ions. It is also conceivable that classical ions formed from a stepwise reaction rearrange to these nonclassical intermediates.

The species,

$$
\begin{array}{c}
\qquad\quad \underset{\diagup\quad\diagdown}{R} \\
R-C\!\!=\!\!\overset{+}{=}\!\!=\!\!C-R \\
\diagup\qquad\qquad\diagdown \\
R\qquad\qquad\quad R
\end{array}
$$

44

which best represents the transition state for an equilibrium between two classical cations, has in some cases been proposed as an actual intermediate. This question is one of the more intriguing problems in organic chemistry, and it is still being debated. Some reactions are best explained by assuming that the intermediate cations have a classical structure. Others are best explained by postulating nonclassical bridged intermediates. A third group of reactions is explained by assuming that both types of carbonium ions are present. We next present some of the arguments for and against these nonclassical intermediates.

The first point that is usually raised, questions whether an intermediate with such a nonclassical structure could actually exist. This question can be answered readily. Since the basic premise of molecular orbital theory is that the electrons in a molecule are delocalized over the entire system, an intermediate having partial bonds and delocalized electrons is certainly conceivable. A comparison of the structure of the nonclassical intermediate with those of similar classical cations can be made most readily using the ideas of valence bond theory, and the differences in structure are not so great as they may at first appear.

Consider an equilibrium between two classical carbonium ions:

$$
\begin{array}{ccc}
\qquad R & & \qquad R \\
\quad | \quad + & & \quad + \quad | \\
R-\overset{|}{C}-\overset{|}{C}-R & \rightleftharpoons & R-\overset{|}{C}-\overset{|}{C}-R \\
\quad | \quad | & & \quad | \quad | \\
\quad R \quad R & & \quad R \quad R
\end{array}
$$

45

What is the likelihood that a reaction involves these classical intermediates rather than the single bridged cation **44**?

We know that according to the valence bond theory, no single valence bond structure gives a complete picture of a species. A whole series of structures is needed to represent the system accurately. Even the classical cations represented by **45** receive contributions from other valence bond contributors. Representing the cations by **45** assumes that two species are involved and that each of these is more or less adequately represented by the structure given. Other valence bond contributors are far less important. On the other hand, representing the cation by **44** assumes that only a single species is formed and that this species is not adequately represented by any single valence bond contributor, at least three contributors being necessary for even an adequate description. The valence bond contributors to **44** are:

$$R-\underset{R}{\overset{R}{C}}\overset{+}{=\!=\!=}\underset{R}{\overset{}{C}}-R$$

44

$$R-\underset{R}{\overset{R}{\overset{+}{C}}}\!\!-\!\!-\!\!-\underset{R}{\overset{}{C}}-R \quad\longleftrightarrow\quad R-\underset{R}{\overset{R}{\overset{+}{C}}}\!\!-\!\!-\!\!-\underset{R}{\overset{}{C}}-R \quad\longleftrightarrow\quad R-\underset{R}{\overset{R^{+}}{C}}\!\!=\!\!\underset{R}{\overset{}{C}}-R$$

The first two contributors to **44** are very similar to **45**.

We see how subtle the difference between **44** and **45** really is. Subtle distinctions remain (for example, slight differences in geometry between the valence bond contributors to **44** and those contributing to **45**). The major difference is the contribution made by each of the various valence bond structures. In the classical case, a single contributor adequately but not completely describes the system, whereas for the nonclassical structure more than a single contributor is necessary for even an adequate description. The difference between classical and nonclassical structures is only a matter of degree. There is then no question about the possible existence of a nonclassical intermediate. Such intermediates definitely and positively can exist! The basic problem is whether a single cationic species (best represented by **44**) or whether two cationic species (**45**) are involved. The problem actually hinges on the number of intermediates, and the question is unresolved whether a single species or whether two cationic intermediates participate in carbonium ion reactions.

The reaction coordinates are shown in Figure 18–5.

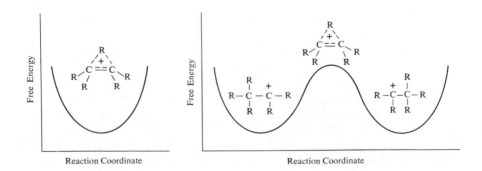

Figure 18–5

Whether classical or nonclassical intermediates are formed in a reaction depends only upon the free energies of the respective cations. The unusual structure of **44** is immaterial. When the free energy of the classical carbonium ions is significantly lower, these will be the intermediates. When the non-classical cation has a lower free energy, it alone will participate. If the free energies of the two are nearly equal, both will be present. Some reactions are best explained on the basis of classical cations; others are best explained in terms of nonclassical carbonium ions. Whether classical or nonclassical inter-mediates are formed in a reaction, depends upon the free energies of these cations, and it is difficult to predict which will be involved.

The solvolysis of the tosylate **46** has been explained in terms of bridged cations whereas the tosylate **47** reacts by way of nonbridged intermediates. In the second case it appears that the nonbridged cation is more stable than the bridged (because of resonance with the phenyl groups), while in the first example it has been suggested that the bridged intermediate is more stable,

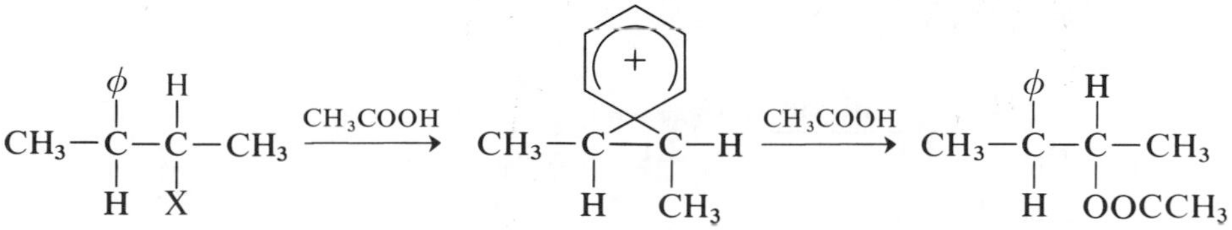

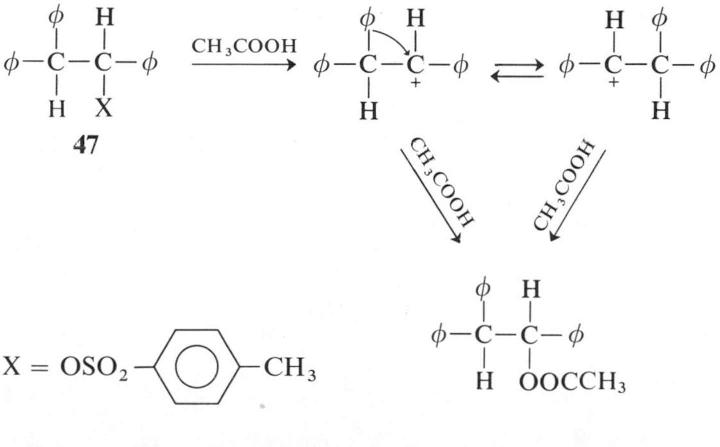

A phenyl group adjacent to an incipient carbonium ion may participate in the first of these processes, yet it is the nonbridged intermediates that are involved in the second. The presence of a group such as phenyl in the system does not insure us of participation by that group in the ionization step, nor does it insure us of bridged ions as intermediates. The more stable intermediate is formed. In some cases this is the bridged ion, and in others it is the non-bridged cation. If the two ions have about the same free energy, then both will participate in the process.

Evidence for the intervention of the bridged ion during the solvolysis of **46** comes from a study of the product geometry. Starting with the *threo* isomer **48** in acetic acid as solvent, a racemic mixture of *threo* products was obtained. This racemic mixture can be explained quite nicely by postulating the cyclic cation as an intermediate. Attack by the solvent at one of the carbon atoms leads to one enantiomer while attack at the other carbon atom produces the mirror image. Further evidence for the participation of cyclic ions in this reaction comes from a similar study on the *erythro* isomer **49**. In this case attack by the solvent at either carbon atom of the cyclic intermediate lead to the same product (*erythro* acetate), and this expected product was, in fact, the major product isolated,

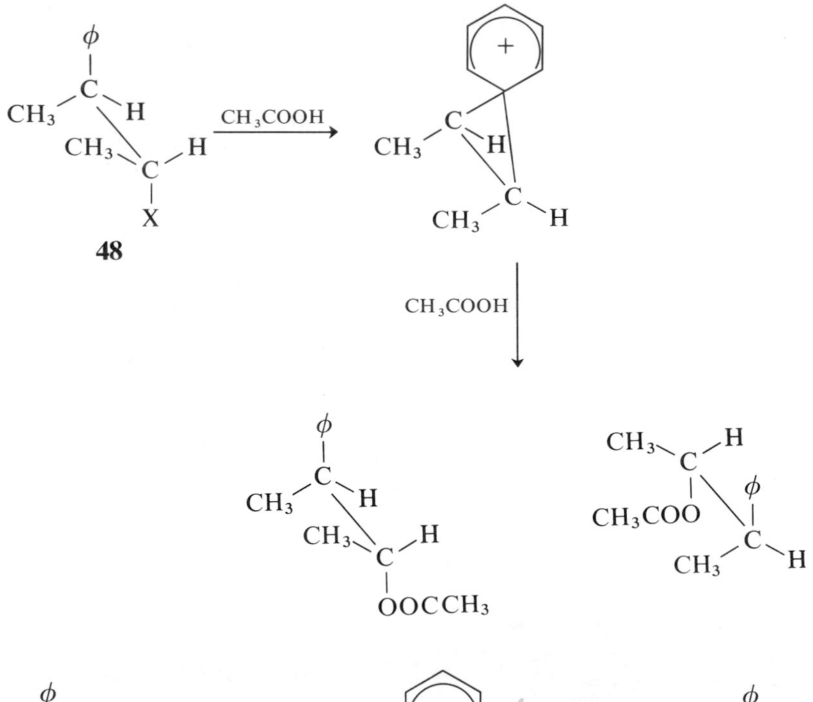

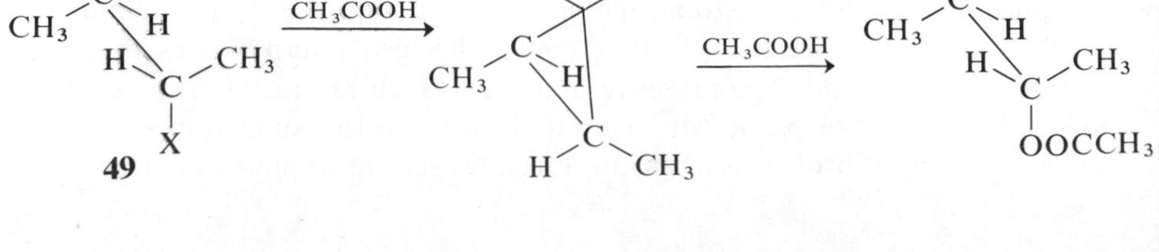

$$X = OSO_2 - \underset{\bigcirc}{\langle\bigcirc\rangle} - CH_3$$

It should be kept in mind that as in any organic reaction, the products just presented are not the only ones formed; they are, however, the major products. Other products include those resulting from hydrogen migration and olefin formation. We shall eventually discuss this more fully.

Evidence for the participation of nonbridged intermediates in the solvolysis of **47** comes from labeling experiments using radioactive carbon. The data demonstrate unambiguously that bridged cationic intermediates are not formed, and nonbridged carbonium ions such as those suggested explain the experimental results in a satisfactory manner.

We have assumed that the solvolyses of **48** and **49** proceed by way of cyclic intermediates. However, a good argument against these nonclassical cations has been presented.

First of all, ion pairs are involved in the reaction, and the racemization of **48** occurs much more rapidly than its solvolysis. While this complicates matters, it does not in any way alter the conclusions. The existence of ion pairs and internal return is not evidence against the cyclic cationic intermediates. The major products formed from acetolysis of the *threo* and *erythro* isomers are still best explained on the basis of cyclic intermediates. However, other complicating factors are present that are not in agreement with participation by the phenyl group and a nonclassical carbonium ion.

Approximately 30% of the product is olefinic material. In addition, products resulting from hydrogen migration are present. In order to account for these olefinic and rearranged products, it becomes necessary to postulate additional carbonium ions. The phenyl bridged structures do not adequately account for all of the observed products. It becomes necessary to assume that classical carbonium ions as well as a hydrogen bridged carbonium ion are also involved. At least three different carbonium ions are now required to explain all of the products, and it has been suggested that the classical intermediates may suffice. Rather than postulate three carbonium ions (a classical and two nonclassical), it has been suggested that rapidly equilibrating classical structures may be sufficient and more reasonable.

A last argument against phenyl participation comes from rate data. If the nonclassical carbonium ion is formed instead of a classical intermediate, it must be because the nonclassical carbonium ion is more stable. (It has been estimated that it would have to be several kilocalories per mole more stable in order to prevent a significant amount of product formation from classical intermediates.) Now, if the nonclassical carbonium ion is significantly more stable than a classical intermediate, the transition state leading to it should also be more stable than the transition state leading to a classical carbonium ion. This leads to the conclusion that tosylates **48** and **49** ought to react at a faster rate than tosylates that do not receive neighboring group assistance. This rate acceleration is not observed. There is no rate enhancement for acetolysis of these tosylates and only moderate rate acceleration in their formolysis (reaction with formic acid). This is further evidence against the nonclassical structures.

The nonclassical carbonium ions explain the major products formed during the acetolysis of **48** and **49**; they do not explain the minor products. It has been suggested that all of the products can be derived from rapidly equilibrating classical carbonium ion pairs such as,

$$
\begin{array}{ccc}
\phi \\
| \\
\mathrm{C} \\
\mathrm{CH_3} \diagdown \mathrm{H} \\
\mathrm{CH_3-\overset{+}{C}-H} \\
\mathrm{X^-}
\end{array}
\quad \rightleftharpoons \quad
\begin{array}{c}
\mathrm{CH_3-\overset{+}{C}-H} \\
\quad \phi \\
\mathrm{X^-} \diagdown | \\
\mathrm{C} \\
\mathrm{CH_3} \diagup \diagdown \mathrm{H}
\end{array}
$$

and

$$
\begin{array}{c}
\phi \\
| \\
\mathrm{C} \\
\mathrm{CH_3} \diagdown \mathrm{H} \\
\mathrm{H-\overset{+}{C}-CH_3} \\
\mathrm{X^-}
\end{array}
\quad \rightleftharpoons \quad
\begin{array}{c}
\mathrm{CH_3-\overset{+}{C}-H} \\
\quad \phi \\
\mathrm{X^-} \diagdown | \\
\mathrm{C} \\
\mathrm{H} \diagup \diagdown \mathrm{CH_3}
\end{array}
$$

The phenyl group is migrating rapidly.

These ion pairs are solvated, and it is assumed that the solvent attacks most readily from the side opposite the phenyl group.

Changes in the reactant geometry, in the solvent, or in the leaving group appear to exert an influence upon the type of intermediate formed during a reaction, and even subtle changes occasionally have a large effect. The solvolyses of **48** and **49** are complex; however, the deamination of the corresponding amine **50** appears to be even more complex. In addition to products resulting from olefin formation, substituted products resulting from hydrogen, methyl, and phenyl migration are found. Again, the results can be explained in terms of bridged and nonbridged cations. The nonbridged carbonium ions are the generally accepted intermediates. Changing the leaving group from tosylate to $\mathrm{N_2^+}$ has a pronounced effect upon the nature and yield of the products. The actual percentage yield of each product depends upon whether the *threo* or *erythro* form of **50** is employed. The following substituted products are found; some of these products were also formed during the solvolyses of **48** and **49**, but the yields were much lower. (The products presented here were first treated with lithium aluminum hydride to convert the esters to alcohols.)

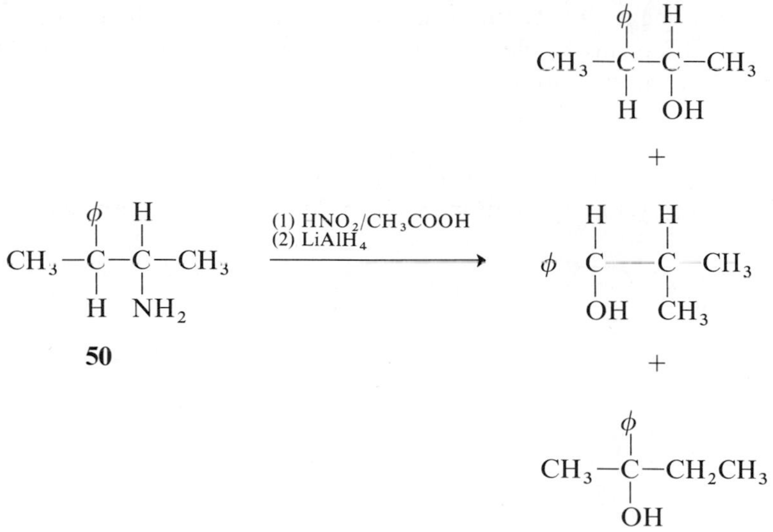

$$CH_3-\overset{\displaystyle\phi}{\underset{\displaystyle H}{C}}-\overset{\displaystyle H}{\underset{\displaystyle OH}{C}}-CH_3$$

+

$$CH_3-\overset{\displaystyle\phi}{\underset{\displaystyle H}{C}}-\overset{\displaystyle H}{\underset{\displaystyle NH_2}{C}}-CH_3 \xrightarrow{\begin{array}{c}\text{(1) HNO}_2/\text{CH}_3\text{COOH}\\ \text{(2) LiAlH}_4\end{array}} \phi-\overset{\displaystyle H}{\underset{\displaystyle OH}{C}}-\overset{\displaystyle H}{\underset{\displaystyle CH_3}{C}}-CH_3$$

50

+

$$CH_3-\overset{\displaystyle\phi}{\underset{\displaystyle OH}{C}}-CH_2CH_3$$

Although participation may not be involved in these reactions, it is certain that such participation can take place. Consider the following sequence where X is tosylate,

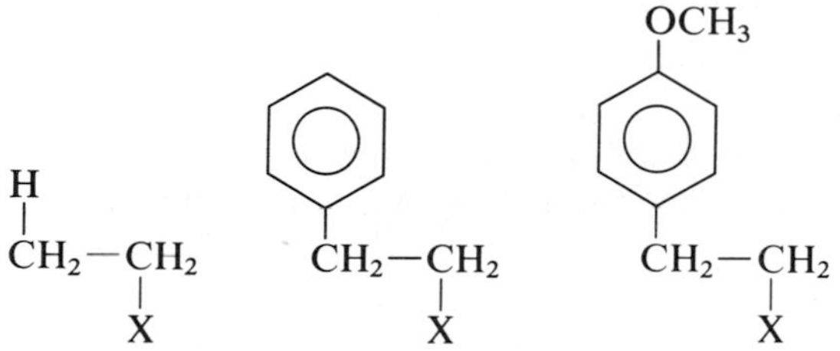

$$\frac{k_R}{k_H} = \qquad\qquad 1 \qquad\qquad 2.1 \qquad\qquad 160$$

It has been observed that the rate constant for formolysis of the second compound is twice that for ethyl tosylate; that of the third is 160 times that of ethyl. While it is not certain that phenyl participates, the data indicate that anisyl certainly does.

The deamination of **50** affords products resulting from hydrogen, methyl and phenyl migration, and migrations of this type occur in many areas of organic chemistry. Examples are encountered with small ring compounds, terpenes, bicyclic compounds, and steroids. The reactions of cyclopropane and its derivatives afford interesting examples. The normal bond angles for the central carbon atom of a carbonium ion are 120°, while the normal angles for a tetrahedrally bonded carbon atom are only 109.5°. Therefore, while the cyclopropyl ring is already strained, converting a tetrahedrally bonded carbon atom into a trigonally bonded one increases the ring strain still further. Because of the increased ring strain that accompanies the process, the cyclopropyl cation is not formed readily, yet some reactions do proceed by way of this intermediate.

Cyclopropyl tosylate is converted to allyl acetate in acetic acid. The reaction is slow, and a cyclopropyl cation can be postulated as an intermediate,

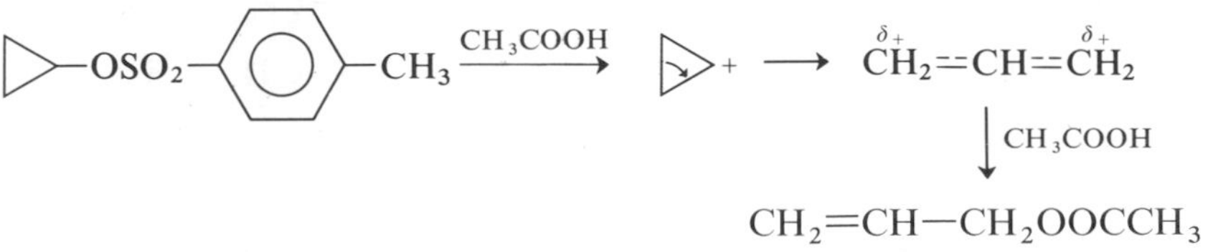

Cyclopropyl amine is converted to allyl alcohol upon treatment with nitrous acid:

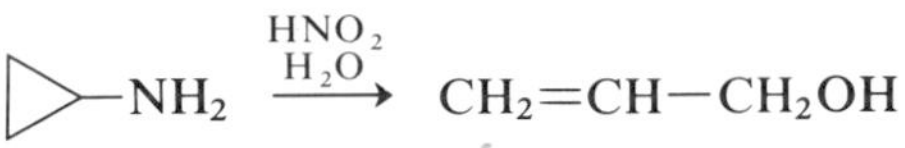

The compound **51** has been prepared, and it rearranges readily to 2-chloronaphthalene. Since the reaction rate is independent of the concentration of added base, the rate limiting step must be a unimolecular ionization. Because of the ease with which this reaction proceeds, it is quite possible that **51** is converted directly to **52** by a concerted mechanism and that the cyclopropyl cation, as such, is not formed as an intermediate,

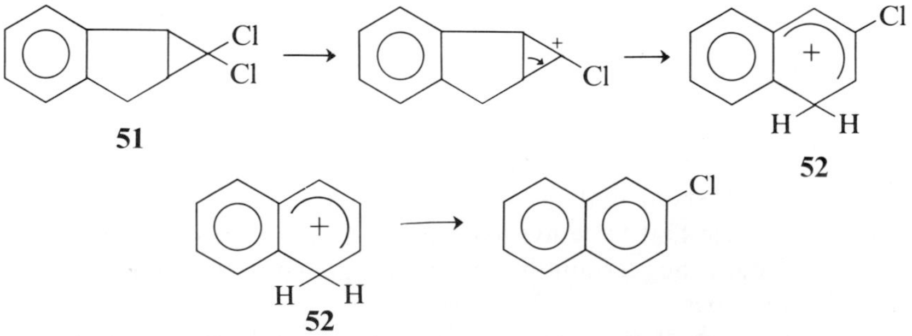

Many other unusual reactions involving cyclopropyl derivatives are known. Upon deamination, the two amines **53** and **54** yield the same mixture of isomeric alcohols. The results (Table 18–1) imply that common intermediates (nonclassical or rapidly equilibrating classical structures) must be involved.

Table 18–1

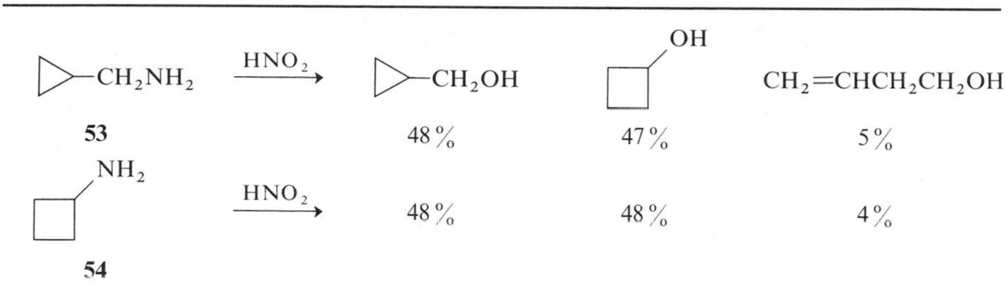

▷–CH₂NH₂	$\xrightarrow{\text{HNO}_2}$	▷–CH₂OH	cyclobutanol (OH)	CH₂=CHCH₂CH₂OH
53		48%	47%	5%
cyclobutyl NH₂	$\xrightarrow{\text{HNO}_2}$	48%	48%	4%
54				

Related to these results are those obtained from the solvolysis of the corresponding chlorides. It turns out that in 50% aqueous ethanol at 50°, the chloride **55** is solvolyzed 27 times as rapidly as **56** and 40 times as rapidly as **57**. It is rather remarkable that the cyclic compounds undergo ionization more rapidly than the allylic halogen, for we know that the allylic carbonium ion and the transition state leading to it are very stable,

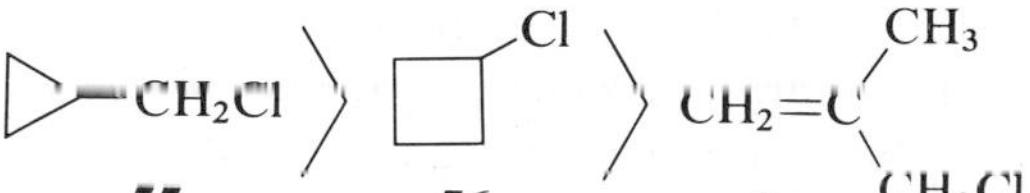

$$\text{▷—CH}_2\text{Cl} \quad \rangle \quad \square^{\text{Cl}} \quad \rangle \quad \text{CH}_2=\text{C}\overset{\text{CH}_3}{\underset{\text{CH}_2\text{Cl}}{\diagdown}}$$

55   **56**   **57**

When **55** is reacted in acetic acid, a mixture of rearranged and solvolyzed products is obtained:

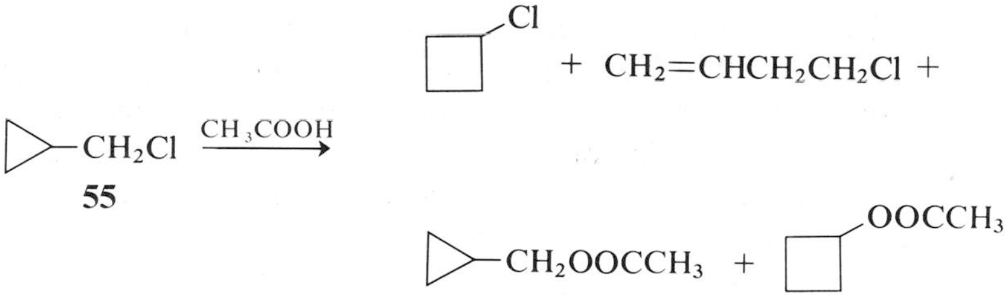

$$\square^{\text{Cl}} \; + \; \text{CH}_2=\text{CHCH}_2\text{CH}_2\text{Cl} \; +$$

$$\text{▷—CH}_2\text{Cl} \xrightarrow{\text{CH}_3\text{COOH}}$$

55

$$\text{▷—CH}_2\text{OOCCH}_3 \; + \; \square^{\text{OOCCH}_3}$$

In order to avoid this complication, this reaction was also conducted in aqueous solution where it was not allowed to proceed to completion. Since **55** is hydrolyzed more rapidly than any isomeric materials that may be formed, it is reasonable to assume that when the reaction is conducted in this manner, all of the alcoholic products are formed from **55**. Two fractions, an alcoholic fraction and a halide fraction, were obtained. The alcoholic fraction contained the same three products in the same proportions that were previously obtained from the deamination of **53** and **54**. The halide fraction contained isomeric materials and unreacted starting material,

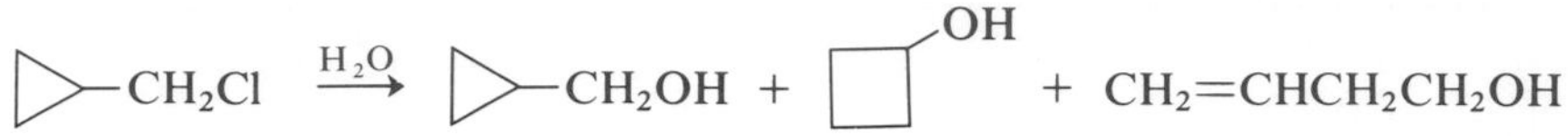

$$\triangleright\!\!-CH_2Cl \xrightarrow{H_2O} \triangleright\!\!-CH_2OH + \square\!\!-OH + CH_2=CHCH_2CH_2OH$$

From the halide fraction were obtained,

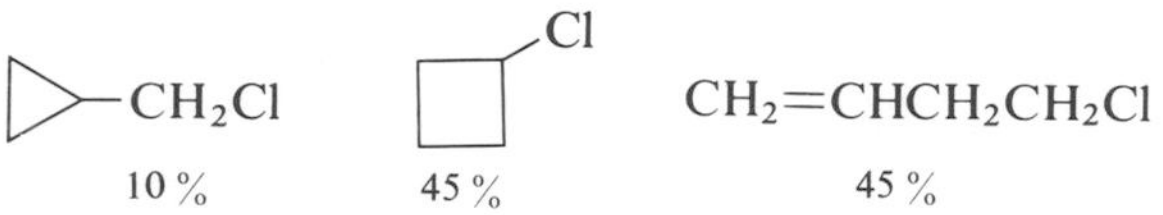

$$\triangleright\!\!-CH_2Cl \qquad \square\!\!-Cl \qquad CH_2=CHCH_2CH_2Cl$$
$$10\% \qquad\qquad 45\% \qquad\qquad 45\%$$

Reaction of cyclobutyl chloride in aqueous solution afforded this same mixture of alcoholic materials:

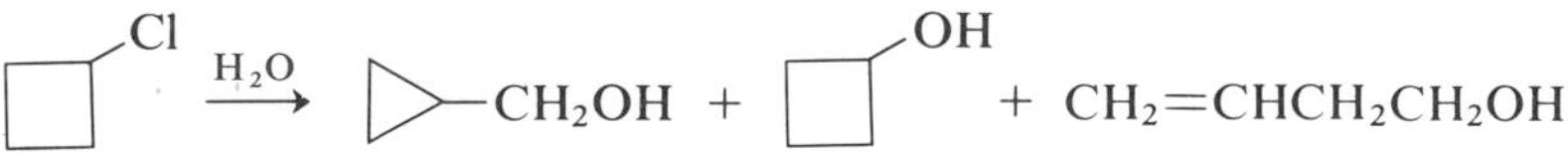

$$\square\!\!-Cl \xrightarrow{H_2O} \triangleright\!\!-CH_2OH + \square\!\!-OH + CH_2=CHCH_2CH_2OH$$

The product distribution can be explained by postulating either rapidly equilibrating classical structures or nonclassical intermediates. The rapid solvolysis rates of the chlorides **55** and **56** and of the brosylate and benzene-sulfonate lead one to favor a nonclassical interpretation,

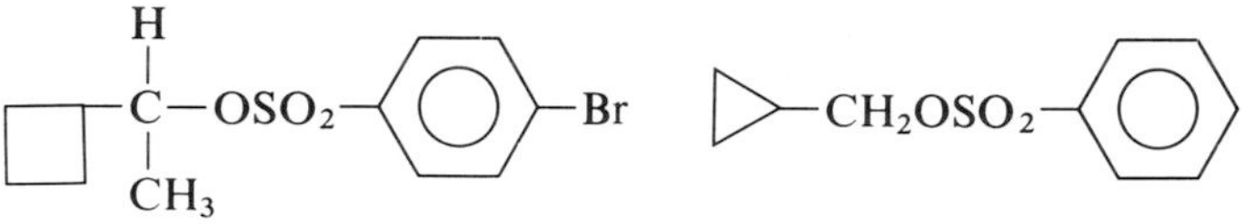

$$\square\!\!-\overset{\displaystyle H}{\underset{\displaystyle CH_3}{C}}\!\!-OSO_2\!\!-\!\!\langle\bigcirc\rangle\!\!-Br \qquad \triangleright\!\!-CH_2OSO_2\!\!-\!\!\langle\bigcirc\rangle$$

It appears from the data that a common intermediate is involved in all of these reactions and that this intermediate is formed quite readily. The ease of formation of this carbonium ion intermediate requires that the positive charge be effectively delocalized in the transition state leading to it. The most likely structure for the cation is one on which the cyclopropyl ring electrons are delocalized out onto the electron deficient carbon atom,

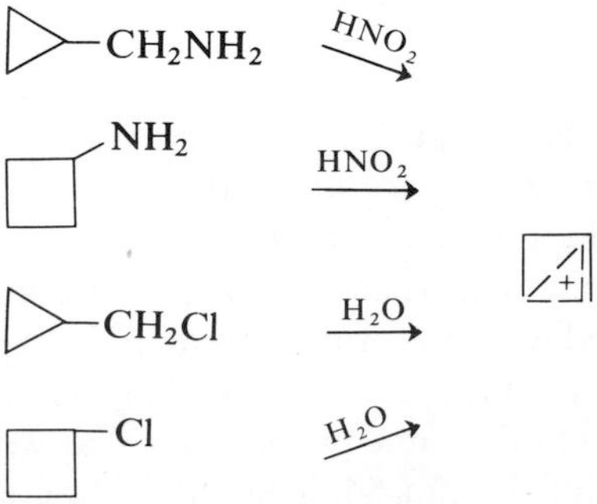

$$\triangleright\!\!-CH_2NH_2 \xrightarrow{HNO_2}$$

$$\square\!\!-NH_2 \xrightarrow{HNO_2}$$

$$\triangleright\!\!-CH_2Cl \xrightarrow{H_2O} \qquad \boxed{\square^{+}}$$

$$\square\!\!-Cl \xrightarrow{H_2O}$$

The electrons in the cyclopropyl ring occupy orbitals that are in a good position to overlap with the incipient carbonium ion. The regions of high electron density for the carbon-carbon bonds of cyclopropane are not directly between these carbon atoms but outside; the bonds are best described as τ type bonds. These electrons are easily delocalized, for good orbital overlap is possible. The cyclobutyl derivatives can also form this cation.

Carbon labeling experiments can also be interpreted in terms of nonclassical intermediates but indicate that more than a single such nonclassical cation must be involved.

Another interesting reaction of cyclopropane and its derivatives is their acid catalyzed ring opening. Cyclopropyl rings are destroyed when treated with Lewis or Brønsted acids. Thus, when treated with aluminum chloride in the presence of benzene, cyclopropane reacts to form *n*-propylbenzene:

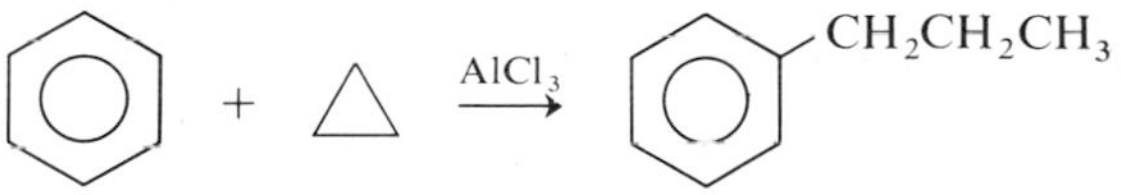

When treated with an acid HX, the product is the *n*-propyl halide:

In these reactions the cyclopropyl ring is first protonated (or complexed with the Lewis acid), and this protonated cyclopropane then reacts. Other reactions of the same type are known. The more complex system **58** opens to form isomeric alkenes when treated with acid:

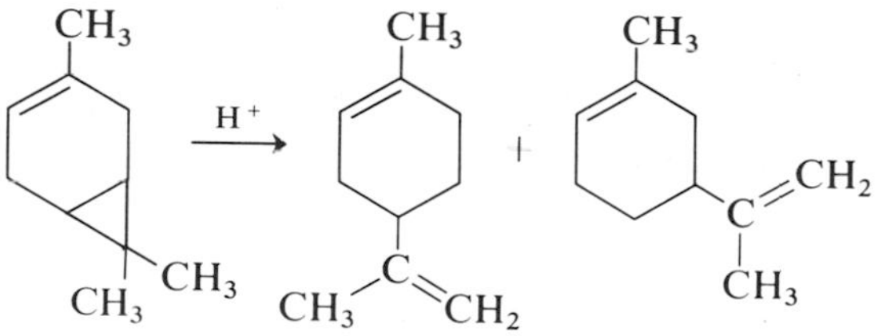

The alcohol **59** suffers an acid catalyzed isomerization, and this rearrangement also involves the opening of a three membered ring:

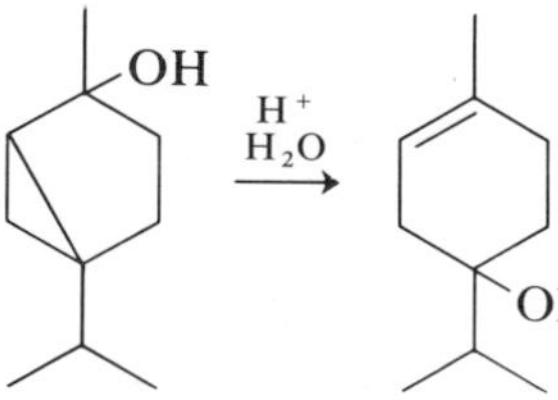

The treatment of a cyclopropyl derivative with an acid catalyst causes the ring to open. The reverse reaction also takes place. It has been found that treatment of open chain systems with acid catalysts effects ring closure, and such cyclizations proceed in a number of systems. Rings of various sizes can be prepared, with six-membered rings the best known examples. When the alcohol **60** is treated with acid, the cyclohexyl derivative is formed:

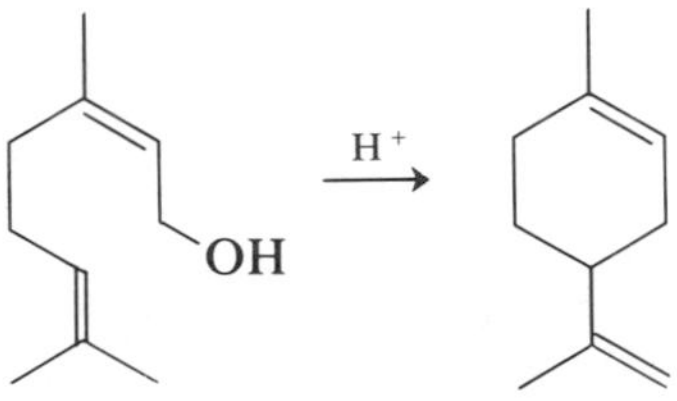

60

The intermediate in this process is assumed to be the allylic carbonium ion,

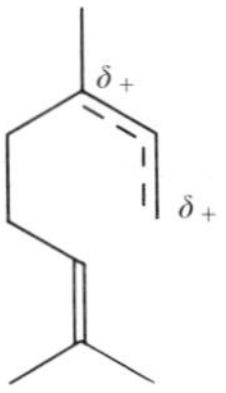

which adds to the olefinic linkage and thereby effects ring closure.

A similar reaction occurs when the alkene **61** is treated with acid.

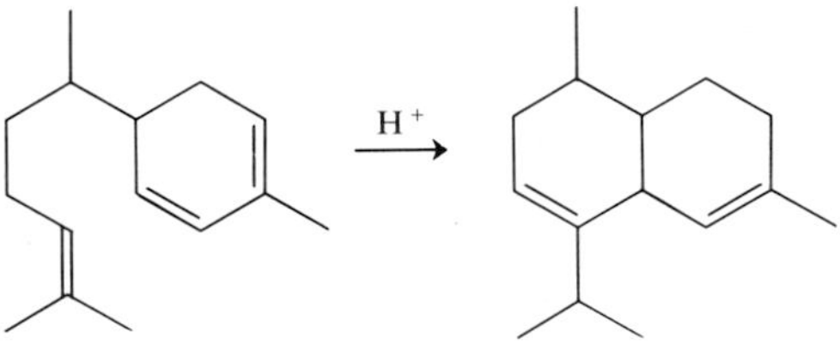

61

More recently it has been shown that the treatment of simple conjugated dienes with concentrated sulfuric acid effects ring closure and yields cyclic allylic cations. The following examples are typical:

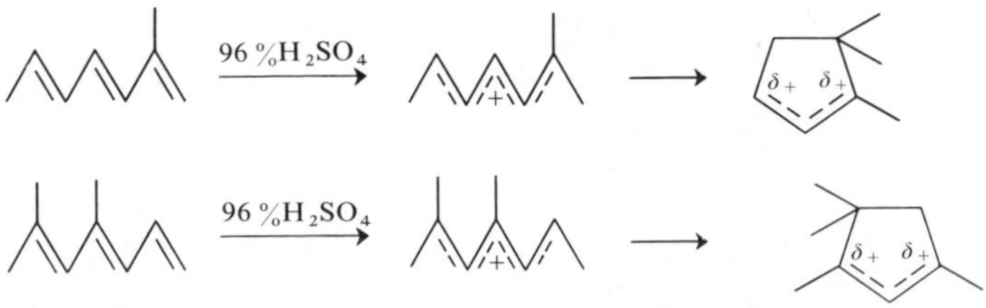

Countless examples of carbonium ion rearrangements exist, and only a few of the more unusual examples have been presented. Whenever a carbonium ion is formed in a system, the possibility of rearrangements must be considered. Of particular importance are the bicyclic compounds. These systems have been studied extensively, and it is here that some of the most unusual and interesting transformations have been observed. These bicyclic systems are more complex, and as their complexity increases, the uniqueness of the rearrangement does also. These compounds suffer alkyl migrations, hydrogen migrations, ring openings, and ring closures. As with the simpler analogues, some of the processes are best explained in terms of classical carbonium ions while for others nonclassical intermediates are postulated. In fact, it is in these systems that the evidence for bridged cations is strongest, and it is here that the largest number of examples can be found in which a nonclassical intermediate is postulated. The most wellknown example of rearrangements in these bicyclic systems is the camphene hydrochloride–isobornynl chloride conversion, and it is with this system that we begin our discussion of bicyclic transformations.

Camphene hydrochloride **62**, as the name implies, is prepared by addition of hydrogen chloride to camphene. This reaction takes place readily. In solution these two materials are in equilibrium:

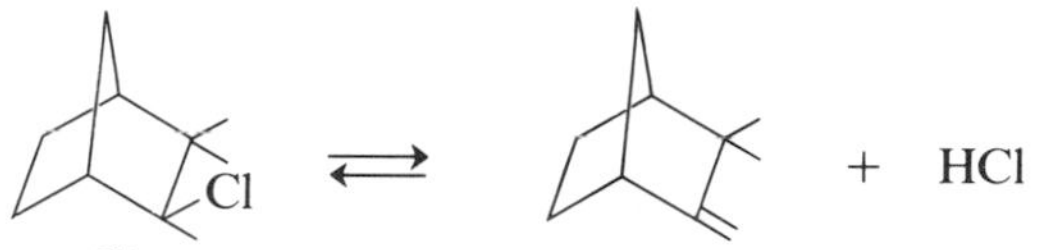

In addition to this equilibrium, camphene hydrochloride also undergoes another reaction, an isomerization to isobornyl chloride **63**. This isomerization takes place more slowly than the equilibrium just presented. It is, however, catalyzed by acids, and the rate also depends upon the polarity of the solvent,

Finally, isobornyl chloride is itself able to undergo a conversion to bornyl chloride **64**. This reaction is also catalyzed by Lewis acids, and it is bornyl

chloride that is the most stable, the thermodynamic, product,

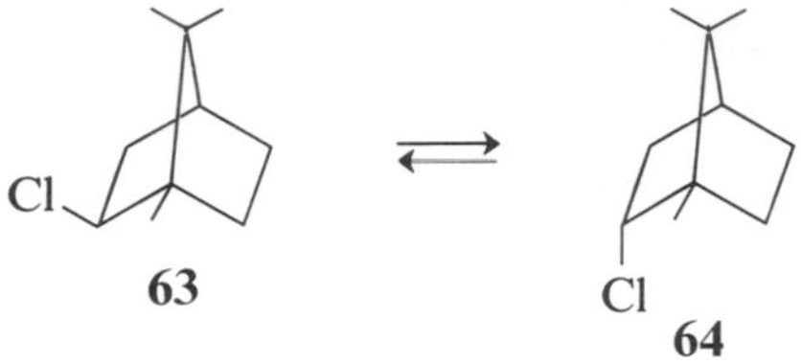

63   **64**

A kinetic study has been made of the isomerization of camphene hydrochloride to isobornyl chloride. It was found that in the absence of an added acid catalyst the increase in the concentration of isobornyl chloride was governed by the rate expression:

$$\frac{d[\mathbf{63}]}{dt} = k[\mathbf{62}]^{3/2}$$

This rate expression, which is somewhat more complex than expected, is consistent with a mechanism in which hydrogen chloride catalyzes the reaction. If the only source of hydrogen chloride is from the first equilibrium, then the concentration of this acid equals that of camphene, and both of these are related to the concentration of camphene hydrochloride by the equilibrium constant for the first reaction:

$$K = \frac{[\text{HCl}]\,[\text{camphene}]}{[\mathbf{62}]}$$

Since,

$$[\text{camphene}] = [\text{HCl}]$$

We obtain

$$K = \frac{[\text{HCl}]^2}{[\mathbf{62}]}$$

or

$$[\text{HCl}] = K^{1/2}[\mathbf{62}]^{1/2}$$

Now if the rate limiting step involves a molecule of hydrogen chloride as well as a molecule of camphene hydrochloride, we have a reaction whose rate is governed by the rate law presented previously,

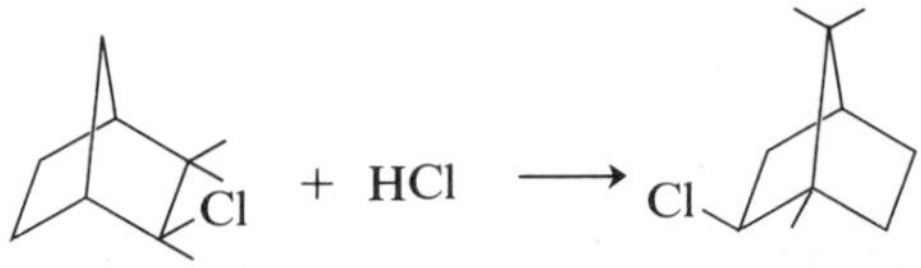

62   **63**

and

$$\frac{d[\mathbf{63}]}{dt} = k_2 K^{1/2}[\mathbf{62}]^{3/2}$$

A more detailed picture of this conversion ($\mathbf{62} \rightarrow \mathbf{63}$) has been postulated. Hydrogen chloride aids in the abstraction of the chloride ion to form a carbonium ion and the species HCl_2^-. The carbonium ion can be formulated as a nonclassical intermediate **65** or as an equilibrium between the classical structures **66**. The carbonium ion (or ions) then reacts with the HCl_2^- and either reverts to camphene hydrochloride or forms isobornyl chloride. Since camphene hydrochloride undergoes chloride exchange (indicated by the incorporation of radioactive chloride) at a faster rate than it isomerizes to isobornyl chloride, the carbonium ion intermediate reverts most frequently to reactant. This result is expected and is also indicated by the rapid equilibrium between camphene and camphene hydrochloride. Camphene hydrochloride actually loses and re-adds hydrogen chloride more readily than it isomerizes. It therefore seems reasonable that it should also exchange chloride more readily.

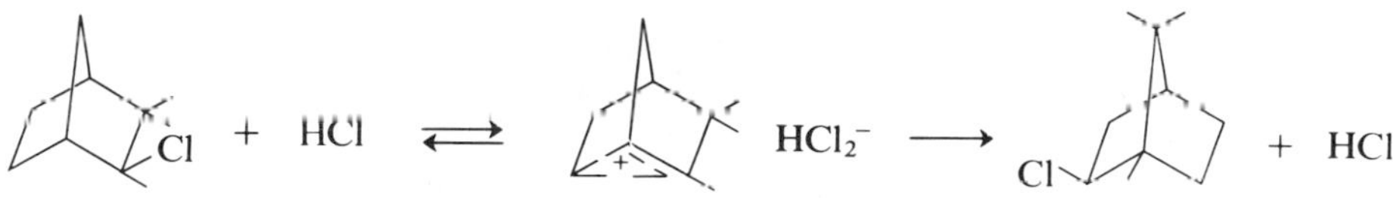

65

In terms of classical structures,

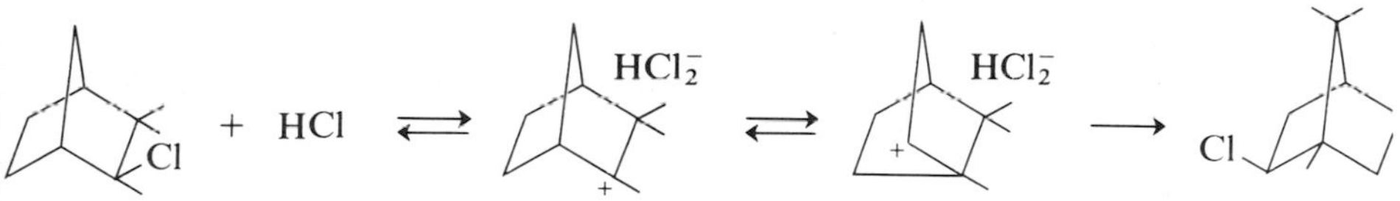

66

The valence bond contributors to the nonclassical structure are,

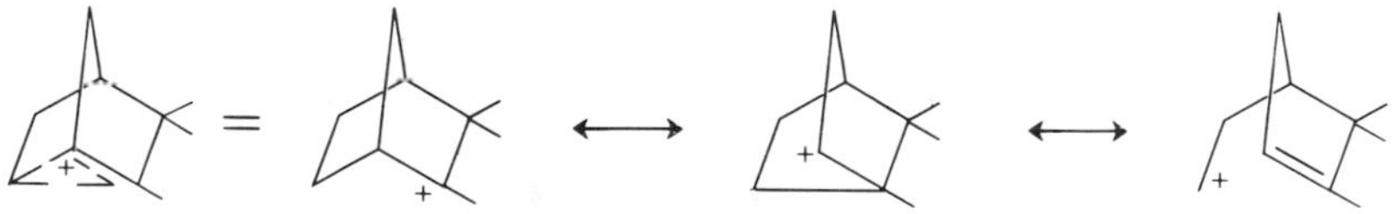

A basic problem in organic chemistry is whether a single cationic species (best represented by **65**) or whether two cationic species (**66**) are involved in this reaction. This question is unresolved. We next present some of the evidence for and against the nonclassical structure.

The very fact that camphene hydrochloride rearranges to isobornyl chloride and not directly to bornyl chloride is evidence in favor of the nonclassical intermediate. Bornyl chloride is more stable, yet it is the kinetic product that is formed almost exclusively. It is difficult to explain the formation of a kinetic product by assuming classical intermediates. On the other hand, a nonclassical structure provides an explanation not only for the formation of a kinetic product but also for its geometry. One can see why the chloride enters *exo*; approach from the other side is hindered, for the delocalized electron pair occupy that side of the molecule:

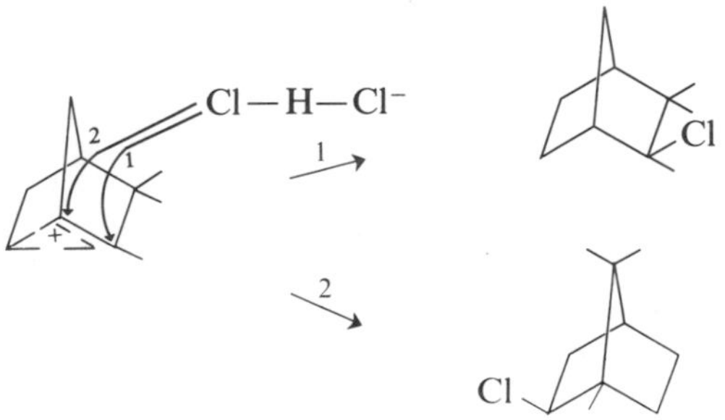

Thus the formation of a kinetic product and its geometry are explained quite simply by postulating a nonclassical intermediate. It is most difficult to explain these observations on the basis of classical intermediates.

The reactivity of camphene hydrochloride and isobornyl chloride in ionization reactions is also explained nicely by assuming a nonclassical intermediate. Both of these materials dissociate more readily than bornyl chloride. The rate enhancement for carbonium ion formation can be explained by assuming neighboring group participation and electronic delocalization in the transition state. However, in bornyl chloride, which has the chloride in the *endo* position, the electrons are not in a good position to assist in the departure of chloride. Consequently, bornyl chloride is not subject to participation and ionizes more slowly,

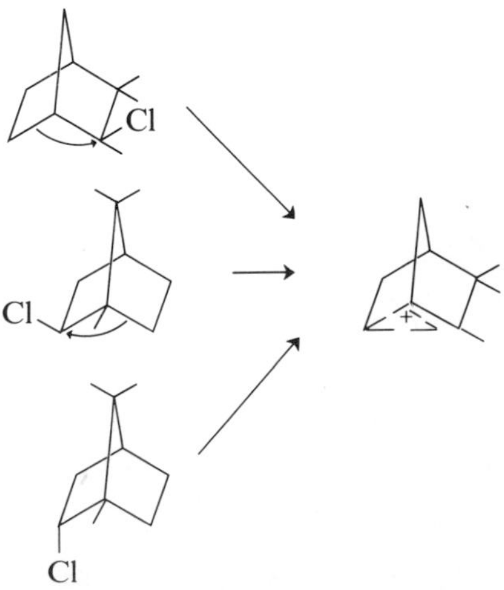

We see that *exo* halides ionize more readily than the corresponding *endo* systems, and this is evidence in favor of nonclassical carbonium ions. It is true that steric interactions exist in these systems and that these contribute to the observed rate differences. It has usually been assumed that these steric factors are not sufficiently pronounced to account for all of the difference; however, it has recently been suggested that steric interactions may play a major role in the reaction.

Another piece of evidence in favor of nonclassical carbonium ions comes from semiempirical rate studies. The rates of acetolysis of a variety of secondary aliphatic tosylates can be calculated with reasonable accuracy by semiempirical means. It is possible to predict the rates of solvolysis of certain tosylates by considering bond angle, torsional and steric strains, and in some cases, inductive effects. Tosylates such as *endo* 2-norbonyl, *endo* 2-norbornenyl, and *endo* 2-benznorbornenyl are treated successfully in this way. However, the treatment fails for the *exo* epimers, which solvolyze at a much faster rate than the calculated value. It is assumed that this rate enhancement of the *exo* isomers above the calculated value is due to nonclassical carbonium ions and to neighboring group participation in the transition states leading to them. The results are tabulated in Table 18–2 (k_{rel} is the solvolysis rate of the tosylate relative to cyclohexyl tosylate in acetic acid at 25°).

Table 18–2. Rates of Solvolysis

Tosylate	Log k_{rel}	
	Calc.	Obs.
7-norbornyl	−7.0	−7.0
endo 2-norbornyl	−0.2	+0.2
endo 2-norbornenyl	−1.0	−1.5
endo 2-benznorbornenyl	−2.4	−2.2
exo 2-norbornyl	−0.6	+2.7
exo 2-norbornenyl	−1.4	+2.4
exo 2-benznorbornenyl	−2.8	+1.6

The evidence in support of nonclassical intermediates in the reactions of these bicyclic systems is excellent. Of course, it is for just this reason that such intermediates have been postulated so frequently. It would certainly be difficult to explain the various experimental observations in some other way. Nevertheless, despite the fact that the evidence for these intermediates is good, equally good evidence is available to demonstrate that some reactions formerly thought to proceed by way of nonclassical cations do not do so and that at least in some reactions, classical carbonium ions must be involved. For example, the semiempirical calculations just presented involve a number of assumptions, one of which is the neglect of steric strain in the various transition states for solvolysis, yet it has been demonstrated that steric strain can exist in the transition states and must be considered.

A piece of evidence against nonclassical cations comes from a comparison of the solvolysis rates of **67** and **68**:

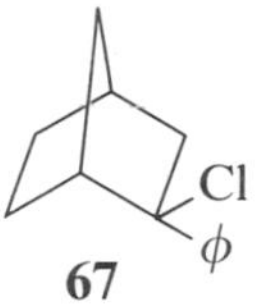

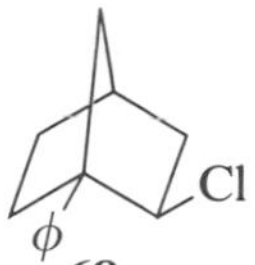

If upon ionization, these two reactants both formed bridged carbonium ions, these intermediates would have the following structures,

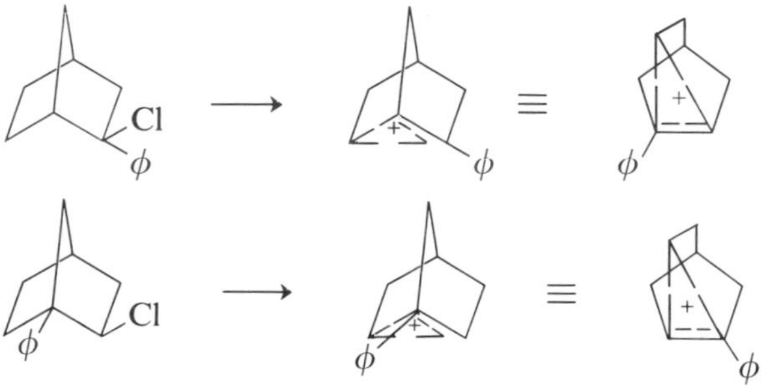

Instead of writing the structures for the ions in the usual way, we rotate the species, and we find that these carbonium ions are equivalent and must have the same energy. The transition states leading to these cations must somewhat resemble them. Therefore, if the carbonium ions have the same energy, the transition states leading to them must have about the same energy. Since the free energy of the reactants is also about the same, this leads us to the conclusion that these two materials should ionize at nearly the same rate.

The fact that **67** undergoes ethanolysis many times faster ($\sim 10^7$) than **68** is not in agreement with this idea. The data do not support the assumption of nonclassical intermediates; however, the facts are compatible with the normal nonbridged carbonium ions. The phenyl group is able to stabilize the transition state resulting from **67** but is unable to stabilize that from **68**.

When alcohols such as **69** ($R_1 = Ar$ or H, $R_2 = Ar$) are treated with strong acids, H_2SO_4 or CF_3COOH, reasonably stable carbonium ions are produced. Determining the chemical and physical properties of these cations provides evidence for their structure,

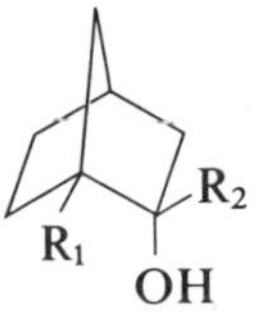

The carbonium ions produced from **69** can be represented either by classical or nonclassical formulations:

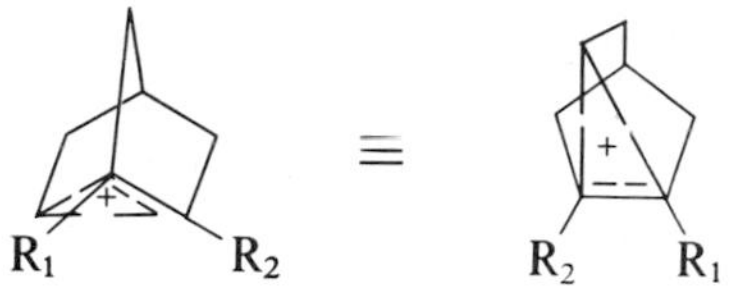

70

In terms of classical structures,

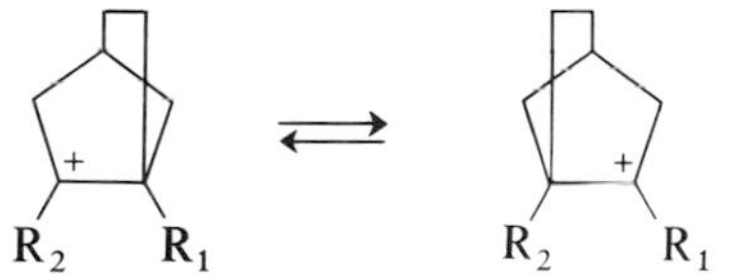

The question of whether a single nonclassical cation or two rapidly equilibrating structures are involved in these cases appears to have been answered.

Since the cationic species that are formed are reasonably stable, it is possible to take ultraviolet spectra. When R_1 and R_2 are both aromatic, these two groups are in conjugation in the nonclassical structure **70** (because of the partial double bond joining the carbon atoms to which these groups are bonded). They are not conjugated in either of the classical structures. Therefore the ultraviolet spectrum of a diaryl substituted cation should differ markedly from that of a monoaryl substituted cation (R_1 = H, R_2 = Ar) if the nonclassical carbonium ion is present, yet these two cations (R_1 = Ar, R_2 = Ar and R_1 = H, R_2 = Ar) should have nearly the same spectrum if only classical intermediates are present. From the results listed in Table 18–3, it can be seen that the observed spectra are in better accord with the idea that equilibrating carbonium ions are present.

These results indicate that nonclassical cations such as **70** do not participate as intermediates, and the data are confirmed by other studies.

Further evidence against the nonclassical intermediates **70** stems from a study of the relative stabilities of the monoaryl and diaryl substituted cations. If nonclassical structures such as **70** are present, then the diaryl carbonium ion,

CH$_3$O   OCH$_3$

Table 18–3

R_1	R_2	$\lambda_{max}(m\mu)$	R_1	R_2	$\lambda_{max}(m\mu)$
 C_6H_5	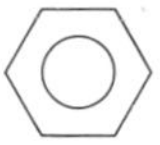 C_6H_5	340	H	 C_6H_5	337
 C_6H_5	$CH_3\text{-}C_6H_4$ 	349	H	$CH_3\text{-}C_6H_4$ 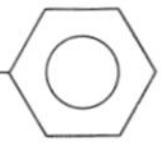	350
$CH_3\text{-}C_6H_4$ 	 C_6H_5	349	H	$CH_3\text{-}C_6H_4$ 	350
$CH_3\text{-}C_6H_4$ 	$CH_3\text{-}C_6H_4$ 	353	H	$CH_3\text{-}C_6H_4$ 	350
$CH_3\text{-}C_6H_4$ 	$CH_3O\text{-}C_6H_4$ 	381	H	$CH_3O\text{-}C_6H_4$ 	381
$CH_3O\text{-}C_6H_4$ 	$CH_3O\text{-}C_6H_4$ 	381	H	$CH_3O\text{-}C_6H_4$ 	381

should be more stable than the monoaryl system,

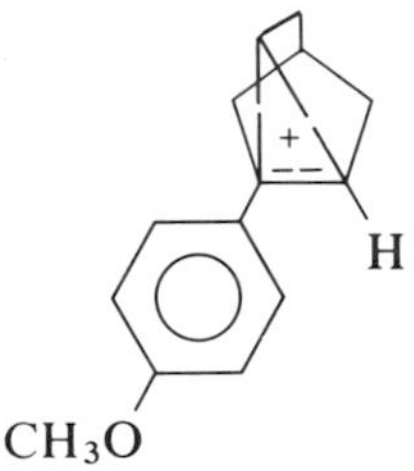

for in the former the positive charge is delocalized into both aromatic rings. However, if these intermediates are not involved, the two carbonium ions (monoaryl and diaryl) are expected to be about equally stable.

A convenient measure of carbonium ion stability is the strength of the aqueous sulfuric acid required to convert half of the starting alcohol **69** to carbonium ion; less stable carbonium ions require more concentrated acid. The diaryl cation requires 51% sulfuric acid, but the monosubstituted system needs only 41% sulfuric acid. It turns out that the monosubstituted system is actually more stable than the disubstituted system. These results are inconsistent with the nonclassical intermediate **70**. The data again support the simple carbonium ions,

Other investigations were made on these systems. Nuclear magnetic resonance studies on the dianisyl cation, as well as studies on the rate of aromatic substitution for the cation also gave results in favor of the usual systems. Four different types of experiments were performed (ultraviolet spectroscopic studies, thermodynamic stabilities in concentrated acid, a nuclear magnetic resonance investigation, and rates of aromatic substitution). All of these support the idea that nonclassical bridged intermediates do not participate, and on the basis of these results, one is forced to conclude that only the usual cations are involved.

The very reasonable suggestion has been made that when the classical carbonium ion is extremely stable, the nonclassical system will not participate as an intermediate. The last investigation dealt with systems where the non-bridged carbonium ions were unusually stable; therefore, intermediates such as **70** were not present. The suggestion has been advanced that nonclassical cations could still be present in other systems. This idea, which appears to be reasonable, can be tested in an indirect way. Direct investigations into the structures of less stable carbonium ions have not yet been successful.

Among the criteria for neighboring group participation and nonclassical carbonium ions was the fact that the *exo* epimer ionizes at a much faster rate than the *endo* epimer. In stable systems, where only classical carbonium ions are involved, neighboring group participation is not expected to take place. The *exo-endo* ratios (k_{exo}/k_{endo}) for such systems are therefore expected to be smaller than those for less stable systems where neighboring group participation does aid the ionization of the *exo* epimer. The *exo-endo* ratio for systems of varying stability serves as a convenient means of testing the hypothesis that nonclassical ions are involved as intermediates in some ionizations.

The rates of acetolysis of *exo* and *endo* norbornyl brosylate **71** have been measured, the solvolysis rate constants determined, and the *exo-endo* ratio evaluated. The value of this ratio is 350,

71

and

$$\frac{k_{exo}}{k_{endo}} = 350$$

If the high value of this *exo-endo* ratio reflects neighboring group participation during the solvolysis of the *exo* epimer, more stable systems, where participation is absent, should give rise to lower values. Accordingly, the solvolysis rates of several *exo-endo* epimeric pairs have been determined. The *para* nitrobenzoate esters (this is also a good leaving group) of several bicyclic alcohols were solvolyzed in 60% aqueous dioxane. The rates were measured at two different temperatures (50° and 75°), and the k_{exo}/k_{endo} values were determined for these systems; the results are presented in Table 18–4.

Table 18–4

Compound	$k \cdot 10^6 \ sec^{-1}$ (50°)	$k \cdot 10^6 \ sec^{-1}$ (75°)	k_{exo}/k_{endo} (50°)
	1.96	41.2	
			83
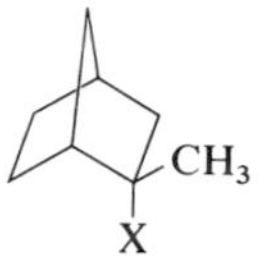	0.024	0.43	
	946	14,100	
			140
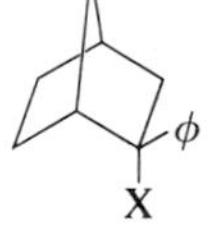	6.74	119	
	16.5	205	
			593
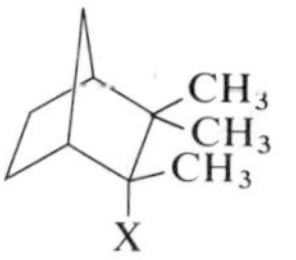	0.028	0.54	

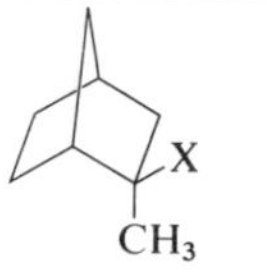

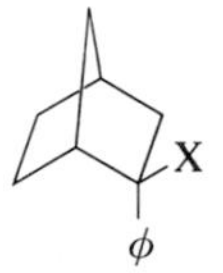

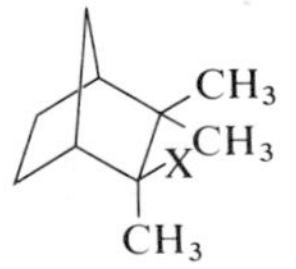

In these systems, $X = OOC\!-\!\!\langle\!\!\bigcirc\!\!\rangle\!\!-NO_2$

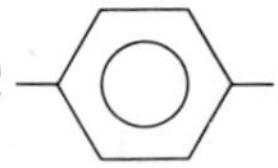

The *exo-endo* ratios for more stable systems are not significantly lower than that observed for solvolysis of the brosylates **71**. The ratio has the same order of magnitude for more stable systems and for less stable systems. Since the value is high even in cases where neighboring group assistance cannot be involved, one can conclude either that this ratio is not a good criterion or that only classical carbonium ions are formed in these reactions.

The *exo-endo* ratios presented here do not consider internal return. Because the brosylate anion from **71** is produced as part of an ion pair and is able to return, the *exo* epimer of **71** is racemized at a greater rate than it is solvolyzed. The same phenomenon does not take place with the *endo* isomer. The brosylate anion must re-enter from the *exo* position (the *exo* isomer is kinetically favored), and such a process, migration by brosylate to the *exo* side, cannot compete favorably with attack by the solvent. With the *endo* epimer, racemized products are brought about only by solvent attack. Consequently, when internal return is considered, the k_{exo}/k_{endo} ratio for ionization of **71** rises to 1225.

While the corresponding data are not available for more stable cationic systems, it is safe to conclude that in these cases also, the phenomenon of internal return increases the ratio. The values of k_{exo}/k_{endo} are expected to increase in an analogous way, and including internal return does not alter the conclusions. The ratio has nearly the same value in all of the systems. This implies that the greater rate of ionization of the *exo* epimer cannot be used to justify neighboring group participation in the transition state and nonclassical carbonium ion intermediates, and some other factor must be found to explain the more rapid dissociation of the *exo* material. The data and these conclusions apply only to bicyclic systems, and nothing can be said concerning the participation of nonclassical cations in other systems.

Evidence exists that strongly supports the concept of nonclassical carbonium ions, but the evidence against such intermediates is equally good. It is certainly difficult to explain the experimental observations, especially the formation of a kinetic product having the *exo* geometry, in any other way. It has been suggested that steric interactions can explain in a satisfactory manner all of the experimental observations, and it remains to be seen if an adequate explanation in terms of these interactions is in fact possible.

We have concerned ourselves almost entirely with alkyl migrations, but hydrogen transfers also take place. In bicyclic systems the most interesting of these transfers is probably the 6,2 transannular hydrogen migration, whereby a cation such as the norbornyl cation is transformed into its mirror image:

If we assume that the norbornyl cation has a classical structure, the transition state for the process looks as follows:

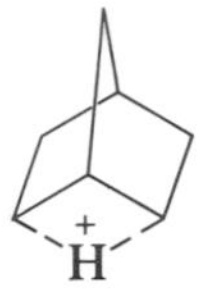

The nonclassical cationic species has the appearance,

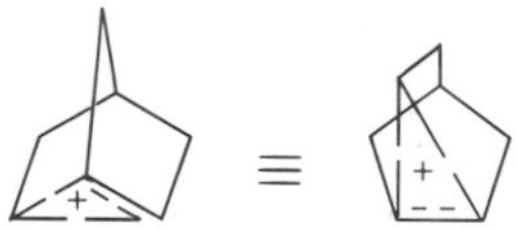

and the transition state becomes

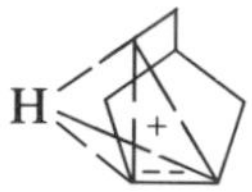

We do not consider here whether the cation is best formulated in classical or nonclassical terms; the pertinent fact is that 6,2 migrations do take place. Several different studies provide evidence for the rearrangement. Investigations employing radioactive carbon as a label to tag the positions support this idea, and confirmatory evidence comes from deuterium exchange studies on related systems. In all of these experiments, results that can be explained readily by postulating the migration, cannot be adequately accounted for in any other way.

When optically active *exo* norbornyl brosylate is solvolyzed in acetic acid, the product is racemic *exo* norbornyl acetate. Nonclassical carbonium ions or rapidly equilibrating classical cations satisfy the data,

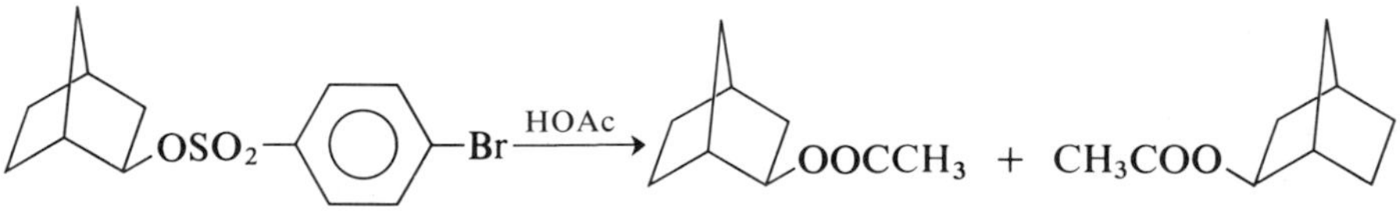

The numbering system for norbornyl derivatives is,

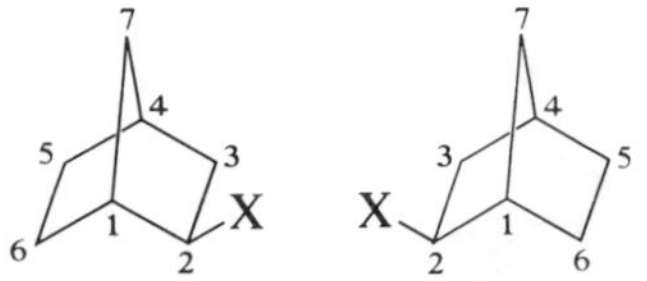

When the reaction is repeated using *exo* norbornyl brosylate labeled with C^{14} in the 2 and 3 positions, a considerable fraction of this C^{14} turns up in positions 5 and 6 of the product. The simple mechanism (the cations are represented by classical structures for simplicity),

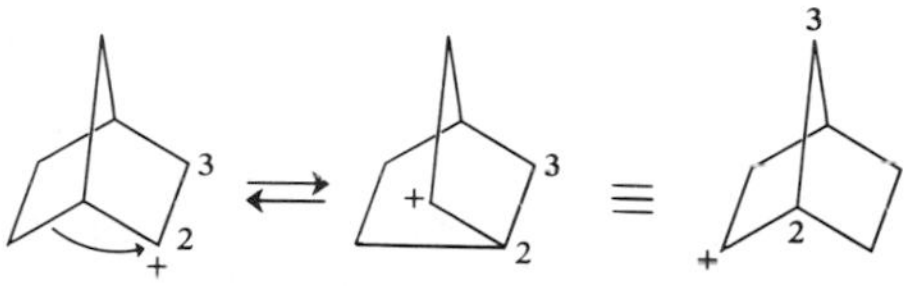

where carbon atoms 2 and 3 now occupy positions 1 and 7, no longer accounts for the experimental results. Some other mechanism that introduces radio-activity into positions 5 and 6 must intervene. A 6,2 transannular migration of hydrogen satisfies the requirements. The labeled carbon atoms, 2 and 3, now occupy positions 5 and 6,

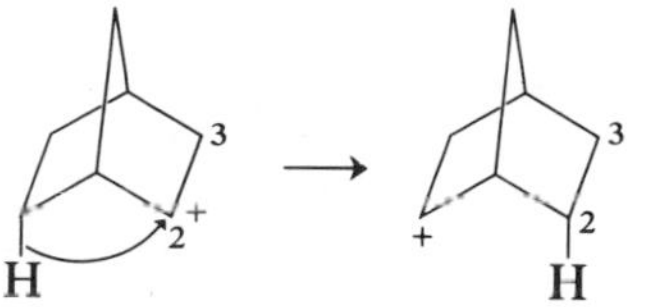

The experimental observations are accounted for in a simple manner by postulating this migration, and it is most difficult to explain them in any other way. Similar studies have been conducted on the formolysis of norbornyl derivatives. Here again, considerable scrambling of the label is observed.

As a result of these studies using labeled norbornyl brosylate, different routes of reaction become evident. Racemization may also take place by way of the migration,

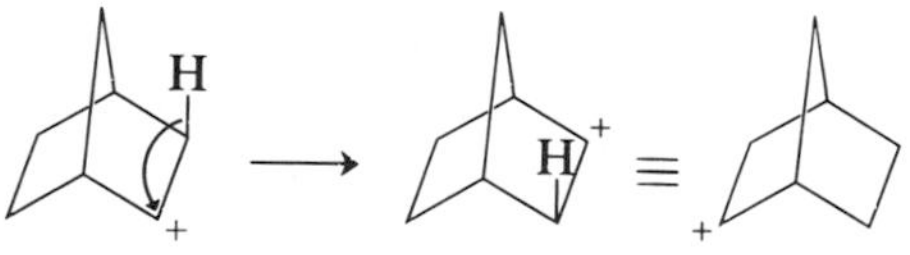

Racemization of norbornyl derivatives can take place by three distinct routes:

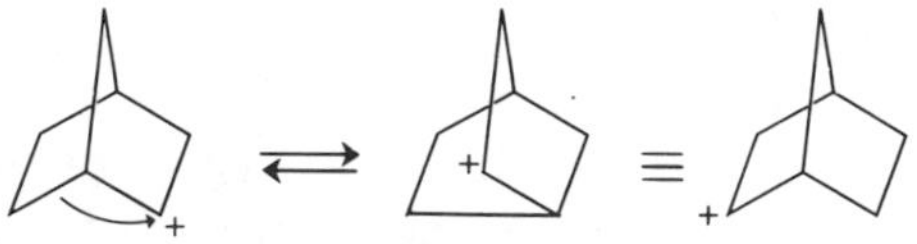

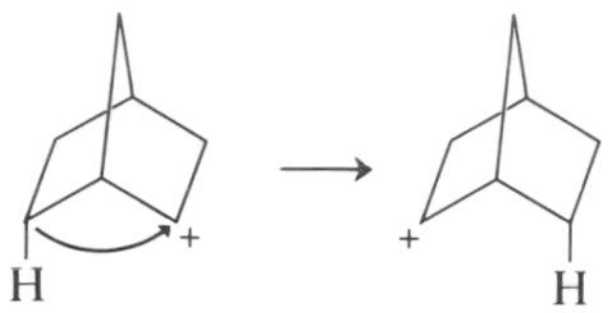

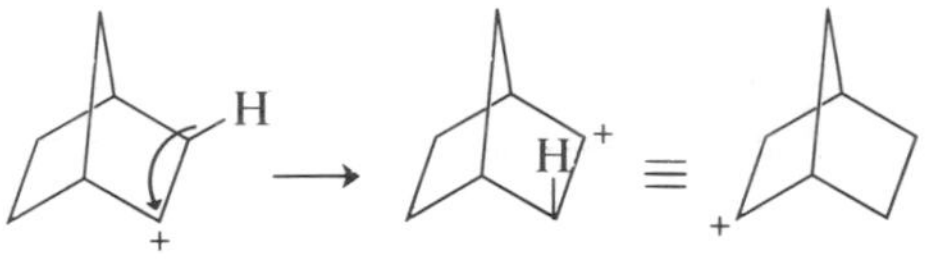

Further evidence supporting these ideas is available. Migration of hydrogen takes place not only in these bicyclic systems but in simpler cases as well. The cyclic diol **72** rearranges to a ketonic product under the influence of acid:

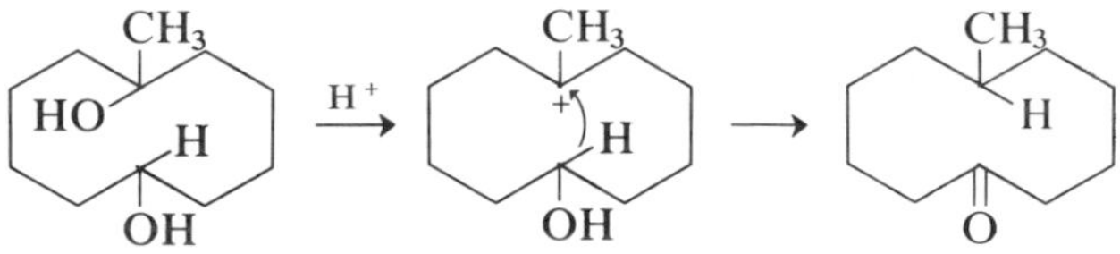

72

The reaction is similar to a pinacol rearrangement, but the migration of hydrogen is across the ring. Evidence that the reaction takes place as indicated comes from the deuterated analogue:

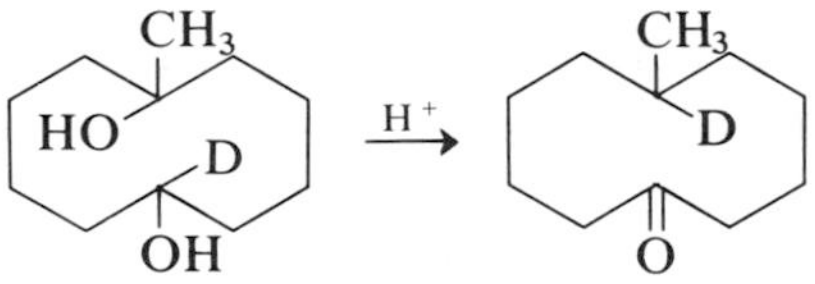

Such transannular migrations of hydrogen are also observed in the reactions of cyclooctene and cyclooctene oxides, and in the reactions of other cyclic systems. We have presented in this chapter just a few examples to illustrate the migration of alkyl, aryl, and hydrogen. Many of these rearrangements are stereospecific, and it has been the custom to explain this stereospecificity in terms of concerted migrations and nonclassical carbonium ions. The idea of a nonclassical carbonium ion is certainly attractive, for it helps to explain quite simply a number of observations that cannot be rationalized easily in any other way. The hypothesis can be employed as long as contradictory evidence is not available. When contradictions with the experimental results appear (as in the case of very stable bicyclic cationic systems), the assumption must be discarded. If at some future date, evidence is brought forth to show that these intermediates are not involved in the reactions, this will not be a setback for organic chemistry but rather an advance, for it is in this way, by hypothesis and experiment, that insight into the behavior of molecules is gained and progress is made.

Supplementary Reading

1. Bartlett, P. D., *Nonclassical Ions.* New York, Benjamin, 1965.
2. De Mayo, P. (editor), *Molecular Rearrangements.* New York, Interscience, Vol. 1 (1963), Vol. 2 (1964).
3. Gould, E. S., *Mechanism and Structure in Organic Chemistry.* New York, Holt, 1959.
4. Hine, J., *Physical Organic Chemistry.* New York, McGraw-Hill, 1962.

Chapter 19

Aromatic Rearrangements and Rearrangements Involving Heteroatoms

19.1 Aromatic Rearrangements

Aromatic systems are known to suffer rearrangement, and the processes, depending upon their nature, are catalyzed by acids, bases, heat, or light. In those to be considered, a group attached to an aromatic side chain is introduced into the aromatic ring:

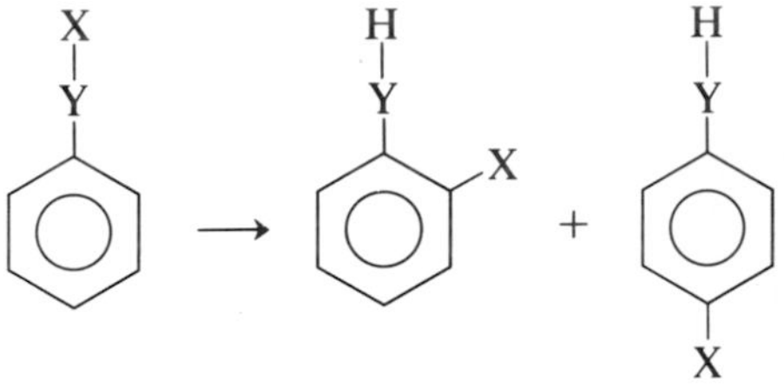

Among the transformations of this type are the Orton, the Fries, the benzidine, and the Claisen rearrangements, and it is with these that we shall deal in this chapter.

19.2 The Orton Rearrangement

When N-chloro- or N-bromoacetanilide is treated with the corresponding halogen acid, a rearrangement takes place and the halogen enters the aromatic ring:

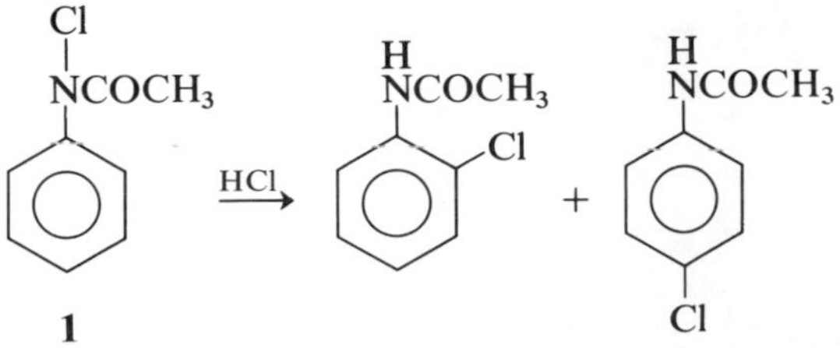

The observed *ortho-para* ratio is virtually the same as that obtained from the direct halogenation of acetanilide,

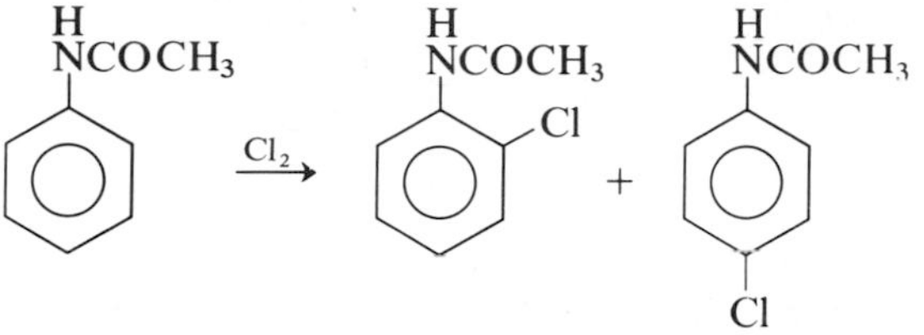

This evidence makes it reasonable to assume that the first stage in the transformation is a conversion of **1** into acetanilide and molecular chlorine. The chlorine thus generated attacks the aromatic system,

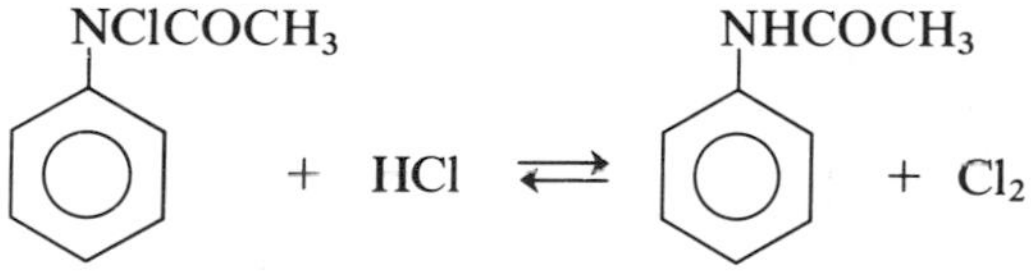

In support of this hypothesis is the fact that molecular chlorine can actually be obtained from solutions containing hydrogen chloride and an N-chloro-acetanilide.

If free molecular chlorine is actually present, then this species need not reenter the same molecule from which it was generated; the reaction ought to be intermolecular. Introduction of a second aromatic system causes cross-halogenation to take place, and this provides evidence concerning the inter-molecular nature of the reaction and additional evidence for the mechanism proposed:

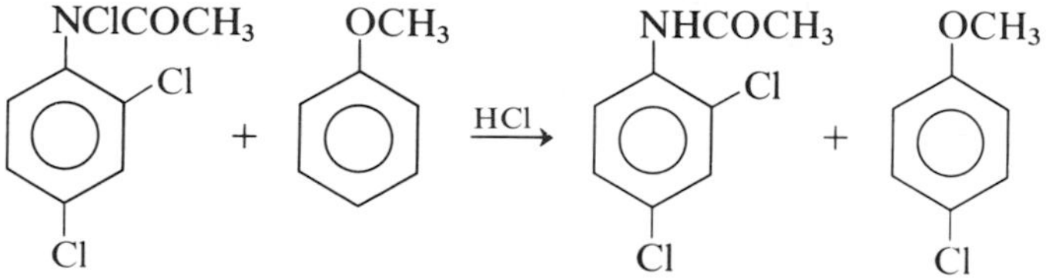

The general rate law that governs the transformation is,

$$-\frac{d[\mathbf{1}]}{dt} = k[\mathbf{1}][H^+][Cl^-]$$

It appears that both a proton and chloride ion enter into the rate limiting step. Studies employing radioactive chloride demonstrate that the formation of molecular chlorine is reversible. Thus the rate limiting step is attack at the

aromatic ring,

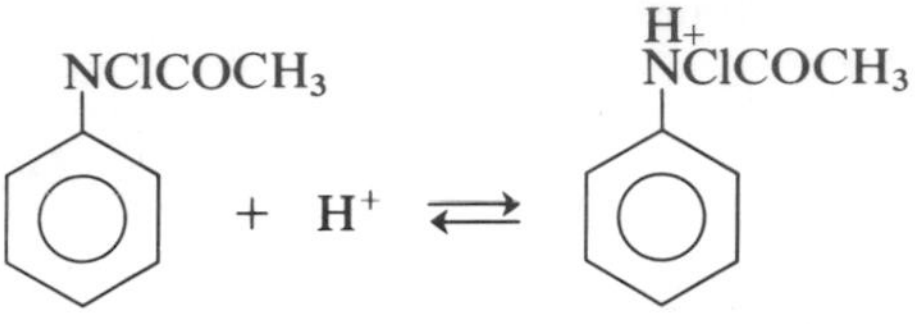

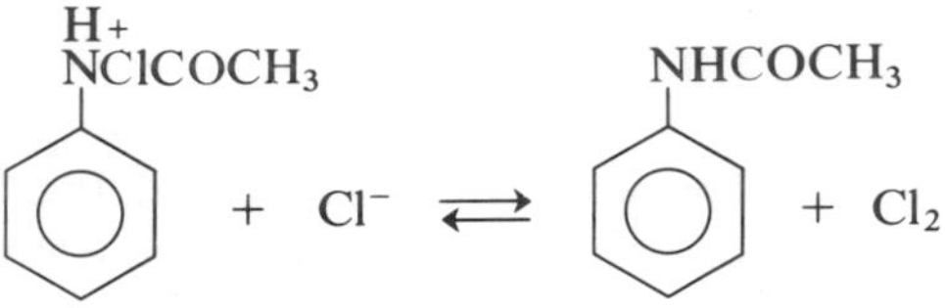

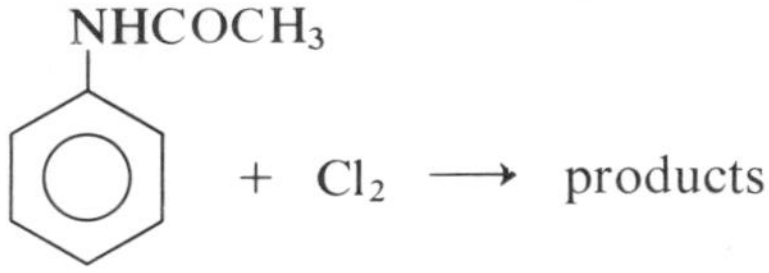

Superficially related to the Orton rearrangement is the acid catalyzed conversion of N-nitroaniline to *ortho* nitroaniline:

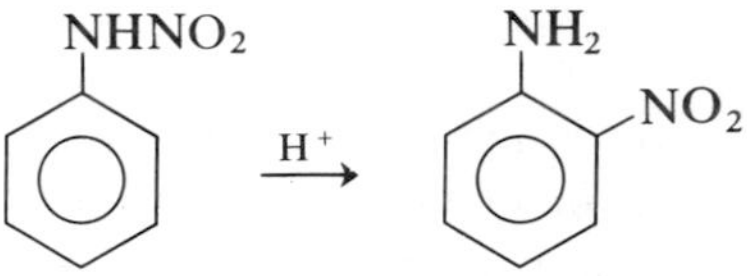

One distinction that becomes apparent immediately is the fact that the *ortho* isomer is formed almost exclusively. This result differs dramatically from that obtained from nitration of aniline. The isomeric distributions for the different reactions are shown in Table 19–1.

Table 19–1

	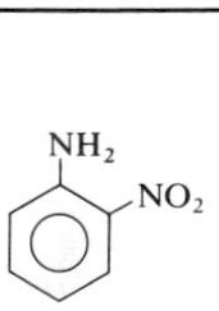 NH_2, NO_2 (ortho)	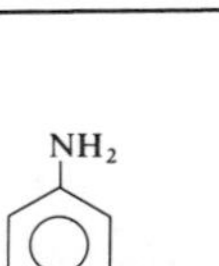 NH_2, NO_2 (meta)	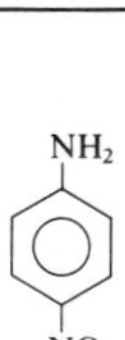 NH_2, NO_2 (para)
Rearrangement of $\phi NHNO_2$	93%	0%	7%
Nitration of ϕNH_2	6%	34%	60%

In both cases the temperature (10°C) and the solvent (85% H_2SO_4) were the same.

Since the product distribution in these two reactions is entirely different, the mechanism by which the nitro group enters the aromatic ring must also differ. When the rearrangement is conducted in the presence of $HN^{15}O_3$, no enrichment of the ring nitro group is observed, this result seems to indicate that, in contrast to the Orton rearrangement, this isomerization is intramolecular.

Several other reactions are known that bear a superficial resemblance to the Orton rearrangement. Some of these proceed by intramolecular pathways; others are intermolecular. When N-alkyl anilines ϕNHR are treated with nitrous acid under mildly acidic conditions, N-nitrosoanilines are produced. These compounds rearrange in the presence of aqueous HCl to *para* nitrosoanilines. The migration, which is generally assumed to be intermolecular, is known as the Fischer-Hepp rearrangement:

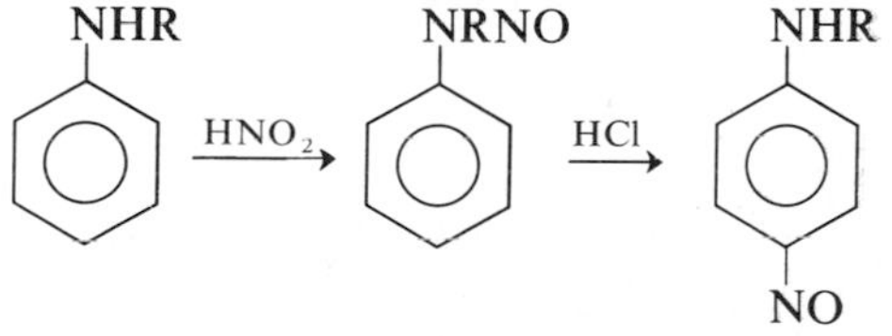

Perhaps the most well-known and certainly the most important of these rearrangements is the benzidine rearrangement. Treatment of hydrazobenzene (**2**) with acid causes the compound to isomerize, and a mixture composed of several isomeric products is obtained:

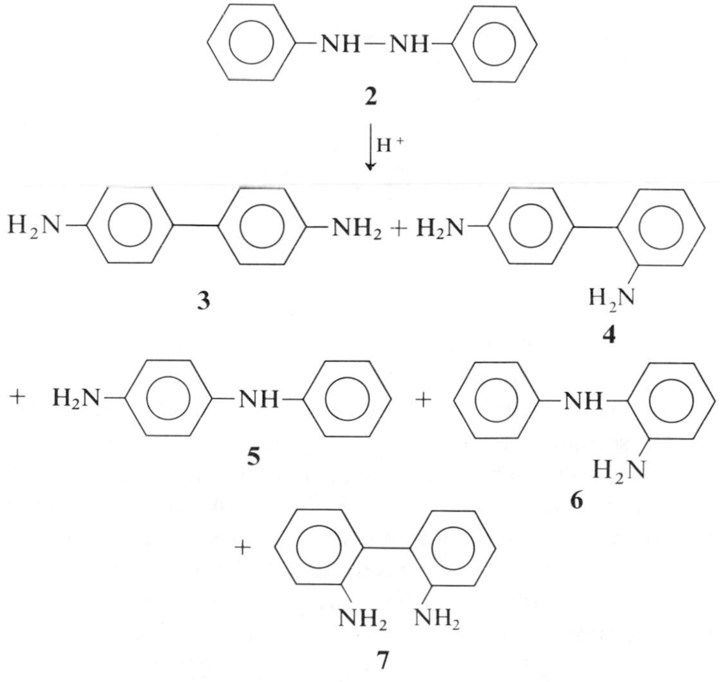

The major product of the reaction is benzidine **3** (hence the name), but isomeric products are obtained.

The reaction is intramolecular as is evidenced by a variety of results. Carbon labeling experiments and crossover experiments both indicate that there is no exchange of aryl groups during the rearrangement. One of the more elegant experiments demonstrating this fact involves the isomerizations of **8** and **9** carried out together.

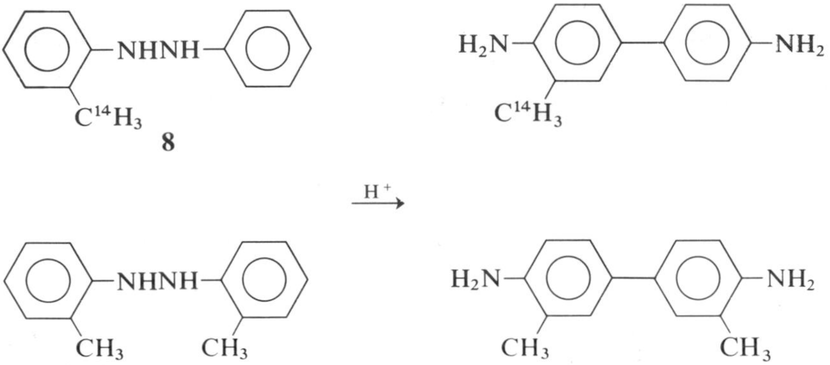

A mixture of (**8**) and (**9**) was isomerized and the product (**10**) examined for excess C^{14}. It was found that this material was not enriched in radioactive carbon and therefore that the reaction was intramolecular. Had the rearrangement been intermolecular, the substance **11** would have been present,

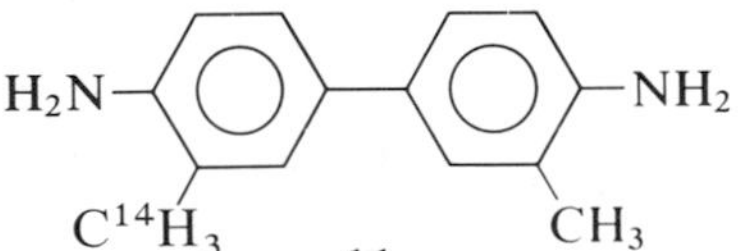

Various attempts have been made to elucidate the mechanism of the rearrangement. The kinetics of isomerization have been investigated. Early data on the subject conflicted. One such study lead to the conclusion that the reaction was a second order process, first order in hydrazobenzene and first order in hydrogen ion. This result is particularly appealing; however, the results of another investigation disagree. Other investigators conclude that the rearrangement is a third order process overall, first order in hydrazobenzene and second order in hydrogen ion. It is more difficult to formulate a mechanism consistent with these kinetics, but later investigations confirm the third order nature of the reaction.

It is difficult to formulate a mechanism consistent with a third order process. Formation of the acid,

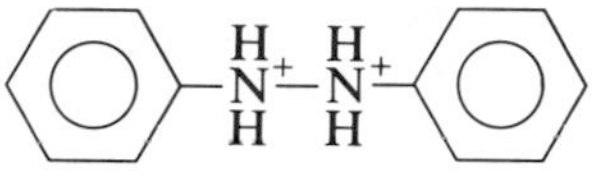

which then rearranges to benzidine, satisfies the data, but this is somewhat unsatisfying. Breakage of the N—N bond might take place, but during the rearrangement both aromatic rings would bear partial positive charges, and a recombination between two even partially positively charged species is unattractive. Alternatively, one species could become neutral and the other doubly charged; however formation of a doubly positively charged species appears equally unattractive. It is much more satisfying to postulate a rearrangement involving the simple conjugate acid,

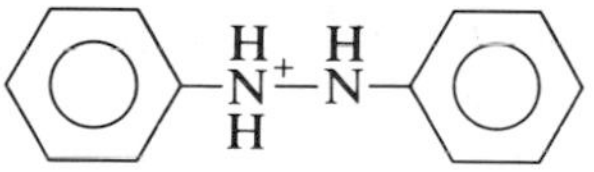

but this does not satisfy the kinetics. We are forced to conclude that no simple mechanistic picture satisfies all the known data, and more work on the benzidine rearrangement is required.

19.3 The Fries Rearrangement

The preparation of keto phenols from the corresponding phenolic esters in the presence of aluminum chloride is called the Fries rearrangement,

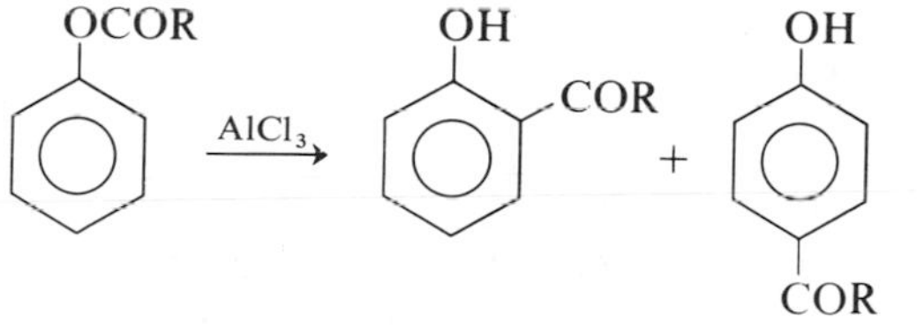

The isomeric distribution can depend to a large extent upon the reaction temperature, and lower temperatures generally lead to *para* substituted products, while higher temperatures often cause the *ortho* isomer to become the chief component of the product mixture.

Examples of this rearrangement include,

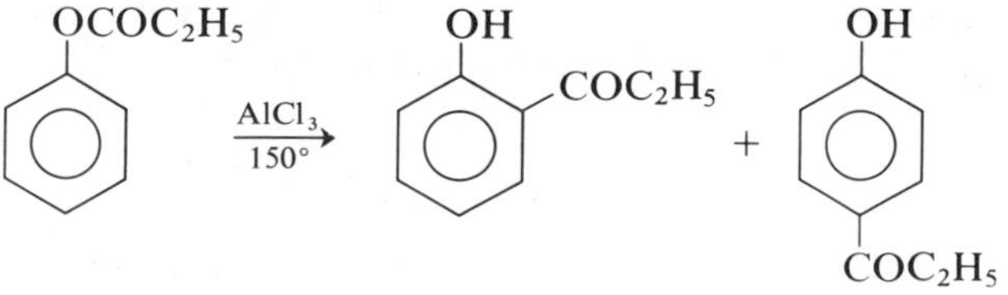

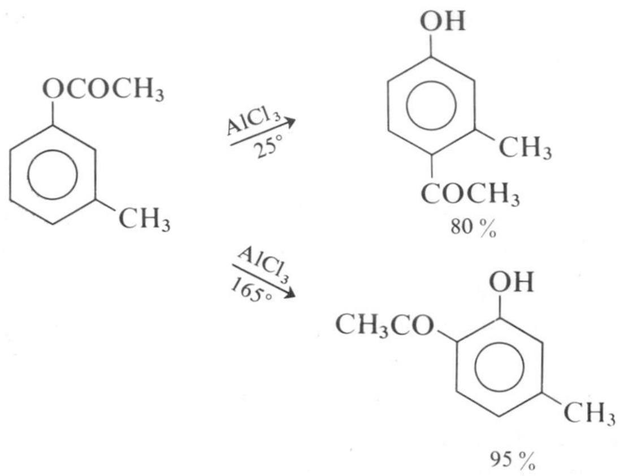

The Fries rearrangement is an equilibrium process, and reversals have been reported. Under the proper conditions some ketones revert to esters.

The introduction of the acyl group into the aromatic ring takes place by both intramolecular and intermolecular routes. The postulated mechanism is,

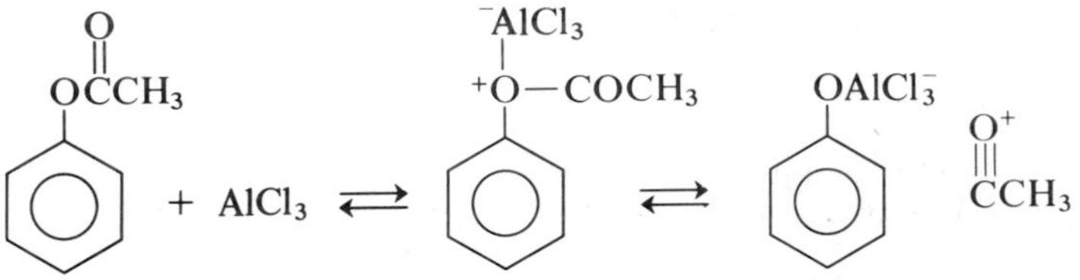

and **12** then goes on to products.

Reaction by the intramolecular pathway is best explained in terms of ion pairs or π complexes. If it is assumed that **12** exists as an ion pair or as a π complex with the electrons of the aromatic system bonding to the cation, this accounts for the intramolecular process. The intermediate **12** collapses to *ortho* and *para* substituted products. The intermolecular process requires that **12** react with another species just like itself or that it attack a molecule of the starting ester. In any case it appears that the species CH_3CO^+ participates (as part of an ion pair or complexed), for this species is known to be formed readily in the presence of aluminum chloride. The ester is similar to an acid chloride because the group ϕO is a good leaving group:

$$RCOCl + AlCl_3 \rightleftharpoons RCO^+ \ AlCl_4^-$$

$$RCOO\phi + AlCl_3 \rightleftharpoons RCO^+ \ AlCl_3O\phi^-$$

19.4 The Claisen Rearrangement

Another reaction involving derivatives of phenols, this one usually brought about by heat, is the Claisen rearrangement. The reaction proceeds readily with allyl phenyl ethers such as **13** and also works with allyl vinyl ethers **14**,

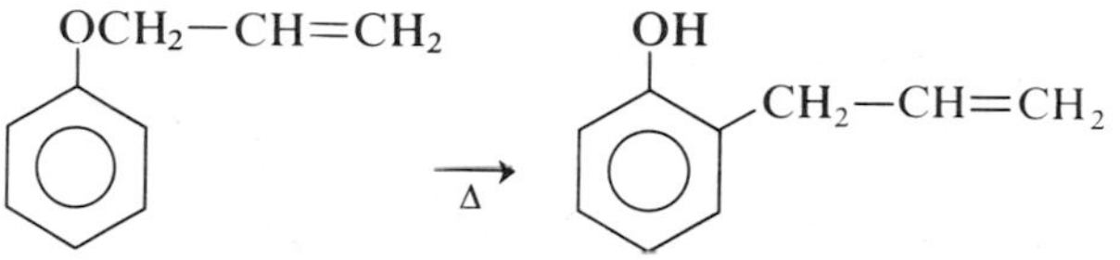

13

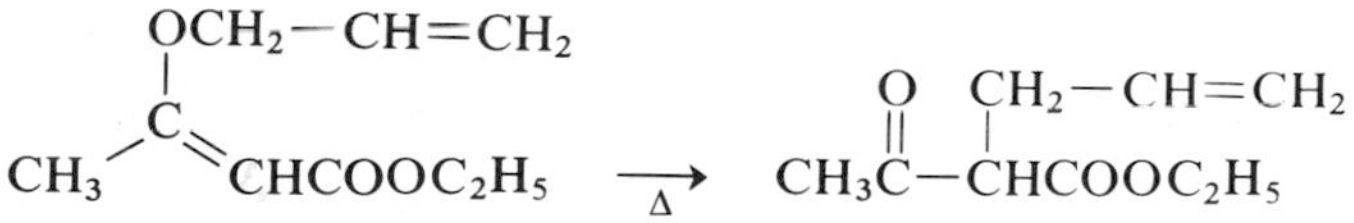

14

Evidence that the thermal reaction does not involve cither the allylic carbonium ion $\overset{\delta+}{C}H_2 = CH = \overset{\delta+}{C}H_2$ or the allylic radical $\overset{\delta\cdot}{C}H_2 = CH = \overset{\delta\cdot}{C}H_2$ as intermediates stems from isotopic labeling experiments. When **13**, labeled in the γ position with C^{14}, undergoes the isomerization, the α-C^{14} product is formed exclusively. This implies that the methylene positions do not become equivalent during the rearrangement:

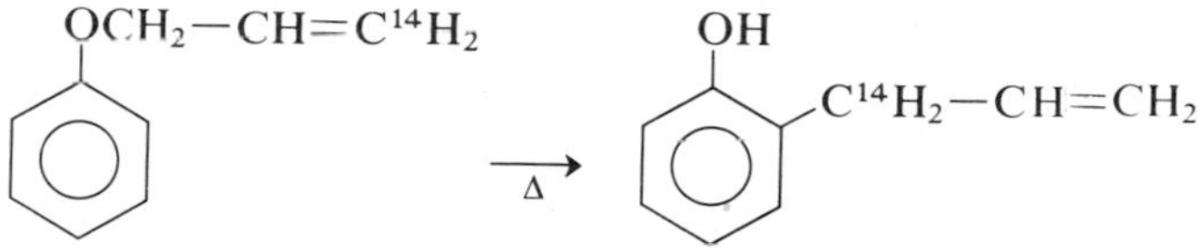

13

Consistent with these results is the cyclic intramolecular mechanism,

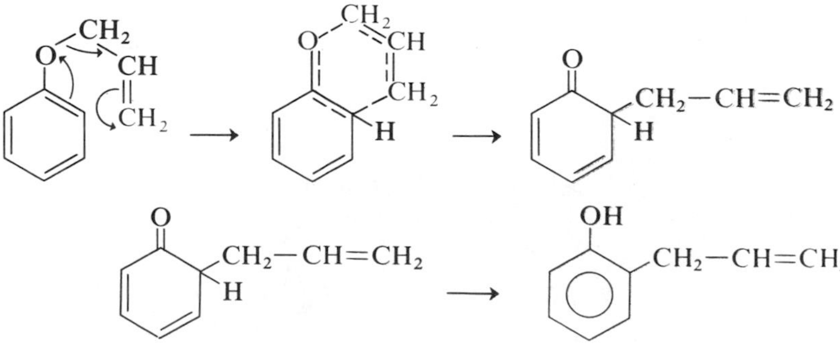

The dienone intermediate enolizes readily to the phenol.

Considerable evidence exists to support this mechanism. The C^{14} data already presented certainly favor this idea. In addition, the fact that no crossed products are formed during crossover experiments indicates the intramolecular nature of the reaction,

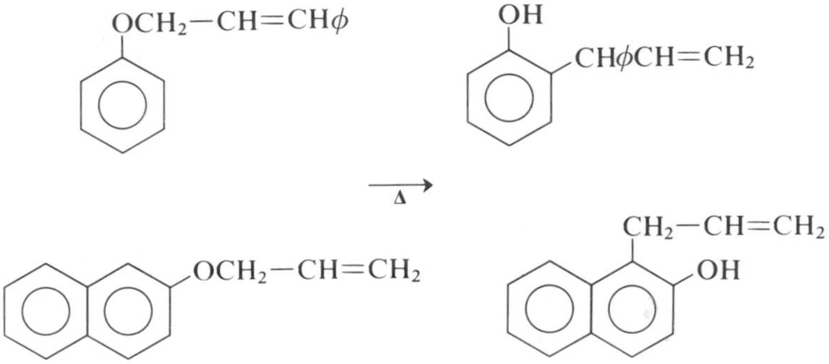

Optical activity is conserved when an optically active form of **15** is subjected to the rearrangement conditions, and this lends further support to the mechanism:

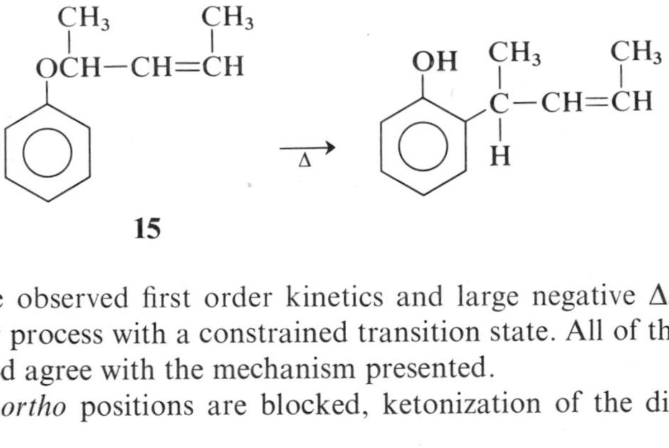

Finally the observed first order kinetics and large negative $\Delta S^{\ddagger}$ require a unimolecular process with a constrained transition state. All of these facts are consistent and agree with the mechanism presented.

When the *ortho* positions are blocked, ketonization of the dienone intermediate

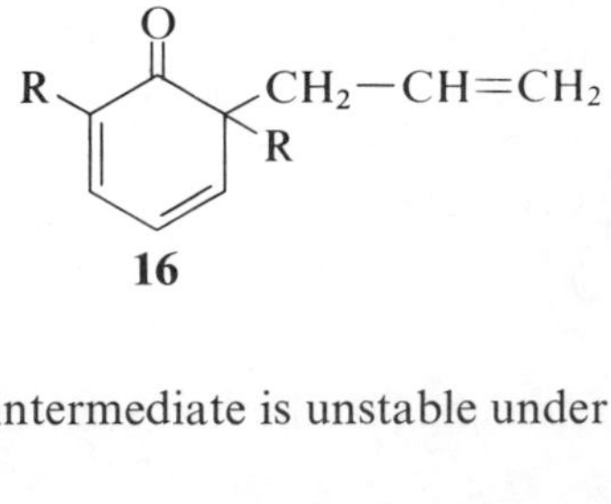

cannot take place. This intermediate is unstable under the reaction conditions, and it rearranges to the *para* phenol:

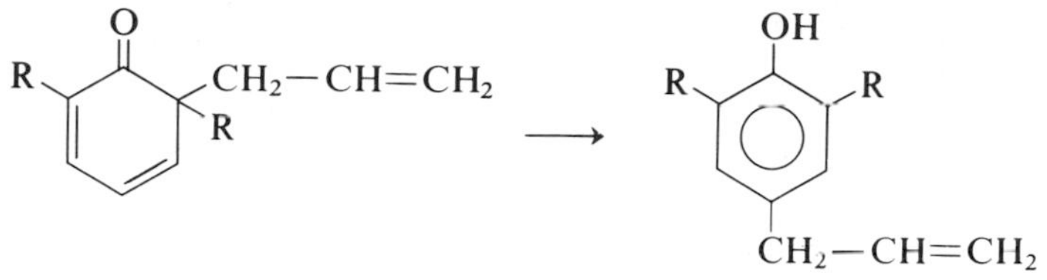

Thus, blocking the *ortho* positions gives rise to the *para* Claisen rearrangement. The intermediate **16** has actually been trapped as the Diels-Alder adduct with maleic anhydride:

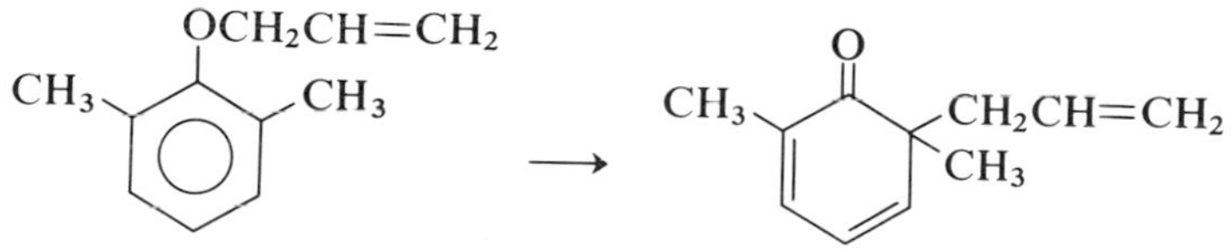

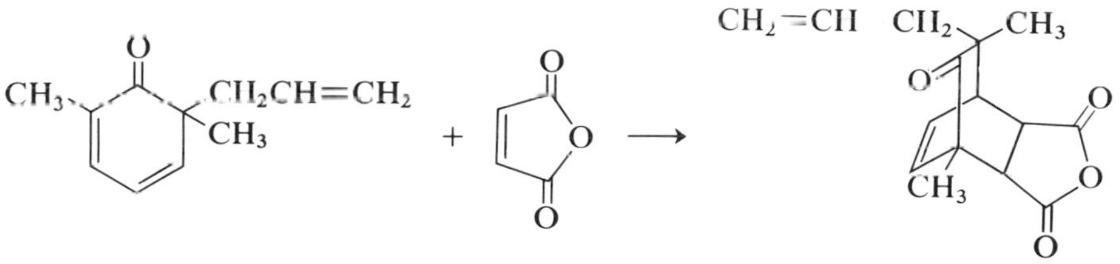

Heating the adduct reverses the Diels-Alder reaction; the expected product is generated:

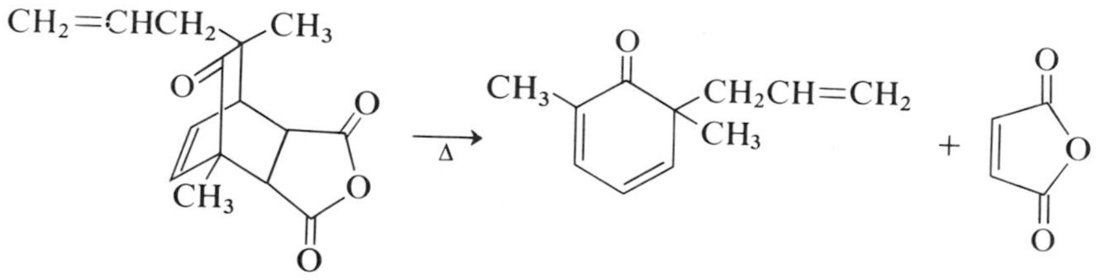

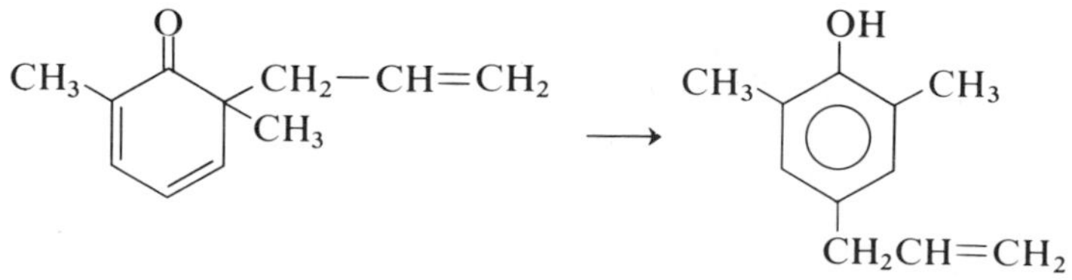

The dienone has, in fact, been prepared at low temperatures and its conversion to ether and phenol studied:

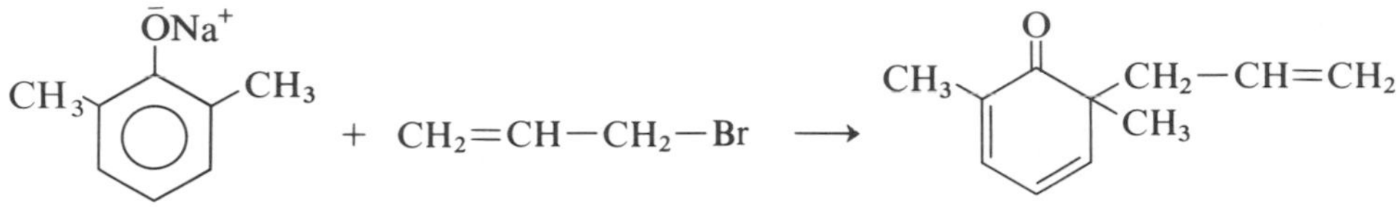

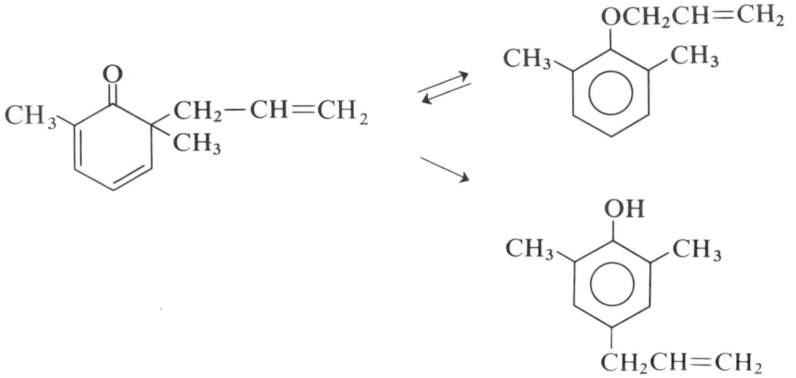

When the starting ether contains C^{14} in the γ position, the result is,

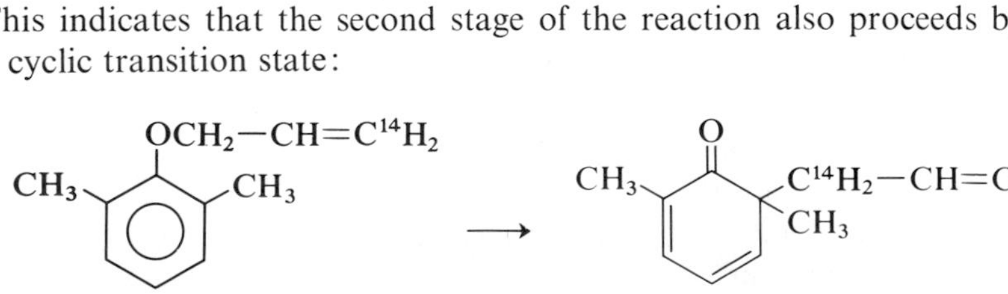

This indicates that the second stage of the reaction also proceeds by way of a cyclic transition state:

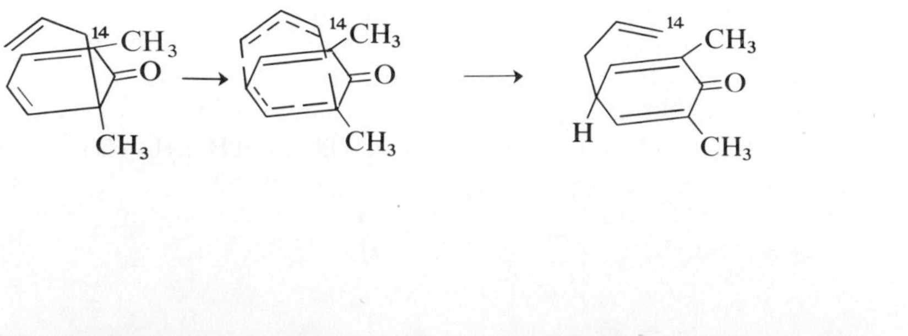

The second transition state also involves a six-membered cyclic system. This process is similar to the Claisen rearrangement but does not involve an ether. The migration appears as follows,

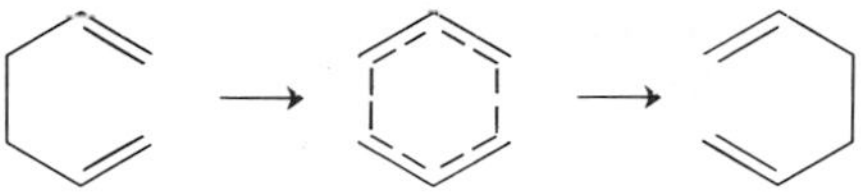

and the reaction is known as a Cope rearrangement.

Other examples of the Cope rearrangement are the equilibrium that exists between **17** and **18** and the isomerizations of **19** and **20**,

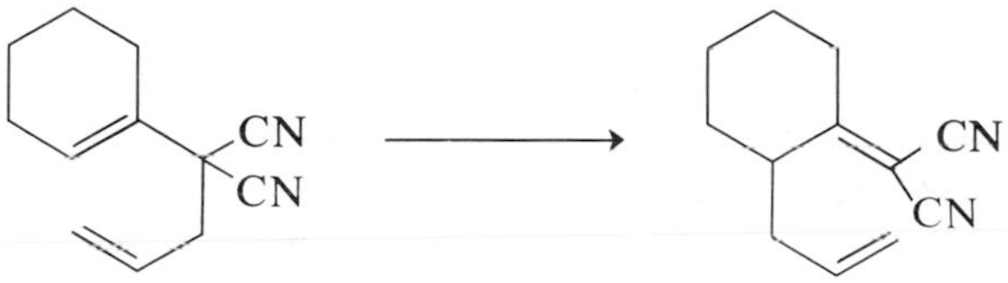

19.5 Rearrangements Involving Heteroatoms

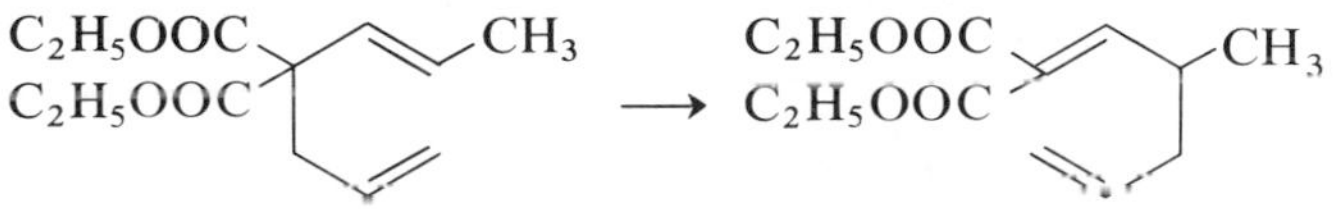

In the previous sections we discussed several rearrangements of aromatic systems, and heteroatoms participated in many of them. There are known, in addition to these aromatic rearrangements, a number of transformations of simple aliphatic systems that also involve heteroatoms. Most of the reactions that we shall present next are mechanistically related and are similar to the Wolff rearrangement.

When treated with silver oxide or with silver benzoate and triethylamine in methanol, a diazo ketone is converted into a ketene. The decomposition can also be effected photochemically or thermally. The ketene then reacts with any nucleophilic reagents that are present to form acid derivatives, and the conversion is known as the Wolff rearrangement.

$$RCOCRN_2 \longrightarrow R_2C{=}C{=}O + N_2$$

$$R_2C{=}C{=}O \quad \overset{\overset{H_2O}{\longrightarrow}}{\underset{\underset{NH_3}{\searrow}}{\overset{ROH}{\longrightarrow}}} \quad \begin{matrix} R_2CHCOOH \\ R_2CHCOOR \\ R_2CHCONH_2 \end{matrix}$$

The Wolff rearrangement just presented is used for converting an acid into the next higher homologue:

$$R{-}COOH \longrightarrow RCH_2COOH$$

The conversion involves treating an acid chloride with diazomethane CH_2N_2,

$$CH_2{=}\overset{+}{N}{=}\overset{-}{N} \longleftrightarrow \overset{-}{CH_2}{-}\overset{+}{N}{\equiv}N$$

When an acid chloride is treated with excess diazomethane, the diazo ketone is formed. The entire sequence for the transformation is,

$$RCOOH \xrightarrow{SOCl_2} RCOCl \xrightarrow{CH_2N_2} RCOCHN_2$$

$$RCOCHN_2 \xrightarrow[H_2O]{Ag_2O} RCH_2COOH$$

This entire process is also given a name, the Arndt-Eistert reaction.

The interesting step in the Arndt-Eistert reaction is the Wolff rearrangement, the conversion of the diazo ketone into the ketene, and much work has gone into elucidating the mechanism. More than a single mechanism is probably operative in this rearrangement step, the process varying with the reaction conditions. It has been suggested that those processes catalyzed by silver oxide or silver benzoate are free radical in nature, for free radical inhibitors quench the rearrangement.

It is thought that the thermal and photochemical reactions, (perhaps the silver ion catalyzed process also), involve carbenes as intermediates. Both singlet and triplet carbenes are conceivable, and it is quite likely that some rearrangements involve the singlet species of carbene while others involve the triplet. Data concerning the nature of the intermediate are sparse, and it is also possible that the migration is concerted with no distinct carbene intermediate being generated. We assume that a distinct carbene **21** is generated, but make no distinction between singlet and triplet intermediates. The mechanism becomes,

$$\overset{O}{\overset{\|}{RCCH}}{-}N_2 \xrightarrow{h\nu} \overset{O}{\overset{\|}{R{-}C}}{-}\ddot{C}H + N_2$$

21

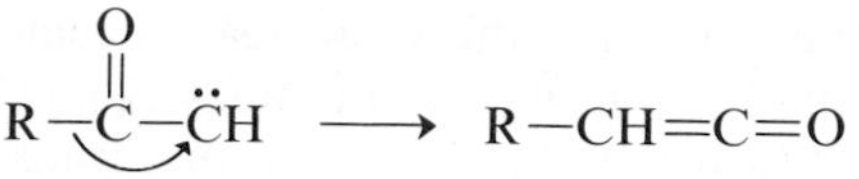

$$R-\overset{\overset{\displaystyle O}{\|}}{C}-\overset{\cdot\cdot}{C}H \longrightarrow R-CH=C=O$$

Typical examples of the rearrangement are,

$$\phi_3C-COCHN_2 \xrightarrow[\text{H}_2\text{O}]{\text{h}\nu} \phi_3CCH_2COOH$$

22

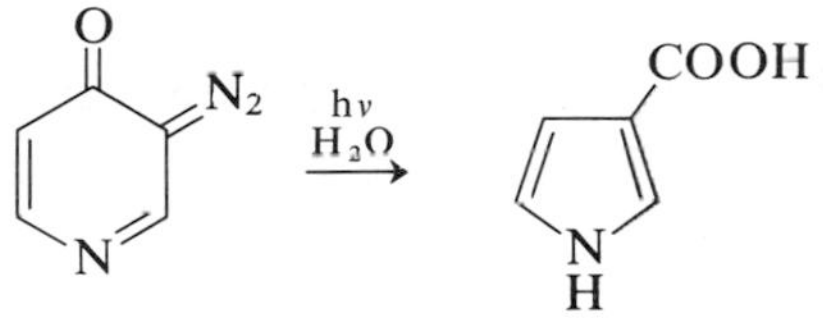

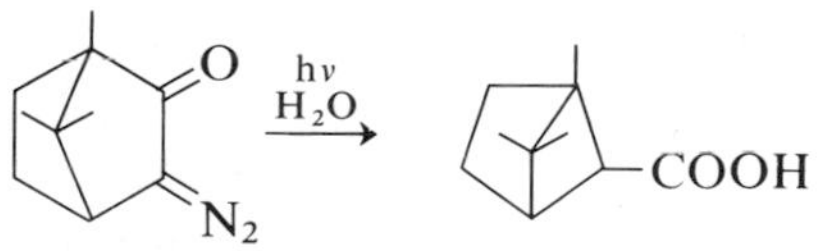

It has been shown in a number of cases that the migrating group in the Wolff rearrangement migrates with retention of configuration,

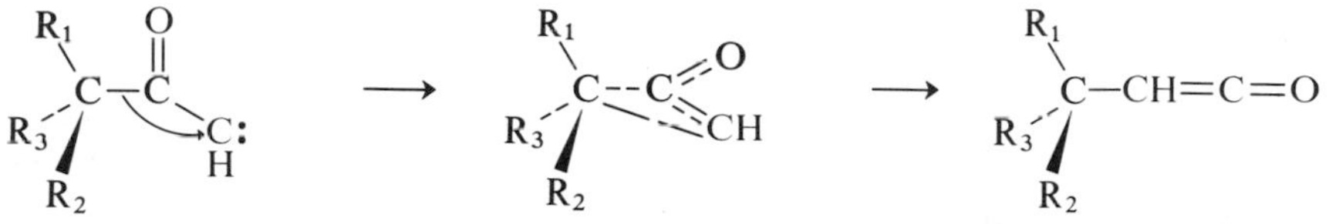

When the reaction is conducted using isotopically labeled carbon, the product is formed without scrambling of the label,

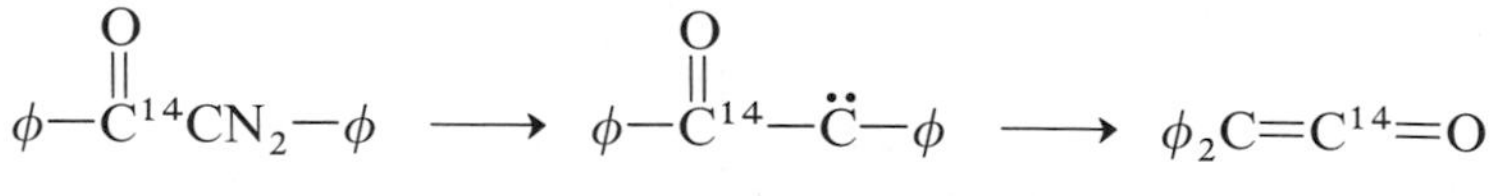

$$\phi-\overset{\overset{\displaystyle O}{\|}}{C}{}^{14}CN_2-\phi \longrightarrow \phi-\overset{\overset{\displaystyle O}{\|}}{C}{}^{14}-\overset{\cdot\cdot}{C}-\phi \longrightarrow \phi_2C=C^{14}=O$$

$$\phi_2C=C^{14}=O \xrightarrow{\text{H}_2\text{O}} \phi_2CHC^{14}OOH$$

This result demonstrates that the α-carbon atom never becomes equivalent to the carbonyl carbon atom, and on this basis intermediates such as,

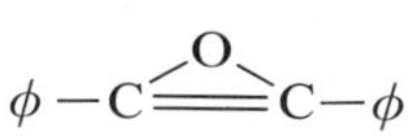

$$\phi-C\overset{\displaystyle O}{=\!\!=}C-\phi$$

can be excluded.

Not all diazo ketones undergo the Wolff rearrangement, and some that do, only do so under certain conditions. Compounds **22** and **23** behave as expected upon irradiation, but their thermal decomposition leads to different products:

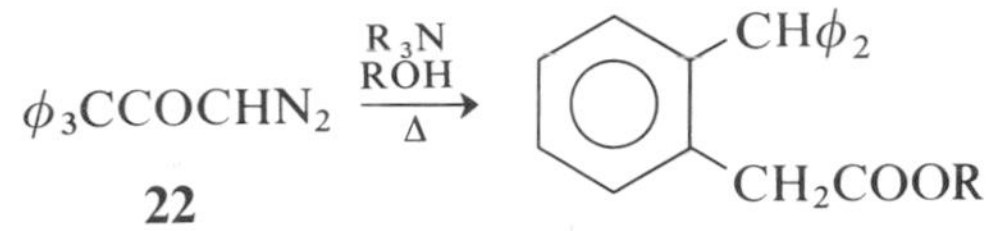

Reactions related to the Wolff rearrangement include the Hofmann reaction, the Lossen rearrangement, and the Curtius and Schmidt reactions. The general characteristics of these processes are similar, that is, migration to an electron deficient atom is involved, and the intermediates in some of them resemble the carbenes encountered in the Wolff rearrangement. We consider the Curtius rearrangement first.

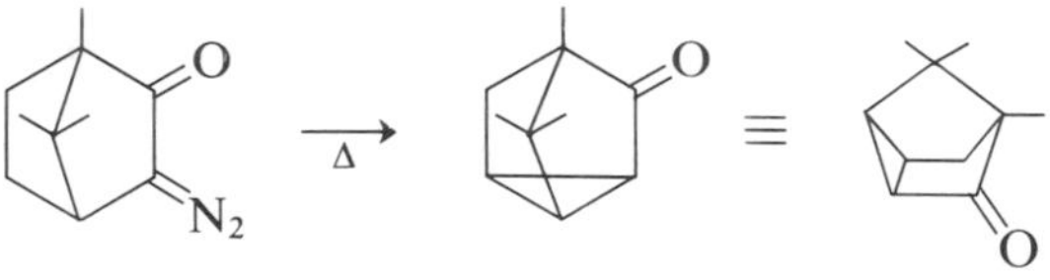

When an acid chloride is treated with sodium azide NaN_3, the corresponding acid azide is obtained:

$$\underset{O}{\overset{\parallel}{R}}CCl + NaN_3 \longrightarrow \underset{O}{\overset{\parallel}{R}}CN_3 + NaCl$$

Other methods of preparation are known; for example, the following scheme has occasionally been employed:

$$RCOOC_2H_5 \xrightarrow{NH_2NH_2} RCONHNH_2 \xrightarrow{HNO_2} RCON_3$$

This acid azide can be decomposed by chemical catalysts or by thermal or irradiative techniques. The reaction, the Curtius reaction, most closely resembles the Wolff rearrangement. However, in view of the greater electronegativity of nitrogen, we do not assume here that a true nitrene is involved; instead we postulate concerted migration,

$$R\overset{O}{\overset{\parallel}{-}}C\overset{\cdot\cdot}{-}N\overset{\frown}{-}N_2 \longrightarrow R-N{=}C{=}O + N_2$$

24

The isocyanates **24** that are formed as products of the decomposition are hydrolyzed readily to primary amines:

$$R-N{=}C{=}O \xrightarrow[H_2O]{OH^-} RNH_2$$

Primary amines are also prepared by way of the Hofmann and Schmidt rearrangements. When a primary amide $RCONH_2$ is treated with halogen in the presence of a base, a primary amine RNH_2 results; the conversion is referred to as the Hofmann rearrangement,

$$RCONH_2 \xrightarrow[OH^-]{X_2} RNH_2$$

The mechanism for the transformation is,

$$R-\overset{\overset{O}{\|}}{C}NH_2 \xrightarrow[OH^-]{Br_2} R-\overset{\overset{O}{\|}}{C}-NHBr$$

25

$$R-\overset{\overset{O}{\|}}{C}-NHBr + OH^- \longrightarrow R-\overset{\overset{O}{\|}}{C}-\ddot{N}=Br + H_2O$$

26

$$R-\overset{\overset{O}{\|}}{C}-\ddot{N}-Br \longrightarrow R-N=C=O$$

$$R-N=C=O \xrightarrow[H_2O]{OH} RNH_2$$

The Hofmann rearrangement is analogous to the Wolff and Curtius reactions. For the reason stated previously, we postulate a concerted migration. The intermediates **25** have in some cases been isolated and have been shown to be acidic. The conjugate bases thus formed are generally unstable and rearrange readily. Under the usual conditions of the Hofmann reaction, the isocyanates are not isolable but hydrolyze directly to the amines. It has also been demonstrated that like the previous rearrangements, retention of configuration accompanies the process:

$$\underset{R_2}{\overset{R_1}{\underset{R_3}{\diagdown}}}\overset{\overset{O}{\diagup\!\!\!\diagdown}}{C-C}\overset{\overset{O}{\diagup\!\!\!\diagdown}}{\underset{Br}{\diagup}}\ddot{N}^- \longrightarrow \underset{R_2}{\overset{R_1}{\underset{R_3}{\diagdown}}}C\text{--}C\overset{O}{\diagup}\overset{\delta-}{N}\underset{Br^{\delta-}}{\diagdown} \longrightarrow \underset{R_2}{\overset{R_1}{\underset{R_3}{\diagdown}}}C-N=C=O$$

In the previous example the leaving group was bromide ion; however, other good leaving groups can be employed. When the reaction involves hydroxamic acids $RCONHOH$ and their derivatives, the process is called the Lossen rearrangement. In these cases the isocyanates can be isolated,

$$R-\overset{\overset{O}{\|}}{C}-\ddot{N}=O-\overset{\overset{O}{\|}}{C}CH_3 \longrightarrow R-N=C=O + CH_3COO^-$$

In the Lossen rearrangement the halogen has been replaced by another leaving group. The rearrangement can actually be effected under a variety of conditions; for example, treating the hydroxamic acid itself with materials such as thionyl chloride or phosphorus pentoxide brings about the conversion to isocyanate. However, most commonly the isocyanate is formed by treating an O-acyl derivative of the hydroxamic acid with base:

$$
\underset{\substack{\| \\ R-CNHOH}}{O} \xrightarrow[\substack{(2)\ KOCH_3}]{(1)\ RCOCl} \underset{\substack{\| \qquad\quad \| \\ R-C-\ddot{N}-OCR}}{\overset{O \qquad\quad O}{}} \longrightarrow R-N{=}C{=}O
$$

The three reactions, Hofmann, Lossen, and Curtius, are very closely related. In one the leaving group is Br^-, in the second ^-OOCR, and in the third N_2. Qualitatively, the mechanism appears to be the same for all three; however, since the leaving group and the reaction conditions differ, we naturally expect the degree of bond making and bond breaking in the transition state to differ also. In some of the transformations the migrating group R may begin to form the R—N bond as soon as the leaving group begins its departure. In others, bond breakage to the leaving group may be almost complete and an incipient nitrene may develop before the migration of R begins. The kinetic orders of these reactions have been determined, and as expected, all of them are first order in organic reactant. Hammett plots and ρ values have been obtained for reactions where the migrating group is aromatic. While the expected linear agreement is not always good, the value of ρ is decidedly negative for the Hofmann and Lossen reactions. Electron donors accelerate the rate of these reactions. The Curtius rearrangement is not as sensitive to substituent changes as the other two processes, and this result certainly indicates that the transition state is not the same in all three cases.

The rate of the Lossen rearrangement is increased by introducing electron withdrawers into the leaving group and electron donors into the migrating group. The fact that both the leaving group and the migrating group influence the rate of reaction is best explained by postulating concerted migrations. Since similar effects are found in the Hofmann rearrangement, the rate limiting step in both reactions is postulated to be the departure of the leaving group coupled with a concerted migration. The Curtius reaction is also represented as a single-step process:

$$
\underset{\substack{\| \\ R-CN_3}}{O} \longrightarrow R-N{=}C{=}O + N_2
$$

The Curtius reaction can be catalyzed by Brønsted and by strong Lewis acids, and in these catalyzed migrations the rate expression for the rearrangement is first order in each material; the value of ρ is negative. In the acid catalyzed Curtius reaction the conjugate acids of the various species are involved:

$$R-\overset{O}{\overset{\|}{C}}-N_3 \xrightarrow{H^+} R-\overset{O-H}{\overset{|}{C}}=N-\overset{+}{N}\equiv N \longrightarrow R-N=C=\overset{+}{O}-H$$
                                                                                    27

The conjugate acid **27** can be hydrolyzed to the amine.

This last process is similar to still another reaction that leads to primary amines, the Schmidt reaction. In the Curtius reaction an acid chloride is treated with sodium azide; the product is an acid azide which can be converted to the amine. The Schmidt rearrangement involves the reaction of a carboxylic acid with hydrazoic acid in concentrated sulfuric acid. The product is an amine, and the azide is an intermediate. The rearrangement step is analogous to the acid catalyzed Curtius reaction:

$$R-\overset{O}{\overset{\|}{C}}OH + HN_3 \xrightarrow{H^+} R-\overset{O}{\overset{\|}{C}}N_3 \xrightarrow{H^+} R-N=C=O \xrightarrow{H^+} RNH_3^+$$

As in the other reactions of this type, R migrates with retention of configuration, and ρ is negative. At constant pH, the Schmidt reaction follows second order kinetics. The rate expression is first order in carboxylic acid and first order in hydrazoic acid.

Aldehydes and ketones also react with hydrazoic acid in the presence of a strong acid. Aldehydes are converted to nitriles under these conditions, while ketones form amides. All these processes are considered to be within the scope of the Schmidt reaction,

$$RCHO + HN_3 \xrightarrow{H^+} RCN$$
$$RCOR + HN_3 \xrightarrow{H^+} RNHCOR$$

The mechanism is, in both cases, assumed to involve intermediates of the type,

$$\underset{R}{\overset{}{\underset{}{}}}\overset{N-\overset{+}{N}\equiv N}{\underset{\overset{\|}{C}}{\overset{|}{N}}}R$$

which are formed from the carbonyl compound, acid, and hydrazoic acid,

$$R-\overset{O}{\overset{\|}{C}}-R + HN_3 + H^+ \longrightarrow R-\overset{\overset{+}{N}-N\equiv N}{\overset{\|}{C}}-R + H_2O$$

When one of the R groups is hydrogen, loss of nitrogen and loss of a proton lead to the nitrile:

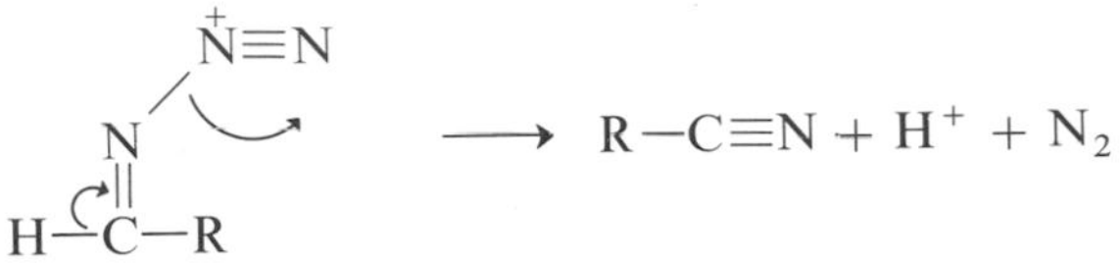

$$\overset{+}{N}\equiv N$$

$$\longrightarrow \quad R-C\equiv N + H^+ + N_2$$

When the groups are both alkyl or aryl groups, migration takes place; the intermediate **28** is produced:

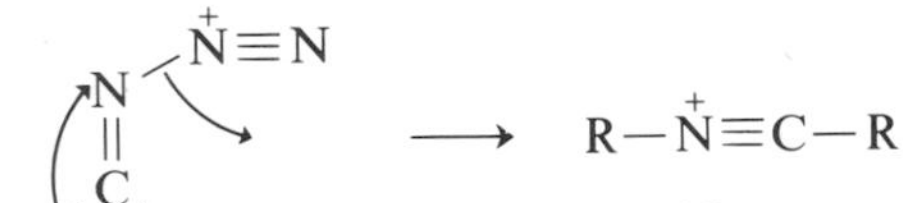

$$\longrightarrow \quad R-\overset{+}{N}\equiv C-R$$

28

The positive charge in **28** is delocalized,

$$R-\overset{+}{N}\equiv C-R \longleftrightarrow R-N=\overset{+}{C}-R$$

and this species reacts with the water that is present and is converted to the amide:

$$R-\overset{+}{N}\equiv C-R \xrightarrow{H_2O} R-\overset{H}{N}-\overset{O}{\overset{||}{C}}-R$$

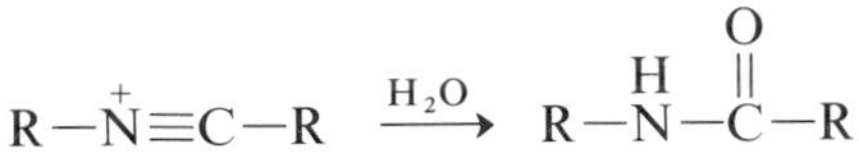

Evidence supporting **28** as an active intermediate in the Schmidt reaction of ketones comes from the conversion of these carbonyl systems to tetrazoles **29** when excess hydrazoic acid is employed. Since the amides themselves do not react to form **29**, an intermediate formed at some stage prior to the amide must be involved in the reaction leading to tetrazoles.

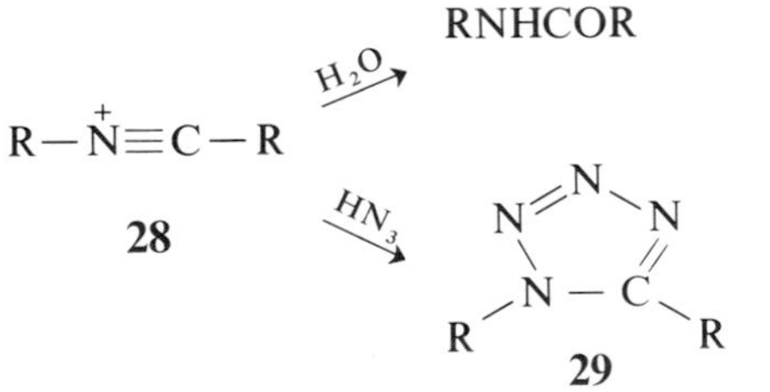

$$R-\overset{+}{N}\equiv C-R \quad \overset{H_2O}{\nearrow} \quad RNHCOR$$

28

$$\searrow^{HN_3}$$

29

The postulated cation **28** satisfies the data. It is converted to the amide under one set of conditions and into **29** in the presence of excess hydrazoic acid.

In the migration step,

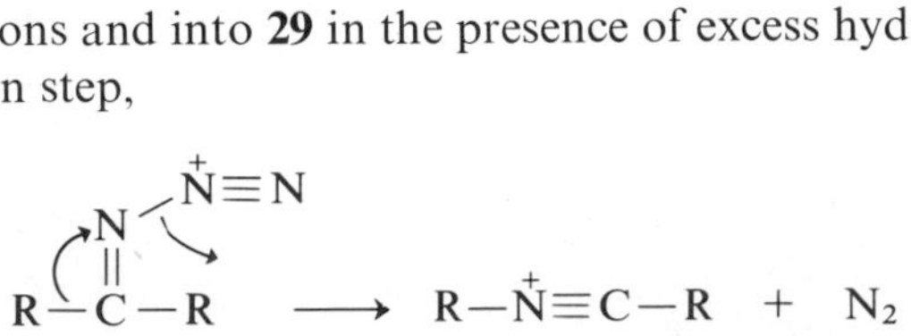

$$R-C-R \longrightarrow R-\overset{+}{N}\equiv C-R \quad + \quad N_2$$

it is the group best situated (*anti* to the leaving group) that migrates and not the group that is best able to stabilize the positive charge. This has been demonstrated by conducting the Schmidt reaction with *para* substituted benzophenones **30**. In these cases, mixtures containing nearly equal quantities of the isomeric amides were obtained. If electronic factors had been influential, a preponderance of a single isomer would have been observed,

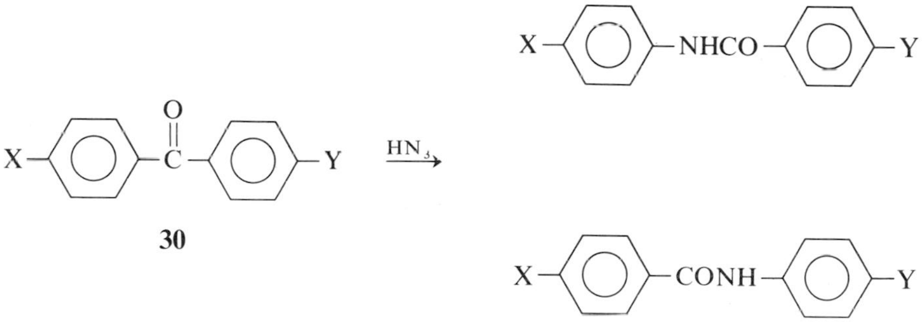

$$X-\langle\bigcirc\rangle-NHCO-\langle\bigcirc\rangle-Y$$

$$X-\langle\bigcirc\rangle-\overset{\overset{O}{\parallel}}{C}-\langle\bigcirc\rangle-Y \xrightarrow{HN_3}$$

30

$$X-\langle\bigcirc\rangle-CONH-\langle\bigcirc\rangle-Y$$

Another reaction that should be considered at this time is the Beckmann rearrangement. This process, related to the Schmidt reaction, provides more conclusive evidence that the migrating group is *anti* to the leaving group. In this reaction oximes are converted to nitriles or amides, a transformation that resembles closely the Schmidt rearrangement,

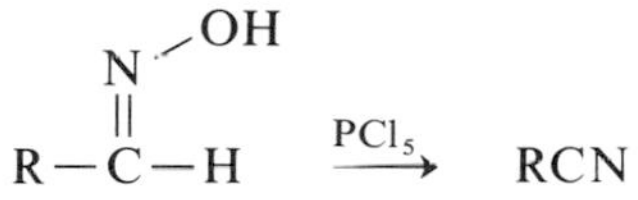

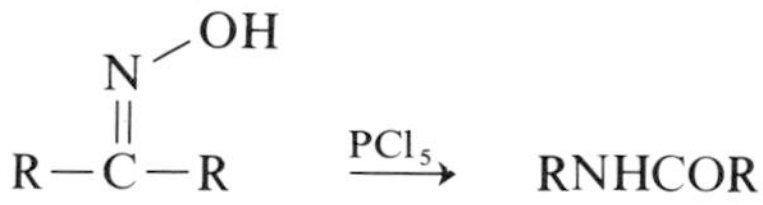

$$\overset{\overset{\displaystyle N^{\diagup OH}}{\parallel}}{\underset{R-C-H}{}} \xrightarrow{PCl_5} RCN$$

$$\overset{\overset{\displaystyle N^{\diagup OH}}{\parallel}}{\underset{R-C-R}{}} \xrightarrow{PCl_5} RNHCOR$$

In these reactions it is possible to determine the geometry of the starting oxime, and it is observed that in the amide, the group initially *anti* to the leaving group has become attached to the nitrogen. This group migrates with retention of configuration, and as usual ρ is negative.

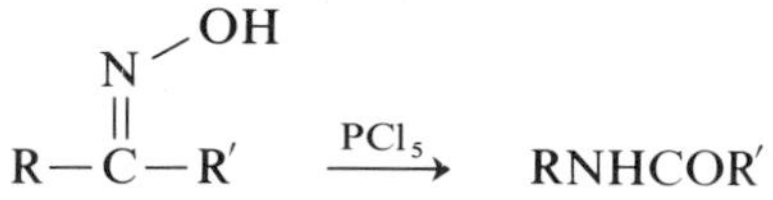

$$\overset{\overset{\displaystyle N^{\diagup OH}}{\parallel}}{\underset{R-C-R'}{}} \xrightarrow{PCl_5} RNHCOR'$$

In some cases, the oximes are readily interconvertible, and then it is the group that is best able to migrate that actually does so. This is possible because in one of the configurations it becomes properly situated.

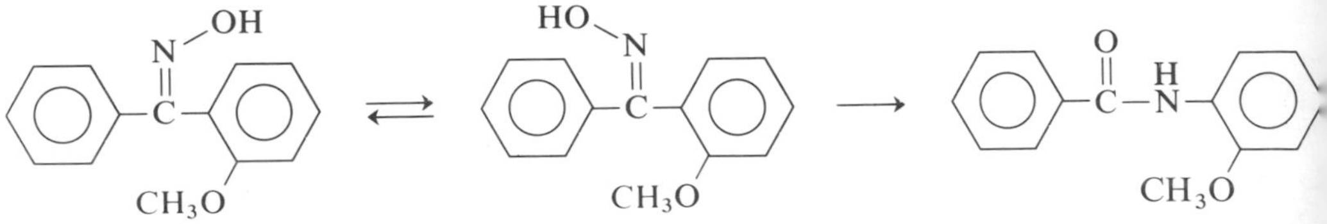

The mechanism usually proposed for the Beckmann rearrangement is a concerted one in which R migrates simultaneously with the departure of the leaving group:

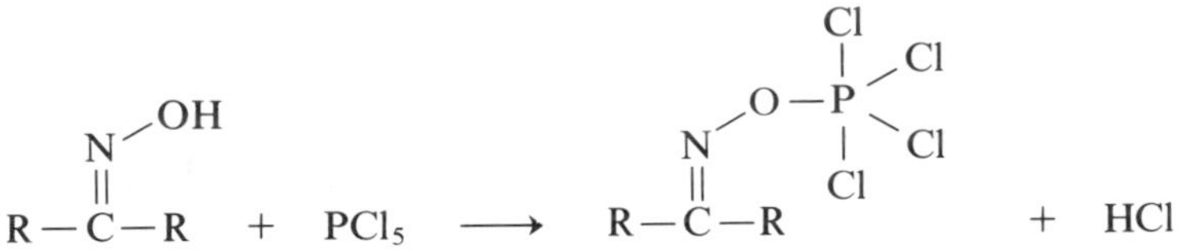

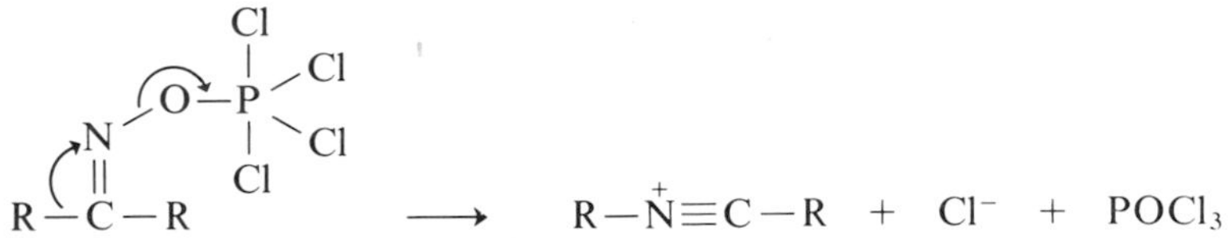

The $POCl_3$ continues the process, the same cation suggested as an intermediate in the Schmidt reaction is proposed here, and this combines with the chloride ion to form the chloride **31**. The last species is subsequently hydrolyzed to the amide:

$$R-\overset{+}{N}\equiv C-R + Cl^- \longrightarrow R-N=\overset{\underset{|}{Cl}}{C}-R$$

31

$$R-N=\overset{\underset{|}{Cl}}{C}-R \xrightarrow{H_2O} RNHCOR$$

Other leaving groups besides OH and other reagents besides PCl_5 can be employed in the reaction. The mechanism is nearly the same in all cases.

The reactions discussed in this section involve migration to electron deficient nitrogen. There are, in addition, processes where the alkyl group migrates to an electron deficient oxygen atom. One of these is the Baeyer-Villiger reaction, and we discuss this process in the next section.

19.6 The Baeyer-Villiger Reaction

A ketone treated with a peroxyacid is converted into an ester:

$$\underset{\substack{\| \\ R-C-R}}{O} \xrightarrow{\substack{O \\ \| \\ R-C-O-OH}} \underset{\substack{\| \\ R-C-OR}}{O}$$

When cyclic ketones are employed, the products are lactones:

$$\xrightarrow{H_2SO_5}$$

The question was frequently raised concerning which oxygen atom in the product came from the peroxyacid. By treating benzophenone containing O^{18} with peroxyacid, it was established that the carbonyl oxygen atom remains intact, and any mechanism postulated for this reaction must be consistent with the result of this investigation. The carbonyl oxygen atom can neither migrate nor become equivalent to the oxygen atom being introduced by the peroxyacid,

$$\underset{\substack{\| \\ \phi-C-\phi}}{O^{18}} \xrightarrow{RCO_3H} \underset{\substack{\| \\ \phi-C-O-\phi}}{O^{18}}$$

In the absence of a strong acid the Baeyer-Villiger reaction may well proceed without acid catalysis. However, when a strong acid is present, it becomes evident that acid catalysis does take place. Kinetic investigations lead to the conclusion that the general rate expression for the reaction is third order, first order in each reactant and first order in acid catalyst. Thus all three species must be accommodated in the transition state.

The first step is undoubtedly an addition of the peroxyacid to the carbonyl group, and this adduct **31** then decomposes into the product:

$$\underset{\substack{\| \\ R-C-R}}{O} + \underset{\substack{\| \\ R'C-O-OH}}{O} \underset{}{\overset{HX}{\rightleftharpoons}} \underset{\substack{| \\ R}}{\overset{OH}{\underset{|}{R-C-O-O-CR'}}} \underset{\substack{\| \\ }}{O}$$

31

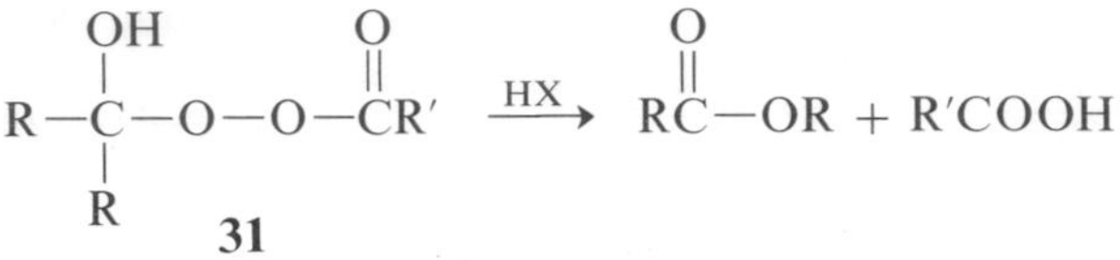

$$\underset{\underset{R}{\overset{OH}{|}}}{R-\overset{}{\underset{}{C}}-O-O-\overset{\overset{O}{||}}{C}R'} \quad \xrightarrow{HX} \quad R\overset{\overset{O}{||}}{C}-OR + R'COOH$$

$$\mathbf{31}$$

It is the hydroxy oxygen atom in **31** that was originally the carbonyl oxygen atom, and it again becomes the carbonyl oxygen atom in the product. This is consistent with the results of the O^{18} study.

There is some question concerning which step in the reaction is rate limiting. The observed kinetic expression can be accommodated either by a rate determining addition of the peroxyacid with the aid of the catalyst, or by a rate limiting decomposition of the adduct **31**, or by a process in which neither step is clearly rate limiting. The fact that electron withdrawers in the leaving group OOCR' and electron donors in the migrating group R increase the rate of reaction is more consistent with a rate limiting second step. It seems reasonable to assume that the first step in the process is a reversible addition of peroxyacid to the carbonyl compound and that the adduct **31** then decomposes with the aid of the catalyst into the product.

The catalyst HX probably also aids in the addition step, but the contribution by HX in this step does not show up in the general rate expression.

The migration of R is concerted with the departure of the leaving group, and either of the R groups can migrate. The value of ρ is negative, and the group best able to stabilize a positive charge is the one that actually rearranges (steric effects occasionally lead to exceptions),

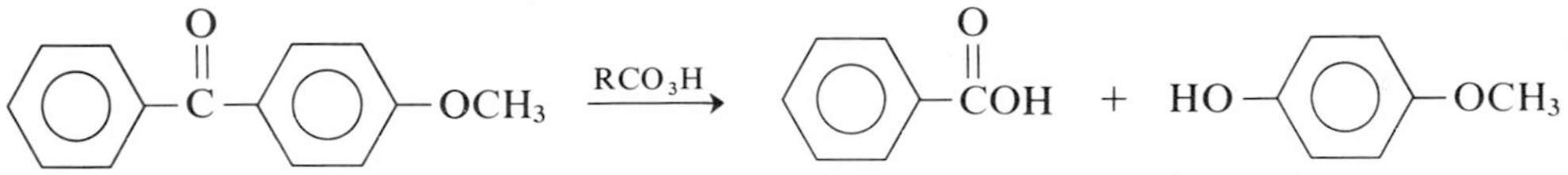

Furthermore, using an optically active migrating group, it has been shown that retention of configuration accompanies the process,

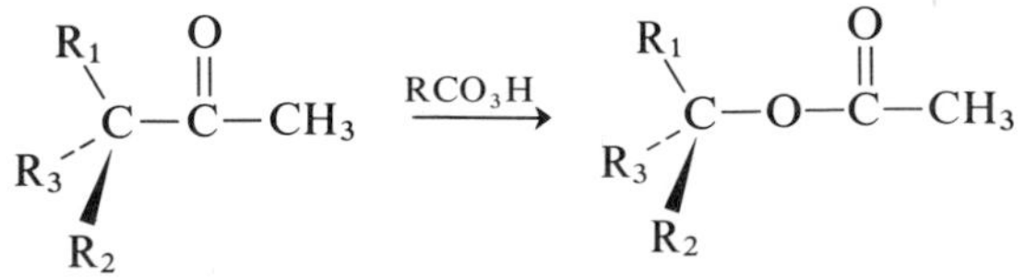

Although it involves a migration to oxygen, the Baeyer-Villiger reaction is, in principle, no different from the migrations discussed previously. It most

closely resembles the acid catalyzed Curtius, the Schmidt, and the Beckman rearrangements. In these processes the group migrates with retention of configuration, and electron donors in the migrating group enhance the rate of reaction (ρ is negative).

Related reactions exist. The commercial preparation of phenol and acetone takes advantage of this sort of behavior. Cumene hydroperoxide, treated with acid, is transformed into a mixture of acetone and phenol. The reaction involves migration of phenyl to an electron deficient oxygen atom, and either classical or nonclassical cations can be postulated as intermediates:

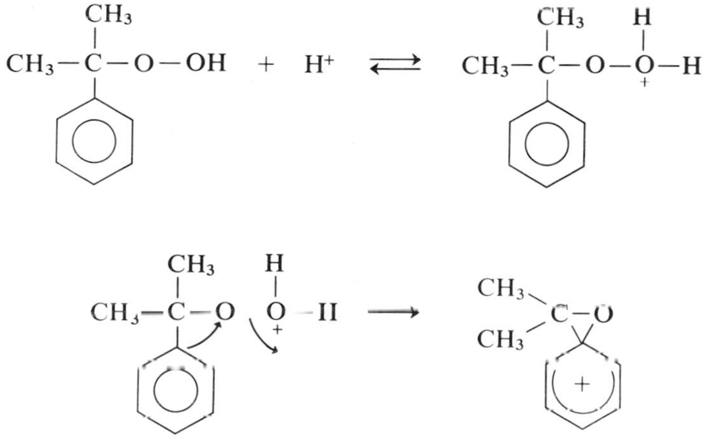

This intermediate can react with water directly, or it can be in equilibrium with the classical intermediate, the latter reacting with water:

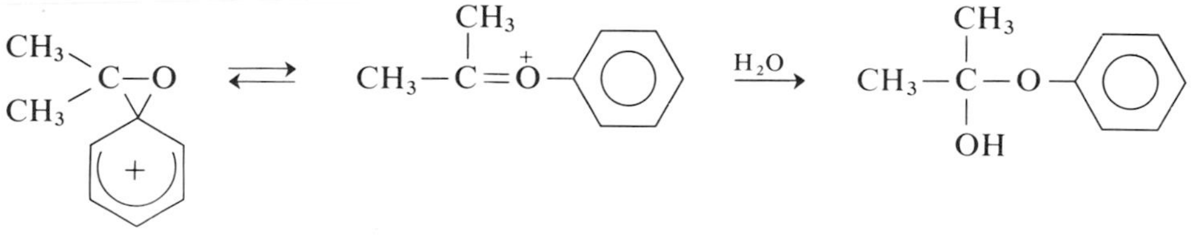

This last material is a hemiketal which readily decomposes into acetone and phenol:

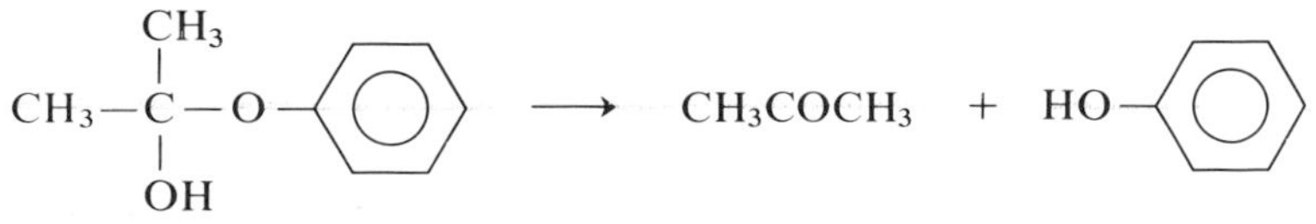

Supplementary Reading

1. De La Mare, P. B. D. and Ridd, J. H., *Aromatic Substitution*. New York, Academic, 1959.

2. De Mayo, P. (editor), *Molecular Rearrangements*. New York, Interscience, Vol. 1 (1963), Vol. 2 (1964).

3. Gould, E. S., *Mechanism and Structure in Organic Chemistry*. New York, Holt, 1959.

4. Hine, J., *Physical Organic Chemistry*. New York, McGraw-Hill, 1962.

5. Surrey, A. R., *Name Reactions in Organic Chemistry*. New York, Academic, 1961.

Chapter 20

Free Radical and Photochemical Reactions

20.1 Free Radical Halogenations

Certainly the most familiar free radical reaction is the halogenation of hydrocarbons. When a hydrocarbon RH is treated with bromine or chlorine, free radical substitution is effected. The mechanism is,

$$X_2 \longrightarrow 2X\bullet \qquad \text{initiating}$$

$$RH + X\bullet \longrightarrow R\bullet + HX \left.\vphantom{\begin{array}{c}a\\b\end{array}}\right\} \text{ propagating}$$

$$R\bullet + X_2 \longrightarrow RX + X\bullet$$

The reaction is a chain reaction with the usual initiating, propagating, and terminating steps, the last being any processes by which radicals are destroyed. This reaction proceeds in a satisfactory manner for hydrocarbons such as CH_4, CH_3CH_3, and $C(CH_3)_4$, which have only one type of replaceable hydrogen. It also works well for toluene, which has more than a single type of hydrogen, because the methyl hydrogens are most readily abstracted. However, the reaction is not always satisfactory for halogenation of hydrocarbons such as $(CH_3)_3CH$ which have several types of hydrogens, for here a mixture of products is sometimes obtained. Chlorination accords a mixture, but bromination, which is more selective, yields almost exclusively *t*-butyl bromide:

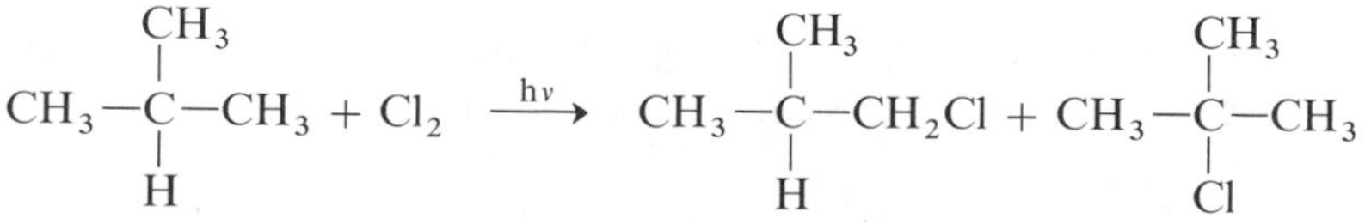

$$CH_3-\overset{\displaystyle CH_3}{\underset{\displaystyle H}{C}}-CH_3 + Cl_2 \xrightarrow{\ h\nu\ } CH_3-\overset{\displaystyle CH_3}{\underset{\displaystyle H}{C}}-CH_2Cl + CH_3-\overset{\displaystyle CH_3}{\underset{\displaystyle Cl}{C}}-CH_3$$

48 %   29 %

+ polyhalogenated
materials

667

The monobromides resulting from bromination give the result,

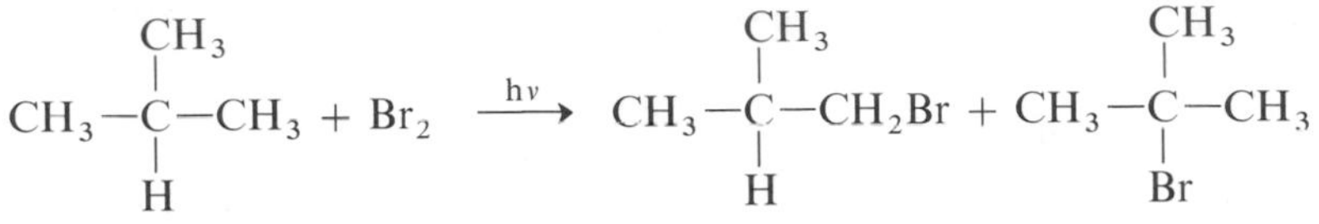

$$CH_3-\underset{\underset{H}{|}}{\overset{\overset{CH_3}{|}}{C}}-CH_3 + Br_2 \xrightarrow{h\nu} CH_3-\underset{\underset{H}{|}}{\overset{\overset{CH_3}{|}}{C}}-CH_2Br + CH_3-\underset{\underset{Br}{|}}{\overset{\overset{CH_3}{|}}{C}}-CH_3$$

$$1\% \qquad\qquad 99\%$$

We mentioned previously that some radicals have nonplanar conformations. In connection with this idea, halogenations of optically active starting materials have been carried out. If the radical that is involved as an intermediate has a nonplanar geometry, optically active products might be obtained:

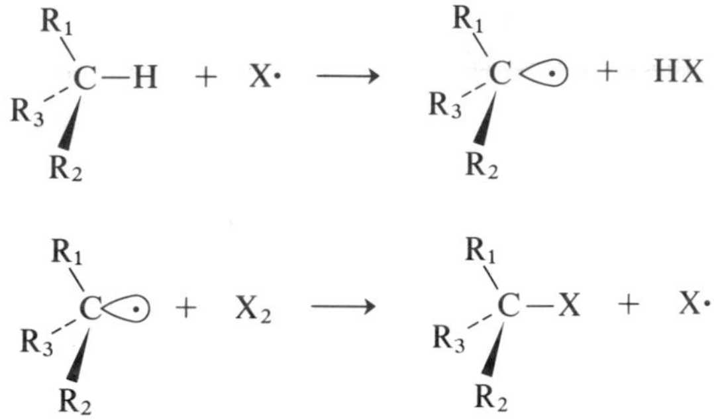

$$\underset{R_2}{\overset{R_1}{\underset{R_3}{\diagdown}}}C-H + X\cdot \longrightarrow \underset{R_2}{\overset{R_1}{\underset{R_3}{\diagdown}}}C\langle\odot + HX$$

$$\underset{R_2}{\overset{R_1}{\underset{R_3}{\diagdown}}}C\langle\odot + X_2 \longrightarrow \underset{R_2}{\overset{R_1}{\underset{R_3}{\diagdown}}}C-X + X\cdot$$

Now the chlorination of optically active **1** leads to an optically inactive mixture of **2**, and this implies that radicals either suffer rapid inversion or that they have a planar geometry:

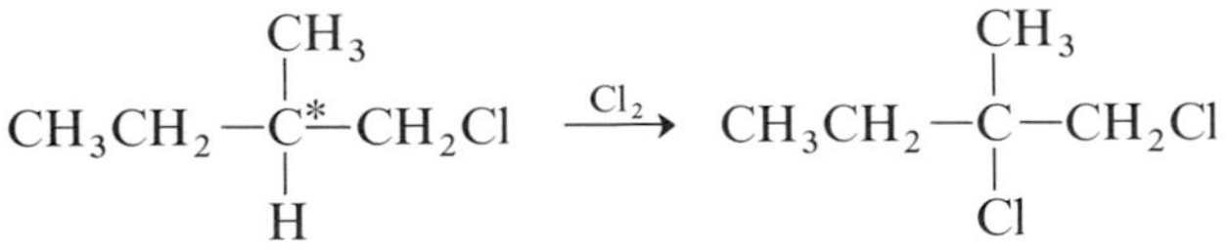

$$CH_3CH_2-\underset{\underset{H}{|}}{\overset{\overset{CH_3}{|}}{C^*}}-CH_2Cl \xrightarrow{Cl_2} CH_3CH_2-\underset{\underset{Cl}{|}}{\overset{\overset{CH_3}{|}}{C}}-CH_2Cl$$

$$\mathbf{1} \qquad\qquad\qquad \mathbf{2}$$

$$\text{racemic}$$

Since carbanions and amines are known to invert readily, the negative results of the previous experiment are inconclusive. The radical is capable of rapid inversion,

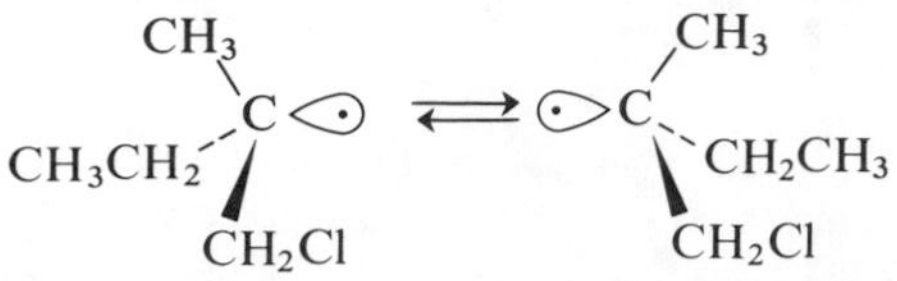

$$\underset{CH_2Cl}{\overset{CH_3}{\underset{CH_3CH_2}{\diagdown}}}C\langle\odot \rightleftharpoons \odot\rangle C\underset{CH_2Cl}{\overset{CH_3}{\diagup}}CH_2CH_3$$

When the same compound is brominated, some optically active product is obtained,

$$CH_3CH_2-\overset{\overset{\displaystyle CH_3}{|}}{\underset{\underset{\displaystyle H}{|}}{\overset{*}{C}}}-CH_2Cl \xrightarrow{Br_2} CH_3CH_2-\overset{\overset{\displaystyle CH_3}{|}}{\underset{\underset{\displaystyle Br}{|}}{\overset{*}{C}}}-CH_2Cl$$

and when instead of the chloride, the optically active bromide is brominated, similar results are obtained. One possibility is that an optically active radical is formed in these reactions, and that this reacts to form products before it undergoes complete racemization. The results are at least consistent with the formation of an optically active radical.

Although the results are consistent with this interpretation, another explanation has been proposed in order to account for the experimental findings. It has been suggested that a nonclassical bridged radical of the type,

$$CH_3CH_2-\overset{\overset{\displaystyle Cl}{\underset{\displaystyle \cdot}{\diagdown}}}{\underset{\displaystyle CH_3}{\diagup}}C-\overset{\displaystyle H}{\underset{\displaystyle H}{C}}$$

is formed in these reactions, and that this bridged radical, which is incapable of racemization, reacts with bromine to form optically active products. This explanation requires that the bridged halogen atom expand its octet, but such an expansion is possible with chlorine and bromine. The idea is similar to the bromonium ion and requires *trans*-addition of the entering bromine:

$$\underset{\underset{\displaystyle H}{\diagup}\overset{\displaystyle C}{\diagdown}H}{\overset{\overset{\displaystyle Cl\cdot}{\diagup\diagdown}}{\underset{\displaystyle R}{\overset{\displaystyle C}{\diagup}}}} \quad \xrightarrow{Br_2} \quad$$

Bridged radicals have also been postulated as intermediates in other reactions. When **3** is treated with bromine under free radical conditions a mixture of **4** and **5** is obtained. The migration of chlorine to give **5** must proceed by way of a bridged radical either as a transition state or as an intermediate. Bromination of **3** under ionic conditions affords the normal adduct:

$$CCl_3CH{=}CH_2 + Br_2 \xrightarrow{h\nu} CCl_3CHBrCH_2Br + CCl_2BrCHClCH_2Br$$

$$\qquad\quad \textbf{3} \qquad\qquad\qquad\qquad \textbf{4} \qquad\qquad\qquad \textbf{5}$$

The free radical addition of hydrogen bromide to **3** leads to a similar result:

$$CCl_3CH{=}CH_2 + HBr \longrightarrow CHCl_2CHClCH_2Br$$

$$\qquad\quad \textbf{3}$$

Hydrogen bromide adds by way of free radical intermediates to a number of olefins, and this addition is frequently stereospecific. Thus, the reaction of hydrogen bromide with propyne leads to *cis*-1-bromopropene **6**, and the reaction of deuterium bromide with *cis*- and *trans*-2-butenes leads to the *threo* and *erythro* adducts, **7** and **8**. All of these additions are *trans*-additions, and they can be explained by assuming bridged radicals as intermediates,

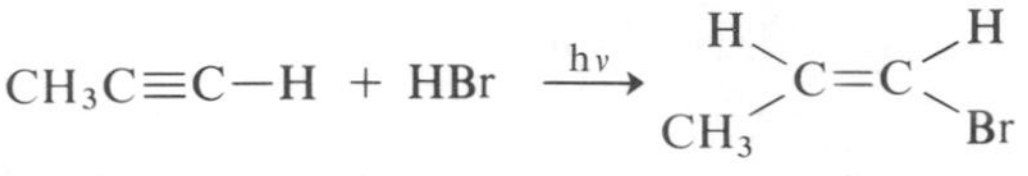

$$CH_3C\equiv C-H + HBr \xrightarrow{h\nu}$$

6

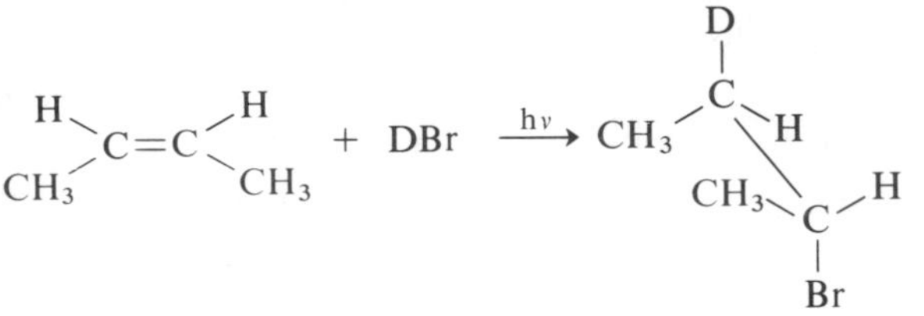

7

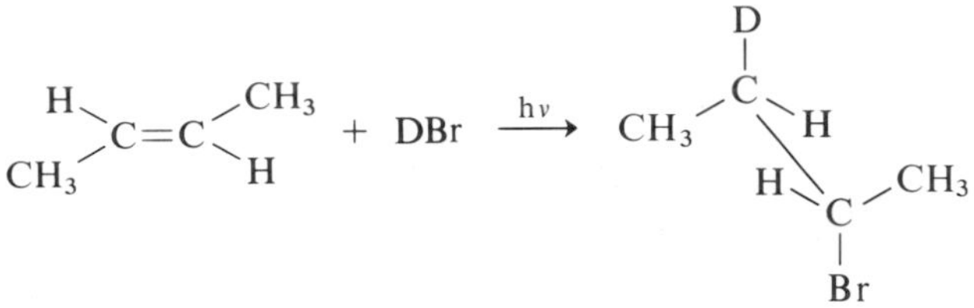

8

Although bridged intermediates account for these stereospecific reactions, such intermediates need not be postulated to explain the experimental results. The data can be explained equally well by assuming planar radicals **9**, slow rotation, and attack from the side opposite the bromine; or by assuming nonplanar radicals **10**, slow rotation, and attack from the less hindered side. Much more work is necessary before any of these other possibilities can be dismissed. The fact that stereospecific *cis*-additions of HBr and Br$_2$ also take place can be used as evidence against the bridged intermediates,

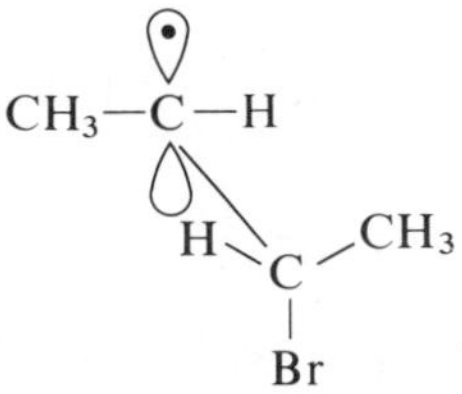

9

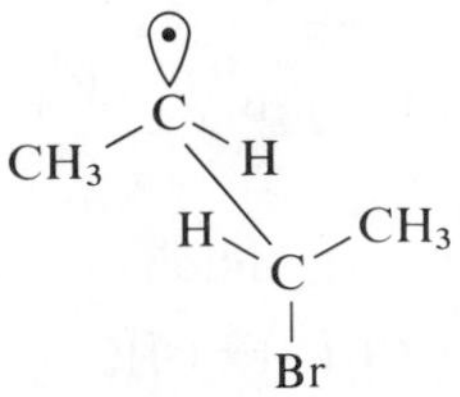

10

Halogen atoms can be introduced into organic systems by reacting a hydro-carbon with molecular halogen, or by treating an alkene with the hydrogen halide or molecular halogen. The first reaction is a free radical process; the second can be conducted under either ionic or free radical conditions. Ionic additions are promoted by polar solvents and Lewis acid catalysts, while the free radical additions are accelerated by light, heat, and free radical initiators such as peroxides, hydroperoxides, tetraethyl lead, and so forth. The products obtained by the different processes are not always the same. The ionic addition of HBr to an alkene proceeds by way of the most stable carbonium ion and leads to the "normal" product. Free radical addition proceeds by way of the most stable free radical and leads to the "abnormal" product:

$$RCH{=}CH_2 + HBr \xrightarrow[\text{radical}]{\text{ionic}} \begin{array}{l} RCHBrCH_3 \\[2mm] RCH_2CH_2Br \end{array}$$

The differences can be more subtle. For example, the *exo* bicyclic system **11** reacts with molecular bromine under ionic conditions to form only the *trans*-product. Under free radical conditions a mixture of *cis*- and *trans*-isomers is produced:

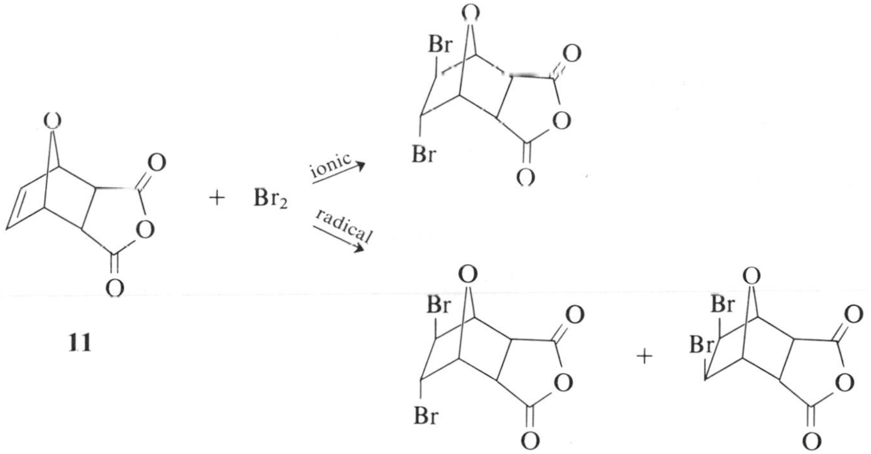

11

Another technique is available for incorporating halogen atoms into organic systems. This procedure employs N-halosuccinimides **12** as the halogenating agents, and the halogen is introduced into the allylic position:

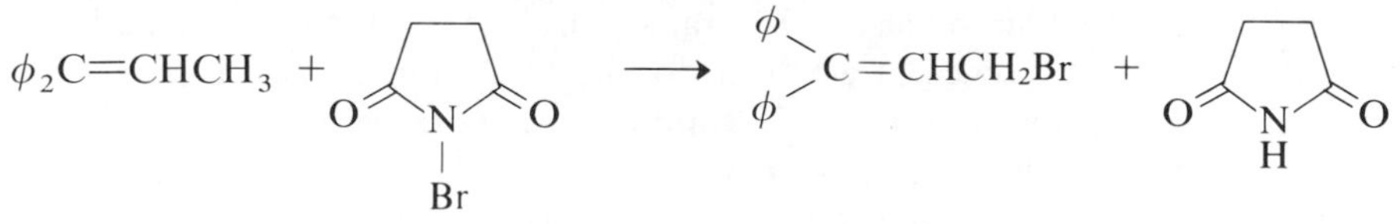

12

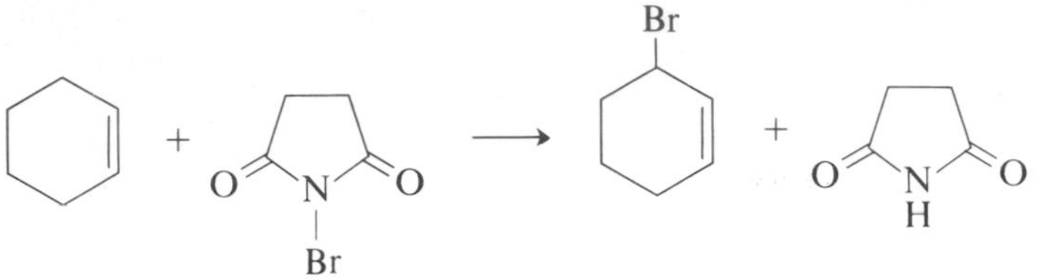

This process, by which a halogen atom is introduced into the allylic position, has widespread synthetic significance, and a rather interesting phenomenon accompanies the halogenation. The reaction is usually carried out as a two-phase reaction with the N-bromosuccinimide insoluble in the solvent. At the start of the reaction the N-bromosuccinimide, being denser than the solvent, is at the bottom of the reaction flask. It reacts, and the product is succinimide, which is lighter than the solvent. Thus, as the reaction proceeds, the crystals of insoluble material rise to the surface. When all of the material has risen, the reaction is complete.

The halogenation is a free radical process involving abstraction of an allylic hydrogen atom and formation of an allylic radical:

$$R\overset{\delta\cdot}{C}H\!=\!\!=\!CH\!=\!\!=\!\overset{\delta\cdot}{C}H_2$$

This allylic radical reacts to form the product. Since both allylic positions are capable of reacting, it is not surprising that in some cases mixtures of products are obtained,

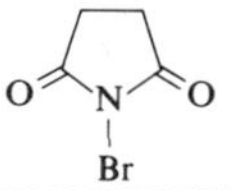

$$C_5H_{11}-CH_2CH\!=\!CH_2 \xrightarrow{\quad} \begin{array}{l} C_5H_{11}-CHBrCH\!=\!CH_2 \\[2mm] C_5H_{11}-CH\!=\!CHCH_2Br \end{array}$$

A study of these reactions is complicated by the fact that the allylic halides formed as products isomerize readily. However, toluene can be brominated in the methyl group by using N-bromosuccinimide as the source of halogen. It appears that this reaction has a polar transition state, for the rate of reaction is promoted by the presence of electron donors and retarded by electron withdrawers in the aromatic system. The value of ρ is negative, and this indicates that the aromatic side chain is electron deficient in the transition state.

Two different mechanisms have been proposed for halogenation by N-bromosuccinimide. The first of these assumes that the material plays a direct role in the reaction:

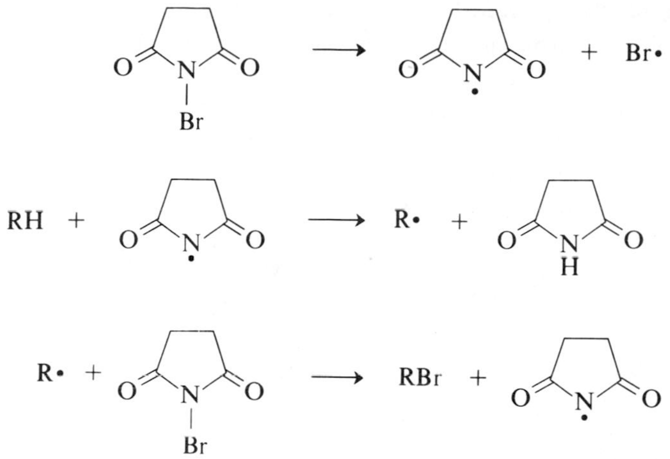

$$\text{(N-bromosuccinimide)} \longrightarrow \text{(succinimidyl radical)} + \text{Br}\cdot$$

$$\text{RH} + \text{(succinimidyl radical)} \longrightarrow \text{R}\cdot + \text{(succinimide, N-H)}$$

$$\text{R}\cdot + \text{(N-bromosuccinimide)} \longrightarrow \text{RBr} + \text{(succinimidyl radical)}$$

The second mechanism assigns no direct role to the material. Instead it is proposed that the compound merely serves as a source of molecular bromine. Since hydrogen bromide is formed when bromine atoms abstract hydrogen atoms,

$$\text{Br}\cdot + \text{RH} \longrightarrow \text{HBr} + \text{R}\cdot$$

and since hydrogen bromide decomposes N-bromosuccinimide according to the equation,

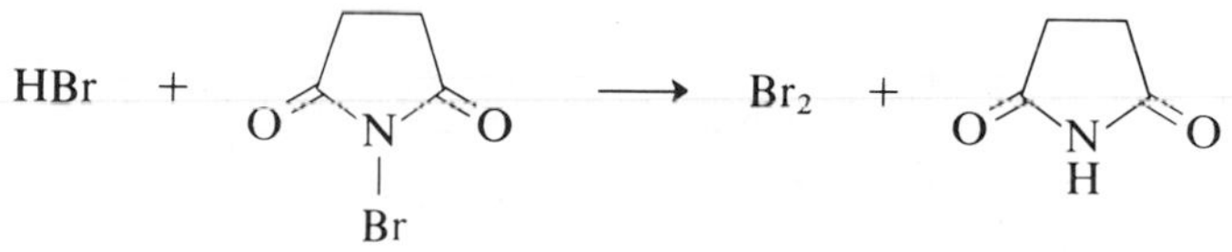

$$\text{HBr} + \text{(N-bromosuccinimide)} \longrightarrow \text{Br}_2 + \text{(succinimide, N-H)}$$

it is assumed that the substance merely serves as a source of molecular bromine in low concentration and that the actual halogenation is accomplished by the bromine:

$$\text{Br}\cdot + \text{RH} \longrightarrow \text{R}\cdot + \text{HBr}$$

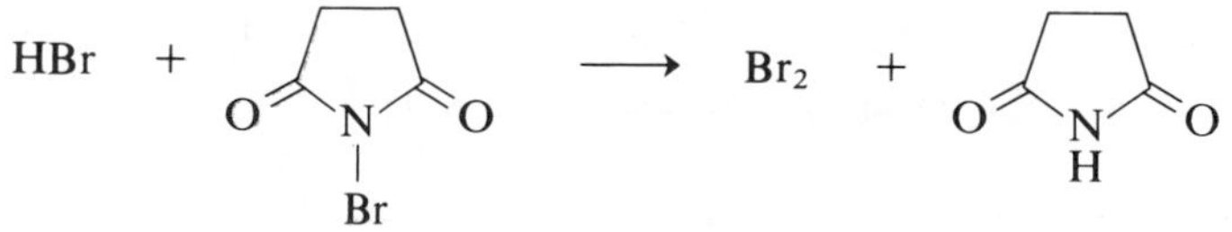

$$\text{HBr} + \text{(N-bromosuccinimide)} \longrightarrow \text{Br}_2 + \text{(succinimide, N-H)}$$

$$\text{R}\cdot + \text{Br}_2 \longrightarrow \text{RBr} + \text{Br}\cdot$$

This second mechanism is generally assumed to be correct. Therefore, one naturally expects brominations by N-bromosuccinimide to be similar to those effected by molecular bromine when the latter is present in low concentration, and there is evidence to show that this is the case. One may well ask why addition to the double bond does not take place, for such behavior is more typical of bromine atoms. It turns out that the addition step is reversible and that when the bromine concentration is low, the radical **13** loses its bromine atom more rapidly than it can react with a molecule of bromine,

$$RCH_2-CH=CH_2 + Br\bullet \rightleftarrows RCH_2-\overset{\bullet}{C}H-CH_2-Br$$

13

The reaction

$$RCH_2-\overset{\bullet}{C}H-CH_2Br + Br_2 \longrightarrow RCH_2CHBrCH_2Br + Br\bullet$$

is slow when the concentration of bromine is low. Loss of the bromine atom takes place instead, and the materials then react according to the equations,

$$RCH_2-CH=CH_2 + Br\bullet \longrightarrow R\overset{\delta\bullet}{C}H \!=\!\!=\! CH \!=\!\!=\! \overset{\delta\bullet}{C}H_2 + HBr$$

and

$$HBr + \underset{\underset{Br}{\overset{|}{N}}}{\overset{O}{\diagup}\diagdown}{}^{O} \longrightarrow Br_2 + \underset{\underset{H}{\overset{|}{N}}}{\overset{O}{\diagup}\diagdown}{}^{O}$$

Other halogenating agents are available. Organic compounds can be chlorinated by alkyl hypohalites, and the use of *t*-butyl hypochlorite **14** as a chlorinating agent has been studied. Under free radical conditions *t*-butyl hypochlorite is moderately selective. Furthermore, it possesses an advantage over molecular chlorine in that it does not produce acidic byproducts.

In most cases this substance also brings about allylic halogenation rather than addition, but it appears that in this instance the *t*-butoxy radical is actively involved in the process:

$$\underset{\underset{\underset{\underset{14}{Cl}}{\overset{|}{O}}}{\overset{|}{CH_3-C-CH_3}}}{\overset{CH_3}{|}} \longrightarrow Cl\bullet + \underset{\underset{\overset{\bullet}{O}}{\overset{|}{CH_3-C-CH_3}}}{\overset{CH_3}{|}}$$

Then,

$$RO\bullet + RH \longrightarrow R\bullet + ROH$$

$$R\bullet + ROCl \longrightarrow RCl + RO\bullet$$

When 1-butene, and *cis*- and *trans*-2-butenes are chlorinated by this material, the products are formed in varying proportions; see Table 20–1.

Table 20–1

	$CH_3CHClCH{=}CH_2$	$\begin{array}{c}H\\ \diagdown\\ CH_3\end{array}C{=}C\begin{array}{c}H\\ \diagup\\ \diagdown CH_2Cl\end{array}$	$\begin{array}{c}H\\ \diagdown\\ CH_3\end{array}C{=}C\begin{array}{c}CH_2Cl\\ \diagup\\ \diagdown H\end{array}$
$CH_3CH_2CH{=}CH_2$	31%	21%–28%	41%–49%
$\begin{array}{c}H\\ \diagdown\\ CH_3\end{array}C{=}C\begin{array}{c}H\\ \diagup\\ \diagdown CH_3\end{array}$	37%	63%	0%
$\begin{array}{c}H\\ \diagdown\\ CH_3\end{array}C{=}C\begin{array}{c}CH_3\\ \diagup\\ \diagdown H\end{array}$	27%	0%	73%

The 1-butene can form either allylic radical, but the *cis*-2-butene forms only the *cis*-radical while the *trans*-2-butene forms only the *trans*-counterpart:

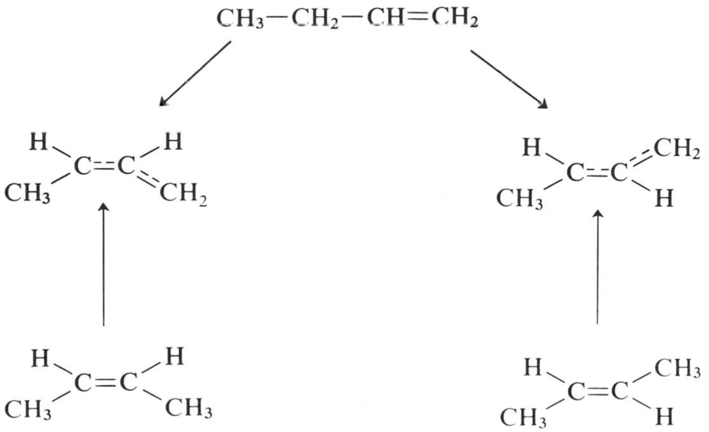

$$CH_3{-}CH_2{-}CH{=}CH_2$$

The fact that the *cis*- and *trans*-radicals maintain their stereochemical integrity and do not isomerize is consistent with the ideas of orbital overlap and stabilization by delocalization of the electrons over the entire system. In order to isomerize, rotation about the central carbon-carbon bond must take place, and this is a high energy process. Orbital overlap in the allylic radical would be destroyed during the process:

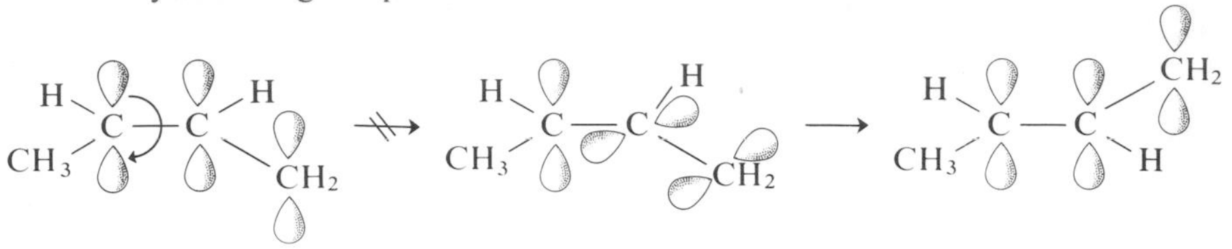

20.2 Polymerization

Polymerization of an unsaturated monomer leads to the formation of a high molecular weight product. These polymers unlike most organic compounds do not have a definite molecular weight. Instead, a polymer is a mixture of related materials with different molecular weights, and one usually speaks of the average molecular weight and the molecular weight distribution when discussing polymers. The physical properties depend not only upon the average molecular weight of the material but also on the molecular weight distribution, and two different materials with the same average molecular weight but different distributions have different properties. The properties also depend upon the molecular weight itself. Even this cannot be determined readily, for it varies with the method used for the determination. When referring to the molecular weight of a polymer, one must also state on what basis this was determined. One frequently refers to the number average molecular weight $\overline{M}_n$ defined by,

$$\overline{M}_n = \frac{\sum_i n_i M_i}{\sum_i n_i}$$

where,

M_i = the molecular weight of a given polymer molecule
n_i = the number of molecules having that molecular weight.

and to the weight average molecular weight $\overline{M}_w$.

$$\overline{M}_w = \frac{\sum_i m_i M_i}{\sum_i m_i}$$

where

m_i = the weight of polymer having a molecular weight M_i.

A simple method for comparing the molecular weights of various polymers is to measure their viscosity. For polymers having similar molecular weight distributions, the lower molecular weight material flows more readily. One heats the polymer to a temperature at which it flows readily and allows the melt to pass through an orifice of given diameter. One determines the weight of material flowing through the orifice during a fixed time period. Since the lower molecular weight material flows more readily, more material passes through. This method, admittedly crude, is rapid. More refined methods are known.

Another phenomenon that affects the behavior of a polymer is its crystallinity. Polymers are heterogeneous materials containing crystalline regions where the polymer chains are regularly oriented and amorphous regions where a random orientation exists. A low degree of crystallinity can be due to the presence of side chains that prevent the formation of a crystalline lattice; hydrogen bonds and other dipole-dipole interactions also exert an influence. Even the rate of cooling of a polymer melt to room temperature affects the crystallinity, and such properties as transparency, hardness, softening point, density, and tensile strength depend upon this characteristic. High density polyethylene produced by the ionic polymerization of ethylene is a more crystalline material than the low density free radically polymerized product, and the two find completely different uses. The low density material contains more side chains generated by the free radical environment under which it is produced. Some of the more common polymers formed by free radical initiation are low density polyethylene, polystyrene, and polyacrylonitrile. The mechanism for these polymerizations involves addition of radicals to the unsaturated linkage:

$$\text{Initiator} \longrightarrow 2R\cdot$$

$$R\cdot + CH_2{=}CHR \longrightarrow R{-}CH_2\overset{\cdot}{C}H \atop \overset{|}{R}$$

$$R{-}CH_2\overset{\cdot}{C}H \atop \overset{|}{R} \; + CH_2{=}CHR \longrightarrow R{-}CH_2{-}\overset{|}{\underset{R}{C}H}{-}CH_2{-}\overset{\cdot}{\underset{R}{C}}H$$

$$R{-}CH_2{-}\overset{|}{\underset{R}{C}H}{-}CH_2{-}\overset{\cdot}{\underset{R}{C}}H \xrightarrow{n(CH_2{=}CHR)} R{-}\left(CH_2{-}\overset{|}{\underset{R}{C}H}\right)_{n+1}{-}CH_2{-}\overset{\cdot}{\underset{R}{C}}H$$

14

This last long chain radical forms the polymer by way of a chain transfer or a terminating step. The terminating reactions are combination and disproportionation:

$$R-\left(CH_2-\underset{\underset{R}{|}}{CH}\right)_{n+1}-CH_2-\overset{\bullet}{CH}_{\underset{R}{|}} + R-\left(CH_2-\underset{\underset{R}{|}}{CH}\right)_m-CH_2-\overset{\bullet}{CH}_{\underset{R}{|}}$$

combination

$$R-\left(CH_2-\underset{\underset{R}{|}}{CH}\right)_{n+2}-\left(\underset{\underset{R}{|}}{CH}-CH_2\right)_{m+1}-R$$

disproportionation

$$R-\left(CH_2-\underset{\underset{R}{|}}{CH}\right)_{n+1}-CH_2CH_2-R + R-\left(CH_2-\underset{\underset{R}{|}}{CH}\right)_m-CH=CHR$$

The chain transfer step is,

$$R-\left(CH_2-\underset{\underset{R}{|}}{CH}\right)_{n+1}-CH_2-\overset{\bullet}{CH}_{\underset{R}{|}} + RH \longrightarrow R\bullet + R-\left(CH_2-\underset{\underset{R}{|}}{CH}\right)_{n+1}-CH_2CH_2R$$

It is possible to decrease the average molecular weight of a polymer by deliberately adding chain transfer agents to the mixture. This increases the probability of chain transfer, thus terminating the old polymer chain at an earlier stage. One polymer chain is terminated, but the reaction yields another radical that is capable of initiating a new one. The average molecular weight of a polymer can be increased by decreasing the concentration of initiator.

Polymers are known in which more than a single monomer has been incorporated into the molecule. One method of synthesizing such copolymers is by graft polymerization, that is, by generating a free radical site on a previously formed polymer and utilizing this free radical to initiate the polymerization of a second monomer. This leads to copolymers composed of two large units, one of each monomer,

$$(M_1)_a M_1(M_1)_b + R\bullet \longrightarrow (M_1)_a \overset{\bullet}{M_1}(M_1)_b$$

$$(M_1)_a \overset{\bullet}{M_1}(M_1)_b + M_2 \longrightarrow (M_1)_a \underset{\underset{\overset{|}{\overset{\bullet}{M_2}}}{}}{M_1}(M_1)_b$$

$$(M_1)_a \underset{\underset{\overset{|}{\overset{\bullet}{M_2}}}{}}{M_1}(M_1)_b + cM_2 \longrightarrow (M_1)_a \underset{\underset{(M_2)_{c+1}}{|}}{M_1}(M_1)_b$$

Another method consists of copolymerizing two monomers to form a single polymer chain, and this leads to a molecule containing M_1 and M_2 either in a random distribution **15** or in an alternating pattern **16**:

$$M_1M_1M_1M_2M_2M_1M_1M_2M_1M_2M_2M_2M_2M_1$$

15

$$M_1M_2M_1M_2M_1M_2M_1M_2M_1M_2M_1M_2M_1M_2$$

16

Since it is important to know the extent to which these processes, **15** and **16**, take place, theories have been developed to enable us to predict the result of a copolymerization. Consider two monomers M_1 and M_2 that are copolymerizing to form a long chain polymer molecule. During the polymerization the odd electron of the polymer radical is on the last unit of the chain. We have long chains terminating in either an M_1 radical, designated as $M_1\cdot$, or an M_2 radical represented by $M_2\cdot$. These long chain radicals $M_1\cdot$ and $M_2\cdot$ extend the chain by adding more monomer. We assume that the ability of the polymer radical to discriminate between M_1 and M_2 depends upon the unit bearing the odd electron and is independent of the rest of the chain. Thus all chains $M_1\cdot$ will react with M_1 at the same rate, and of course, the same applies to addition of M_2, and to reactions for $M_2\cdot$. There are then four possible routes for extension of the chain:

$$M_1\cdot + M_1 \xrightarrow{k_{11}} M_1\cdot$$
$$M_1\cdot + M_2 \xrightarrow{k_{12}} M_2\cdot$$
$$M_2\cdot + M_1 \xrightarrow{k_{21}} M_1\cdot$$
$$M_2\cdot + M_2 \xrightarrow{k_{22}} M_2\cdot$$

The decrease in the concentration of M_1 is given by,

$$-\frac{d[M_1]}{dt} = k_{11}[M_1\cdot][M_1] + k_{21}[M_2\cdot][M_1]$$

While the disappearance of M_2 follows the rate expression,

$$-\frac{d[M_2]}{dt} = k_{12}[M_1\cdot][M_2] + k_{22}[M_2\cdot][M_2]$$

The ratio of these expressions is time independent and yields the result,

$$\frac{d[M_1]}{d[M_2]} = \frac{k_{11}[M_1\cdot][M_1] + k_{21}[M_2\cdot][M_1]}{k_{12}[M_1\cdot][M_2] + k_{22}[M_2\cdot][M_2]}$$

We next assume a steady state in $M_1\cdot$ and $M_2\cdot$, that is, we assume that $M_1\cdot$ is being converted to $M_2\cdot$ at the same rate that $M_2\cdot$ is converted to $M_1\cdot$. Then,

$$k_{12}[M_1\cdot][M_2] = k_{21}[M_2\cdot][M_1]$$

and substituting this into the previous expression affords,

$$\frac{d[M_1]}{d[M_2]} = \frac{k_{11}[M_1\cdot][M_1] + k_{12}[M_1\cdot][M_2]}{k_{21}[M_2\cdot][M_1] + k_{22}[M_2\cdot][M_2]}$$

or

$$\frac{d[M_1]}{d[M_2]} = \frac{[M_1\cdot]}{[M_2\cdot]}\left(\frac{k_{11}[M_1] + k_{12}[M_2]}{k_{21}[M_1] + k_{22}[M_2]}\right)$$

Now, multiplying the first term in the numerator by k_{12}/k_{12} and then factoring k_{12} leads to,

$$\frac{d[M_1]}{d[M_2]} = \frac{k_{12}[M_1\cdot]}{[M_2\cdot]}\left(\frac{\dfrac{k_{11}}{k_{12}}[M_1] + [M_2]}{k_{21}[M_1] + k_{22}[M_2]}\right)$$

Carrying out a similar operation with k_{21}/k_{21} in the second term of the denominator affords,

$$\frac{d[M_1]}{d[M_2]} = \frac{k_{12}[M_1\cdot]}{k_{21}[M_2\cdot]}\left(\frac{\dfrac{k_{11}}{k_{12}}[M_1] + [M_2]}{[M_1] + \dfrac{k_{22}}{k_{21}}[M_2]}\right)$$

From the steady state assumption we know that,

$$\frac{k_{12}[M_1\cdot]}{k_{21}[M_2\cdot]} = \frac{[M_1]}{[M_2]}$$

and this leads to the result,

$$\frac{d[M_1]}{d[M_2]} = \frac{[M_1]}{[M_2]}\left(\frac{\dfrac{k_{11}}{k_{12}}[M_1] + [M_2]}{[M_1] + \dfrac{k_{22}}{k_{21}}[M_2]}\right)$$

This expression gives the relative rate of incorporation of two monomers M_1 and M_2 into the polymer chain, and the rate of incorporation depends upon the concentrations of these monomers and the specific rate constants for their reaction. The ratios k_{11}/k_{12} and k_{22}/k_{21} are usually represented by the symbols r_1 and r_2:

$$r_1 = \frac{k_{11}}{k_{12}}$$

$$r_2 = \frac{k_{22}}{k_{21}}$$

If r_1 is greater than unity, this implies that $M_1\cdot$ prefers to react with M_1 rather than M_2. If r_1 is equal to unity, $M_1\cdot$ reacts equally readily with both M_1 and M_2; it shows no discrimination. But r_1 less than unity, indicates that $M_1\cdot$ reacts more readily with M_2. An analogous interpretation is given to r_2; r_2 greater than unity indicates a preference for M_2, and so forth.

For most copolymers, both r_1 and r_2 are less than unity. Therefore, $M_1\cdot$ reacts more readily with M_2, while $M_2\cdot$ reacts preferably with M_1, and this leads to polymeric chains consisting largely of alternating units of M_1 and M_2.

20.3 Free Radical Rearrangements

A number of interesting free radical rearrangements and free radical decompositions are known. In these reactions, as in their ionic counterparts, changes in the carbon skeletal network take place. When β-pinene **17** is treated with a variety of different reagents under free radical conditions, the four-membered ring opens and alkenes such as **18** are formed:

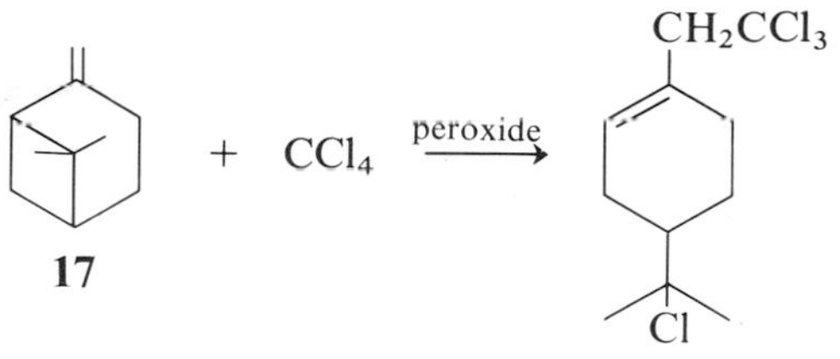

The mechanism for the transformation involves attack of the alkene by $CCl_3\cdot$,

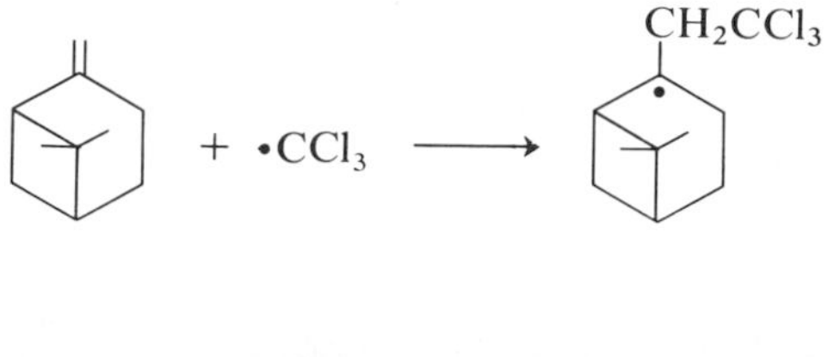

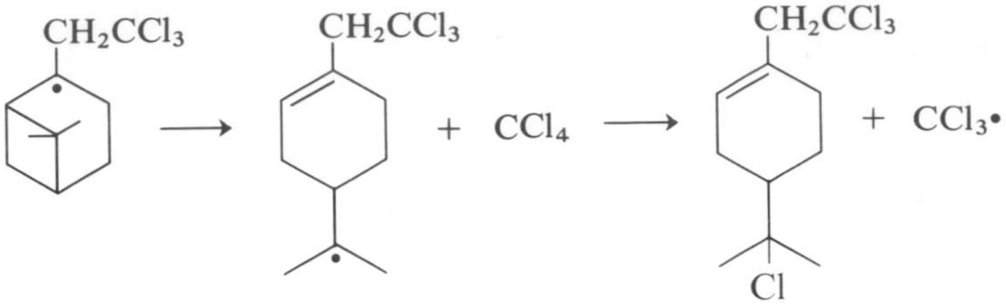

The reaction of β-pinene with chloroform under free radical conditions also leads to a rearranged product, and materials such as $BrCH_2COOEt$, and CCl_3CHO afford analogous results. Carbon tetrachloride adds to most alkenes under free radical conditions, and with butadiene at 110°C, the 1,4-adduct results:

$$CH_2{=}CH{-}CH{=}CH_2 + CCl_4 \longrightarrow CH_2ClCH{=}CHCH_2CCl_3$$

Aldehydes are known to react with halogens under radical conditions, and α,α-dichloropropanal **19** is reported to yield the corresponding acid chloride with chlorine, while free radical bromination of the α,β-unsaturated material **20** leads to the acid bromide:

$$CH_3CCl_2CHO + Cl_2 \longrightarrow CH_3CCl_2COCl$$
$$\mathbf{19}$$

and,

$$CCl_2{=}CHCHO + Br_2 \longrightarrow CCl_2{=}CHCOBr$$
$$\mathbf{20}$$

The mechanism,

$$Cl_2 \longrightarrow 2Cl\bullet$$
$$RCHO + Cl\bullet \longrightarrow RCO\bullet + HCl$$
$$RCO\bullet + Cl_2 \longrightarrow RCOCl + Cl\bullet$$

accounts for the observed results.

When radicals of the type $RCO\bullet$ are generated in the absence of a suitable reagent, decarbonylation occurs:

$$RCO\bullet \longrightarrow R\bullet + CO$$

Thus, the peroxide initiated decomposition of **21** leads to mixtures of *t*-butyl- and isobutylbenzene:

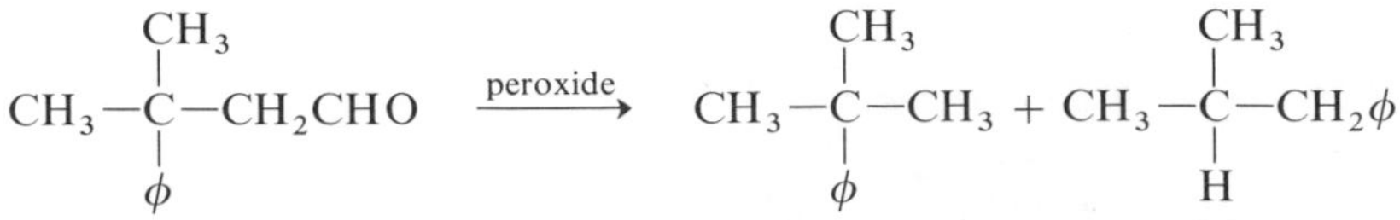

The results can be explained in terms of a decarbonylation of the initial radical to yield a new radical that forms the final products,

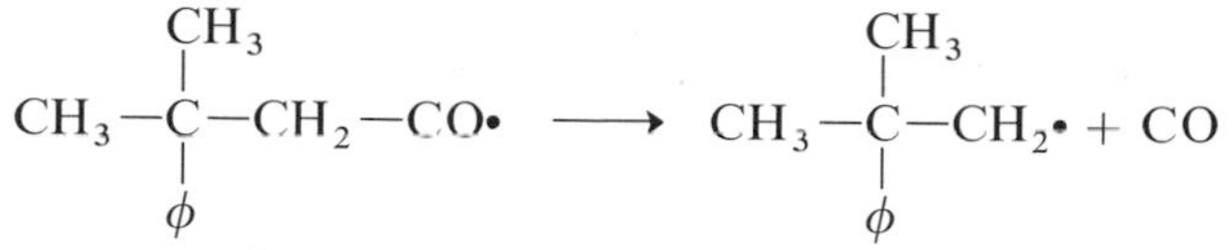

$$CH_3-\underset{\underset{\phi}{|}}{\overset{\overset{CH_3}{|}}{C}}-CH_2-CO\bullet \longrightarrow CH_3-\underset{\underset{\phi}{|}}{\overset{\overset{CH_3}{|}}{C}}-CH_2\bullet + CO$$

and

$$CH_3-\underset{\underset{\phi}{|}}{\overset{\overset{CH_3}{|}}{C}}-CH_2\bullet \longrightarrow CH_3-\underset{\underset{\phi}{\bullet}}{\overset{\overset{CH_3}{|}}{C}}-CH_2\phi$$

$$CH_3-\underset{\underset{\phi}{|}}{\overset{\overset{CH_3}{|}}{C}}-CH_2CHO \qquad\qquad CH_3-\underset{\underset{\phi}{|}}{\overset{\overset{CH_3}{|}}{C}}-CH_2CHO$$

$$CH_3-\underset{\underset{\phi}{|}}{\overset{\overset{CH_3}{|}}{C}}-CH_3 \qquad\qquad CH_3-\underset{\underset{H}{|}}{\overset{\overset{CH_3}{|}}{C}}-CH_2\phi$$

$$+ \qquad\qquad\qquad\qquad +$$

$$CH_3-\underset{\underset{\phi}{|}}{\overset{\overset{CH_3}{|}}{C}}-CH_2CO\bullet \qquad CH_3-\underset{\underset{\phi}{|}}{\overset{\overset{CH_3}{|}}{C}}-CH_2CO\bullet$$

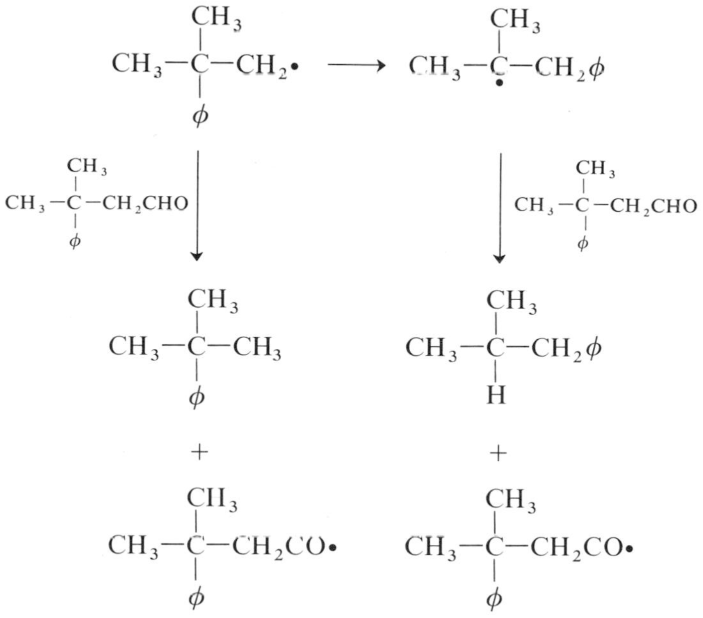

The isobutylbenzene results from a migration of phenyl, and a species such as

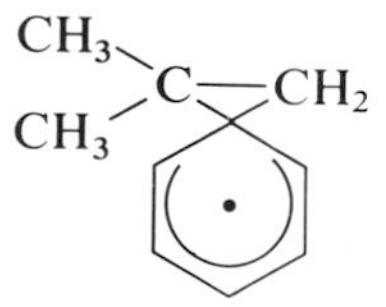

$$\underset{CH_3}{\overset{CH_3}{\diagdown}}C{=\!=\!=}CH_2$$

must be involved either as a transition state or as an intermediate.

This migration has been studied in detail. The possibility of a concerted formation of the bridged intermediate has been eliminated. Migratory aptitudes for substituted phenyl groups and a ρ value for the process have been obtained. It is found that the ρ value is positive, and therefore, in the transition state for phenyl migration, the aromatic ring must bear a partial negative charge. Although the process involves the conversion of one radical to another, a transition state with some polar character must be written.

Aryl groups are observed to migrate during radical reactions but analogous behavior on the part of alkyl groups is seldom observed. It is interesting to note that free radical additions to bicyclic systems frequently result in *exo* products, yet no evidence of skeletal rearrangement is found. Thus, the photochemical addition of acetone to norbornylene yields the *exo* product as does the reaction with *para* thiocresol:

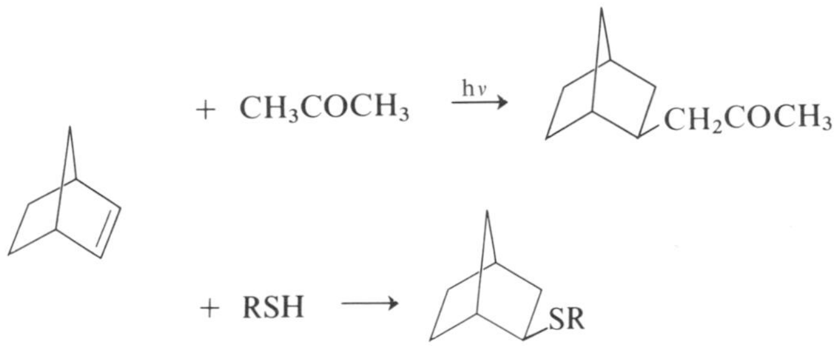

$$+ \quad CH_3COCH_3 \quad \xrightarrow{h\nu}$$

$$+ \quad RSH \quad \longrightarrow$$

A number of thermal isomerizations are known; for example, β-pinene is reported to yield **22**, and the cyclopropyl system **23** isomerizes to the phenol:

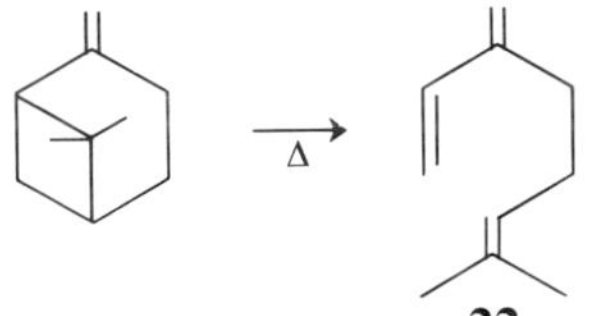

22

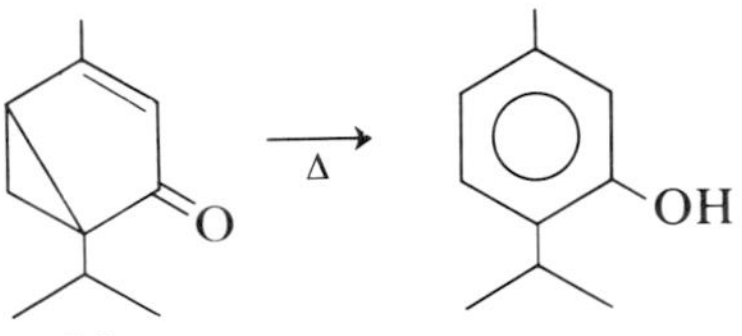

23

Some thermal isomerizations proceed by way of diradical intermediates while others appear to be concerted processes with rupture of the old bond and formation of the new one taking place simultaneously. It is sometimes possible to distinguish between these two processes by determining $\Delta H^{\ddagger}$ and $\Delta S^{\ddagger}$ for the isomerization. A reaction proceeding by way of a diradical intermediate exhibits a larger $\Delta H^{\ddagger}$ but a more favorable $\Delta S^{\ddagger}$ than a concerted process. The transition state in the diradical process is less constrained than that in the concerted reaction, and this results in a more favorable $\Delta S^{\ddagger}$. On the other hand, if diradicals are formed prior to or in the rate limiting step, $\Delta H^{\ddagger}$ will be larger; in these cases it must at least equal the bond dissociation energy for the bond being ruptured and is usually larger.

The isomerizations of cyclopropane and its derivatives have been studied in detail. Cyclopropane decomposes thermally into propene:

$$\triangle \xrightarrow{\Delta} CH_3CH=CH_2$$

The reaction involves ring opening and migration of a hydrogen atom. Either step could be rate limiting or the isomerization could be concerted. The term $\Delta S^{\ddagger}$ indicates that a diradical is formed but gives no information concerning the rate limiting step:

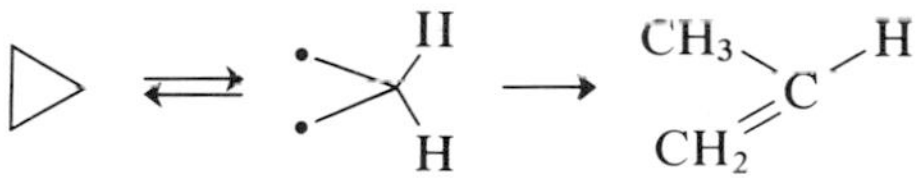

$$\triangleright \rightleftharpoons \cdot \overset{H}{\underset{H}{\times}} \cdot \longrightarrow \overset{CH_3}{\underset{CH_2}{\diagdown}} C \overset{H}{\diagup}$$

However, the fact that **24** and **25** are partially equilibrated under the reaction conditions, and that hexadeuterocyclopropane shows a primary kinetic isotope effect implies that hydrogen migration is rate limiting,

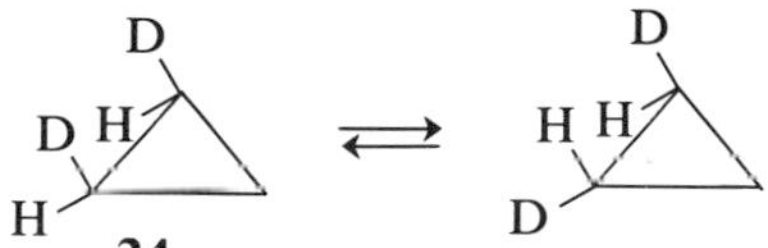

$$\underset{24}{\overset{D\ H}{\underset{H}{\diagup}}\triangle} \rightleftharpoons \underset{25}{\overset{H\ H}{\underset{D}{\diagup}}\triangle}$$

At the pressures usually employed for this reaction, migration of hydrogen is the rate limiting step; however, the reaction can be made to follow different kinetics under certain conditions. In order to form the diradical, cyclopropane must first become vibrationally excited. It does this by colliding with other molecules. This vibrational excitation of cyclopropane by way of collision can be written as,

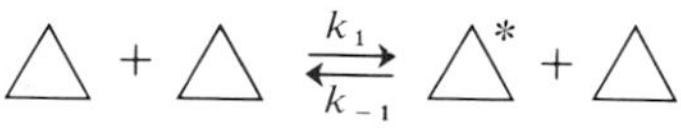

$$\triangle + \triangle \underset{k_{-1}}{\overset{k_1}{\rightleftharpoons}} \triangle^* + \triangle$$

Of course, subsequent collisions of $\triangle^*$ with less energetic molecules deactivate this species. In addition, the excited molecule opens up to the diradical $\overset{\cdot}{\wedge}\cdot$

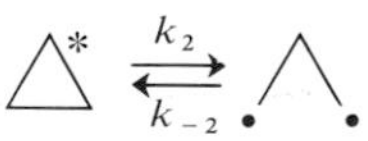

$$\triangle^* \underset{k_{-2}}{\overset{k_2}{\rightleftharpoons}} \overset{\cdot}{\wedge}\cdot$$

This unimolecular decomposition leads to a diradical that then isomerizes to propene.

$$\overset{\cdot}{\wedge}\cdot \xrightarrow{k_3} CH_3CH=CH_2$$

The general rate expression can be obtained by using the steady state approximation and the fact that

$$-\frac{d[\triangle]}{dt} = \frac{d[CH_3CH{=}CH_2]}{dt}$$

The resultant general rate expression is,

$$\frac{d[CH_3CH{=}CH_2]}{dt} = \frac{k_1 k_2 k_3 [\triangle]^2}{(k_{-1}k_{-2} + k_{-1}k_3)[\triangle] + k_2 k_3}$$

While this expression appears complex, it can be written in the simple form,

$$\frac{d[CH_3CH{=}CH_2]}{dt} = \frac{a[\triangle]^2}{b[\triangle] + c}$$

where a, b, and c are composite terms.

The concentration of cyclopropane enters into both the numerator and denominator of the general rate expression. When this concentration is sufficiently high, the term $b[\triangle]$ is much greater than c, and the reaction appears to be first order. On the other hand, at very low concentrations of cyclopropane, c is larger, and the process is expected to follow second order kinetics. Under these conditions the species goes on to propene more readily than it is deactivated. The general rate expression becomes simply,

$$\frac{d[CH_3CH{=}CH_2]}{dt} = k_1 [\triangle]^2$$

and the rate limiting step is activation by collision.

When activation by collision is rate limiting, adding chemically inert molecules to the system brings about rate acceleration. Adding molecules increases the number of collisions and enhances the rate of product formation. Although many examples of this type of behavior are known, not all added molecules are equally effective at providing activation. The effectiveness of an added molecule in activating cyclopropane to the vibrationally excited state required for radical formation varies with the material. Nor are all molecules equally good at quenching the excited cyclopropane after it has formed. It is possible to tabulate the efficiency of added materials by calculating collision diameters and collision cross sections σ.

Cyclopropane is a gas at ordinary temperatures and gas phase collisions are less frequent than collisions in solution. Molecules of the solvent provide ample opportunity for collision when a reaction is conducted in the liquid phase.

Free radical reactions play an important role in preparative organic chemistry. In addition, much information concerning the behavior of molecules comes from their study. Certainly, polymer research has stimulated investigations in free radical chemistry, and a large number of advances have recently been made.

20.4 Organic Photochemistry

Reactions are known that are initiated by irradiating organic compounds with light of frequency v. Absorption of this light leads to a gain in energy by the absorbing molecule equal to hv. The molecule enters an excited state, and the energy gained is equal to the energy of the light absorbed:

$$\Delta E = hv$$

The excited molecule, in order to regain some stability, undergoes certain chemical and physical reactions.

When an excited state is deactivated to a lower energy state by transferring energy to other components in the system, thus preventing some more desirable process from taking place, the excited state is said to suffer quenching. Since quenching involves energy transfer, the process certainly depends upon the concentration of the recipient molecule. Furthermore, not all molecules are equally effective quenchers, and one usually speaks of quenching cross sections σ_Q to express their efficiency. The larger the quenching cross section the more effective is the recipient molecule as a quencher. This idea can be stated as a probability that quenching will take place when a given molecule is introduced into the presence of an excited molecule. However, one difficulty is that quenching takes place by a number of different pathways, and it would be desirable to separate the various mechanisms for deactivation and speak of cross sections for each process. This has not yet been possible. For the reaction between an excited molecule M^* and a quencher Q, the quenching cross section σ_Q is given by collision theory:

$$M^* + Q \xrightarrow{k_2} M + Q + T \text{ (translational kinetic energy)}$$

The quenching cross section for this reaction is,

$$\sigma_Q = \frac{10^3}{4N}\left(\frac{\pi\mu}{8kT}\right)^{1/2} k_2$$

The term N is Avogadro's number, and the quantity $10^3/N$ converts the number of effective collisions per cubic centimeter into units of moles per liter. The quantity μ is the reduced mass $(m_M m_Q / m_M + m_Q)$ while $(\pi\mu/8kT)^{1/2}$ is the reciprocal of the average velocity; k is Boltzmann's constant.

These quenching cross sections also apply to reactions involving thermal excitation, for any excited molecule can be quenched by collision. The previous example was an ideal process where the quencher Q deactivated M^* without a chemical reaction accompanying the process and where the excess energy was converted completely to translational kinetic energy. It frequently occurs that chemical reactions do accompany deactivation; however, quenching cross sections can still be determined.

Mercury can be converted readily into a number of electronically excited states. One of these states, an excited triplet Hg*, and the quenching reactions of this species, have been studied in detail. It appears that electron donation by the quenching molecule is a desirable property in the reaction, for the quenching cross section increases with electron donating ability. Methane is a poor quencher, water better, and ammonia is better than either. However, compounds such as PH_3 and H_2S containing second row elements have greater cross sections than any of these. When olefins are utilized, the cross section increases with the electron donating ability of the alkene. The data in Table 20–2 indicate that the mercury atom is electrophilic in this excited state.

Table 20–2

Compound	σ_Q
CH_4	0.06
H_2O	1.00
NH_3	2.94
H_2S	23.0
PH_3	26.2
$CH_2{=}CH_2$	26
$CH_3CH{=}CH_2$	32
$(CH_3)_2C{=}C(CH_3)_2$	43

Other phenomena such as fluorescence and phosphorescence are of interest, and processes such as internal conversion and intersystem crossing must also be considered. A number of processes can take place between the time radiation is absorbed by a molecule and its reemission. These changes alter the frequency and therefore the energy of the emitted radiation. Furthermore, to the extent that these processes occur, they prevent the molecule from undergoing chemical reaction, for they dissipate the energy. Possible routes for deactivation of an excited molecule are presented in Figure 20–1.

A molecule in the ground state S_0 absorbs electromagnetic radiation and enters the singlet excited state S_2. It can enter this state both vibrationally and rotationally excited; however, loss of this excess vibrational and rotational energy to the environment is possible. The molecule remains electronically excited in the state S_2, and it may then, by internal conversion, enter an upper level of the state S_1. No energy is lost during this transition, and no radiation is emitted. The process is accordingly called a radiationless transition. The S_1 state is a lower energy state; however, since no energy is assumed to be lost, the molecule must enter an upper level of this state. Internal conversions are nonradiative transitions between states of like multiplicity, that is, singlet–singlet transitions or triplet–triplet transitions. Now a molecule in an upper level of S_1, again loses its excess vibrational and rotational energy to the environment and it can return to the ground state by emission of radiation.

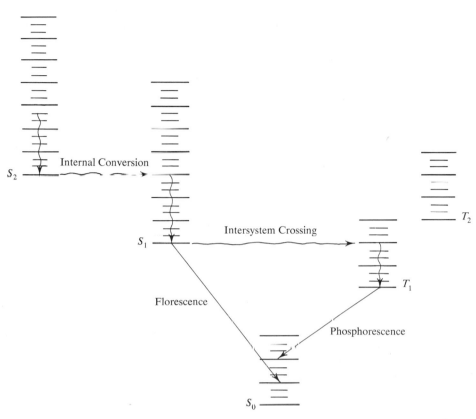

Figure 20–1

This process, singlet–singlet conversion, accompanied by emission of radiation is called fluorescence. A triplet–triplet conversion accompanied by emission of electromagnetic radiation is also called fluorescence.

Other possible routes for the deactivation of singlet excited states are inter-system (singlet–triplet) crossings followed by phosphorescence. Intersystem crossings and phosphorescence, which are singlet–triplet conversions, are in principle spin forbidden. However, changes in spin multiplicity are observed with diminished intensity and can be attributed to spin-orbital coupling. Phosphorescence is a radiative transition between states of different spin multiplicity; hence, the process ought to take place slowly. The molecule is expected to spend some time in the state T_1 before it is able to emit radiation and enter S_0. Consequently, the lifetime of T_1 is expected to be relatively long, and the radiation may well be emitted at some time after removal of the external electromagnetic field.

One frequently refers to the quantum yield in a process and two types of quantum yields should be considered. The primary quantum yield ϕ is the number of molecules emitting or chemically reacting from a particular excited state divided by the number of quanta ($h\nu$) absorbed. The total quantum yield Φ is the number of product molecules formed per quantum of energy absorbed.

20.5 Photochemical Reactions

Although a number of photochemically initiated reactions are known, those most interesting to the organic chemist involve reactions of organic compounds having an electron in an antibonding molecular orbital π^*.

The two π electrons in ethylene occupy the molecular orbital,

$$\psi_1 = \frac{1}{\sqrt{2}}(p_1 + p_2)$$

This orbital is a bonding orbital; there exists another orbital, the antibonding orbital, that is vacant:

$$\psi_2 = \frac{1}{\sqrt{2}}(p_1 - p_2)$$

In the ground state of ethylene both electrons occupy ψ_1 (designated hereafter as π). However, irradiation of this alkene causes one of the electrons to be promoted into ψ_2 (henceforth designated as π^*). This is shown in Figure 20–2.

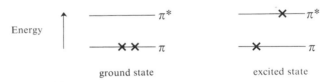

Figure 20–2

Other orbitals are present. For example, the electrons in the carbon-hydrogen bonds occupy σ bond molecular orbitals, and both σ and σ^* orbitals exist. We shall not consider these further.

There are two different excited states in ethylene; an excited state S_1 in which the two electrons, although in different orbitals, still have opposite spins, and a state T_1 where the two π electrons have parallel spins. The triplet state has lower energy due to the decreased interelectronic repulsion in this state. In S_0 both electrons occupy π. In S_1 and T_1, one electron occupies π and the other is in π^*. However, the spins are different in the two excited states; see Figure 20–3.

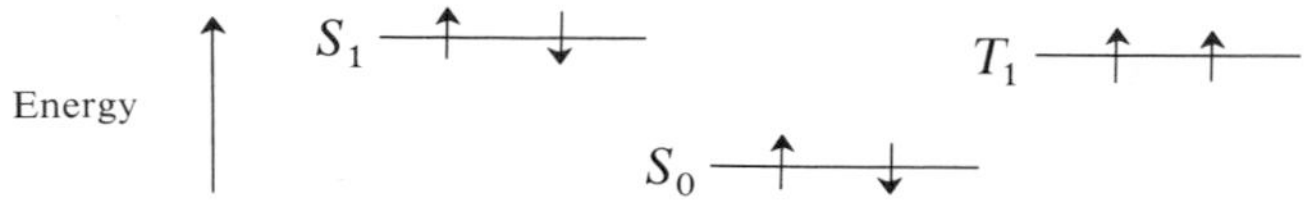

Figure 20–3

In addition to π—π^* transitions, n—π^* transitions frequently take place. In a carbonyl compound such as formaldehyde, there are, in addition to the σ electrons, the two π electrons in the carbonyl bond and the unshared electrons on the oxygen atom. The two π electrons occupy the bonding π bond molecular orbital, and there is a vacant π^* antibonding molecular orbital. Excitation of one of the π electrons into the π^* orbital is a π—π^* transition (singlet and triplet states are possible). The unshared electrons associated with the oxygen atom can also be excited into the π^* orbital. These unshared electrons occupy nonbonding orbitals n, and it is possible to promote one of these electrons into the antibonding orbital of the carbonyl group. This transition is an n—π^* excitation:

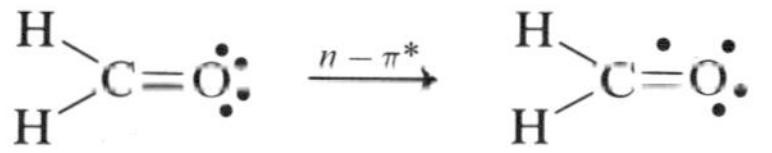

In the excited state resulting from the n—π^* transition, an electron that was originally associated with the oxygen atom is now being shared by the carbon atom and the oxygen atom; therefore, the electron density at the oxygen atom has decreased while that at the carbon atom has increased. In addition, the polarization of the antibonding electron is towards carbon, and this differs considerably from the polarization observed in the ground state. We indicate in the following structure the polarization of the antibonding electron,

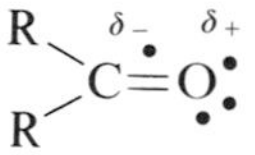

Both n—π^* and π—π^* transitions can lead to excited singlets and excited triplets, and energy-level diagrams of the various states generally appear as presented in Figure 20–4.

Since the electrons in the bonding π molecular orbital of the carbonyl group are more stable than the electrons in the nonbonding orbitals, excitation to the state S (n—π^*) requires less energy than the transition leading to S (π—π^*). Furthermore, interelectronic repulsion decreases in proceeding to the triplets; therefore, the triplet states are of lower energy than the corresponding singlets.

The general scheme presented here by no means applies in all cases; however, it does apply for a number of carbonyl systems.

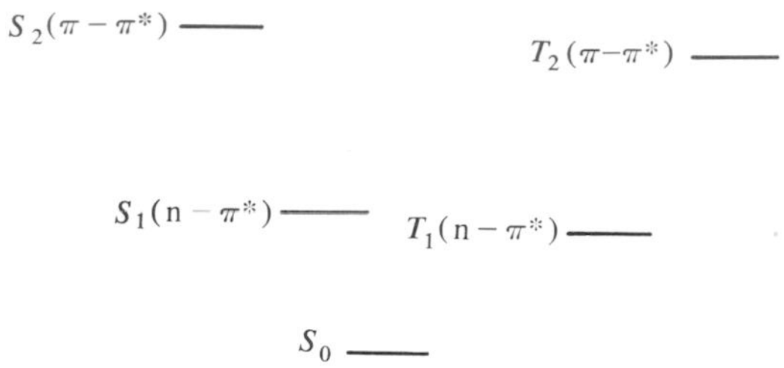

$$S_2(\pi - \pi^*) \; \text{———}$$

$$T_2(\pi-\pi^*) \; \text{———}$$

$$S_1(n - \pi^*) \; \text{———}$$

$$T_1(n - \pi^*) \; \text{———}$$

$$S_0 \; \text{———}$$

Figure 20–4

Alkenes and carbonyl compounds absorb radiation of frequency v and are converted into high energy species. These metastable states can lose this excess energy by any of the physical processes described earlier—quenching, phosphorescence, fluorescence, and so forth. Alternatively, excitation leads to dissociation of the molecule or to subsequent chemical reaction. In solution, the solvent can influence the course of a reaction, for molecular collisions are frequent when solvent molecules are present. Quenching and chemical reactions with the solvent proceed rapidly. Furthermore, the solvent need not participate directly in order to influence the outcome of a reaction, for the solvent also exerts a cage effect. Excited molecules may dissociate, but the radicals that result are held in close proximity by the solvent cage. This favors recombination followed by one or more of the physical processes. In the vapor phase where molecular collisions are less frequent, dissociation takes place without subsequent recombination. For example, acetone in the vapor phase, when irradiated with light of appropriate frequency, dissociates into acetyl radicals and methyl radicals:

$$\underset{\text{CH}_3\overset{\text{O}}{\overset{\|}{\text{C}}}\text{CH}_3}{} \xrightarrow{h\nu} \text{CH}_3\overset{\text{O}}{\overset{\|}{\text{C}}}\text{CH}_3^*$$

$$\text{CH}_3\overset{\text{O}}{\overset{\|}{\text{C}}}\text{CH}_3^* \longrightarrow \text{CH}_3{-}\overset{\text{O}}{\overset{\|}{\text{C}}}{\cdot} + \text{CH}_3{\cdot}$$

$$\text{CH}_3\overset{\text{O}}{\overset{\|}{\text{C}}}{\cdot} \longrightarrow \text{CH}_3{\cdot} + \text{CO}$$

The initial products of the decomposition are acetyl radicals and methyl radicals. The former ultimately lose carbon monoxide and are themselves converted into methyl radicals. These eventually combine to form ethane:

$$2\text{CH}_3{\cdot} \longrightarrow \text{C}_2\text{H}_6$$

Dissociation is not the only chemical process that an excited molecule can undergo. The reactions of these metastable materials are interesting and unusual, and in many cases they afford products that could not have been prepared in any other way.

The chemically active excited state of benzophenone ϕ_2CO is a diradical state, and the reactions of this species are typical radical reactions. This excited state can, in fact, be used to convert other ground state molecules into triplets, and the process serves as a convenient method for generating a triplet system.

Benzophenone undergoes a π—π^* transition to form an excited singlet S (π—π^*). This species suffers internal conversion to the more stable singlet S (n—π^*). By using radiation of appropriate frequency, it is possible to excite benzophenone directly to the S (n—π^*) state. The molecule in the state S (n—π^*) by intersystem crossing affords the triplet T (n—π^*). The yield of triplet is excellent, and this by reacting with other molecules transforms them into triplets. The process is known as spin conservation.

When a triplet reacts with a ground state singlet, the total spin angular momentum remains unaltered. The energy transfer process involves the conversion of benzophenone into its ground state singlet while the ground state molecule is converted into the triplet state. The reaction is illustrated for cyclopentadiene:

$$\phi_2C \doteq \ddot{O} . \; + \; \underset{}{\boxed{}} \; \longrightarrow \; \phi_2C = \ddot{O} . \; + \; . \underset{}{\boxed{}} .$$

This process can be employed in preparative organic chemistry, for it is frequently difficult to generate such interesting intermediates in any other way. Benzophenone reacts from the state $T(n$—$\pi^*)$. Since it is a diradical, it behaves in a fashion similar to other radicals, and the ability of this state to abstract hydrogen atoms parallels the ability of free radicals to do so. It appears in these cases that the unpaired electron associated with the oxygen atom is involved. The system behaves like an alkoxy radical. The resulting product is an alkyl radical which subsequently couples or undergoes some other radical reaction:

$$\phi_2C = O \; \xrightarrow{h\nu} \; \phi_2C \doteq \ddot{O} .$$

$$\phi_2C \doteq \ddot{O} . + R - H \; \longrightarrow \; \phi_2\dot{C} - \ddot{O} - H + R \cdot$$

When two radicals of the type $\phi_2\dot{C}OH$ combine, the product is benzpinacol,

$$2\phi_2C \cdot \; \longrightarrow \; \phi - \underset{OH}{\overset{\phi}{\underset{|}{\overset{|}{C}}}} - \underset{OH}{\overset{\phi}{\underset{|}{\overset{|}{C}}}} - \phi$$

When *ortho* methylbenzophenone is irradiated, it is converted into its enol **26**. This intermediate then undergoes a Diels-Alder reaction, and the adduct dehydrates readily to the substituted naphthalene **27**. The Diels-Alder reaction was used to trap **26**, thereby showing that it actually was the product of the irradiation. The first step, the enolization to **26**, proceeds by way of an intramolecular abstraction of hydrogen by the excited ketone,

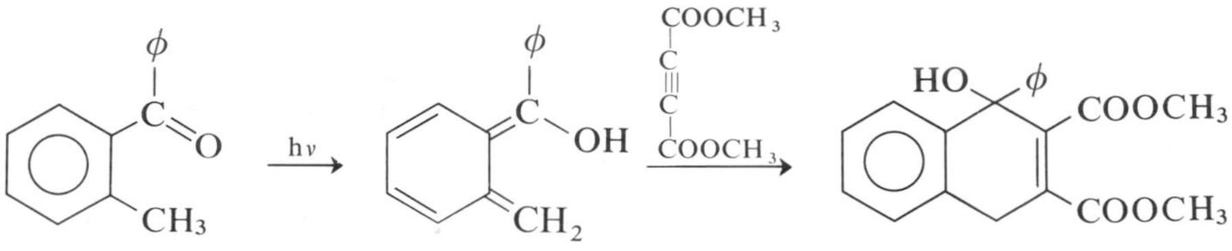

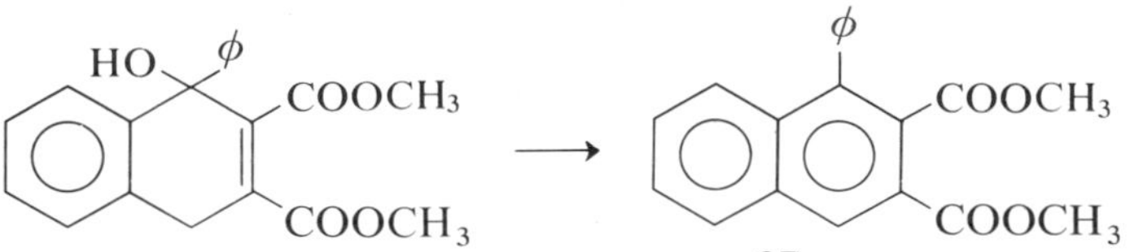

The formation of **26** involves scission of a carbon-hydrogen bond. The reaction is a typical radical reaction, and apparently the species T $(n—\pi^*)$ participates. Furthermore the unpaired electron associated with the oxygen atom actually performs the abstraction of hydrogen, a six-membered cyclic transition state being involved:

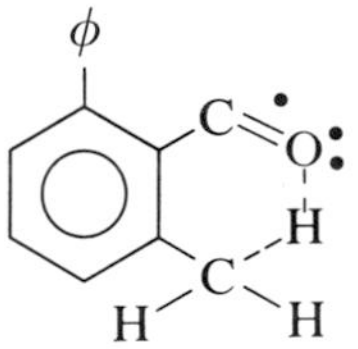

A similar reaction takes place with *trans* dypnone oxide **28**. Photolysis of this material leads to a number of products; however, the hydroxy ketone **29** is the major component of the product mixture:

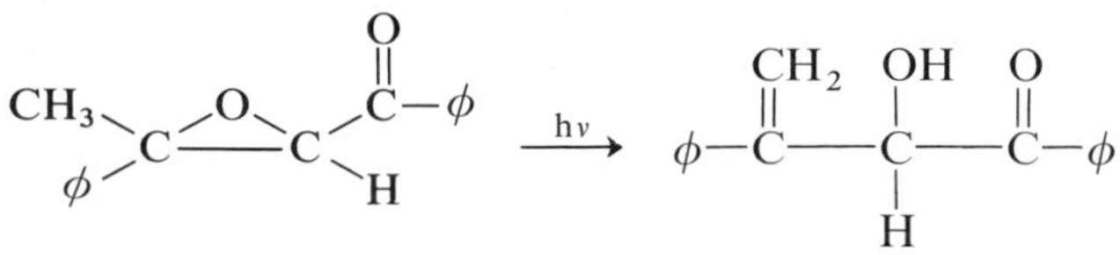

Here again, an $(n—\pi^*)$ excited state is involved and the unpaired electron on the oxygen atom abstracts a methyl hydrogen.

The photochemical reactions of dienones are of interest. Dienones rearrange when treated with acid. The product of the acid catalyzed isomerization is a phenol, and the reaction is known as the dienone-phenol rearrangement. Dienone systems also suffer photochemically induced rearrangements. The skeletal changes are even more dramatic in these reactions, and the mechanisms by which they proceed are of interest,

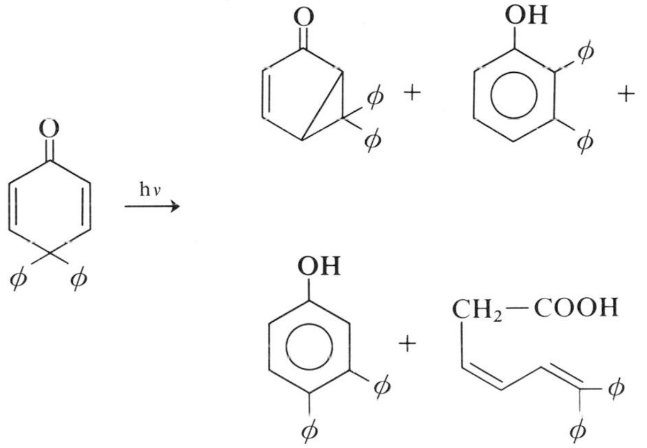

It appears that the cyclopropyl system eventually forms the other products, for it decomposes, when irradiated, into a mixture of the unsaturated acid and 2,3-diphenylphenol.

The rearrangement can be envisioned as involving two processes, the formation of the cyclopropyl intermediate and its destruction to yield other products. The first of these is simply the result of an $(n—\pi^*)$ transition.

The reaction proceeds by $(n—\pi^*)$ excitation followed by rearrangement of the excited state. The initial state is the $S(n—\pi^*)$ state, which undergoes a singlet–triplet conversion to the system $T\ (n—\pi^*)$. It is this $T\ (n—\pi^*)$ system that rearranges:

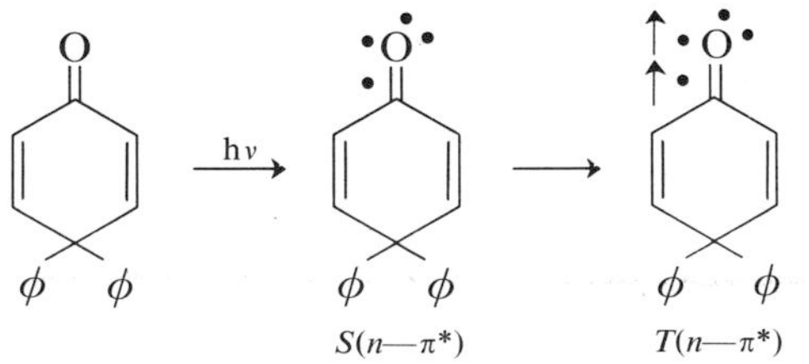

30

Since the π electrons are delocalized over the entire system, it is difficult to picture the transformation in terms of molecular orbitals. Valence-bond theory gives a simpler picture of the reaction. The system **30** can be equally well represented as a superposition of several valence-bond contributors. One of these contributors has the structure **31**, and it has been suggested that the reaction proceeds in the following manner:

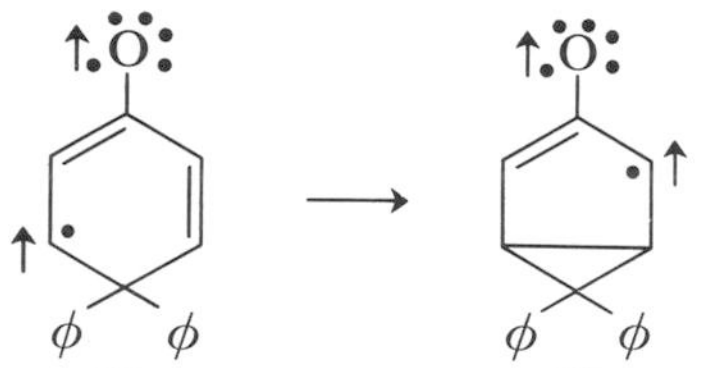

31   **32**

If the antibonding electron in **32** now returns to its original nonbonding orbital, a ground state intermediate **33** is obtained:

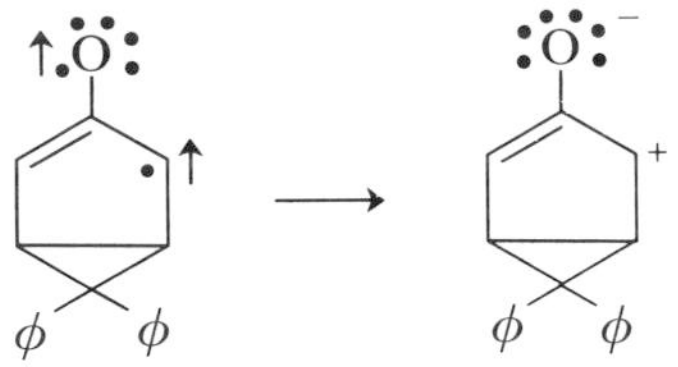

32   **33**

Since the process must be accompanied by spin inversion, this is an example of intersystem crossing. The species **32** is an excited state of **33**, and the return from the electronically excited state to the ground state must be accompanied by loss of energy. The ground state system **33** then reacts by a more familiar pathway to form the cyclopropyl product:

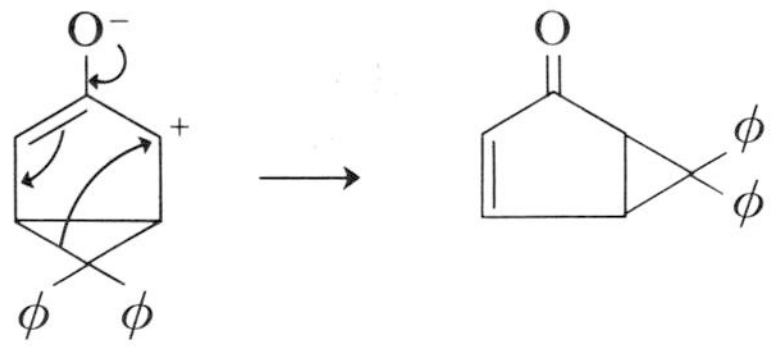

33

Formation of the other products from the cyclopropyl intermediate can be explained by postulating similar mechanisms, this time involving the cyclopropyl system. An (n—π*) transition leads to the excited state **34**,

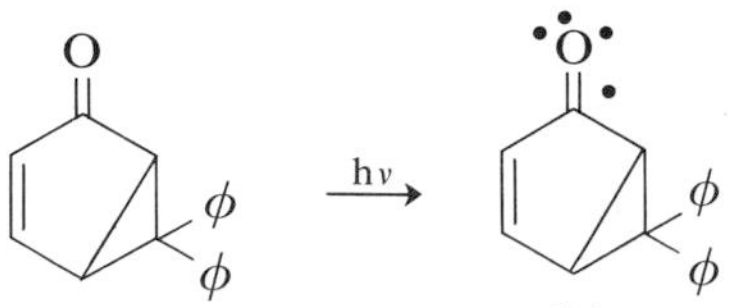

34

which we picture for convenience as **35**:

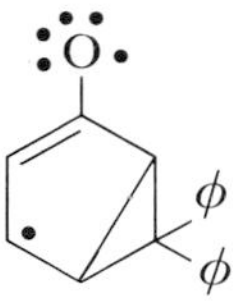

35

The remaining three products are assumed to result from reactions of **35**. The phenolic products are accounted for, by postulating the following,

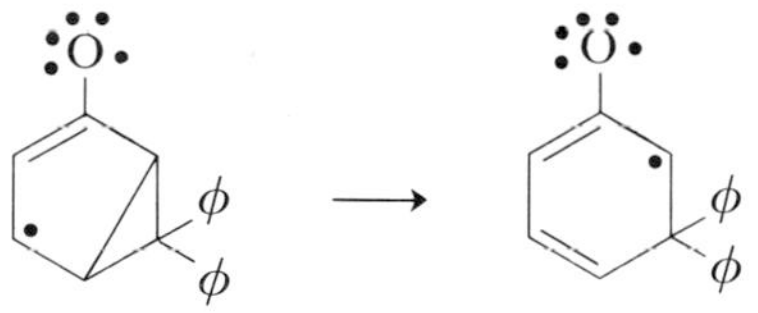

A return of the antibonding electron to the nonbonding orbital (accompanied by loss of energy) leads to the ionic intermediate **36**,

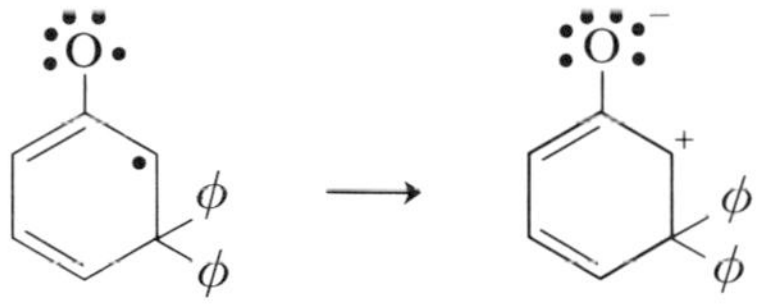

36

The positive charge (and the negative charge also) in **36** is delocalized, and other valence bond structures can be written. This positive charge resides at the positions,

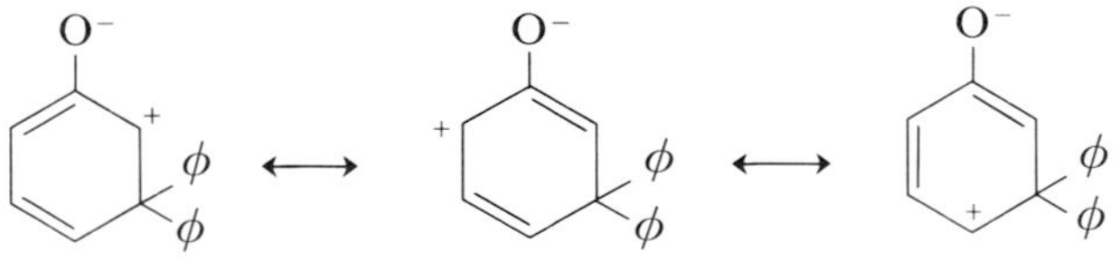

and migration of phenyl to the neighboring carbon atoms gives rise to the phenolic products:

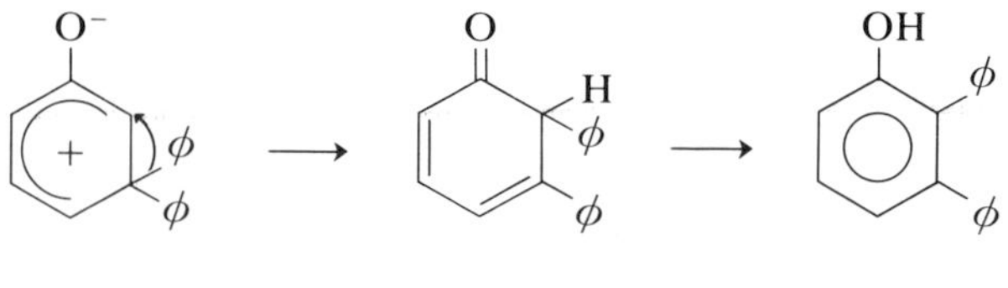

and

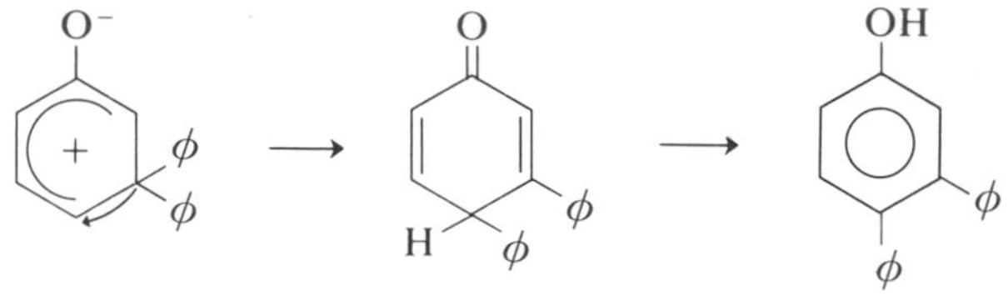

The unsaturated acid also results from a rearrangement of **35**; however, the process is somewhat different from that leading to the phenols:

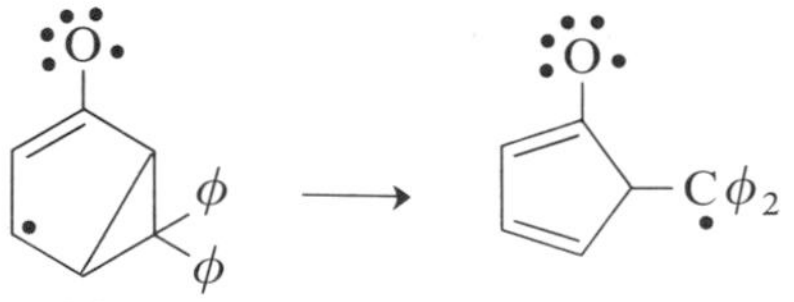

Two pathways can be imagined for the transformation of **37**. One of these involves a return of the antibonding electron to the nonbonding orbital at this stage. This leads to the ionic intermediate,

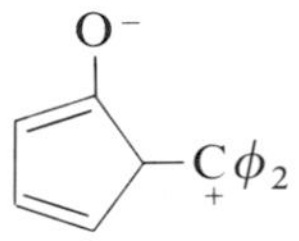

which forms a ketene,

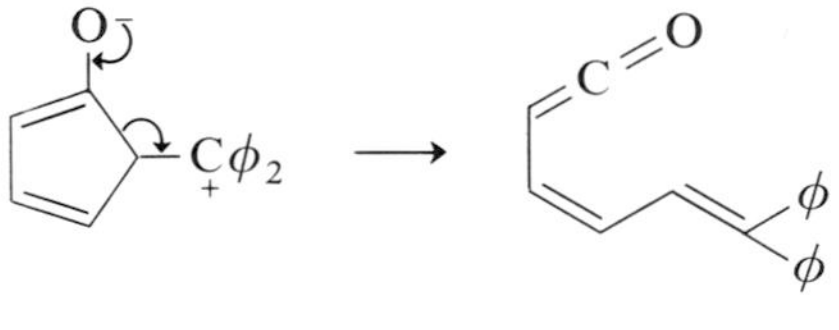

Since the reaction was conducted in aqueous dioxane, water was present in the system. The ketene would naturally be expected to react under these conditions, thereby forming the unsaturated acid:

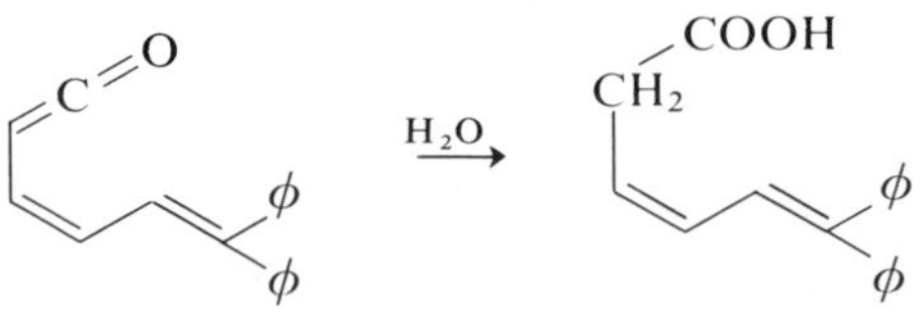

Another mechanism can be written that also accounts for formation of the acid. In this mechanism the unpaired electron on the oxygen atom of **37** causes it to behave like an alkoxy radical. The following radical step can be envisioned (the process is similar to the cleavage of acetone),

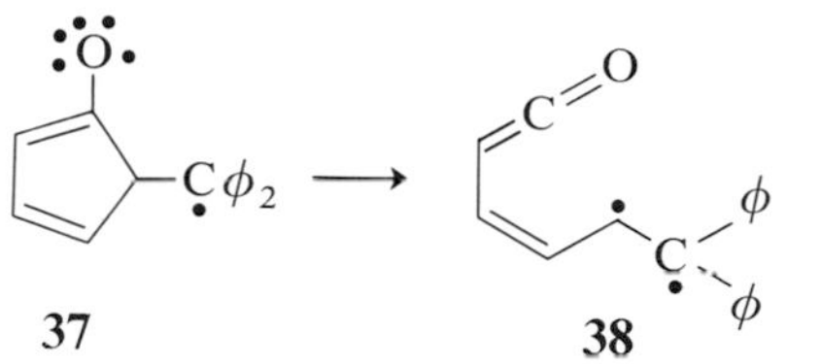

Deexcitation of the excited species **38** causes it to form the ketene, and this ultimately goes on to the unsaturated acid:

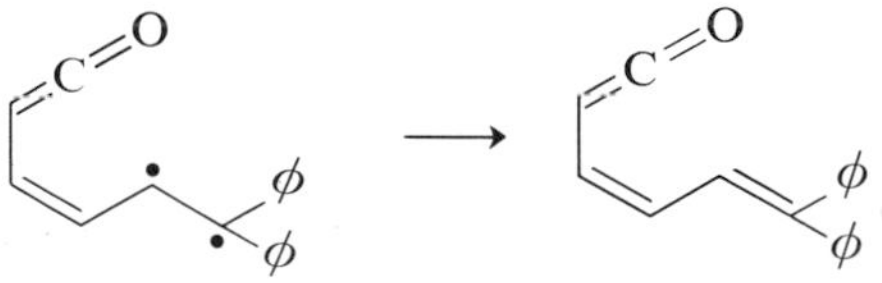

We have presented possible mechanisms for the conversion of the dienone into its products. The mechanisms written here are by no means the only possible schemes that account for the experimental results. For example, the following scheme has been suggested as an additional possibility.

The dienone undergoes an $(n—\pi^*)$ transition to form **31**:

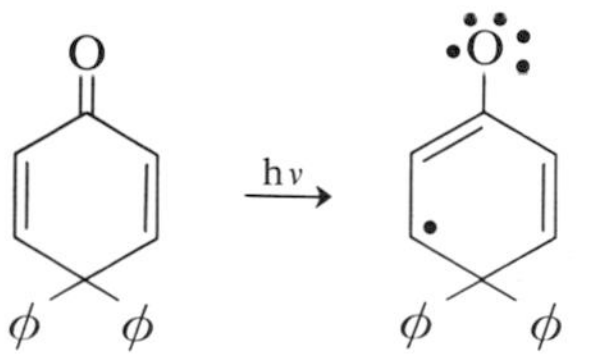

We write this simply as,

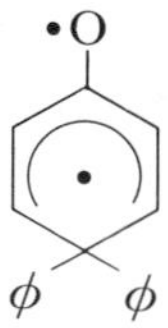

This species forms the intermediates **39** and **40**, and these intermediates then afford the products:

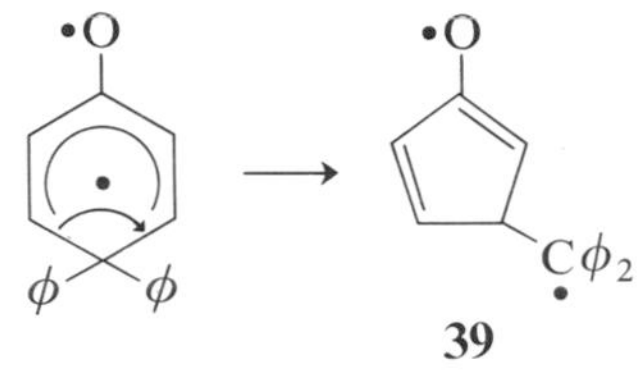

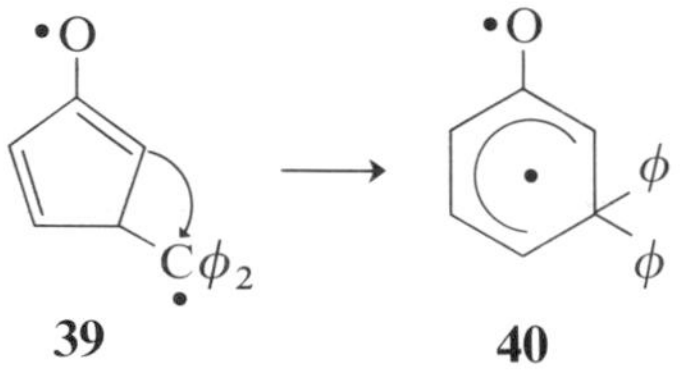

This intermediate **40** is the same as that which we obtained previously. It can go on to the phenolic products. The species **40** can also yield the cyclopropyl derivative, and the latter is known to afford the acid,

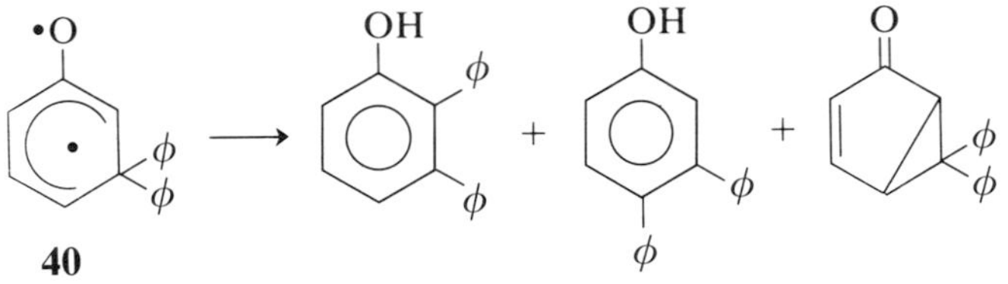

A number of reactions yield similar products to those obtained in this system. Consequently, analogous mechanisms can be written for the conversions. The steroid **41** behaves similarly when irradiated in dioxane:

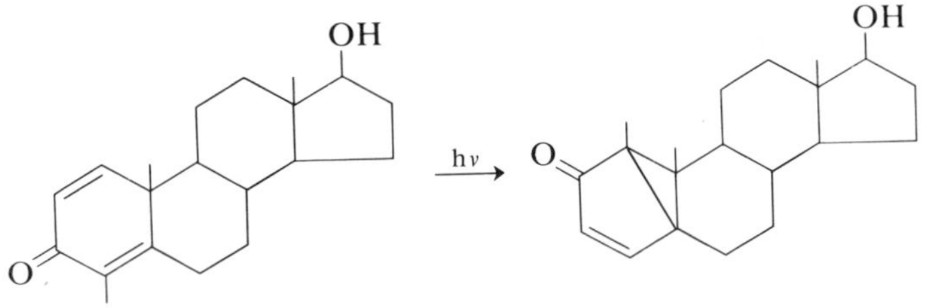

A simple cyclohexadienone such as **42** yields a carboxylic acid when irradiated in the presence of water; the ketene **43** is most likely the intermediate,

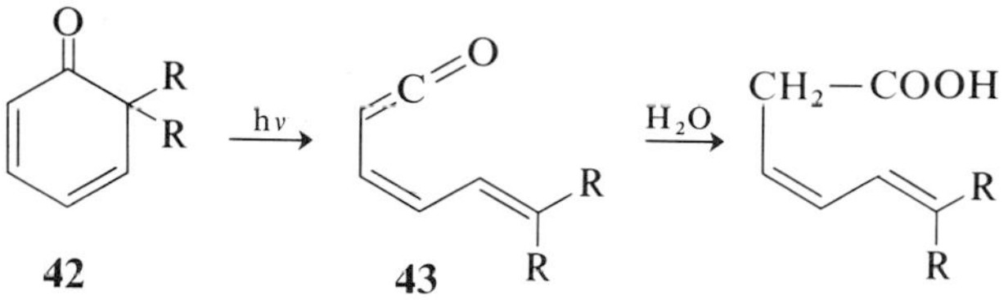

The irradiation of **44** leads to the interesting cyclobutanone **45**:

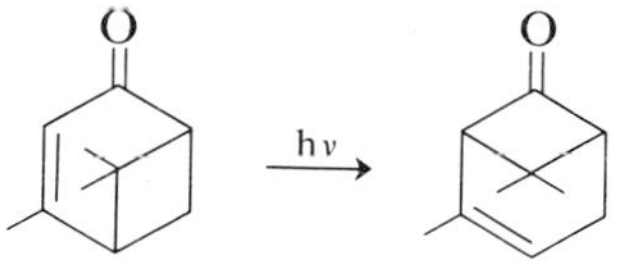

Mechanisms involving $(n-\pi^*)$ excited states can be written for these transformations. The insight that has been gained in organic photochemistry in a comparatively short time is truly amazing. Reactions that baffled the chemist just a few years ago can now be explained adequately by postulating the proper electronically excited states as intermediates. Nor is the gain purely theoretical, with a better understanding of the principles involved, synthetic utilization of these processes becomes possible. We are able to prepare new and interesting materials by irradiating an organic compound with light of the proper frequency. Irradiation transforms the compound into a known excited state that we know will behave in a certain way. Employment of such procedures has led to a number of interesting compounds that could not have been synthesized in so simple a manner in any other way. Not all excitations involve $(n-\pi^*)$ excited states, for the reactions of $(\pi-\pi^*)$ states are equally interesting and useful. Both transitions lead to excited systems that afford unusual products. A few interesting photochemical results are,

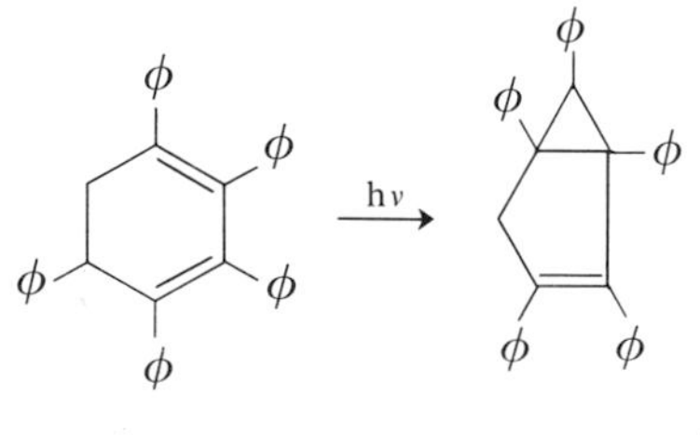

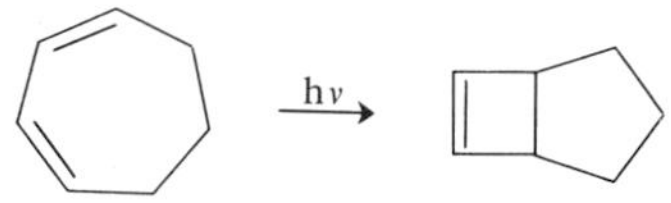

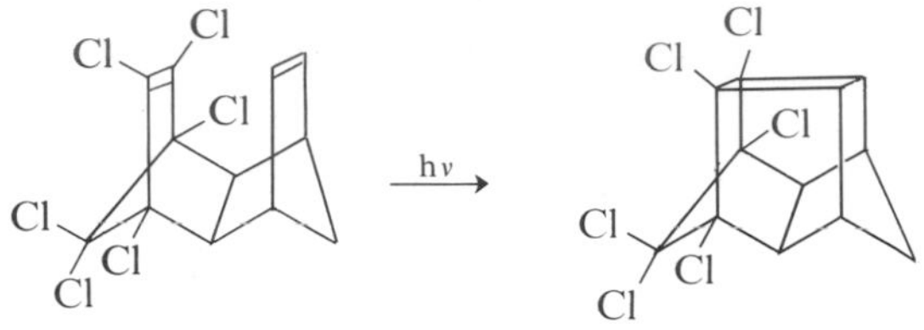

Consider the excited state resulting from promotion of one of the π electrons in ethylene into π^*. Prior to excitation both electrons were in π, and this orbital is described as a linear combination of the p atomic orbitals,

$$\pi = \frac{1}{\sqrt{2}}(p_1 + p_2)$$

Here p_1 refers to the $2p$ atomic orbital of carbon atom one while p_2 refers to that from carbon atom two. After excitation one electron is still in this orbital; the other occupies π^*,

$$\pi^* = \frac{1}{\sqrt{2}}(p_1 - p_2)$$

The electrons occupy molecular orbitals; however, since it is difficult to picture these molecular orbitals, we shall transform them into a more familiar set of equivalent orbitals. As long as the same number of electrons occupy each orbital, such an equivalent set of orbitals can be employed. (Using Hückel molecular orbitals, these equivalent orbitals will turn out to be the p atomic orbitals).

Let us construct new orbitals of the form,

$$\frac{1}{\sqrt{2}}(\pi + \pi^*)$$

and

$$\frac{1}{\sqrt{2}}(\pi - \pi^*)$$

These new orbitals will give us a more familiar picture of the positions occupied by the electrons in the (π—π^*) excited state. We are justified in using these new orbitals as long as measurable quantities such as the electron density and charge density (dipole moment), and energy remain invarient under the transformation.

We find that

$$\frac{1}{\sqrt{2}}(\pi + \pi^*) = p_1$$

while

$$\frac{1}{\sqrt{2}}(\pi - \pi^*) = p_2$$

Thus the $(\pi—\pi^*)$ excited state of ethylene can be described by the picture,

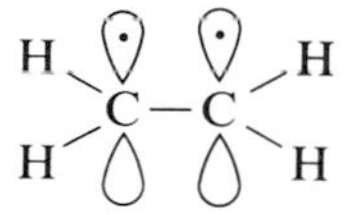

where we have broken the π bond and returned the electrons to the respective atomic orbitals. According to the Hückel theory, the excitation energy must then equal the energy required for breakage of the π bond, and it does (-2β). Actually, some rehybridization accompanies the excitation.

We mentioned previously that two $(\pi—\pi^*)$ excited states exist, a singlet state S $(\pi—\pi^*)$ and a triplet state T $(\pi—\pi^*)$. The singlet state has the geometry just presented,

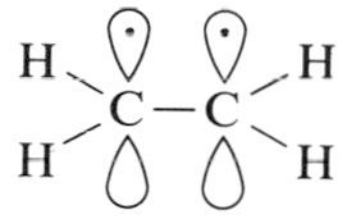

The triplet state, on the other hand, has a preferred geometry in which the methylene groups are perpendicular:

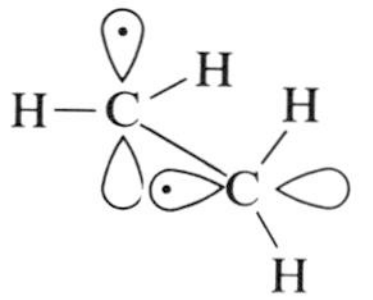

Furthermore, since there is less interelectronic repulsion in the triplet state where the electrons are on the average farther apart, the triplet is the more stable excited state.

A plot of the energy of the various states S_0, S $(\pi—\pi^*)$, and T $(\pi—\pi^*)$ as a function of the angle of rotation about the carbon-carbon bond is presented in Figure 20–5.

Acetylene also undergoes $(\pi—\pi^*)$ transitions, and rehybridization is known to accompany the excitation. The singlet excited state S $(\pi—\pi^*)$ is best

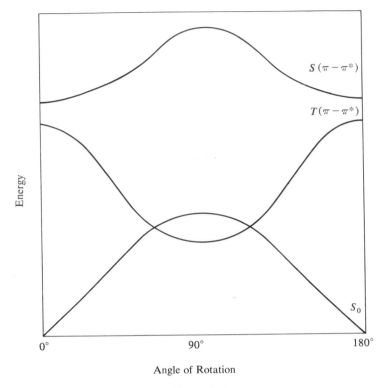

Angle of Rotation

Figure 20–5

described in terms of sp^2 hybridization at carbon, with the pertinent electrons occupying sp^2 orbitals and with a *trans*-geometry:

These ideas concerning the structures and electronic distributions of $(\pi - \pi^*)$ states can be used to explain a number of phenomena. For example, *cis-trans* isomerizations of olefins and azo compounds are photochemically induced, and the processes can be described in terms of $(\pi - \pi^*)$ states,

$$\phi\!-\!N\!=\!N\!-\!\phi \quad \underset{h\nu'}{\overset{h\nu}{\rightleftarrows}} \quad \phi\!-\!N\!=\!N\!-\!\phi$$

$$\underset{HOOC}{\overset{H}{>}}C\!=\!C\underset{COOH}{\overset{H}{<}} \quad \underset{h\nu'}{\overset{h\nu}{\rightleftarrows}} \quad \underset{HOOC}{\overset{H}{>}}C\!=\!C\underset{H}{\overset{COOH}{<}}$$

When a geometric isomer of the type,

$$\underset{R}{\overset{H}{>}}C\!=\!C\underset{R}{\overset{H}{<}}$$

undergoes a photochemically induced isomerization, the first step is absorption of radiation accompanied by a transition to the singlet excited state S (π—π^*). The singlet can be formed at a vibrationally and rotationally excited level, and this species can itself undergo isomerization. The direct isomerization of the singlet excited *cis* to the singlet excited *trans* state, followed by deexcitation to ground state *trans*, requires that the singlet be formed with enough excess energy to pass over the energy barrier to internal rotation. See for example, S (π—π^*) in Figure 20–5.

A lower energy route exists for the isomerization. The singlet excited *cis* S (π π^*) is converted by intersystem crossing into the state T (π—π^*), and the latter can undergo intersystem crossing once again to form the *trans* ground-state product. See Figure 20–5. Isomerization by either route is conceivable. The second pathway requires less energy than the first, but both can take place.

The chemistry of (π—π^*) states is interesting, and a number of reactions are explained in terms of these excited systems. They participate in the *cis-trans* isomerizations of alkenes and in certain ring openings. In some cases, differing electron density and charge density distributions lead to reactive sites in the electronically excited species that differ from the usual sites of reaction in the molecule. Only recently has some mechanistic insight into the behavior of these systems been gained, and future studies will advance the subject still further. One interesting reaction, the ring openings of substituted cyclobutenes, has been explained quite recently. In these and in other cyclic systems, photochemical ring opening involves (π—π^*) states and leads to stereospecific products. Stereospecificity is also observed when thermal ring openings and ring closures are effected, and the ideas of molecular orbital theory are employed to explain these results.

Cyclobutenes undergo thermal ring opening to form butadienes, and the process can be written as,

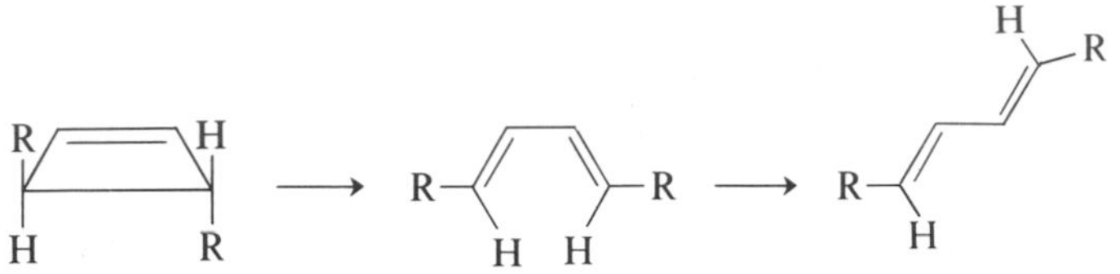

Such a process is described as *conrotatory* because both groups rotate in the same direction, in this case counterclockwise, to form the open chain product:

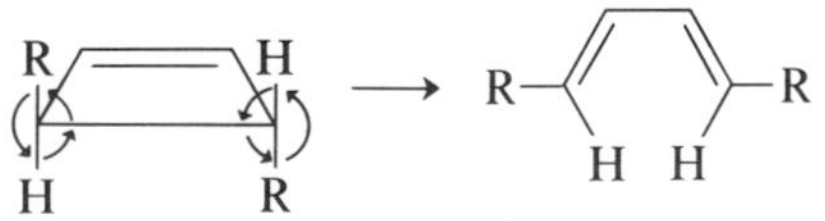

Photochemical ring openings and ring closures in the hexatriene system are also conrotatory,

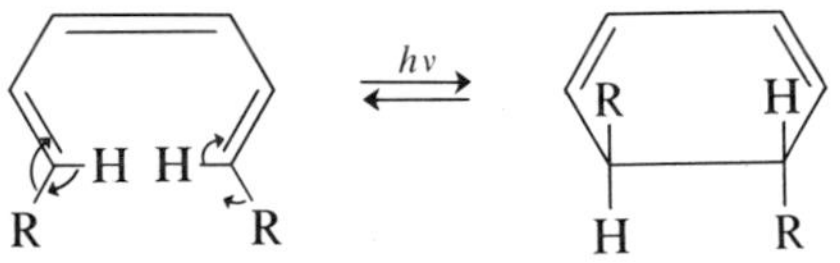

The opening is also conrotatory,

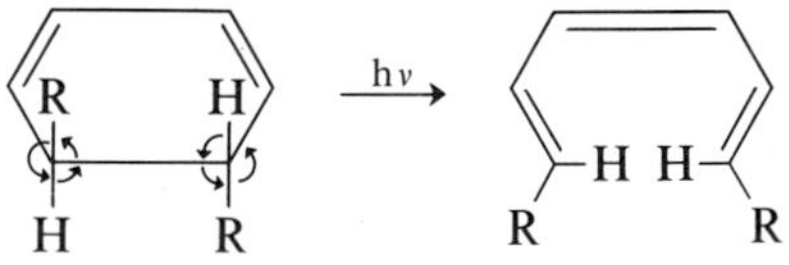

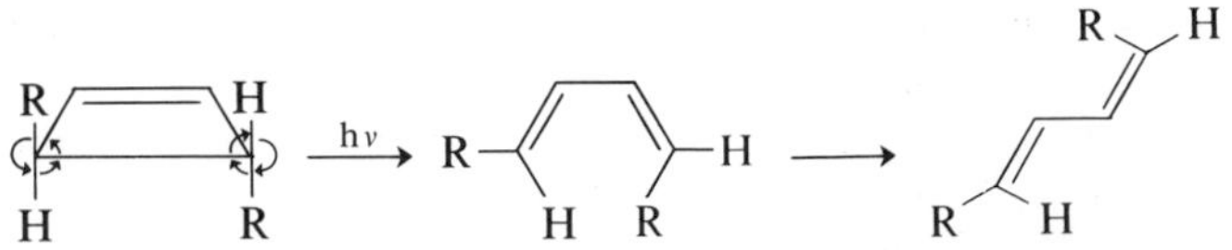

Disrotatory processes in which the groups rotate in opposite directions are also known. The photochemical ring openings of cyclobutenes are disrotatory, as are thermal closures in the hexatriene system,

To explain these results we first review the following.

A *p* atomic orbital has two lobes, a positive lobe and a negative lobe,

and bond formation comes from greater overlap between lobes of like sign. Thus a π bond results from sidewise overlap,

while a σ bond results from endwise overlap.

When lobes of opposite sign have greater overlap, the interaction is said to be antibonding.

σ*   π*

Cyclobutenes open thermally in a conrotatory manner to yield butadienes. The reactant, which has two electrons in the ethylenic linkage and two electrons in the carbon-carbon bond, can be represented as,

This reactant is transformed into butadiene in which two electrons occupy the π molecular orbital of lowest energy ψ_1, and the remaining two π electrons occupy that of next lowest energy ψ_2. The four molecular orbitals of butadiene are,

$$\psi_1 = 0.37p_1 + 0.60p_2 + 0.60p_3 + 0.37p_4$$

$$\psi_2 = 0.60p_1 + 0.37p_2 - 0.37p_3 - 0.60p_4$$

$$\psi_3 = 0.60p_1 - 0.37p_2 - 0.37p_3 + 0.60p_4$$

$$\psi_4 = 0.37p_1 - 0.60p_2 + 0.60p_3 - 0.37p_4$$

At this time we are interested only in ψ_1 and ψ_2, which we present as,

We assume that in the transformation the two π electrons in cyclobutene enter ψ_1 and that the two σ electrons enter ψ_2.

During the transformation,

and

In order for the σ electrons to enter ψ_2, one lobe of the σ bond must rotate up and the other down. This is just the conrotatory motion that is observed.

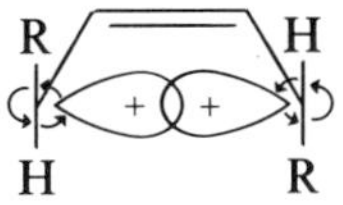

It is possible to explain the thermal ring openings by assuming that only electronic ground states are involved and that the electrons in the σ bond enter the higher energy molecular orbital in the ground state of the product (ψ_3

and ψ_4 are unoccupied in the ground state of butadiene). Just the converse takes place during ring closures. For hexatrienes the thermal conversion is,

46

The six π molecular orbitals for hexatriene are,

$$\psi_1 = 0.23p_1 + 0.42p_2 + 0.52p_3 + 0.52p_4 + 0.42p_5 + 0.23p_6$$

$$\psi_2 = 0.42p_1 + 0.52p_2 + 0.23p_3 - 0.23p_4 - 0.52p_5 - 0.42p_6$$

$$\psi_3 = 0.52p_1 + 0.23p_2 - 0.42p_3 - 0.42p_4 + 0.23p_5 + 0.52p_6$$

$$\psi_4 = 0.52p_1 - 0.23p_2 - 0.42p_3 + 0.42p_4 + 0.23p_5 - 0.52p_6$$

$$\psi_5 = 0.42p_1 - 0.52p_2 + 0.23p_3 + 0.23p_4 - 0.52p_5 + 0.42p_6$$

$$\psi_6 = 0.23p_1 - 0.42p_2 + 0.52p_3 - 0.52p_4 + 0.42p_5 - 0.23p_6$$

In the ground state of hexatriene ψ_1, ψ_2, and ψ_3 are occupied; each contains two electrons. It is assumed that the highest energy electrons, those in ψ_3, are used to form the σ bond in the cyclohexadiene **46**. We assume that the electrons in the σ bond of the product originally occupied the highest energy of the three π molecular orbitals in the reactant. The σ bond is formed by utilizing the electrons in the orbital of highest energy. On the other hand, in those reactions such as butadiene formation, where breakage of a σ bond is involved, this breakage causes the electrons to enter the higher energy molecular orbital. We write ψ_3 for hexatriene as,

In order to form the σ bond, orbital overlap must take place between lobes of like sign. This requires a disrotatory motion, and such a motion is the one observed in product formation:

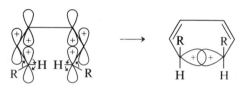

The thermal rearrangements are explained in a satisfactory manner by assuming that the electrons occupying the highest energy molecular orbital are used to form the σ bond whereas σ bond breakage introduces electrons into the highest energy occupied molecular orbital. Only the electronic ground states of product and reactant are involved. We have worked with ψ, but remember that only ψ^2 has physical significance; it represents electron density.

In contrast to the thermal isomerizations, the photochemical processes involve $(\pi-\pi^*)$ excited states.

With cyclobutenes, the photochemical ring opening is disrotatory:

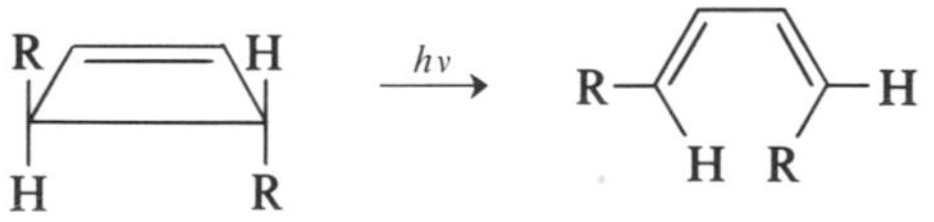

Photochemical excitation promotes one of the π electrons of cyclobutene into the π^* orbital, and this $(\pi-\pi^*)$ state isomerizes to the first excited state of butadiene, where two electrons are in ψ_1, one in ψ_2, and one in ψ_3 of butadiene. The excited state then loses energy and is converted into the ground state molecule. The process can be written as,

$$\sigma^2\pi^2 \xrightarrow{h\nu} \sigma^2\pi\pi^* \longrightarrow \psi_1{}^2\psi_2\psi_3 \longrightarrow \psi_1{}^2\psi_2{}^2$$

where σ^2 implies that there are two electrons in the σ bond, and so forth.

By making use of orbital symmetries it is possible to explain both this result and the observation that photochemical ring opening and ring closure in the hexatriene-cyclohexadiene system are conrotatory.

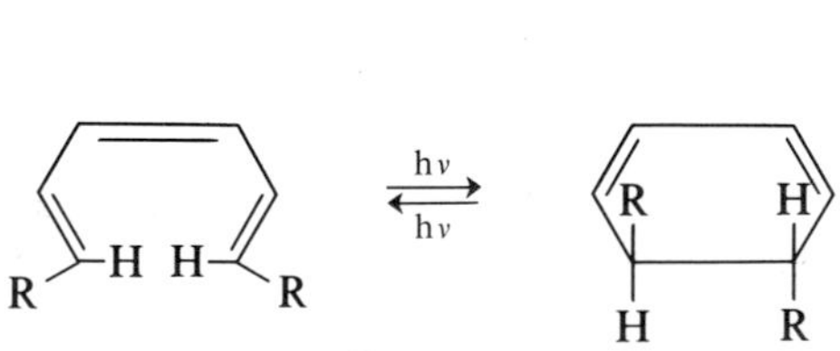

The $(\pi-\pi^*)$ states participate in these photochemical isomerizations, and the ideas of molecular orbital theory can be employed to explain the results. The major advances in organic photochemistry are recent and exciting, and in the near future many new discoveries will certainly be made.

Supplementary Reading

1. De Mayo, P. (editor), *Molecular Rearrangements.* New York, Interscience, Vol. 1 (1963), Vol. 2 (1964).

2. Gould, E. S., *Mechanism and Structure in Organic Chemistry.* New York, Holt, 1959.

3. Hine, J., *Physical Organic Chemistry.* New York, McGraw-Hill, 1962.

4. Noyes, W. A., Jr., Hammond, G. S., and Pitts, J. N., Jr. (editors), *Advances in Photo-chemistry.* New York, Interscience, 1963.

5. Pryor, W. A., *Free Radicals.* New York, McGraw-Hill, 1966.

6. Turro, N. J., *Molecular Photochemistry.* New York, Benjamin, 1965.

Index

Alpha (α), 135
Amides, 561, 585
  reactions, 563, 565, 586
  restricted rotations, 561
Amines, 13, 81, 82, 85, 86, 89, 494, 502
  addition to carbonyl compounds, 502
  basicity and hybridization, 89
  basicity and hydrogen bonding, 87
  basicity and inductive effects, 77
  basicity and resonance, 81, 82
  basicity and solvent effects, 86, 87
  basicity and steric effects, 85
  basicity and steric inhibition of reso-
    nance, 82
  inversion, 13, 502
Ammonia, 13, 86, 176, 193
  bond angles, 86
  dipole moment, 193, 194
  hybridization, 86
  inversion, 13, 502
Anionic rearrangements, 594
Antibonding molecular orbitals, 138, 690,
  707, 710
Arndt-Eistert reaction, 654
Aromatic rearrangements, 642
Aromatic substitution, 423
  complexes, 428
  environmental effects, 445
  Friedel-Crafts reaction, 434, 468
  halogenation, 457
  mechanism, 425
  nitration, 445, 450, 451, 452
  nucleophilic, 473
  orientation, 439
  ortho-para ratio, 449
  partial rate factors, 438
  selectivity-reactivity, 443
  sulfonation, 465
Aromaticity, 151, 161
Arrhenius equation, 6, 17
Asymmetrical top, 252
Autoprotonation, 62, 67

Baeyer-Villiger reaction, 663
Base, 54, 57, 64, 72, 73, 77, 432
  amines, 13, 81, 82, 85, 86, 89, 494, 502
  hybridization effects, 88
  hydrocarbons, 432
  hydrogen bonding, 86, 87
  inductive effect, 75, 78
  resonance effect, 80
  solvent effects, 85
  steric effects, 85
  steric inhibition of resonance, 82
Base acceleration, 532, 565
  benzilic acid rearrangement, 558, 595
  ester hydrolysis, 565
  halogenation of ketones, 531, 532
Basic catalysis, 54, 57
  aldol condensation, 535
  general, 54
  keto-enol tautomerism, 525
  specific, 57
Basicity of hydrocarbons, 432
Beckmann rearrangement, 661
Bending vibrations, 33, 37, 247, 248
Bent bonds, 183, 184, 348
Benzene, 138, 162, 166, 169

aromatic substitution, 423
  resonance energy, 138, 162, 169, 170
  valence-bond treatment, 166
Benzidine rearrangement, 645
Benzilic acid rearrangement, 558, 595
Benzoin condensation, 551
Benzophenone, photochemical reactions,
  693
Benzpinacol, formation, 693
Benzylic radical, 220
Benzyne, 357
  Diels-Alder reactions, 361
  orientation, 363
Beryllium dichloride, 178
Beryllium difluoride, 178
Beta (β), 135
Bimolecular elimination, 327
Bimolecular nucleophilic substitution, 295
Bimolecular reaction, 44
Bisulfite addition, 485
Bond angles, 175, 177
Bond dipole moment, 188, 189
Bond dissociation energy, 185, 220
Bond lengths, 184
Bond strengths, 185, 220
Bonding molecular orbitals, 138, 690, 707
Boron trifluoride, 178, 191
Bredt's rule, 303, 526
Bridgehead reactivity, 219, 302, 526
  enolization, 526
  nucleophilic substitution, 302
  radicals, 219
N-Bromosuccinimide, 671
Brønsted catalysis law, 107
Brown equation, 107, 438
t-Butyl carbonium ion, 178, 205, 206

Cannizzaro reaction, 553
Carbanions, 503
Carbenes, 344
  Wolff rearrangement, 654
Carbon dioxide, vibrational transitions, 247
Carbon-hydrogen bond moment, 192
Carbonium ions, 178, 204, 208, 279, 294,
  594, 602, 614, 621, 630
  homoallylic, 312
  nonclassical, 206, 210, 312, 614, 624, 630
  rearrangements, 291, 307, 594, 602, 614,
    623, 627
  stability, 208, 210
  stability and isotope effects, 213
  structure, 204, 206, 617, 624, 630, 633
Carbonyl compounds, 480, 525
  addition, 480, 535
  hydration, 482, 489
  ultraviolet absorption, 235, 241
Catalyst, 29, 54, 55, 57, 484
  acid, 54, 57
  addition to carbonyl compounds, 484
  base, 54, 57
  solvent, 55
Cationic rearrangements, 291, 307, 594,
  602, 614, 623, 627
Chemical shift, 270
Chemical spectroscopy, 224
Chloroacetylene, dipole moment, 199
Chloroethylene, dipole moment, 199
Chugaev reaction, 340